COMMISSION OF THE EUROPEAN COMMUNITIES

9789400982663

W0230399

AGREP

PERMANENT INVENTORY
OF
AGRICULTURAL RESEARCH
PROJECTS IN THE
EUROPEAN COMMUNITIES

VOL. I MAIN LIST: RESEARCH PROJECTS

(containing data on approx. 21,000 research projects)

MAY 1980

SPRINGER-SCIENCE+BUSINESS MEDIA, B.V.

This volume has a Library of Congress Cataloging in Publication classification.

ISBN 978-94-009-8266-6   ISBN 978-94-009-8264-2 (eBook)
DOI 10.1007/978-94-009-8264-2

Publication arranged by:
Commission of the European Communities,
Directorate-General Information Market and Innovation,
Luxembourg

Data processing by
I/S Datacentralen af 1959,
Retortvej 6-8,
2500 Valby,
Denmark

EUR 5895

LEGAL NOTICE
Neither the Commission of the European Communities nor any person acting on behalf of
the Commission is responsible for the use which might be made of the following information.

Photocomposition by Special-Trykkeriet Viborg a-s

Table of Contents

INTRODUCTION

The Permanent Inventory of AGricultural REsearch Projects (AGREP) is an information system on current projects in agriculture and related fields in the Member States of the European Communities (Belgium, Denmark, Federal Republic of Germany, France, Ireland, Italy, Luxembourg, the Netherlands and the United Kingdom). Its creation is based upon a regulation of the Council of Ministers of the European Communities concerning the coordination of agricultural research (Council Regulation No 1728/74 of 27 June, 1974).

AGREP covers agriculture in an extensive sense of the word, i.e. including fields like fisheries and forestry, land use and development, conservation of nature, veterinary medicine, food science and technology, as well as agricultural economics and rural sociology. A detailed scope description is given in the subject classification facets "fields of research" and "subject areas" as presented on the introductory pages of the two printed volumes.

The data base is fully computerized. It is available in printed form and on magnetic tape. On-line access is offered by EURONET/DIANE (DIrect Access Network for Europe). The data base is updated annually.

The 1980 issue of AGREP contains about 21.000 title citations of agricultural research projects.

AGREP is a cooperative system. The national focal points (NFPs) collect input and provide it in an agreed format to the Commission which sponsors the management of the system and the provision of output to the Member Countries. The Commission is advised by the Standing Committee on Agricultural Research (SCAR) and its sub-group, the AGREP Advisory Board. Data processing and technical assistance are carried out by a contractor to the Commission. The AGREP publication consists of two volumes:

Vol. I contains the Main List with the titles (both in the original language and in English) of the research projects, complemented by some basic information on each project, i.e. name(s) of researcher(s), country and research organisation (in the Main List given as codes), and availability of publications.

Vol. II contains various indexes, i.e.

– a Subject Index which permits the identification of research projects relevant to subject areas,

– the List of Research Organisations ordered by country and within each country by the hierarchical organisation code (see also explanatory note, vol. I, page IX). The names of research organisations are complemented by postal adresses, – the List of Scientists containing the name(s) of scientist(s) involved in the research projects referred to.

Further information may be obtained from the

> AGREP Secretariat
> Mr. G. Trevisan
> Commission of the European Communities
> Bâtiment Jean Monnet
> LUXEMBOURG – KIRCHBERG

or by contacting one of the National Focal Points listed on the following page.

NATIONAL FOCAL POINTS OF EC MEMBER COUNTRIES PROVIDING INPUT TO AGREP.

BELGIUM
Ministère de l'Agriculture
Mr. J. Gooris
Administration de la Recherche Agronomique
Chaussée d'Ixelles 29-31
1050 – BRUXELLES
Telephone: 32-2-5123910

F.R. of GERMANY
Zentralstelle für Agrardokumentation
und -information
Mr. E. Müller
Villichgasse 17
5300 BONN 2
Telephone: (0228) 357097

FRANCE
Ministère de l'Agriculture et du
Développement Rural
Institut National de la Recherche Agronomique
Mme. G. Michel
149, Rue de Grenelle
75341 PARIS CEDEX 07
Telephone: 33-1-5503200

DENMARK
Landbrugets Samråd for Forskning og Forsøg
Mr. O. Kjeldsen Rasmussen
Vesterbrogade 4A^{IV}
1620 COPENHAGEN V
Telephone 45-1-127561

IRELAND
The Agricultural Institute
Headquarters
Mr. V. Reilly
19, Sandymount Avenue
DUBLIN 4
Telephone 353-1-688188
Telex 30459

ITALY
Ministero dell' Agricoltura e delle Foreste
Direzione Generale della Produzione Agricola
Divisione II Informazione Divulgazione
Mr. A. D'Ambrosio
Via XX Settembre
ROMA
Telephone: 39-6-4759580
Telex: 61251

Consiglio Nazionale delle Ricerche
Mr. E. Galante
Piazzale Aldo Moro, 7
ROMA
Telephone: 39-6-4953337
Telex: 610076

THE NETHERLANDS
Nationale Raad Landbouwkundig Onderzoek – TNO
Mr. H. Wansink
Office: Adelheidstraat 84,
Post: Juliana van Stolberglaan 148,
Postbus 297
2501 BD's-GRAVENHAGE
Telephone: 31-70-471021

UNITED KINGDOM
Agricultural Research Council
Mr. W. S. Wise
160, Great Portland Str.
LONDON W1N 6DT
Telephone: 44-1-5806655

COVERAGE

In the table below is indicated the degree of coverage within the different subject areas as defined by the Standing Committee for Agricultural Research (SCAR.).

By coverage is meant the percentage of all current research projects on subject areas A-H in a country, which are registered in AGREP. The figures should be viewed in conjunction with the notes following the table.

It should be noted, that the percentages are estimates and therefore subject to considerable uncertainty.

Percentage coverage of SCAR-recommended subject areas for the 1980 AGREP-inventory.

Subject Area	BE	DE	DK	GB	IE	IT	NL
A. Natural resources							
– Soil science and management of land, water, fauna and flora	90	85	80	40	95	85	80
B. Plant production	90						
– Crop husbandry, breeding and protection		85	95	75	99	85	100
– forestry		85	40	10	100	90	100
C. Animal production	90						
– Livestock husbandry, breeding and veterinary medicine		80	95	75	99	85	100
– Fisheries and fishery products		85	0	75	80	85	75
D. Agricultural engineering and building	90	85	95	85	100	85	100
E. Food and nutrition	85	90	50	85	99	80	75
F. Economic and social aspects	90						
– Management, economy and marketing studies		85	95	20	90	85	100
– Social studies		85	50	–	99	85	80
G. Research related to developing countries (on fields A-F)	90	80	50	5	100	85	90
H. General research methodology and service institutions (related to field A-F)	90	–	95	–	100	85	90

Notes regarding type of research organisation and financing in contributing countries.

Belgium
Both publicly financed and executed and privately financed and executed research projects are included in AGREP. The coverage indicated is the one for research carried out at public institutes – for privately executed research the coverage is considerably less.

Denmark
Mainly research carried out at public and semi-public institutions is included in AGREP.

Federal Republic of Germany
Research projects of public, semi-public and private institutions are included in AGREP. The percentage of coverage indicated relates mainly to public and semi-public organisations. For privately executed research the coverage is considerably less.

Ireland
Research carried out at public institutions – whether it is publicly financed research or done under contract for private industry – has been included in AGREP. Research carried out in private industry has not been included.

Italy
Research projects sponsored by:
– the public Administrations (governmental organizations in the strict sense – e.g. MAF, CNR, CNEN, universities and other research and public bodies),
– the public enterprises which are funded by the Ministry for Public Investment,
– private firms and other bodies,
  are included.

The Netherlands
Both public and private research is included in AGREP. The coverage indicated is the one for public research. Some public research on fishery products, foods and nutrition as well as research carried out at universities other than the Agricultural University and Faculty of Veterinary Medicine is not yet included in AGREP. For privately executed research the coverage is considerably less.

United Kingdom
Only public research is included in AGREP.

EXPLANATORY NOTES

MAIN LIST: Research projects (Vol. I)

Each entry of the main list contains input data collected per research project as listed below.

The entries are ordered

1) according to "Fields of Research" subdivided by "subject areas" (commodities) (table D of the classification scheme, see Table of Contents)
2) within each group according to the AGREP code, i.e. country, research institute and year the project was started. In cases where more than one D-classification code has been assigned to a project, the reference numbers of these projects are listed under the related chapter headings initiated by "see also".

Example of a typical entry:

```
                2)                              3)
1)  3086   Prummel, J.          NL 010103/62/0534
    Bemesting van grove tuinbouwgewassen op
4)  landbouwgronden   Manuring of vegetables in agriculture.   5)
```

6) Publications

1) A computer-assigned sequential number (reference number) at the beginning of each entry.
2) Scientists involved. Up to 6 names of research workers involved; where more than one name is given, the first name is that of the project leader.

3) **AGREP code**

A 14-character alpha-numeric code composed of

a) a 2-character alphabetical country code

BE	Belgium
DE	Federal Republic of Germany
DK	Denmark
FR	France
GB	United Kingdom
IE	Ireland
IT	Italy
NL	Netherlands
XE	The Commission of the European Communities

b) a 6-digit Research Organisation Code (see following page)

c) a 2-digit code indicating the year when the project started (e.g. 75)

For the Federal Republic of Germany only: The code indicates the year in which the project became known to the Focal Point.

d) a 4-digit current number assigned by the research organisations or by the National Focal Point.

4) **Title of the research project in the original language** except English

5) **English title** (original or translated) in bold face

6) **Publications**

"Publications" means that documents relevant to the research project are available.

RESEARCH ORGANISATION CODES

The organisation code is a six digit, three-level hierarchical numeric code, assigned by the National Focal Points. With the exception of the Federal Republic of Germany, the code should be interpreted in the following way:

Digit 1-2: Highest level   (e.g. ministry)
Digit 3-4: Intermediate level   (e.g. university)
Digit 5-6: Lowest level   (e.g. institute)

For the Federal Republic of Germany only, the code should be interpreted as follows:

Digit 1-3: Highest level   (e.g. university)
Digit 4-5: Intermediate level   (e.g. institute)
Digit   6: Lowest level   (e.g. department)
Note: Digit 1 may also be a code for the type of the organisation (e.g. Federal)

This three-level hierarchical code makes it possible to identify the different units in the chain of responsibility, e.g. AA.02.03.04:

AA   Country Code
    02.   Faculté des Sciences Agronomiques de
                          l'Université Catholique
        03.   Département de Phytotechnique Tropicale
                          et Subtropicale
            04.   Laboratoir de Phytotechnique Tropicale et
                          Subtropicale

In the list of Research Organisations, each organisation code is followed by the name of the corresponding organisation, while the address in general is given only if it is different from the next higher level.

Example: AA.06.00.00. Faculté de Médecine
                                Vétérinaire de l'Université
                            45, Rue des Vétérinaires

                               AA.06.01.00   Chaire d'Anatomie
                               AA.06.02.00   Chaire de Bactériologie
                               AA.06.03.00   Chaire de Génétique
                               AA.06.04.00   Chaire d'Histologie
                               AA.06.06.00   Chaire d'Inspection des Denrées Alimentaires

Main List – Fields of Research

(Fields of Research are subdivided by Subject Areas, see Vol. II).

D 3100 – Animal management general and animal husbandry

See also 1838, 2153, 2154, 2604, 3552, 3568, 15367

10399 Dagnelie, P.; Claustriaux, J. BE 010010/76/0009 R
Gestion par ordinateur de troupeaux bovins. **Management of a stock of cattle by computer.**

10400 Ectors, F.; Massip, A. BE 060006/76/0003 N
Culture et conservation à basse température d'embryons. **Culture and low temperature preservation of cow embryos.** Publications.

10401 Rixhon, L.; Delhaye, R. BE 080800/78/0012
Etude de la culture associée : soja/maïs. **Study of associate crop : soja/mais.**

10402 Arens, R. DE 506154/75/0001
Untersuchungen über die Wirkungen und Kosten extensiver Schafweide auf Brachflächen. **Studies on effects and costs of extensive sheep grazing on fallow land.**

10403 Sengbusch, R.von DE 903500/75/0001
Domestikation von Warmwasserfischen. **Domestication of warm–water fishes.**

10404 Østergaard, V. DK 010201/77/0009
Afprøvning af eksperimentelle staldsystemer til kvæg. **Testing of experimental stall systems for cattle.**

10405 Petersen, E.O. DK 010300/76/0082
Den sæsonmæssige variation i den danske mælkeproduktion – årsager og virkninger. **The seasonal variation of milk production in Denmark – causes and effects.**

10406 Callesen, O.; Karlsen, P. DK 030171/79/0002 N
Vegetativ formering af storfrugtet blåbær. **Propagation of highbush blueberry by soft wood cuttings.**

10407 Ollivier–Bousquet, M. FR 010213/70/7546
Migration intracellulaire et exocytose des protéines sécrétées. **Intracellular transit and secreted proteins exocytosis.**

10408 Pétrissant, G.; Boisnard, M. FR 010213/74/7548
Synthèse protéigue chez les mammifères: Rôle des isoaccepteurs d'un T Arn spécifique au cours de la traduction. **Function of the isoaccepting species of a specific T Rna during the translation step.**

10409 Pétrissant, G.; Boisnard, M. FR 010213/74/7549
Synthèse protéique chez les mammifères: Association des aminoacyl T Arn synthétases en un complexe multienzymatique. **Aminoacyl T Arn synthetases complexes in mammalian cells.**

10410 Ollivier–Bousquet, M. FR 010213/76/7547
Migration intracellulaire et sécrétion des globules lipidiques. **Intracellular transit and milk fat globule secretion.**

10411 Taylor GB 030201/00/0026 R
Examination of chemical composition, bacteriological quality and somatic cell count of milk.

10412 Conchie; Hay GB 030602/00/0004 R
Structure of ovomucoid glycopeptide.

10413 McAllister; Lee GB 040402/75/0021 R
Optimal treatment of animal slurry.

10414 Briggs GB 040902/76/0002
Experimental palourde cultivation.

10415 Gracey GB 041101/00/0014 R
Field studies on pollution caused by land disposal of animal slurries.

10416 Researcher not indicated GB 050170/00/0008
Hill grazing: production and management.

10417 Jason; Kent GB 051005/00/0027 R
Thermo–physical properties of fish and fish products.

10418 Dodds GB 060108/00/0001
Milk production systems.

10419 McCarthy, R. IE 050100/76/9154 N
Energy from forests. Publications.

10420 Lynch, T. IE 050100/77/9155 N
Effect of silviculture on wood quality. Publications.

10421 Whelan, J.; Brennan, E. IE 120101/78/9176 N
The rearing, release and survival of pheasants (phasianus co lchicus) in the natural habitat.

10422 Lee, T.; Kelly, T. IE 180111/78/8760 R
Survey of trawl grounds off the south west coast of Ireland.

Animals and parts of their bodies (B 2300)

See also 11628, 11632, 11633

10423 Desnoyers, F.; Vodovar, N. FR 010205/70/9563 N
Etudes morphologiques des tissus adipeux. **Morphological studies of adipose tissues.**

10424 Meslin, J.C. FR 010205/70/9567
Intéractions flore microbienne, morphologie et renouvellement de l'épithélium intestinal. **Microbial interactions on morphology and renewal of the small intestinal epithelium.**

10425 Kann, G.; Martinet, J.; Fevre, J. FR 010213/69/7556
Mécanismes de régulation de la sécrétion de prolactine. **Prolactin secretion: Mechanisms of regulation.**

10426 Delouis, C.; Pont, J. FR 010213/71/7555
Rôle des stéroides ovariens au cours de la différenciation de la cellule épithéliale mammaire. **Role of ovarian steroids during epithelial mammary cell differentiation.**

10427 Djiane, J. FR 010213/73/7554
Récepteurs membranaires aux hormones prolactiniques et de croissance. **Prolactin and growth hormone receptors.**

10428 Kann, G.; Martinet, J.; Schirar, A. FR 010213/74/7557
Anoestrus de lactation. **Anoestrus of lactation.**

10429 Houdebine, L–M.; Devinoy, E. FR 010213/78/7551

Transcription et stabilisation des ARN messagers mammaires. **Transcription and stabilization of the mammary messenger RNAs.**

10430 Houdebine, L.-M.; Djiane, J.; Delouis, C.
FR 010213/78/7553
Mécanismes moléculaires de transfert de l'information prolactinique dans la cellule mammaire. **Molecular mechanisms involved in the transfer of prolactin information in the mammary cell.**

10431 Bacou, F.; Vigneron, P.; Cordesse, R.; Nougues, J.
FR 011203/67/7566
Etude histochimique et biochimique de la myogénése et de la différenciation des types de fibres musculaires in vivo et in vitro. **Histochemical and biochemical study of myogenesis and muscle fibers differentiation in vivo and in vitro.**

10432 Mariana, J.C.; Reviers, M.M. de   FR 011501/63/7518
Analyse des paramètres de la folliculogénèse ovarienne. **Ovarian folliculogenesis.**

10433 Dacheux, J.L.; Paquignon, M.   FR 011501/72/7508
Maturation et métabolisme des spermatozoides au cours de leur transit épididymaire. **Maturation and metabolism of epididymal sperm.**

10434 Dubois, M.; Martinat, N.; Caraty, A.
FR 011501/72/7530
Localisation de neuropeptides hormonaux dans le cerveau et dans l'organisme. **Hormonal neuropeptides in the brain and at the periphery.**

10435 Courot, M.; Dacheux, J.L.; Blanc, M.; Hochereau de Reviers, M.T.; Cahoreau, C.   FR 011501/74/7505
Existence et rôle de substances protéiques d'origine testiculaire, qui contrôlent la croissance testiculaire et la spermatogenese. **Testicular proteineceous substances controlling testicular growth and spermatogenesis.**

10436 Mauléon, P.; Corteel, M.; Lemon–Resplandy, M.; Loir, M.   FR 011501/75/7523
Hétérogénéité du corps jaune. **Two–cell status in corpus luteum.**

10437 Terqui, M.   FR 011501/77/7520
Récepteurs ovariens aux stéroides: Maturation folliculaire in vivo. Effet d'une immunisation passive aux steroides. **Steroid receptors in the ovarian follicle.**

10438 Signoret, J.P.   FR 011501/77/7543
Equilibre hormonal du comportement sexuel du mâle. Variations saisonnières de sensibilité. **Hormonal balance of male sexual behaviour and seasonal variation of reactivity.**

Animal and plant communities as ecological systems (B 2500)

See also 10542

Domestic animals in general (B 4000)

See also 2170, 2393, 2751, 2848, 3536, 3683, 11692, 11704, 11743, 13651, 15551, 17378, 17487, 17488, 18023

10439 Vandenbyvang, P.; Bodart, A.; François, E.

BE 010003/73/0005
Application de la radioimmunologie aux problèmes de physiologie animale et zootechnie. **Application of radioimmunology to problems in animal physiology and animal husbandry.**

10440 Vandenbyvang, P.; Bulteau, M.; Fabry, J.; Bodart, C.
BE 081200/75/0007
Relations entre physiologie hormonale (prolactine, GH, hormones thyroïdiennes) et productions zootechniques. **Relations between hormonal physiology (prolactine, GH, thyroid hormones) and animal productions.**

10441 Mülling, M.   DE 104400/70/0005
Perinatale Untersuchu‧‧gen bei Haustieren. **Perinatal investigations of domestic animals.**

10442 Merck, C.C.; Jacob, A.   DE 104400/70/0009
Darstellung des physiologischen Zellgehalts der Milch unter Berücksichtigung verschiedener Umwelteinflüsse. **Presentation of physiological cell content in milk regarding different environmental conditions.**

10443 Rohloff, D.; Laiblin, C.   DE 104400/72/0006
Untersuchung der Spermienproduktion bei Haustieren. **Estimation of sperm production in domestic animals.**

10444 Rohloff, D.; Kelami, A.; Seppelt, G.; Blohm, B.; Schroeter, A.; Laiblin, C.   DE 104401/75/0001
Artifizielle Spermatocelen im Tierexperiment. **Artificial spermatocele in animal experiments.** Publications.

10445 Horst, P.; Weniger, J.H.; Peters, K.-J.
DE 105550/71/0002
Züchtungstechnische Studie an tropischen Standorten. **Study on breeding methods in the tropics.**

10446 Enbergs, H.   DE 111405/78/0001 N
Endokrinologische Untersuchungen an verschiedenen Haustierarten. **Endocrinological investigations on different farm animals.**

10447 Kellner, P.; Schinke, E.   DE 129380/75/0005 R
Schlachttier– und Fleischproduktion in der DDR. **Products in the GDR.**

10448 Kellner, P.; Pospelowa, G.; Fliess, H.; Schinke, E.
DE 129380/75/0007
Schlachttier– und Fleischproduktion in Bulgarien. **Production of animals for slaughter and of meat and meat products in Bulgaria.**

10449 Kellner, P.; Jaehne, G.; Schinke, E. DE 129380/75/0008
Schlachttier– und Fleischproduktion in der Sowjetunion. **Production of animals for slaughter and of meat and meat products in the Soviet Union.**

10450 Stuhrmann, H.   DE 129400/75/0006
Analytische Betrachtungen und modelltheoretische Untersuchungen zur Bestimmung der optimalen Kanalabmessungen beim Flüssigmistverfahren. **Analytical considerations and model theoretical investigations concerning the determination of optimal channel dimensions for liquid manure.**

10451 Fischer, H.; Scheurmann, E.   DE 129540/71/0005

Untersuchungen über Haltung, Nutzung und Zucht der einheimischen Wild– und Haustierpopulationen in den Tropen. **Contribution to husbandry, breeding and utilization of indigenous wild and domestic animals in the tropics.**

10452 Goller, H.   DE 129605/72/0001
Vergleichende Neuroanatomie unserer Haustiere. **Comparative neuroanatomy of our domestic animals.**

10453 Meinecke, B.   DE 129860/77/0002
Untersuchungen zur in vivo Befruchtung in vitro gereifter Oozyten. **Investigations in fertilizing oocytes matured in vitro.**

10454 Brummer, H.   DE 129861/77/0001
Verhaltensstörungen bei den Haustieren. **Disorders of behaviour in domestic animals.** Publications.

10455 Paufler, S.; Müller–Schlösser, F.   DE 132335/72/0001 N
Untersuchung über die Verarbeitung, Lagerung und Anwendung von Sperma bei Haustieren. **Investigations into the dilution, preservation and insemination of sperm in domestic animals.** Publications.

10456 Schwarz, R.   DE 139050/72/0001
Untersuchungen an der äusseren Haut von Haustieren. **Investigations on outer skin of domestic animals.**

10457 Hill, H.; Agthe, O.; Kolm, H.P.; Himmler, V.   DE 139205/78/0001 N
Physiologie und Pathologie der Fortpflanzung. **Physiology and pathology of reproduction.** Publications.

10458 Comberg, G.   DE 139350/73/0002
Private Organisationen und Staatliche Förderungsmassnahmen in der deutschen Tierzucht und ihre Bedeutung für den züchterischgenetischen Fortschritt. **Self–aid of private organizations and state promotion measures in the German animal production and their effects on the genetic breeding progress.**

10459 Schulze, W.; Mickwitz, G.von   DE 139750/78/0011 N
Ethophysiologische Aspekte des Tiertransportes. **Ethophysiological aspects of animal transport.** Publications.

10460 Lotthammer, K.–H.   DE 139800/70/0004
Zusammenhänge zwischen Fütterung und Fruchtbarkeit unter besonderer Berücksichtigung der Veränderung der Blutwerte von Glucose, Bilirubin, Cholesterin, LDH und GOT. **Correlations between feeding and fertility with special regard to changes in serum values of glucose, bilirubin, cholesterol, LDH, and GOT.**

10461 Schneider, U.; Hahn, J.   DE 139803/77/0001
Untersuchungen zur Verbesserung der Ergebnisse bei der Eizellübertragung verschiedener Spezies. **Optimisation of zygote transfer in different species.**

10462 Faber, H.von; Hartner, L.   DE 144141/74/0003
Die Wirkungsweise von DDT, seinen Metaboliten und PCBs bei ihrer Beeinflussung reproduktiver Prozesse. **The mode of action of DDT, its metabolites and PCBs on processes of reproduction.**

10463 Siebert, G.; Groha, C.   DE 144190/78/0002 N
Verhalten von Palatinit und verwandten Verbindungen gegenüber Darmbakterien. **The reaction of Palatinitol and**

related substances to intestinal microorganisms.

10464 Hinrichsen, J.K.; Jopski, E.; Buchenauer, D.   DE 144675/77/0003
Untersuchungen über die Eignung ausgewählter physiologischer Parameter zur Beurteilung des sog. Wohlbefindens bei landwirtschaftlichen Nutztieren. **Investigations on qualification of some physiological parameters in relation to the well–being of farm animals.**

10465 Vollmerhaus, B.   DE 160430/78/0001 N
Anatomie der Blutgefässe und der Lymphgefässe bei Haustieren. **Anatomy of blood vessels and lymphatic vessels in domestic animals.**

10466 Walter, P.; Liebich, H.–G.   DE 160460/70/0001
Experimentell–morphologische Untersuchungen an immunologisch kompetenten Zellen. **Experimental and morphological investigations of immuno– logical competent cells.**

10467 Walter, P.; Rüsse, I.   DE 160460/73/0001
Morphologie der weiblichen Geschlechtsorgane der Haussäugetiere. **Morphology of the genital organs in female domestic animals.**

10468 Walter, P.; Liebich, H.–G.   DE 160460/74/0001
Strukturveränderungen an Gefässen nach Transplantation. **Structural changes in vessels after transplantation.**

10469 Petry, H.   DE 160600/72/0002
Quantitative Beziehung zwischen Energieumsatz und Tiermotilität. **Quantitative correlations between energy metabolism and body activity of animals.**

10470 Gropp, J.; Beck, H.   DE 160600/72/0018 N
Wachstumsförderer. **Growth stimulants.**

10471 Scharrer, E.   DE 160600/75/0012
Entwicklung des Nährstofftransports. **Development of nutrient transport.**

10472 Rüsse, M.W.   DE 160910/70/0001
Über den Einfluss der neuroendokrinen Regulation auf die bioelektrischen Vorgänge der glatten Muskelzellen des Uterus. **Influence of neuro–endocrine regulation on bio–electric events of smooth uterine muscle cells.**

10473 Leidl, W.; Schefels, W.; Kuhn, A.; Stidl, G.; Braun, H.   DE 160910/73/0004
Superovulation und Eitransplantation – Fortsetzung –. **Superovulation and transplantation of ova – continuation –.**

10474 Leidl, W.; Wendt, V.; Klenner, A.; Prinzen, R.; Kleeberg, S.; Boryczko, Z.   DE 160910/73/0005
Enzyme bei Sperma und Spermien – Fortsetzung –. **Enzymes in semen and spermatozoa – continuation –.**

10475 Leidl, W.; Prinzen, R.; Grägl, M.; Kraussmüller, H.   DE 160911/73/0004
Die Steuerung der Gonaden. **Regulating mechanisms in gonadal growth.**

10476 Kirchgessner, M.; Spörl, R.   DE 161280/72/0001
Spurenelement Stoffwechsel bei Reproduktionsvorgängen bei Ratten. **Trace element metabolism in rat reproduction.**

D 3100 – Animal management general and animal husbandry

10477 Pirchner, F.; Rottmann, O.   DE 161300/78/0001 N
Chromosomenanalyse bei Embryonenmanipulation.
Chromosome analysis in manipulation of early embryos.

10478 Wander, J.–F.   DE 201080/77/0001
Auswirkung verschiedener Haltungssysteme auf qualitative
und quantitative Merkmale der Leistung und des Verhaltens
landwirtschaftlicher Nutztiere. **Effects of different keeping
systems on qualitative and quantitative characteristics of
performance and behaviour of agricultural livestock.**

10479 Schlünsen, D.   DE 201090/75/0019
Gesundheitskontrolle und Ermittlung des
Konzeptionsoptimums durch physiologische Kenndaten.
**Health control and finding out of the optimum of conception
by physiological data.**

10480 Meinhold, K.; Walter, K.   DE 201100/78/0006 N
Ökonomische Analyse technischer und züchterischer
Fortschritte in der tierischen Produktion. **Economic analysis of
technical and genetical progresses in animal production.**

10481 Pfau, A.   DE 201200/75/0003
Radiobiologische Untersuchungen zu
Körperzusammensetzung und Stoffwechselvorgängen bei
Haustieren. **Radiobiological investigations on whole body
composition and metabolism of domestic animals.**

10482 Farries, E.   DE 201200/77/0001
Biologische Grundlagen des Wachstums landwirtschaftlicher
Nutztiere. **Biological principles of the growth of productive
livestock.**

10483 Unshelm, J.   DE 201200/77/0002
Untersuchung der biologischen Rhythmik physiologischer
Konstitutionsmerkmale bei Haustieren. **Investigations on
biological rhythm of physiological constitution features in
domestic animals.**

10484 Andreae, U.   DE 201200/77/0005
Studien zur Relativierung von Verhaltensansprüchen der
Haustiere zur Anpassung. **Studies on relativity between
behavioral requirements of domestic animals and adaptation.**

10485 Ellendorff, F.   DE 201200/77/0008
Endokrinologie und Neuroendokrinologie des zyklisch
ablaufenden Sexualgeschehens. **Endocrinology and
neuroendocrinology of sexual cycle.**

10486 Smidt, D.   DE 201200/77/0009
Endokrinologie und Neuroendokrinologie der Gravidität und
Geburt. **Endocrinology and neuroendocrinology of gravidity.**

10487 Ellendorff, F.   ' DE 201200/77/0010
Steuerung männlicher Sexualfunktionen. **Control of sexual
functions in male animals.**

10488 Schilling, E.   DE 201200/77/0017
Brunststeuerung und Brunstdiagnostik. **Control and diagnostic
of oestrus.**

10489 Elsaesser, F.   DE 201200/77/0018
Steuerung von Fortpflanzungsvorgängen mittels
Immunisierung gegen endogene Hormone. **Control of
reproductive processes by immunization against endogenous
hormones.**

10490 Werhahn, E.   DE 201200/77/0021
Konstitutionsbiologische Untersuchungen zur Aufzucht von
Jungtieren. **Constitution biological examination for rearing of
young animals.**

10491 Andreae, U.   DE 201200/77/0026
Entwicklung praktikabler telemetrischer Verfahren zur
Erfassung ethologischer und verhaltensphysiologischer
Parameter. **Development of practicable telemetric methods for
collection of ethological and behaviour physiological
parameters.**

10492 Elsaesser, F.   DE 201200/77/0029
Endokrine und neuroendokrine Grundlagen der sexuellen
Differenzierung und Entwicklung. **Endocrine and
neuroendocrine principles of sexual differentiation and
development.**

10493 Schön, L.; Scheper, J.   DE 210010/78/0007 N
Ermittlung des quantitativen Schlachtwertes am lebenden
Tier. **Estimation of the quantitative slaughter value on the live
animal.**

10494 Mason, V.C.; Bech–Andersen, S.   DK 010206/72/0008
Udarbejdelse og afprøvning af blodanalysemetoder (proteiner,
enzymer og metaboliter). **Development and testing of methods
for blood analyses.**

10495 Scmidt, M.; Vestergaard, K.   DK 030135/74/0006 R
Etologiske undersøgelser. e. Etologi, fysiologi og
husdyrproduktion. **Ethological investigations. (e) Ethology,
Physiology and Domestic animal production.**

10496 Desmoulin, B.   FR 010206/74/2935
Etude du stade optimal d'abattage selon le sexe, les types
génétiques et les conditions nutritionnelles. **Optimal age of
slaughtering according to sex, genetic types and nutritional
conditions.**

10497 Gaye, P.; Mercier, J.C.   FR 010213/77/7550
Etude des mécanismes de synthèse et de sécrétion des
protéines du lait. **Mechanisms involved in the biosynthesis and
secretion of milkproteins.**

10498 Tissier, M.; Theriez, M.; Robelin, J.
    FR 010805/76/6540
Détermination des réserves corporelles in vivo. **Determination
of body in vivo.**

10499 Rayssiguier, Y.; Kopp; Larvor, P.   FR 010817/77/8031
Minéraux et parturition : influence du magnésium. **Effect of
magnésium on parturition.**

10500 Langlet, A.; Flamand.; Gibon, A.   FR 011401/76/6212
Problèmes agronomiques de l'élevage en milieu pyrénéen.
Agronomical problems for breeding in mountains "Pyrénées".

10501 Hall; Purser   GB 010103/00/0005 R
**Commercial and biological significance of blood groups in
sheep.**

10502 Nicholson; Maxwell   GB 010105/76/0005
**Database management systems for experimental livestock
breeding projects.**

10503 Slee; Bateman   GB 010106/00/0007 R
Growth/temperature/nutrition interactions.

10504 Slee   GB 010106/00/0009 R
Physiology of cold stress and its effect on food intake and growth.

10505 Baldwin; Paterson   GB 010301/00/0032 R
Behavioural cardiovascular and endocrine responses to stress in pigs and ruminants.

10506 Holtzbauer–sharman; Sharman   GB 010301/00/0043 R
Monoamine oxidase in the young rat and pig.

10507 Holzbauer–sharman   GB 010301/00/0044 R
Responses of the endocrine system to environmental stresses including extremes of temperature.

10508 Sharman; Stephens   GB 010301/00/0052 R
The neurochemical basis for abnormal behaviour in domesticated animals.

10509 Mount; James   GB 010301/00/0056 R
Heat loss from man in relation to body type, diet and activity.

10510 Sharman   GB 010301/00/0064 R
Chemical methods for estimation of substances involved in transmission of nerve activity and their metabolites.

10511 Baldwin   GB 010301/75/0075
The role of olfaction in the behaviour of pigs and ruminants.

10512 Holzbauer–sharman   GB 010301/76/0045 R
Subcellular distribution of steroids in the adrenal gland.

10513 Stephens   GB 010301/76/0076 R
Physiological concomitants of transportation in domestic farm animals.

10514 Holzbauer–sharman   GB 010301/77/0080 R
The function of the dopaminergic nerves in the pituitary gland in laboratory and farm animals.

10515 Mann; Banns   GB 010301/77/0082 R
Metabolism of acetylcholine and choline.

10516 Mount   GB 010301/77/0083 R
Heat transfer between the organism and its environment.

10517 Sharman   GB 010301/79/0089 N
The origin of dopamine in the blood following feeding.

10518 Munn   GB 010302/00/0041 R
Structural and functional properties of mitochondria.

10519 Dawson; Hemington   GB 010302/76/0045 R
Increased phosphatidylinositol turnover during secretion of hormones.

10520 Evans; Rydzewski   GB 010304/00/0035 R
Neural control of respiration and autonomic functions with particular reference to the rostral brainstem.

10521 Wakerley; Leng   GB 010304/77/0056 R
Control of oxytocin and vasopressin neurones.

10522 Dyer; Leng   GB 010304/77/0057 R
Neuronal mechanisms in the secretion of hypothalamic hormones.

10523 Wakerley; Cross   GB 010304/77/0058 R
Neurohormonal effects of suckling.

10524 Silver   GB 010305/18/0012 N
Functional innervation of the pineal gland of farm animals.

10525 Bligh   GB 010305/76/0059 R
Thermoregulation and other processes of homeostasis in farm animals.

10526 Bligh; Bacon   GB 010305/76/0060 R
Process of acclimatization of farm animals to seasonal and other environmental changes.

10527 Bangham   GB 010307/00/0001 R
Cell membranes: behaviour of models made from phospholipids.

10528 Bangham; Hill   GB 010307/00/0004 R
Adhesion, fusion and perforation of membranes at a molecular level.

10529 Miller; Joggard   GB 010307/00/0006 R
Extraction, purification and identification of lipids.

10530 Bangham; Hill   GB 010307/00/0007 R
Use of liposomes in investigating anasthesia, sleep and hibernation.

10531 Eriksdottir; Bangham   GB 010307/00/0010 R
Compositional adaptation by membranes to physical and chemical assault.

10532 Bangham; Wale   GB 010307/78/0013 R
Actin microfilament interaction with cell or model membranes.

10533 Wooding; Peacock   GB 010308/19/0017 N
Ultrastructure of secretory and absorbing epithelia.

10534 Munn   GB 010308/76/0005 R
Interactions of proteins with membranes.

10535 Gordon; Carleton   GB 010308/76/0014 R
Cellular receptors involved in concentrative transport and responses to stimuli.

10536 Heitzman; Hoare   GB 010404/75/0829 R
Mode of action, hazards and therapeutic uses of steroids.

10537 Enser   GB 010601/00/0100 R
Define factors controlling accumulation and physical characteristics of adipose tissue fat in meat animals.

10538 Lister   GB 010601/00/0120 R
Define neuroendocrine factors controlling metabolism, carcass composition and meat quality.

10539 Fisher   GB 010602/00/0020 R
Define parameters of live animals for predicting carcass composition.

10540 Skinner; Knight   GB 010907/00/0002

Develop rigid–wall isolators for mouse breeding and large scale production of clean foundation stock.

10541 Robertson; Hill   GB 021007/79/0001 N
Genetic interrelationships between rate of lean deposition, appetite and body composition in mice.

10542 Peaker   GB 030204/00/0019 R
Environmental factors, particularly cold exposure, on metabolism and production.

10543 Smith; Palmer   GB 030601/00/0006 R
Structure and metabolism of intramuscular collagen during growth (cattle, rabbit).

10544 Smith; RH   GB 030601/00/0007 R
Physico–chemical characterization of aortic collagen.

10545 Dawson; Smith   GB 030601/00/0025 R
Effect of diet, age and pregnancy on the collagen of skin and other major tissues.

10546 Harris   GB 030601/00/0029 R
Metabolism of muscle protein during growth of farm animals.

10547 Robins   GB 030601/76/0030 R
Collagen turnover rates.

10548 Williams; Dawson   GB 030604/78/0029 N
The effects of copper deficiency on the development of the heart and other tissues in young growing animals.

10549 Fell; Dinsdale   GB 030608/00/0013 R
Effect of hormones on structure of the alimentary canal.

10550 Researcher not indicated   GB 050166/00/0002
Farm waste: effect on soil and crops.

10551 Researcher not indicated   GB 050434/00/0003 R
Studies of serum gamma globulin levels in relation to productivity.

10552 Dodsworth   GB 060208/00/0015
Monitoring traditional animal husbandry practices and the use of proprietary products in animal production.

10553 Clancy, M.J.   IE 060100/72/0817 R
Growth, development and differentiation of skeletal muscle in meat animals. Publications.

10554 Lee, J.; Gardiner, M.; Finch, T.F.   IE 060200/75/1084 R
The potential of Irish land for livestock production (Meath). Publications.

10555 Cole, A.   IE 060201/71/0417
The effects of different stocking rates on animal production on sod peat cutaway bog. Publications.

10556 Enne, G.   IT 040613/77/0659
Induzione, sincronizzazione dell'ovulazione e dell'estro in diverse specie di interesse zootecnico. **Induction, synchronisation of ovulation and oestrum in different species of farm animals.**

10557 Matassino, D.   IT 040722/77/0570 R
Valutazione –in vivo– degli animali destinati alla produzione della carne e quantizzione delle caratteristiche qualitative della carne. **"In vivo" evaluation of animals bred for their meat; quantification of qualitative characteristics of the meat.**

10558 Bergström, P.L.   NL 010112/67/1199
De invloed van afstamming, sexe, voeding, voedersysteem en opfokintensteit op het groeiritme van landbouw huisdieren. **The influence of descent, sex, feeding, feeding–system and rearing intensity on growth rhythm in farm animals.** Publications.

10559 Wiel, D.F.M. van de   NL 010112/75/6182
Onderzoek van de normale huishouding der vrouwelijke geslachtshormonen bij landbouwhuisdieren. **Research of the normal status of female sex–hormones in farm animals.** Publications.

10560 Brake, J.H.A. te   NL 010112/75/6183
Drachtigheidsdiagnose bij landbouwhuisdieren. **Pregnancy diagnosis in farm animals.** Publications.

10561 Boekholt, H.A.   NL 020017/74/5452
Energie– en eiwithuishouding van warm– en koudbloedige dieren m.i.v. de bepaling van de energetische voederwaarde van veevoeders met behulp van energiebalansproeven. **Energy and protein metabolism of homeo– and poikilotherm animal including the determination of energetic feedingvalue of feeds for livestock on energy–balance–trials.**

10562 Hoek, J. van den   NL 020017/77/7309
De biologische activiteit van geconfugeerde oestrogenen op verschillende tijdstippen van de ovariële cyclus. **The biological activity of conjugated oestrogens at different points of time of the ovarian cycle.**

10563 Brant, A.   NL 030013/76/6122 R
Het diepvriezen van embryonen van landbouwhuisdieren. **Deep freezing of embryos of farm animals.** Publications.

Equines (B 4100)

See also 10710, 10871, 11034, 13910

10564 Rohloff, D.; Jacob, L.   DE 104400/75/0002
Histometrische Untersuchungen an Hengsthoden. **Histometrical investigations of testes in stallion.**

10565 Heidrich, H.J.; Degenhardt, H.C.   DE 104400/77/0003
Der Hämagglutinationstest 'MIP–Rest' zur Trächtigkeitsdiagnose bei der Stute. **Hemagglutination test 'rest of MIP' for diagnosis of pregnancy in mare.**

10566 Wintzer, H.–J.; Biber, V.   DE 104450/73/0002 N
Untersuchungen zur Aufzucht und zum Training von Vollblutpferden. **Studies of thoroughbred horse rearing and training.**

10567 Hartung, K.; Herrmann, W.   DE 104451/74/0001
Untersuchungen zur Schilddrüsenfunktion bei Trabrennpferden mit Hilfe des T3– und des T4–Testes. **Analysis of the thyroid function in trotting racers by means of T3 and T4 tests.**

10568 Keller, H.; Keulertz, K.   DE 104452/75/0002
Das weisse Blutbild des Pferdes. **White blood cells in horses.**

D 3100 – Animal management general and animal husbandry

10569 Sommer, H.; Best, I.　　　　DE 111400/77/0001
Untersuchungen zur Ermittlung des Referenzbereiches
verschiedener Blutparameter bei Vollblutpferden.
**Investigations on reference values of different blood
constituents in thoroughbred horses.**

10570 Sommer, H.; Järgen, A.; Enbergs, H.
　　　　　　　　　　　　　DE 111400/77/0002
Untersuchungen zur Verbesserung der Fruchtbarkeit bei
Warmblutstuten. **Investigations on the improvement of fertility
in warmblood mares.**

10571 Sommer, H.; Lotzemer–Jentges, K.; Enbergs, H.
　　　　　　　　　　　　　DE 111400/77/0003
Untersuchungen zur Verbesserung der Fruchtbarkeit von
Traberstuten. **Investigations on the improvement of fertility in
trotter mares.**

10572 Eikmeier, H.; Schmidt, K.–H.; Schmidt, B.
　　　　　　　　　　　　　DE 129881/78/0002 N
Verhalten von Serumenzymen beim Pferd unter verschiedenen
äusseren Einflüssen und Belastungen. **Behaviour of serum
enzymes in horse in dependence on different outer influences
and stress impacts.**

10573 Bader, H.; Genn, H.J.　　　DE 139400/78/0002 N
Vaginalzytologische Untersuchungen bei der hochtragenden
Stute zur Vorausbestimmung des Geburtstermines. **Vaginal
cytological studies on mares advanced in pregnancy at term to
estimate the time of parturition.** Publications.

10574 Günzel, A.–R.; Himmler, V.; Kolm, H.P.
　　　　　　　　　　　　　DE 139400/78/0004 N
Versuche zur Beeinflussbarkeit des Fortpflanzungsgeschehens
der Stute mittels intrazervikaler Elektrostimulation
verdeutlicht durch die Progesteronkonzentration im
peripheren Serum. **Trials on taking influence on reproduction
of mare by intracervical electro–stimulation using progesterone
concentration in peripheral serum.**

10575 Bader, H.; Nesseler, D.　　DE 139400/78/0005 N
Vaginalzytologische Untersuchungen bei zyklischen Stuten.
Vaginal cytological investigations on cycling mares.

10576 Bader, H.; Krause, A.　　　DE 139401/78/0003 N
Untersuchungen über Transport und Verteilung der Spermien
im Genitale der Stute nach künstlicher Besamung.
**Investigations on transport and distribution of sperm in the
genitals of mare after artificial insemination.**

10577 Bader, H.; Baumgartl, C.; Drommer, W.
　　　　　　　　　　　　　DE 139401/78/0004 N
Licht– und elektronenmikroskopische Befunde an
Hengstspermien in Abhängigkeit von der
Spermakonservierung. **Light and electron microscopical
investigations on stallion spermatozoa in relation with semen
preservation.**

10578 Bader, H.　　　　　　　DE 139401/78/0005 N
Spermienkapazitation beim Pferd. **Sperm capacitation in
horses.**

10579 Deegen, E.; Buntenkötter, E.; Holsten, H.H.;
Mattiesen, T.　　　　　　　DE 139850/71/0005
Herz– und Kreislaufuntersuchungen beim Pferd. **The analysis
of the heart and circulation in horse.**

10580 Hertsch, B.; Flores, C.　　DE 139850/77/0006
Hautthermographie beim Pferd. **Skin thermography in horse.**

10581 Hörnicke, H.; Meixner, R.　DE 144140/77/0001
Telemetrische Messung von Atmungsgrössen und
Sauerstoffverbrauch bei Pferden in der Bewegung. **Telemetric
measurement of respiratory parameters and oxygen
consumption in exercising horses.**

10582 Schulz, H.; Pirkelmann, H.　DE 502602/72/0002
Untersuchungen über moderne Haltungsverfahren für
Nutzund Sportpferde 1972. **Studies of present–day methods of
keeping horses for productive and sports purposes.**

10583 Sønnichsen, H.V.; Falk–Rønne, J.; Kristoffersen, J.
　　　　　　　　　　　　　DK 030130/78/0006 N
Blodanalyser vedr. Hg, leukocyter og enzymerne ASAT og
ALP. **Laboratory investigations in riding horses. Blood
analyses concerning Hg, leucocytes and enzymes ASAT and
ALP.**

10584 Kristoffersen, J.; Thuen, J.; Sønnichsen, H.V.
　　　　　　　　　　　　　DK 030130/79/0001 N
Undersøgelse af ændringer i 4 standard blodparametre hos
konkurrencerideheste. **Investigations on changes in 4 standard
blood parameters in competition horses.**

10585 Kristoffersen, J.; Sønnichsen, H.V.; Smith, M.;
Reimann, I.; Christensen, S.B.; Mortensen, S.
　　　　　　　　　　　　　DK 030130/79/0002 N
Undersøgelse vedr. trykforhold i led og omgivende knogler hos
hest. **Investigations on tension in joints and adjoining bones in
horse.**

10586 Petit, M.; Beranger, C.; Garel, M.　FR 010813/70/6533
Elevage des génisses dans un troupeau allaitant. **Rearing of
heifers in a suckling herd.**

10587 Martin–Rosset, W.　　　　FR 010813/73/6536
Production de poulain de boucherie. **Horse meat production.**

10588 Martin–Rosset, W.　　　　FR 010813/74/6534
Exploitation et alimentation de troupeaux de juments
allaitantes. **Managements of brood mares'herds.**

10589 Bosc, M.; Locatelli, A.; Durand, P.; Prud'Homme,
M.J.; Fevre, J.; Terqui, M.　　　FR 011501/69/7538
Etude du contrôle de la parturition des mammifères
domestiques et de la survie des nouveaux–fies. **Study of the
control of parturition in domestic mammals and of the survival
of the young born.**

10590 Prud'Homme, M.J.　　　　FR 011501/69/7540
Facteurs de régulation de l'activité utérine chez les
mammiferes domestiques. **Factors of regulation of the uterine
activity in domestic Mammals.**

10591 Palmer, E.; Driancourt, M.A.; Mariana, J.C.
　　　　　　　　　　　　　FR 011501/72/7527
Maîtrise de la reproduction chez la jument. **Control of
reproduction in the mare.**

10592 Brophy, P.O.; Gordon, I.; Hannan, J.; Collins, J.D.
　　　　　　　　　　　　　IE 120105/79/9215 N
An investigation into factors affecting the health and survival of

the newborn foal.

10593 Vecchiotti´Antaldi, G.　　　　IT 040411/77/0310 R
Sulla fertilità del cavallo da corsa, con particolare riferimento
alla eventuale influenza su di essa dell'attività sportiva.
**Fecundity in the race horse, stressing the eventual influence of
racing.**

10594 Mey, G.J.W. van der; Bos, H.　　　NL 030009/70/5724
Analyse van de waarde van prestatieproeven van dekhengsten
die voor het merendeel kruisingen zijn. **Performance tests in
horses.**

10595 Sasse, H.H.L.　　　　　　　NL 030011/71/5811 R
Longfunktietest bij paarden. **Lungfunctiontest in horses.**
Publications.

10596 Taverne, M.A.M.　　　　　　NL 030013/76/6981 R
Myometriumactiviteit tijdens de oestrische cyclus, graviditeit
en geboorte bij de merrie. **Myometrial activity during the
oestrous cycle, gestation and parturition in the mare.**
Publications.

Ruminants in general (B 4200)

See also 2446, 3545, 10586, 10589, 10590, 11825, 11839, 11843,
12965, 14059, 19169

10597 Greve, T.; Lehn–Jensen, H.; Jensen, A.M.
　　　　　　　　　　　　　　　DK 030128/79/0001 N
Bovine ovulationsmekanismer. **Bovine ovulatory mechanisms.**

10598 Lehn–Jensen, H.; Greve, T.　　　DK 030128/79/0002 N
Dybfrysning af bovine embryoner. **Low temperature
preservation of bovine embryos.**

10599 Champredon, C.; Pion, R.; Prugnaud, J.
　　　　　　　　　　　　　　　FR 010815/68/9582 N
Etude de l'aminoacidémie libre des ruminants. **Free amino
acids in blood of ruminants.**

10600 Morand–Fehr, P.; Chilliard, Y.; Bas, P.
　　　　　　　　　　　　　　　FR 011712/70/9509 N
Métabolisme lié à la sécrétion lactée des femelles hautes
productrices de lait chez les ruminants. **Metabolism in relation
with milk secretion of high milk yielding producers in
ruminants.**

10601 Thompson; Silver　　　　　GB 010305/78/0071 R
Effect of cold exposure on organ function in ruminants.

10602 Young; Mansfield　　　　　GB 010308/76/0004 R
**Investigation of ruminant erythrocyte metabolism and funtion
with emphasis on membrane transport processes.**

10603 McLean; Watts　　　　　　GB 030204/00/0006 R
Investigation of heat storage by calorimetry and thermometry.

10604 Jenkinson; Lloyd　　　　　GB 030204/00/0025 R
Factors affecting the microbial population of the skin.

10605 Hodgson; Milne　　　　　GB 030303/00/0003
**The improvement of hill and upland pasture utilisation by
grazing cattle and sheep.**

10606 Brockway　　　　　　　GB 030606/00/0007

Effects of exercise and stress on domestic animals.

10607 Gordon; Webster　　　　　GB 030606/00/0010 R
Environmental studies on intensively reared livestock.

10608 Greenhalg; Reid GW　　　　GB 030611/00/0018
Use of roughages by ruminants.

10609 Chalmers; White　　　　　GB 030612/00/0003 R
Metabolism of urea and amino acids.

10610 Prescott　　　　　　　GB 060102/00/0034
Forage systems for livestock.

10611 Mackie; Girvan　　　　　GB 060214/00/0015
Grazing systems for beef and sheep production.

10612 Dickson; Frame　　　　　GB 060315/00/0006
**Herbage utilisation employing cattle and sheep,and
conservation,under intensive grassland management.**

10613 Dickson　　　　　　　GB 060315/00/0007
**Animal production from lowland sheep grazing systems with
and without cattle.**

10614 McClelland　　　　　　GB 060319/00/0001
**A system of hill sheep and suckler calf production involving
more extensive use of hill land.**

10615 McClelland　　　　　　GB 060319/00/0002
**The improvement of output from a traditional hill farm
environment.**

10616 Auxilia, M.T.; Puppo, S.; Terramoccia, S.; De Maria,
C.　　　　　　　　　　　　　IT 020700/78/0003 R
Tenore in oligoelementi del colostro di diverse specie in
ruminanti a differenti distanze dal parto –. **Trace element
content in colostrum of different ruminant species at varius
post–partum intervals.**

10617 Piva, G.F.　　　　　　　IT 040412/77/0576 R
Nuove indagini sul condizionamento della microflora ruminale
per migliorare le sintesi protidiche. **New investigations on
microflora conditioning in ruminants as a means of improving
protein synthesis.**

10618 Faustini, R.　　　　　　　IT 040630/77/0552 R
Motilità e secrezioni nell'apparato gastroenterico dei
ruminanti, effetti di vari polipeptidi. **Motility and secretions of
the gastroenteric track in ruminants, the action of various
polypeptids.**

10619 Colombani, B.　　　　　　IT 041118/74/0537
Variazioni dei livelli ematici in macro e microelementi nelle
lattifere della litoranea toscana in rapporto alle conndizioni
agropedologiche, al livello produttivo ed alle manifestazioni di
ipofecondità rilevate nelle aree studiate. **Variations of hematic
levels in macro and microelements in dairy cows of the tuscan
littoral zone according to agricultural soil conditions, to levels of
productivity and to the occurrence of low fecundity in the areas
surveyed.**

Cattle (B 4210)

See also 2076, 2085, 3367, 3613, 3665, 5590, 10399, 10400,
10404, 11035, 11037, 11054, 11057, 11060, 11066, 11361, 12006,

12055, 12056, 12067, 12197, 12305, 12974, 13019, 13081, 13084, 13144, 13147, 14113, 14136, 14365, 15374, 15422, 15655, 15674, 15679, 15689, 15690, 15784, 15787, 15805, 16288, 17194, 17493, 19355

10620 Antoine, A.; Fraselle, J.; Rondia, G.; Dekker, A.; Dachet, P.   BE 010003/69/0001 R
Etude technique et économique dans le Nord Tunisien portant sur la production bovine intensive. **Technical and economical study in North Tunisia on intensive bovine production.** Publications.

10621 Vandenbyvang, P.; Antoine, A.   BE 010003/69/0002
Production intensive de viande bovine sans traire. **Research on intensive bovine meat production without milking.** Publications.

10622 De Corte, G.   BE 030001/62/0003 R
Vergelijkende studie van het wit rood Oostvlaams vee en het zwartbont vee van Belgie. **Comparative study of the white and red cattle of Oost Vlaanderen and the black and white cattle of Belgium.** Publications.

10623 Vandeplassche, M.; Bouters, R.; Geldof, A.; Moyaert, I.   BE 050300/77/0005 R
Invloed van verlossing door keizersnede op latere vruchtbaarheid van het rund. **Influence of delivery by ceasarean section on the subsequent fertility of the cow.**

10624 Vandeplassche, M.; Bouters, R.; Vereecke, D.
                              BE 050300/78/0008
Post partumstoornissen bij het rund. **Post partumtroubles in the cow.**

10625 Peeters, G.; Burvenich, C.; Vandeputte–Van Messom, G.   BE 050800/69/0002 R
Studie van de bloedvloei door de melkklier van geit en koe. **Studies on bloodflow trough the mammary of goats and cows.** Publications.

10626 Peeters, G.   BE 050800/70/0004
Studie over de fysiologie van de tepelspieren bij de melkkoe. **Study on the physiology of the teat muscles in lactating cows.** Publications.

10627 Ectors, F.; Beckers, J.   BE 060006/79/0002 N
Recherche sur la physiologie de la production, la stérilité hormonale et le diagnostic de gestation chez la vache. **Investigation of physiologie of production, hormonal sterility and pregnancy diagnosis by the cow.** Publications.

10628 Bienfet, V.; Lomba, F.; Cordiez, E.; Chavaux, G.; Van Stalle, A.; Lekeux, G.   BE 060009/79/0007 N
Etude des problèmes hygiéniques, sanitaires et techniques posés par la conduite rationnelle de grosses unités de production bovines et porcines. **Study of hygienic, sanitary and technical problems in managing large bovine and porcine production units.**

10629 Maton, A.; Daelemans, J.   BE 070300/72/0017 R
Studie van de kwetsuren bij melkvee in verschillende staltypen. **Study of the wounds of cows in different types of houses.** Publications.

10630 Boucqué, C.   BE 070700/71/0019 R
Vleesproduktie met zoogkoeien. **Beefproduction with suckling cows.** Publications.

10631 Buysse, F.X.; Boucqué, C.; Fiems, L.
                              BE 070700/73/0018 R
Intensieve vleesproduktie met vaarzen. **Intensive beefproduction with heifers.** Publications.

10632 Vandenbyvang, P.   BE 081200/70/0008
Vêlage précoce des génisses de la race Bleu Blanc belge. **Early calving of heifers of Blue White Belgian breed.**

10633 Thines, G.; Zayan, R.; Collignon, G.
                              BE 140000/76/0049 R
Comportement d'animaux domestiques en élevages industriels. **Behaviour of cattle and poultry in big economic farms.** Publications.

10634 Niepage, H.; Pomsel, T.   DE 104151/78/0003 N
Das Blutbild normaler Kühe in Abhängigkeit von Lebensalter und Trächtigkeit. **The blood picture of normal cows in relation to age and gestation.**

10635 Rohloff, D.; Patel, B.   DE 104400/75/0001
Untersuchungen zur Brunstdiagnostik beim Rind mittels Messung der elektrischen Leitfähigkeit des Vaginalschleims. **Studies on the detection of estrus in cattle by electrical measurements of vaginal mucus.** Publications.

10636 Horst, P.; Peters, K.–J.   DE 105550/77/0001
Körpergrössenentwicklung und Reproduktionseffizienz von Fleischrindern unterschiedlicher genetischer Struktur am subtropischen Standort. **Longterm bodyweight development and reproductive efficiency of beef cattle of different genetic structure in a subtropical environment.**

10637 Reinhardt, V.   DE 111403/78/0003 N
Untersuchungen zum Verhalten des Rindes. **Investigations on behavior of cattle.**

10638 Schmitten, F.; Müsch, W.; Lüke, F.; Trappmann, W.
                              DE 111500/75/0001
Schätzung von Parametern für Mastleistung und Körperform beim Rind. **Estimation of parameters for fattening performance and physical shape in cattle.**

10639 Schmitten, F.; Griese, J.   DE 111500/78/0002 N
Untersuchungen zur Steigerung der Wirtschaftlichkeit der Fleischrinderhaltung durch biotechnische Massnahmen. **Investigations for increasing the economy of beef cattle husbandry by biotechnical means.**

10640 Wassmuth, R.; Behrendt, W.   DE 129383/77/0002
Probleme der Bestandsgrösse und der Haltungstechnik in industriemässigen Tierhaltungen in der Sowjetunion u.a. osteuropäischen Staaten. **Problems of stock size and keeping system in large–scale livestock husbandry in the Soviet Union and other East European countries.**

10641 Steinbach, J.; Ottaro, J.   DE 129553/78/0002 N
Ökologische Einflüsse auf die Leistungen von Rindern in den Hochland– und Tieflandregionen Kenyas. **Ecological factors affecting cattle performance in the highland and lowland regions of Kenya.**

10642 Langholz, H.–J.; Bradly, M.; Claus, J.
                              DE 132270/78/0001 N

D 3100 – Animal management general and animal husbandry

Die Leistungsentwicklung schwarzbunter Importrinder und deren Nachzucht in Marokko. **Development of performance of black–and–white cattle imported to Morocco and of their progeny. Publications.**

10643 Langholz, H.–J.; Smidt, D.; Saage, H.–J.
DE 132273/70/0003
Entwicklung eines praktisch einsetzbaren Verfahrens zur Lebendbeurteilung von Schlacht– und Zuchtrindern mit Hilfe der Biophotogrammetrie. **Development of a practicable method for the valuation of live slaughter and breeding cattle by means of biophotogrammetry.**

10644 Langholz, H.–J.; Jürgens, H.   DE 132273/72/0003
Bestimmung der Umwelteinflüsse auf die Erstlaktation des Rindes unter besonderer Berücksichtigung ihrer Bedeutung für die Zuchtwertschätzung. **Determination of environmental effects on first lactation in cattle with special reference to their importance for estimation of breeding value.**

10645 Langholz, H.–J.; Kanning, K.   DE 132273/72/0006
Mutterkuhhaltung mit Rassen unterschiedlicher Nutzungsrichtung zur Nutzung des Grünlandes im Mittelgebirge – Solling. **Suckler cow keeping and breeds of different specialization for the utilization of grassland in the Solling uplands.**

10646 Langholz, H.–J.; Jongeling, C.   DE 132273/77/0003
Reaktion von Mutterkühen unterschiedlicher Nutzungsrichtung auf arbeits– und einstreusparende Stallformen. **Reaction of different breeds of suckler cows on housing in cubicles. Publications.**

10647 Holtz, W.; Voss, H.J.   DE 132276/75/0003
Zyklussteuerung beim Rind – Ein Vergleich verschiedener Verfahren. **Estrus control in cattle by different techniques.**

10648 Holtz, W.; Hahn, J.   DE 132276/77/0004
Erhöhung der Mehrlingshäufigkeit beim Rind auf dem Wege der Eitransplantation. **Increase of the twinning rate in cattle by way of embryo transfer.**

10649 Holtz, W.; Ehlers, K.   DE 132276/78/0004 N
Steuerung des Geburtstermins durch Corticoidgaben bei Färsen. **Control of parturition in heifers by treatment with corticoids.**

10650 Bader, H.; Stephan, E.   DE 139260/70/0006
Zur Problematik der Klimaempfindlichkeit bei Haustieren. Auswirkungen experimenteller Wärmebelastungen auf Bullen. **Problems of climatic tolerance in domestic animals. Effects of experimental heat stress on bulls.**

10651 Stephan, E.; Krause, D.   DE 139261/78/0001 N
Prägung von Jungrindern durch Kurzbelastung. **Young cattle as affected by short–term stress.**

10652 Stephan, E.; Roth, R.   DE 139261/78/0004 N
Prüfung auf Interaktionen zwischen Milchleistungsparametern beim Rind und medizin–meteorologischen Wirkungskomplexen. **Testing of interactions between parameters of milk yield in cow and medicinal–meteorological complexes of effects.**

10653 Geldermann, H.   DE 139352/77/0002
Einfluss polymorpher Enzyme auf den Milchstoffwechsel beim Rind. **Influence of polymorphic enzymes on the milk metabolism in cattle.**

10654 Stephan, E.; Bader, H.; Boehnke, H.–J.; Frädrich, G.; Hanschke, G.; Fink, C.   DE 139400/78/0001 N
Klimatische Einflüsse auf Reproduktionsleistungen beim Rind. **Climatic influences on reproduction performance in cattle.**

10655 Boehnke, H.–J.; Tormann, B.   DE 139401/78/0002 N
Zervikale und intrauterine Insemination beim Rind. **Cervical and intrauterine insemination in cattle.**

10656 Frerking, H.   DE 139800/70/0010
Untersuchungen über Mineralstoffgehalt der Kälber und der Fruchtwässer des Rindes in den verschiedenen Trächtigkeitsmonaten. **Investigations on mineral content in calves and in amniotic fluids of cows in different months of pregnancy.**

10657 Frerking, H.   DE 139800/70/0016
Geburtsauslösung beim Rind mit Glukokortikoiden. **Inducing of labour with glucocorticoids.**

10658 Meyer, H.; Lotthammer, K.–H.; Ahlswede, L.
DE 139800/73/0002 N
Beziehungen zwischen Fütterung und Fruchtbarkeit beim Rind. **Relations between feeding and fertility of dairy cattle.**

10659 Lotthammer, K.–H.; Volger, H.; Zinke, H.
DE 139800/74/0001
Vergleichende Untersuchungen über ernährungsbedingte Fruchtbarkeitsstörungen beim Rind in Grünlandbetrieben unter besonderer Berücksichtigung der Futtererzeugung. **Comparative studies on bovine fertility disturbances caused by nutritional errors in grassland farms with special regard to feed production.**

10660 Grunert, E.; Ruhe, F.   DE 139800/74/0002 R
Nachweis der Frühträchtigkeit beim Rind mit Hilfe von Progesteron–Bestimmungen in der Milch. **Diagnosis of early pregnancy in cattle by means of determining progesterone in milk. Publications.**

10661 Grunert, E.; Schwarz, R.   DE 139800/74/0003
Untersuchungen über die Wirkung von Human–Choriongonadotropin auf die Ovartätigkeit des Rindes. **Examinations of effects on the ovarian human chorionic gonadotrophin activity in cattle.**

10662 Frerking, H.   DE 139800/74/0006 R
Versuche zur hormonalen Geburtsauslösung beim Rind durch ACTH–Injektion bei Muttertier und Fetus. **Hormonal onset of labour in cattle by ACTH injections applied to dam and fetus.**

10663 Grunert, E.; Peukert, I.   DE 139800/78/0001 N
Untersuchungen über Häufigkeit, Entstehung und Funktion von Luteinzysten beim Rind. **Occurrence, development and function of Lutein cysts in cows.**

10664 Grunert, E.; Hornig, B.   DE 139800/78/0003 N
Vergleichende rektale und hormonanalytische Untersuchungen beim Rind zur Feststellung des Zyklusstandes. **Comparison of rectal and hormone analytical tests to determine the cycle of cows.**

10665 Grunert, E.; Blesenkemper, L.   DE 139800/78/0004 N
Untersuchungen über die Auswirkung der verkürzten
Zwischenkalbezeit auf die spätere Fruchtbarkeit beim Rind.
**Influence of shorter calving interval on subsequent fertility of
cows.**

10666 Lotthammer, K.–H.; Garibay, M.; Farries, E.
DE 139800/78/0007 N
Einfluss einer unterschiedlichen Nährstoffversorgung vor und
nach der Geburt von Milchrindern auf die Gesundheit und
Fruchtbarkeit. **Influence of different intake of energy and
digestible protein pre– and postpartum on health and fertility of
dairy cows.**

10667 Lotthammer, K.–H.; Knippenberg, R.
DE 139800/78/0009 N
Beziehungen zwischen Blutserumwerten von Kühen und prä–
und perinatalen Kälberverlusten. **Relations between serum
values of cows and pre– and perinatal calves–losses.**

10668 Hahn, J.; Schneider, U.   DE 139803/73/0001
Versuche zur in vitro–Befruchtung und Konservierung der
Eizellen von Maus, Kaninchen und Rind. **Experiments of in
vitro–fertilization and preservation of mouse, rabbit and cattle
ova.**

10669 Hahn, J.; Hahn, R.; Schneider, U.; Zoder, H.F.;
Baumgärtner, G.   DE 139803/74/0002
Versuche zur Gewinnung, Konservierung und Transplantation
von Rindereizellen. **Experiments on collection, preservation
and transfer of bovine ova.**

10670 Marx, D.   DE 144605/72/0003
Regelmässige Fertilitäts– und Sterilitätsuntersuchungen sowie
therapeutische Massnahmen in den Rinderherden der
Universität Hohenheim als Beispiel einer kontinuierlichen
Fruchtbarkeitsüberwachung. **Regular investigations of fertility
respectively sterility and therapeutic measures in the herds of
cattle of the Hohenheim University as an example of continuous
control of fertility.**

10671 Hinrichsen, J.K.; Neher, T.   DE 144675/77/0005
Analyse der Mutterkuhhaltung und Entwicklungstendenzen in
Baden–Württemberg. **Analysis of calf–suckling–system and
development in Baden–Wuerttemberg.**

10672 Buchenauer, D.; Dannenmann, K.
DE 144675/78/0004 N
Kälberverhalten bei unterschiedlichen
Beleuchtungsintensitäten. **Behavior of calves at different light
intensities.**

10673 Fewson, D.; Börner, H.; Momm, H.
DE 144680/78/0004 N
Organisationspraxis der Zuchtplanung beim Rind. **Practical
organization of breeding planning with cattle.**

10674 Rabold, K.; Gaiser, H.   DE 144690/78/0003 N
Ein Beitrag zur Involution der Rindermilchdrüse. **A
contribution to the involution of the mammary gland of cows.**

10675 Rabold, K.; Grimm, H.   DE 144690/78/0004 N
Einfluss von Melkverfahren auf das Verhalten von Milchkühen
beim Melken. **Influence of milking procedures on some
ethological parameters of cows during milking.**

10676 Ernst, E.; Kalm, E.; Schubert, U.
DE 148350/75/0005 R
Reaktionen von Rinderrassen auf verschiedene
Haltungsverfahren. **Reactions of cattle races to different
systems of husbandry.**

10677 Ernst, E.; Appel, W.   DE 148352/78/0002 N
Ultraschallmessungen am lebenden Rind. **Ultrasonic
measurements of cattle.**

10678 König, H.E.   DE 160430/78/0002 N
Zur Anatomie und Entwicklung der Blutgefässe in der
Schädelhöhle der Hauswiederkäuer – Rind, Schaf und Ziege –.
**Anatomy and evolution of blood vessels in the brain cavity of
domestic ruminants – cow, sheep and goat –.**

10679 Frahm, K.; Graf, F.   DE 160705/75/0001
Enzymaktivitäten in Rinderorganen. **Enzyme activity in organs
of cattle.**

10680 Sambraus, H.H.; Steinel, H.   DE 160705/75/0006
Hinweise auf eine soziale Rangordnung in einer Kälbergruppe.
Indications of a social hierarchy in a group of calves.

10681 Sambraus, H.H.; Fries, B.   DE 160705/75/0007
Das Sozialverhalten in einer Hochleistungsrinderherde. **The
social behaviour in a herd of high–efficiency cattle.**

10682 Kräusslich, H.; Lampeter; Wagner, H.G.; Graf, F.
DE 160705/77/0004
Unblutige Gewinnung und Übertragung von Embryonen beim
Rind. **Bloodless transfer of embryos in cows.**

10683 Frahm, K.; Kögel, S.; Claus, R.; Kräusslich, H.
DE 160705/77/0005
Einfluss der unilateralen Orchidektomie bei Bullen auf den
Verlauf der Testosteron–Konzentration im peripheren
Blutplasma sowie auf Mastleistung und
Schlachtkörperzusammensetzung. **Influence of unilateral
orchidectomy on peripheral plasma testosterone concentration,
growth and carcass criteria in bulls.**

10684 Graf, F.; Osterkorn, K.; Tenhumberg, H.
DE 160705/78/0001 N
Biochemische Parameter im Blut beim Rind. **Biochemical
parameters in bovine blood.** Publications.

10685 Leidl, W.; Stolla, R.   DE 160910/75/0001
Die Messung des elektrischen Widerstandes der
Scheidenschleimhaut als Hilfsmittel der Brunsterkennung
beim Rind. **Measurement of the electric conductance of the
vaginal mucus in cows as an aid for heat detection.** Publications.

10686 Walser, K.; Schmid, G.; Zahn, V.   DE 160910/75/0008
Kardiotokographie am gebärenden Rind. **Cardiotocography in
cows during parturition.**

10687 Researcher not indicated   DE 160911/73/0005
Die essentiellen Verhaltensmuster des Kalbes. **The essential
behaviour patterns of calf.**

10688 Kirchgessner, M.; Roth–Maier, D.A.
DE 161280/74/0007
Einfluss der Aufzuchtintensität auf die Reproduktionsleistung.
**Influence of the rearing intensity on the reproductive
performance.**

10689 Kirchgessner, M.; Müller, H.L.   DE 161280/78/0001 N
Untersuchungen zum Energiestoffwechsel von Rind und
Schwein. **Experiments on energy metabolism in cattle and
swine.**

10690 Pirchner, F.; Fehlings, R.   DE 161300/75/0001
Zusammenhänge zwischen männlicher und weiblicher
Fruchtbarkeit beim Rind. **Correlations between male and
female fertility in cattle.**

10691 Eichinger, H.; Krippl, J.; Niedermaier, H.
    DE 161305/78/0002 N
Untersuchungen über den Einfluss von Fütterungsintensität
und Nüchterungsdauer auf die physiologischen
Belastungsreaktionen beim Transport von Mastkälbern.
**Investigations on the influence of feeding intensity and of the
duration of fasting condition on the physiological stress
reactions of fattening calves during transport.**

10692 Hoffmann, B.; Karg, H.   DE 161320/77/0002
Weiterentwicklung des Milch–Progesteronverfahrens zur
Fertilitätskontrolle beim Rind durch direkte Bestimmung von
Progesteron im Milchfett. **Further development of the
milk–progesterone assay for fertility control in cattle by
determining progesterone in milk fat.**

10693 Hoffmann, B.   DE 161320/77/0003
Hormonale Kontrolle der Gravidität und des
Geburtszeitpunktes beim Rind. **Hormonal control of
pregnancy and date of parturition in cows.**

10694 Karg, H.   DE 161320/78/0002 N
Erzielung einer grösseren Zahl lebensfähiger Kälber durch
bessere Überwachung der Fortpflanzung. **Control of
reproduction in cattle for producing a great number of viable
calves.**

10695 Karg, H.; Arnstadt, K.–I.   DE 161320/78/0003 N
Entwicklung eines Enzym–Immuno–Assay für die
Progesteronbestimmung in der Milch und Anwendung für die
Fertilitätskontrolle bei Kühen. **Development of enzyme
immuno–assay for fertility control in cows by determining
progesterone in milk.**

10696 Schön, H.; Weber   DE 161524/73/0002
Beeinflussung von Melkgeschwindigkeit und Milchabgabe
durch verschiedene technische Parameter. **Milking speed and
milking capacity in dependence on divers technical parameters.**

10697 Daenicke, R.   DE 201050/78/0002 N
Optimierung von Verfahren der Kälberaufzucht. **Optimization
of calf rearing systems.**

10698 Artmann, R.   DE 201090/77/0001 N
Auswirkung verschiedener technischer Einrichtungen von
Laufställen auf die tierische Leistung. – Kraftfutterfütterung
ausserhalb des Melkstandes –. **Effects of different installations
in Loose housing on animal performance. Feeding of
concentrates outside of the milking parlour.**

10699 Andreae, U.   DE 201200/77/0003
Untersuchungen zur Frage der "Biostimulation" bei
Milchkühen im Laufstall. **Studies on the problem of
biostimulation of dairy cows in loose housing.**

10700 Huth, F.W.   DE 201200/77/0006
Vergleichende Wachstumsstudien an Rindern extrem
unterschiedlicher Wachstumskapazität. **Comparative studies
on growth of cattle of extremely different growth capacity.**

10701 Smidt, D.   DE 201200/77/0012
Untersuchung ökonomisch bedeutender
Fruchtbarkeitskriterien bei Rindern, Schafen und Schweinen.
**Analysis of fertility criteria of economic interest in cattle,
sheep and pigs.**

10702 Schilling, E.   DE 201200/77/0015
Untersuchungen zum Einfluss der Aufzuchtintensität bei
weiblichen Rindern, Schafen und Schweinen auf den Eintritt
der Geschlechtsreife, die Fortpflanzungsleistung und die
Reaktion auf hormonale Brunstinduktion. **Studies on the
influence of the intensity in rearing cows, ewes and sows on the
initiation of pubescence, on the reproductive performance and
on the reaction to oestrus induction.**

10703 Smidt, D.   DE 201200/77/0016
Eitransplantation, Superovulation und Geschlechtskontrolle
beim Rind. **Transfer of zygote, superovulation and sexual
control.**

10704 Farries, E.   DE 201200/77/0019
Physiologische Steuerung der Dynamik von graviditäts– und
laktationsabhängigen Veränderungen der stofflichen
Körperzusammensetzung beim Rind, Schwein, Schaf.
**Physiological control of the dynamics of changes in substantial
body composition of cows, sows and ewes depending on
gravidity and lactation.**

10705 Andreae, U.   DE 201200/77/0024
Vergleichende ethologische und verhaltensphysiologische
Untersuchungen an Mastbullen in unterschiedlichen
Laufstallformen. **Comparative ethological and behaviour
physiological studies on fattening bulls in different loose housing
systems.**

10706 Andreae, U.   DE 201200/77/0025
Ethologische und verhaltensphysiologische Studien an
Milchkühen unter unterschiedlichen Bedingungen der
Kraftfuttervorlage. **Ethological and behaviour physiological
studies on dairy cows under different conditions of concentrate
feeding.**

10707 Huth, F.W.   DE 201200/77/0027
Zusammenhänge zwischen der Höhe der Milch– und
Milchfettleistung und klimatischen Kennwerten. **Correlations
between levels of milk and milk fat performance and climatic
parameters.**

10708 Andreae, U.   DE 201200/77/0034
Laktationsphysiologische Untersuchungen an Milchkühen.
Lactation physiological studies on dairy cows.

10709 Researcher not indicated   DE 501320/77/0001
Einfluss der Raumstruktur auf das Verhalten von Rindern in
Laufställen und auf der Weide. **Influence of spatial structures
on the behaviour of cattle in loose housing stables and on
pasture.**

10710 Zeeb, K.   DE 501321/71/0001
Angewandte Ethologie bei Rind und Pferd zur Verbesserung
der Haltung. **Applied ethology of cattle and horses for
improvement of husbandry.**

D 3100 – Animal management general and animal husbandry

10711 Kögel, S.; Alps, H.   DE 502303/75/0002
Einfluss der einseitigen Kastration auf Mast– und
Schlachtleistung beim Rind. **Influence of unilateral
orchidectomy on the rate of androgen secretion, growth and
carcass quality in cattle.**

10712 Kögel, S.; Ferstl, R.; Alps, H.   DE 502303/77/0001
Mast– und Schlachtleistung von Kreuzungskälbern Red
Holstein x Fleckvieh im Vergleich zu reinem Fleckvieh.
**Fattening performance and carcass quality of crossbred Red
Holstein x German Simmental calves in comparison to
purebred Simmental calves.**

10713 Kögel, S.; Alps, H.; Strasser, H.   DE 502303/77/0002
Mast– und Schlachtleistung männlicher und weiblicher Rinder
aus der Winter– und Frühsommerkalbung einer
Mutterkuhherde. **Fattening performance and carcass quality of
male and female cattle from winter and early summer calvings
out of a single suckling herd.**

10714 Hammer, K.; Süss, M.; Koller, G.
                                                 DE 502306/78/0002 N
Untersuchungen über den Einfluss eines wärmegedämmten
und eines nicht wärmegedämmten Laufstalles mit
Fress–Liegeboxen auf Parameter der tierischen Leistung von
Milchkühen. **Investigations on the influence of an insulated and
a non–insulated loose housing barn with feeding cubicles on
parameters of animal production of dairy cows.**

10715 Larsen, J.B.; Sejrsen, K.   DK 010201/62/0001
Kælvningsalderens indflydelse på produktion og frugtbarhed.
The influence of age at calving on production and fertility.

10716 Christensen, L.G.   DK 010201/68/0005
Langtidsopbevaring af tyresæd med henblik på etablering af
gen–pulje og beregning af genetisk fremgang. **Preservation and
storage of bull semen with a view to establishing a gene–pool
and calculating genetic gain.**

10717 Østergaard, V.; Neimann–Sørensen, A.
                                                 DK 010201/68/0006
Belysning af tekniske og økonomiske relationer i forskellige
kvægbrugssystemer. **A critical examination of technical and
economic relationship in various systems of cattle husbandry.**

10718 Konggaard, S.P.; Neimann–Sørensen, A.
                                                 DK 010201/69/0006
Forsøg med forskellige staldtyper til kvæg. **Studies of various
types of cattle–shed.**

10719 Kruse, V.; Neimann–Sørensen, A.   DK 010201/71/0003
Sammenhængen mellem dyrenes hormonaktivitet og deres
produktionsegenskaber. **The relationship between hormone
aktivity and production potential.**

10720 Larsen, J.B.; Sejrsen, K.   DK 010201/72/0004
Betydningen af forholdet mellem grovfoder og kraftfoder for
tilvækst og kælvningsalder. **Importance of the ratio of roughage
to concentrates for growth and age of calving.**

10721 Nielsen, S.M.   DK 010201/73/0004
Malkning i båsestalde med fast maskintid og fast malkerutine.
**Milking in conventional type stalls with fixed machine time and
milking routine.**

10722 Andersen, B.B.   DK 010201/74/0016
Udvikling af nyt ultralydudstyr til måling af kødindhold på
levende kvæg. **Development of new ultra–sound equipment for
the measurement of the meat–content of living cattle.**

10723 Konggaard, S.P.; Krohn, C.   DK 010201/74/0019
Undersøgelser vedrørende løsdriftsystemets indflydelse på
malkekøernes sociale adfærd, stresstilstand m.m. under
forskellige foderstyringsbetingelser. **Studies of the influence of
the loose–drift–system on the social behaviour, state of stress,
etc., of dairy cows under various systems of feeding
management.**

10724 Andersen, P.E.   DK 010201/75/0005
Foderstyring i mælkeproduktionen. **Feed manipulation in milk
production.**

10725 Andersen, P.E.   DK 010201/77/0001
Styringsfaktorer for malkekøers optagelse af ensilage. **Factors
controlling the intake of silage by milch cows.**

10726 Pedersen, S.; Hansen, K.   DK 010400/78/0005 N
Indsamling af data fra praksis vedrørende klima og indretning i
kalvestalde. **Collected field–data on climatic conditions and
technical arrangements in calfhouses.**

10727 Keller, P.   DK 010400/78/0006 N
Arbejdsundersøgelser i kostalde. **Labour requirement in
cowhouses.**

10728 Rasmussen, S.   DK 010500/78/0002 N
Vurdering af investeringsklimaet i husdyrproduktionen. **The
profitability of investments in animal husbandry.**

10729 Elleby, F.   DK 010702/76/0001
Miljø– og fodringsforhold samt ressourceudnyttelse og
besætningsprognoser i kvægbruget. **Environmental and feeding
conditions, resource utilisation and stock prognoses in cattle
production.**

10730 Koefoed–Johnsen, H.H.   DK 030128/77/0016 N
Systematisk anvendelse af mælkeprogesteronanalyser ved
reproduktionskontrol i malkekvægbesætninger. **Reproduction
control in dairy herds by means of systematic milk progesterone
assays.**

10731 Philipsen, H.; Pedersen, K.M.; Pedersen, H.
                                                 DK 030128/79/0003 N
Brunstkontrol hos malkekøer med estrumat. **Heat control in
dairy cows using Estrumate.**

10732 Flagstad, T.   DK 030129/74/0001 N
Påvisning af anlægsbærertyre med den genetiske defekt A 46.
Registration of carrier–bulls with the genetic defect A 46.

10733 Riis, P.M.   DK 030141/78/0001 N
Regulering af mælkekirtlens næringsstofforsyning og
mobilisering fra energi– og proteindepoter hos køer. **Regulation of nutrient partition and nutrient release from body
pools in cows.**

10734 Henriksen, J.; Pedersen, K.M.; Pedersen, H.; Nielsen,
F.; Andersen, O.   DK 030142/79/0002 N
Årsager til nedsat frugtbarhed hos kvæg. **Causes of reduced
fertility in cattle.**

10735 Mocquot, J.C.; Poutous, M.; Flamant, J.C.
FR 010202/62/2547
Méthodes de contrôle laitier bovin et ovin. **Milk recording methods in sheep and cattle.** Publications.

10736 Renault, P.; Garel, J.P.　　　FR 010804/70/3010
Hivernage de troupeaux bovins de race Sapers sous abris légers en montagne (1 000m). **Winter management of Sapers cattle under light shelters in mountainous district (1 000 m).** Publications.

10737 Renault, P.; Garel, J.P.　　　FR 010804/70/3011
Etude du comportement de vaches laitières à forte productivité en montagne. **Study of the behaviour of high producing dairy cows in mountainous district.** Publications.

10738 Renault, P.; Garel, J.P.　　　FR 010804/70/3012
Elevage intensif de vaches allaitantes en montagne. Adoption de veaux. **Intensive management of suckling cows in mountainous districts: adoption of calves.** Publications.

10739 Garel, J.P.; Petit, M.; Maronne, P.
FR 010804/74/9022 N
Etude de l'activité ovarienne des vaches allaitantes de race Salers. **Study of ovarian activity of Salers Suckler cows..**

10740 Garel, J.P.; Le Neindre, P.; Maronne, P.
FR 010804/77/9025 N
Influence du mode d'élevage des génisses Salers et F.F.P.N. sur leur comportement social et maternel. **Effects of a rearing pattern on Salers and Friesian heifers on their future social and maternal behaviour.**

10741 Garel, J.P.; Didienne, M.; Devoyod, J.J.; Pigeau, P.
FR 010804/77/9027 N
Influence de facteurs zootechniques (race, alimentation) sur les caractères organoleptiques et la qualité du fromage.. **Consequences of feeding and breed on cheese quality made of milk obtained from dairy cows fed either on grass silage of hay (high land pastures).**

10742 Gouet, Ph.; Dubourguier, H.C.; Riou, Y.; Contrepois, M.　　　FR 010809/71/9527 N
Technologie de production et d'élevage de jeunes ruminants axéniques (Chevreaux, veaux). **Techniques for obtaining, fistulization and rearing of axenic or gnotoxenic lambs, kids and calves.**

10743 Robelin, J.; Geay, Y.　　　FR 010813/62/6521
Estimation de la composition corporelle des bovins. **Estimation of body composition of cattle.**

10744 Robelin, J.; Geay, Y.　　　FR 010813/62/6522 N
Evolution de la composition corporelle chez les bovins : variations avec la race et le sexe. **Evolution of the corporeal composition of bovines : variations in relation with breed and sex.**

10745 Geay, Y.; Robelin, J.; Beranger, C.　FR 010813/72/6528
Production de boeufs, taureaux et génisses de 2 ans. **Steers, bulls, heifers production for slaughtering at 2 years.**

10746 Geay, Y.; Boccard, R.; Robelin, J.; Beranger, C.
FR 010813/74/6524
Caractéristiques d'élevage et d'engraissement des bovins de race limousine : taurillons, taureaux, boeufs, génisses.

Growing and fattening cattle performances in Limousin breed: young and older bulls, esters and heifers.

10747 Vermorel, M.; Bouvier, J.C.　　　FR 010816/73/2767
Etudes de thermogènése et de thermolyse chez le jeune préruminant pendant la période néonatale. **Neonatal thermogenesis and thermolysis by the young preruminant. Trials and calves and lambs.** Publications.

10748 Vermorel, M.; Bouvier, J.C.; Geay, Y.
FR 010816/75/9516 N
Etude de la croissance des jeunes bovins d'aptitudes et de précocités différentes. **Study of growth in growing cattle with various growth potential and rate of maturity.**

10749 Bonnemaire, J.; Teissier, J.H.; Roux, M.
FR 011013/76/6567
Utilisation intensive des génisses des troupeaux laitiers pour la production de viande ; intérêt d'un vêlage très précoce. **Very early calving of heifers for slaughter.**

10750 Labussiére, J.; Combaud, J.F.; Ruiz, M.C.
FR 011310/78/7560
Action des prostaglandines sur l'ejection du lait et la motricite des canaux galactophores chez la vache et la brebis. **Effects of prostaglandin on milk ejection of cows and ewes.**

10751 Chupin, D.; Pelot, J.; André, D.; Fontaubert, Y. de; Terqui, M.　　　FR 011501/69/7528
Maîtrise des cycles sexuels chez les bovins. **Control of reproduction in cattle.**

10752 Bouissou, M.F.　　　FR 011501/76/7541
Rôle des équilibres hormonaux sur l'apparition et l'expression des relations de dominance – subordination chez les bovins. **Role of endocrine balance on dominance – submission relationships in cattle.**

10753 Delouis; Parrassin, P.　　　FR 012224/77/9010
Induction hormonale de la lactation chez les vaches. **Hormonal induction of lactation on dairy cows.**

10754 Pelot; Parrassin, P.　　　FR 012224/77/9011
Comparaison de deux méthodes de synchronisation de chaleurs chez les vaches. **Comparison of two methods for inducing the synchronization of individual heat periods among cows.**

10755 Hinks　　　GB 010101/76/0018
Cattle industry consultation.

10756 Baldwin　　　GB 010301/78/0085
Illumination preferences in calves.

10757 Manston　　　GB 010404/00/0806 R
Metabolic profiles of cattle – future development.

10758 Manston　　　GB 010408/00/0806 R
Metabolic profiles of cattle – future development.

10759 Williams　　　GB 010601/00/0070 R
Relating anatomical physiological and metabolic parameters to carcass composition and production efficiency in cattle breeds.

10760 Wood　　　GB 010601/79/0080 N
Study effects of changing sex hormone metabolism on growth

efficiency and body composition in cattle.

10761 Le, Du.   GB 011205/79/0605 N
Nutrition and management factors affecting the herbage intake and milk production of grazing dairy cows.

10762 Leaver   GB 011704/00/0004
Rearing systems for young dairy stock.

10763 Line; Westgarth   GB 011704/00/0009
Influence of feed allocation during lactation on milk yield and quality liveweight change and profit margin.

10764 Connell   GB 011704/00/0011 R
Production and feeding of artificially dried forages to milking cows.

10765 Phipps; Leaver   GB 011704/00/0012 R
Production and feeding of maize silage to milking cows and dairy replacements.

10766 Leaver; Broster   GB 011704/00/0023
Influence of rearing practice on the adult performance of dairy cattle.

10767 Roy; Stobo   GB 011707/00/0001 R
Factors affecting the growth and health of the calf; diet, breed and physical environment.

10768 Roy; Gillies   GB 011707/00/0002
Effect of plane of nutrition on early breeding. Effect of early breeding on health, lactation and fertility.

10769 Broster; Clough   GB 011707/00/0008
Apply improved rationing systems to practical management.

10770 Bines; Hart   GB 011707/00/0010 R
Hormonal control of energy metabolism in lactating cattle.

10771 Glover   GB 011709/00/0003
Disposal of effluent.

10772 Castle; Watson   GB 030201/00/0009 R
Feeding value of red clover silage for milk production.

10773 Muir; Taylor   GB 030201/75/0033 R
The effect of modern methods of milk production and handling on the quality of milk and milk products.

10774 Jenkinson; Smith   GB 030204/00/0018 R
Skin glands and the composition of their secretions.

10775 Boyd   GB 041102/00/0008
Breed comparison in outwintered spring–calving hill suckler herd.

10776 McGaughey   GB 041102/76/0010
Summer calving in a hill suckler herd.

10777 Gordon   GB 041302/00/0001
Milk production from the spring–calving dairy herd.

10778 Gordon   GB 041302/00/0003
Rearing dairy replacement stock.

10779 Gordon   GB 041302/77/0004
Milk production from the autumn calving dairy herd.

10780 McIlmoyle   GB 041303/00/0001
The effect of the management of the sward upon the production of silage for fattening cattle.

10781 Lee   GB 041304/00/0001
Low cost housing for rearing cattle.

10782 Chestnutt   GB 041307/76/0001
To compare the effects of weaning calves from the single suckling cow at various stages of lactation.

10783 Chestnutt   GB 041307/76/0002
Influence of seasonal liveweight change in the suckler cow on grassland utilisation and beef production.

10784 Bartholomew   GB 041309/76/0003
The influence of grazing animals on production and utilisation of pasture subjected to different managements.

10785 Reed   GB 041401/00/0001 R
The role of body reserves in the function and productivity of the dairy cow.

10786 Researcher not indicated   GB 041401/76/0002 R
Beef production from grass–clover and grass–N swards.

10787 Barnes   GB 041406/00/0005
Interaction of stocking rate, nitrogen application and grazing cycle on the production of beef from grass.

10788 Researcher not indicated   GB 050123/00/0001 R
Beef: suckler calf production on hill grazing.

10789 Researcher not indicated   GB 050123/00/0002 R
Beef: suckler calf production on enclosed upland.

10790 Researcher not indicated   GB 050123/00/0003 R
Beef: suckler calf production on lowland grass.

10791 Researcher not indicated   GB 050123/00/0004 R
Beef: feeding and finishing of suckler calves.

10792 Researcher not indicated   GB 050123/00/0006 R
Beef: intensive beef production.

10793 Researcher not indicated   GB 050123/00/0007 R
Beef: production from dairy bred cattle.

10794 Researcher not indicated   GB 050124/00/0002 R
Dairy heifer replacement: rearing system.

10795 Researcher not indicated   GB 050124/00/0003 R
Dairy cows: large herd management.

10796 Researcher not indicated   GB 050124/00/0004 R
Dairy cows: management of the spring calving cow.

10797 Researcher not indicated   GB 050124/00/0005 R
Dairy cows: grazing management.

10798 Researcher not indicated   GB 050124/00/0006 R
Dairy cows: milking equipment, cow management and behaviour studies.

10799 Researcher not indicated GB 050163/00/0001
Beef: suckler calf production on hill grazing.

10800 Researcher not indicated GB 050163/00/0002
Beef: suckler calf production on enclosed land.

10801 Researcher not indicated GB 050163/00/0003
Beef: feeding and finishing of suckler calves.

10802 Researcher not indicated GB 050163/00/0005
Beef: intensive beef production.

10803 Researcher not indicated GB 050163/00/0006
Beef: production from dairy bred cattle.

10804 Researcher not indicated GB 050163/00/0007
Suckler calf production on lowland grass.

10805 Researcher not indicated GB 050164/00/0002
Dairy heifer replacements: rearing systems.

10806 Researcher not indicated GB 050164/00/0003
Dairy cows: large herd management.

10807 Researcher not indicated GB 050164/00/0005
Dairy cows: grazing management.

10808 Researcher not indicated GB 050164/00/0006
Dairy cows: milking equipment, cow management and behaviour studies.

10809 Researcher not indicated GB 050464/00/0001
Dairy heifer rearing project.

10810 Bell GB 060102/00/0001
Large dairy herd management.

10811 Prescott GB 060102/00/0003
Evaluation of management practices for high yielding dairy cows.

10812 Hinks GB 060102/00/0006
Husbandry, health and nutrition of artificially reared calves.

10813 Lowman GB 060102/00/0007
Evaluation of management systems in suckler beef herds.

10814 Owen; Allen GB 060208/00/0001
Development of intensive feeding systems based on complete diets for winter and summer use:(1) dairy cattle.

10815 Petchey; Dodsworth GB 060208/00/0002
Development of artificial calf rearing systems.

10816 Owen GB 060208/00/0004
Development of intensive systems based on complete diets for winter and summer use–beef cattle.

10817 Broadbent GB 060208/00/0005
Response of suckler cow genotypes to winter environment and nutrition.

10818 Johnston GB 060212/79/0012 N
Biochemical examination of milk from suckler cows with clotting abnormalities.

10819 Thompson GB 060219/00/0001 R
Factors affecting blood composition of the dairy cow.

10820 Galbraith GB 060219/00/0002 R
The effect of anabolic compounds on the performance and blood characteristics of finishing cattle.

10821 Galbraith GB 060219/00/0003 R
Control of milk secretion in spring calving suckler cows.

10822 Chesworth GB 060219/79/0015 N
Changes in the mobilisation of lipids which occur during lactation in beef cow.

10823 Bruce GB 060224/79/0025 N
Thermal simulation of a suckler cows.

10824 Knox GB 060226/00/0001
Cattle grazing in forest plantations. Integration of forestry and agriculture.

10825 Sargent; Waterson GB 060311/00/0001 R
Milk production systems investigation.

10826 Lindsay GB 060311/00/0002
A study of labour and machinery utilisation on the dairy farm.

10827 Hunt; Groves GB 060311/00/0003
An investigation into recent trends in beef production in Scotland.

10828 Sargent GB 060311/00/0004
Beef production systems investigation.

10829 Parkinson; Martin GB 060313/00/0002
Dairy cow herd health and productivity.

10830 Rees GB 060315/00/0002
Environment studies related to performance of housed calves fed at different levels of nutrition.

10831 Rees GB 060315/00/0003
Management and nutrition of a summer–calving, low ground suckler herd.

10832 Rees GB 060315/00/0004
Management and feeding aspects of calf rearing systems in the West of Scotland.

10833 Leaver GB 060316/00/0001
Farm unit studies of dairying systems.

10834 Leaver; Land GB 060316/00/0003
The effect of body condition on milk production and reproduction in dairy cattle.

10835 Leaver GB 060316/78/0004
The development of efficient grazing systems for dairy cattle.

10836 Cunningham, E.P. IE 060100/75/1082 R
Evaluation of canadian holstein dairy cattle for dairy and beef production. Publications.

10837 Roche, J.F. IE 060100/77/1394 N
The use of growth promoters in beef cattle. Publications.

10838 Harte, F.J.; Collins, D.P. IE 060103/70/0314 N
Bull beef production. Publications.

10839 Maguire, M.F.; Roche, J.F. IE 060103/77/1393 N
Synchronization of oestrus in cows.

10840 Fallon, R.J.; Tuite, P.J.; Harte, F.J.; Daly, O.G.
IE 060103/77/2085 R
Calf housing design and evaluation.

10841 Gleeson, P.A.; Kavanagh A.J. IE 060400/74/2041 R
Rearing dairy replacement heifers. Publications.

10842 Gleeson, P.A. IE 060400/75/1093 R
The effect of age and weight at first calving on life time
performance. Publications.

10843 Joseph, R.L.; Hanrahan, T.J. IE 060400/76/1308 R
Examination of incidence of boar odour. Publications.

10844 O'Farrell, K.J. IE 060400/76/1397 N
The conception rate of dairy cows inseminated with semen
containing enzyme additives. Publications.

10845 O'Farrell, K.J. IE 060400/77/2080 R
Heat detection in dairy cows.

10846 Mulqueen, J. IE 060701/72/0657 N
Dairy cattle production on marginal land. Publications.

10847 Flanagan, S.P.; Daly, P.J. IE 060702/76/1248 R
Intensified beef production from western lowland pastures.
Revised project. Publications.

10848 Gordon, I.; Boland, M.F.; Crosby, F.
IE 120105/78/9025
An investigation of nuclear transplantation in cattle.

10849 Caffrey, P.; Brophy, P.; Gordon, I.; Crosby, F.; Rath,
M. IE 120105/78/9027 R
An investigation of beef production techniques from calf to
slaughter at two years. Publications.

10850 Boland, M.P. IE 120105/78/9028 R
Studies in the in vitro fertilization of cattle oocytes.

10851 Boland, M.P.; Crosby, F.; Gordon, I.; McDonnell, H.
IE 120105/78/9036 R
Studies in the evaluation of cattle eggs for transfer.
Publications.

10852 Boland, M.P.; Crosby, F.; Gordon, I.; Kennedy, L.;
McDonnell, H. IE 120105/78/9037 R
A study of superovulation in the beef heifer after treatment with
gonadotrophins and prostaglandins. Publications.

10853 Gordon, I.; Boland, M.P.; Crosby, F.; McDonnell, H.;
Kennedy, L. IE 120105/78/9039 R
The use of egg transfer for the production of twin calves in beef
and dairy cattle. Publications.

10854 Lucey, M.; Mehigan, C.; Crinion, R. IE 120204/76/9021
The recovery of fertilised ova from superovulated cows and the
transfer of these embryos to synchronised recipients.

10855 Crinion, R.A.P.; Mehigan, C.; Lucey, M.P.; Burke, P.

IE 120206/73/9135 N
Bovine embryo transfer using non–surgical collection methods
for embryo.

10856 Dodd, V.A.; Doyle, H.J. IE 120301/76/9055 N
Development of building designs for beef and dairy cattle based
on slatted floors and cubicles. Publications.

10857 Dodd, V.A.; Kelly, T.A.; Ruane, D.
IE 120301/78/9234 N
Study of calf house design and its environment on calf
performance.

10858 Gosling, J.P.; Morgan, P.; Sreenan, J.M.
IE 130102/77/9216 N
Gonadotropin receptors on ovarian granulosa cells from
naturally cycling cows, and cows induced to superovulate.
Publications.

10859 Romita, A.; Pilla, A.M.; Borghese, A.; Gigli, S.
IT 020700/76/0011
Parto precoce di meticce frisone x tori da carne. Early calving
of (beefbull x friesian) crossbred cows.

10860 Malossini, F. IT 020700/77/0700 R
Meccanizzazione della raccolta dei foraggi per gli allevamenti
vacca–vitello, utilizzazione paglia e deiezioni, aspetti
zootecnici. Mechanization of fodder crops harvesting for
broodcow farms, utilisation of litter and excreta, aspects related
to livestock rearing.

10861 Masoero, G.; Terramoccia, S.; Auxilia, M.T.
IT 020700/78/0007
Creatininemia in bovini Piemontesi in rapporto al carattere "
coscia". Serum creatinine in Piemontese cattle with muscolar
hypertrophy. Publications.

10862 Bergonzini, E. IT 020700/78/0008
Studio delle condizioni e delle possibilità di sviluppo
dell'allevamento bovino al pascolo in aziende della fascia
superiore dell'Appennino settentrionale. A study of the
conditions and possibilities of expansion of the cattle breeding
on pasture on farms in the North Appennines upper belt.
Publications.

10863 Auxilia, M.T.; Puppo, S.; Terramoccia, S.; De Maria,
C. IT 020700/79/0012 N
Relazione tra le immunoglobuline del colostro di vacche di
razza Piemontese. Relationship between colostral
immunoglobulins of Piemontese cows and surwival and growth
of newborn.

10864 Toppino, P.M.; Bossi, M.G.; Cabrini, A.
IT 022200/78/0004
Clostridi nel tratto digerente delle bovine da latte. Clostridia in
digestive tract of milk cow.

10865 Chiesa, F. IT 040228/77/0547 R
Studio della incidenza della mortalità embrionale nella specie
bovina e del significato fisiologico della prostaglandina PGF2
in diretta specie, durante il ciclo estrale, la gravidanza ed il
parto. A study of foetal mortaly frequency in cows and the
physiological indirect action of prostaglandin PGF2 in pure
breeds, during the oestral cycle, gestation and delivery.

10866 Cerutti, F.M. IT 040613/74/0533

Studi sulla fertilità nell'allevamento bovino e in quello suino. **Studies on fertility in cattle and pig production.** Publications.

10867 Cerutti, F.M.   IT 040613/77/0143 R
Studi sulla fertilità dell'allevamento bovino e sulla dinami–ca delle popolazioni bovine allevate in funzione dell'azione selettiva. **Study on the fertility of cattle hand on the dynamics of the cattle population bred in view of selection.**

10868 Cicogna, M.   IT 040613/78/1045 N
Il comportamento dei bovini, in funzione di alcuni fattori ambientali connessi ai ricoveri ed alle tecniche di gestione degli allevamenti. **Bovine cattle behaviour depending on certain environmental factors connected with byres and breeding management methods.**

10869 Carenzi, C.; Dell'Orto, V.; Rognoni, G.; Campitelli, S.; Crimella, M.; Giuliani, M.G.   IT 040638/74/0001
Studio sulla fertilità dell'allevamento bovino, equino, suino e conicolo. Indagine sugli aspetti ambientali e genetici per un migliore sfruttamento della successiva carriera riproduttiva. **Study on cattle, equine, swine, rabbit herd fertility. Research on the genetic and environmental aspects allowing a better exploitation of subsequent cow's reproductive career.** Publications.

10870 Dell'Orto, V.; Polidori, F.; Carenzi, C.; Lechi, F.; Rognoni, G.; Calvo, V.   IT 040638/75/0001
Studio per un modello di assistenza tecnica per la riproduzione e l'alimentazione nell'allevamento bovino da latte. Utilizzazione della programmazione lineare per l'ottimizzazione economica dell'azienda agro–zootecnica. **Research on the assistance technical model for reproduction and feeding in dairy farm. Utilisation of linear program for the dairy farm improvement.** Publications.

10871 Verga, M.; Oberosler, R.; Carenzi, C.; Campitelli, S.; Dell'Orto, V.; Crimella, C.   IT 040638/77/0001
Indagini comportamentali della specie bovina, equina, suina e cunicola. Ricerche di base per il trasferimento delle tecniche di condizionamento classico ed operante nella pratica zootecnica. **Behaviour studies of cattle, horse, swine and rabbit species. Basic researches on transfer of classic and operant conditioning techniques to practical husbandry.** Publications.

10872 Bettini, T.M.; Matassino, D.   IT 040722/67/0001
Efficienza riproduttiva e produttiva in bovini da latte e da carne, nel bufalo, negli ovini. **Reproductive and productive efficiency in dairy and milk cattle, in buffalo, in sheep.** Publications.

10873 Matassino, D.   IT 040722/74/0586
Studio sulla produzione di carne bovina. Aspetti zootecnici e zooeconomici. **Study on beef production. Economical and technical aspects.**

10874 Bonsembiante, M.   IT 040810/73/1809
Ricerche sulla produzione della carne bovina. L'allevamento della manza in confinamento per la produzione del vitello da ristallo. **Research on beef production. The breeding of Heifer in "confinamento" for the production of fattening calf.** Publications.

10875 Rioni, M.; Bittante, G.   IT 040810/77/0004 N
Effetto della castrazione e del trattamento con un androgeno anabolizzante sull'ingrasso delle manze. **Heifers meat production: effect of spaying and of TBA implantation.** Publications.

10876 Bonsembiante, M.   IT 040810/77/0539 R
Relazioni tra alcuni parametri ematici e la fertilità di bovine. **Relation between certain blood parameters and bovine fertility.**

10877 Lanari, D.   IT 040810/77/0698 R
Meccanizzazione della raccolta dei foraggi per gli allevamenti vacca–vitello, utilizzazione stocchi, recupero zone marginali, aspetti zootecnici. **Mechanization of fodder crops harvesting for brood–cow farms, uses of stalks, reclaiming marginal lands, aspects in zootechny.**

10878 Abbozzo, P.; Ciani, A.   IT 041009/75/0001
Aspetti tecnici ed economici degli allevamenti bovini in Umbria. **The technical and economical aspects of breeding cows in the Umbria country.**

10879 Valfrè, F.   IT 041028/77/0609
Rapporti tra i fattori dell'ambiente e attività riproduttiva nei bovini. **Relationship between environmental factors and the reproductive activity of bovine cattle.**

10880 Lucifero, M.   IT 041113/77/0563 R
Indagine conoscitiva delle situazioni attinenti i parametri riproduttivi nella specie bovina ed ovina e ricerche sulla fertilità degli ovini. **Preliminary research on the present parameters of bovine and sheep reproduction, research on sheep fertility.**

10881 Trimarchi, G.; Ferruzzi, G.; Rossi, G.; Secchiari, P.   IT 041113/79/0001 N
Stimolazione elettronica dei capezzoli della vacca e produzione lattea. **Electronic stimulation of the teat cow and milk production.**

10882 Maletto, S.   IT 041217/77/0564 R
Produzione quali–quantitativa di carne in bovini di razza piemontese e loro derivati da incrocio. **Qualitative and quantitative data on beef production from Piedmont races and their crossbreeds.**

10883 Ubertalle, A.   IT 041217/77/0590 R
Linea vacca–vitello nella produzione di meticci da carne, con minimo impiego di manodopera e massima valorizzazione dei piani alimentari adottabili in aree marginali. **The brood–cow line in the production of beef crosses, using a minimum of labourforce and maximising the efficiency of feeding plans suitable for marginal areas.**

10884 Manunta, G.   IT 041315/77/0568
Sincronizzazione dei calori nei bovini e nei piccoli ruminanti. **Synchronisation of heat in bovine cattle and small ruminants.**

10885 Cantarelli, F.   IT 041502/74/0523
Indagine sull'utilizzabilità di terreni marginali per la produzione di vitelli da ristallo nel paese. **Investigation on the possible use of marginal lands for the production of beef calves in Italy.**

10886 Bonomi, A.   IT 041521/74/0650
I rapporti fra livello nutritivo della razione, produttività e fecondità nelle bovine da latte. **Relation between feeding level of ration, productivity and fecundity in milk cattle.**

10887 Bonomi, A.　　　　　IT 041521/77/0119 R
I rapporti fra livello nutritivo della razione produttiva e fecondita nelle bovine da latte. **Relations between nutritional level of production and fertility in dairy cows.**

10888 Bonadonna, T.; Succi, G.　　　IT 050100/76/0001
Ricerche sulla introduzione per via transvaginale degli ovuli fecondati nelle bovine incubatrici. **Researches on the introduction of fertilized eggs in incubator cows through vagina.** Publications.

10889 Valpreda, M.　　　　IT 050500/77/0591 R
Problemi connessi con la fecondazione artificiale per la produzione della carne. Cause di ipofecondità, ipofertilità e infertilità nei bovini. Ricerca sulle cause infettive tossiche da additivi. Studio sul contributo maschile all'infertilità. **Problems related to artificial insemination used in meat production. The causes of hypo–fecundity, hypo–fertility, sterility in bovine cattle. Research on the toxic and infective action of additives. Study on the male component of sterility.**

10890 Ferrara, L.　　　　IT 060800/77/0610
Interazioni genotipo–ambiente nella razza–popolazione bovina del Cubante Mirabellano. **Fenotype–environment interactions in the bovine breed of the "Cubante–Mirabellano".**

10891 Meyboom, F.W.　　　NL 010102/77/6945 R
Frequentie en oorzaak van urinebrandplekken. **Frequency of urine scorch patches.**

10892 Smits, A.C.　　　　NL 010106/60/4749
De invloed van de huisvestings– en inrichtingssystemen op het gedrag van melkvee. **The influence of housing systems and equipment on the behaviour of dairy cattle.**

10893 Rossing, W.　　　　NL 010106/73/6146
De betekenis van het meten van de lichaamstemperatuur via de melk voor het onderkennen van bronst en ziekten bij koeien. **The meaning of measuring the body temperature by way of milk temperature for detection of heat and diseases of cows.** Publications.

10894 Brandsma, S.; Maatje, K.　　NL 010112/60/1172
De invloed van de melktechniek op de produktie en de uiergezondheid van koeien. **Influence of milking methods on production and udder health of cows.** Publications.

10895 Brandsma, S.　　　　NL 010112/67/1194
De invloed van de huisvesting in ligboxenstallen op gedrag, produktie en voederopname van rundvee. **Influence of the cubicle–system on behaviour and feed uptake of cattle.** Publications

10896 Brandsma, S.　　　　NL 010112/68/2309
De invloed van erfelijke aanleg en melktechnieken op het gehalte aan vrije vetzuren in melk. **Influence of hereditary predisposition and milking technique on content of free fatty acids in milk.**

10897 Putten, G. van　　　　NL 010112/73/5394
Onderzoek naar de ruimte die een mestkalf nodig heeft om onbelemmerd te kunnen liggen. **The space fattening calves need to lie down without being restrained.** Publications.

10898 Brake, J.H. te; Wiel, D.F.M. van de; Maatje, K.

NL 010112/73/6146
De betekenis van het meten van de lichaamstemperatuur via de melk voor het onderkennen van bronst en ziekten bij koeien. **The meaning of measuring the body temperature by way of milk temperature for detection of heat and diseases of cows.** Publications.

10899 Putten, G. van　　　　NL 010112/75/6151
De gevolgen van het verstrekken van enig stro aan vleeskalveren. **The consequences of feeding some straw to veal–calves.** Publications.

10900 Brake, J.H.A. te; Oldenbroek, J.K.　NL 010112/75/6181
Onderzoek naar de relatie tussen oestrus–symptomen en fertiliteit bij het rund. **Research into the relation between oestrus symptoms and fertility in cattle.**

10901 Elshof, W.J.; Putten, G. van　　NL 010112/77/7842
Een onderzoek naar alternatieven voor de huisvesting van vleeskalveren. **Experiments with alternative housing–systems for veal calves.** Publications.

10902 Wierenga, H.K.　　　　NL 010112/77/7844
Sociaal gedrag van melkkoeien en de sociale organisatie van een kudde melkvee in relatie tot huisvestingssystemen. **Social behaviour of dairy cattle and the social organisation in a herd of dairy cattle in relation to housing systems.**

10903 Oostendorp, D.　　　　NL 010208/70/8739 N
Invloed van isolatie, ventilatie en hokbezetting op de groei van vleesstieren in roostervloerstallen. **Effects of isolation, ventilation and number of animals per pen on growth of beef bulls in slatted floor sheds.** Publications.

10904 Kommerij, R.　　　　NL 010208/73/8736 N
Management omstreeks het drachtig worden van melkvee. **Management in relation to conception of dairy cattle.** Publications.

10905 Kommerij, R.　　　　NL 010208/75/8754 N
Huisvesting en management met betrekking tot het afkalven van melkvee. **Lay–out of accomodation and management in relation with calving of dairy cows.**

10906 Meijer, A.B.　　　　NL 010208/75/8761 N
Invloed van huisvesting van fokkalveren op gezondheid en ontwikkeling. **Influence of housing young–stock for breeding on health and development.** Publications.

10907 Boer, D.J. den; Keuning, J.A.　NL 010208/77/6945 R
Frequentie en oorzaak van urinebrandplekken. **Frequency of urine scorch patches.**

10908 Snijders, P.J.M.　　　　NL 010208/77/8741 N
Mogelijkheden van een geconcentreerd in de herfst afkalvende veestapel. **Possibilities of a herd calving in autumn.**

10909 Schipper, C.J.; Jellema, A.　　NL 010213/63/3379
Onderzoek naar de oorzaken waardoor het gebrek rans in boerderijmelk kan ontstaan en naar de wijze waarop het kan worden tegengegaan (gevoeligheid van de melk, invloed voeding, ontwikkeling controle methoden). **Research for the causes of rancidity in farm milk and the factors combatting this defect (sensibility of the milk, influence of nutrition, development control methods).** Publications.

10910 Jellema, A. NL 010213/70/3385
Onderzoek naar de invloed van de koe op de hygiënische hoedanigheid van boederijmelk. **The influence of the cow on the hygienic quality of farm milk.**

10911 Akkermans, J.P.W.M.; Pomper, W. NL 010401/62/7741
Fertiliteitsstoornissen bij rund, schaap en varken met inbegrip van abortus. **Fertility problems of cattle, sheep and pigs including abortion.** Publications.

10912 Osinga, A. NL 020058/66/6275
Nadere bestudering van het geboorteproces (bij runderen en schapen) met de nadruk op de endocrinologische achtergronden van moeilijke geboortes en doodgeboortes. **Further study of the parturition process (with cattle and sheep) with special attention to the endocrinological mechanism of difficult calvings and stillbirths.** Publications.

10913 Montsma, G. NL 020058/72/4642
Aanpassing van westerse veerassen in een tropische ontwikkelingsland (Kenya). **Adaption of improved cattle breeds in a developing country in the tropics (Kenya).** Publications.

10914 Osinga, A. NL 020058/73/6146
De betekenis van het meten van de lichaamstemperatuur via de melk voor het onderkennen van bronst en ziekten bij koeien. **The meaning of measuring the body temperature by way of milk temperature for detection of heat and diseases of cows.** Publications.

10915 Metz, J.H.M. NL 020058/76/6857
Sociaal gedrag van runderen. **Social behaviour of domestic cattle.** Publications.

10916 Metz, J.H.M. NL 020058/76/7356
Onderzoek naar ethologische maatstaven voor het welzijn van runderen. **Study of ethological criteria for the well–being of cattle.** Publications.

10917 Kloosterman, A. NL 020058/78/8811 N
De invloed van resistentie tegen maag– en darmworm op de groei en stofwisseling van geïnfecteerde kalveren. **The effect of resistance to gastro–intestinal nematodes on growth performance and metabolism of infected calves.**

10918 Boender, J. NL 030001/77/7746 R
In vitro capacitatie van bere– en stierespermatozoa. **In vitro capacitation of boar and bull spermatozoa.**

10919 Elving, L.; Govers, J.P. NL 030009/68/7814
Milieu– en erfelijke invloeden op het oestruspatroon bij het rund. **Genetical and environmental influences on the oestrus in cattle.**

10920 Elving, L. NL 030009/73/6146
De betekenis van het meten van de lichaamstemperatuur via de melk voor het onderkennen van bronst en ziekten bij koeien. **The meaning of measuring the body temperature by way of milk temperature for detection of heat and diseases of cows.** Publications.

10921 Elving, L.; Govers, J.P. NL 030009/75/6181
Onderzoek naar de relatie tussen oestrus–symptomen en fertiliteit bij het rund. **Research into the relation between oestrus symptoms and fertility in cattle.**

10922 Bois, C.H.W. de NL 030013/76/5509 R
Biochemische aspecten van de normale en de cysteus ontaarde ovariële follikels bij het rund. **Biochemical aspects of the normal and the cystic ovarian follicles in cattle.**

10923 Kruip, Th.A.M. NL 030013/76/5517 R
Functie van de follikelwand bij de maturatie van de eicel in vivo en in vitro. **Function of the follicular wall in the maturation process of the oocyte in vivo and in vitro.** Publications.

10924 Boer, D.J. den; Keuning, J.A. NL 060008/77/6945
Frequentie en oorzaak van urinebrandplekken. **Frequency and cause of urine scorch by grazing cattle.**

Sheep (B 4220)

See also 3370, 3613, 4829, 10402, 10678, 10701, 10702, 10704, 10735, 10742, 10747, 10750, 10872, 10880, 10884, 10911, 10912, 11504, 11534, 11535, 12067, 12304, 12305, 12307, 12348, 12355, 12357, 12358, 13239, 13242, 14573, 15385, 15669, 15670, 15671, 15672

10925 Finger, K.H.; Lembke, V. DE 129250/71/0005
Klimatoleranz verschiedener Schafrassen und Kreuzungen unter besonderer Berücksichtigung der Wasserversorgung. **Climatic tolerance in different races and crosses of sheep with special regard to water supply.**

10926 Matter, H.E. DE 129253/77/0001 N
Fortpflanzung und Fruchtbarkeit beim Steppenschaf. **Reproduction and fertility in the steppe sheep.** Publications.

10927 Wassmuth, R.; Scharf, G. DE 129383/77/0001
Sowjetische Beiträge zur Erforschung der Fruchtbarkeit und der Felleigenschaften bei Karakuls u.a. Pelzschafrassen. **Soviet contributions concerning the research of the fertility and the quality of skins of karakul sheep and other skin races.**

10928 Schäfer, H. DE 129553/72/0006
Die Struktur der Felle eintägiger Karakullämmer in Abhängigkeit vom Mineralstoffgehalt des Bodens, des Wassers und der Weide verschiedener Standorte der Trockensavanne Südwest– afrikas. **The structure of the coat of one day old karakul lambs depending on mineral content in soil, water and pasture at different sites of the dry savanna in South West Africa.**

10929 Holtz, W.; Nitter, G.; Thume, O.
DE 132276/78/0003 N
Zyklussteuerung beim Schaf – eine Feldstudie. **Control of estrus in sheep – a field trial.** Publications.

10930 Hinrichsen, J.K.; Rudloff, S. DE 144675/73/0005
Transportprobleme bei Schafen. **Problems of sheep transport.**

10931 Nitter, G. DE 144680/78/0003 N
Prüfung von Zuchtmethoden auf der Basis von Suffolk– und Merinolandschafen unter herkömmlichen Haltungsformen. **Examination of breeding methods in conventional sheep production systems based on Suffolk and German Merino breeds.**

10932 Benthin, G.; Röstel, W. DE 148350/78/0003 N
Brunststimulation durch Hormonbehandlung beim Schaf. **Heat stimulation in sheep by treatment with hormones.** Publications.

D 3100 – Animal management general and animal husbandry

10933 Benthin, G.   DE 148351/78/0001 N
Untersuchungen zur Verbesserung der Fleischleistung –
insbesondere zur Methodik von Leistungprüfungen auf
Lebendgewichtszuwachs – beim Schaf. **Studies for
improvement in meat production of sheep especially
investigations on the methods of production tests on live weight
gain.**

10934 Kalm, E.; Benthin, G.   DE 148351/78/0002 N
Zusammenhänge zwischen Teil– und Gesamtleistung im
Lebendgewichtszuwachs beim Schaf. **Correlations between
partial and total performance of live weight gain in sheep.**

10935 Kallweit, E.   DE 201200/77/0004
Vergleichende ethologische und verhaltensphysiologische
Untersuchungen an Schafen verschiedener Rassen und
Kreuzungen sowie unter unterschiedlichen
Haltungsbedingungen. **Comparative ethological and behaviour
physiological investigations on sheep of different breed and
cross and under different keeping conditions.**

10936 Kallweit, E.   DE 201200/77/0014
Vergleichende Untersuchungen über die Saisonalität des
Brunstzyklus bei Schafen verschiedener Rassen und
Kreuzungen. **Comparative studies on the seasonality of oestrus
cycle in sheep of different race and cross.**

10937 Schön, I.   DE 210050/78/0001 N
Schlachtwert von Schafen. **Slaughter value of sheep.**

10938 Burgkart, M.   DE 502305/74/0001
Untersuchungen zur Ermittlung objektiver Massstäbe zur
Schätzung des Schlachtwertes von Mastlämmern. **Derivation of
objective standards for determining the slaughter value of
fattening lambs.**

10939 Burgkart, M.   DE 502305/74/0002
Untersuchung der Auswirkung einer ganzjährigen Stallhaltung
von Schafen auf die Gesundheit und Fortpflanzungsleistung.
**The effect of indoor stock keeping throughout the year on
health and reproduction of sheep.**

10940 Schlolaut, W.; Heinemann, G.   DE 506220/74/0001
Vergleichende Untersuchungen über die
Reproduktionsleistung bei permanenter Decksaison zwischen
Mutter– schafen der Rassen Merino–Landschaf und Tiroler
Berg– schaf. **Comparison between German Merino landrace
sheep and Tyrol mountain sheep in lambing rate and lambing
interval.**

10941 Christiansen, I.J.; Greve, T.; Lehn–Jensen, H.;
Schmidt, M.   DK 030128/78/0001 N
Ægtransplantation på får. **Embryo transplantation in sheep.**

10942 Møller, A.J.   DK 030191/77/0005 N
Betydningen af slagtevægt og slagtealder for kødets konsistens
hos lam af forskellige racer. **Studies on meat tenderness in ovine
longissimus dorsi from different breeds.**

10943 Soulier, S.; Gaye, P.; Clauser, H.   FR 010213/73/7552
Structure des oligosaccharides des caséines k de lactation et
colostrales de la brebis. **Structure of the polysaccharide chains
from the k–caseins of the ewe, during the colostral and
lactational phases.**

10944 Martal, J.; Lacroix, M.–C.; Chene, N.

                                        FR 010213/73/7558
Structure, activité, régulation de la somatomammotrophine
chorionique ovine. **Structure, activity and regulation of the
ovine chorionic somatomammotropin.**

10945 Martal, J.; Lacroix, M.–C.   FR 010213/73/7559
Facteurs antilutéolytiques et lutéotrophiques du trophoblaste
ovin. **Antiluteolytic and luteotrophic factors of ovine
trophoblast.**

10946 Theriez, M.; Houssin, Y.   FR 010805/74/6541
Evolution de la composition corporelle de l'agneau. **Evolution
of body composition of lambs.**

10947 Houssin, Y.; Theriez, M.   FR 010805/77/6543
Effet du poids de naissance sur le développement de l'agneau.
Effects of birth weight on lambs development.

10948 Combe, E.; Obled, C.; Arnal, M.; Ferrara, M.

                                        FR 010815/77/9588 N
Synthèse protéique dans les tissus intestinaux chez l'agneau au
cours du développement. **Evolution with age of protein
synthesis in the lamb intestinal tissues.**

10949 Vezinhet, A.; Dulor, J.P.; Nougues, J.; Charrier, J.

                                        FR 011203/74/7565
Etudes de l'activité métabolique du tissu adipeux et du rôle de
certaines hormones (Insuline, GH), chez l'agneau et le lapin de
croissance. **Adipose tissue metabolic activity and hormonal
effects (insulin and Growth hormone) studies, in growing Lamb
and Rabbit.**

10950 Flamant, J.C.   FR 011405/73/2552
Etude des performances de reproduction et de croissance en
élevage extensif chez les ovins. **Reproduction and growth
characters of sheep in extensive conditions.**

10951 Loir, M.   FR 011501/68/7501
Qualité des spermatozoides de bélier. **Quality of the
spermatozoa in the ram.**

10952 Blanc, M.R.; Courot, M.   FR 011501/68/7534
Mécanisme de régulation de la secrétion de FSH (hormone
folliculo–stimulante) chez le mouton. **Regulatory mecanism of
FSH secretion in the ram.**

10953 Cognie, Y.; Saumande, J.; Locatelli, A.

                                        FR 011501/70/7525
Activités ovarienne et hypophysaire pendant l'anoestrus
post–partum chez la brebis. **Ovarian and hypophyseal activities
during post–partum anoestrus in the ewe.**

10954 Colas, G.   FR 011501/73/7511
Collecte du sperme déférentiel par canulation chez le bélier.
Etude des propriétés du sperme recueilli. **Collection of
spermatozoa by canulation of vas deferens in the ram.**

10955 Mauléon, P.; Terqui, M.; Bezard, J.; Saumane, J.;
Berthelot, F.   FR 011501/74/7517
Organisation et fonction des cellules somatiques au cours du
développement embryonnaire de la gonade chez la brebis.
Embryonic gonadal development in sheep.

10956 Courot, M.; Monet–Kuntz, C.; Hochereau de Reviers,
M.T.; Courtens, J.L.   FR 011501/75/7503
Endocrinologie de la spermatogénèse du bélier. **Endocrine**

D 3100 – Animal management general and animal husbandry

control of spermatogenesis in the ram.

10957 Mariana, J.C.; Dufour, J.; Cahill, L.; Mauleon, P.; Hulot, F.   FR 011501/75/7519
Folliculogénèse et niveaux hormonaux particuliers aux races prolifiques ovines. **Ovarian and endocrine status in ovine prolific breeds.**

10958 Ortavant, R.; Blanc, M.; Ravault, J.P.; Dubois, M.P.; Pelletier, J.   FR 011501/75/7537
Mise en évidence d'une phase photosensible chez le bélier action de la prolactine chez le mâle. **Evidence for a photoinducible phase for PRL in male Action of PRL in ram.**

10959 Courtens, J.L.; Courot, M.   FR 011501/76/7502
Modifications cytochimiques au cours de la différenciation des spermatides du bélier, essai de définition des facteurs morphologiques impliqués dans la différenciation des cellules germinales mâles. **Spermiogenesis in the ram: E.M. study of the morphogenesis of the spermatids.**

10960 Courot, M.; Dacheux, J.L.; Blanc, M.; Cahoreau, C.; Hochereau de Reviers, M.T.   FR 011501/76/7504
Endocrinologie de la spermatogénèse du bélier et de l'agneau, rôle de l'inhibine. **Inhibine and spermatogenesis in the ram.**

10961 Jegou, B.; Courot, M.   FR 011501/76/7506
Etude des protéines de liaison spécifiques des androgènes (Androgen Binding Protein: Abp; Sex Steroid Binding Protein: SBP) chez les ovins. **Studies of the specific binding proteins of androgens (androgen binding protein: Abp; Sex steroid binding protein: Sbp) in sheep.**

10962 Kuntz, C.; Terqui, M.; Courot, M.   FR 011501/76/7507
Caractérisation et quantification des récepteurs aux androgenes dans le testicule du bélier. **Characterization and quantification of androgen receptors in ram testis.**

10963 Delpech, S.; Flechon, J.E.; Courot, M.; Courtens, J.L.
                                              FR 011501/76/7509
Glycoprotéines à affinité con a de la membrane du spermatozoide de bélier (Maturation épididymaire et capacitation). **Membraneous Con A affinity of the ram spermatozoa during maturation and capacitation.**

10964 Delpech, S.; Colas, G.; Courot, M.   FR 011501/76/7510
Compétence fonctionnelle du spermatozoide dans l'épididyme (bélier). **Intraepididymal fertilizing ability of the spermatozoa.**

10965 Thimonier, J.; Ortavant, R.; Ravault, J.P.
                                              FR 011501/76/7524
Variations saisonnières et photopériodisme chez les ovins. **Photoperiodism in sheep.**

10966 Pelletier, J.; Blanc, M.; Courot, M.   FR 011501/76/7533
Effet de la cryptorchidie sur le système hypothalamo–hypophysaire du bélier. **Effects of cryptorchidism on levels of hypothalamic and pituitary hormones in the ram.**

10967 Signoret, J.P.; Fabre, C.   FR 011501/76/7544
Equilibre hormonal du comportement spécifique mâle ou femelle: étude de l'effet du rythme de traitement chez la brebis. **Endocrine balance of male–like sexual behaviour in the ewe.**

10968 Pelletier, J.   FR 011501/77/7535
Variations saisonnières des récepteurs cytosoliques hypophysaires aux stéroides chez le bélier. **Variations in the levels of pituitary cytosolic receptors for steroids in the ram during the year.**

10969 Poindron, P.; Le Neindre, P.; Signoret, J.P.
                                              FR 011501/78/7542
Relations mère–jeune chez les ovins domestiques. **Mother young relationships in sheep.**

10970 Baldwin   GB 010301/78/0086
Illumination preferences in sheep.

10971 Coleman; Kemp   GB 010302/00/0058
Effect of change in species of rumen protozoa on growth and quality of lambs.

10972 Greenwood   GB 010303/00/0012 R
The physiology of the sheep blood monocyte and humoral factors which regulate miotic potential.

10973 Beal; Harrison   GB 010305/00/0055 R
Role of adrenal hormones and prostaglandins in the urinary excretion of sodium and potassium in sheep.

10974 Tucker; Kilgour   GB 010308/76/0007 R
Detection of biochemical polymorphism in sheep blood and tissue fluids.

10975 Tucker; Kilgour   GB 010308/76/0008 R
Blood groups in sheep and the production of blood group reagents.

10976 Perry   GB 010601/75/0060 R
Relate anatomy physiology metabolic parameters to carcass, meat quality production efficiency in sheep breeds.

10977 Eales; Mellor   GB 030111/76/0007 R
Physiology of the new born lamb and its association with lamb survival.

10978 Mitchell; Williams   GB 030112/00/0008 R
Establishment of respiratory gas values in sheep during normality, anaesthesia and pneumonia.

10979 Peart; Doney   GB 030301/00/0002
Factors affecting lactation yield and its effect on lamb growth.

10980 Smith; Doney   GB 030301/75/0007
Wool production from blackface and crossbred ewes under improved management systems.

10981 Eadie; Floate   GB 030303/00/0002
Effect of hill land improvement on nutrition and productivity on a range of pasture and soil types.

10982 Maxwell   GB 030303/00/0005
Develop off wintering systems of animal production from hill pastoral resources.

10983 Maxwell; Eadie   GB 030303/00/0006
Economic evaluation of hill farming production systems.

10984 Maxwell; Eadie   GB 030303/00/0008
Improved systems of sheep production from upland pastoral

resources.

10985 Fell; Campbell   GB 030608/00/0006 R
Cell division, cell death and total DNA in the livers of breeding
ewes.

10986 Mackie   GB 030608/00/0008 R
Synthesis of macroglobulins in sheep.

10987 Boyne   GB 030608/00/0012 R
Morphology, histochemistry and function of leucocytes.

10988 Robinson; Kay   GB 030611/00/0028
Relationships between nutrition and hormones in ruminants :
effect on breeding frequency and litter size.

10989 Robinson; Fraser   GB 030611/00/0029
Nutrient requirements for reproduction and lactation in prolific
sheep.

10990 Adams   GB 040402/78/0025 R
Sheep grazing in forests.

10991 Chestnutt   GB 041306/00/0002
Effect of rations fed to early–weaned lambs on liveweight gain
and carcass characteristics.

10992 McLaughline   GB 041406/75/0008
The intensification of the traditional lowland sheep flock in
Northern Ireland.

10993 Researcher not indicated   GB 050128/00/0001 R
Sheep: production in hill farming systems.

10994 Researcher not indicated   GB 050128/00/0002 R
Sheep: production in arable farming systems.

10995 Researcher not indicated   GB 050128/00/0003 R
Sheep: mixed stocking systems.

10996 Researcher not indicated   GB 050128/00/0004 R
Sheep: intensive grass sheep systems.

10997 Researcher not indicated   GB 050128/00/0005 R
Sheep: new developments in sheep husbandry.

10998 Researcher not indicated   GB 050128/00/0006 R
Sheep: evaluation of the Finnish landrace, ADAS/ABRO trials.

10999 Researcher not indicated   GB 050168/00/0001
Sheep: production in hill farming systems.

11000 Researcher not indicated   GB 050168/00/0002
Sheep: production in arable farming systems.

11001 Researcher not indicated   GB 050168/00/0003
Sheep: mixed stocking systems.

11002 Researcher not indicated   GB 050168/00/0004
Sheep: intensive grass sheep systems.

11003 Researcher not indicated   GB 050168/00/0005
Sheep: new developments in sheep husbandry.

11004 Researcher not indicated   GB 050168/00/0006
Sheep: evaluation of finnish landrace, ADAS/ABRO trials.

11005 Researcher not indicated   GB 050434/00/0005
Sheep management survey (in association with M.L.C.).

11006 Researcher not indicated   GB 050483/00/0004
Performance and project testing of Welsh mountain rams.

11007 Researcher not indicated   GB 050483/00/0005
Minimal housing of sheep.

11008 Black   GB 060102/00/0012
Development of ewe feeding systems.

11009 Rutter   GB 060102/00/0013
Hill sheep development.

11010 Speedy   GB 060102/00/0014
Upland farm development.

11011 Rutter   GB 060102/00/0017
Grassland based sheep systems.

11012 Speedy   GB 060102/00/0018
Store lamb finishing systems.

11013 Knox   GB 060206/78/0001 N
Achany sheep stocking policy 1 1.

11014 Owen   GB 060208/00/0008
Development of low cost grass based systems to maximise lamb
output:(1) use of highly prolific ewes.

11015 Thomas   GB 060208/00/0010
Development of efficient grazing systems suitable for
management of ewe flocks in caithness.

11016 Vipond   GB 060208/00/0011
Methods of reducing neonatal lamb mortality in upland and
lowground flocks.

11017 Galbraith   GB 060219/00/0007 R
The effect of anabolic compounds on the performance, blood
characteristics and carcase composition of sheep.

11018 Knox   GB 060226/00/0002
Achany sheep stocking policy.

11019 Grant   GB 060226/00/0003
Modified systems of hill sheep management.

11020 MacPherson   GB 060311/00/0005
An economic study of lowland sheep production.

11021 McClelland   GB 060319/00/0003
An investigation of the use of limited improved land in an
otherwise unimproved, unfenced hill situation.

11022 McClelland   GB 060319/00/0004
Hill sheep development project.

11023 Jennings, J.; Lawlor, M.J.   IE 060100/71/0279 R
Increased lambing frequency. Publications.

11024 Lawlor, M.J.; Poole, D.B.R.   IE 060100/74/1203 R
A study of tailendness and compensatory growth in lambs.
Publications.

D 3100 – Animal management general and animal husbandry

11025 More O'Ferrall, G.J.; O'Toole, M.A.; Sheehan, W.
IE 060100/74/1210 R
Comparison of scottish blackface strains and cheviot rams for hill lamb production. Publications.

11026 Kearney, A.
IE 060700/71/0447 R
Effects of mating ewe lambs prior to 'self care'. Publications.

11027 Flanagan, S.P.; Daly, P.J.
IE 060702/72/0439 R
Early lamb production. Publications.

11028 Gordon, I.; Boland, M.P.; Crosby, F.
IE 120105/76/9026 R
Prostaglandin synchronization of ovulation and oestrus in sheep: a comparison with standard progestagen procedures. Publications.

11029 Gordon, I.; Boland, M.P.; Crosby, F.
IE 120105/77/9031 R
Effect of prostaglandins as semen additives in sheep artificial insemination.

11030 Gordon, I.; Boland, M.P.; Crosby, F.; McDonnell, H.
IE 120105/78/9032 R
Studies in the hormonal augmentation of fertility in galway ewes by the application of progestagen and pmsg. Publications.

11031 Gordon, I.; Crosby, F.; Boland, M.P.; McDonnell, H.
IE 120105/78/9033 R
Studies in the induction of parturition in sheep by the use of synthetic corticosteroids.

11032 Gordon, I.; Boland, M.F.; Crosby, F.
IE 120105/78/9035 R
Studies in the artificial insemination of sheep with texel semen. Publications.

11033 Gordon, I.; Boland, M.F.; Crosby, F.
IE 120105/78/9038 R
Effect of sexual preparation procedures on semen characteristics in the ram. Publications.

11034 Gordon, I.; Boland, M.P.; Crosby, F.
IE 120105/78/9210 N
Studies in sheep egg transfer using equine pituitary extract as the agent for inducing superovulation. Publications.

11035 Gordon, I.; Crosby, F.; McDonnell, H.; Boland, M.P.
IE 120105/79/9207 N
Oestrogen assay in detection of multiples in sheep and cattle.

11036 Gordon, I.; McDonnell, H.; Crosby, F.; Boland, M.
IE 120105/79/9209 N
Progestagen–prostaglandin treatment in oestrus/ovulation control in cyclic ewes.

11037 Gordon, I.; Boland, M.P.; Crosby, F.
IE 120105/79/9211 N
Freezing of cattle and sheep embryos.

11038 Crinion, R.A.P.
IE 120206/77/9133 N
Establishing normal biochemical and haemetological values for breeding sheep in Ireland.

11039 Pelosi, A.; Taibi, L.; Di Taranto, F.; Dell'Aquila, S.
IT 020700/77/0012 N
Indagine statistica sulla interferenza della sincronizzazione dei calori sulla carriera economica e riproduttiva delle pecore. **Statistical survey on the interference on the synchronization of oestrus in the economic–reproductive life in the scheeps.**

11040 Matassino, D.; Di Taranto, F.P.; Pilla, A.M.; Dell'Aquila, S.; Pelosi, A.; Taibi, L.
IT 020700/77/0013 N
Contributo sperimentale per gli effetti della sincronizzazione dei calori sull'equilibrio ormonale degli ovini –.. **Experimental contribution for effects synchronization's oestrus on the sheep's ormonal balance –..**

11041 Pelosi, A.
IT 020700/77/0575 R
Indagine conoscitiva della situazione attinente i parametri riproduttivi della specie ovina. **Preliminary research on the present parameters of sheep reproduction.**

11042 Pelosi, A.; Puppo, S.; Dell'Aquila, S.; De Maria, C.
IT 020700/78/0002 R
Influenza della soppressione di una mungitura giornaliera sulla produzione e su talune caratteristiche fisico–chimiche del latte in pecore di razza Comisana. **Effect of omitting one daily milking on milk yield and some physical and chemical properties of milk from Comisana ewes.**

11043 Pilla, A.M.; Dell'Aquila, S.; Taibi, L.
IT 020700/78/0013
La produzione di lana nelle pecore Gentile di Puglia. II Influenza del peso e di alcune misure somatiche. **Wool production in Gentile di Puglia sheep. II Effect of weight and measure.** Publications.

11044 Pilla, A.M.; Dell'Aquila, S.
IT 020700/78/0014
Produzione di latte delle pecore e indice di conversione negli agnelli di razza Comisana nella fase di allattamento. **Production of milk by sheep and index of conversion by suckling Comisana lambs.** Publications.

11045 Pelosi, A.; Taibi, L.; Di Taranto, F.; Pilla, A.M.; Dell'Aquila, S.
IT 020700/78/0015 R
Prove d'impiego di PGF_2 per la sincronizzazione dei calori nelle pecore. Effetti su alcune costanti biologiche e sulle carni. **Use of PGF_2 for synchronization of oestrus in ewes. Effects on some biological parametres and meat characteristics.** Publications.

11046 Pelosi, A.; Taibi, L.; Dell'Aquila, S.; Di Taranto, F.
IT 020700/79/0016 N
Ricerca sulle modificazioni del contenuto plasmatico delle gonadotropine e degli steroidi sessuali (estradiolo e progesterone) sulle pecore di razza Gentile di Puglia durante il normale ciclo sessuale. **Changes of plasmatic contents of gonadotropin and sexual steroids during normal sexual cycle of Gentile di Puglia sheep.**

11047 Pelosi, A.; Di Taranto, F.; Dell'Aquila, S.; Taibi, L.
IT 020700/79/0017 N
Indagine sulla utilizzazione di sostanze tocolitiche per regolare e condizionare il parto delle pecore. **Use of tocolytic substances to regulate and conditionate lambing.**

11048 Cianci, D.
IT 040105/73/1812
Ambiente climatico e fattori nutrizionali nella produzione dell'agnello da macello. **Climatic environment and nutritional factors in the production of lambs for slaughter.**

11049 Bufano, G.   IT 040105/77/0125 R
Razzologia e produzione quanti–qualitativa di latte negli ovini.
Study of races: yield and quality of milk in ewes.

11050 Celi, R.   IT 040105/77/0595 R
Interazioni genotipo–ambiente nel quadro delle attidudini
produttive e riproduttive negli ovini. **Genotype – environment
interaction regarding sheep productive and reproductive
qualities.**

11051 Martemucci, G.   IT 040111/77/0569 R
Il miglioramento della fecondità, della fertilità e della
prolificità nella specie ovina. **Improved fecundity, fertility and
prolificacy in sheep.**

11052 Russo, V.   IT 040245/77/0291
Ricerche sul polimorfismo del latte nelle popolazioni ovine e
caprine. **Research on ewe's and goat's milk polymorphism.**

11053 Lanza, A.   IT 040303/77/0561 R
Ristrutturazione dell'allevamento ovino siciliano allo scopo di
incrementare in particolare la produzione della carne.
**Reorganisation of sheep farming in Sicily with a view to
increase production, particularly of meat.**

11054 Beghelli, V.   IT 041028/77/0536
Sincronizzazione degli estri nella specie ovina, bovina e suina.
Synchronisation of oestrus in sheep, bovine cattle and pigs.

11055 Trimarchi, G.; Ferruzzi, G.; Rossi, G.; Secchiari, P.
    IT 041113/76/0002 N
Studi e ricerche sugli aspetti agronomici zootecnici ed
economici degli allevamenti ovini della Regione Toscana.
**Studies and researches on agronomic, zootecnic and economic
aspects of Toscana sheep breeding..**

11056 Trimarchi, G.   IT 041113/77/0589 R
Studio sulla funzionalità e sull'igiene dei ricoveri per ovini e
caprini. **A study on sheep and goat shelters: functionality and
hygiene.**

11057 Cenni, B.   IT 041127/77/0545 R
Sincronizzazione degli estri nella specie ovina e bovina.
Synchronisation of oestrus in sheep and bovine cattle.

11058 Ubertalle, A.; Errante, J.; Bianchi, M.; Mazzocco, P.
    IT 041217/79/0001 N
Ricerca sulle attitudini produttive e riproduttive degli ovini e
dei caprini. **Research on productive and reproductive
performances of sheep and goats.**

11059 Lucifero, M.   IT 041313/73/0931
Ricerche sulla produzione di carne ovina. **Research on the
production of sheep meat.** Publications.

11060 Bonadonna, T.; Succi, G.   IT 050100/76/0003
La sincronizzazione degli estri nelle pecore e nelle bovine con
l'impiego di idonei prodotti sintetici sostitutivi delle
prostaglandine naturali. **Oestrus synchronization in sheep and
cows using synthetic products in substitution of natural
prostaglandine.** Publications.

11061 Aalbers, J.G.   NL 010112/74/5399
De ontwikkeling van diepvriesmethoden voor ramme–sperma.
The development of deep freezing methods for ram semen.

11062 Oostendorp, D.   NL 010208/71/8751 N
Verhoging van het aantal lammeren per ooi door
bronstinductie of kruising. **Increasing the number of lambs per
ewe by heat induction or crossbreeding.** Publications.

11063 Oostendorp, D.   NL 010208/72/8766 N
Eenvoudige systemen voor huisvesting en verzorging van
schapen en lammeren. **Simple systems for housing and
management of sheep and lambs.** Publications.

11064 Weyden, G.C. van der   NL 030013/76/5476 R
Myometriumactiviteit tijdens de oestrische cyclus bij het
schaap. **Myometrial activity during the oestrous cycle in the
ewe.** Publications.

11065 Weyden, G.C. van der   NL 030013/76/5477 R
De invloed van foetaal oxytocine op de uteruscontracties bij
het schaap. **The influence of fetal oxytocin on uterine
contractions in the ewe.**

Goats, farm deer and other ruminants (B 4290)

See also 3370, 10625, 10678, 10742, 10872, 10884, 11052,
11056, 11058, 11519, 12357, 14587, 15385

11066 Peeters, G.; Roets, E.; Massart–Leen, A.M.
    BE 050600/55/0003
Studies van de precursoren voor de melksynthese bij geit en
koe (geperfuseerde melkklieren, tracer experimenten,
methode der arterio veneuze verschillen doorheen de uier).
**Studies on the precursors of milksynthesis in goat and cow
(perfusion of isolated udder, tracer experiments, method of
arterio venous differences accross the udder).** Publications.

11067 Peeters, G.; Van Sichem–Reynaert, R.
    BE 050800/71/0001 R
Studies over de release van ocytocine bij herkauwers. **Studies
on the release of ocytocine in ruminants.** Publications.

11068 Peeters, G.; Vandeputte, –Van Messom, G.
    BE 050800/77/0005 R
Invloed van de inplanting van perfenazine in de hypothalamus
van de lacterende geit op de melksecretie. **Influence of
inplantation of perphenazine in the hypothalamus of the
lactating goat on the secretion of milk.** Publications.

11069 Finke, K.; Pietrowski, R.; Schmitten, F.
    DE 111503/78/0002 N
Untersuchungen zum Verhalten von Damtieren in
Gehegehaltung an unterschiedlichem Biotop. **Studies on the
behaviour of fallow deer fenced in areas in different biotopes.**

11070 Kuhlmann, F.; Jack, M.   DE 129301/78/0006 N
Intensivierung der Ziegenhaltung in den Tropen. **Intensifying
of goat keeping in the tropics.**

11071 Fischer, H.; Scheurmann, E.   DE 129540/71/0004
Die Bedeutung des Wasserbüffels als landwirtschaftliches
Haustier in den Tropen. **The importance of the water buffalo in
tropical agriculture.**

11072 Fischer, H.; Scheurmann, E.   DE 129540/74/0005
Probleme der Ziegenhaltung, –gesundheit und Zucht in
tropischen Ländern. **Problems of goat husbandry, health and
production in tropical countries.**

D 3100 – Animal management general and animal husbandry

11073 Fischer, H.; Mann, J.   DE 129540/78/0003 N
Andrologische Untersuchungen an afrikanischen Zwergziegen
unter besonderer Berücksichtigung der Spermatogenese.
**Andrological investigations on African dwarf goats with special
reference to spermatogenesis.**

11074 Steinbach, J.; Sidibe, M.   DE 129553/78/0001 N
Physiologische Reaktionen auf Wärmebelastung bei der
Bunten Deutschen Edelziege, der westafrikanischen
Waldziege und der südafrikanischen Burenziege. **Physiological
reactions to heat stress in different goat breeds of temperate –
German – and tropical – West and South African – origin.**

11075 Holtz, W.; Herrmann, H.H.   DE 132276/78/0006 N
Zyklussteuerung und Embryotransfer bei der Ziege. **Control of
estrus cycle and embryo transfer in goats.**

11076 Hinrichsen, J.K.; Merkel–Gottlieb, A.
                                          DE 144675/78/0005 N
Rechtliche Aspekte der Damtierhaltung. **Legal aspects of
fallow deer production.**

11077 Bogner, H.   DE 502300/75/0003
Damwild unter extensiven Fütterungs– und
Haltungsbedingungen zur Erzeugung von Wildbret. **Keeping of
fallow deer – dama dama – under extensive feeding and housing
conditions for venison production.**

11078 Corteel, J.M.; Chemineau, P.; Bariteau, F.
                                          FR 011501/65/7516
Maîtrise de la fertilité caprine: Production et conservation des
gamètes mâles par congelation. Maîtrise du cycle sexuel de la
femelle. Conditions d'insémination artificielle. Diagnostics de
gestation. **Production and deep freezing of goat spermatozoa.
Oestrus control in the goat. Early pregnancy diagnosis.**

11079 Cunningham; Hamilton   GB 030305/00/0001
Study husbanding of red deer.

11080 Kay; Goodall   GB 030612/00/0001
Nutrition of red deer.

11081 Kay   GB 030612/00/0002
Deer farming studies.

11082 Young   GB 060208/79/0019 N
**Establishment and management of a herd of farmed red deer
from the wild.**

11083 Romita, A.   IT 020700/74/0616
Confronti fra gli accrescimenti, le caratteristiche chimico
fisiche ed organolettiche delle carni di vitelli bovini e bufalini
macellati a diverse età, 4–6–8 mesi. **Compared weight
increments, chemical, physical and organoleptic characteristics
of buffalo and cattle calves slaughtered at different ages, 4–6–8
months.**

11084 Intrieri, F.   IT 040738/74/0571
La produzione lattea nella bufala. Effetti della doppia
mungitura meccanica, tempo di mungitura, studi chimici e
biochimici sul latte prodotto, caseificabilità. **Milk yields of
buffalo cows. Effects of double machine milking, milking time,
chemical and biochemical studies on milk yielded,
cheese–making quality.**

11085 Brandano, P.; Congiu, F.   IT 041313/75/0001
Studio conoscitivo della popolazione caprina sarda, delle sue
attitudini produttive e dell'influenza dei fattori ambientali sulla
produzione del latte. **Cognitive study of the Sardinian goat
population, its productive capacities, and the environmental
effects on the milk production.** Publications.

11086 Wiel, D.F.M. van de   NL 010112/77/7845
De progesteron–test: een snelle methode voor oestrus–detectie
bij de waterbuffel. **The progesterone–test: a rapid method for
oestrus detection in the swamp buffalo.**

11087 Adrichem Boogaert, D.H. van   NL 010112/78/7901
Studie omtrent de mogelijkheden van het houden van geiten.
Study on the possibilities of goat farming.

11088 Montsma, G.   NL 020058/78/8812 N
Biologische efficiëntie van vleesproductie bij dwerggeiten.
**Biological efficiency of meat production on dwarf (pygmy)
goats.**

Pigs (B 4300)

See also 10589, 10590, 10628, 10689, 10701, 10702, 10704,
10866, 10871, 10911, 10918, 11054, 12384, 12485, 12487, 12496,
12500, 12502, 12504, 12546, 12572, 13264, 13352, 14647, 14757,
14777, 15677, 15678, 16352, 17193, 19256, 19588

11089 Van der Heyde, H.; Lievens, R.   BE 030028/70/0001 R
Studie van de kunstmatige biggenopfok. **Artificial rearing of
piglets.** Publications.

11090 Vandeplassche, M.; Spincemaille, J.; Bonte, P.;
Dossche, L.   BE 050300/69/0006
Geprogrammeerde partus bij de zeug. **Planned parturition in
the sow.** Publications.

11091 Bouquet, Y.; Lampo, P.   BE 051000/75/0002
Stressgevoeligheid bij varkens. **Stress susceptibility in pigs.**
Publications.

11092 Casteels, M.; Bekaert, H.   BE 070700/76/0023 R
Zootechnische en economische aspecten van
produktieregelende stoffen bij biggen en mestvarkens
(paysone, antibiotica, fumaarzuur..). **Zootecalhnic and
economic aspects of growth promoting additives for pigs
(paysone, antibiotics, fumaric acid...).** Publications.

11093 Bodart, C.; Thielemans, M.F.; François, E.; Thewis,
A.   BE 081200/76/0009
Etude du transit gastro–intestinal chez le porc. **Study of the
rate of passage of food trough the alimentary tract of the pig.**

11094 Van Aelten, G.; Sterkens, L.   BE 140000/77/0009
Invloed van het slachtgewicht op het vetmesten van varkens.
Influence of a higher slaughterweight on the fattening of pigs.

11095 Bronsch, K.; Schneider, D.   DE 104550/70/0002
Bedingungen optimaler Haltung und Ernährung für die
optimale Fruchtbarkeit und Langlebigkeit von Zuchtsauen.
**Effects of environmental and nutritional factors on
reproductive performance and longevity of sows.**

11096 Weniger, J.H.; Steinhauf, D.; Boremann, H.;
Bissinger, E.   DE 105550/72/0005
Verhaltensstudien an Hausschweinen unter modernen

Haltungsbedingungen Auswirkungen unterschiedlicher Haltungsformen auf Bewegungs– aktivität im Tagesablauf, Mastleistung und Schlachtkörper– zusammensetzung. **Studies on the behaviour of domestic swine in modern keeping system Effects of different keeping conditions on moving activity in the course of day, on fattening performance and on composition of carcass.**

11097 Steinhauf, D.; Weniger, J.H.; Unterholzner, J.; Teuscher, T.   DE 105550/73/0001
Untersuchungen zur Reaktion von Ebern auf hohe Umwelttemperaturen. **Studies on the reaction of boars to high environmental temperatures.**

11098 Sommer, H.; Petersen, B.   DE 111403/78/0002 N
Beziehungen zwischen Blut– und Harninhaltsstoffen und dem MMA–Komplex der Sau. **Relations between blood and urine constituents and the MMA–complex of sow.**

11099 Finke, F.; Bergenthal, U.; Finke, K.; Schmitten, F.
          DE 111503/78/0001 N
Untersuchungen zur tiergerechten Haltung von Sauen und Ferkeln. **Investigations on keeping sows and piglets with view to animal welfare.**

11100 Seufert, H.   DE 129400/75/0001
Verbesserungen an Füllkörperwäschern zur Einschränkung von Emissionen aus Schweineproduktionsanlagen. **Amendments to outgoing air foil cleaners for the restriction of emissions from pig production plants.**

11101 Seufert, H.; Sens, K.   DE 129400/75/0003
Untersuchungen zur Rückgewinnung von Wärmeenergie aus der Abluft intensiv belegter Mastschweineställe mit Hilfe von Wärmepumpen. **Studies on the recovery of thermal energy from the outgoing air of intensively stocked pig fattening houses by means of heat pumps.**

11102 Lorenz, J.   DE 129400/75/0010
Arbeitszeitbedarf in der Schweinemast bei Anwendung von Flüssigfütterungsanlagen. **Working time requirements in pig fattening using wet feeders.**

11103 Seufert, H.; Jungbluth, T.   DE 129402/78/0002 N
Physikalische und physiologische Grundlagen des Wärmehaushalts bei Ferkeln zur Ermittlung der Kennwerte von Heizungssystemen. **Physical and physiological principles of heat balance in piglets for determination of characteristics of heating systems.**

11104 Herzog, A.; Müller, K.B.   DE 129680/78/0009 N
Elektronenmikroskopische Untersuchungen an der Herzmuskulatur bei Haus– und Wildschweinen. **Electron microscopic examinations of heart muscles of domestic and wild pigs.**

11105 Herzog, A.; Finger, K.W.   DE 129680/78/0010 N
Elektronenmikroskopische Untersuchungen an der Skelettmuskulatur bei Haus– und Wildschweinen. **Electron microscopic examinations of skeletal musculature of domestic and wild pigs.**

11106 Holtz, W.; Kaufmann, F.von   DE 132276/75/0001
Steuerung des Ovulationszeitpunktes bei Jungsauen. **Control of ovulation in gilts.**

11107 Holtz, W.; Herrmann, H.H.   DE 132276/75/0002 N
Aufbewahrung und Befruchtung von Schweineeizellen im Eileiter des Kaninchens. **Storage and transport of pig egg cells in the rabbit oviduct.**

11108 Holtz, W.; Hassan, F.   DE 132276/77/0002
Struktur und Funktion des Nebenhodens beim Schwein. **Structure and function of the epididymis in the pig.**

11109 Holtz, W.; Hartig, A.; Hahmeier, W.; Vahl, U.
          DE 132276/77/0003
Cortisol– und Testosteronsekretion nach ACTH–Gaben an intakte, kastrierte und adrenalektomierte Eber des Göttinger Miniaturschweins. **Secretion of cortisol and testosterone after ACTH injection in intact, castrated and adrenalectomized boars of the Goettingen miniature pig.**

11110 Holtz, W.; Pich, S.   DE 132276/77/0005
Beschreibung und Quantifizierung der Spermatogenese beim Göttinger Miniaturschwein. **Spermatogenesis in the Goettingen miniature pig.**

11111 Holtz, W.; Kaufmann, F.von   DE 132276/78/0001 N
Der Einfluss von Prostaglandin F2alpha auf den Gelbkörper des Schweins in vitro. **Effect of prostaglandin F2alpha on Corpus Luteum of pig in vitro.**

11112 Holtz, W.   DE 132276/78/0002 N
Geburtsauslösung beim Schwein durch Prostaglandin F2alpha. **Induction of parturition in pigs by prostaglandin F2alpha.**

11113 Holtz, W.   DE 132276/78/0005 N
Vergleich verschiedener Geräte zur Trächtigkeitsfeststellung beim Schwein mit dem Echolot–Verfahren. **Comparison of different ultrasonic apparatuses for pregnancy diagnosis in pigs.**

11114 Holtz, W.   DE 132276/78/0007 N
Das Sperma des Göttinger Miniaturschweins. **Semen of the Goettingen miniature pig.**

11115 Paufler, S.   DE 132330/74/0001
Untersuchungen zur Steigerung der Fruchtbarkeit durch Verwendung von Mischsperma beim Kaninchen und Schwein. **Studies on the increase of fertility by application of mixed sperma to rabbits and pigs.**

11116 Szentkuti, L.   DE 139203/78/0001 N
Untersuchung der physiologischen Eigenschaften einzelner Motoneurone im Rückenmark von Schweinen unter Anwendung der Mikroelektrodentechnik. **Studies of physiological properties of single motor neurons in spinal cord of pigs by microelectrodes.**

11117 Szentkuti, L.; Riffelmann, D.; Steinmetz, F.
          DE 139203/78/0002 N
Physiologische und histochemische Eigenschaften einzelner Muskelfasertypen in der Skelettmuskulatur von Haus– und Wildschweinen. **Physiological and histochemical properties of single muscle fiber types in skeletal muscle of domestic and wilde–life pigs.**

11118 Stephan, E.   DE 139261/78/0006 N
Hybridschweine und ihre Reaktionslage gegenüber Umweltstressoren. **Hybrid pigs and their response to environmental stressors.**

11119 Plonait, H.; Heuser, H.   DE 139750/78/0001 N
Elekromechanische Aufzeichnung des Ruheverhaltens von
Mastschweinen. **Electromechanical recording of resting
behaviour of fattening pigs.** Publications.

11120 Schulze, W.; Luebbers, H.   DE 139750/78/0006 N
Der Kastrationszeitpunkt als oekonomischer Faktor in der
Schweineproduktion. **Time of castration as an economic factor
in pig production.**

11121 Schulze, W.; Mickwitz, G.von   DE 139750/78/0012 N
Tierschutzgerechter Transport von Schweinen. **Transport of
pigs, according to animal welfare.** Publications.

11122 Bickhardt, K.; Flock, D.K.; Richter, L.
    DE 139750/78/0020 N
Creatin–Kinase–Test 'CK–Test' als Selektionsmerkmal zur
Schätzung der Stressresistenz und Fleischqualität bei
Schweinen. **Creatine–kinase–test 'CK–test' as selection
criterion to estimate stress resistance and meat quality in pigs.**
Publications.

11123 Bickhardt, K.; Wirtz, A.   DE 139750/78/0021 N
Zum Ruhe–Lactatstoffwechsel bei nüchternen und gefütterten
Schweinen. **Lactate metabolism in resting pigs before and after
feeding.** Publications.

11124 Faber, H.von; Fewson, D.; Ensinger, U.; Rogdakis, E.
    DE 144141/78/0001 N
Hormon– und Enzymmuster und deren Beziehung zur
Fleischqualität beim Schwein. **Hormone and enzyme patterns
and their relation to meat quality in pigs.**

11125 Siebert, G.; Sturm, G.   DE 144190/75/0003
Die Rolle der Acetyl–CoA–Carboxylase bei der Lipogenese
des Schweines. **On the role of acetyl–CoA–carboxylase in the
lipogenesis of pigs.**

11126 Siebert, G.; Karl, I.   DE 144190/78/0001 N
Charakterisierung der Fettschichten im Subcutanfett des
Schweins. **Characterization of the layers of subcutaneous
adipose tissue in the pig.**

11127 Loeffler, K.; Marx, D.   DE 144605/71/0002 N
Untersuchungen der Möglichkeiten der besseren Ausnutzung
der Reproduktionskapazität der Sau mit Hilfe moderner
Haltungsverfahren. **Studies on possibilities of increasing
efficiency of the reproducing capacity of sows by modern raising
methods.**

11128 Loeffler, K.; Marx, D.; Schrenk, H.–J.
    DE 144605/73/0001
Ethologische Untersuchungen an Saugferkeln und
frühabgesetzten Ferkeln in Flatdeckhaltung. **Ethological
studies on suckling piglets raised conventionally and on early
weaned piglets kept in flatdecks.** Publications.

11129 Loeffler, K.; Flemisch, R.   DE 144605/74/0002
Untersuchungen an den Klauen und Klauengelenken von
Schweinen in verschiedenen Haltungssystemen. **Studies on the
clows and coffin joints of swines in different breeding systems.**

11130 Loeffler, K.; Marx, D.; Schrenk, H.–J.
    DE 144605/75/0006
Spielverhalten von Saugferkeln und frühabgesetzten Ferkeln in

Käfiggruppenhaltung – Flatdecks –. **Playing behaviour of
suckling respectively early weaned piglets kept in cages –
flatdecks –.** Publications.

11131 Loeffler, K.; Schuster, H.; Marx, D. DE 144605/77/0005
Verhalten frühabgesetzter Ferkel in Flatdecks mit
verschiedenen Bodenbelägen. **Behaviour of early weaned
piglets kept in flatdeck–cages with different floor performance.**

11132 Menke, K.H.; Berschauer, F.; Ehrensvärd, U.
    DE 144621/78/0006 N
Protein– und Fettansatz verschiedener Schweinerassen im
Gewichtabschnitt 3–100 kg. **Protein– and fat gain of pigs of
different breed from 3–100 kg live weight.** Publications.

11133 Buchenauer, D.   DE 144675/77/0007
Die Aktivität von ferkelführenden Sauen in Abhängigkeit vom
Haltungsverfahren. **Activity of nursing sows depending on
housing systems.**

11134 Buchenauer, D.   DE 144675/77/0008
Einfluss von Umweltfaktoren auf das Verhalten von
Schweinen. **Influence of the environment on the behaviour of
pigs.**

11135 Buchenauer, D.   DE 144675/78/0002 N
Verhalten von Mastschweinen auf verschiedenen Böden.
Behavior of fattening pigs on different floors.

11136 Buchenauer, D.   DE 144675/78/0003 N
Der Einfluss des Geburtsgewichts auf Mastverlauf und
Mastleistung von Schweinen. **The influence of birth weight on
fattening rate and fattening performance of pigs.**

11137 Hinrichsen, J.K.   DE 144675/78/0006 N
Haltungseinflüsse bei Sauen und ihre Beziehung zu
Leistungsmerkmalen. **Effects of environment on sow keeping
and the relations to productivity parameters.**

11138 Hinrichsen, J.K.; Ehlers, K.   DE 144675/78/0007 N
Einflüsse von Haltungs– und Fütterungsfaktoren auf die
Leistung und das Verhalten von Ebern. **Effects of stable
systems and feeding on performance and behavior of boars.**

11139 Hinrichsen, J.K.; Lukanc, A.; Fliegner, H.
    DE 144675/78/0008 N
Die systematische Erfassung und Auswertung täglicher und
jahreszeitlicher Schwankungen des Stallklimas in
Schweineställen. **Systematic inquiry and evaluation of daily and
seasonal variations of the climate in piggeries.**

11140 Fewson, D.; Bischoff, T.; Böckenhoff, E.; Fender, M.;
Zeddies, J.   DE 144680/75/0005
Ermittlung der Wirtschaftlichkeitskoeffizienten für die
Leistungsmerkmale beim Schwein. **Determination of
economically relevant coefficients for production traits in swine.**

11141 Rogdakis, E.   DE 144680/78/0002 N
Fettzellenwachstum beim Schwein. **Fat cells growth in pigs.**

11142 Kalm, E.   DE 148350/78/0001 N
Landwirtschaftliche Nutziere in modernen Haltungsverfahren
– Tiermaterial für intensive Schweinehaltung. **Farm livestock
under modern management systems – animal material for
intensive pig production.**

11143 Kalm, E.; Otto, H.   DE 148350/78/0002 N
Haltungsverfahren beim Schwein. **Various methods of pig keeping.**

11144 Ernst, E.; Sönnichsen, M.-L.   DE 148352/78/0001 N
Stressanfälligkeit des modernen Fleischschweines. **Predisposition of modern fattened pigs to stress.**

11145 Waibl, H.   DE 160430/78/0003 N
Zur Morphologie des Thymus beim Schwein. **Morphological investigations on the thymus of swine.**

11146 Sambraus, H.H.; Sommer, B.   DE 160705/77/0003
Das Verhalten von Zuchtsauen in Kastenställen und Laufställen mit Einzelfressständen. **The behaviour of breeding sows in pens and in loose houses with separate feeding stands.**

11147 Sambraus, H.H.   DE 160705/78/0007 N
Analmassage und Kotfressen bei Mastschweinen. **The massage of the anus and eating of faeces by fattening pigs.**

11148 Sickel, E.; Giesen, D.   DE 160912/70/0001
Über den Einfluss prä– und perinataler Momente auf die künstliche Aufzucht von Ferkeln. **Influence of pre– and perinatal facts on artificial raising of piglets.**

11149 Spörl, R.; Kirchgessner, M.   DE 161280/78/0003 N
Zum Trächtigkeitsanabolismus von Spurenelementen beim Schwein. **Anabolic effects of trace elements on pregnant sows.**

11150 Blöchinger, J.; Krippl, J.   DE 161305/78/0001 N
Untersuchungen über Tierverluste und vorzeitige Abgänge in der Schweineproduktion. **Investigations on animal losses and premature exits in pig production.**

11151 Claus, R.; Jacobi, W.   DE 161320/77/0004
Radioimmunologische und enzymimmunologische Messung des Ebergeruchssteroids und verwandter Verbindungen beim Schwein. **Radioimmunological and enzyme immunological determination of the boar–taint steroid and related compounds in pig.**

11152 Claus, R.; Alsing, W.   DE 161320/77/0005
Radioimmunologische Messung des Ebergeruchssteroids 5a–Androst–16–en–3–on im peripheren Plasma und im Fettgewebe von Ebern. **Radioimmunological determination of the boar–taint steroid 5a–androst–16–en–3–on in peripheral plasma and fatty tissue of boars.**

11153 Krumper, H.   DE 161360/73/0003
Hygiene der Wasserversorgung des Schweines Trinkverhalten von Sauen und Ferkeln. **Water supply hygiene of pig Drinking behaviour of sow and piglet.**

11154 Bogner, H.; Schumm, H.R.; Berner, H.
     DE 161360/75/0005
Reproduktionsleistung von Muttersauen. **Reproductive efficiency of sows.**

11155 Meinhold, K.; Hinrichs, P.   DE 201100/78/0008 N
Die Entwicklung der Wettbewerbsfähigkeit von Ferkelerzeugung und Schweinemast seit 1957. **The development of the competitiveness of piglet and hog production since 1957.**

11156 Ellendorff, F.   DE 201200/77/0013
Fertilitätskontrolle in Sauenbeständen mittels PlasmaProgesteronbestimmung. **Control of fertility in sows by determination of plasma progesterone.**

11157 Unshelm, J.   DE 201200/77/0020
Konstitutionsbiologische Untersuchungen am wachsenden und erwachsenen Fleischschwein. **Constitution biological examinations of growing and grown–up heavy baconer.**

11158 Kallweit, E.   DE 201200/77/0023
Physiologische Anpassungsfähigkeit des Fleischschweins an belastende Umweltverhältnisse. **Physiological adaptation of heavy baconer to stress of environmental conditions.**

11159 Augustini, C.; Fischer, K.   DE 210010/77/0006
Auswirkungen verschiedener Ruhezeiten auf die Fleischbeschaffenheit von Schweinen nach kontrollierter Klimaund Laufbelastung. **Effects of different rest periods on meat quality of pigs after control of climatic and running stress.**

11160 Schumm, H.R.   DE 502300/75/0001
Untersuchungen zur Reproduktionsleistung bei Zuchtsauen in Verbindung mit dem Frühabsetzen von Ferkeln. **Investigations of reproductive performance of breeding sows in connection with early weaning of piglets.**

11161 Blendl, H.M.   DE 502300/77/0004
Objektive Erfassung der Stressresistenz am lebenden Schwein. **Objective measurement of stress resistance in living pigs.**

11162 Blendl, H.M.   DE 502300/77/0005
Trächtigkeitsdiagnose beim Schwein mit Ultraschall. **Pregnancy diagnosis in pigs by an ultrasonic method.**

11163 Süss, M.   DE 502306/77/0001
Der Einfluss unterschiedlicher Käfigböden auf die Entwicklung von abgesetzten Ferkeln. **The influence of different floors in cages on the development of weaned piglets.**

11164 Reusse, U.; Geister, R.; Messow, C.
     DE 505100/78/0001 N
Untersuchungen über die Reproduzierbarkeit und Ursachen der nach Verfütterung von strahlenpasteurisiertem Fischmehl bei Mastschweinen aufgetretenen erhöhten Mitoseraten. **Studies on the reproduction and causes of increased mitoses in fattening pigs fed with irradiated fishmeal.**

11165 Pedersen, O.K.   DK 010202/67/0002
Kontrol af anvendte metoder og udvikling af nye metoder til bestemmelse af svinenes slagtekvalitet. **Control of current methods, and the development of new methods for the measurement of carcass quality in pigs.**

11166 Pedersen, O.K.   DK 010202/73/0003
Kødkvalitetsundersøgelser hos Dansk Landrace. **Investigations of meat quality in the Danish Landrace pig.**

11167 Madsen, A.; Nielsen, E.K.   DK 010202/74/0001 R
Nærmiljø i en åben stald til slagtesvin. **The environment for growing pigs in an open housing system.**

11168 Nielsen, H.E.   DK 010202/75/0003
Effekten af forskellige fravænningstidspunkter på søer, samt på smågrise, der opdrættes henholdsvis på gulv og i bur. **The effect of weaning at different ages on sows and piglets, reared on**

floors and in cages.

11169 Madsen, A.   DK 010202/75/0013
Slagtesvinenes adfærd. **The behaviour of the bacon pig.**

11170 Nielsen, H.E.   DK 010202/76/0006
Fravænning ved 3 eller 8 uger med anvendelse af søer af ren race eller krydsninger. **Weaning at 3 or 8 weeks from pure and cross bred sows.**

11171 Pedersen, O.K.   DK 010202/76/0017
Dissektion og beregning i forbindelse med klassificering af slagterisvin. **Dissection and calculations in connection with the classification of bacon pigs.**

11172 Pedersen, O.K.   DK 010202/77/0015
Bestemmelse af forskellige faktorers indflydelse på kødkvaliteten hos svin. **Calculation of the influence of various factors on meat quality of pigs.**

11173 Danielsen, V.; Hansen, L.L.; Nielsen, E.K.; Ruby, V.
     DK 010202/78/0007 N
Billige staldtyper til slagtesvin. **Uninsulated stables for growing – finishing pigs.**

11174 Danielsen, V.; Bresson, S.; Ruby, V.
     DK 010202/78/0008 N
Afprøvning af nye og eksperimentelle staldtyper til svin. **Tests of new and experimental types of stables for pigs.**

11175 Jakobsen, P.E.; Jakobsen, K.   DK 010206/70/0011
Mitokondriemængde og –kvalitet i relation til kødmængde og kødkvalitet hos svin. **The amount and quality of mitochondria in relation to the quantity and quality of meat in pigs.**

11176 Keller, P.   DK 010400/77/0003 N
Arbejdsbehov i billige staldtyper til slagtesvin. **Labour requirement in low cost houses for bacon pigs.**

11177 Pedersen, S.; Møller, F.   DK 010400/78/0003 N
Tekniske konsekvenser samt skader på søer ved anvendelse af forskellige bindelstyper. **Technical consequences and sow injuries using various tieing systems.**

11178 Pedersen, S.; Guul–Simonsen, F.; Møller, F.
     DK 010400/78/0004 N
Undersøgelse af nyt ventilationsprincip til slagtesvin. **Investigations of a new ventilation principle in houses for bacon pigs.**

11179 Pedersen, S.; Møller, F.   DK 010400/78/0007 N
Klimaundersøgelser i slagtesvinestalde. **Investigations of climatic conditions in houses for bacon pigs.**

11180 Strøm, J.S.   DK 011000/76/0004
Høje, varierende lufthastigheders indflydelse på slagtesvins tilvækst og foderforbrug. **Influence of high, varying air speeds on the growth and feed consumption of bacon pigs.**

11181 Friis, C.   DK 030123/78/0004 N
Den funktionelle udvikling af nyrer hos smågrise. **Development of renal function in piglets.**

11182 Hansen, N.E.; Sørensen, P.H.   DK 030125/77/0004
Stråle– og rumopvarmning i smågrisestalde. **Radiant heating in sucking pig pens.**

11183 Aalund, O.   DK 030129/77/0016 N
Adfærdsmæssige og fysiologiske konsekvenser af tidlig fravænning af smågrise. **The influence of early weaning on behaviour and physiology of pigs.**

11184 Vestergaard, K.   DK 030135/74/0005
Etologiske undersøgelser. d. Adfærd hos bundne og løsgående søer. **Ethological investigations. (d) The behaviour of bound and untethered sows.**

11185 Bresson, S.   DK 030142/78/0005 N
Belastningers indflydelse på udviklingen af skeletmuskulaturens glykolysehastighed hos svin. **Influence of prolonged stress on development of glycolytic rate in skeletal muscle of pigs.**

11186 Charlet–Lery, G.; Laplace, J.P.   FR 010205/75/2723
Utilisation du porc trachéotomisé pour l'étude des dépenses énergétiques. **Use of tracheotomized pigs for evaluation of heat production.**

11187 Fremont, L.; Corring, T.   FR 010205/77/9553 N
Analyse des lipoprotéines plasmatiques de Porc. **Analysis of pig plasma lipoproteins.**

11188 Aumaitre, L.   FR 010206/65/2903
Sevrage précoce et productivité de la truie. **Early weaning and sow productivity.**

11189 Aumaitre, L.; Rettagliati, J.; Bina, L.; Le Dividich, J.
     FR 010206/67/2902
Sevrage précoce du porcelet et environnement. **Early weaning of piglets and environment.**

11190 Desmoulin, B.; Bonneau, M. ( )   FR 010206/69/2938
Conditions de production et utilisation des viandes de porcs mâles entiers (non castrés) : étude organoleptique et méthodes de contrôle du Boar taint. **Breeding and husbandry systems of entire (uncastrated) pig males on meat quality : detection method and control of Boar taint.** Publications.

11191 Seve, B.; Etienne, M.; Desmoulin, B.; Henry, Y.
     FR 010206/74/2918
Effets à long terme du sevrage précoce (avant 3 semaines) sur la croissance, la qualité de la carcasse et les performances de reproduction dans l'espèce porcine. **Long term effects of early weaning (before three weeks of age) upon growth, carcass quality and reproductive performance in the pig.**

11192 Le Dividich, J.; Berbigier   FR 010206/74/2937
Importance de l'environnement thermique en production porcine. **Importance of the thermal environment in pig production.**

11193 Perez, J.M.   FR 010206/75/2932
La gestion technique des troupeaux de truie en France. **Technical interpretation of data collected from French sows.**

11194 Paquignon, M.; Bariteau, F.   FR 011501/72/7513
Insémination artificielle porcine avec de la semence congelée. **Artificial insemination with deep–frozen boar spermatozoa.**

11195 Botte, F.; Mauléon, P.; Bariteau, F.; Locatelli, A.
     FR 011501/74/7529
Maîtrise des cycles sexuels chez la truie (nullipare et multipare

postarissement). **Oestrus synchronization of gilts and post–weanning sows.**

11196 Courot, M.; Bariteau, F.; Paquignon, M.
FR 011501/75/7512
Insemination artificielle porcine en semence fraîche. **Artificial insemination in the pig with fresh semen.**

11197 Ingram GB 010301/00/0009 R
Mechanisms of thermoregulation and acclimatization in pigs.

11198 Ingram GB 010301/00/0010 R
Influence of body temperatures and environment on food and water intake and behaviour in pigs.

11199 Close GB 010301/00/0059
The effects of environmental variation on the energy metabolism of groups of pigs.

11200 Sharman; Stephens GB 010301/00/0067 R
Cerebral metabolism of dopamine and other neurotransmitter substances in relation to abnormal pig behaviour.

11201 Walser GB 010301/00/0069
Behaviour of piglets during suckling and following weaning.

11202 Mount GB 010301/76/0084
Heat loss and behaviour of penned pigs in relation to ventilation.

11203 Baldwin GB 010301/78/0088 R
Ingestive and thermoregulatory behaviour in pigs.

11204 Feinstein; Holliman GB 010303/00/0038 R
Reconstitution of lymphocyte membranes in pig and man with respect to membrane bound antigen receptors.

11205 Newport GB 011711/00/0001
Artificial rearing and early weaning of piglets.

11206 Braude GB 011711/00/0008
Field response of nutritional treatments.

11207 Pitman GB 011711/00/0010
Factors affecting the performance of pigs (eg castration).

11208 Braude GB 011711/76/0011
Genetic–nutrition interactions.

11209 Weekes GB 023503/79/0009 N
Physiological control of growth and carcass quality in pigs.

11210 Fuller; Livingstn GB 030611/00/0035 R
Comparison of factors affecting performance in pigs of different genotypes.

11211 Fowler; Pennie GB 030611/76/0038 R
Artificial prematurity and subsequent development in the pig.

11212 Fowler; Stockdale GB 030611/76/0041 R
Effects of hormones and their analogues on growth and efficiency of pigs.

11213 Chalmers; Grant GB 030612/77/0027 R
Transport of nutrients in the vascular system of pigs.

11214 Moss GB 040404/79/0008 N
Pig meat quality and stress sensitivity as influenced by genetic selection.

11215 Walker; Lee GB 041301/00/0015
Effect of housing upon young pigs.

11216 Walker GB 041301/00/0017
ARC co–ordinated sow experiments.

11217 Walker; McCracken GB 041301/00/0022
Optimal nutritional environment for early–weaned pigs.

11218 Patterson GB 041301/76/0036
The value of silage effluent for pig production.

11219 Walker; Eddie GB 041301/77/0018
A study of the effects of early weaning upon reproduction in sows.

11220 Researcher not indicated GB 050122/00/0001 R
Pigs: sow productivity.

11221 Researcher not indicated GB 050122/00/0004 R
Pigs: EHF/Rowett collaborative trials.

11222 Hillyer GB 060102/00/0021
Sow and litter performance under different environmental conditions.

11223 Hillyer GB 060102/00/0022
Improved management practices for weaned pigs.

11224 Elsley GB 060102/00/0023
Reductions in weaner production costs.

11225 Whatson GB 060102/00/0026
Studies of pig behaviour.

11226 English GB 060208/00/0013
Factors affecting piglet rearing, their control and implementation in systems of production.

11227 Crabtree GB 060223/00/0001
Economic models of protein and energy nutrition in bacon pigs.

11228 Robertson GB 060224/78/0013 N
The comparative assessment of perforated flooring materials for piglets.

11229 Robertson GB 060224/79/0017 N
The assessment of containerised accomodation for weaned pigs.

11230 Robertson GB 060224/79/0019 N
Assessment of tiered flat deck cages for early weaned pigs.

11231 Robertson GB 060224/79/0020 N
The use of tri–form slats in flat–deck pens for weaned pigs.

11232 McGloughlin, P. IE 060100/65/0529 R
Studies on genetic and environmental aspects of pig production, using pig records from test stations, pedigree herds and commercial units. Publications.

11233 Lynch, P.B. IE 060400/74/1024 R
Environmental conditions for sows and litter. Publications.

11234 O'Grady, J.F.　　IE 060400/78/1410 N
Management influences in the post weaning period on fertility of the sow. Publications.

11235 Lynch, P.B.; Hanrahan, T.J.　　IE 060400/78/1413 N
Study of environmental conditions in large pig houses. Publications.

11236 O'Grady, J.F.　　IE 060400/79/1411 N
Rearing replacement gilts. Publications.

11237 Gordon, I.; Boland, M.P.; Craig, J.
　　IE 120105/77/9030 R
The induction of parturition in pigs by prostaglandin treatm ent.

11238 Bergonzini, E.; Matassino, D.; Quadri, G.; Pilla, A.M.
　　IT 020700/77/0007 N
Rilievi qualitativi a livello muscolare nei suini. **Qualitative reliefs on some muscles of pigs.**

11239 Bergonzini, E.; Rosi, M.A.; Poletti, E.
　　IT 020700/78/0009
Svezzamento precoce di suinetti in gabbie e in ambiente condizionato. **Early weaning of piglets in cages and in controlled environment.**

11240 Manfredini, M.　　IT 040218/74/0583
Ricerche sulla produzione della carne suina mediante l'utilizzazione di animali interi. **Research on pork production using whole animals.**

11241 Semprini, P.　　IT 040218/77/0586 R
Verifica di un metodo di allevamento suino a ciclo chiuso volto ad ottenere la riduzione dell'incidenza del costo dell'alimentazione. **Trial of a closed circuit method of pig breeding aiming at reducing feeding costs.**

11242 Geri, G.　　IT 040520/74/0560
Influenza di alcuni fattori individuali, nutrizionali e di allevamento sulle caratteristiche chimiche fisiche e istologiche della carne suina. **Influence of some individual, nutritional and breeding factors on the chemical, physical and histological characteristics of pork.**

11243 Succi, G.　　IT 040613/73/0953
Ricerche sperimentali sulla possibilità di aumentare la prolificità delle scrofe mediante trattamenti con ossitocina. **Experimental research on the possibility of increasing the reproductivity of sows by means of oxytocin treatments.** Publications.

11244 Curto, G.M.　　IT 040613/77/0549 R
Trattamenti con ossitocina e prolificità delle scrofe. **Oxytocine tratment and fertility in sows.**

11245 Crimella, C.; Roncoroni, G.; Navarotto, P.; Campitelli, S.; Pasi, A.; Giuliani, M.G.　　IT 040638/77/0003 N
Studio sugli aspetti ambientali dell'allevamento suino. Indagini comparative delle strutture di allevamento ai fini di un miglioramento riproduttivo e produttivo.. **Researches on environmental aspects of swine breeding. Comparative studies of breeding structures aimed to production and reproduction improvement.** Publications.

11246 De Franciscis, G.　　IT 040709/77/0550 R
Produzione di carne suina magra in soggetti Fl casertana di tipo grande con suini a spiccate attitudini alla produzione della carne magra. **Lean pork production in large type Caserta Fl pigs using swine with a definite tendency to produce lean meat.**

11247 Salerno, A.　　IT 040724/78/1105 N
Valutazione della massa muscolare nei suini mediante la ricerca del K–40. **Evaluation of the muscular mass of pigs through K–40 detection.**

11248 Haartsen, P.　　NL 010106/67/1179
Stalklimaatsinvloeden op de mestresultaten van varkens. **Effect of indoor climate on fattening pigs.** Publications.

11249 Koomans, P.　　NL 010106/72/4771
Ontwikkeling en verbetering van huisvestingsmethoden en bijbehorende voorzieningen voor biggen. **Development and improvement of housing methods and related facilities for piglets.** Publications.

11250 Koomans, P.　　NL 010106/78/8368
Onderzoek naar mogelijke aanpassingen van huisvestings– en inrichtingssystemen in relatie tot het gedrag en het welzijn van varkens. **Improvement of housing and equipment systems from the point of view of welfare of swine.**

11251 Brake, J.H.A. te　　NL 010112/67/1174
Optimalisering van bevruchting en toom grootte bij varkens. **Optimal fertilization and litter size in pigs.** Publications.

11252 Mateman, G.　　NL 010112/67/1179
Stalklimaatsinvloeden op de mestresultaten van varkens. **Effect of indoor climate on fattening pigs.** Publications.

11253 Walstra, P.　　NL 010112/67/1209
Het opheffen van bezwaren verbonden aan de produktie van gemeste beertjes (fokkerij– en mesterijmaatregelen, gedrag en bepaling van geslachtsgeur in het vlees).**Elimination of the difficulties connected with the production of meat from entire male pigs (breeding and fattening measures, quantification and behaviour of sex odours in meat).** Publications.

11254 Walstra, P.　　NL 010112/67/2307
De invloed van castratie /partiële castratie van mannelijke mestvarkens op groeisnelheid, slachtkwaliteit en voederverbruik bij verschillende voedersystemen. **The influence of castration /partial castration of male pigs for fattening on rapidity of growth, slaughtering –quality and feed consumption with different feeding –systems.** Publications.

11255 Brake, J.H.A. te; Wiel, D.F.M. van de
　　NL 010112/74/5401
Onderzoek naar achtergronden en oorzaken van onvruchtbaarheid, c.q. verminderde vruchtbaarheid bij zeugen. **Investigation into background and causes of infertility or reduced fertility in sows.** Publications.

11256 Eikelenboom, G.　　NL 010112/74/7899
De ontwikkeling van experimenteel–chirurgische technieken t.b.v. het endocrinologisch voortplantingsonderzoek bij het vrouwelijk varken. **The development of experimental surgical techniques for the study of reproductive endocrinology in the female pig.**

11257 Wiel, D.F.M. van de; Eikelenboom, G.; Vos, E.

D 3100 – Animal management general and animal husbandry

NL 010112/75/6150
De maternale herkenning van de graviditeit bij het varken. **Maternal recognition of pregnancy in the pig.** Publications.

11258 Aalbers, J.G.; Brake, J.H.A. te   NL 010112/75/6178
De ontwikkeling van diepvriesmethoden voor beresperma. **The development of deep freezing methods for boar semen.** Publications.

11259 Putten, G. van   NL 010112/76/6143
Het vaststellen van het welzijn van vleesvarkens bij drie lichtniveaus. **To establish the welfare of fattening pigs, kept at three different light intensities.** Publications.

11260 Wiel, D.F.M. van de   NL 010112/76/6149
Neuro–endocrine controle–mechanismen van de gonaden functie bij het vrouwelijk varken. **Neuro–endocrine control mechanism of gonad function in the female pig.** Publications.

11261 Wiel, D.F.M. van de   NL 010112/77/7897
Ovulatie–inductie in prepuberale gelten. **Induction of precocious ovulation in gilts.**

11262 Verstegen, M.W.A.   NL 020058/74/4812
Invloed van klimaatsfactoren en genotype op de eiwitaanzet en energiebalans van groeiende varkens (en van muizen). **Influence of climate factors and genotype on protein deposition and energy balance in growing pigs (and mice).** Publications.

11263 Lange, A.W. de   NL 020058/77/7357
Het gedrag van zeugen rond de partus. **The behaviour of sows about the time of parturition.**

11264 Goedegebuure, S.A.   NL 030005/76/5809
Onderzoek naar erfelijke en milieuinvloeden op locomotiestoornissen bij varkens, o.a. klinische en pathologische parameters voor osteochondropathieën. **Genetic and environmental influences on locomotion disturbances in pigs, a.o. clinical and pathological parameters for osteochondrosis.** Publications.

11265 Hoogerbrugge, A.   NL 030009/70/5717 R
Een onderzoek naar de perinatale biggensterfte. **An investigation on perinatal mortality of pigs.**

11266 Taverne, M.A.M.   NL 030013/76/6139
Functionele analyse van het partusgebeuren bij het minivarken. **Physiology of parturition in the minipig.** Publications.

11267 Willemse, A.H.   NL 030013/76/7780 R
Onderzoek naar de oorzaken van het bestaan van ovariële inaktiviteit tijdens de laktatie bij de zeug (prolactine, lactatie, ovarium, gonadotrope hormonen, zeug). **Investigation to the cause of the existence of ovarian inactivity during lactation in the sow (prolactin, lactation, ovary, gonadoptropins, sow).** Publications.

11268 Amerongen, J.J. van   NL 030017/76/7778 R
Een onderzoek naar registratiesystemen op varkensfokbedrijven. **An investigation of registration technics on pig breeding farms.**

Poultry and domestic birds in general (B 4400)

See also 17155, 19169

11269 Krampitz, G.   DE 111401/72/0003
Vergleichende Untersuchungen an Schalenproteinen von Eischalen und Mollusken. **Comparative studies on proteins in egg shells and molluscan shells.**

11270 Krampitz, G.; Meisel, H.   DE 111401/78/0002 N
Ca–Bindungsmechanismen in Eischalen. **Ca–binding mechanisms in egg shells.**

11271 Scholtyssek, S.; Ehinger, F.; Gschwindt, B.
DE 144685/75/0001
Transportversuche mit Mastgeflügel. **Transport experimentation on broilers.**

11272 Bessei, W.; Jezierski, T.   DE 144685/75/0005
Die Entwicklung neuer Messverfahren zur quantitativen Bewertung des Verhaltens von Legehennen in verschiedenen Haltungssystemen. **Development of new methods of measurement for quantitative evaluation of the behaviour of laying hens in different management systems.**

11273 Scholtyssek, S.; Fehrentz, H.   DE 144685/75/0011
Fruchtbarkeitsverhältnisse der Hähne in der modernen Geflügelhaltung. **The situation of cock fertility in modern poultry management.**

11274 Scholtyssek, S.; Bessei, W.; Gschwindt, B.
DE 144685/75/0012
Anpassungszüchtung von Legehennen auf bestimmte Haltungssysteme. **Breeding of laying hens for adaptation to certain management systems.**

11275 Scholtyssek, S.   DE 144685/78/0003 N
Technologie in Geflügelstallungen und Eiqualität. **Technology in fowl housing and egg quality.** Publications.

11276 Kirchgessner, M.; Voreck, O.   DE 161280/77/0002
Energieaufwand für die Proteinsynthese beim Ei. **Energy costs for egg protein formation.**

11277 Löliger, H.–C.; Hanschke, S.   DE 201300/75/0009
Vergleichende Untersuchungen über die Entwicklung von Schilddrüsen und Nebennieren sowie des Herzmuskels, des Magens, der Leber und Milz unter Einschluss karyometrischer Analysen der Endokrinorgane von Hennen aus Boden– und Käfighaltung mit unterschiedlicher Besatzdichte. **Comparative studies on the development of thyroid glands and adrenal glands as well as of heart muscles, stomach, liver and spleen including karyometric analyses of the endocrinal organs of hens from freeland and cage housing with different stocking rate.**

11278 Torges, H.–G.; Matthes, S.   DE 201300/75/0012
Untersuchungen zur Eiqualität in Abhängigkeit von der Haltungsform der Legehennen. **Investigations of egg quality in dependence on layer housing systems.**

11279 Rauch, H.–W.; Heil, G.; Hartmann, W.
DE 201300/77/0003
Einfluss von Bruteibehandlung, Brutbedingungen und Eigenschaften der Bruteier auf den Bruterfolg. **Influence of treatment of hatching eggs, of hatching conditions and properties of hatching eggs on the hatching success.**

11280 Hartmann, W.; Rauch, H.–W.; Heil, G.

D 3100 – Animal management general and animal husbandry

DE 201300/77/0004
Untersuchung erblicher und maternaler Einflüsse auf die Embryonalsterblichkeit in verschiedenen Abschnitten der Brutperiode und deren Vorhersagewert für Lebensfähigkeit. **Examination of hereditary and maternal influences on the mortality of embryos in different stages of the hatching period and their prognostic value for viability.**

11281 Matthes, S.　　　　　DE 201300/78/0009 N
Einfluss der Haltungsmethode auf die hygienische Qualität von Kleintierprodukten. **Influence of the management system on the food hygienic quality of eggs.**

11282 Wegner, R.–M.; Otto, C.; Rauch, H.–W.; Sodeikat, G.; Torges, H.–G.; Wennrich, G.　　DE 201300/78/0017 N
Haltung von Legehennen in verschiedenen Käfigtypen. **New types of cages for laying hens.**

11283 Wegner, R.–M.; Otto, C.; Rauch, H.–W.; Sodeikat, G.; Torges, H.–G.; Wennrich, G.　　DE 201300/78/0018 N
a.Haltung von Legehennen im Volierensystem b.Haltung von Legehennen in kostengünstigen Ställen. **New systems for keeping laying hens – aviary systems and lowcost poultry houses – plastic foil –.**

11284 Wegner, R.–M.; Torges, H.–G.; Rauch, H.–W.
　　　　　　　　　　DE 201300/78/0019 N
Überprüfung verschiedener Beleuchtungsprogramme für Legehennen. **Testing of effects of different lighting–regimes on layers.**

11285 Schön, L.; Ristic, M.; Freudenreich, P.
　　　　　　　　　　DE 210010/77/0002
Qualitätsuntersuchungen an Produkten von Wirtschaftsgeflügel aus neuzeitlichen Haltungssystemen. **Investigations on quality of commercial poultry from modern systems of husbandry.**

11286 Simonsen, H.B.　　　　　DK 030135/76/0007
Radiotelemetrisk måling af legemstemperaturens døgnrytme hos høns. **Measurement of the diurnal rhythm of body temperature in hens using radio–telemetry.**

11287 Siller　　　　　GB 010701/00/0002 R
Tissue structure in normal and stressed birds.

11288 Maxwell　　　　　GB 010701/00/0007 R
Ultrastructure of leucocytes in normal and stressed bids.

11289 Macleod　　　　　GB 010703/00/0004 R
Effect of genotype, environment and activity on the production and loss of heat in poultry.

11290 Gentle　　　　　GB 010704/00/0004 R
Behavioural and physiological responses to painful stimuli.

11291 Duncan　　　　　GB 010704/00/0005 R
Behavioural response to stress correlated with physiological parameters.

11292 Wells　　　　　GB 010708/00/0008 R
Adrenal activity in relation to stress.

11293 Evans; Bannister　　　　　GB 010708/00/0018 R
Formation, transport and utilisation of blood lipids in the growing chicken.

11294 Evans　　　　　GB 010708/00/0019 R
Formation, transport and utilisation of blood lipids in the laying chicken.

11295 Bannister　　　　　GB 010708/00/0022 R
Intermediary metabolism in the growing and laying bird.

11296 Sharp; Gilbert　　　　　GB 010708/74/0023 R
Neuroendocrine factors and egg production in poultry.

11297 Crawford　　　　　GB 041406/00/0004 R
The biodegradation of broiler litter and its subsequent use.

11298 Researcher not indicated　　　　　GB 050129/00/0005 R
Table poultry : production.

11299 Researcher not indicated　　　　　GB 050169/00/0005
Table poultry: production.

11300 Researcher not indicated　　　　　GB 050455/00/0001
Some aspects of production and mortality amongst pheasants.

11301 Emmans　　　　　GB 060102/00/0028
Feeding laying hens.

11302 Brocklehurst　　　　　GB 060102/00/0030
Poultry management scheme.

11303 Shirlaw　　　　　GB 060102/00/0032
An examination of the growth,marketing and organoleptic properties of different types of poultry.

11304 Morgan–Jones　　　　　GB 060113/00/0002 R
Microbiology associated with hatching,rearing and processing poultry.

11305 Michie　　　　　GB 060209/00/0001
Poultry meat production.

11306 Crinion, R.A.P.　　　　　IE 120206/77/9134 N
Establishing normal biochemical and haematological parameters for broiler and laying hens.

11307 Giordani, G.　　　　　IT 040212/78/1159 N
Influenza delle tecniche di allevamento e delle condizioni fisioclimatologiche sulla qualità dei prodotti avicoli. **Influence of breeding techniques, physiological and climatic factors on the quality of avian products.**

11308 Olivetti Rason, A.　　　　　IT 040520/74/0592
Indagini sull'alimentazione e sull'allevamento del pollo da carne e del coniglio da carne. Riflessi produttivi ed igienico–sanitari. **Investigations on the feeding and rearing of meat poultry and rabbits. Productive, hygienic and sanitary aspects.**

11309 Haartsen, P.I.　　　　　NL 010106/72/4775
Huisvesting van pluimvee en konijnen. **Housing of poultry and rabbits. Publications.**

11310 Brantas, G.C.　　　　　NL 010109/65/7858
Bedrijfstechnische verbetering van huisvesting en verzorging van pluimvee in verband met het gedrag. **Improvement of housing and management of poultry in relation to behaviour. Publications.**

11311 Brantas, G.C.　　　　　NL 010109/70/7733
Gedrag en welzijn van pluimvee. **Behaviour and poultry welfare.** Publications.

11312 Goosen, H.　　　　　NL 030009/74/6018 R
De invloed van geïsoleerde opfok, door middel van FAPP–housing op het optreden van lymfoide leucose bij pluimvee (isolatie, FAPP–housing, lymfoide leucose, pluimvee). **The role of isolation by means of FAPP–housing on the frequency of lymphoid leucosis (isolation, FAPP–housing, lymphoid leucosis, poultry).**

11313 Visschedijk, A.H.J.　　　　　NL 030014/74/6054
Het geleidingsvermogen van de eischaal voor gassen. **Gas conductance of egg–shells.** Publications.

Chickens (B 4410)

See also 10633, 17281

11314 Horst, P.; Petersen, J.; Wolf, M.　　　DE 105550/72/0001
Auswirkungen hoher Umwelttemperaturen auf die Leistungsreaktion von Legehennen unterschiedlichen Körpergewichts. **The influence of high environmental temperatures on the production performance of laying hens with different body weight.**

11315 Researcher not indicated　　　　　DE 108000/77/0001
Hormonphysiologische Untersuchungen an Legehennen unter verschiedenen Haltungsbedingungen. **Hormone physiological investigations on layers under different keeping conditions.**

11316 Petersen, J.　　　　　DE 111501/78/0002 N
Methodische Untersuchungen zur Regulierung von Legepausen beim Huhn. **Investigations on methods for controlling laying intervals in hen.**

11317 Petersen, J.; Kreuer, G.　　　　　DE 111501/78/0003 N
Untersuchungen zur Besatzdichte bei der Käfighaltung von Legehennen. **Research on stock density in cage husbandry of laying hens.**

11318 Petersen, J.; Schaten, M.　　　　　DE 111501/78/0004 N
Die Bedeutung der Jugendentwicklung von Legehennen für die spätere Leistungsfähigkeit. **The importance of juvenile development of laying hens for later performance.**

11319 Scholtyssek, S.; Bessei, W.　　　　　DE 144685/77/0001
Neue Methoden zur Induzierung einer Legepause bei Hühnern. **New methods for induction of laying interval in poultry.**

11320 Lösch, U.; Scharrer, E.　　　　　DE 160600/72/0029
Untersuchungen an gnotobiotischen Küken. **Experiments on gnotobiotic chicks.**

11321 Wittmann, J.　　　　　DE 160600/74/0001 R
Regulierung des perinatalen Stoffwechsels beim Küken. **Regulation of perinatal metabolism at the time of hatching.**

11322 Wennrich, G.　　　　　DE 201300/75/0010
Untersuchungen über den Einfluss der Raumbeschränkung auf Bewegungsaktivität und Komfortverhalten des Huhnes. **Investigations of the influence of room restrictions to moving activity and comfort behaviour of chickens.** Publications.

11323 Wennrich, G.　　　　　DE 201300/77/0010
Untersuchungen zum Lautinventar des Huhnes bei freier Bewegungsmöglichkeit und im Deprivationsversuch. **Studies on sound inventory of chick in free exercise and in deprivation.**

11324 Wegner, R.–M.; Torges, H.–G.; Wennrich, G.; Otto, C.; Sodeikat, G.　　　　　DE 201300/77/0011
Qualitative und quantitative Untersuchungen zum Verhalten, zur Leistung und zum physiologisch–anatomischen Status von Legehennen in unterschiedlichen Haltungssystemen. **Qualitative and quantitative studies on behaviour performance and physiological–anatomical status of layers in different keeping conditions.**

11325 Torges, H.–G.　　　　　DE 201300/77/0013
Untersuchungen über den Einfluss der Haltungssysteme auf den Fettgehalt der Leber von Legehennen verschiedener Herkünfte. **Studies on the influence of keeping conditions on the fat content in the liver of layers of different provenience.**

11326 Löliger, H.–C.　　　　　DE 201300/77/0014
Untersuchungen zur Kokzidiostatica–freien Aufzucht von Junghühnern. **Trials on rearing ckicks without coccidiostatica.**

11327 Matthes, S.　　　　　DE 201300/78/0010 N
Einfluss der Haltungsmethode auf die Antikörperbildung beim Huhn. **Influence of the management system on the development of antibodies in chickens.**

11328 Löliger, H.–C.　　　　　DE 201300/78/0013 N
Klinisch–chemische Substrat– und Enzymmessungen an wachsenden und adulten Hennen in unterschiedlichen Haltungsmethoden. **Clinico–chemical evaluation of substrate and enzyme levels in growing and adult chickens under different keeping conditions.**

11329 Fuhrken, E.　　　　　DE 511250/78/0001 N
6 Beleuchtungsversuche 'Broilermast'. **6 trials on light intensities 'broiler fattening'.**

11330 Laughlin　　　　　GB 010703/00/0003
Factors influencing hatchability in commercial hatcheries.

11331 Hughes　　　　　GB 010704/00/0007
Social behaviour in fowls in large groups and in cages under various conditions.

11332 Duncan　　　　　GB 010704/00/0009 R
Behavioural modifications during domestication.

11333 Pearce　　　　　GB 040403/00/0003 R
Effects of hormonal status on enzyme activity in the domestic fowl.

11334 Purvis　　　　　GB 041405/75/0006
The effects of stocking density and colony size on the performance of broiler parent stock housed in cages.

11335 Researcher not indicated　　　　　GB 050129/00/0003 R
Laying hens: environment.

11336 Researcher not indicated　　　　　GB 050129/00/0004 R
Laying hens: rearing replacements.

11337 Researcher not indicated　　　　　GB 050169/00/0003

Laying hens: environment.

11338 Researcher not indicated GB 050169/00/0004
Laying hens: rearing replacements.

11339 Emmans GB 060102/78/0037 N
Broiler production.

11340 Michie GB 060209/78/0003 N
Broiler production: study of systems environment feeding and their interactions.

11341 Michie GB 060209/78/0004 N
Poultry meat production (other than broilers) study of systems environment feeding.

11342 Michie GB 060209/78/0005 N
Egg production: feed utilisation studies.

11343 Michie GB 060209/78/0006 N
Egg production: study of environment/nutrition.

11344 Whittle GB 060305/00/0003
Broiler breeding stock in cages.

11345 Kaltofen, R.S. NL 010109/69/7856
Ontsmetting van broedeieren met formaldehyde gas.
Formaldehyde fumigation of hatching eggs. Publications.

11346 Haye, U.; Middelkoop, J.H. van; Voorst, A. van
  NL 010109/70/7739
Spermakenmerken bij hanen van de slachtrassen in verband met de fertiliteit. **Sperm characteristics of broiler males in relation to fertility.**

11347 Beuving, G. NL 010109/72/3888
Biochemische aspekten van stress bij pluimvee. **Biochemical aspects of stress in poultry.** Publications.

11348 Kuit, A.R. NL 010109/73/3891 R
Onderzoek naar de vetaanzet bij slachtkuikens. **Research into fatdeposition in broilers.** Publications.

11349 Kaltofen, R.S. NL 010109/74/5958
De invloed van de afkoeling van het ei na de leg op de embryonale ontwikkeling en de broeduitkomsten. **The influence of cooling of eggs after laying on the embryonic development and hatching results.**

11350 Kaltofen, R.S. NL 010109/75/6065
Sterfte preventie tijdens het vervoer per vliegtuig van eendagskuikens. **Prevention of mortality in one day old chicks during transport in aeroplanes.**

11351 Tijen, W.F. van; Gerritsen, G.; Brantas, G.C.
  NL 010109/75/7859
Het leggedrag van kippen in verband met eischaalbreuk. **The laying behaviour of hens in relation to eggshell breakage.** Publications.

11352 Brantas, G.C. NL 010109/77/7728 R
Paringsaktiviteit bij zware hanen in verband met de natuurlijke voortplanting. **Mating activity of meat type cocks in relation to reproduction.**

11353 Simons, P.C.M.; Teunis, G.P.; Jansonius, F.A.T.;

11354 Folkerts, J.; Erdtsieck, B.; Frijters, J.E.R.; Gerrits, A.R.; Helder, J.F.; Janssen, W.M.M.A. NL 010109/77/7866
De produktie van een slachtkuiken met een verbeterde kwaliteit. **Production of a broiler of improved quality.**

11355 Mulder, R.W.A.W.; Haye, U.; Kaltofen, R.; Pelgröm, R. NL 010109/77/7867
De produktie van Salmonella–vrije slachtkuikens. **Production of Salmonella–free broilers.** Publications.

11356 Schenk, P.M. NL 020047/78/8804 N
Sociaal gedrag en sociale organisatie bij kippen. **Social behaviour and organization of poultry.**

11357 Huisman, G.H. NL 030014/76/6922 R
Acclimatisatie van kippen aan verschillende klimatologische omstandigheden (voedselbeperking, vetgroeiremming). **Acclimation to physical factors in chickens (feed restrictions, fatgrowth inhibition).** Publications.

11358 Huisman, G.H. NL 030014/77/7785 R
Waterbalans van kippen bij diverse omgevingstemperaturen. **Water balance in chickens at different ambient temperatures.**

11359 Schothorst, M. van NL 040011/76/7453
Onderzoek naar de mogelijkheden van het Salmonella–vrij opfokken van slachtkuikens. **Investigation on the possibilities of Salmonella–free breeding of broilers.**

Geese, turkeys and other domestic birds (B 4490)

See also 10421, 12716

11360 Merne, O. IE 050100/68/7229 N
Monitoring wintering population of white–front goose. Publications.

11361 Cavalchini, L.G. IT 040613/77/0544 R
Indagini sulla produzione di carne di tacchino e bovina attraverso ricerche interessanti l'efficienza riproduttiva, l'incubazione, l'ingrasso con particolare riferimento all'alimentazione. **Research on turkey and beef meat production taking into account fertility, incubation and fattening in relation to feeding.**

11362 Cavalchini, L.G. IT 040638/74/0531
Ricerche sulle attività riproduttive dei tacchini in funzione di differenti tecnologie di allevamento e di diversi piani alimentari. Approfondimento delle conoscenze riguardanti la fertilità dell'allevamento del coniglio. **Research on reproductive activity of turkeybirds as influenced by different breeding technologies and different feeding programs. Further research on fertility in rabbit breeding.**

11363 Cavalchini, L.; Campitelli, S.; Roncoroni, G.; Giuliani, M.G. IT 040638/77/0002
Indagine sull'allevamento delle specie avicole. Ricerche sulla tecnologia con particolare riferimento al microclima e alle caratteristiche produttive nel tacchino. Studio genetico per l'intensificazione della prod. anatra. **Research on poultry breeding. Studies on tecnology, with particolar emphasis on microclimate, and production in turkey species. Genetic studies**

aimed to the duck's production improvement. Publications.

11364 Fedeli Avanzi, C.   IT 041113/77/0553 R
Effetti del clima sui parametri riproduttivi dell'anatra muschiata e prove di adattamento in ambienti diversi. **The effects of climate on the musk–duck reproductive parameters and adaptation trials on different environments.**

11365 Kuit, A.R.; Ehlhardt, D.A.; Middelkoop, J.H. van; Zegwaard, A.   NL 010109/77/7860
De geschiktheid van kleine erfdieren voor produktie van vlees en eieren. **The suitability of native farm animals (birds) for meat and egg production.**

Fishes, crustacea, shell fish and frogs in general (B 4500)

See also 2043, 2056, 10422

11366 Gérard, P.   BE 130000/79/0024 N
Biologie, croissance, reproduction de diverses espèces d'écrevisses. **Biology, growth and reproduction of different species of crayfish.**

11367 Koeniger, N.; Ritter, W.   DE 123100/77/0001
Temperaturregulation im Bienenvolk mit und ohne Brut. **Temperature regulation in honeybee colonies with and without brood.** Publications.

11368 Wassmuth, R.; Kellner, P.   DE 129383/74/0001
Fischerei und Fischproduktion in der UdSSR. **Fishing and fish production in the USSR.**

11369 Braum, E.; Klinger, H.; Peters, G.
          DE 135250/78/0001 N
Das Blutbild gestresster Fische aus Intensivzuchten. **Stress effects on hematological parameters of fish in intensive culture.**

11370 Braum, E.; Delventhal, H.; Peters, G.; Liemann, J.
          DE 135250/78/0002 N
Plasmacortisol–Konzentration und Kohlenhydrat–Stoffwechsel von gestressten Fischen unter verschiedenen Hälterungsbedingungen. **Stress effects on plasmacortisol concentration and carbohydrate metabolism of fish under various rearing conditions.**

11371 Peters, G.   DE 135250/78/0003 N
Stresssymptome bei Fischen aus Intensivzuchten. **Symptoms of stress in fish in intensive culture.** Publications.

11372 Lamina, J.; Bayrle, H.; Stein, H. DE 161361/78/0001 N
Gefrierkonservierung von Fischsperma. **Cryopreservation of fish spermatozoa.** Publications.

11373 Lamina, J.; Stein, H.   DE 161361/78/0004 N
Anwendung spezieller Verdünnungsmedien bei der künstlichen Besamung bei Fischen. **Application of special dilution media in the artificial insemination of fish.**

11374 Sengbusch, R.von   DE 903500/73/0001
Studium der biologischen Klärung des Wassers zur Fisch– bzw. Wassertierhaltung im geschlossenen Kreislauf sowie Studium des gezielten Aufbaus biologischer Ketten zur Umwandlung unverwertbarer organischer Substanz in verwertbare und die Verwertung von N–Endprodukten. **Study on biological water clarification for keeping fish resp. aquatic animals in closed**

cycle as well as on the systematic structure of biological chains for transforming unavailable organic matter into available one and utilization of N–final products.

11375 Billard, R.; Upadhyay, S.; Fostier, A.; Breton, B.
          FR 010203/65/5544
La spermatogénése des poissons téléostéens: morphologie et régulation endocriniennes. **Spermatogenesis in teleost fish: morphology and endocrinology.**

11376 Breton, B.; Jalabert, B.   FR 010203/70/5545
Purification des hormones gonadotropes de poissons. **Purification of the fish gonadotropins.**

11377 Jalabert, B.; Campbell, C.; Breton, B.; Fostier, A.
          FR 010203/71/5550
Etude du déterminisme de la maturation ovocytaire et de l'ovulation chez les poissons. **Studies of physiological control of ovocyte maturation and ovulation in the fish.**

11378 Weil; Breton, B.; Billard, R.   FR 010203/72/5535 N
Etude de l'axe hypothalamus–hypophyse, gonades au cours du cycle reproducteur. **Study of axis hypotalamus–hypophyse, gonads during the reproductive cycle.**

11379 Billard, R.; Dupont, J.; de Montalembert; Escaffre, A.M.; Sanchez, M.   FR 010203/72/5541
Insémination artificielle et conservation des gamètes chez les poissons téléostéens. **Artificial insemination and gamete preservation in teleost fish.**

11380 Billard, R.; de Montalembert   FR 010203/72/5543
La spermiation chez les poissons téléostéens. **The spermation and sperm release in teleost fish.**

11381 Billard, R.; Fostier, A.; Weil, C.; Dubois, M.; Breton, B.   FR 010203/73/5542
Fonctionnement de l'axe gonadotrope hypothalamo–hypophysaire chez les poissons téléostéens. **Hypotalamo–pituitary axis and control of reproduction in teleost.**

11382 Billard, R.; Sanchez, M.; Breton, B.; Montalembert de   FR 010203/74/5539
La physiologie du sperme chez les poissons téléostéens. **Physiology of sperm in teleost fish.**

11383 Billard, R.; Gillet, C.; Breton, B.   FR 010203/74/5540
Effets de divers micropolluants sur la reproduction des poissons. **Effects of various micropolluants on fish reproduction.**

11384 Gillet, C.; Billard, R.; Breton, B.   FR 010203/75/5530
Effets de la température sur la reproduction des poissons. **Effects of temperature on fish reproduction.**

11385 Fostier, A.   FR 010203/77/5532
Sexage des poissons marins. **Sexing sea fish.**

11386 Breton, B.; Fostier, A.; Billiard, B.
          FR 010203/77/5546 N
Contrôlle de la sécrétion gonadotrope. Etude des cycles de reproduction. **Endocrine control of reproductive cycles.**

11387 Lesel, R.; Juste, C.   FR 010204/73/5508
Productions aquicoles intégrées. **Integrated aquatic**

D 3100 – Animal management general and animal husbandry

production.

11388 Laurent   FR 012218/75/5567
Evolution quantitative des stocks de poissons vivants dans les lacs. **Quantitative estimations of lakes fish standing crop by mean of echointegration.**

11389 Jason; Kent   GB 051005/00/0021 R
Diffusion and sorption of monolayer water in fish at sub–zero temperatures.

11390 Jason; Sanders   GB 05100⁵/00/0024 R
Heat transfer in fish.

11391 Lee, T.; Kelly, T.   IE 180111/79/9194 N
Pair demersal bobbin trawling and exploratory fishing off Irelands south–east coast.

11392 Lee, T.; Kelly, T.   IE 180111/79/9197 N
Single boat pelagic trawling trials in the Irish sea.

11393 Ferrero, L.; Gelosi, E.   IT 022700/74/0002
Studio dell'inquinamento di un lago vulcanico laziale: il L. di Nemi. Conseguenze dell'alterazione dell'ambiente sulla produzione ittica. **Study on pollution of a vulcanic lake in Lazio (Lake of Nemi). Consequence of environmental degradation on fishery production.** Publications.

11394 Boddeke, R.   NL 010702/74/7095
Onderzoek naar de mogelijkheden van het op economisch rendabele basis kweken van zeevissoorten ten behoeve van de ontwikkeling van de aquacultuur. **Research on the culture of marine fishes and shellfish on an economic remunerative base in behalf of the development of the aquaculture.** Publications.

11395 Timmermans, L.P.M.   NL 020071/77/8393
Herkomst en differentiatie van de oergeslachtscellen bij vissen. **Origin and differentation of the primordial germ cells in fishes.**

Carp (B 4510)

See also 2055

11396 Timmermans, J.; Gérard, P.   BE 130000/77/0020 R
Elevage de poissons dans une eau chauffée. **Fish culture heating water.**

11397 Kausch, H.   DE 126800/75/0002
Belastbarkeit und Optimierung einer Wasserkreislauf–Anlage mit zweistufiger Reinigung durch Belebtschlamm bei Intensivhaltung von Karpfen – Cyprinus carpio L. –. **Capacity and optimization of water circulation plant with two–stage cleaning by activated sludge in confined husbandry of Cyprinus carpio L..**

11398 Kausch, H.   DE 126800/75/0003
Experimentelle Untersuchungen zur P–Remobilisierung durch junge Karpfen – Cyprinus carpio L. –. **Experiments on phosphorus remobilization in young Cyprinus carpio L..**

11399 Bohl, M.; Rieger, G.   DE 160772/78/0001 N
Untersuchungen über den Einfluss von Grasfischen und Silberfischen in Karpfenteichen auf Primärproduktion und Wasserqualität. **Investigations on the influence of grass–fish and silver–fish in carp ponds on primary production and water quality.**

11400 Jalabert, B.; Breton, B.; Fostier, A. FR 010203/76/5551
Induction artificielle de l'ovulation chez la carpe par utilisation d'hormones stéroïdes. **Artificial induction of ovulation in carps using steroid hormones.**

Salmon (B 4520)

See also 2055, 2057

11401 Prunet; Breton, B.   FR 010203/76/5547
Purification et dosage de la prolactine chez le saumon. **Purification and radioimmunoassay of salmon prolactin.**

11402 Jalabert, B.; Bry, C.; Breton, B.; Fostier, A.
                                      FR 010203/76/5549
Induction précoce de l'ovulation chez les salmonidés par traitements hormonaux. **Precoucious induction of ovulation in salmonids using hormonal treatments.**

11403 Lesel, R.; Rico, A.   FR 010711/68/5521
Environnement biotique de l'alevin de salmonidés. **Biotic environment of salmonid embryos.**

11404 Davaine, P.; Fostier, A.; Beall, E.; Bergot, P.
ponctuellement   FR 010711/70/5523
Ecologie des populations de salmonidés (Salmo trutta, Salvelinus fontinalis) introduites en milieux naturels vierges de poissons. **Ecology of Salmonid populations (S. trutta, S. fontinalis) introduced in natural fishless environments.**

11405 Dumas, J.   FR 010711/71/5526
Amélioration des techniques d'élevage des salmonidés de repeuplement (truites et saumons) et contrôle de la qualité des produits. **Rearing technics improvement for stocking with salmonids (Trout and Salmon) and fish quality control.**

11406 Heland, M.; Détermination invertébrés:; Neveu, A.
                                      FR 010711/72/5528
Compétition entre alevins et tocans de saumon atlantique. **Competition between yearling and underyearling atlantic salmon.**

11407 Davaine, P.; Beall, E.   FR 010711/75/5524
Introduction du saumon atlantique (Salmo salar) en milieu subantarctique. **Introduction of Atlantic Salmon (S. salar) into the subantarctic waters.**

11408 Laurent   FR 012218/75/5568
Mise au point d'une technique d'élevage et de production d'ombles chevaliers (Salvelinus alpinus). **Arctic char breeding.**

11409 Kennedy   GB 040901/78/0020 R
A study of the factors influencing the production of salmon and trout in the Riiver Bush.

11410 Gosling, J.P.; Murphy, T.M.; McHugh, A.M.; Fottrell, P.F.   IE 130102/77/9217 N
The control of precocious sexual maturity in male atlantic salmon.

11411 Roycroft, E.N.   IE 180119/74/8802
Sea farming of atlantic salmon.

Trout (B 4530)

See also 2055, 11402, 11403, 11404, 11405, 11409

11412 Breny, R.; Biernaux, J.   BE 010011/69/0006
La biologie de la truite et l'aménagement des territoires
piscicoles. **The biologie of trout and the management of
piscicultural territories.** Publications.

11413 Langholz, H.–J.; Keesen, H.   DE 132273/75/0001
Leistungsvergleich unterschiedlicher Forellenherkünfte unter
intensiven Haltungsbedingungen. **Comparison of performance
of different trout proveniences under intensive conditions of
production.**

11414 Holtz, W.; Stoss, J.   DE 132276/77/0001
Biotechnische Verfahren zur Verbesserung der
Fortpflanzungsleistung bei der männlichen
Regenbogenforelle. **Biotechnical techniques to improve
reproductive performance in the male rainbow trout.**

11415 Lamina, J.; Hoch, J.; Stein, H.   DE 161361/78/0002 N
Spezielle Untersuchungen zur Dauer der
Befruchtungsfähigkeit von Regenbogenforellen unter
verschiedenen Bedingungen. **Preservation of eggs of
rainbow–trout under different conditions and duration of
fecundation ability.**

11416 Lamina, J.; Stein, H.   DE 161361/78/0003 N
Hormoninduzierte Ovulation bei der Äsche.
Hormone–induced ovulation in the grayling.

11417 Researcher not indicated   DE 502650/78/0019 N
Teichkreislaufhaltung von Regenbogenforellen. **Breeding of
rainbow trout in circulatory system of ponds.**

11418 Researcher not indicated   DE 502650/78/0023 N
Auswirkungen von Kupfersulfat zur Algenbekämpfung in
Salmonidenteichen und Anreicherung in der
Forellenmuskulatur. **Effects of copper sulphate for control of
algae in ponds with Salmonidae stock and accumulation in the
muscles of trouts.**

11419 Chevassus, B.; Petit, J.   FR 010203/72/5538
Analyse génétique de la croissance chez la truite Arc–en–ciel.
Genetic analysis of growth in rainbow trout.

11420 Fostier, A.; Terqui, M.; Campbell, C.
                    FR 010203/73/5531
Niveaux plasmatiques stéroïdiens chez la truite. **Steroids levels
in trout plasma.**

11421 Fostier, A.; Terqui, M.; Jalabert, B.; Breton, B.
                    FR 010203/73/5533
Liaisons spécifiques de stéroïdes à des protéines chez la truite.
Specific binding of steroids with proteins in trout.

11422 Campbell; Jalabert, B.   FR 010203/75/5534
Contrôle endocrinien de la vie vitellogénèse : caractérisation et
purification de la vitellogénone. Mécanismes de synthèse
hépatique de transport plasmatique et d'incorporation dans les
ovocytes de truite. **Endocrine regulation of vitellogenesis :
characterisation of vitellogenin. Liner synthesis, plasmatic
transport and incorporation into trout oocytes.**

11423 Lebrun, C. Melle; Jalabert, B.   FR 010203/76/5536
Etude de la chronologie de différenciation des gonades chez la
truite Arc–en–ciel. **Investigation of the time course of gonadal
differenciation.**

11424 Choubert, G.   FR 010204/74/5509
Métabolisme des pigments caroténoïdes chez la truite.
Carotenoids metabolism in rainbow trout.

11425 Fremont, L.; Léger, C.; Bergot, P. FR 010205/77/9554 N
Analyse des lipoprotéines plasmatiques de Truite. **Analysis of
trout plasma lipoproteins.**

11426 Danaine, P.; Heland, M.; Dumas, J.; Badia, J.; Beall,
E.; Laurent, M.   FR 010711/64/5522
Dynamique de la population de truites communes (S. trutta m.
fario L.) d'un ruisseau du Pays Basque : le Lizunia. **Population
dynamics of a Brown trout stream (S. trutta) in the Basque
country : the Lizunia.**

11427 Heland, M.   FR 010711/71/5529
Compétition interspécifique entre le vairon et la truite
commune juvénile. **Interspecific competition between minnow
and juvenile brown trout.**

11428 Dumas, J.; Heland, M.; Neveu, A. ponctuellement
                    FR 010711/74/5525
Etude écologique et aménagement d'un cours d'eau à truites.
Ecological study and salmonid stream improvement.

11429 Fauconneau, B.; Arnal, M.; Luquet, P.
                    FR 010815/78/9579
Synthése protéique in vivo dans différents tissus et organes
chez la truite Arc en ciel (Salmo Gairdneri R.) en croissance.
**Protein synthesis, in vivo, in various tissus of growing rainbow
trouts (Salmo Gairdneri R.).**

11430 Badia, J.; Poltronieri   FR 011409/75/8272
Dynamique population de truite: estimation paramètres
population (3). **Dynamics of a trout population: estimation of
population parameters.**

11431 Dubois, M.; Billard, M.; Breton, M. FR 011501/74/7531
Poissons: étude du complexe hypothalamo–hypophysaire
identification des centres encéphaliques sérétant des
neuropeptides hormonaux (lh–rf, srif) chez la truite.
**Localization of hormonal neuropeptides in the brain of the
trout.**

11432 Roycroft, E.N.; Whelan, B.   IE 180119/78/8801 R
Cage rearing of brown trout.

Eel (B 4550)

See also 2262, 11396

11433 Greuel, E.; Schule–Lohmöller, H.
                    DE 111404/73/0001 N
Untersuchungen zur Intensivhaltung von Aalen – Anguilla
anguilla L. – unter besonderer Berücksichtigung der
Wassertemperatur und des Nährstoffbedarfs. **Studies on
confined management of eels – Anguilla anguilla L. – with
special reference to water temperature and nutrient
requirement.**

11434 Boyd   GB 040901/77/0019 R
**Investigation of the freshwater eel and its fishery in the Lough
Neagh area.**

11435 Conway, M.; Whelan, B.; Roycroft, E.N.
IE 180119/76/8800 R
Eel rearing in warm water effluent from thermal stations.

11436 Bilio, M.   IT 121600/77/0513 R
Razionalizzazione dell'anpuillicoltura intensiva, efficienza dei
metodi di pesca, campionamento e selezionatura,
differenzialità dell'accrescimento, influenza dell'ecosistema.
**Rationalisation of intensive eel–farming; efficiency of fishing
methods; sampling and selection; differences in growth;
influence of the ecosystem.**

Crustacea, shell fish, frogs (B 4560)

See also 11269

11437 Krampitz, G.; Samata, T.   DE 111401/78/0003 N
Ca–Bindungssysteme in Austernschalen. **Ca–binding systems
in oyster shells.**

11438 Briggs   GB 040902/77/0006 R
**Productivity and population dynamics of mussel (Mytilus edulis
L.) beds and related environmental factors.**

11439 Reynolds, J.D.; O'Keefe, C.F.   IE 140202/77/9049 N
**Food and environmental studies of freshwater crayfish with a
view towards potential aquaculture.** Publications.

11440 Aldrich, J.C.   IE 140202/78/9051 N
**In situ measurements of oxygen consumption in marine
decapods.** Publications.

11441 Lee, T.; Bates, R.   IE 180111/79/9193 N
**Exploratory fishing for scallops, pecten maximus l. in Galway
bay.** Publications.

11442 Lee, T.; Bates, R.   IE 180111/79/9195 N
**Survey of crab, cancer pagurus l.. resources in Donegal bay
area, with emphasis on offshore grounds not previously fished.**
Publications.

11443 Gelosi, E.; Mancini, A.; Cataudella, S.; Ferrero, L.
IT 022700/79/0001 N
Ricerche sulla biologia del gambero di fiume italiano
(Austropotamobius pallipes). Allevamento comparato con il
Gambero della sp. Pontastacus leptodactylus. **Researches on
biology of freshwater crayfish (Austropotamobius pallipes).
Breeding compared with crayfish Pontastacus leptodactylus.**

11444 Faranda, F.M.   IT 041714/77/0514 R
Allevamento di Penaeus kerathurus, realizzazione
dell'impianto pilota, indagine ambientale, alimentazione,
fisiologia della riproduzione, censimento delle aree costiere di
insediamenti stabili del Penaeus, raccolta bibliografica.
**Breeding farms for Penaeus kerathurus, construction of the
pilot scheme plant; environmental investigation, diet,
reproduction physiology; survey of the coastal areas suitable
for Penaeus settlement; bibliography.**

11445 Lumare, F.   IT 064100/77/0617
Definizione di metodologie di base per l'allevamento
commerciale di Penaeus kerathurus. **Draft of basic methods for
the commercial breeding of Penaeus kerathurus.**

11446 Arena, P.   IT 091904/77/0611 R

Indagine sui popolamenti di gambero imperiale o mazzancolla
– Penaeus kerathurus – della Sicilia sud–orientale, nell'ambito
delle esperienze pilota per un allevamento intensivo. **Research
on the populations of Penaeus kerathurus in south–eastern
Sicily in the context of a pilot scheme of intensive breeding.**

11447 Drinkwaard, A.C.   NL 010702/69/7001
Onderzoek naar de samenstelling en bestandsgrootte van
mosselen in de Nederlandse kustwateren, alsmede in de
Grevelingen en de factoren, die deze samenstelling en
bestandsgrootte beïnvloeden, ten behoeve van een doelmatig
beheer ten bate van de visserij. **Biological research concerning
mussels and the culture of mussels in the Dutch coastal waters
and the Grevelingen.**

11448 Drinkwaard, A.C.   NL 010702/73/7005 N
Fundamenteel oecofysiologisch onderzoek bij schelpdieren,
gericht op de fysiologische en biochemische aspecten (gedrag
en stofwisseling) ten aanzien van de levensverrichtingen en
levenskans zowel bij de produktie als bij de behandeling.
**Fundamental oecophysiological research on molluscan
(physiological and biochemical aspects about life conditions
during production and handling).**

11449 Drinkwaard, A.C.   NL 010702/76/7000
Onderzoek naar de samenstelling en bestandsgrootte van
oesters in de Nederlandse kustwateren, alsmede in de
Grevelingen en de factoren, die deze samenstelling en
bestandsgrootte beïnvloeden, ten behoeve van een doelmatig
beheer ten bate van de visserij; oesterbroedwinning in het
Grevelingenmeer en de opkweekmogelijkheden daarvan tot
zaaigoed. **Biological research concerning oysters and the
culture of oysters in the Dutch coastal waters and the
Grevelingen; development of a natural oysterspat collecting
system in the "stagnant" sea–water Lake Grevelingen, with
special attention to the first growing period into the sowable
stage.**

11450 Drinkwaard, A.C.   NL 010702/77/7003
Onderzoek naar de samenstelling en bestandsgrootte van
andere schelpdieren dan oesters, mossels en kokkels in het
Nederlandse kustwater en in het aangrenzende deel van de
Noordzee en de faktoren die deze samenstelling en
bestandsgrootte beïnvloeden ten behoeve van een doelmatig
beheer ten bate van de visserij. **Biological research concerning
molluscan shellfish excluding oysters, mussels and cockles in the
Dutch coastal waters and the North Sea.**

Other fishes (B 4590)

See also 11396

11451 Schubert, G.; Steineck, W.   DE 144151/77/0003
Die Beeinflussung des 'Raumfaktors' bei Pterophyllum scalare
durch chemische und filter–technische Massnahmen. **The
influence of chemical conditioning and filteringtechnique on the
'raumfaktor' in Pterophyllum scalare.**

11452 Jalabert, B.; de Montalembert; Bry, C.
FR 010203/76/5548
Induction artificielle de l'ovulation chez les géniteurs de
brochet capturés à l'état immature. **Artificial induction of
ovulation in pike.**

11453 Lee, T.; Kelly, T.; Bates, R.   IE 180111/79/9196 N
Feasability study of longlining for hake, merluccius merluccius,

off the south–west coast of Ireland.

11454 Gelosi, E.; De Bonfils, G. IT 022700/70/0002 R
Osservazioni sulla biologia di Esox lucius (luccio) in alcuni
laghi dell'Italia centrale. **Reserches into the biology of Esox
lucius in some lakes in Central Italy.**

11455 Ferrero, L.; Gelosi, E.; Cataudella, S.
IT 022700/74/0001 R
Tentativo di introduzione di una specie ittica sud americana:
Basilichtys bonariensis (pesce re). **Endeavour of introduction in
Italy of a South American species of fish: Basilichtys
bonariensis.**

11456 Gelosi, E.; Cataudella, S.; De Bonfils, G.
IT 022700/77/0001
Contributi allo studio della biologia del Coregone (Coregonus
sp.) dell'Italia Centrale. **Contribution to the study of the
biology of the Central Italy Whitefish (Coregonus sp.).**

11457 Richter, C.J.J. NL 020058/76/7358 R
Voortplanting van de meerval, Clarias lazera. **Reproduction of
the catfish Clarias lazera.** Publications.

Invertebrates (bees, silk–worm) (B 4600)

See also 7987, 8896

11458 Drescher, W.; Verbeck, B. DE 111201/77/0001
Die Steuerung der Flugperiodizität von Drohnen der
Honigbiene, Apis mellifica L.. **The regulation of flight
periodicity of drones of the honeybee.**

11459 Lindauer, M. DE 123070/72/0001
Lernmechanismen bei Honigbienen Magnetfeldorientierung
bei Bienen. **Mechanisms of learning in honeybee Magnetic field
orientation of bee.**

11460 Koeniger, N. DE 123100/75/0001
Biologie und Haltungsbedingungen der asiatischen
Riesenhonigbiene – Apis dorsata –, Sri Lanka/Ceylon. **Biology
and keeping conditions of Apis dorsata in Sri Lanka/Ceylon.**

11461 Neese, V. DE 176050/75/0001 N
Verhaltensanalyse bei Bienen: Die Entfernungsmessung der
Flugstrecke und ihre Wiedergabe durch die Sammelbienen.
**Behaviour analysis of bees: ranging of flying distance and
swarming reproduction by collecting bees.**

11462 Weiss, K. DE 502350/73/0002
Versuche mit künstlichen Bienenwaben. **Experiments with
artificial honey–combs.**

11463 Weiss, K. DE 502350/75/0002
Versuche zur Afterweiselentstehung. **Investigations on the
development of laying worker bees.**

11464 Weiss, K. DE 502350/77/0001
Versuche mit Pollenfallen. **Experiments with pollen traps.**

11465 Weiss, K. DE 502350/77/0002
Versuche zum Brutfrass der Bienen. **Investigations of
broodeating bees.**

11466 Weiss, K. DE 502350/77/0003
Versuche mit künstlichen Weiselbechern. **Trials with artificial
queen–cell cups.**

11467 Weiss, K. DE 502350/77/0005
Beobachtungen zur Verpuppung der Bienenmade.
Investigation of pupation of the bee larva.

11468 Schaper, F. DE 502350/78/0001 N
Untersuchungen zum Kohlehydratgehalt von Pollenhöschen.
Investigations on the carbon hydrate content of pollen loads.

11469 Pouvreau, A.; Marilleau, R. FR 010114/62/5139
Biologie et élevage des Bourdons (Bombus sp.). **Bumblebee
(Bombus sp.) biology and rearing.**

11470 Louveaux, J. FR 010114/63/5140
Génétique et écologie des populations d'abeilles. **Genetics and
ecology of honeybee populations.**

11471 Louveaux, J.; Lavie, P. FR 010114/64/1750
Cycle biologique annuel de la colonie d'abeilles. **Annual
biological cycle of the bee colony.** Publications.

11472 Louveaux, J.; Tassencourrt, L. Mme
FR 010114/73/5141
Analyse morphométrique des races d'abeilles domestiques.
Morphometric analysis of honeybee races.

11473 Pain, J.; Roger, B.; Theurkauff, J. FR 010114/73/5142
Production et physiologie des mâles d'abeilles. **Production and
physiology of drones.**

11474 Pain, J.; Roger, R. FR 010114/73/5143
Rythmes biologiques et sécrétions phéromonales chez l'abeille.
Biological rythms and pheromonal secretions in the honeybee.

11475 Louveaux, J.; Douault, Ph.; Pouvreau, A.
FR 010114/75/5146
Elevage de micro–colonies d'abeilles en milieu entièrement
contrôlé. **Rearing of honeybee micro–colonies in a fully
controlled environment.**

11476 Bounias, M.; Poitout, S.; Massonie, G.
FR 010602/73/5135
Biochimie comparée de différentes lignées d'insectes d'intérêt
agronomique. **Comparative Biochemistry of different strains of
insects of Agronomic importance.**

11477 Bounias, M. FR 010602/75/5136
Recherches sur le métabolisme glucidique : la glycémie et sa
régulation chez divers insectes d'intérêt agronomique. **On
glucidic metabolism : glycemia and its regulation in insects of
agronomic interest.**

11478 Fresnaye, J.; Lavie, P. FR 010608/73/5278
Insémination artificielle des reines d'abeilles. **Instrumental
insemination of honeybee queens.**

11479 Cornuet, J.M.; Fresnaye, J.; Tassencourt, L. Mme
FR 010608/75/5280
Structure d'une population d'abeilles dans les Cévennes.
Structure of a honeybee population in the Cévennes.

11480 Mesquida, J. FR 011306/70/5120
Etude de la variabilité de la production de couvain de mâles
chez l'abeille domestique. **Study of the variability of male
brood–comb production in honey–bees.**

11481 Simpson; Free   GB 012004/78/0048 R
Development of behaviour controlling chemicals for managing honeybee colonies and promoting pollination.

11482 Simpson   GB 012004/78/0049 R
Effects of nutrition and physical environment on honeybee colonies.

11483 Free   GB 012004/78/0054 R
Social behaviour and foraging of honeybees.

11484 Mobus   GB 060218/00/0001 R
Brood initiation within winter cluster of honey bees.

11485 Reali, G.; Meneghini, A.; Cappellozza, L.
     IT 020400/73/0007
Meccanizzazione della bachicoltura. **Mechanization of the silkworm rearing.** Publications.

11486 D'Ambrosio, M.; Ricciardelli, G.; Battaglini, M.; Intoppa, F.; Persano, L.   IT 020400/75/0006
Studio sull'apicultura nomade in Italia e dei fattori che la influenzano. **Studies on beekeeping transhumance in Italy and on its conditioning factors.** Publications.

11487 Vidano, C.   IT 041204/74/0643
Attività impollinatrice dell'ape flora mellifera. Patologia apicola. **Pollinating activity of the bee flora mellifera. Pathology of bees.**

11488 Merletto, F.   IT 041204/77/0229 R
Attività impollinatrice dell'ape, flora mellifera, patologia apicola. **The pollinating activity of bees, honey–producing flora and bee pathology.**

11489 Beetsma, J.   NL 020014/67/4408
Onderzoek van factoren, die de bouw van koninginnecellen bevorderen of remmen bij de honingbij. Zwermverhindering. **Study of the factors which promote or counteract the development of queen–cells. Prevention of swarming.**

11490 Beetsma, J.   NL 020014/76/6789
Regulatie van de kasten differentiatie bij bijen. **Regulation of the caste differentiation of bees.** Publications.

11491 Beetsma, J.   NL 020014/76/6790
Effecten van synthetische insektegroeiregulatoren op de honigbij. **Effects of insect growth regulators on the honeybee.**

11492 Wilde, J. de   NL 020014/78/8644 N
Rol van voedingsgedrag en de voedselsamenstelling gedurende de broedzorg bij de kaste bepaling van de honingbij (Apis mellifera L.). **The role of nursing behaviour and food composition during broodcare on caste differentiation in the honey bee (Apis mellifera L.).**

Rabbits (B 4910)

See also 10589, 10590, 10668, 10871, 10949, 11107, 11115, 11308, 11309, 11362, 11530, 12794, 12795, 13439

11493 De Groote, G.; Okerman, F.   BE 070200/76/0031 R
Vergelijking van het koloniekooi kweeksysteem met de kweek van konijnen in klassieke batterijkooien. **Comparison of the colony cage system with the classical battery cages for the breeding of rabbits.**

11494 Enbergs, H.; Hardebeck, H.   DE 111400/77/0005
Untersuchungen zur Verbesserung der Reproduktionsleistung beim Wirtschaftskaninchen. **Investigations on the improvement of reproduction in rabbits.**

11495 Paufler, S.; Munsel, M.; Pakzad, R.; Schlolaut, W.
     DE 132335/78/0001 N
Untersuchungen zur Verbesserung der Reproduktionsleistung bei Kaninchen. **Investigations to improve fertility in rabbits.** Publications.

11496 Stephan, E.; Schlolaut, W.   DE 139261/78/0002 N
Einfluss des natürlichen und des künstlich veränderten 'optimierten' Mikroklimas im Kaninchennest auf Mortalität und Entwicklung von Kaninchen. **Influence of natural and of artificially modified 'optimized' microclimate in rabbit nest on mortality and growth of rabbits.**

11497 Stephan, E.   DE 139261/78/0003 N
Erfassung von Genotyp–Umwelt–Interaktion bei der Produktion von Normal– und Diätfleisch durch Kaninchenbroiler. **Determination of interactions between genotype and environment in production of normal and dietetic meat by rabbit broilers.**

11498 Stephan, E.   DE 139261/78/0005 N
Einfluss einer Erhöhung des Anteils negativ geladener Luftionen in der Atmungsluft auf Mast– und Schlachtleistung von Fleischkaninchenbroilern. **Fattening and carcass performance of rabbit broilers as affected by an increase of negatively charged ions in respiratory air.**

11499 Hörnicke, H.; Clauss, W.   DE 144140/78/0001 N
Phasenbeziehungen circadianer Rhythmen beim Kaninchen. **Phase–relationships of circadian rhythms in rabbits.**

11500 Loeffler, K.   DE 144605/75/0002
Entwicklung der sekundären Patella beim Kaninchen. **Development of the secondary patella in rabbits.**

11501 Schilling, E.   DE 201200/77/0011
Grundlegende Untersuchungen zur Fortpflanzungsphysiologie an Kaninchen. **Basic studies on reproduction physiology of rabbits.**

11502 Berbigier, P.   FR 010101/76/5029 N
Optimalisation de l'ambiance thermique dans les nids à lapereaux. **Optimization of thermal ambiance in new–born rabbits nests.**

11503 Lebas, F.   FR 010206/53/2930
Etude des conditions de mise en service et d'exploitation des lapins reproducteurs. **Preparation of young rabbits to the reproduction and management of adult rabbits during the reproduction.**

11504 Bacou, F.; Vigneron, P.; Garambois, X.
     FR 011203/75/7567
Etude des populations de fibres musculaires d'animaux (lapins, ovins) de souches ou de races différentes. Liaison avec la qualité de la viande. **Study of muscle fibers populations from sheeps and rabbits of various breeds and strains – Interactions, implications on meat quality.**

11505 Vrillon, J.L.; Roustan, A.   FR 011404/69/2574

Recherche appliquée et développement en vue de l' amélioration de la production de viande de lapin. **Applied research and development to improve the efficiency of meat production in rabbit.**

11506 Hulot, F.; Roustan, A.   FR 011404/71/2575
Insémination artificielle répétée chez la lapine en différents états physiologiques (nullipare, allaitante). **Repeated artificial insemination in the rabbit under different physiological stages (nulliparous, lactating).**

11507 Vrillon, J.L.   FR 011404/73/2582
Contrôle de performances de reproduction du lièvre, en captivité étroite. **Performance testing of reproduction characters in the hare, in closed environment.**

11508 Fisher   GB 010702/00/0004 R
Rabbit breeding and husbandry.

11509 Giavarini, I.   IT 040212/77/0557 R
Ricerche sull'allevamento del coniglio. **Research on rabbit breeding.**

11510 Proto, V.   IT 040722/77/0578 R
Funzioni del cieco e significato nutrizionale del ciecotrofo nel coniglio. **Rabbit : functions of the caecum and nutritional mexming of cecofrophum.**

Domestic pets and zoo animals (B 4920)

11511 Niepage, H.; Sjöberg, A.   DE 104151/78/0001 N
Vergleich des Erythrocytenstatus, insbesondere der Retikulocyten, im Venenblut und im Knochenmarksblut zweier Hunde nach Aderlass und bei physiologischer Blutmauserung. **Morphology and quantity of reticulocytess in venous and bone marrow blood of two dogs after bleeding and in physiological blood regeneration.**

11512 Niepage, H.   DE 104151/78/0002 N
Die physiologische Schwankungsbreite des Blutbildes beim Hund. **The physiological variation of the blood picture in the dog.** Publications.

11513 Niepage, H.; Wedding, S.   DE 104151/78/0004 N
Das Blutbild von 3 Kamelen und einem Lama in den ersten drei Lebensmonaten. **The blood picture of three camels and a llama in the first three months of life.**

11514 Niepage, H.; Fäthke, I.   DE 104151/78/0005 N
Methodische Untersuchung zur Messung der Thrombocytenaggregation beim Hund mit dem Aggregometer Modell Giessen. **The aggregation of thrombocytes in the dog. A methodological investigation using the "Model–Giessen"–aggregometer.** Publications.

11515 Kasbohm, C.; Saar, C.   DE 104500/72/0003
Untersuchungen über die Wirkung von Östrogenen auf das Knochenmark von Hunden. **Studies of dogs as to the effects of estrogenic hormones on the bone marrow.**

11516 Schwartz–Porsche, D.; Lettow, E.; Opitz, M.
          DE 104500/77/0007
Untersuchungen zum Wasser–Elektrolyt– und SäureBasenhaushalt des Hundes und der Katze. **Investigations of the water–electrolyte– and acid– base–balance of dog and cat.**

11517 Günzel, A.–R.; Ertelt, H.   DE 139400/78/0003 N
Zum Fortpflanzungsgeschehen beim Elefanten – Elephas maximus und Loxodonta africana – unter besonderer Berücksichtigung der Zyklusdiagnose beim Indischen Elefanten – Elephas maximus – in europäischer Gefangenschaft. **On the reproduction of elephant – Elephas maximus and Loxodonta africana – with special regard to cycle diagnosis in Indian elephant – Elephas maximus – in European captivity.**

11518 Frank, W.; Pflugfelder, M.   DE 144130/78/0002 N
Serum–Harnsäurekonzentration bei Reptilien nach unterschiedlich langer Gefangenschaftshaltung. **Uric acid concentration in the serum of reptiles in captivity of different duration.**

11519 Engelhardt, W.von; Heller, R.   DE 144140/73/0001
Funktion der Vormägen des Lamas. **Secretion in proventriculi of llama.**

11520 Loeffler, K.; Rodenbeck, H.; Ficus, H.–J.
          DE 144605/78/0002 N
Histologische und histochemische Untersuchungen an Nickhautdrüsen gesunder Hunde. **Histological and histochemical studies on nictidand glandulae in sound dogs.** Publications.

11521 Sambraus, H.H.; Klotz, K.   DE 160705/78/0004 N
Mutter–Kind–Verhalten von Meerschweinchen. **Mother–infant–behaviour in guinea–pig.**

11522 Sambraus, H.H.; Sälzle, E.   DE 160705/78/0005 N
Das Verhalten von Moschusochsen. **The behaviour of musk–oxen.**

11523 Sambraus, H.H.; Hegel, G.von   DE 160705/78/0006 N
Fortpflanzungsverhalten von Gemsen. **Reproductive behaviour of chamois.**

11524 Sambraus, H.H.; Schmidt–Pauli, W.
          DE 160705/78/0008 N
Fremdprägung von Rehen. **Foreign imprinting in roe–deer.**

11525 Vogt   GB 010304/00/0034 R
Release of noradrenaline and choline esterase into perfused cerebral ventricles of cats.

11526 Weyden, G.C. van der   NL 030013/76/6138 R
Enkele aspekten van de normale geboorte bij de hond (intrauteriene ligging, kop– stuitligging, volgorde bij partus). **Some aspects of normal parturition in the dog (intra–uterine position, posterior anterior presentation, birth order).**

11527 Vogel, F.   NL 030013/77/7782 R
Mikromorfologische en endokrinologische aspecten van het puerperium bij de hond. **Micromorphological and endocrinological aspects of the puerperium of the dog.**

11528 Huisman, G.H.   NL 030014/78/8950 N
De invloed van fysieke en psychische belasting op verdeling van het bloedvolume bij de hond, in het bijzonder op de grootte van de bloeddoorstroming van het splanchnicus–gebied. (tredmolen, zwemmen, bloedvolume, bloeddoorstroming, art. renalis). **Influence of physical and psychological stress on distribution of blood volume in the dog,**

especially on blood flow in the spanchnic area. (treadmill, swimming, blood volume, blood flow, renal artery). Publications.

Fur animals (B 4930)

11529 Habermehl, K.–H.   DE 129601/73/0003
Die Altersbestimmungen bei Pelztieren und beim jagdbaren Wild. **Age determination in fur–bearing animals and game.**

11530 Schlolaut, W.; Lange, K.   DE 506221/74/0001
Der Einfluss von Alter, Geschlecht und Fütterung auf die Wolleistung von Angorakaninchen. **Influence of age, sex and nutrition on wool yield of angora rabbits.**

Laboratory animals (B 9120)

See also 10668, 12860, 12866

11531 Rohloff, D.; Laiblin, C.; Schroeter, A.; Schilderoth, M.

DE 104401/75/0002
Untersuchungen über die Befruchtungsfähigkeit von Nebenhodenspermien. **Investigations on fertility of spermatozoa taken from epididymidis.** Publications.

11532 Plonait, H.; Reinhard, H.J.   DE 139750/74/0035
Der Einfluss sozialer und ökologischer Faktoren auf telemetrisch messbare Grössen bei Versuchstieren. **The influences of social and ecological factors on the telemetric parameters in experimental animals.**

11533 Hahn, J.; Schneider, U.   DE 139803/78/0001 N
Gewinnung, Kultivierung und Übertragung von Eizellen der Maus, Ratte und Kaninchen. **Collection, cultivation and transfer of mouse, rat and rabbit ova.**

11534 Arnal, M.; Ferrara, M.; Fauconneau, G.; Obled, C.
FR 010815/74/9574 N
Synthése protéique in vivo dans le muscle, le foie et la peau au cours du développement du rat et de l'agneau. **Muscle and skin protein turnover in rats and lambs throughout development.**

11535 Arnal, M.; Fauconneau, G.; Obled, C.
FR 010815/75/9575 N
Etude du catabolisme oxydatif des acides aminés au cours du développement du rat et de l'agneau. **Amino acid oxydation in rats and lambs throughout their development.**

11536 Martinez, M.C.; Pelletier, J.; Hochereau–de–Reviers, M.T.   FR 011501/70/7536
Mode d'action des anti–androgènes chez le mâle prépubère. **Comparative action of two anti–androgens in immature male rat.**

11537 Buis, R.C.   NL 020058/78/8547
Hormoonspiegels in het bloed van muizen in relatie tot hun vruchtbaarheid. **Hormone levels in the blood of mice in relation to their fertility.**

D 3200 – Animal nutrition

See also 1062, 3333, 3346, 3425, 3428, 3429, 3430, 3553, 5565, 6629, 12878, 12879, 12880, 13512, 13513, 13516, 13518, 15862, 15890, 15894, 15910, 15911, 15912, 15913, 15914, 16331, 16722, 16726, 18853, 18854, 18948, 20026

11538 Antoine, A.; Compère, R.   BE 010003/76/0010 R
Utilisation des "Triticale" dans l'alimentation animale. **Utilization of "Triticale" in animal nutrition.**

11539 Burny, A.; Piérard, J.; Compère, R.; Thielemans, M.F.; Thévis, A.   BE 010003/76/0015 R
Etude microbiologique, biochimique et économique de la Rumensine (Monensine Sodium) ajoutée aux rations des bovidés à l'engrais. **Microbiological, biochemical and economical study of Rumensin (Monensin Sodium) added to the rations of growing–fattening steers.**

11540 Piérard, J.; Bergans, J.   BE 010007/63/0006 R
Economie de l'alimentation des gros bovins et des veaux. **Economy of the feeding of big bovidae and calves.** Publications.

11541 Vanbelle, M.; Moreels, A.; Vervack, W.
BE 020601/60/0006 R
Dépistage des oestrogènes dans les aliments. **The detection of oestrogenic matters in feeds and foods.** Publications.

11542 Vanbelle, M.; Vervack, W.   BE 020601/75/0002 R
Influence des traitements industriels sur la composition en acides aminés des protéines alimentaires. **Influence of industrial treatments on the amino acid composition of feeds and foods.**

11543 Vanbelle, M.; Meurens, M.; Allart, B.
BE 020601/79/0016 N
Etude sur la qualité alimentaire des pulpes de betteraves déshydratées. **Study of the feed quality of dried sugar beetpulps.**

11544 Cordiez, E.; Bienfait, J.M.; Delhaye, J.P.; Forceille, M.J.; Lambert, J.; Nogarede, P.   BE 020602/77/0013
Utilisation maximale des protéines de l'herbe par le bétail à haute production laitière. **The maximum use of grass proteins by high milk production cattle.** Publications.

11545 Cordiez, E.; Bienfait, J.M.; Lambert, J.; Nogarede, P.; Delhaye, J.P.   BE 020602/78/0014 R
Etude de l'extraction des protéines (crop fractionation) pour différentes associations de graminées et légumineuses. **Study of crop fractionation for different graminaceae and legumes associations.**

11546 Behaeghe, T.; Van Bockstaele, E.   BE 030017/76/0005
Inkuilen met formaldehyde. **Silage with formaldehyde.**

11547 Lousse, A.; Godeau; Génicot–Dandien; Teller; Debaere, R.   BE 060011/51/0001
Alimentation azotée et énergétique de la vache laitière. **Nitrogen and energetic alimentation of the dairy cow.** Publications.

11548 Bienfait, J.M.; Lambert, J.; Toussaint, A.; Gielen, M.
BE 060012/79/0007 N
Dans la langue originale : étude de l'influence du traitement à la soude des foins sur les performances zootechniques de taurillons en croissance–engraissement. **Study of the effect of NaOH treatment of hay on the zootechnical performances obtained with young growing–fattening bulls.**

11549 Bienfait, J.M.; Lambert, J.; Toussaint, A.; Legros, P.; Gielen, M.   BE 060012/79/0008 N

Etude comparative de trois types d'ensilages de maïs chez le jeune bétail destiné à la production de viande. **Comparative study of three maize silage types in rations for young beef cattle.**

11550 Bienfait, J.M.; Noirfalise, L.; Limbourg, P.; Gielen, M.

BE 060012/79/0009 N
Etude de la valorisation comparée selon différents modes d'exploitation, du pâturage tournant et pâturage continu chez la vache en lactation et le jeune bétail en croissance. **Comparative study of pasture valorization by lactating cows and by young growing beef cattle using different management techniques with paddock and stock grazing systems.**

11551 Bienfait, J.M.; Gielen, M.   BE 060012/79/0010 N
Action des anabolysants chez les taurillons précoces et les vaches de réforme. **Effectiveness of treatments with anabolic agents by young bulls and fathening dry cows.**

11552 Bienfait, J.M.; Lambot, O.; Van Eename, C.

BE 060012/79/0011 N
Effets zootechniques des agents anabolisants sur taurillons et vaches de réforme – Variation des régimes. **Zootechnic al effects of anabolicagenta and performances growing–fattening by young bulls and dry cows – Different feed methods.**

11553 De Groote, G.; Maertens, L.; Okerman, F.

BE 070200/71/0002 R
Onderzoek van voederadditieven bij konijnen. **Research of feed additives for rabbits.** Publications.

11554 De Groote, G.; Maertens, L.; Okerman, F.

BE 070200/76/0028 R
Onderzoek over de bepaling van de verteerbare– en metaboliseerbare energie van konijnenvoeders en grondstoffen. **Study of the determination of the digestible– and metabolisable energy of rabbit feeds and ingredients.**

11555 De Groote, G.; Fontaine, G.   BE 070200/76/0043 R
Het effect van de toevoeging van niet eiwit N bronnen aan laag eiwit rantsoenen voor W.L. hennen. **The effect of the supplementation of non protein N sources of low protein diets for W.L. hens.** Publications.

11556 De Groote, G.; Huyghebaert, G.   BE 070200/77/0048
Biologische beschikbaarheid van P–in voederfosfaten. **Biological availability of phosphorus in feed grade phosphates.**

11557 De Groote, G.; Fontaine, G.   BE 070200/78/0053
Energetische voederwaardebepaling van vismelen. **Energetic evaluation of fishmeals.**

11558 De Groote, G.; Huyghebaert, G.   BE 070200/79/0057 N
Biologische voederwaarde – bepaling van koolzaadschroot; energieinhoud en verteerbaarheid der aminozuren – bruikbaarheid in kuikenrantsoenen. **Biological evaluation of the nutritional value of rape seed meals. Energy content and digestibility of amino acids – feeding value in chick diets.**

11559 De Groote, G.; Huyghebaert, G.   BE 070200/79/0058 N
De invloed van het zuur–base evenwicht en het F–gehalte op de biologische beschikbaarheid van P in enkele voederfosfaten. **The influence of acid–base equilibrium and F content on the biological availability of P in a number of feed phosphates.**

11560 Vyncke, A.; Van Hee, L.; Vandepitte, H.

BE 070400/69/0014 R
Onderzoek der voornaamste voedingselementen N, P, K, Ca en Mg alsmede de voedingswaarde van graszaadstro. **Research of the important nutrition elements as N, P, K, Ca and MG also the feeding–value of the straw of grass crops for seed.**

11561 Andries, A.; Van Hee, L.   BE 070400/76/0024 R
Voederwaarde en scheikundige samenstelling van R.v.P. cultivars. **Fodder quality and chemical composition of R.v.P. varieties.**

11562 Droeven, G.; Rixhon, L.; Raimond, Y.; Crohain, A.; Couvreur, J.; Destain, J.P.   BE 080100/75/0011 R
Influence de la valorisation agronomique du lisier sur les rendements, sur la qualité des récoltes sur les principales propriétés du sol et sur la protection du milieu. **Influence of the agricultural use of the slurry on crop yield and quality and on the principal soil properties while minimizing environmental pollution hazards.**

11563 Biston, R.; Faem, J.; Thill, N.   BE 080900/78/0010 R
Détermination objective de la digestibilité de diverses productions fourragères dans la région du Sud–Est. **Objective determination of digestibility of various forages in the South Eastern region.** Publications.

11564 Vandenbyvang, P.   BE 081200/60/0005
Nutrition minérale des bovins. **Mineral nutrition of bovine.**

11565 Vandenbyvang, P.; Thill, N.; François, E.

BE 081200/69/0004 R
Détermination de la quantité et de la digestibilité de l'herbe ingérée par la vache laitière au pâturage. **Quantity and digestibility determination of the grass ingested by the grazing dairy cow.** Publications.

11566 Bodart, C.; Thielemans, M.F.   BE 081200/75/0006
La cellulose dans l'alimentation des porcs à l'engrais. **Cellulose in the diet for fattening pig.**

11567 Janiesch, P.   DE 164050/78/0003 N
Mineralstoffhaushalt von Erlenbruchwäldern sowie deren Kontaktgesellschaften A. Edaphische Faktoren B. Physiologie und Ökologie von Bruchwaldpflanzen. **Mineral cycling in Alnus forests and contact communities A. Edaphic factors B. Physiology and ecology of swamp forest plants.** Publications.

11568 Schwarz, O.   DE 501504/73/0001
Anwendungsmöglichkeiten von kompostierten Abfällen bei Douglasienund Roteichenkulturen sowie in Altbeständen – im Raum Schwetzingen –. **The use of refuse compost in Douglas fir and red–oak plantations as well as in mature forests – area Schwetzingen –.**

11569 Burgkart, M.   DE 502300/73/0001
Zucht–, Fütterungs– und Haltungsmassnahmen zur wirtschaftlichen Erzeugung von Qualitätslammfleisch. **Feeding and management operations for profitable production of lamb meat of high quality.**

11570 Papendick, K.   DE 506152/70/0001
Der Futterwert von konserviertem Grünfutter. **The feed value of preserved grass.**

11571 Mølle, KG.; Skovborg, E.B.   DK 010114/75/0007

D 3200 – Animal nutrition

Udnyttelse af ensilagesaft og af saft udpresset af grønne afgrøder (del af EF–projekt). **Utilisation of silage effluent and sap extracted from green crops (part of EEC project).**

11572 Andersen, P.E.; Kristensen, V.F.; Skovborg, E.B.
DK 010201/75/0003 R
Helsædsensilage til malkekøer. **Whole seed silage for dairy cows.**

11573 Brolund Larsen, J.   DK 010201/76/0005
Kemisk behandlet halm til opdræt. **Chemical treated straw and rearing.**

11574 Sørensen, M.   DK 010201/77/0006
Majsensilage til ungtyre. **Maize silage for young bulls.**

11575 Petersen, V.E.; Weidner, K.   DK 010203/76/0001
Afblanding af foderblandinger til fjerkræ og svin. **Segregation of feedstuff mixtures for poultry and pigs.**

11576 Weidner, K.   DK 010206/75/0001
Undersøgelse af fedtfraktionens stabilitet i henholdsvis formalet og uformalet majs. **An investigation into the stability of the fat fraction in milled and unmilled maize.**

11577 Mason, V.C.   DK 010206/75/0007
Kvaliteten af fiskemel i forbindelse med lagring. **Quality of fish meal in connection with storage.**

11578 Mason, V.C.; Just, A.   DK 010206/75/0008
Undersøgelse af proteinkvaliteten i byggens proteinfraktioner. **Investigation of the protein quality of the protein fraction of barley.**

11579 Mason, V.C.   DK 010206/76/0003
Tannins indflydelse på næringsværdien af vegetabilske fodermidler. **The influences of tannins on the nutritive value of vegetable feedstuffs.**

11580 Weidner, K.   DK 010206/77/0006
Formalingstidspunktets og opbevaringsforholdenes indflydelse på forskellige kvalitetsegenskaber i byg. **The influence of the time of milling and storage conditions on various quality–attributes of barley.**

11581 Rexen, B.; Holm, F.   DK 010800/77/0001
Foderets rheologiske egenskaber – biologisk effekt af plantefibre. **Rheological characteristics of feed – biological effect of plant fibre.**

11582 Hartley   GB 011201/00/0004
Cell wall constituents of forage plants in relation to nutritional quality.

11583 Jones   GB 011201/00/0005
Mineral content of forage plants in relation to nutritional quality.

11584 Harris   GB 011203/00/0012
Investigate anatomy, fine structure and aspects of chemistry of grasses in relation to nutritional quality.

11585 Terry; Osbourn   GB 011205/79/0010 N
Develop and evaluate methods to assess forage nutritive value.

11586 Ford   GB 011708/00/0003

Nutritional quality of proteins.

11587 Andrews   GB 011712/77/0015 R
Mechanism of glycosyl transfer in glycoprotein and oligosaccharide synthesis.

11588 Barman; Andrews   GB 011712/77/0016 R
Bacterial lactate dehydrogenases dependent on fructose diphosphate.

11589 Jones; Hayward   GB 012102/00/0005
Variation in the cell wall constituents of forages and their hydrolysis in–vitro and in–vivo.

11590 Gosden   GB 012102/00/0009
Determination and distribution of oestrogenic compounds in legumes.

11591 Welch   GB 012102/00/0012
Factors influencing the chemical composition and feed quality of oats.

11592 Welch   GB 012102/00/0013
Factors influencing the chemical composition and feed quality of barley.

11593 Gosden   GB 012102/00/0014
Determination and distribution of goitrogenic and other toxic substances in Brassica fodder crops.

11594 Griffiths   GB 012102/00/0016
Assessment of nutritive quality in field beans for animal feeding.

11595 Gosden   GB 012102/00/0017
Determination and distribution of water soluble proteins and protein precipitants in plants.

11596 Jones; Hayward   GB 012102/76/0019
Nonstructural constituents of forages; estimation of distribution and nutritional significance.

11597 Walters; Evans EM   GB 012105/00/0015
The voluntary intake of herbage varieties as determined by physical and chemical characteristics.

11598 Munro; Davies DA   GB 012105/00/0020
Nutritive quality of selected varieties and native species in different hill and upland situations.

11599 Milne; MacRae   GB 030302/00/0004
Nutritive value of heather.

11600 MacRae; Wilson   GB 030302/00/0005
Supplementation of low quality roughage diets.

11601 Macklon; Sim   GB 030404/00/0007 R
Salt absorption: physical and metabolic aspects.

11602 Pusztai   GB 030601/00/0008
Toxic and anti–nutritional factors in the kidney bean.

11603 Ellinger   GB 030601/00/0013 R
Structural studies of chemically modified proteins related to availability of their constituent amino acids.

D 3200 – Animal nutrition

11604 Wood;MacRae GB 030602/00/0001
Cellulases and other enzymes degrading plant cell walls.

11605 Wainman; Smith GB 030606/00/0014
Evaluation of the contribution of individual compounds to the metabolizable energy of feed mixtures.

11606 Dewey GB 030606/00/0018
Laboratory analysis and prediction of the nutritive value of feeds.

11607 King GB 030608/76/0020
Cytopathology of bean lectins.

11608 Jones;Houseman GB 030611/00/0002
Fractionation of grass and use of liquor in pig feeding and residue for cattle.

11609 Livingstn GB 030611/00/0016
Intensification of land use: the evaluation of bulky feeds using liquid feeding systems.

11610 Jackson GB 040401/00/0018
A comparison of the nutrient loss and feeding value of high and low nitrogen silages.

11611 McDougall GB 040401/76/0024
The use of different silage–making techniques to control silage quality and dry matter intake by sheep.

11612 McCullough GB 041101/00/0005
Evaluation of silage additives.

11613 McCullough GB 041306/77/0009
Feeding value of sodium hydroxide treated barley straw.

11614 Ewart GB 060101/00/0005
Ruminent metabolism with particular reference to silage.

11615 Edwards GB 060103/00/0006
Nutritional evaluation of silage.

11616 Lewis GB 060103/00/0007
Intakes of silage dry matter.

11617 Bruce;Baines GB 060308/00/0007 R
Utilisation of animal waste for animal feed.

11618 Frame; Simpson GB 060314/00/0004 R
The yield and quality responses of grasses and clovers to fertiliser nitrogen.

11619 Griffiths, T.W.; Wilson, R.K. IE 060100/72/0288 R
Factors affecting the intake and utilization of nutrients in grass silage. Publications.

11620 O'Shea, J.; Griffiths, T.W. IE 060100/72/0296 R
Development of a ready reckoner or slide rule for the interpretation of silage results at farm level. (B) applicable to winter milk systems. Publications.

11621 Maguire, M.F. IE 060300/71/0153
Biological value of wheat proteins. Biochemistry, u.C.D. Publications.

11622 Comerford, P.J.; Flynn, A.V. IE 060500/71/0167 N

Comparison of single, double and precision–chop silages for self–feeding and trough feeding. Publications.

Plants and animals in general (B 2000)

11623 Lints, F.; Gruwez, G.; Kuo, T. BE 020304/66/0002
Génétique de la longévité et du vieillissement. **Genetics of longevity and ageing.** Publications.

Animals and parts of their bodies (B 2300)

See also 11946, 13523

11624 Patzelt, R. DE 129760/74/0002
Wirkungsweise von Vitamin E auf den LipidStoffwechsel. **Mode of action of vitamin E in lipid metabolism.**

11625 Jakobsen, P.E. DK 010206/75/0009
Linolsyrens betydning for skeletmuskulaturens funktion. **The importance of linolic acid for the function of the skeletal muscles.**

11626 Thorbek, G. DK 010206/75/0010
Linolsyrens betydning for musklernes mitocondriefunktion, kødmængde og kødkvalitet. **The influence on muscle–mitochondrial function, meat quality and quantity of linolic acid.**

11627 Demarne, Y.; Durand, G.; Etienne, M.; Pascal, G.; Henry, Y. FR 010205/72/9545 N
Contrôle par voie nutritionnelle de la lipogenèse du jeune monogastrique en croissance. **Nutritional control of lipogenesis in the non–ruminant growing animals.**

11628 Vodovar, N.; Desnoyers, F. FR 010205/74/9566
Effets des acides gras des lipides alimentaires sur le système cardiovasculaire et sur le vieillissement cellulaire. **Effects of fatty acid composition of dietary lipids on the cardiovascular system and on the ageing of cells.**

11629 Durand, M.; Dumay, C.; Gueguen, L. FR 010205/75/9562 N
Influence des oligoéléments sur la digestion microbienne au niveau du rumen. **Influence of trace elements on microbial digestion in the rumen.**

11630 Demarne, Y.; Ducluzeau, R.; Lhuillery; Raibaud, P. FR 010205/76/9546
Influence des lipides du lait sur l'implantation de différentes bactéries dans le tractus digestif. **Relationship between dietary lipids and bacterial ecology, in the G.I. tract.**

11631 Pascal, G.; Vodovar, N.; Durand, G.; Desnoyers, F.; Parodi, M. FR 010205/77/9560 N
Contribution à l'appréciation du risque toxique entraîné par la consommation de deux antioxygènes alimentaires : les gallates d'octyle et de dodécyle. **Determination of toxicological risk of octyl and dodecyl gallate intake.**

11632 Rozen, R. FR 010205/77/9568
Métabolisme hépatique des acides gras. **Hepatic metabolism of free fatty acids.**

11633 Vodovar, N.; Desnoyers, F.; Pascal, G.; Durand, G.; Parodi, A.L.; Etienne, M. FR 010205/78/9565
Effets de la nutrition et du niveau de l'apport énergétique sur

le développement des tissus adipeux suivant l'âge. **Effects of diet and energy intake on adipose tissues development.**

11634 Raibaud, P.; Galpin, J.V.　　FR 010216/70/9594 N
Ecologie microbienne : isolement de souches bactériennes métabolisant les sels biliaires chez l'animal gnotoxénique. **Microbial ecology : isolation of bacterial strains metabolizing the bile acids in gnotoxenic animals.**

11635 Obled, C.; Grizard, J.; Arnal, M.　　FR 010815/70/9580
Influence du comportement alimentaire sur le rythme de l'utilisation métabolique des acides aminés au cours de la journée. Régulation hormonale. **Influence of feeding schedule on amino acid metabolism throughout the day. Hormonal regulation.**

11636 Pion, R.; Prugnaud, J.; Champredon, C.
　　　　　　　　　　　　　　　FR 010815/72/9570 N
Etude de la composition des matières azotées des contenus intestinaux. **Amino acid composition of nitrogenous maters of ruminant intestinal contents.**

Animal communities as ecological systems (B 2400)

See also 1827

Domestic animals in general (B 4000)

See also 3063, 3315, 3342, 3481, 3634, 5516, 5658, 6805, 10319, 10460, 10499, 10546, 10548, 10549, 10558, 10561, 11538, 11570, 11622, 11748, 12930, 12931, 12932, 12933, 13684, 13690, 13692, 13694, 13745, 13747, 13879, 15411, 15860, 15866, 16325, 16348, 16488, 17089, 17111, 18950, 19241, 19243, 19412, 19413, 19414

11637 Hartfiel, W.; Steinkamp, U.　　DE 111451/78/0001 N
Veränderungen des Gehaltes an Antioxidantien und des Fettsäuremusters im Mischfutter durch oxidative Einwirkungen. **Changes in the content of antioxidants and fatty acids in mixed feeds by oxidative reactions.**

11638 Brune, H.; Bruns, H.; Pallauf, J.; Niemann, E.;
Kreuder, K.; Schmidt, M.　　　　DE 129270/77/0007
Noxen in biosynthetischen Proteinträgern. **Noxious components in biosynthetic protein carrier.**

11639 Hadlok, R.; Christen, U.; Binzel, R.-M.
　　　　　　　　　　　　　　　DE 129700/73/0003
Untersuchungen zur Zusammensetzung von vom Tier stammenden Nahrungsmitteln. **Investigations into the composition of animal food.**

11640 Leitzmann, C.; Menden, E.; Wagner, B.
　　　　　　　　　　　　　　　DE 129900/74/0001
Der Gastrinspiegel bei Mensch und Tier während der Adaptation an veränderte Ernährung. **The gastrin level in man and animal during adaptation to changed nutrition.**

11641 Molnar, S.; Günther, K.-D.　　DE 132300/74/0003
Die Proteinbewertung verschiedener Hydrogenomonas–Mutanten im Tierversuch. **Biological protein evaluation of different Hydrogenomonas mutants in experimentation on animals.**

11642 Günther, K.-D.; Meulen, U.ter; Struck, S.
　　　　　　　　　　　　　　　DE 132300/77/0002
Untersuchungen über die intermediäre Wirksamkeit

wachstumsfördernder Substanzen. **Metabolism of growth promoting agents.**

11643 Molnar, S.　　　　　　　DE 132300/77/0005
Methoden zur Qualitätsprüfung von Futterfetten. **The quality of fat in animal feedstuffs.**

11644 Bassler, R.; Putzka, H.-A.　　DE 135056/74/0002
Es wird eine Übersicht über den Gehalt an chlorierten Kohlenwasserstoffen und an Aflatoxin B1 in Futtermitteln insbesondere tropischer und subtropischer Herkunft erstellt. **Chlorinated hydrocarbon and aflatoxin B1 content in feeding stuffs especially of tropical and subtropic origin.**

11645 Bassler, R.; Putzka, H.-A.　　DE 135056/74/0003
Für die Bewertung von Futtermitteln wird der Einfluss verschiedener Fettbestimmungsmethoden auf die quantitativen Ausbeuten und auf die qualitative Zusammensetzung der gewonnenen Rohfette untersucht. **Feed evaluation: the influence of various fat determination methods on the quantity of yield and the quality of composition of the crude fats extracted.**

11646 Haendler, H.; Lai–Dinh, D.　　DE 144030/75/0002
Verbesserung der Informationen über tropische und subtropische Futtermittel. **Improvement of information on tropical and subtropical feeds.**

11647 Menke, K.H.; Kühl, J.　　DE 144620/78/0001 N
Voraussage der Proteinqualität aus der Aminosäurenzusammensetzung der Ration bei Ratten. **Prediction of the protein quality from the amino acid composition of the ration of rats.**

11648 Menke, K.H.; Raab, L.　　DE 144621/78/0001 N
Futtermittelbewertung mit Hilfe vereinfachter Methoden. **Feed evaluation with simplified methods.**

11649 Zucker, H.; Rambeck, W.　　DE 160600/75/0007
Calcinose–Wirkung von Trisetum flavescens. **Calcinosis activity of Trisetum flavescens.**

11650 Scharrer, E.　　　　　　DE 160600/75/0010
Untersuchungen zur Verzehrregulation. **Studies on control of food intake.**

11651 Gedek, B.　　　　　　　DE 160761/70/0003
Richtlinien für die Beurteilung von Einzel– und Mischfuttermitteln. **Principles for valuation of single and of mixed feeds.**

11652 Kirchgessner, M.; Roth, P.　　DE 161280/71/0003
Einfluss der Zinkversorgung auf die Aktivität von Enzymen und Insulin. **Influence of zinc status in animals on enzyme and insulin activity.**

11653 Kirchgessner, M.; Schwarz, F.　　DE 161280/71/0004
Untersuchungen zur intestinalen Cu– Zn– und Mn–Absorption in vitro. **In vitro studies on intestinal copper, zinc and manganese absorption.**

11654 Kirchgessner, M.; Schnegg, A.　　DE 161280/72/0003
Essentialität von Nickel im tierischen Stoffwechsel. **The essentiality of nickel in the animal body.**

11655 Kirchgessner, M.; Kellner, R.　　DE 161280/74/0002

Ausarbeitung von in–vitro–Methoden zur Bestimmung der Verdaulichkeit von Futtermitteln. **Development of an analysis in vitro for the determination of the digestibility of feeds.**

11656 Kirchgessner, M.; Ranfft, K.   DE 161280/74/0008
Detergentienanalysen in Grundfuttermitteln zur Futterbewertung. **Estimation of the nutritive value of forages by analysis of detergents.**

11657 Kirchgessner, M.; Heiseke, D.   DE 161280/77/0001
Mangan–Stoffwechsel im tierischen Organismus. **Manganese metabolism in animals.**

11658 Kirchgessner, M.; Weigand, E.   DE 161280/77/0003
Zur Bestimmung der Absorption von Spurenelementen mittels der Radioisotopen–Verdünnungsmethode. **The use of the radioisotope dilution method for measuring the absorption of trace elements.**

11659 Paul, C.   DE 201030/78/0002 N
Evaluierung von Qualitätsparametern des Futterwertes, insbesondere der Verdaulichkeit bei Futterpflanzen. **Evaluation of parameters for nutritive value, especially digestibility of different forage crops.**

11660 Vemmer, H.   DE 201050/77/0001
Carry–over von Blei und Cadmium aus verschiedenen Bindungsformen. **Carry–over of lead and cadmium from different compounds.**

11661 Rohr, K.   DE 201050/77/0005
Einfluss futterbaulicher und technologischer Massnahmen auf den Nährwert von Halmfutter. **Influence of fodder cropping and technological measures on the nutritional value of grain fodder.**

11662 Vemmer, H.   DE 201050/77/0007
Carry–over von Blei und Cadmium unter steigender Zufuhr. **Carry–over of lead and cadmium by increasing supply.**

11663 Schulz, E.   DE 201050/78/0003 N
Ernährungsphysiologische Bewertung von unkonventionellen oder speziell aufbereiteten Futtermitteln. **Nutritional evaluation of unconventionally and specially prepared feedstuffs.**

11664 Schulz, E.   DE 201050/78/0004 N
Ermittlung des Nährwerts und der Einsatzmöglichkeiten von biotechnischem Protein – SCP –. **Determination of nutritive value and applications of biotechnical Protein – SCP –.**

11665 Schlünsen, D.; Meinhold, K.; Walter, K.
          DE 201090/72/5009
Quantifizierung der Beziehungen zwischen Fütterungsfrequenz, Futteraufnahme und Leistung. **To quantify the relation between feeding frequence, fodder intake and yield.**

11666 Farries, E.   DE 201200/77/0030
Untersuchungen über die Verwendung unkonventioneller Grundstoffe zur Erzeugung von tierischem Eiweiss und tierischen Produkten. **Experiments on the use of unconventional basic substances for production of animal protein and animal products.**

11667 Stephan, R.; Bulling, E.   DE 305030/75/0053
Auftreten und Ausbreitung von Resistenzfaktoren bei Haustieren unter Einfluss von Antibiotikafütterung. **Occurrence and spread of R–factors in domestic animals under the influence of antibiotics feeding.** Publications.

11668 Thalmann, A.; Gruber, S.; Rückemann, H.
          DE 501011/78/0001 N
Vorkommen von Mykotoxinen in Futtermitteln und mögliche Auswirkungen auf die Leistung landwirtschaftlicher Nutztiere, mit besonderer Berücksichtigung von Betrieben in Baden. **The occurrence of mycotoxins in feedstuffs and their possible effects on the performance of productive livestock especially in Baden.**

11669 Researcher not indicated   DE 501011/78/0002 N
Untersuchungen über das Vorkommen von Mykotoxinen – ausser Aflatoxin – in Futtermitteln und mögliche Zusammenhänge mit futterbedingten Leistungsminderungen und Erkrankungen bei landwirtschaftlichen Nutztieren. **Investigations on the occurrence of mycotoxins – aflatoxin excluded – in feeds and potential correlations to reductions in performance caused by feed and to diseases of farming livestock caused by feed.**

11670 Beringer, H.; Burgdorf, H.   DE 902001/78/0002 N
Untersuchungen zur Bewertung der Nährstoffe in Stroh und Rübenblatt. **Evaluation of nutrient efficiency in straw and sugar–beet leaves.**

11671 Møller, P.D.; Thomsen, K.V.   DK 010201/78/0004 N
Foderemnes næringsværdi til husdyr vurderet ud fra laboratoriemetoder. **The nutritive value of feeds for farm animals evaluated by laboratory methods.**

11672 Mason, V.C.; Eggum, B.O.   DK 010206/68/0002
Bestemmelse af aminosyrernes sande tilgængelighed. **Determination of the true availability of amino acids.**

11673 Weidner, K.; Andersen, J.O.   DK 010206/69/0001
Udarbejdelse af metoder til gaskromatografisk bestemmelse af fedtsyrer. **Development of methods for the determination of fatty acids by gas chromatography.**

11674 Mason, V.C.; Bech–Andersen, S.   DK 010206/71/0010
Udvikling af hurtigmetoder til bestemmelse af individuelle aminosyrer med henblik på fodermiddelvurdering. **Development of rapid methods for the determination of individual amino acids with a view to feed evaluation.**

11675 Jakobsen, P.E.; Rotenberg, S.   DK 010206/73/0005
Forskellige kulhydratfraktioners indflydelse på lipogenesens omfang. **Influence of various carbohydrate fractions on the extent of lipogenisis.**

11676 Jakobsen, P.E.; Riis, P.M.   DK 010206/74/0001
Væksthormonvirkning og proteinaflejringens regulering. **Growth hormone and the regulation of protein deposition.**

11677 Mason, V.C.; Eggum, B.O.   DK 010206/74/0004
Undersøgelse af de forskellige kornmutanters proteinkvalitet samt fordøjelig og omsættelig energi. **Investigation of the protein quality of various cereal mutants, together with their digestibility and metabolizable energy.**

11678 Mason, V.C.; Eggum, B.O.   DK 010206/74/0007 R
Bestemmelse af proteinkvalitet, fordøjelig energi samt omsættelig energi i alternative fodermidler. **Determination of**

protein quality, digestible energy and metabolizable energy in alternative feedstuffs.

11679 Jensen, A.T.; Jensen, E.   DK 030106/75/0036 N
Undersøgelse af reaktiviteten af vanduopløselige oxider, carbonater og phosfater, der forhandles som komponenter til husdyrs mineralstofblandinger. **Investigation of reactivity profiles of water–insoluble oxides, carbonates and phosphates used as components in mineral additives for domestic animals.**

11680 Moustgaard, J.; Wegger, I.   DK 030126/76/0001
Bestemmelse af latent mangel på sporelementer som zink, selen m.m. hos huspattedyr. **A determination of the latent scarcity of trace elements such as zinc, selenium etc., in domesticated mammals.**

11681 Flanzy, J.; Pihet, A.; Demarne, Y.; Boudon, M.; Leger, C.   FR 010205/60/2711
Métabolisme des acides gras. **Metabolism of fatty acids.**

11682 Durand, G.; Penot, E.   FR 010205/63/2710
Développement des tissus et organes en relation avec les facteurs alimentaires en particulier développement du muscle, des tissus adipeux, du foie et du coeur. **Development of tissus and organs in relationship with alimentary factors in particular muscle development, adipose tissues, liver and heart.**

11683 Pascal, G. et Durand, G.; Delpech, P. et Desmoulin, B.
    FR 010205/67/2700
Développement et agents antioxygènes:. **Development and antioxygen agents.**

11684 Flanzy, J.; Pihet A.; Demarne, Y.; Boudon, M.; Leger, C.   FR 010205/68/2712
Utilisation digestive des lipides. **Digestive utilization of lipids.**

11685 Rerat, A.; Aumaitre, L.   FR 010205/69/2722
Mesure quantitative et qualitative de l'absorption des produits de la digestion de divers glucides. **Quantitative and qualitative measurement of the absorption of the products of the digestion of various carbohydrates.** Publications.

11686 Demarne, Y.; Flanzy, J.; Sacquet, E.; Raibaud, P.
    FR 010205/70/2707
Influence de la flore gastro–intestinale sur la digestion et l'absorption des lipides alimentaires chea les monogastrique. Influence de la composition en acides gras des lipides alimentaires sur l'écologie microbienne du tube digestif. **Influence of the gastro–intestinal flora on the digestion and the absorption of dietary fat in monogastric animals. Influence of the fatty acids composition of dietary fats on the microbial ecology of the G.I. tract.** Publications.

11687 Rerat, A.   FR 010205/70/2721
Mesure quantitative et qualitative de l'absorption des acides aminés au cours de la digestion de régimes contenant des taux variés de diverses protéines supplémentées ou non avec des acides aminés libres. **Quantitative and qualitative measurement of the absorption of aminoacids during the digestion of meals with different levels of various proteins, added or not with free aminoacids.** Publications.

11688 Ducluzeau, R.; Raibaud, P.; Dubos, F.
    FR 010205/71/2752
Cinétique de l'implantation de la flore microbienne chez les animaux nouveaux–nés. **Kinetic of the implantation of the microbial flora in new–born animals.** Publications.

11689 Flanzy, J.; Demarne, Y.   FR 010205/73/2708
Relation entre qualité de l'énergie ingérée et lipogénèse chez le monogastrique. **Studies of the relationship between different types of energy in the diet (Carbohydrates and different kinds of lipids) on the lipogenesis in monogastric animals.** Publications.

11690 Gueguen, L.; Durand, M.; Dumay, C.
    FR 010205/74/2706
Influence des éléments minéraux sur l'activité de la microflore du tube digestif. **Influence of minerals upon the activity of digestive microflora.** Publications.

11691 Pascal, G. and Durand, G.; Vodovar, N.
    FR 010205/74/2709
Développement des tissus adipeux;évolution de leur composition et de leur capacité de lipogénèse. **Adipose tissues development, evolution of their composition and their lipogenesis capacity.**

11692 Laplace, J.P.; Lebas, F.   FR 010217/70/9533 N
Adaptation fonctionelle du tube digestif. **Adaptation changes of the gastro intestinal tract.**

11693 Bellanger, J.   FR 010807/65/8007
Diagnostic analytique des carences en oligoéléments. **Analytical determination of trace elements deficiencies.**

11694 Levieux, D.; Pardon, P.; Querboeuf, D.
    FR 010807/77/8010
Carence en zinc et immunité. **Zinc deficiency and immune responsiveness.**

11695 Piel, H.   FR 010807/77/8011
La carence en iode en France. **Iodine deficiency in France.**

11696 Journet, M.; Hoden, A.   FR 010812/72/6517
Méthodes de complémentation azotée (et minérale) des fourrages pauvres. **Methods of nitrogen and mineral supplementation of low quality forages.**

11697 Dulphy, J.P.; Demarquilly, C.; Xandé, A.
    FR 010814/72/6507
Valeur alimentaire des fourrages pauvres et son amélioration. **Feeding value of straws. Improvement of this value.**

11698 Demarquilly, C.; Dulphy, J.P.   FR 010814/75/6508
Etude de la valeur nutritive et de l'utilisation des pulpes de betteraves surpressées. **Study of nutritive value and utilisation of beet pulp.**

11699 Andrieu, J.   FR 010814/77/6501
Tableaux de la valeur alimentaire des fourrages. **Tables of composition and nutritive value of roughages.**

11700 Michalet–Doreau, B.   FR 010814/77/6503
Prévision de la valeur nutritive et alimentaire des ensilages d'herbe. **Prevision of silage nutritive value.**

11701 Michalet–Doreau, B.; Dulphy, J.P.   FR 010814/77/6505
Variation des quantités d'ensilage ingérées: influence de la finesse de hachage et de la qualité de conservation. **Silage intake: Influence of chopping and quality of conservation.**

11702 Patureau–Mirand, P.; Prugnaud, J.; Pion, R.

FR 010815/70/9576 N

Quelques aspects de la valeur nutritionnelle des aliments protéiques susceptibles d'être incorporés dans les aliments d'allaitement. **Some aspects of the nutritional value of new proteins for milkreplacers.**

11703 Vermorel, M.; Pion, R.; Mendes–Pereira, E.
FR 010816/66/2760
Valeur énergétique et azotée de diverses céréales ou sources d'azote pour l'animal monogastrique en croissance. Etudes sur rats. **Energy and nitrogen value of various grains or nitrogen sources for growing monogastric animals. Trials on rats.** Publications.

11704 Aurousseau, B.; Flanzy, J.; Vermorel, M.; Toullec, R.; Fauconneau, MM. FR 010816/68/9518 N
Utilisation énergétique de chaînes carbonées particulières chez les animaux en croissance. **Energy utilization of various carbon chains by growing animals.**

11705 Vermorel, M.; Bouvier, J.C.; Dulphy, J.P.
FR 010816/78/9514
Valeur énergétique des pailles traitées ou non à la soude et complémentées par des aliments concentrés à base de céréales ou de pulpes. **Energy value of diets based on alcali reated straw with various concentrate mixtures.**

11706 Larvor, P.; Rayssiguier, Y. FR 010817/69/8032
Métabolisme du magnésium et pathologie associée au déficit magnésique. **Magnesium metabolism and pathological problem caused by magnesium deficiency.**

11707 Levieux; Rayssiguier, Y.; Larvor, P. FR 010817/77/8033
Relations nutrition immunité : rôle du magnesium. **Nutrition and immunity : effect of magnesium.**

11708 Recamier, A.; Hutter FR 011801/75/9069
Valeur énergétique des pailles de céréales. **Energy value of cereal straw recuperation.**

11709 Lafon, E.; Jeannin, B.; Beranger, C. FR 012201/78/9054
Production de génisses de boucherie de 26–30 mois sur prairie permanente de marais intensifiée. **Production of 26–30 month–old butchery heifers on intensive permanent marsh–land meadows.**

11710 Dronne, Y.; Janet, C. FR 012205/69/8517
Les substitutions au tourteau de soja en alimentation animale. **Substitutes to soybean meal in animal feeds.**

11711 Janet, C.; Gorse, P. FR 012205/75/8518
La consommation des additifs en alimentation animale en France. **Chemical addings use in French feeding industry.**

11712 Sharman; Mann GB 010301/77/0077 R
Perinatal development of enzymes in the nervous system and the effects of early weaning in laboratory rodents and pigs.

11713 Close; Stanier GB 010301/77/0078
The energy cost of pregnancy and lactation in the rat.

11714 White; Lindsay GB 010302/00/0002 R
Alcohol production and effects in new–born animals on artificial diets wth glucose. Stomach yeast population.

11715 Lindsay GB 010302/00/0008 R
Hormonal changes in declining lactation.

11716 Leat GB 010302/00/0065 R
Comparative lipid metabolism of herbivores and omnivores.

11717 Harrison; Bunnett GB 010305/18/0073 N
Isolation and location of peptide hormones in the gastrointestinal tract.

11718 Thompson GB 010305/78/0070 R
Mobilisation and circulation of nutrients in farm animals.

11719 Symonds; Baird GB 010403/00/0809 R
Dynamics of liver metabolism.

11720 Symons GB 010404/00/0809 R
Dynamics of liver metabolism.

11721 Sansom; Gibbons GB 010404/76/0835 R
Diseases associated with a deficient dietary intake and poisoning associated with an excessive intake of Se.

11722 Wood GB 010601/00/0140 R
Defining the physiological basis for differences in growth efficiency and nutrient parition in animals.

11723 Wilkins GB 011202/79/0049 N
The utilization of white clover/grass swards by grazing and by conservation as silage.

11724 Nutbrown; Geisler GB 011207/79/0019 N
Quantitative analysis of animal production systems based on grass and other forage crops.

11725 Iggo GB 021004/79/0004 N
Duodenal sensory and reflex mechanisms.

11726 Smith GB 022001/79/0014 N
Metabolite utilisation in lactating mammary tissue.

11727 Noble; Steele GB 030202/00/0001 R
Metabolism of polyunsaturated fatty acids in the tissues of ruminants and non–ruminant animals.

11728 Christie; Vernon GB 030202/00/0004 R
Comparative aspects of lipid synthesis in mammary gland and adipose tissue of ruminants and non–ruminants.

11729 Christie; Hunter GB 030202/00/0006 R
Structure of lipid components of tissues of ruminant and non–ruminant animals.

11730 Wahle; Garton GB 030603/00/0001 R
Desaturation and hydroxylation of fatty acids in tissues of the sheep,rat and hen.

11731 Lough GB 030603/00/0004 R
Metabolism of branched–chain fatty acids in animals.

11732 Wahle; Paterson GB 030603/77/0005 R
Control of fatty acid synthesis and lipid deposition.

11733 Davies GB 030604/77/0020
Influence of dietary factors on zinc availability.

11734 Bremner; Mills GB 030604/77/0022 R

D 3200 – Animal nutrition

Antagonistic interactions of molybdenum and sulphur upon copper metabolism.

11735 Davies   GB 030604/77/0023
Role of copper in mitochondrial and microsomal oxidative reactions.

11736 Bremner; Davies   GB 030604/77/0024 R
Role of metallothioneins in absorption retention and excretion of metals.

11737 Chesters; Will   GB 030604/77/0027 R
Metabolism of zinc and copper during infection and stress in farm livestock.

11738 Davies   GB 030604/78/0030 N
Methylation of inorganic mercury by intestinal micro–organisms of rat, rabbit and ruminants.

11739 Davies; Mills   GB 030604/78/0032 N
Copper absorption, physiological and dietary factors affecting.

11740 Pullar; Spreadbry   GB 030606/76/0021
Energy exchanges in growing rabbits.

11741 Jones   GB 030611/77/0044
Control and measurement of energy reserves in neonates pigs lambs.

11742 Goodall; Kay   GB 030612/00/0013 R
Propulsion of food through the alimentary tract of ruminant animals.

11743 Scott   GB 030612/77/0022 R
Hormonal control of water and mineral balance in young farm animals.

11744 Rhind; Rayner   GB 030612/78/0029 N
Hormonal and metabolic responses to digestion and absorption.

11745 Anderson   GB 040401/79/0032 N
The effect of wilting on the nitrogenous components of grass silage.

11746 Singer   GB 051101/79/0026 N
Availability and composition of swill from catering establishments etc.

11747 McLellan   GB 060102/00/0033
Calorimetric investigations with farm animals.

11748 McGrath, D.; Poole, D.B.R.; Fleming, G.A.
     IE 060200/76/1178 R
A study of the hazards to pasture and animal health arising from the land spreading of copper containing pig manures. Publications.

11749 Crinion, R.A.P.   IE 120206/75/9136 N
Epidemiological survey of selenium toxicity in farm animals in County Meath, Ireland. Publications.

11750 Perniola, M.; Ferri, D.; Convertini, G.
     IT 020500/73/0003
Indagini qualitative sulla loiessa. Research on ryegrass forage quality. Publications.

11751 Martillotti, F.; Pace, V.; Verna, M.; Malossini, F.
     IT 020700/79/0010 N
Ricerca di fattori antinutrizionali per l'utilizzazione zootecnica del triticale e caratteristiche chimiche e nutrizionali della pianta intera di triticale prima e dopo insilamento a diversi stadi di maturazione. Antinutritional factors in triticale for animal feeding and some chemical and nutritional characteristics of whole plant before and after ensiling at different stages.

11752 Malossini, F.; Pace, V.; Settineri, D.
     IT 020700/79/0011 N
Impiego del residuo acido insolubile come indicatore per la stima della digeribilità. Acid insoluble ashes as marker for to digestibility evaluation.

11753 Ceruzzi, B.   IT 040105/74/0535
Utilizzazione digestiva di alcuni alimenti del bestiame in relazione alla loro composizione in aminoacidi. Digestive utilization of certain feeds according to their aminoacid composition.

11754 Bellitti, E.   IT 040111/73/0144
Nutrizione e ambiente climatico. Nutrition and the climatic environment.

11755 Manfredini, M.   IT 040236/77/0566 R
Ricerche sull'impiego di sottoprodotti industriali ed agricoli nell'alimentazione di animali in produzione zootecnica. Research on the use of industrial and agricultural bye–products in feeding animals for live–stock breeding.

11756 Mordenti, A.; Scipioni, R.; Zaghini, G.; Parisini, P.
     IT 040236/78/0001 N
Ricerche su effetti e possibili meccanismi d'azione di pools aminoacidici in alimentazione animale. Research on the effects and possible actions of aminoacid pools in animal nutrition. Publications.

11757 D'Urso, G.; Sinatra, M.C.; Nicolosi, C.
     IT 040303/79/0001 N
Ricerche sulla composizione chimica e valore nutritivo delle vinacce. Research on chemical composition and nutritive value of grape marc.

11758 Cappa, V.   IT 040411/73/0162
Sulla possibilità di identificare le carenze di oligoelementi attraverso il controllo dell'eliminazione fecale. On the possibility of identifying oligoelement deficiencies through the control of fecal elimination. Publications.

11759 Antongiovanni, M.   IT 040518/78/0105 R
Ulteriori indagini sui metodi in vitro come strumento di valutazione degli alimenti zootecnici. Further investigation in vitro methods as a means of assessing foods for animals.

11760 Antongiovanni, M.   IT 040520/78/1025 N
Valutazione delle caratteristiche nutritive di diete contenenti paglia trattata con alcali ed urea come fonte azotata non proteica. Evaluation of the nutritional characteristics of diets containing straw treated with alkali and urea as a source of non proteinic nitrogen food.

11761 Cerletti, P.; Restani, P.; Duranti, M.; Bonomi, F.
     IT 040620/75/0002 R
Alcuni parametri molecolari, proprietà nutrizionali e

funzionali di proteine di Lupinus Albus e di Zea Mais. **Some molecular parameters, nutritional and functional properties of proteins from Lupinus Albus and Zea Mais.** Publications.

11762 Bonsembiante, M.   IT 040810/77/0538 R
Utilizzazione di foraggi e sottoprodotti di varia origine nell'alimentazione del bestiame da macello e da riproduzione. **The utilisation of fodder and by–products of various origin in feeding cattle for slaughter and for reproduction.**

11763 Fedeli Avanzi, C.   IT 041116/73/1814
Ricerche sui fabbisogni alimentari e sulle tecniche di alimentazione delle piccole specie animali. **Research on nutritional requirements and feeding techniques of smaller animal species.** Publications.

11764 Congiu, F.   IT 041313/75/0003
Ricerche pluriennale sul ciclo biologico e sul valore nutritivo delle principali essenze arbustive presenti nelle zone pascolive della Sardegna. **Pluriannual researches on the biological cycle and on the nutritional values of the main shrub plants present in the grazing grounds of Sardinia.** Publications.

11765 Caretta, G.   IT 041802/73/0163
Analisi qualitativa e quantitativa delle aflatossine prodotte da funghi saprofiti di sostanze vegetali e foraggi usati nell'alimentazione del bestiame. **Qualitative and quantitative analysis of aflatoxins produced by saprophyte fungi of plant material and fodders used in animal feeding.** Publications.

11766 Calaresu, G.; Pulina, C.   IT 051100/77/0002
Sulla presenza di Mercurio, Cadmio, Piombo in mangimi preparati in Sardegna ed in mangimi importati. **Investigation on the Mercury, Cadmium and lead residues present in some integrated feeds prepared in Sardinia (Italy) and imported.**

11767 Canale, A.   IT 062500/74/0198
L'energia metabolizzabile, la digeribilità delle proteine e degli aminoacidi e l'utilizzazione nutritiva di proteine non convenzionali provenienti da lieviti coltivati su n–paraffine. **Metabolizable energy, protein and amino–acids digestibility and nutritive utilization of not conventional proteins from yeasts grown on n–paraffines.**

11768 Sarra, C.   IT 062500/74/0201
Le caratteristiche bromatologiche dei melassi in relazione alla identificazione ed al dosaggio degli zuccheri per mezzo della cromatografia in fase gassosa. **Bromatologic characteristics of molasses in relation with their identification and sugars content by means of gaschromatography.**

11769 Sarra, C.   IT 062500/74/0202
La composizione chimico–bromatologica dei semi di alcune piante dell'America Latina:prime indagini su differenti varietà di "Quinua"(Chenopodium quinoa L.). **Chemical–bromatological composition of seeds from a few Latin American plants:preliminary investigations on different "Quinua" varieties (Chenopodium quinoa L.).**

11770 Albonico, F.   IT 062600/77/0883
Utilizzo del permeato di ultrafiltrazione nell'alimentazione zootecnica. **Use of the residue of ultrafiltration for animal feeding.**

11771 Nassimbeni, P.; Parente, G.   IT 090701/76/0001
Prove di confronto varietale tra diverse essenze foraggere nella zona montana della Regione Friuli Venezia Giulia e studi sulla loro conservazione. **Variety comparison tests among different forage essences in the Friuli Venezia Giulia mountain zone and studies on their conservation.** Publications.

11772 Kemp, A.; Geurink, J.H.; Hemkes, O.J.
          NL 010102/76/6732
Minerale bestanddelen in de relatie bodem–plant–dier. **Mineral compounds in the relation soil–plant–animal.** Publications.

11773 Janssen, W.M.M.A.; Versteegh, H.A.J.; Helder, J.F.; Kan, C.A.; Mulder, R.W.A.W.   NL 010109/77/7874
Onderzoek naar de toepassingsmogelijkheden van gedroogde kippemest als veevoedergrondstof. **The applicability of dried chicken manure as feedstuff.**

11774 Honing, Y. van der   NL 010115/54/5452
De bepaling van de energetische voederwaarde van veevoeders met behulp van energiebalans–proeven. **The determination of energetic feeding–value of feeds for livestock on energy–balance–trials.** Publications.

11775 Vreman, K.   NL 010115/73/5456
Overdracht van milieukritische stoffen uit het voer via het dier naar het verkoopbare dierlijke produkt. **Transfer of compounds which might cause environment and health problems from feed via the domestic animal to the marketable animal product.** Publications.

11776 Meer, J.M van der   NL 010115/74/5431
Ontwikkelen, toetsen en op peil houden van chemische bepalingsmethoden en laboratoriumtechnieken voor veevoedingsonderzoek. **Development, testing and controlling of analytical laboratory techniques.** Publications.

11777 Beers, A. van   NL 010115/74/5432
Ontwerpen en vervaardigen van technische hulpapparatuur voor veevoedingsonderzoek met dieren. **Designing and constructing technical equipment to be used in animal nutrition research.**

11778 Vuuren, A.M. van   NL 010115/74/5433
Het aanpassen en het ontwikkelen van chirurgische technieken bij landbouwhuisdieren t.b.v. het veevoedingsonderzoek. **Modifying and developing surgical technics on (farm) animals for research purposes on animal feeding.**

11779 Meer, M.J. van der   NL 010115/76/7227
Onderzoek naar de voederwaardebepaling uitgaande van de chemische samenstelling. **Research into the nutritive value determination by means of the chemical constituents.** Publications.

11780 Boer, F. de   NL 010115/77/7617
Verhogen voedselproduktie in ontwikkelingslanden via voederwaardeonderzoek. **Stimulation of food–production in developing countries by feed value evaluation.**

11781 Smits, B.   NL 010115/78/8616 N
Valorisatie van vlokkingsslib van slachterijen en zuivelfabrieken als voedermiddel. **Evaluation of flocculation–flotation sludge from slaughter houses and dairy factories as a feedstuff.**

11782 Binnerts, W.T.   NL 020017/51/4686

D 3200 – Animal nutrition

Het metabolisme en de functie van sporenelementen. **The trace element metabolism and the function of trace elements.** Publications.

11783 Boekholt, H.A.   NL 020017/54/4687
Invloed van milieufactoren op energiehuishouding van landbouwhuisdieren. **Influence of environmental factors on energy metabolism of farm animals.** Publications.

11784 Schothorst, M. van   NL 040011/55/7439
Het voorkomen van nabesmetting van eindprodukten van destructoren en het vaststellen van eisen welke aan deze produkten kunnen worden gesteld. **Prevention of after–contamination of the end–product of destructors and determination of quality requirements for these products.** Publications.

11785 Greve, P.A.   NL 040011/69/7510
Onderzoek naar residuen van bestrijdingsmiddelen behorende tot de groep van de cyclische gechloreerde koolwaterstoffen in veevoeders. **Examination on residues of pesticides belonging to the group of cyclic chlorinated carbohydrates in animal feeds.** Publications.

11786 Schuller, P.L.   NL 040011/75/7468
Het ontwikkelen van een multi–mycotoxine detectiemethode in veevoer. **Development of a multi–mycotoxin detection method for animal feeds.** Publications.

11787 Schuller, P.L.   NL 040011/75/7469
Het ontwikkelen van een methode van onderzoek voor het bepalen van aflatoxine B_1 in samengestelde veevoeders. **The development of a detection method for determination of aflatoxin B_1 in mixed animal feeds.** Publications.

11788 Vos, R.H. de   NL 050301/72/5305
Onderzoek naar de contaminatie van veevoeders en veevoedergrondstoffen met gechloreerde koolwaterstoffen. **Study of the contamination of feeds and feed raw materials with chlorinated hydrocarbons.** Publications.

11789 Bloksma, A.H.   NL 050302/74/6242
Het ontwikkelen en verbeteren van onderzoekmethoden voor grondstoffen en eindprodukten voor de mengvoederindustrie. **Quality testing of feed; development and standardization of methods for feed analysis.**

11790 Onck, W.S.   NL 050305/72/8043
Automatisering van analyses in veevoeder en dierlijk materiaal. **Automation of analyses in animal feed and material of animal origin.**

11791 Schutte, J.B.   NL 050305/75/8018
De waarde van op verschillende wijze behandelde varkens– en pluimveemest voor de veevoeding. **Evaluation of differently treated pig and poultry excreta as a component for animal feed.**

11792 Onck, W.S.   NL 050305/76/8042
Analyse van residuen van anabool werkende stoffen in dierlijke weefsels, organen en excreta m.b.v. dunne laag chromatografie. **Analysis of residues of anabolic agents in animal tissues, organs and excreta by thin–layer chromatography.**

11793 Wal, P. van der   NL 050305/77/8037
De immunologische reaktie van landbouwhuisdieren op voederbestanddelen in relatie tot gezondheidstoestand, groei en voederconversie. **Immunological response of farm animals to feed constituents and its effect on state of health and performance.**

11794 Wal, P. van der   NL 050305/78/8032
Zware metalen, in het bijzonder cadmium, in relatie tot de conditie van landbouwhuisdieren, hun omgeving en de consument van dierlijke produkten. **Heavy metals, in particular cadmium, effect on farm animals, their environment and the consumer of their products.**

Equines (B 4100)

See also 10586, 10588

11795 Kielwein, G.; Storch, G.; Zollmann, H.   DE 129701/78/0002 N
Untersuchungen über die Zusammensetzung von Stutenmilch und Kumyss. **Investigation into composition of mare's milk and kumyss.** Publications.

11796 Meyer, H.; Schwabenbauer, K.; Schyns, V.   DE 139300/78/0002 N
Untersuchungen über den Einfluss verschiedener Futtermittel und Fütterungstechniken auf Futterpassage und Caecumstoffwechsel beim Pferd. **Studies on passage of feeds and metabolism of caecum in horse as affected by different feeds and feeding systems.**

11797 Meyer, H.; Mundt, H.–C.   DE 139300/78/0003 N
Untersuchungen über die Verdaulichkeit von aufgeschlossenem Stroh. **Studies on the digestibility of treated straw.**

11798 Drepper, K.   DE 148300/78/0007 N
Nährstoffbedarf von Sport– und Zuchtpferden. **Nutrient requirements of sport horses and brood mares.**

11799 Gueguen, L.; Pointillart, A.   FR 010205/62/2704
Utilisation digestive et métabolisme du phosphore et du calcium chez les mammifères domestiques. Influence des facteurs alimentaires. **Digestive and metabolic utilization of phosphorus and calcium in domestic mammalia. Influence of dietary factors.** Publications.

11800 Doreau, M.   FR 010812/76/6513
Nutrition de la jument en fin de gestation et début de lactation. Comparaison avec la vache. **Nutrition of the mare in late pregnancy and early lactation Comparison with the cow.**

11801 Le Neindre, P.; Petit, M.; Muller, A.   FR 010813/66/6531
Allaitement double et multiple. **Double or multiple suckling.**

11802 Martin–Rosset, W.; Molenat, G.   FR 010813/74/6535
Utilisation comparée de l'herbe et des fourrages par le cheval et les ruminants. **Compared utilization of grass and forages by horses and ruminants.**

11803 Rayssiguier, Y.; Remesy, C.; Poncet; Demigne, C.; Thivend, P.   FR 010817/76/8034
Influence des modifications des fermentations digestives sur l'absorption des minéraux chez le monogastrique et le ruminant. **Effect of changes in digestive fermentations on mineral absorption in monogastric animals and ruminants.**

11804 Masson, C.; Tisserand, J.L.   FR 011013/72/6562
Etude de la digestion microbienne dans le gros intestin du
cheval (travaux réalisés sur poneys). **Microbial digestion in
horses (ponies).**

11805 Klooster, A.Th. van 't   NL 030009/74/6020 N
Verteringsproeven met ontsloten voedermiddelen bij ponies
(extruderen, verteringsproeven, verteringskoëfficiënten,
pony). **Ponies: digestion trials with extruded feedings stuffs
(extrusioncooking, digestion trials, digestibility coefficients,
ponies).** Publications.

11806 Klooster, A.Th. van   NL 030009/76/6956 R
De relatie tussen Fe–gehalte van het rantsoen en het
Hb–gehalte van het bloed van paarden. **Relationship between
Fe–content of the ration and the Hb–content of the blood of
horses.**

11807 Schee, W. van der   NL 030009/77/7752
Het metabolisme van vitamine B12 bij paarden. **Vitamin B12
metabolism in the horse.**

Ruminants in general (B 4200)

See also 3398, 3405, 3406, 3534, 3545, 3546, 3564, 3637, 5632,
8505, 10251, 10253, 10586, 10600, 10609, 11543, 11548, 11550,
11560, 11797, 11799, 11801, 11802, 11803, 12957, 12964, 13984,
16338, 17508, 19673, 20128

11808 Hennaux, L.; François, E.; Compère, R.; Thewis, A.;
Bodart, C.   BE 010003/68/0003
Etude de la vitesse de transit des résidus alimentaires chez les
ruminants et le porc. **Study of the rate of transit of food residus
in ruminants and pigs.** Publications.

11809 Vanbelle, M.; Allard, B.; Meurens, M.
    BE 020601/73/0001 R
Etude de la granulométrie des aliments et son effet sur leur
digestibilité par les ruminants. **Study on the granulometry of
animal concentrated food and the digestibility response in
ruminants.**

11810 Weik, H.   DE 104100/77/0003
Ketosis der Wiederkäuer. **Ketosis of ruminants.** Publications.

11811 Simon, U.; Daniel, P.   DE 129142/74/0001
Die Beliebtheit von Futterpflanzenarten und –sorten beim
Wiederkäuer. **Palatibility of forage species and varieties and
intake by ruminants.**

11812 Pfeffer, E.; Schiele, B.   DE 132302/77/0003
Futterwert von Gräsern in den Usambara–Bergen 'Tansania'.
**Feeding value of grasses in the Usambara Mountains
'Tansania'.**

11813 Pfeffer, E.   DE 132304/72/0001
Untersuchungen über die Protein–Verwertung bei
Wiederkäuern. **Studies on utilization of proteins in ruminants.**

11814 Harmeyer, J.; Grabe, C.von   DE 139200/78/0002 N
Stöchiometrische Messungen an Pansenmikroorganismen.
Stoichiometrical measurements of rumen fermentation.
Publications.

11815 Engelhardt, W.von; Rechkemmer, E.; Wirthensohn,

K.; Rübsamen, K.   DE 144142/77/0002
Der Einfluss kurzkettiger Fettsäuren auf die Resorption von
Wasser und von Ionen im Colon. **Influence of short–chain fatty
acids on the absorption of water and ions in the colon.**

11816 Giesecke, D.; Stangassinger, M.; Emmanual, B.
    DE 160600/78/0003 N
Ruminale Ketogenese. **Ruminal ketogenesis.**

11817 Rohr, K.   DE 201050/77/0010
Versuche zur Quantifizierung des Stickstoffumsatzes von
Wiederkäuern. **Experiments on quantification of nitrogen
metabolism in ruminants.**

11818 Rohr, K.   DE 201050/78/0001 N
Überprüfung neuer Energiebewertungssysteme für
Wiederkäuer. **Testing of food energy evaluation systems for
ruminants.**

11819 Kaufmann, W.; Hagemeister, H. DE 207010/78/0001 N
Proteinstoffwechsel bei Wiederkäuern einschliesslich
"protected protein". **Protein metabolism in ruminants incl.
protected protein.**

11820 Gross, F.   DE 502300/77/0001
Untersuchungen zum Nährstoffgehalt und zur Verdaulichkeit
bei Wiederkäuern und Schweinen von Silomais, Maiskolben
und Körnermais und deren Silagen aus frühen bis mittelfrühen
Maishybriden. **Investigations on ruminants and pigs as to
nutrient content and digestibility of silage maize, maize cobs
and grain maize and their silages of early to medium–early
maize hybrids.** Publications.

11821 Thomsen, K.V.; Neimann–Sørensen, A.
    DK 010201/63/0001
Bestemmelse af fodermidlers fordøjelighed og foderværdi på
grundlag af in vitro bestemmelser. (laboratoriemetoder).
**Determination of the digestibility and nutritional value of
feedingstuffs using in vitro methods (Laboratory methods).**

11822 Jensen, A.T.; Jensen, E.   DK 030106/78/0001 N
Undersøgelse af årsagerne til virkningen af el–filterstøv fra
cementfabrikation som mineralstof til drøvtyggere. **A chemical
investigation of the causes of the effect of cement kiln dust as a
mineral feed additive for ruminants.**

11823 Madsen, J.   DK 030142/79/0003 N
Udarbejdelse af et nyt proteinvurderingssystem til drøvtyggere
og undersøgelser til fastlæggelse af proteinets nedbrydning i
vommen. **Preparation of a new protein evaluation system for
ruminants and investigations on protein degradation in the
rumen.**

11824 Durand, M.; Dumay, C.; Gueguen, L.
    FR 010205/75/9561 N
Influence de l'acidité du régime sur la digestion microbienne au
niveau du rumen. **Influence of acid diets on microbial digestion
in the rumen.**

11825 Jeannin, B.; Béranger, C.; Louyot, J.M.; Petit, M.;
Garel, J.P.; de Montard, F.   FR 010804/77/9017 N
Etude sur les possibilités de conduite d'un troupeau d'animaux
en croissance sur prairie de montagne non mécanisable.. **Study
of the grazing management of youngstock on highlands where
haymaking is not feasing.**

11826 Jouany, J.P. FR 010805/72/6548
Rôle des protozoaires du rumen dans la digestion. **Biology and digestive role of rumen protozoa.**

11827 Poncet, C. FR 010805/73/6550
Etude quantitative de la digestion de l'azote : influence de la nature de la ration (fourrage ou aliment concentré). **Factors affecting the digestion of nitrogen in the rumen : protein solubility level of intake, nature of the energy.**

11828 Thivend, P.; Poncet, C. FR 010805/73/6551
Digestion du lactose par le ruminant. **Digestion of lactose by ruminants.**

11829 Poncet, C.; Dardillat, C. FR 010805/76/6546
Méthode de mesure quantitative de la digestion chez le ruminant: détermination du débit du contenu intestinal. **Quantitative studies of digestion: measurement of intestinal flow using an electromagnetic method.**

11830 Dardillat, C. FR 010805/76/6547
Etude de la motricité gastro–intestinale : son rôle dans la digestion des aliments et en physiopathologie (cas du jeune). **Relationship between gastro–intestinal motility, digestive processes and physiopathological aspects.**

11831 Jouany, J.P.; Thivend, P.; Poncet, C.
FR 010805/78/6549
Etude des inter–relations entre les protozoaires et les bactéries du rumen dans les phénomènes de la digestion, mise au point des techniques. Applications préliminaires. **Relationship between protozoa and bacteria in rumen digestion.**

11832 Lamand, M. FR 010807/77/8008
Digestibilité des oligoéléments chez les ruminants. **Trace elements availability in ruminants.**

11833 Journet, M.; Hoden, A.; Muller, A. FR 010812/72/6518
Utilisation des sous–produits d'origine industrielle par les ruminants. **Utilization by the ruminants of by products from industry.**

11834 Verite, R. FR 010812/73/6510
Digestion de l'azote chez le ruminant et valeur azotée réelle des aliments et des rations. **Nitrogen digestion in ruminant and actual nitrogen value of feeds and diets.**

11835 Champredon, C.; Pion, R.; Grizard, J.
FR 010815/70/9583 N
Besoins en acides aminés des ruminants laitiers. **Amino acid requirements of dairy ruminants.**

11836 Champredon, C.; Pion, R.; Prugnaud, J.
FR 010815/72/9581
Utilisation digestive et métabolique de divers composés soufrés par les ruminants. **Digestive and metabolic utilisation of some sulfur compounds by ruminants.**

11837 Barry, J.L.; Campredon, C. FR 010815/76/9586
Estimation de la valeur alimentaire des nutriments par mesure de l'absorption des composés azotés provenant de la digestion chez le ruminant. **Estimation of the nutritive value of feedstuffs by measuring nitrogenous compounds absorption from the digestive tract in ruminant.**

11838 Bauchart, D.; Aurousseau, B. FR 010816/77/9521
Préparation de l'acide heptadécénoique (pureté>, 99%) et de plusieurs substances lipidiques étalons contenant l'acide heptadécénoique. **Preparation of pure heptadecenoic acid and several standard heptadecenoic acid esters.**

11839 Bouvier, J.C.; Thivend, P.; Vermorel, M.
FR 010816/78/9517
Détermination de la production d'acides gras volatils (agv) chez le ruminant. Etude des variations en fonction de la nature du régime et de l'âge des animaux. **Measurement of volatile fatty acids (ufa) production in the ruminant. Variations with diet composition and age.**

11840 Tisserand, J.L. FR 011013/70/6564
Utilisation des graines protéagineuses (féverole, pois, lupin) dans l'alimentation du ruminant. **Utilization of protein seeds in ruminants nutrition.**

11841 Tisserand, J.L.; Teissier, J.H. FR 011013/78/6563
Etude de l'utilisation d'un aliment à base de bois dans l'alimentation des ruminants adultes. **Processed Wood in Ruminant feeding.**

11842 Giovanni, R.; Grongnet, J.F. FR 011304/75/6561
Influence des facteurs antinutritionnels des crucifères sur l'état sanitaire et les performances des ruminants. **Kale anemia and goitrogenic factors in ruminants.**

11843 Morand–Fehr, P. FR 011712/65/9510 N
Etude des précurseurs des acides gras des triglycérides du lait de ruminants : facteurs influençant leur utilisation par la mamelle. **Study of fatty acids precursors of milk triglycerides in ruminants factors influencing their utilization in the mammary gland.**

11844 Decourt, N.; Brun, A. FR 012303/78/8542
Recherche bibliographique sur le pâturage en forêt. **Grazing in forests : a review.**

11845 Munn; Orpin GB 010302/00/0001 R
E.M. Studies of the structure of ruminant bacteria and flagellates correlated with biochemical analyses.

11846 Orpin GB 010302/00/0003 R
Biochemistry of bacterium – Eadies oval – from the rumen and its significance in rumen metabolism.

11847 Lindsay; Setchell GB 010302/00/0009 R
Utilisation of ketones, volatile fatty acids and glucose by ruminant brain and muscle.

11848 Lindsay; Barker GB 010302/00/0011 R
Factors affecting the production of glucose by ruminants and its relation to their protein metabolism.

11849 Kemp; Dawson GB 010302/00/0020 R
Structural and metabolic studies in lipids from rumen micro–organisms.

11850 Coleman GB 010302/00/0025 R
Role of nine species of ciliate protozoa in rumen function as shown by studies on their metabolism.

11851 Coleman; Hall GB 010302/00/0028 R
Role of bacteria in the metabolism of rumen protozoa as shown by studies in the electron microscope.

11852 Coleman   GB 010302/00/0029 R
Degradation and metabolism of cellulose by cellulolytic protozoa from the rumen.

11853 Mangan; Wright   GB 010302/00/0034 R
Protein metabolism in the rumen, measurement of rumen volumes and digesta flow, effect of tannins in legumes.

11854 Mangan; Wright   GB 010302/00/0035 R
Plasma and erythrocyte amino acids in relation to protein feeding/insulin/hormones in ruminants.

11855 Mangan   GB 010302/00/0036 R
Release of soluble protein from chloroplasts and plant leaves and effect of aldehyde treatment on rumen digestion.

11856 Munn   GB 010302/00/0038 R
Functional organisation of rumen and omasum epithelium, and structure and properties of subcellular fraction.

11857 Leat; Harrison   GB 010302/00/0059 R
The role of pancreatic enzymes and bile in the absorption, synthesis and transport of lipids in the sheep.

11858 Orpin   GB 010302/00/0062 R
Population, cultural and biochemical studies on rumen flagellates.

11859 Leat   GB 010302/00/0066 R
Metabolic changes in the ruminant between birth and maturity.

11860 Mongan; Harrison   GB 010302/19/0072 N
Digestion of protected protein by ruminant animals.

11861 Mangan; Wright   GB 010302/75/0068 R
Arginase in erythrocytes of ruminants.

11862 Hazlewood; Mangan   GB 010302/77/0070
Isolation and characterisation of proteolytic bacteria in the rumen.

11863 Harrison   GB 010305/00/0056 R
Active transport of salts across rumen and omasum epithelium.

11864 Wilkinson; Cook   GB 011202/00/0018 R
Nutritive value of silage for ruminants.

11865 Harris; Lawton   GB 011203/76/0020 R
Ultra–structural studies of forage plants in relation to their nutritional quality for ruminants.

11866 Beever; Outen   GB 011205/00/0002 R
Factors influencing and the products of ruminal digestion of structural carbohydrate.

11867 Siddons; Beever   GB 011205/00/0003 R
Factors influencing digestion, synthesis and absorption of protein in the ruminant.

11868 Thomson; Beever   GB 011205/00/0004 R
Utilization of digested nutrients in grazed and conserved forage and forage based diets by sheep and cattle.

11869 Outen; Beever   GB 011205/00/0005 R
The transformation synthesis and absorption of lipids during digestion by ruminants.

11870 Penning; Treacher   GB 011205/79/0705 N
To develop techniques to measure intake, behaviour and energy expenditure of grazing animals.

11871 France   GB 011207/79/0017 N
Quantitative studies of grazing animal/ sward interactions.

11872 Geisler   GB 011207/79/0018 N
Quantitative studies of ruminant animal response to nutritional inputs.

11873 Sharpe; Latham   GB 011701/00/0016
Microflora of rumen.

11874 Latham   GB 011701/77/0025
Digestion of plant cell walls by rumen bacteria.

11875 Knight; Sutton   GB 011707/75/0011 R
Factors affecting microbial synthesis in the rumen.

11876 Coates; Harrison   GB 011708/00/0010 R
Influence of the gut microflora on nutrient metabolism and utilization.

11877 Coates; Rolls   GB 011708/00/0013 R
Effects of the gut microflora on the growth of young animals.

11878 Smith   GB 011708/79/0022 N
Exchanges of major minerals and some other nutrients at specific sites along the ruminant alimentary tract.

11879 Andrews   GB 011712/00/0012 R
Function of calcium binding proteins in the transport of calcium in the ruminant.

11880 Jones; Hayward   GB 012102/00/0006 R
Evaluation of lab techniques as selection criteria for improved voluntary intake of grasses by ruminants.

11881 Suttle   GB 030101/00/0007 R
Availability of copper in ruminant diets.

11882 Field; Munro   GB 030101/00/0018
Availability of calcium and phosphorus in ruminant diets.

11883 Sykes   GB 030101/00/0023 R
Biochemical indices of protein status.

11884 Suttle   GB 030101/78/0029 N
Vitamin B12 metabolism in ruminants.

11885 Kelly; Thomas   GB 030201/00/0027 R
Ingestion and metabolism of conserved forages, particularly silage, by ruminants.

11886 Noble; Moore   GB 030202/00/0007 R
Metabolism of lipids in young ruminants.

11887 Czerkawski; Brecken   GB 030202/00/0009 R
Fate of metabolic hydrogen in fermentation, microbial synthesis and in methane production and its inhibition.

11888 Czerkawski; Brecken   GB 030202/00/0013
Gross changes in the microbial population in the rumen with

diet and dietary additives.

11889 Martin   GB 030202/00/0017 R
The role of intestinal micro–organisms in the metabolism of aromatic compounds by ruminants.

11890 Victor; Zammit   GB 030202/78/0023 N
Lipid and carbohydrate metabolism in ruminants.

11891 Manson; Annan   GB 030203/00/0003
Stability of the phosphate centre of beta–casein to attack by enzymes of the gastrointestinal tract.

11892 Vernon   GB 030204/75/0026 R
Regulation of nutrient utilisation at different body sites during pregnancy and lacation.

11893 Bacon   GB 030602/00/0006 R
Plant cell walls from forage species; their composition and digestion by ruminants.

11894 Cochie   GB 030602/77/0007
Detailed chemical structure of the products of digestion of plant cell walls by ruminants.

11895 Garton; Duncan   GB 030603/00/0002 R
Occurrence and biosynthesis of propionate–derived fatty acids in animal tissues.

11896 Arthur; Rahim   GB 030604/77/0018
Dietary factors influencing availabilty of selenium to ruminants.

11897 Arthur; Price   GB 030604/77/0026 R
Selenium deficiency in live stock in North Scotland: detection relationship to geochemical enviroment.

11898 Hobson   GB 030605/00/0001
Factors determining growth and metabolism of anaerobes in continuous culture.

11899 Mann; Barr   GB 030605/00/0003
Enumeration of rumen bacteria concerned in digestion of feeds and illness of digestive tract origin.

11900 Eadie   GB 030605/00/0004
Ciliate protozoa and feed digestion in the rumen.

11901 Eadie   GB 030605/00/0007
The distribution of ciliate protozoa in different species of ruminant and ruminant like animals.

11902 Henderson   GB 030605/00/0009
Production and utilization of hydrogen by rumen bacteria; interdependence of these bacteria in the rumen.

11903 Stewart   GB 030605/76/0012
Cellulolysis and digestion of herbages in the rumen and the bacteria concerned.

11904 Wallace   GB 030605/78/0013 R
The influence of rumen ammonia concentration on microbial metabolism and rumen function.

11905 Wainman   GB 030606/00/0011 R
Effect of physical processing on the energy value of feeds for ruminants.

11906 Wainman   GB 030606/00/0012 R
Measurement of net energy value of feeds for ruminants.

11907 Wainman   GB 030606/00/0017 R
Measurement of the metabolizable energy of feeds for ruminants.

11908 MacRae; Smith   GB 030606/78/0022 R
Biochemical / metabolic aspects of energy exchange and glucose requirement in ruminants.

11909 MacRae; Sharman   GB 030606/78/0023 R
Effects of parasitic infestation,infection and hyperpyrexia on energy and nitrogen metabolism of animals.

11910 Brockway; Gordon   GB 030606/78/0024 N
Evaluation of methods for estimating energy exchange in the grazing situation.

11911 Greenhalg; Reid GW   GB 030611/00/0019
Feed intake regulation.

11912 Greenhalg; Orskov   GB 030611/00/0021
Nutritional factors affecting body and carcass characteristics of ruminants.

11913 Kay   GB 030611/00/0023 R
Use of forage crops and by–products by ruminants.

11914 Orskov; Kay   GB 030611/00/0025
Digestion and metabolism of nutrients by ruminants.

11915 Greenhalgh   GB 030611/76/0043 R
Effects of processing feeds on their utilization by ruminants.

11916 Laidlaw; McBratney   GB 040301/00/0012 R
In vitro digestibility of various grass species.

11917 Todd; Thompson   GB 040401/00/0019
Investigations of selenium in ruminant nutrition in Northern Ireland.

11918 Pearce   GB 040403/76/0015
A study of the effects of diet and physiological state on liver metabolism in ruminants.

11919 Researcher not indicated   GB 050464/00/0005 R
Survey of copper levels in cattle and sheep blood.

11920 Edwards   GB 060103/00/0004 R
Chemically treated barley straw.

11921 Mathieson   GB 060116/00/0010
Trace element status of ruminant animals.

11922 MacPherson; Voss   GB 060306/00/0001
Copper and cobalt deficiency in ruminants.

11923 Harkess   GB 060314/00/0003 R
Herbage digestibility in relation to ear emergence.

11924 Griffiths, T.W.; Rogers, P.A.M.   IE 060100/78/1398 N
Nutritive value of protein sources for ruminants with particular reference to silage. Publications.

11925 Griffiths, T.W.; O'Shea, J.; Lawlor, M.J.; Drennan, M.J.; Sheehan, W.; Gleeson, P.A.   IE 060103/76/1255 R
To formulate an energy feeding system for ruminants under Irish conditions. Publications.

11926 Leek, B.F.; Upton, P.K.; Ryan, J.P.; Woods, M.J.
IE 120203/77/9052 N
An investigation of the mechanisms by which acids inhibit ruminant stomach movements. Publications.

11927 Malossini, F.; Pace, V.; Settineri, D.
IT 020700/79/0009 N
Studio dell'attività inibitrice dei tannini sugli enzimi digestivi dei ruminanti. **Inhibition of ruminants digestive enzymes by tannins.**

11928 Marcotrigiano, G.   IT 040104/77/0227 R
Utilizzazione nei ruminanti di micro–elementi complessati con amminoacidi e loro N–ACIL derivati. **Utilization in ruminants of micro–elements compounded with amino–acids and their N–ACIL derivates.**

11929 Galvano, G.; Lanza, A.   IT 040319/75/0002
Ricerche sul valore nutritivo della paglia grano, sottoposta ad idrolisi chimica, nell'alimentazione dei ruminanti. **Reasearch on the nutritive value of wheat straw chemically hydrolized in the feeding of the ruminants.**

11930 Piana, G.   IT 040411/74/0603
Ricerche dirette a ridurre i costi di produzione della carne attraverso un condizionamento dei microrganismi ruminali atto a stimolare le sintesi proteiche a partire da fonti di azoto non protidico ad elevato livello di innocuità. **Research in the reduction of meat production costs through a conditioning of rumen microorganisms aiming at the stimulation of protein synthesis from highly safe non–protidic nitrogen sources.**

11931 Piana, G.   IT 040411/77/0260 R
Effetti di trattamenti fisico–chimici ai cereali sulle caratteristiche chimiche e biochimiche dell'amido alle interferenze dei cereali trattati sulla digeribilità e sulle fermentazioni ruminali. **Effects of the physical and chemical treatment of cereals on the chemical and bio–chemical properties of starch, on their digestibility and on fermentations in ruminants.**

11932 Geri, G.   IT 040520/74/0561
Ricerche sulla composizione chimica, digeribilità, consume volontario e valore nutritivo degli alimenti destinati all'alimentazione dei ruminanti. **Research on the chemical composition, digestibility, voluntary consumption and nutritive value of feeds for ruminants.**

11933 Steg, A.   NL 010115/32/5434
Verteerbaarheidsonderzoek van ruw– en krachtvoeders bij herkauwers. **Digestability research of roughages and concentrates by ruminants.** Publications.

11934 Steg, A.   NL 010115/69/5435
De gebruikswarde van bestaande en nieuwe voedermiddelen voor herkauwers, gemeten in (vergelijkende) voederproeven. **Possible use and nutritive value of existing and newly introduced feeding stuffs for ruminants, as measured in (comparative) feeding experiments.** Publications.

11935 Tamminga, S.   NL 010115/69/5453
Onderzoek naar N–metabolisme in het verteringskanaal van herkauwers. **Research about the N–metabolism in the digestive tract of ruminants.** Publications.

11936 Bruchem, J. van   NL 020017/66/4684
Onderzoek naar de functie van het maagdarm kanaal bij zoogdieren m.n. bij herkauwers. **Research to the function of the gut in mammals esp. in ruminants.** Publications.

11937 Hart, M.L. het   NL 020025/70/5036
Voederopname door en produktiviteit van weidend vee. **Feed intake by growing cattle.** Publications.

11938 Boer, H.   NL 020059/76/4505
Chemie van de koolhydraten in relatie tot de verteerbaarheid van celwandbestanddelen. **Chemistry of the carbohydrates in relationship to the digestibility of cell–wall constituents.**

11939 Huisman, J.   NL 050305/70/8004
Methionine behoefte van herkauwers alsmede de passage door de pens en de biologische beschikbaarheid van methionine modifikaties. **Requirements of ruminants for methionine together with the passage through the rumen and the biological availability of methionine–compounds.**

11940 Terluin, R.W.   NL 050305/72/8034
Soja–lecithinen en andere emulgatoren in rantsoenen voor vleeskalveren. **Soy lecithin and other fat emulsifying agents in rations for veal calves.**

11941 Hellemond, K.K. van   NL 050305/75/8029
Invloed van additieven op stofwisseling en samenstelling van de pensflora. **The effect of additives on the metabolism and composition of the rumen microflora.**

11942 Huisman, J.   NL 050305/77/8020
De voederwaarde van gehydrolyseerde stro voor herkauwers. **Nutritional value of hydrolised straw for ruminants.**

11943 Huisman, J.   NL 050305/78/8019
Voorkoming van eiwitafbraak in de pens van herkauwers. **Prevention of degradation of protein in the rumen.**

Cattle (B 4210)

See also 3084, 3344, 3373, 3505, 3522, 3595, 3613, 3621, 5612, 10658, 10666, 10688, 10698, 10720, 10725, 10736, 10738, 10741, 10742, 10746, 10757, 10761, 10785, 10886, 10887, 10895, 10899, 10909, 11361, 11539, 11540, 11544, 11546, 11547, 11549, 11551, 11552, 11561, 11564, 11565, 11572, 11573, 11574, 11620, 11800, 12305, 12310, 12390, 12391, 12449, 13021, 13113, 14168, 14169, 14222, 14301, 14376, 15382, 15443, 15676, 15829, 15843, 16297, 16815, 16892, 18464, 19321

11944 Henderickx, H.; Demeyer, D.; Van Nevel, C.
BE 030026/57/0001 N
Studie van het pensmetabolisme. **Study of the rumen metabolism.** Publications.

11945 Henderickx, D.; Demeyer, D.; Van Nevel, C.
BE 030026/57/0002 N
Studie van het pensmetabolisme. **Study of the rumen metabolism.** Publications.

11946 De Vos, N.; Lauwers, H.   BE 050400/69/0001

Histochemisch onderzoek van de voormagenwand van het rund met het doel een verklaring te geven van zijn actief resorptievermogen. **Histochemical study of the wall of the bovine forestomachs with special reference to its absorptiveability.** Publications.

11947 Buysse, F.; Aerts, J.; Cottyn, B.; De Brabander, D.
BE 070700/70/0002 R
Verteerbaarheid van diverse voedermiddelen bij koeien en schapen en de relatie met in vitrotechnieken. **Digestibility of different feedstuffs with dairy cows and sheep and the relationship with in vitro –techniques.** Publications.

11948 Boucqué, C.; Cottyn, B.
BE 070700/70/0012 R
Studie van de verschillende energieniveaus bij grazend jongvee op de ontwikkeling van dieren en de weerslag ervan op de economie van de rundvleesproduktie. **The effect of different feeding–levels viewing an economical meatproduction by young bulls in pasture.** Publications.

11949 Buysse, F.; De Brabander, D.; Aerts, J.
BE 070700/71/0001 R
Economisch optimaal voederopnamevermogen bij melkvee tijdens de stalperiode. **Study of the factors affecting feed intake by dairy cows during the indoor period.** Publications.

11950 Boucqué, C.; Cottyn, B.
BE 070700/71/0010 R
Studie van de voederwaarde van deegrijpe maïs onder zijn verschillende vormen in de rundvleesproduktie. **Research on the feed–value of dough–dent maize under its different forms in beef production.** Publications.

11951 Boucqué, C.; Cottyn, B.
BE 070700/72/0017 R
Studie van de bruikbaarheid van diverse N–P–N bronnen in complete droogvoederrantsoenen voor jonge vleesstiertjes. **Study of the suitability of different N–P–N products in all–concentrate rations by intensive beef production.** Publications.

11952 Boucqué, C.; Cottyn, B.
BE 070700/76/0026 R
Studie van de bruikbaarheid van diverse N.P.N. verbindingen in mais kuilvoeder bij mestvee. **Study of the suitability of different N.P.N. products in corn silage by beef production.** Publications.

11953 Boucqué, C.; De Meyer, E.
BE 070700/76/0027 R
Studie van het optimaal eiwitniveau in het krachtvoeder voor fokkalveren. **The optimum protein level in concentrates for calves.**

11954 Boucqué, C.; Cottyn, B.
BE 070700/77/0028 R
Studie van de voederwaarde van druivenpitschroot voor de rundvleesproduktie. **Feed value of grape seed oil meal in rations for beef production.** Publications.

11955 Boucqué, C.; Cottyn, B.
BE 070700/77/0030 R
Studie \ an de pensregulerende stoffen nl. rumensin en avoparein in rundvleesproduktierantsoenen. **Study of rumensin and avoparein as rumen regulating factors in beef cattle.**

11956 Buysse, F.; De Brabander, D.; Aerts, J.
BE 070700/77/0032 R
Maiskuilvoeder als enig ruwvoeder voor melkvee gedurende de stalperiode. **Maize silage as the sole roughage for dairy cattle during the indoor period.**

11957 Boucqué, C.; Cottyn, B.
BE 070700/78/0029 R
Voederwaarde van ingekuilde geperste suikerbietpulp voor de rundvleesproduktie. **Feed value of ensiled pressed sugarbeetpulp in rations for beefproduction.** Publications.

11958 Boucqué, C.; De Meyer, E.
BE 070700/78/0031 R
Studie omtrent het gebruik van verscheidene eiwitbronnen in het krachtvoeder voor fokkalveren. **The use of different protein sources in the concentrates of rearing calves.**

11959 Boucqué, Ch.
BE 070700/78/0039 N
De bruikbaarheid van rauwe aardappelen in de rundvleesproduktie. **The use of raw potatoes for beef production.**

11960 Cottyn, B.; Aerts, J.
BE 070700/79/0037 N
Schatting van de netto–energiewaarde van krachtvoeders voor melkvee op basis van de ruwe nutrienten. **Prediction of the net energy value of concentrates for dairy cows, based on the crude nutrients.**

11961 Thill, N.; François, E.
BE 080100/75/0016 R
Détermination de la ration consommée par le bovin à l'herbage. **Determination of forage intake by the cow in the pasture.**

11962 Vandenbyvang, P.; Thill, N.
BE 140000/74/0052 R
Etude de la quantité et de la qualité de l'alimentation de la vache laitière à l'herbage. **Study of quantity and quality for feeding dairy life stock in pasture.** Publications.

11963 Paquay, R.; Doize, Fr.
BE 140000/75/0050
Mise au point d'une méthode de contrôle du rapport ingestion d'aliments et dépôts de graisses chez le bétail. **Search for a controlmethod for rapport alimentation and fat content by cattle.**

11964 Van Aelten, G.
BE 140000/78/0012
Nieuwe krachtvoeders bij melkvee. **New concentrates of milking cows.**

11965 Sommer, H.; Shabbir, S.M.
DE 111400/77/0004
Mineralstoffgehalt im Speichel und Pansenmikroorganismen bei Milchkühen unter dem Einfluss von Laktationsstadium und Fütterung. **Mineral elements of saliva and rumen microorganisms in dairy cows as influenced by lactation period and feeding regime.**

11966 Sommer, H.; Kowertz, D.
DE 111403/74/0001
Untersuchungen zur Mineralstoff- und Spurenelementversorgungslage von Milchkühen aufgrund von Futter– mittel– und Bodenanalysen. **Analyses of feeds and soil for examining the state of mineral and trace elements supply in dairy cows.**

11967 Pallauf, J.; Brune, H.; Kreuder, K.; Walz, O.P.
DE 129270/77/0009
Einfluss der Kalttränke auf Stoffwechselleistungen des Aufzuchtkalbes. **Effect of cold drinks on the metabolism of rearing calves.**

11968 Steinbach, J.; Hakam, M.
DE 129553/78/0003 N
Jahreszeitliche Einflüsse auf Futterverfügbarkeit und Milchmenge und Milchzusammensetzung in Bangladesh. **Feed supply and effects on milk yield and composition depending on**

the seasons in Bangladesh.

11969 Günther, K.–D.; Nolting, J.; Erkek, R.; Abel, H.
DE 132300/73/0001
Der Mineralstoffumsatz der Milchkuh. **Mineral metabolism in dairy cow.**

11970 Günther, K.–D.; Rosenow, H.; Cheva–Isarakul, B.
DE 132300/78/0002 N
Der Einfluss eines unterschiedlichen Nitratgehaltes auf Leistung und Gesundheit beim Rind. **Influence of different nitrate level on performance and health of cattle.**

11971 Pfeffer, E.; Soller, H.
DE 132302/77/0002
Wirkung des Futterzusatzes Rumensin in der Bullenmast. **Effect of the feed additive Rumensin in fattening bulls.**

11972 Günther, K.–D.; Meulen, U.ter; Gimpel, W.
DE 132303/75/0001
Möglichkeiten des Ersatzes von Milchproteinen durch pflanzliche Proteinfuttermittel im Rahmen der Kälbermast. **Plant proteins as possible milk protein substitute in calf fattening.**

11973 Gütte, J.O.; Helfferich, B.; Poeschel, F.
DE 132305/75/0002
Einfluss der Düngung des Graslandes auf Gewichtsentwicklung und Fruchtbarkeit von Mutterkühen und deren Saugkälber. **The effect of grassland fertilizing on weight and fertility of cows and their sucking calves.**

11974 Harmeyer, J.; Brendler, H.; Breves, G.
DE 139200/78/0001 N
Untersuchungen zur Nebennierenrindefunktion bei boviner Ketose. **Function of the adrenal cortex in bovine ketosis.**

11975 Meyer, H.; Scholz, H.
DE 139300/78/0001 N
Über die Eignung hochmelassierter Trockenschnitzel für die Rindermast. **Suitability of highly molassed dry pulp for cattle fattening.**

11976 Stöber, M.; Waechter, K.
DE 139900/78/0010 N
Synopsis der Symptome der Stoffwechselstörungen und Mangelkrankheiten des Rindes. **Synopsis of symptoms of metabolic disorders and deficiency diseases in cattle.**

11977 Menke, K.H.; Fritz, D.; Schneider, W.
DE 144620/78/0002 N
Einfluss unterschiedlicher Protein– und Energiegaben auf die Verwertung von Protein und Energie für die Milchbildung bei der Kuh. **Effect of different levels of protein and energy on the utilization of protein and energy for milk production in cows.**

11978 Reichl, J.R.
DE 144622/78/0001 N
Bestimmung der Umsatzraten von Aminosäuren in Pansen, Darm und Leber beim Rind. **Estimation of turnover rates of amino acids in the rumen, intestinum and liver of cattle.**

11979 Isensee, E.; Langhammer, E.K.; Kaufmann, W.
DE 148150/77/0001
Auswirkungen mehrmaliger Kraftfuttergaben im praktischen Milchviehhaltungsbetrieb. **Effect of multiple concentrate feeding in dairy farming.**

11980 Pulss, G.
DE 148300/71/0004
Nährstoffbilanz von Milchkühen mit spontaner Acetonämie

bei unterschiedlicher Fütterung. **Nutrient balance in dairy cows with spontaneous acetonaemia depending on different feeding.**

11981 Langbehn, C.; Raue, F.
DE 148401/75/0003
Spezielle Probleme der Rindermast. **Special problems in cattle fattening.**

11982 Researcher not indicated
DE 160000/78/0001 N
Untersuchungen zur Erfassung des Übergangs von Cadmium 'Cd' aus dem Futter auf Fleisch und Organe von Schlachtrindern und dessen Abhängigkeit von bestimmten Umweltfaktoren. **Investigations on the detection of the carry–over of Cd from feeds into meat and organs of cattle–for–slaughter in dependence on certain environmental conditions.**

11983 Gropp, J.; Erbersdobler, H.; Beck, H.
DE 160600/72/0012
Proteinbedarf des Mastkalbes sowie die Verwertung verschiedener Proteinquellen. **Protein requirement of the veal calf and the utilization of different protein sources.**

11984 Gropp, J.
DE 160600/72/0013
Die Verwertung von Nahrungskohlenhydraten beim Mastkalb. **The utilization of feed carbohydrates by veal calf.**

11985 Erbersdobler, H.; Wangenheim, B.von
DE 160600/78/0002 N
Übergang von Maillardprodukten aus heissluftgetrocknetem Grünfutter in die Milch. **Carry–over of Maillard products from hot–air dried green forage into milk.**

11986 Kirchgessner, M.; Roth–Maier, D.A.
DE 161280/73/0001
Zum Pantothensäurebedarf von Mastküken, Mastschweinen und Mastkälbern. **The requirement of pantothenic acid for broiler chicks, fattening pigs and veal calves.**

11987 Kirchgessner, M.; Weigand, E.
DE 161280/74/0004
Zum Futterwert von Vinassen für Wiederkäuer und Schweine. **The feeding value of vinasses for ruminants and swine.**

11988 Kirchgessner, M.; Roth, F.
DE 161280/74/0009
Einsatz von Einzellerprotein und die Verwertung von Nucleinsäuren. **The use of single–cell protein and the utilization of nucleic acids.**

11989 Lindner, H.–P.; Sax, J.; Kirchgessner, M.
DE 161280/78/0004 N
Zum Einfluss verschiedener Fütterungstechniken auf Kriterien der Verdauung und Leistung von Milchkühen. **Influence of various feeding systems on parameters of digestibility and performance of dairy cows.**

11990 Rollwagen, C.
DE 161440/78/0001 N
Zur Ökonomik des Einsatzes von Maisstroh in der Färsenmast. **Economic aspects of fattening heifers with maize straw.**

11991 Daenicke, R.
DE 201050/77/0008
Ermittlung der optimalen Proteinversorgung für Mastbullen. **Determination of optimum protein supply of fattening bulls.**

11992 Huth, F.W.
DE 201200/77/0033
Einfluss unterschiedlicher Energiezufuhr bei Jungmastbullen der Rassen Deutsche Schwarzbunte und Fleckvieh. **Influence of different energy supply on young fattening bulls of "Deutsche**

Schwarzbunte" and "Fleckvieh".

11993 Kaufmann, W. DE 207010/78/0002 N
Bakterielle Vitaminsynthese in den Vormägen. **Bacterial
vitamin synthesis in the rumen of cattle.**

11994 Blüthgen, A.; Heeschen, W.; Hamann, J.
DE 207020/77/0006
Zur Bedeutung von Futtermitteln für die Ausscheidung von
Umweltchemikalien und Bioziden mit der Milch. **Importance
of feeds for secretion of environmental chemicals and biocides
via milk.**

11995 Scheller, H.; Rieder, J.B. DE 502050/71/0001 R
Pflanzenbauliche Aspekte zum Problem der
Fruchtbarkeitsstörungen bei Hochleistungsrindern 1971. **Plant
production aspects of the problem of fertility disturbances in
high–performance cattle.**

11996 Bogner, H.; Pranckh, G.von DE 502300/77/0002
Die Mast von Kälbern mit Milchaustauscher bei gleichzeitiger
Verabreichung strukturierter Futterstoffe unter besonderer
Berücksichtigung ethologischer und physiologischer Aspekte.
**Fattening of calves with milk replacer and additional feeding of
feeds of structured crude fiber with special emphasis on
ethological and physiological aspects.**

11997 Burgstaller, G. DE 502302/77/0006
Proteinversorgung von Jungbullen bei intensiven
Mastverfahren. **Protein supply of young bulls in intensive
fattening system.** Publications.

11998 Burgstaller, G.; Mayer, J. DE 502302/78/0005 N
Untersuchungen zum Einsatz von aufgeschlossenem Stroh
'Na–OH–Aufschluss' in der Milchviehfütterung. **Studies on
feeding treated straw 'Na–OH–treatment' to dairy cattle.**

11999 Kögel, S.; Karnbaum, B.; Jänisch, D.
DE 502303/75/0005
Mutterkuhhaltung mit Deutschem Fleckvieh auf
niederschlagsreichem Grünlandstandort. **Calf production with
single suckler cows of the German Fleckvieh breed on grassland
with high rainfall.**

12000 Papendick, K. DE 506152/75/0001
Ausnutzung der Mineralstoffe von Maisgärfutter durch
wachsende Bullen. **Exploitation of the minerals in maize silage
by growing bulls.**

12001 Leffers, G. DE 507350/78/0001 N
Vergleich der milchleistungsbezogenen Kraftfutterzuteilung an
Milchkühe im Melkstand und am Transponder–Automaten im
Hinblick auf Futteraufnahme, Milchleistung, Arbeitsaufwand
und Kosten. **Comparison of concentrate feeding of dairy cows
in milking parlour and by transponder automaton regarding
feed intake, milk yield, labour input and costs.**

12002 Leffers, G. DE 507350/78/0002 N
Ertragsleistungen von Standweiden bei steigenden N–Gaben
und Ermittlung der Produktionskosten pro KSTE. **Yield
performance of continuous grazing after increasing N–supply
and determination of production costs per KSTE.**

12003 Bothmer, G.von DE 507350/78/0003 N
Der Einfluss der Kraftfutterzufütterung auf
Gewichtsentwicklung, Schlachtkörperwert und

Wirtschaftlichkeit bei Weidebullen in der Endmastperiode.
**Influence of concentrate additive on weight gain, carcass
quality and profitability of grazing bulls in the final fattening
period.** Publications.

12004 Bothmer, G.von DE 507350/78/0008 N
Der Einfluss der Kalttränkmethode bei Kälbern auf
Gewichtsentwicklung, Verlustrate, Futterkosten und
Arbeitsaufwand mit magermilchpulverreichen und –losen
Milchaustauschfuttermitteln sowie Magermilch. **Influence of
cold watering of calves on weight gain, loss rate, feed costs and
labour input with milk substitutes rich or poor in skim milk
powder and with skim milk.** Publications.

12005 Krohn, C.; Neimann–Sørensen, A. DK 010201/71/0001
Differentieret energi– og proteinbehov i første del af
laktationsperioden hos malkekøer. **Energy and protein
requirements for dairy cows in the first part of the lactation
period.**

12006 Østergaard, V. DK 010201/71/0006
Fastlæggelse af optimal fodringsintensitet til mælkeproduktion
hos kvæg. **Establishment of optimal feeding intensity for dairy
cattle.**

12007 Kristensen, V.F.; Andersen, P.E. DK 010201/72/0003 R
Natriumhydroxyd– og ammoniakbehandlet halm som foder til
malkekøer. **Sodium hydroxide–and ammonia–treated straw for
dairy cows.**

12008 Møller, P.D. DK 010201/74/0002 R
Undersøgelser over indflydelsen af forskellige
NPN–forbindelser på N–omsætningen i vommen samt
N–udnyttelsen hos malkekøer og kalve. **The influence of
various NPN–compounds on N–metabolism in the rumen and
N–utilization by dairy cows and calves.**

12009 Andersen, P.E.; Kirsgaard, E. DK 010201/74/0004
Ensilage af kløvergræs eller rene græsser til malkekøer. **Clover
grass– or pure grass–silage to dairy cows.**

12010 Andersen, H.R.; Sørensen, M. DK 010201/74/0009
Forskellig slagtevægt og forskellig foderstyrke i forsøg med
tyre og stude. **Various slaughter weights and feeding intensities
in experiments with bulls and steers.**

12011 Detlef Møller, P. DK 010201/75/0002
Undersøgelser over kvægets proteinforsyning, herunder
relationer mellem den mikrobielle proteinsyntese i vommen og
aminosyreabsorptionen fra tarmen. **Investigations of protein
supply, including relationships between microbial protein
synthesis in the rumen and amino acid adsorption from the
intestinal tract of the bovine.**

12012 Østergaard, V. DK 010201/75/0006
Metionin–supplement i laktationens begyndelse. **Metionin
supplement at the beginning of lactation.**

12013 Østergaard, V. DK 010201/75/0007
Animalsk fedt i laktationens begyndelse. **Animal fat at the start
of lactation.**

12014 Andersen, P.E.; Skovborg, E.B. DK 010201/76/0004 R
Afgræsningsforsøg med malkekøer; Afgræsning af kløvergræs
og rene græsser. **Cropping experiments with dairy cows;
Cropping of clovergrass and pure grass stands.**

12015 Østergaard, V. DK 010201/76/0008
Proteinniveauets indflydelse i mælkeproduktionen. I.
Mælkeydelse, tilvækst, reproduktion og sundhed. **The
influence of protein level on milk production. I. Milk yield,
growth, reproduction and health.**

12016 Østergaard, V. DK 010201/76/0010
Grovfoderkvalitetens indflydelse på foderoptagelsen hos
malkekøer. **The influence of feed quality on the feed
consumption of milch cows.**

12017 Nielsen, S.M. DK 010201/76/0011
Proteinniveauets indflydelse i mælkeproduktionen. II.
Yversundhed og mælkekvalitet. **The influence of protein level
on milk production. II. Udder health and milk quality.**

12018 Andersen, P.E. DK 010201/77/0002
Metionin til malkekøer omkring kælvning. **Metionin for milch
cows round about calving time.**

12019 Andersen, P.E. DK 010201/77/0003
Anvendelse af beskyttet protein til malkekøer. **Use of protected
proteins for milch cows.**

12020 Andersen, P.E. DK 010201/77/0004
Rapskager til malkekøer. **Crushed rape for milch cows.**

12021 Brolund Larsen, J. DK 010201/77/0005
Erstatning for kolostrum til spædkalve. **A replacement for
colostrum for young calves.**

12022 Sørensen, M. DK 010201/77/0007
Rumensin (Monensin natrium) i foderblandinger til ungtyre.
Rumensin (Monensin natrium) in feed mixes for young bulls.

12023 Sørensen, M. DK 010201/77/0008
Roe– og rørmelasse i varierende mængde til ungtyre. **Root and
cane melasses in various amounts for young bulls.**

12024 Konggaard, S.P. DK 010201/77/0011
Undersøgelser over malkekøernes optagelse af forskellige
fodermidler ved selvvalg. **Own–choice consumption of various
feedstuffs by milch cows.**

12025 Andersen, B.B.; Andersen, H.R.
  DK 010201/78/0001 N
Fodringssystemer ved individprøver af ungtyre. **Feeding
systems in performance tests of young bulls.**

12026 Andersen, B.B.; Andersen, H.R.; Jensen, J.
  DK 010201/78/0002 N
Holstein–Frisian, optimal slagtevægt, appetit og
foderudnyttelse. **Optimal weight at slaughter, and genetic
variation in appetite and feed utilization in young bulls of the
Holstein–Frisian breed.**

12027 Møller, P.D.; Hvelplund, T. DK 010201/78/0003 N
Undersøgelser over forskellige proteinfodermidlers
nedbrydning i vommen hos kvæg. **Determination of protein
degradation in the rumen of cattle fed different protein feeds.**

12028 Andersen, P.E.; Møller–Madsen, A.
  DK 010201/78/0005 N
Fodermidlernes indflydelse på ostemælkens kvalitet. **The
influence of feedstuffs on the quality of milk for cheese making.**

12029 Larsen, J.B.; Foldager, J. DK 010201/78/0006 N
Optimal fodringsintensitet i opdrætningsperioden hos kvier af
malkerace. **Optimum feeding intensity during rearing of heifers
of the Red Danish breed.**

12030 Andersen, H.R.; Klausen, S. DK 010201/78/0007 N
Valle og permeat som foder til ungtyre. **Whey and ultra
filtrated skim milk for young bulls.**

12031 Sørensen, M.; Lykkeaa, J. DK 010201/78/0008 N
Komælkserstatninger til kalve. **Milk replacers for calves.**

12032 Thorbek, G.; Neergaard, L. DK 010206/73/0010
Undersøgelser over spædekalves ernæring, specielt virkningen
af tilsætning af stivelsesspaltende enzymer til
sødmælkserstatninger. **Studies on the nutrition of baby calves,
especially the effect of adding starch–splitting enzymes to
milk–replacers.**

12033 Thorbek, G. DK 010206/75/0011
Energetisk vedligeholdesesbehov hos kalve, svin og mink.
Energetic maintenance needs of calves, pigs and minks.

12034 Thorbek, G. DK 010206/77/0004
Calcium– og fosfatomsætning hos voksende kalve og svin.
Calcium and phosphate turnover in growing calves and pigs.

12035 Weidner, K. DK 010206/77/0007 N
Animalka som mineralstoftilskud til malkekøer. **Animalka as a
mineral supplement to dairy cows.**

12036 Møller–Madsen, A. DK 010300/76/0061
Proteinniveauets indflydelse på mælkens kvalitet. **The
influence of the protein level on milk quality.**

12037 Larsen, C.S.; Israelsen, M.; Waagepetersen, J.
  DK 010800/78/0001 N
Industriel forarbejdning af foder til kvæg med henblik på at
forøge proteinudnyttelsen. **Industrial processing of feed for
cattle with special reference to increase the protein utilization.**

12038 Wolstrup, J. DK 030108/75/0009
Bestemmelse af mikrobiel biomasse og aktivitet i
fordøjelseskanalen hos køer. **The determination of the
microbial biomass and activity in the alimentary canal of cows.**

12039 Jensen, K. DK 030125/75/0001
Kvantitative undersøgelser over foderomsætningen i kvægets
vom i relation til teorien om vommen som en kontinuert
fermentator. **Quantitative studies of food metabolism in the
rumen of cattle in relation to the concept of the rumen as a
continuous fermentor.**

12040 Flagstad, T. DK 030129/74/0003
Zinkmetabolisme hos kalve med den genetiske defekt A46.
Zinc metabolism in calves with the genetic defect A46.

12041 Henriksen, J. DK 030142/76/0011
Undersøgelser vedrørende fodermiddelvurdering baseret på
laboratoriemetoder og på fedekalves tilvækst. **Investigations to
evaluate feedstuffs based on laboratory methods and the growth
rate of fattened calves.**

12042 Thilsted, S.H. DK 030142/77/0013
Energimobiliseringens regulering hos malkekøer. **The
regulation of energy mobilization in dairy cows.**

12043 Nørgaard, P.; Neimann–Sørensen, A.; Møller, P.D.
DK 030142/77/0016 N
Betydningen af foderets fysiske struktur for forgæringsprocesserne og foderomsætningen i formaverne hos malkekøer. **The influence of physical structure in feeds on fermentation and metabolism in the rumen of lactating cows.**

12044 Garel, J.P.; Hoden, A.; Journet, M.
FR 010804/71/9019 N
Alimentation des veaux femelles d'élevage de la naissance à trois mois.. **Rearing dairy heifer calves (from birth to 3 months)..**

12045 Jeannin, B.; Béranger, C.; Louyot, J.M.; Petit, M.; Garel, J.P.
FR 010804/72/9016 N
Etude de l'utilisation de zones pastorales d'altitude par le pâturage de vaches allaitantes.. **Study of the rational use of highland pastures by suckler cows..**

12046 Garel, J.P.; Petit, M.
FR 010804/72/9020 N
Alimentation hivernale des vaches allaitantes. **Winter feeding of suckler cows..**

12047 Jeannin, B.; Journet, M.; Louyot, J.M.; Hoden, A.; Garel, J.P.
FR 010804/74/9015 N
Etude de l'utilisation de zones pastorales d'altitude par le pâturage de vaches laitières. **Study of the rational use of highland pastures by dairy cows..**

12048 Garel, J.P.; Journet, M.; Jaworek, M.; Hoden, A.
FR 010804/74/9018 N
Etude sur la comparaison de deux systèmes d'alimentation du troupeau laitier de Marcenat (FFPN et MONTBELIARDE). **Trial comparing two feeding methods on the dairy herd of Marcenat (FFPN and MONTBELIARDE)..**

12049 Garel, J.P.; Maronne, P.; Le Neindre, J.
FR 010804/74/9021 N
Allaitement simultané de deux veaux par vache en race Salers.. **Salers cows suckling two calves.**

12050 Garel, J.P.; Petit, M.; Maronne, P.
FR 010804/77/9026 N
Niveau d'alimentation hivernal et estival d'un troupeau de vaches allaitantes Salers. **Winter and summer feed intake of a herd of Salers suckler cows.**

12051 Garel, J.P.; Petit, M.; Maronne, P.
FR 010804/78/9023 N
Niveau d'alimentation énergétique hivernal des vaches allaitantes en gestation.. **Study of the effects of feeding restrictions on suckler cows during the period of gestation.**

12052 Thivend, P.; Toullec, R.; Vermorel, M.
FR 010805/70/6553
Utilisation de l'amidon et de ses dérivés par le veau préruminant. **Utilization of starch and its derivatives by the preruminant calf.**

12053 Thivend, P.; Besle, J.M.
FR 010805/74/6554
Digestion des galastosides et des autres glucides complexes. **Digestion of galactosides and other unsual carbohydrates by the preruminant calf.**

12054 Thivend, P.; Toullec, R.; Dardillat, C.; Lefaivre, J.
FR 010805/77/6552
Etude de la sécrétion biliaire chez le jeune veau. **Biliary secretion in the young calf.**

12055 Chassaque, M.
FR 010811/76/8060
Nutrition et fertilité des vaches: Influence des apports alimentaires énergétiques, quantitatifs et qualitatifs. Méthodes d'exploration du niveau de ces apports. **Nutrition and fertility in the cow. Influence of energi and essential fatty acid intakes.**

12056 Jarrige, R.; Journet, M.; Grappin, R.; Decaen, C.; Hoden, A.; Remond, B.
FR 010812/55/6515
Facteurs zootechniques de la composition des laits de vache (matières grasses et matières azotées) et de leurs qualités fromagères. **Effect of animal and feed factors on chemical composition of milk and its quality for cheesemaking.**

12057 Journet, M.; Muller, A.; Demarquilly, C.; Hoden, A.
FR 010812/59/6516
Pâturage des vaches laitières. **Grazing of dairy cows.**

12058 Journet, M.; Troccon, J.L.
FR 010812/70/6519
Alimentation du veau de la naissance a 6 mois (période d'élevage). **Calf feeding from birth to six months.**

12059 Verite, R.; Journet, M.
FR 010812/71/6509
Alimentation azotée des vaches laitières. **Nitrogen feeding of dairy cows.**

12060 Journet, M.; Troccon, J.L.
FR 010812/71/6520
Vêlage précoce des génisses laitières. **Early calving for dairy heifers.**

12061 Remond, B.; Colleau, J.J.; Journet, M.
FR 010812/74/6511
Alimentation énergétique et azotée des vaches laitières en fin de gestation et en début de la lactation et capacité de mobilisation des réserves corporelles. **Energetic and nitrogen feeding of dairy cows at the end of pregnancy and at the beginning of lactation.**

12062 Remond, B.; Doreau, M.
FR 010812/74/6512
Evolution des paramètres comportementaux, digestifs et métaboliques chez la vache laitière en fin de gestation et début de lactation. **Variations of feeding behaviour, digestive and metabolic processes in late pregnancy and early lactation in the dairy cow.**

12063 Rulquin, H.
FR 010812/77/6514
Etude des relations existant entre les éléments terminaux de la digestion et le prélèvement des métabolites énergétiques sanguins par la mamelle chez la vache laitière. **Relations between the end products of the digestion and mammary uptake of blood energetic metabolites in lactaging cows.**

12064 Geay, Y.; Thivend, P.; Malterre, C.; Poncet, C.; Beranger, C.
FR 010813/66/6526
Alimentation azotée des bovins en croissance. **Utilization of nitrogen by growing and fattening cattle.**

12065 Geay, Y.; Beranger, C.; Malterre, C.
FR 010813/66/6527
Utilisation des différents aliments pour la croissance et l'engraissement des bovins. **Utilization of different feed for growing and fattening cattle.**

12066 Le Neindre, P.; Petit, M.; Garel, M. FR 010813/66/6530
Production laitière des vaches allaitantes et son influence sur la croissance des veaux. **Milk production of the suckling cow and its effect on the growth rate of the calves.**

12067 Le Neindre, P.; Garel, M. FR 010813/68/6529
Relations mère–jeune chez les bovins et les ovins. **Mother young relations in cattle and sheep.**

12068 Geay, Y.; Robelin, J.; Beranger, C. FR 010813/70/6525
Alimentation énergétique des bovins en croissance. **Utilization of energy by growing and fattening cattle.**

12069 Petit, M.; Garel, M. FR 010813/72/6532
Alimentation hivernale des vaches allaitantes. **Winter feeding of suckling cows.**

12070 Dulphy, J.P.; Demarquilly, C.; Bony, J.
FR 010814/69/6506
Utilisation de l'ensilage d'herbe par un troupeau laitier. **Utilization of grass silage by dairy herd.**

12071 Patureau–Mirand, P.; Grizard, J.; Prugnaud, J.; Arnal, M.; Pion, R. FR 010815/70/9577 N
Utilisation métabolique des acides aminés chez le veau et l'agneau préruminants : détermination des besoins en acides aminés indispensables. **Amino acid metabolism in preruminant calves and lambs.**

12072 Vermorel, M.; Beranger, C.; Bouvier, J.C.; Geay, Y.
FR 010816/72/2762
Evolution de la composition du croît des jeunes ruminants. Influence de la race, du sexe, du type d'alimentation. Etude sur bovins. **Evolution of gain composition of growing ruminants. Influence of breed, and diet. Trials on beef.** Publications.

12073 Aurousseau, B.; Thivend, P.; Vermorel, M.; Patureau Mirand, Ph.; Theriez, M. FR 010816/74/2764
Influence de divers types de chaînes carbonées employées comme source d'énergie sur la nutrition du jeune mammifère pendant la période néonatale. Etudes sur veaux et agneaux. **Influence of various energy sources according to the type of carbon chain on neonatal nutrition of young mammals. Trials on lambs and calves.**

12074 Vermorel, M.; Thivend, P.; Bouvier, J.C.; Geay, Y.
FR 010816/77/9515
Utilisation de l'énergie par les bovins en croissance. **Energy utilization by growing cattle.**

12075 Bauchart, D.; Demigne, C.; Aurousseau, B.; Remezy, C. FR 010816/77/9519
Influence de la nature des matières grasses incorporées aux aliments d'allaitement sur le métabolisme des lipides plasmatiques du veau préruminant. **Effect of the kind of triglycerides introduced in milk substitutes on the metabolism of the plasma lipids of the veal calf.**

12076 Aurousseau, B.; Bauchart, D.; Valin, C.
FR 010816/78/9520
Etude de la composition des tissus adipeux de veaux préruminants de races différentes : veaux limousins allaités par la mère, veaux frisons recevant du lait entier ou un lait artificiel de remplacement. **Adipose tissu composition of veal calves from different breeds : suckling limousins or frisian calves bucket fed**

whole milk or milk replacers.

12077 Demigne, C.; Remesy, C. FR 010817/76/8039
Aspects nutritionnels et métaboliques de la diarrhée du veau. **Nutritional and metabolic aspects of calf diarrhea.**

12078 Toullec, R.; Guilloteau, P.; Patureau–Mirand, P.
FR 011304/66/6557
Utilisation du lait et des aliments d'allaitement par le veau préruminant. **Milk and milk substitutes utilization by the preruminant calf.**

12079 Guilloteau, P.; Toullec, R. FR 011304/68/6556
Rôle de la caillette dans la digestion chez le veau préruminant. **Digestive processus in the preruminant calf abomasum.**

12080 Guilhermet, R.; Patureau–Mirand, P.; Toullec, R.
FR 011304/72/6558
Besoin en acides aminés du veau sevré précocement. **Amino and requirements of the early weaned calf.**

12081 Giovanni, R. FR 011304/72/6560
Utilisation du pâturage par le veau d'élevage. **Calf rearing on grass.**

12082 Guilhermet, R.; Giovanni, R.; Toullec, R.
FR 011304/73/6559
Utilisation de différentes sources azotées par le veau sevré précocement. **Use of differents nitrogen sources by the early weaned calf.**

12083 Guilloteau, R.; Toullec, R.; Patureau–Mirand, P.
FR 011304/75/6555
Digestion du lait et des laits de remplacement dans l'intestin grêle du veau préruminant. **Digestion of milk and milk substitutes in the small intestine of the preruminant.**

12084 Bertin, G.; Huguet, L. FR 012223/70/0149
Utilisation du maïs plante entière ensilée (variété commerciale, nouveaux types variétaux, stade de récolte) des graminées pérennes (ray-grass d'Italie, dactyle, fétuque élevée) et de la luzerne ensilées pour la production de viande de jeunes bovins. **Use of maize as ensiled entire plant (commercial varieties, new varietal types, harvest stage), of ensiled perennial grasses (italian raygrass, cocks'foot, weed feswe) and of ensiled lucerne for the production of young cattle meat.**

12085 Huguet, L.; Mourguet, A. FR 012223/73/0148
Etude comparative de 2 modèles fourragers en vue de la production de lait d'hiver ou d'été. **Comparative study of two fodder patterns for winter or summer milk production.**

12086 Jeannin, B.; Parrassin, P.; Guinot, J.P.; De Vaubernier, E. FR 012224/75/9002
Etude du pâturage de la prairie permanente par des vaches laitières en région lorraine et de sa complémentation par des prairies temporaires. **Study of the grazing of permanent meadows by dairy cows in the Lorrain region and of the complementary need for temporary meadows.**

12087 Journet, M. FR 012224/76/9004
Comparaison de deux rations hivernales de vaches laitières : ensilage d'herbe et ensilage maïs. **Comparing two winter rationing systems for dairy cows : grass silage and maize.**

12088 Dawson   GB 010302/00/0043
Isolate and characterise micro–organisms which catabolise complex lipids in the rumen.

12089 Roberts   GB 010401/00/0821
Factors involved in the response of dairy cows to undernutritional debility.

12090 Roberts   GB 010403/00/0821
Factors involved in the response of dairy cows to undernutritional debility.

12091 Roberts   GB 010404/00/0821
Factors involved in the response of dairy cows to undernutritional debility.

12092 Thomas   GB 011205/00/0001 R
Evaluation of conserved forages alone or with other feeds for beef production.

12093 Thomas; Osbourn   GB 011205/00/0007 R
Evaluate conserved forages and their use with other feeds for beef production.

12094 Thomas; Aston   GB 011205/00/0009 R
Evaluation of conserved forages alone or with other feeds for milk production.

12095 Baker; Young   GB 011205/79/0603 N
The influence of winter feeding and grazing management on the feed intake and productivity of beef cattle.

12096 Le, Du; Wade   GB 011205/79/0606 N
The effect of sward type and management upon herbage growth and utilization by grazing cattle.

12097 Messer; Lindsay   GB 011610/78/0008 N
Mechanised feeding of dairy cows from bunker silos.

12098 Storry; Brumby   GB 011703/00/0002
Properties of protected fats, their use in ruminant nutrition and milk production.

12099 Brumby   GB 011703/00/0003
Fatty acid composition of cow milk in relation to stage of lactation, endocrine and genetic factors.

12100 Line   GB 011704/00/0013
Grazing experiments with milking cows.

12101 Broster   GB 011707/00/0003
Nutrition of growing heifer.

12102 Bines; Balch   GB 011707/00/0004
Factors affecting voluntary food intake.

12103 Sutton   GB 011707/00/0006 R
Dietary factors affecting digestion and utilisation of energy for milk production; milk composition.

12104 Broster   GB 011707/00/0007
Responses of lactating cows to variations in nutrient inputs.

12105 Oldham; Sutton   GB 011707/75/0012 R
Protein metabolism in the gut and body of dairy cows in relation to energy metabolism and protein needs.

12106 Smith; Salter, R.H.   GB 011708/00/0006
Nitrogen metabolism in the ruminant.

12107 Smith; R.H. McAllan   GB 011708/00/0007
Factors influencing amount and origin of dietary and microbial carbohydrate entering the small intestine.

12108 Smith; Sissons   GB 011708/79/0021 N
Basic studies of nutrient utilization by the preruminant calf.

12109 Evans   GB 011709/00/0005
Physical changes in, and movement of rumen digesta.

12110 Barman   GB 011712/00/0013 R
Properties of alkaline phosphatase.

12111 Castle; Watson   GB 030201/00/0011 R
Efficiency of different grazing systems for milk production.

12112 Castle; Watson   GB 030201/00/0028 R
Maximising the use of grass by dairy cows.

12113 Banks; Ferrie   GB 030201/00/0030
Factors affecting milk fat composition when cows are fed diets containing soya bean oil (with WSAC).

12114 Banks; Ferrie   GB 030201/00/0031 R
Dietary manipulation of the yield and composition of milk; effect of composition on manufacturing properties.

12115 Morrison   GB 030202/00/0019
Characterization of ruminant dietary polysaccharides.

12116 Morrison; Williams   GB 030202/00/0020
Degradation of purified hemicelluloses and production of hemicellulases by rumen micro–organisms.

12117 West   GB 030203/78/0025 R
The influence of calcium transport in the mammary glands with reference to the bioassembly of casein micelle.

12118 Russel   GB 030302/00/0008
Nutrition of beef suckler cow in pregnancy and lactation.

12119 Price; Chesters   GB 030604/75/0017
Field investigations on the zinc status of ruminant livestock in North Scotland.

12120 Phillipo; Humphries   GB 030604/77/0019
Reproductive function in cattle of low copper status.

12121 Webster; Brockway   GB 030606/00/0008 R
Energy studies in growth in cattle.

12122 Kay; McLeod   GB 030611/00/0022
Nutrient requirements of pre–ruminant calves; meeting requirements in practice.

12123 Kay; Greenhalg   GB 030611/00/0024
The determination of the nutrient requirements of calves and fattening cattle.

12124 Robinson; Fraser   GB 030611/00/0030
Age at first mating nutritional status and reproductive performance.

12125 Fuller   GB 030611/00/0036 R
The effect of dietary energy on the utilisation of protein of
various qualities.

12126 O'Neill   GB 040501/00/0002 R
Value of creep feed for autumn–borne single suckler calves.

12127 O'Neill   GB 040501/00/0003 R
Grazing systems for suckler cows.

12128 O'Neill   GB 040501/00/0005 R
Suckler cow feeding trials.

12129 McCullough   GB 041101/00/0016 R
Effect of method of feeding on silage intakes by beef cattle.

12130 McCullogh   GB 041101/00/0021 R
Development of a high quality silage system for beef production.

12131 McCullough   GB 041101/77/0027 R
Red clover silage for beef cattle.

12132 Boyd   GB 041102/00/0007
Winter diets for suckler cows.

12133 Gordon   GB 041302/00/0002
Effect of calorie:protein ratio of supplementary concentrates on
milk production.

12134 McIlmoyle   GB 041303/76/0002 R
Legume silage for beef production.

12135 McIlmoyle   GB 041303/76/0003 R
Brassicas as supplements to silage for beef production.

12136 Marsh   GB 041309/76/0002 R
A comparison of hay and wilted and unwilted silage at two levels
of concentrate feeding for young calves.

12137 Reed   GB 041401/79/0006 N
Effect of metabolisable energy intake on autumn calving dairy
cows.

12138 McCoullgh   GB 041406/75/0007
Roughages for calf rearing.

12139 Researcher not indicated   GB 050123/00/0005 R
Calves: artificial rearing.

12140 Researcher not indicated   GB 050124/00/0001 R
Dairy cows: nutrition of the autumn calving cows.

12141 Researcher not indicated   GB 050163/00/0004 R
Calves: artificial rearing.

12142 Researcher not indicated   GB 050164/00/0001
Dairy cows: nutrition of the autumn calving cow.

12143 Lowman   GB 060102/00/0004
Suckler and calf nutrition.

12144 Prescott   GB 060102/00/0005
Grazing intake and grazing behaviour of cattle.

12145 Prescott   GB 060102/00/0008
Feeding and grazing systems for beef cattle.

12146 Edwards   GB 060103/00/0001
Selection and evaluation of feeding regimes for dairy cattle.

12147 Edwards   GB 060103/00/0002
Selection and evaluation of feeding regimes for beef cattle.

12148 Petchey   GB 060208/00/0003 R
Voluntary food intake of dairy cows.

12149 Dodsworth   GB 060208/00/0006 R
Voluntary food intake of beef cattle.

12150 Kay   GB 060208/79/0020 N
The use of forage crops in beef production systems.

12151 Halliday   GB 060212/00/0002 R
Study of copper deficiency in beef herds in the North East of
Scotland.

12152 Topps   GB 060219/00/0004
Performance of calves on different suckling regimes.

12153 Iopps   GB 060219/79/0016 N
Nutrient requirement of autumn–calving beef cows with
reference to different amounts of dietary protein.

12154 Laird   GB 060315/00/0001
Protein supplementation of silage based diets for dairy cows.

12155 Rees   GB 060315/00/0005
Management and feeding components in beef from the dairy
herd.

12156 Laird   GB 060315/79/0011 N
Beef production from alkali treated whole grain.

12157 Leaver; Moisey   GB 060316/00/0002
The effect of silage quality and supplementary feeding regime
on milk production.

12158 O'Shea, J.; Spillane, T.A.; Wheeler, B.M.
     IE 060100/70/0297 R
Development of a ready reckoner or slide rule for the
interpretation of silage analysis results in cattle farming
systems. (A) applicable to winter beef systems. Publications.

12159 Collins, D.P.   IE 060100/71/0809 R
Nitrogen fertilising of pasture for cattle production.
Publications.

12160 Wilson, R.K.   IE 060100/72/0291 R
Application of radio telemetry to agricultural research with
particular reference to jaw movements in beef cattle as
indicators of time spent eating, cudding and loafing.
Publications.

12161 Griffiths, T.W.   IE 060100/73/0801 R
Studies on the protein requirements of young growing beef
cattle. Publications.

12162 Harte, F.J.   IE 060100/76/1264 R
System of beef production from calf to finishing in which the
calves are multiple suckled using charolais and hereford cross

calves. Publications.

12163 Drennan, M.J.; Lawlor, M.J.; O'Shea, J.
IE 060100/77/1330 R
To evaluate chemically treated straw in rations for storing and fattening cattle. Publications.

12164 Poole, D.B.R.; Rogers, P.A.M.   IE 060100/79/1416 N
Survey of mineral status of herds around Cahirciveen, Co.Kerry. Publications.

12165 Keane, M.G.; Fallon, R.J.   IE 060103/00/1400 N
Effect of supplement type on grass intake and utilization by calves. Publications.

12166 Drennan, M.J.; Harte, F.J.   IE 060103/66/0307 R
Effect of plane of nutrition during early life on subsequent performance of cattle for beef. Publications.

12167 Drennan, M.J.   IE 060103/70/0306 N
To determine the type, quantity and protein level (and source of nitrogen) of the supplement to feed to cattle of different ages receiving basal diets of silage, hay or straw. Publications.

12168 Flynn, A.V.; O'Shea, J.   IE 060103/75/1105 N
Evaluation of additives for hay. Publications.

12169 Drennan, M.J.   IE 060103/76/1252 R
Fattening of culled cows. Publications.

12170 Drennan, M.J.; Cole, A.; Murphy, W.E.; Downey, N.E.; Nicholl, G.   IE 060103/77/1261 R
Calf to beef systems on cut–over peat. Publications.

12171 Keane, M.G.   IE 060103/78/1401 R
Effect of dietary energy intake on efficiency of energy utilization and carcass composition in beef cattle. Publications.

12172 Flynn, A.V.; O'Kiely, P.; Wilson, R.K.; O'Shea, J.; Spillane, T.A.   IE 060103/78/1415 R
The effects of forage dry matter content on production, carcass composition, feed conversion efficiency and rumen parameters in beef cattle. Publications.

12173 Keane, M.G.   IE 060103/79/1418 N
Determination of the net energy values of silages relative to barley for maintenance and liveweight gain in beef cattle. Publications.

12174 MacNaeidhe, F.; Cassidy, J.C.; Prendiville, M.D.; Murphy, R.F.; Prendergast, A.G.   IE 060200/76/1140 R
Extension trials on hand cutover peat. Publications.

12175 Walsh, J.P.   IE 060400/00/2084 N
Concentrate supplements for spring calving cows. Publications.

12176 Cogan, T.   IE 060400/74/2049 R
Evaluation of feeds for dairy cattle. Publications.

12177 McCarthy, D.D.   IE 060400/77/1296 R
The study of feed intake by grazing dairy cattle. Publications.

12178 Cogan, T.; Gleeson, P.A.   IE 060400/77/1357 R
The effect of crude protein and energy levels on milk production in early lactation. Publications.

12179 Gleeson, P.A.; Murphy, J.   IE 060400/78/1373 R
Inclusions of high fat levels in dairy rations. Publications.

12180 Gleeson, P.A.   IE 060400/78/1375 R
A study of stocking rate/concentrate supplementation relationships in a total grassland – based feeding system for spring–calving dairy cows. Publications.

12181 Nolan, T.; Connolly, J.   IE 060700/76/1258 R
Mixed grazing of cattle and sheep. Publications.

12182 Fitzgerald, S.; Daly, P.J.   IE 060702/76/1287 R
Evaluation of red clover as a source of feed for store lambs. (A)when conserved as silage for winter feeding (b)when grazed in autumn. Publications.

12183 Grubb, L.; Daly, P.J.   IE 060706/77/1370 R
Calf to beef system on reclaimed blanket peat integrated with reclaimed shallow peat. Publications.

12184 Raftery, T.F.; O'Donovan, S.F.; Kett, J.J.
IE 110104/79/9224 N
The influence of NAOH treated barley on the 95312500f silage and milk output of dairy cows. 0000000.

12185 Caffrey, P.J.; Brophy, P.O.; Bermingham, P.
IE 120105/79/9208 N
Effect of alkali treatment and physical processing on the utilization of barley by cattle.

12186 Collins, J.D.; Brophy, P.O.   IE 120206/79/9239 N
Hypomagnesemia in dairy cows : herd monitoring of effects on milk yield. Publications.

12187 Colzani, G.; Martillotti, F.; Verna, M.
IT 020600/78/0003
Meccanizzazione dell'alimentazione dei bovini da carne e da latte. **Mechanization of feeding for cattle and cows.**

12188 Malossini, F.   IT 020700/73/0933
Influenza di alte dosi di concentrati somministrate in fasi diverse del ciclo produttivo nelle vacche da latte. **Influence of high doses of concentrates fed to dairy cows at different phases of the productive cycle.** Publications.

12189 Malossini, F.   IT 020700/74/0581
Composizione chimica dei semi e delle farine di estrazione di brassica napus e brassica campestris ed influenza della somministrazione di queste su alcune caratteristiche del latte di vacca. **Chemical composition of brassica napus and brassica campestris seeds and flours and their influence on some milk characteristics when fed to dairy cows.**

12190 Bergonzini, E.; Piva, G.C.; Borlenghi, G.
IT 020700/78/0010
Utilizzazione degli idrolizzati proteici nell'alimentazione dei vitelloni. **Feeding protein hydrolyzates to steers.**

12191 Bergonzini, E.; Borlenghi, G.   IT 020700/78/0012
Farina di pianta intera di mais disidratata quale fonte di energia in razioni per vitelloni. **Dehydrated corn meal from the whole plant as a source of energy in the rations for steers.**

12192 Bergonzini, E.; Borlenghi, G.   IT 020700/79/0005 N
Effetti dell'aggiunta di monensin e acido nicotinico in razioni per vitelloni. **Effect of addition of monensin and nicotic acid to**

rations for fattening young bulls.

12193 Falaschini, A.   IT 040218/73/0200
Ricerche sulla utilizzazione di latti ricostituiti per vitelli contenenti nuove fonti proteiche e diversi tassi lipidici in presenza o meno di enzimi. **Research on the use of reconstituted milks for calves, containing new sources of protein and various lipid rates, in presence or not of enzymes.**

12194 Falaschini, A.   IT 040218/74/0549
Ulteriori ricerche sulla utilizzazione di latti ricostituiti per vitelli contenenti nuove fonti proteiche non convenzionali. **Further research on the use of reconstituted milks containing new non conventional protein sources for calf–feeding.**

12195 Minoccheri, F.   IT 040218/77/0244 R
Condizioni metaboliche e qualità delle masse muscolari dei vitelli a carni bianche e quadro ematochimico ed ematologico in condizioni diverse di alimentazione. **Metabolic conditions and quality of the muscular mass of white meat producing calves. Blood chemistry and hematology depending on different feeding programs.**

12196 Cappa, V.   IT 040411/74/0524
Rapporti fra alimentazione; condizioni metaboliche delle bovine, produzione del latte e sue proprietà. **Relationships between feeding and metabolic conditions of dairy cows, milk yields and milk properties.**

12197 Cappa, V.   IT 040411/77/0541 R
Studio delle cause alimentari delle ipofertilità bovine mediante l'impiego del profilo metabolico. **A study of the nutritional causes of bovine low fertility based on metabolic profiles.**

12198 Curto, G.M.   IT 040613/73/2137
Ricerche sperimentali sull'impiego di concentrati ad elevatissimo valore calorico nell'alimentazione delle bovine durante le prime fasi della terza lattazione. **Experiments on the use of concentrates of very high caloric value in the feeding of cows during the first periods of second lactation.** Publications.

12199 Curto, G.M.   IT 040613/74/0540
Variazioni quanti–qualitative del latte e variazioni metabolico funzionali delle bovine per somministrazioni di dosi elevate di vit. A, foraggi a sospetta azione gozzigena, insilati tradizionali mais e nuovi soja. **Quantitative and qualitative variations in milk and functional and metabolic variations in cows caused by their feeding on high doses of vit. A, forages suspected of causing goiter, traditional silage fodders maize and new silage fodders soybeans.**

12200 Piva, G.   IT 040613/74/0605
Ricerche dirette a ridurre i costi di produzione del latte attraverso la identificazione degli aminoacidi essenziali usualmente limitanti, onde realizzare opportuni interventi con apporti supplementari. **Research in the reduction of milk production costs through the identification of usually limiting essential aminoacids with a view to perform suitable supplementations.**

12201 Curto, G.M.   IT 040613/77/0157 R
Variazioni quanti–qualitative e variazioni metabolico–fun–zionali delle bovine per somministrazione di dosi elevate di vit. A foraggi a sospetta azione gozzigena, insilati tradizionali e nuovi, mais e soja. **Qualitative and quantitative variations, functional and metabolic variations in**

cows after feeding high doses of Vit. A; fodder with a suspected goitre inducing action, common and new ansilages, aize and soya.

12202 Rioni Volpato, M.   IT 040810/74/0612
Ricerche sull'utilizzazione di fonti proteiche diverse e di azoto non proteico nello svezzamento precoce del vitello. **Research on the use of different protein sources and of non–protein nitrogen in early weaning of calves.**

12203 Bonsempiante, M.; Bittante, G.; Ceselli, P.; Andrighetto, I.; Cinetto, M.   IT 040810/78/0002 N
Effetto del trattamento della granella di mais sulla digeribilità, sul metabolismo e sulle prestazioni produttive di vitelloni, manze e vacche sottoposti all'ingrasso. **Effect of physical form of maizegrain on metabolism and performances of calves, heifers and cows during fattening.**

12204 Bonsempiante, M.; Bittante, G.; Andrighetto, I.
    IT 040810/79/0001 N
Confronto fra diete basate sul fieno e sul silomais nell'allevamento confinato delle bovine per la produzione del vitello. **Comparison between diets based on hay and on maize silage in the confinated breeding of beef heifers and cows.**

12205 Monti, F.   IT 041126/77/0572 R
Indagini sul metabolismo lipidico, protidico e aminoacidico e sull'emostasi fisiologica in vitelli allevati con latte ricostruito. **Research on fat, protein, aminoacid metabolism and on physiological hemostasis in calves fed on reconstituted milk.**

12206 Ubertalle, A.; Errante, J.; Bianchi, M.; Mazzocco, P.
    IT 041217/77/0001 N
Contributo alla conoscenza dei pascoli naturali in Valle di Susa.. **Contribution to knowledge of the grazing lands of Susa Valley.**

12207 Giardini, A.   IT 062400/73/0111
Confronto tra diverse modalità di integrazione proteicae minerale della razione per bovini all'ingrasso alimentati con silomais e farina secca di granella di mais. **Comparison of different methods for mineral and protein integration in fodder–rations for beef cattle fed with corn silage and dry corn grain meal.**

12208 Baldoni, R.   IT 062400/77/0952
Confronto tra alcuni sottoprodotti dell'industria saccarifera ed i foraggi di mais nell'ingrasso del bovino. **Comparison between some by–products of the sugar industry and maize fodder for the purpose of fattening beef cattle.**

12209 Canale, A.   IT 062500/74/0196
L'utilizzazione digestiva della dieta in vitelli sperimentalmente infestati con Ostertagia ostertagi sottoposti a differenti regimi alimentari. **The digestive utilization of the ration in calves experimentally infested with Ostertagia ostertagi and subjected to different rations.**

12210 Maletto, S.   IT 062500/77/0974
L'utilizzazione delle proteine nei vitelli preruminanti in accrescimento: l'influenza della sostituzione parziale delle proteine del latte con quelle provenienti dalla soia. **The use of proteins in growing milk–sucking calves; influence of the partial substitution of soya proteins for milk proteins.**

12211 Fagnoni, P.; Alberini, B.; Fantuzzi, U.

D 3200 – Animal nutrition

IT 090301/78/0002 N
Impiego dei grassi nell'alimentazione delle bovine da latte. **Fat utilization on milk cow feeding.** Publications.

12212 Kemp, A. NL 010104/73/3962
De hoedanigheid en de samenstelling van ruwvoer in relatie met het optreden van nitriet–vergiftiging bij rundvee. **Quality and composition of roughage in relation to nitrate accumulation and toxicity in cattle.** Publications.

12213 Wierenga, H.K.; Brandsma, S. NL 010112/77/7843
De mogelijkheden en gevolgen van krachtvoederverstrekking aan het voerhek voor melkkoeien in loopstalsystemen. **Possibilities and consequences of supplying concentrates at the feed–gate to dairy cattle in loose–housing systems.**

12214 Boer, F. de NL 010115/67/5439
Toepassing van NPN in de mestveevoeding gecombineerd met onderzoek naar de eiwitbehoeftenormen bij deze categorie dieren. **Application of NPN in fattening cattle, combined with assessment of their N–requirements.**

12215 Meijs, J.A.C. NL 010115/67/5440
Voederopname onderzoek bij grazend rundvee en bij rundvee in loopstallen. **Research on feed intake in cattle grazing in pasture or kept in loose – housing.** Publications.

12216 Visser, H. de NL 010115/67/5441
Onderzoek naar de factoren die de voerderopname van rundvee bepalen. **Research into factors which influence the feed intake of dairy cows.** Publications.

12217 Vuuren, A.M. van NL 010115/67/5442
Ruwvoer–krachtvoer–verhouding in de melkveevoeding. **Roughage–concentrates–ratio in the nutrition of dairy cows.** Publications.

12218 Smits, B. NL 010115/67/5446 R
Bepaling van de voerderwaarde van veevoeders door middel van verteringsproeven met varkens en/of kalveren. **Determination of the feeding value of feed in digestion trials with pigs and/or veal calves.** Publications.

12219 Meijs, J.A.C. NL 010115/68/5437
Gebruikswaarde en het effect van technologische en conserveringstechnieken op ruwvoeders voor rundvee. **Nutritive value of and technological or conservation methods on roughages for cattle.** Publications.

12220 Rijpkema, Y.S. NL 010115/74/5436
Energie– en N–behoeftenormen voor melkvee, gemeten met behulp van voederproeven. **Energy– and N–requirements for dairy cattle (feeding trials).** Publications.

12221 Boer, F. de NL 010115/74/5445
Onderzoek naar de relatie tussen voederbehoefte en ras– of type verschillen bij meststieren, samenhangend met het groeirytme onderzoek. **Research on the relation of feed–requirements and breed – or type differences in young bulls in connection with growthcurve–research.**

12222 Steg, A. NL 010115/76/6943 R
De waarde van met ammoniak ontsloten stro en toepassingsmogelijkheden daarven in de veevoeding. **Research into the value of straw decomposed with ammonia and application possibilities in livestock feeding.**

12223 Jongbloed, A.W. NL 010115/76/7615
Beïnvloeding van de vetzuursamenstelling in lichaamsvet (in vlees) en melk via de voeding, in het bijzonder m.b.t. meervoudig onverzadigde vetzuren. **Manipulation the fatty acid pattern in bodyfat (meat) and milk by means of feeding, with special reference to the polyunsaturated fatty acids.**

12224 Vreman, K. NL 010115/77/7614
Overdracht van zware metalen uit voer naar melk en vlees. **Transfer of toxic metals from feed into milk and meat.** Publications.

12225 Oostendorp, D. NL 010208/70/8737 N
Toepassing van industriële afvalstoffen als voedermiddel voor vleesstieren. **Application of by–products of the industry in rations for beef bulls.** Publications.

12226 Oostendorp, D. NL 010208/70/8738 N
Invloed van de aard en samenstelling van het voer en van de hoeveelheid op de groei van stieren voor vleesproduktie. **Influence of nature, composition and quantity of feeds on growth of bulls for beef.** Publications.

12227 Schukking, S.; Hengeveld, A.G.; Overvest, J.
NL 010208/71/3507
Zelf– en voorraadvoedering van ruwvoer. **Self–feeding and stock feeding of roughage.** Publications.

12228 Meijer, A.B. NL 010208/71/8772 N
Opname van diverse voedermiddelen door melkvee. **Intake of different feedstuffs by dairy cattle.** Publications.

12229 Meijer, A.B. NL 010208/72/8746 N
Invloed van het energieniveau op groei en ontwikkeling van jongvee. **Energy level by young stock in relation to growth rate and development.** Publications.

12230 Meijer, A.B. NL 010208/72/8748 N
Onderlinge beïnvloeding in opname van voedermiddelen bij melkvee. **Interrelation between the total intake of feedstuffs by dairy cows.** Publications.

12231 Boer, D.J. den; Keuning, J.H. NL 010208/73/3962
De hoedanigheid en de samenstelling van ruwvoer in relatie met het optreden van nitriet–vergiftiging bij rundvee. **Quality and composition of roughage in relation with nitrate accumulation and toxicity in cattle.** Publications.

12232 Meijer, A.B. NL 010208/73/8747 N
Ontwikkelen en testen van arbeid– en grasbesparende beweidingssystemen voor melkvee. **Developing and testing labour and grass saving grazing systems for dairy cows.** Publications.

12233 Snijders, P.J.M. NL 010208/74/8744 N
Invloed van zomerstalvoedering op de gezondheid van melkvee. **Influence of zero grazing on health of dairy cattle.** Publications.

12234 Meijer, A.B. NL 010208/74/8763 N
Produktie en gezondheid van melkvee bij diverse methoden van ruwvoer– en krachtvoer verstrekking. **Production and health of dairy cattle with several methods of roughage and concentrate feeding.** Publications.

12235 Kommerij, R. NL 010208/76/6941 R
Maatregelen ter voorkoming van stofwisselingsziekten bij melkvee. **Measures to prevent metabolic diseases in dairy cows.**

12236 Boer, D.J. den NL 010208/76/6943 R
De waarde van met ammoniak ontsloten stro en toepassingsmogelijkheden daarvan in de veevoeding. **Research into the value of straw decomposed with ammonia and application possibilities in live–stock feeding.**

12237 Meijer, A.B. NL 010208/76/8750 N
Invloed van rantsoensamenstelling op de pensfunctie van melkvee. **Effect of composition of the ration on the rumen function by dairy cows.** Publications.

12238 Meijer, A.B. NL 010208/76/8762 N
Invloed van voederfrequentie op voeropname, gezondheid en produktie van melkvee. **Effect of feeding frequency on feed intake, health and performance of dairy cows.** Publications.

12239 Boxem, Tj. NL 010208/78/8749 N
Ontwikkelen van beweidingssystemen voor jongvee in de zomer. **Developing young–stock grazing systems in summer.**

12240 Meijer, A.B. NL 010208/78/8773 N
Voersystemen voor jongvee in de winter. **Feeding systems for young–stock in winter.**

12241 Luten, W. NL 010208/79/8774 N
Mogelijkheden en knelpunten van intensieve standweidesystemen. **Possibilities and difficulties of intensive permanent pasture systems.**

12242 Binnerts, W. T. NL 020017/76/6792
Somatomedine en andere groeifactoren in runderplasma. **Somatomedine and other growthfactors in bovine plasma.** Publications.

12243 Hoek, J. van den NL 020017/77/7310
De stofwisseling van water en van tritium bij de lacterende koe. **The metabolism of water and of tritium in the lactating cow.**

12244 Zemmelink, G. NL 020058/71/4643
Schatten van de voederopname van tropische ruwvoeders. **Estimation of feed intake of tropical forages.** Publications.

12245 Hof, G. NL 020059/70/4803
Onderzoek naar de relatie tussen de fysisch–chemische eigenschappen van het dier en de voederopname door herkauwers. **Some aspects of the relation between voluntary feed intake in ruminants and the physical/chemical patterns of the ration.** Publications.

12246 Hof, G. NL 020059/71/8038
De vertering van koolhydraten bij vleeskalveren beoordeeld aan het verloop van de verteringsprocessen en de relatie tot het optreden van diarrhee. **The digestion of carbohydrates in veal calves judged by the course of the digestion processes and its relation to diarrhoa.**

12247 Hof, G. NL 020059/76/4499
De invloed van het rantsoen tijdens de opfok op de voederopname op oudere leeftijd bij melkvee. **The relationship between the composition of the rearing ration and the feedintake capacity of adult dairy cattle.**

12248 Klooster, A.Th. van NL 030009/73/3962 R
De hoedanigheid en de samenstelling van ruwvoer in relatie met het optreden van nitriet–vergiftiging bij rundvee. **Quality and composition of roughage in relation with nitrate accumulation and toxicity in cattle.** Publications.

12249 Prins, R.A. NL 030009/75/7811 R
De rol van lactaat als intermediair in de pensfermentatie. **The role of lactate as an intermediate in the rumen fermentation.** Publications.

12250 Klooster, A.T. van 't; Malestein, A.; Prins, R.A. NL 030009/76/7812
Voeding van melkkoeien rond de partus. **Feeding of dairy cows near parturition.** Publications.

12251 Prins, R.A. NL 030009/78/8961 N
Microbiële adaptatie in de pens (pensmikroben, rund, adaptatie). **Microbial adaptation in the rumen (rumen microbes, cattle, adaptetion).** Publications.

12252 Schotman, A.J.H. NL 030011/74/6044 R
De invloed van het lipidentype in de voeding van mestkalveren op het optreden van atheroschlerotische afwijkingen. **The influence of the type of lipids in the food of calves on the occurrence of aetherosclerotic deviation.**

12253 Breukink, H.J. NL 030011/76/7822 R
Het voorkomen, de diagnostiek en de therapie van de zogenaamde "luxe acetonaemie" (subklinische ketose type II) bij het rund. **Occurrence, diagnosis and treatment of the so–called "luxe–acet acetonaemia" (subclinical ketosis type II) in the dairy cow.**

12254 Breukink, H.J. NL 030011/78/8963 N
De pathofysiologische konsekwenties van melkverlagende rantsoenen (structuur, melkvet, glucose, insuline, vluchtige vetzuren, samenstellingen van pensvloeistof). **The pathophysiological consequences of milkfat depressing rations (volatile fatty acids, composition of ruman content, insulin, glucose, milkfat–structure).**

12255 Verhoeff, J. NL 030017/77/7779 R
Het loodgehalte in het serum van runderen, die gevoederd worden met hooi afkomstig van de berm van een snelweg. **Serum lead levels in cattle, fed on hay, taken from the sides of motorways.**

12256 Schuller, P.L. NL 040011/76/7474
Oriënterend onderzoek d.m.v. dunnelaagchromatografie naar de aanwezigheid van trenbolone, trenbolone–acetaat, methyltestosteron, oestradiol en ethyniloestradiol in kalverkunstmelkpoeders. **Preliminary investigation by means of thin layer chromatography on the presence of trenbolone, trenbolone–acetate, methyltestosterone, oestradiol and ethylniloestradiol in artificial milk powders for fattening calves.**

12257 Schuller, P.L. NL 040011/76/8033
Dynamische en kinetische aspecten van nitraat, nitriet en nitrosaminen in rantsoenen voor vleeskalveren. **Dynamic and kinetic aspects of nitrate, nitrite and nitrosamines in rations for veal calves.**

12258 Wal, P. van der NL 050305/62/8028
Nuts– en veiligheidsaspecten van nitrofuranen voor

D 3200 – Animal nutrition

vleeskalveren, hun omgeving en de consument van hun produkten. **Efficacy and safety aspects of nitrofurans for veal calves, their environment and the consumer of their products.**

12259 Huisman, J. NL 050305/66/8006
Melkeiwit in het rantsoen van vleeskalveren in relatie tot groei, gezondheidstoestand en het verloop van de verteringsprocessen. **Milk protein in the ration of veal calves in relation to growth, health and the course of the digestion processes.**

12260 Terluin, R.W. NL 050305/67/8012
Nutritionele en toxicologische evaluatie van gist gegroeid op paraffine bij vleeskalveren. **Nutritional and toxicological evaluation of yeast grown on paraffins in veal calves.**

12261 Berende, P.L.M. NL 050305/67/8022
Anabole stoffen bij vleeskalveren, vleesvarkens, vleesstieren, ossen, vaarzen en schapen in relatie tot groei, voederverbruik, slachtkwaliteit en gezondheidstoestand. **Anabolic agents in veal calves, growing pigs, bulls, steers, heifers and sheep in relation to performance, carcass quality and state of health.**

12262 Berende, P.L.M. NL 050305/67/8023
Kinetische aspecten van anabole stoffen bij vleeskalveren, vleesvarkens, vleesstieren, ossen, vaarzen en schapen. **Kinetic aspects of anabolic agents in veal calves, growing pigs, bulls, steers, heifers and sheep.**

12263 Huisman, J. NL 050305/68/8007
De vervanging van melkeiwit in het rantsoen van vleeskalveren, beoordeeld aan het verloop van de verteringsprocessen en aan groei en gezondheidstoestand. **Replacement of milk protein in veal calf rations judged by the course of the digestion processes, growth and health.**

12264 Weerden, E.J. van NL 050305/69/8025
Werkzaamheid en veiligheid van het nieuwe groeibevorderende antibioticum mocimycine ("DelvomycineR") t.b.v. de toepassing hiervan in rantsoenen van pluimvee, varkens en kalveren. **Effectiveness and safety of the new growth promoting antibiotic moimycine ("DelvomycineR") with regard to the application into diets for poultry, pigs and calves.**

12265 Hellemond, K.K. van NL 050305/69/8036
Biologische beschikbaarheid van ijzer uit diverse voedermiddelen voor vleeskalveren. **Bioavailability of iron from different feedstuffs for veal calves.**

12266 Huisman, J. NL 050305/71/8038
De vertering van koolhydraten bij vleeskalveren beoordeeld aan het verloop van de verteringsprocessen en de relatie tot het optreden van diarrhee. **The digestion of carbohydrates in veal calves judged by the course of the digestion processes and its relation to diarrhoa.**

12267 Hellemond, K.K. van NL 050305/72/8039
Ontwikkeling van (re–entrant) fistuleringstechnieken in digestietractus van rundvee, schapen en varkens. **Development of techniques for (re–entrant) cannulation of the digestive tract of cattle, sheep and pigs.**

12268 Weerden, E.J. van NL 050305/73/8003
Aminozuurbehoefte van vleeskalveren. **Amino acid requirements of veal calves.**

12269 Terluin, R.W. NL 050305/73/8013
Nutritionele en toxicologische evaluatie bij varkens en vleeskalveren van bacterieel SCP gegroeid op methanol. **Nutritional and toxicological evaluation in pigs and veal calves of bacterial SCP grown on methanol.**

12270 Weerden, E.J. van NL 050305/73/8021
Eiwit- en energiestofwisseling bij landbouwhuisdieren onder invloed van anabole stoffen. **Protein and energy metabolism in farm animals as influenced by anabolic agents.**

12271 Berende, P.L.M. NL 050305/73/8027
Kinetica van antibiotica en andere groeibevorderaars bij pluimvee, varkens en vleeskalveren. **Kinetic aspects of antibiotics and other growth promoting agents in poultry, pigs and veal calves.**

12272 Hellemond, K.K. van NL 050305/74/8008
Invloed van hoge giften aan plantaardige produkten op de bacterieflora van het colon bij vleeskalveren. **Effect of high doses of vegetable products on the bacterial flora in the colon of veal calves.**

12273 Weerden, E.J. van NL 050305/74/8015
Stofwisseling van koolwaterstoffen en oneven–genummerde vetzuren bij landbouwhuisdieren. **Metabolism of hydrocarbons and odd–numbered fatty acids in farm animals.**

12274 Weerden, E.J. van NL 050305/75/8024
Werkzaamheid en veiligheid van aan rantsoenen van pluimvee, varkens en kalveren toegevoegde antibiotica en andere groeibevorderende stoffen. **Efficacy and safety of antibiotica and other growth promotors added to diets for poultry, pigs and calves.**

12275 Schutte, J.B. NL 050305/76/8017
Nutritionele evaluatie van slachtafvalleneiwit bij kuikens, vleeskalveren en biggen. **Nutritional evaluation of protein from slaughterhouse offal in chickens, veal calves and pigs.**

12276 Terluin, R.W. NL 050305/76/8033
Dynamische en kinetische aspecten van nitraat, nitriet en nitrosaminen in rantsoenen voor vleeskalveren. **Dynamic and kinetic aspects of nitrate, nitrite and nitrosamines in rations for veal calves.**

12277 Berende, P.L.M. NL 050305/77/8026
Combinaties van antibiotica met andere groeibevorderaars in rantsoenen voor slachtkuikens en vleesvarkens in relatie tot groei, voederconversie en veiligheidsaspekten. **Combinations of antibiotics and other growth promoting substances in feed of broilers and growing pigs with regard to performance and safety aspects.**

12278 Boer, D.J. den; Keuning, J.H. NL 060008/73/3962
De hoedanigheid en de samenstelling van ruwvoer in relatie met het optreden van nitriet–vergiftiging bij rundvee. **Quality and composition of roughage in relation with nitrate accumulation and toxicity in cattle.** Publications.

12279 Boer, D.J. den NL 060008/76/6943 R
De waarde van met ammoniake ontsloten stro en toepassingsmogelijkheden daarvan in de veevoeding. **Research into the value of straw decomposed with ammonia and application possibilities in live stock feeding.**

D 3200 – Animal nutrition

See also 3544, 3599, 3613, 10742, 10925, 10948, 10973, 10978, 11048, 11569, 11947, 12067, 12071, 12073, 12181, 12206, 12261, 12262, 12267, 12270, 13215, 14454, 14574, 15669, 15670

12280 Hennaux, L.; François, E.; Compère, R.; Thewis, A.
BE 010003/64/0004
Influence du niveau calcique de la ration sur le métabolisme du phosphore et de l'absorption et de la sécrétion endogène du phosphore et de la valeur comparée de divers phosphates chez le mouton. **Effect of the level of calcium on the metabolisme of phosphorus and the absorption and the endogenous secretion of phosphorus and the comparative value of several phosphates in the sheep.** Publications.

12281 Antoine, A.; Fraselle, J.; Rondia, G.; Dekker, A.; Dachet, P.
BE 010003/69/0008 R
Etude technique et économique dans le Nord Tunisien sur l'alimentation du mouton en saison sèche. **Technical and economical study in North Tunisia on sheep feeding during dry season.** Publications.

12282 Vanbelle, M.; Arnould, R.; Ska, P.
BE 020601/69/0009 R
Contribution à l'utilisation de l'urée par les moutons en croissance. **Contribution to the study of the utilization of urea by growing sheeps.** Publications.

12283 Vanbelle, M.; Deswijsen, A.; Focant, M.
BE 020601/77/0014 R
Etude de l'action du hachage sur l'ingestion et la rumination chez le mouton. **The effect of silage chop length on the voluntary intake and rumination behaviour of sheep.** Publications.

12284 François, E.; Thewis, A.
BE 080100/67/0007
Etude de l'absorption et de la sécrétion du phosphore dans le tractus digestif du mouton. **Study of phosphorus absorption and secretion in the gastrointestinal tract of the sheep.** Publications.

12285 Hartfiel, W.; Potthast, V.
DE 111451/77/0002
Strohaufschluss mit Ammoniak, Verdaulichkeit beim Schaf. **Treatment of straw with ammoniak, digestion trials with sheep.** Publications.

12286 Günther, K.–D.; Nolting, J.; Xantinides, I.; Sabounchi, N.
DE 132300/71/0007
Mineralumsatz und –ansatz in Abhängigkeit vom Ca zum P–Gehalt der Ration beim Schaf. **Influence of the Ca/P ratio in ration on mineral metabolism in sheep.**

12287 Pfeffer, E.; Fenster, N.
DE 132302/77/0004
Nettoenergie für Wachstum von Lämmern in Zucker und Trockenschnitzeln. **Net energy for growth of lambs in sugar and beet pulp.**

12288 Pfeffer, E.; Prigge, H.
DE 132302/77/0005
Zusammenhänge zwischen Purinkörpern im Darminhalt und der Höhe der Allantoinausscheidung im Harn von Schafen. **Influences of purines in the digesta on excretion of allantoin in the urine of sheep.**

12289 Pfeffer, E.; Prigge, H.
DE 132302/78/0001 N
Bestimmung des Netto–Energiegehaltes in aufgeschlossenem

Stroh an wachsenden Schaflämmern. **Net–energy in treated straw, determined in growing lambs.**

12290 Höller, H.; Breves, G.; Buchhop, K.; Gerbaulet, I.
DE 139202/78/0001 N
Umsatz von Thiamin 'Vitamin B1' im Pansen von Schafen. **Metabolism of thiamine 'vitamin B1' in the sheep rumen.**

12291 Martens, H.
DE 139204/78/0001 N
Untersuchungen über die Magnesiumabsorption aus dem Pansen von Schafen und deren Beeinflussung durch Futterinhaltsstoffe und Fermentationsprodukte. **Absorption of magnesium from the rumen of sheep. The influence of components of the diet and of fermentation products on the absorption.** Publications.

12292 Hinrichsen, J.K.; Gladrow, H.
DE 144675/74/0001
Ziegenlämmer–Aufzucht mit Milchaustauscher und Frühabsetzen zur Mast. **Kid rearing with milk replacers and early weaning for fattening.**

12293 Gladrow, H.
DE 144675/77/0009
Untersuchungen zur Entwicklung von Mastleistungen und Schlachtkörperzusammensetzung von Merinolandschaflämmern bei Kraftfuttermast. **Development of fattening performance and carcass composition of merino lambs, fed with concentrates.**

12294 Thomsen, K.V.
DK 010201/66/0002
Bestemmelse af fodermidlers fordøjelighed og foderværdi på grundlag af fordøjelighedsforsøg med får. **Determination of the digestibility and nutritional value of feedingstuffs-using sheep.**

12295 Højland Frederiksen, J.; Jensen, N.
DK 010201/77/0012
Undersøgelser vedrørende tilvækst, slagtekvalitet og kødkvalitet hos lam. **Investigations into growth, slaughter quality and meat quality of lamb.**

12296 Mason, V.C.
DK 010206/71/0011
Kvælstofomsætningen i cæcum og colon hos får. Studier af faktorer som påvirker bestemmelsen af fordøjeligt kvælstof hos drøvtyggere. **Nitrogen metabolism in the caecum and colon of sheep.**

12297 Gueguen, L.
FR 010205/65/9548 N
Utilisation digestive et métabolique de diverses sources de phosphore chez le Mouton et le Porc en croissance. **Digestive and metabolic utilization of different sources of phosphorus by growing sheep and pigs.**

12298 Gueguen, L.; Bouchet, J.
FR 010205/78/9547
Influence de l'acidité du régime sur le métabolisme minéral chez le mouton en croissance. **Influence of dietary acidity on mineral metabolism in growing sheep.**

12299 Theriez, M.; Molenat, G.
FR 010805/69/6539
Allaitement artificiel de l'agneau. **Artificial rearing of lambs.**

12300 Tissier, M.; Theriez, M.
FR 010805/70/6537
Variation de la capacité d'ingestion de la brebis en fin de gestation et en début de lactation. **Variation of voluntary intake in pregnant and lactating ewe.**

12301 Tissier, M.; Theriez, M.; Grizard, J. FR 010805/72/6538
Alimentation de la brebis en fin de gestation et début de lactation: détermination des besoins énergétiques. **Ewe**

nutrition at the end of pregnancy and beginning of lactation energy requirements.

12302 Molenat, G.; Loiseau, P.; Bechet, G.; Flamant, J.C.
FR 010805/72/6544
Utilisation des zones peu productives par les ovins. **Range utilisation by sheep.**

12303 Molenat, G.; Bechet, G.   FR 010805/74/6545
Comportement alimentaire des ovins au pâturage. **Feeding behaviour of sheep at pasture.**

12304 Theriez, M.; Poncet, C.   FR 010805/75/6542
Relation entre l'alimentation, les performances de l'agneau et la composition corporelle. **Relationships between lamb nutrition, growth rate and body composition.**

12305 Contrepois, M.; Goby, J.F.; Thivend, P.; Dubourguier, H.C.; Gouet, Ph.   FR 010809/75/9524 N
Etude écologique de la microflore intestinale de l'agneau et du veau et son rôle dans la digestion des glucides. **Ecological study of intestinal microflora in lamb and calf and its part in digestion of carbohydrates.**

12306 Grenet, E.; Demarquilly, C.   FR 010814/74/6502
Mesure du bilan azote sur moutons en croissance alimentés avec des fourrages verts ou des fourrages conservés. **Nitrogen balance on growing sheep fed with fresh grass, hay and grass silage.**

12307 Grizard, J.; Prugnaud, J.; Tissier, M.; Pion, R.; Champredon, C.; Patureau–Mirand, P.   FR 010815/74/9572 N
Régulation hormonale de l'utilisation des acides aminés chez la brebis en fin de gestation et début de lactation. **Hormonal regulation of amino acid metabolism in pregnant and lactating ewes.**

12308 Aurousseau, B.; Patureau Mirand, Ph.; Vermorel, M.; Theriez, M.   FR 010816/68/2763
Influence de divers types de chaînes carbonées employées comme source d'énergie et de l'équilibre entre les nutriments sur l'utilisation de l'azote et de l'énergie chez le jeune mammifère en croissance intensive. Etudes sur rats et agneaux. **Influence of various sources according to the nature of the carbon chain and of energy nitrogen ratio on nitrogen and energy retention by young fast growing mammals. Trials on rats and lambs.** Publications.

12309 Aurousseau, B.; Vermorel, M.   FR 010816/68/2766
Utilisation métabolique de diverses chaînes des tissus adipeux. Etudes sur rats et sur agneaux. **Metabolic utilisation of various energy sources according to the type of carbon chain. Influence on adipose tissue composition. Trials on rats and lambs.** Publications.

12310 Vermorel, M.; Beranger, C.; Bouvier, J.C.; Demarquilly, C.   FR 010816/72/2761
Valeur énergétique des rations chez les ruminants en croissance. Influence du taux de concentré et du mode de conditionnement des rations. Etudes sur ovins et bovins. **Energy value of rations for growing ruminants. Influence of concentrate to roughage ratio and of conditioning of rations. Trials on sheep and beef.** Publications.

12311 Aurousseau, B.; Nougues; Vermorel, M.; Vezinhet
FR 010816/73/2765

Influence à long terme de divers types de chaînes carbonées employées comme source d'énergie sur la mise en place et le développement des tissus adipeux. Etudes chez l'agneau. **Long term effect of various energy sources, according to the type of carbon chain, on cellularity of adipose tissue. Trials on lambs.**

12312 Hughet, L.; Traineau, R.   FR 012223/72/0147
Etude de la valeur alimentaire de nouveaux types variétaux (graminées, luzerne, sorgho, maïs) sur fourrages verts et en ensilage. Influence des techniques de culture et du stade de rècolte. **Study of the nutritive value of new varietal types (grasses, lucerne, sorghum, maize) as green and ensiled fodders. Influence of cultivation methods and harvest stage.**

12313 Dawson   GB 010302/00/0042 R
Digestion of complex lipids and pigments in grass in sheep rumen.

12314 Orpin   GB 010302/00/0055 R
Effect of absence of certain large bacteria of rumen on growth of lambs fed a high carbohydrate diet.

12315 Newton; Austin   GB 011205/79/0701 N
The nutritional and toxicological evaluation of forage crops for the autumn feeding of sheep.

12316 Newton; Penning   GB 011205/79/0702 N
Evaluation of supplementation for grazing sheep.

12317 Treacher; Newton   GB 011205/79/0703 N
Evaluation of conserved forages for ewes during pregnancy.

12318 Treacher; Newton   GB 011205/79/0704 N
Influence on productivity of interactions between the sheep and sward characteristics and management.

12319 Braithwte   GB 011712/00/0001 R
Effects of environmental and physiological factors on calcium metabolism.

12320 Jones   GB 012102/00/0007 R
Mineral content of grass species, varieties and genotypes in relation to nutritional requirements of sheep.

12321 Moseley; Jones   GB 012102/76/0018 R
Chemical and physical characters of grasses in relation to digestion, utilisation and metabolism by sheep.

12322 Moseley; Jones   GB 012102/76/0021 R
Chemical and physical characteristics of clovers in relation to digestion utilisation metabolism by sheep.

12323 Barnes   GB 020709/79/0003 N
Control of gastrointestinal blood flow in the conscious sheep.

12324 Smith; Wright, B.   GB 030101/00/0010 R
Distribution of plasma copper in sheep.

12325 Sykes; Dingwall   GB 030101/00/0011
Skeletal mineralisation in breeding ewes.

12326 Hodgson   GB 030101/00/0025
Qualitative and quantitative aspects of energy metabolism in pregnant sheep and their developing foetuses.

12327 Mellor; Hodgson   GB 030111/00/0005 R

Qualitative and quantitative aspects of energy metabolism in pregnant sheep and their developing foetuses.

12328 Mellor; Slater   GB 030111/00/0006 R
Factors affecting foetal nitrogen metabolism in the pregnant sheep.

12329 Rook; Strachan   GB 030201/00/0024 R
Sites of absorption and excretion of magnesium in the gut of sheep.

12330 Foot   GB 030302/00/0001
Voluntary intake and change in body composition in lactating ewes on different roughage feeds.

12331 Russel   GB 030302/00/0002
Nutritional physiology of the pregnant ewe.

12332 Foot   GB 030302/00/0003
Interaction between nutrition and body composition.

12333 Whitelaw; Armstrong   GB 030302/73/0009
Mineral nutrition and animal performance.

12334 Maxwell   GB 030303/00/0004 R
Develop improved year round grazing systems for animal production from hill pastoral resources.

12335 Williams; Dalgarno   GB 030604/77/0028 R
Zinc deficiency effects on testicular development and spermatogenesis in sheep and rats.

12336 Hobson   GB 030605/00/0006
Establishment of a defined rumen flora in gnotobiotic lambs.

12337 Orskov; Grubb   GB 030611/00/0026 R
Nutrient requirement of fattening lambs and the formulation of diets for intensive lamb production.

12338 Orskov   GB 030611/00/0027
Nutrient requirements of neo–natal and pre–ruminant lambs.

12339 Unsworth; Morrison   GB 040401/75/0022
The effect of variation in silage composition upon nutrient supplies to surgically modified sheep.

12340 McGaughey   GB 041102/76/0011
Silage diets for hill sheep.

12341 Chestnutt   GB 041306/77/0003 R
Evaluation of silage for sheep.

12342 Speedy   GB 060102/00/0011
Assessment of the meat production potential of different lamb genotypes.

12343 Owen   GB 060208/00/0007 R
The voluntary feed intake of ewes of different genotypes housed indoors.

12344 Vipond   GB 060208/00/0012 R
Voluntary feed intake in breeding ewes.

12345 Vipond   GB 060208/79/0018 N
Voluntary feed intake in breeding ewes.

12346 Calder   GB 060225/00/0001 R
Performance of fattening lambs on Brassicas.

12347 Lawlor, M.J.   IE 060100/69/0300 N
The role of liquid feeding in intensive lamb production. Publications.

12348 Sheehan, W.   IE 060700/73/0915 R
Effect of energy intake during pregnancy and lactation on the subsequent reproductive performance of ewes. Publications.

12349 Fitzgerald, S.; Thomas, T.M.   IE 060700/74/1013 R
Evaluation of root crops as sources of feed for fattening of store lambs trial 3 – comparison of feeding roots outdoor in situ versus outdoor using hill and lowland lambs. Publications.

12350 Fitzgerald, S.   IE 060700/74/1014 R
Studies on the aspects of silage quality which affect silage intake and the performance of store lambs. Trial 1 – effect of grass growth on silage quality, silage intake and on lamb performance. Publications.

12351 Quirke, J.F.; Sheehan, W.; O'Keefe, M.
    IE 060700/76/1271 R
Assessment of growth promoting agents (anabolic compounds) in the finishing of store lambs. Publications.

12352 Fitzgerald, S.   IE 060702/77/1328
Feeding of store lambs on fodder beet grazed in situ.

12353 Fitzgerald, S.   IE 060702/78/1327 R
Protein supplementation of roots for finishing store lambs. Publications.

12354 Malossini, F.; Pace, V.; Settineri, D.
    IT 020700/79/0006 N
Impiego della farina di estrazione di colza (CV Tower) come fonte proteica per la produzione dell'agnello pesante. **Use of rapeseed oil meal (CV Tower) as proteic source in order to produce lambs.**

12355 Bufano, G.   IT 040105/74/0520
Alimentazione e produzione quanti–qualitativa di latte negli ovini. **Sheep feeding, milk quality and milk yields.**

12356 Ciruzzi, B.   IT 040124/77/0548
Piani alimentari e livelli nutritivi nella produzione di soggetti ovini da macello. **Feeding programs and nutritional standards in the production of sheep for slaughter.**

12357 Bonsempiante, M.; Bittante, G.   IT 040810/79/0003 N
L'allevamento confinato, ovini, caprini, per la produzione della carne: studi sull'alimentazione e sul controllo della riproduzione. **Sheep and goats reared in confinement for meat production: studies on feeding and reproduction.**

12358 Trimarchi, G.; Ferruzzi, G.; Rossi, G.; Ghelardoni, F.; Secchiari, P.; Giovannetti, I.   IT 041113/79/0002 N
Livello di ingestione e produttività di pecore da latte. **Ingestion and productivity level of milk sheep.**

12359 Ubertalle, A.; Errante, J.; Bianchi, M.; Mazzocco, P.
    IT 041217/77/0002 N
Ovini delle Langhe e meticci nella produzione dell'agnello "pesante" per la carne.. **Langhe sheep and crossbreeding for heavy lamb for slaughter production..**

12360 Dattilo, M.   IT 041313/72/0444
Studi sull'alimentazione degli ovini da latte. **Studies on the feeding of milk–producing sheep.** Publications.

12361 Dattilo, M.   IT 041313/75/0002
Studi sull'impiego di foraggi conservati nell'alimentazione degli ovini. **Study on the use of the preserved fodders in the feeding of sheep.** Publications.

12362 Dattilo, M.   IT 041313/77/0160 R
Studi sull'alimentazione delle pecore in lattazione. **Studies on the feeding of suckling ewes.**

12363 Kuiper, H.   NL 010115/66/5443
Onderzoek naar de optimale voeding van op stal gemeste lammeren. **Research into optimal feeding of indoor fattened lambs.** Publications.

12364 Kuiper, H.   NL 010115/67/5438
Voedernormen voor ooien, die door foktechnische maatregelen grotere worpfrequentie en grotere worpen leveren. **Feeding standards for ewes – caused by zootechnical measures – a higher breeding frequency and increased lamb numbers.** Publications.

12365 Kuiper, H.   NL 010115/73/5444
Voedingsonderzoek met schapen en lammeren in de weide. **Feeding research with sheep and lambs in the pasture.**

12366 Oostendorp, D.   NL 010208/71/8752 N
Slachtrijp maken van lammeren op stal met behulp van krachtvoer. **Indoor finishing of lambs with concentrates.**

12367 Adrichem, P. W. M. van   NL 020017/76/6793
Vertering en resorptie van eiwitten bij schapen. **Digestion and absorption of protein in sheep.**

Goats, farm deer and other ruminants (B 4290)

See also 1825, 1861, 10742, 12357, 12957

12368 Scheurmann, E.; Diab, A.   DE 129540/78/0002 N
Futteraufnahmeverhalten der afrikanischen Zwergziegen. **Feed intake behaviour of the African dwarf goat.**

12369 Hinrichsen, J.K.; Soumaree, A.; Buchenauer, D.
                    DE 144675/77/0001
Untersuchungen zum Ernährungsverhalten von Ziegen auf der Weide. **Studies on ingestive behaviour of goats on pasture.**

12370 Decaen, C.; Masson, C.   FR 011013/75/6565 N
Alimentation et production laitière de la chèvre. **Feeding and milk production of goat.**

12371 Fehr, P.M.; Bas, P.; Sauvant, D.; Delage, J.
                    FR 011712/64/2741
Influence des facteurs alimentaires sur la secrétion lipidique de la mamelle de chèvre. **Effect of alimentary factors on the secretion of lipids by goat udder.** Publications.

12372 Fehr, P.M.; Bas, P.; Sauvant, D.; Hervieu, J.; Delage, J.   FR 011712/64/2742
Alimentation des caprins. **Feeding of goats.** Publications.

12373 Morand–Fehr, P.   FR 011712/72/9508 N

Alimentation des chèvres laitières. **Feeding of dairy goat.**

12374 Intrieri, F.   IT 040709/78/1064 N
Influenza del tipo di alimentazione su alcune costanti ematiche e loro rapporti con la produzione lattea e con la fertilità nella specie bufalina. **Influence of the type of feeding on certain blood chemistry values; their relation to milk production and to fertility in the buffalo species.**

12375 Prins, R.A.; Lankhorst, A.   NL 030009/76/7813
Pensfermentatie bij wilde herkauwers (hert). **Rumen fermentation in wild ruminants (deer).**

Pigs (B 4300)

See also 1860, 11095, 11123, 11138, 11164, 11187, 11191, 11213, 11241, 11242, 11254, 11566, 11575, 11712, 11748, 11799, 11803, 11808, 11820, 11986, 12033, 12034, 12218, 12223, 12224, 12261, 12262, 12264, 12267, 12269, 12270, 12271, 12273, 12274, 12275, 12277, 12297, 12843, 12845, 12846, 12861, 12862, 13348, 14687, 14725, 16297, 16815, 17062

12376 Henderickx, H.; De Cuypere, J.; Vervaeke, I.; Dierick, N.   BE 030026/72/0006 R
Studie van verteringsprocessen bij enkelmagigen. **Study of digestion processes with monogastric animals.** Publications.

12377 Bouquet, Y.; De Wilde, R.   BE 051100/56/0001 R
Onderzoek over de voeding van varkens en de scheikundige samenstelling van het vlees. **Research on the feeding of pigs and the chemical composition of their meat.** Publications.

12378 Bekaert, H.; Eeckhout, W.; Casteels, M.
                    BE 070700/70/0004 R
Optimale aminozurenbehoefte van biggen en varkens en de verteerbaarheid van aminozuren. **Optimum amino–acid requirements of pigs and the digestibility of amino acids.** Publications.

12379 Eeckhout, W.; Casteels, M.; Bekaert, H.
                    BE 070700/71/0005 R
Eiwitmetabolisme bij mestvarkens. **Protein metabolism by pigs.** Publications.

12380 Eeckhout, W.   BE 070700/76/0024 R
Verteerbaarheid van voedervetten bij mestvarkens. **Digestibility of fats by pigs.** Publications.

12381 Bekaert, H.; Eeckhout, W.   BE 070700/76/0025 R
Het gebruik van vochtig maisgraan voor fokzeugen en mestvarkens. **The use of high moisture corn for sows and pigs.** Publications.

12382 Eeckhout, W.   BE 070700/77/0033 R
Invloed van een alkal–behandeling van sojabloem op de voederwaarde voor varkens. **Influence of alkali–treatment on the feeding value of soy–flour for piglets.**

12383 Eeckhout, W.   BE 070700/79/0036 N
Schatting van de netto–energieinhoud van krachtvoeders voor biggen en mestvarkens op basis van de ruwe nutrienten. **Prediction of the net energy value of concentrates for pigs based on the crude nutrients.**

12384 Bronsch, K.; Schneider, D.   DE 104550/70/0001
Die ernährungsphysiologischen und haltungstechnischen

Bedingungen zur Aufzucht von im Alter von 21 Tagen abgesetzten Ferkeln. **Nutritional and environmental requirements for rearing piglets weaned after 21 days.**

12385 Schneider, D.; Bronsch, K.   DE 104550/73/0001
Wirkungen unterschiedlicher Energieversorgung bei Zuchtsauen. **The effects of different dietary energy supply on breeding sows.**

12386 Schmitten, F.; Jüngst, H.; Finke, K.   DE 111500/75/0002
Einsatz eiweissreicher Getreidearten als Alleinfutter in der Schweinemast. **Utilization of cereals rich in protein as complete feed in fattening pigs.**

12387 Brune, H.; Walz, O.P.   DE 129270/77/0001
Vergleichende Stoffwechsel–Bilanzuntersuchungen an Mensch und Schwein. **Comparative studies of metabolic balance in man and pig.**

12388 Brune, H.; Walz, O.P.   DE 129270/77/0002
Wirkung zeitlich geteilter Gaben von Aminosäuren auf den N–Ansatz beim Mastschwein. **Effect of feeding amino acids at different intervals on the N–retention in fattening pigs.**

12389 Brune, H.   DE 129270/77/0003
Stoffwechsel des Spurenelementes Chrom beim Schwein. **Metabolism of the trace element chromium in pigs.**

12390 Pallauf, J.; Göttert, W.; Brune, H.   DE 129270/77/0004
Einfluss organischer Säuren auf den N–Stoffwechsel bei Ratte, Schwein und Kalb. **Effect of several organic acids on the N–metabolism of rats, pigs and calves.**

12391 Brune, H.; Eckstein, K.; Pallauf, J.   DE 129270/77/0005
Einfluss organischer Säuren auf den Mineralstoffwechsel bei Ratte, Kalb und Schwein. **Effect of several organic acids on the metabolism of minerals in rats, calves and pigs.**

12392 Günther, K.–D.; Nolting, J.; Tekin, C.
   DE 132300/72/0004
Mineralumsatz und –ansatz in Abhängigkeit von Mineralstoffkomplexwirkungen beim Schwein. **Influence of complex effects on metabolism and gain of minerals in pig.**

12393 Günther, K.–D.; Nolting, J.; Tekin, C.
   DE 132300/73/0002
Phytinphosphorverwertung beim wachsenden Schwein. **Phytin phosphorus utilization in growing pig.**

12394 Abel, H.; Rosenow, H.   DE 132300/77/0004
Untersuchungen zum Ansatz und Umsatz von Körperlipiden und –protein beim wachsenden Schwein in Abhängigkeit von der Art des Futterenergieträgers. **The influence of different energy sources on lipid and protein metabolism in growing piglets.**

12395 Günther, K.–D.; Mohme, H.; Helms, W.; Goerke, R.
   DE 132300/78/0001 N
Untersuchungen zur Protein– und Aminosäure–Verwertung beim laktierenden Schwein. **Protein and amino acids utilization in lactating sows.**

12396 Günther, K.–D.   DE 132303/72/0002
Zur Frage der Mineralstoffverwertbarkeit bei wachsenden Schweinen. **The availability of mineral elements in the growing pig.**

12397 Meyer, H.; Drochner, W.   DE 139300/73/0001
Einfluss von Strukturstoffen auf die Futterpassage und Vergärungsvorgänge beim Schwein. **The influence of structural substances on the feed passage and fermentation processes in pig.**

12398 Meyer, H.; Drochner, W.   DE 139300/75/0003
Einfluss verschiedener Futterkomponenten auf Nährstoffumsetzungen im Dickdarm des Schweines. **Influence of different feedstuffs on the digestion and metabolism of nutrients, especially in the colon of pigs.**

12399 Meyer, H.; Drochner, W.   DE 139300/77/0001
Untersuchungen über die Verträglichkeit melassierter Trockenschnitzel bei Sauen. **Investigations on the tolerance of sows to high melassed beet pulps.**

12400 Plonait, H.; Reinhard, H.J.; Hahn, W.; Krieger, H.
   DE 139750/78/0004 N
Elektronische Befunddokumentation und biometrische Auswertung von Rhythmen der Magenbewegung bei Mastschweinen. **Electronic data recording and biometric evaluation of rhythms of stomach movment in fattening pigs.** Publications.

12401 Menke, K.H.; Ehrensvärd, U.; Berschauer, F.
   DE 144621/78/0002 N
Einfluss der Fettsäurenzusammensetzung der Ration auf den Insulinspiegel und auf die Verwertung der ME für den Proteinansatz bei Schweinen. **Influence of fatty acid composition of diets on insulin level and on utilization of ME for protein synthesis in pigs.** Publications.

12402 Menke, K.H.; Berschauer, F.; Ehrensvärd, U.
   DE 144621/78/0003 N
Bestimmung der maximalen Proteinsynthesekapazität von Schweinen. **Determination of maximum capacity for protein synthesis of pigs.**

12403 Menke, K.H.; Cornelius, H.   DE 144621/78/0004 N
Bestimmung der Proteinqualität an Hand chemischer und biochemischer Kenndaten unter Berücksichtigung des Energieund Aminosäuren–Bedarfs beim Schwein. **Determination of protein quality with the aid of chemical and biochemical data taking into consideration energy– and amino acid requirements of the pigs.**

12404 Lantzsch, H.–J.   DE 144621/78/0005 N
Untersuchungen zum Zn– und Cu–Versorgungsstatus von Ratten und Ferkeln mit Hilfe parenteral zugeführter Chelatbildner und Bestimmung der Verfügbarkeit aus Nahrungs– und Futtermitteln. **Investigations on the status of Zn– and Cu–supply of rats and piglets with the aid of parenterally administered chelating agents and evaluation of the availability in foods and feeds.** Publications.

12405 Reichl, J.R.   DE 144622/78/0002 N
Computer–Simulation des Fettstoffwechsels beim Schwein. **Computer simulation of fat metabolism in pig.** Publications.

12406 Rogdakis, E.; Rothfuss, U.; Fewson, D.
   DE 144680/77/0001
Enzymatische Lipogene und lipolytische Parameter im Fettgewebe verschiedener Schweinerassen in Abhängigkeit vom Gewicht und ihre Beziehung zum Fettansatz. **Enzymatic**

lipogenic and lipolytic parameters in adipose tissue in different pig breeds in relation to weight and fat retention.

12407 Isensee, E.; Thomsen, H.   DE 148150/75/0001
Haltungsverfahren der Schweinemast in Offenställen. **Investigations of open–stall systems in swine fattening.**

12408 Henkel, H.; Feige, K.   DE 148300/78/0001 N
Der Nährwert von Inhaltsstoffen pflanzlicher Futtermittel in der Schweinemast. – Die Ermittlung einer neuen Energiebewertung. **The feeding value of nutritive substances in plant feeds for pig fattening. – The determination of a new energy value. Publications.**

12409 Henkel, H.; Hüttmann, A.   DE 148300/78/0002 N
Der optimale Energie– und Aminosäurebedarf von Mastschweinen. **The optimum requirement of fattening pigs for energy and amino acids.**

12410 Henkel, H.; Schwarz, M.   DE 148300/78/0003 N
Die Ermittlung des Körperfettgehaltes in lebenden Schweinen. **The determination of the quantity of body fat in living pigs.**

12411 Kirchgessner, M.   DE 161280/75/0002
Zur Energiebewertung von Schweinefuttermitteln. **Estimation of the energy value of feeds for swine.**

12412 Groth, W.; Berner, H.; Bogner, H.; Gränzer, W.;
Reissig, F.   DE 161360/77/0001
Die Mast von Kälbern unter Einsatz von Milchaustauschern und strukturiertem Futter unter besonderer Berücksichtigung ethologischer und physiologischer Aspekte. **The fattening of calves with milk–replacer and structural forage with special regard to ethological and physiological aspects.**

12413 Schulz, E.   DE 201050/78/0005 N
Differenzierung des Aminosäurebedarfes wachsender Schweine. **Differentiation of the requirement of amino acids in growing pigs.**

12414 Böhme, H.   DE 201050/78/0006 N
Energie– und Proteinumsatz wachsender Schweine unter spezieller Berücksichtigung des kompensatorischen Wachstums. **Energy and protein metabolism of growing pigs with special regard to compensatory growth.**

12415 Petersen, U.; Vemmer, H.   DE 201050/78/0007 N
Bewertung der Mineralstoffversorgung von Schweinen unter praktischen Fütterungsbedingungen. **Studies on mineral supply of pigs under practical feeding conditions.**

12416 Burgstaller, G.   DE 502302/77/0005
Kontrolle des Energiegehaltes in Futtermischungen für Schweine 'Energiemesszahl – Schwein'. **Control of energy content in feed mixtures for pigs 'energy index – pigs'.**

12417 Burgstaller, G.; Kögel, J.   DE 502302/78/0003 N
Untersuchungen zum Einsatz von hohen Trockenschnitzelanteilen mit und ohne Lysinergänzung in der Schweinemast. **Studies on feeding high rates of dry pulp with and without supplementary lysine in pig fattening.**

12418 Madsen, A.   DK 010202/70/0004
Kornproteinets, specielt bygproteinets, sammensætning og dets indflydelse på slagterisvin. **Composition of grain protein, with particular reference to barley, and its influence on bacon**

pigs.

12419 Hansen, V.   DK 010202/73/0010
Stigende mængder bomuldsfrøskrå (indtil 9 pct.) i foderblandinger til slagterisvin. Blandinger med 6 pct. bomuldsfrøskrå tilsat jernsulfat og/eller lysin. **Increasing amounts of cotton seed meal in feed mixtures for bacon pigs. Mixtures of 6 per cent cotton seed meal with added iron sulphate and/or lysine.**

12420 Just, A.   DK 010202/74/0023
Undersøgelser til belysning af faktorer, der påvirker udnyttelsen af foderets omsættelige energi hos svin. **Investigations of factors influencing the efficiency of utilization of metabolizable energy in pigs.**

12421 Just, A.   DK 010202/74/0024
Bestemmelse af fodermidlernes fordøjelighed og foderværdi til svin. **Determination of the digestibility of the individual feedstuffs, and their content of metabolizable energy for pigs.**

12422 Madsen, A.   DK 010202/75/0011
Slagtesvinenes protein– og aminosyrebehov. **Protein and amino acid needs of bacon pigs.**

12423 Madsen, A.   DK 010202/75/0012
Slagtesvinenes protein– og energiforsyning. **Protein and energy supply for bacon pigs.**

12424 Hansen, V.   DK 010202/76/0003
Stigende mængder tørret sukkerroeaffald til slagtesvin. **Increasing quantities of dried sugarbeet waste to bacon pigs.**

12425 Hansen, V.   DK 010202/76/0004
Forskellig foderstyrke, forskelligt proteinniveau. Sogrise og galte hver for sig eller 2 sogrise og 2 galte pr. sti. **Different feeding levels, different protein levels. Female pigs and castrated male pigs, separately or 2 female pigs and 2 castrated male pigs together per sty.**

12426 Nielsen, H.E.   DK 010202/76/0005
Glukose og elektrolytter til tidligt fravænnede grise som forebyggelse af dehydrering i forbindelse med fravænningsdiarree. **Glucose and electrolytes for early weaned pigs as preventative measures against dehydration in connection with weaning–diarrhoea.**

12427 Nielsen, H.E.   DK 010202/76/0007
Pattegrisenes hæmoglobinstatus gennem de første 4 døgn efter fødsel. **Piglet haemoglobin levels during the first 4 days after birth.**

12428 Nielsen, H.E.   DK 010202/76/0011
Proteinnormer i drægtigheds– og diegivningsperioden til søer med kort diegivningsperiode. **Protein levels for sows with short suckling periods, during the gestation and suckling period.**

12429 Just, A.   DK 010202/76/0012
Undersøgelser med fistulerede svin til belysning af tarmfloraens betydning for næringsstoffernes fordøjelighed m.v. **Investigations with fistulated pigs for the elucidation of the intestinal flora's influence on food stuff digestibility.**

12430 Madsen, A.   DK 010202/77/0001
Fodersammensætning og foderkvalitetens betydning for slagtesvin. **The significance of feed composition and feed quality**

for bacon pigs.

12431 Hansen, V. DK 010202/77/0002
Moderat fodring efter norm sammenlignet med fodring efter ædelyst indtil 50 kg efterfulgt af normfodring 50–90 kg. Sogrise og galte hver for sig eller 2 sogrise og 2 galte pr. sti. **Moderate standard feeding compared with feeding according to appetite up to 50 kg followed by normal feeding 50–90 kg. Female pigs and castrated male pigs separated or 2 female pigs and 2 castrated male pigs together per sty.**

12432 Hansen, V. DK 010202/77/0003
Rapsskrå (sorten double low) som proteintilskudsfoder til slagtesvin. **Crushed rape (var. Double low) as protein feed supplement. for bacon pigs.**

12433 Hansen, V. DK 010202/77/0004
Rapskager (eller rapsexpeller) sorten Erglu (double low) som en del af slagtesvinenes proteintilskudsfoder. **Rape cakes (or Rape expeller) var. Erglu (Double low) as a part of bacon pig protein feed supplement.**

12434 Nielsen, H.E. DK 010202/77/0007
Effekten af selen og vitamin E på biokemiske og histologiske paramentre hos svin. **The effect of selenium and vitamin E on biochemical and histological parameters of pigs.**

12435 Nielsen, H.E. DK 010202/77/0008
Formalingstidspunktets indflydelse på forskellige kemiske egenskaber i byg og dettes foderværdi, målt på vækst og sundhedstilstand hos tidligt fravænnede grise. **Influence of stage of milling on various chemical properties and the feeding value of barley measured according to growth and health of early weaned pigs.**

12436 Nielsen, H.E. DK 010202/77/0009
Forskellig proteintildeling til søer af ren race eller krydsning. **Different protein rations for pure and cross bred sows.**

12437 Nielsen, H.E. DK 010202/77/0010
Startblanding til smågrise hos soen til brug ved henholdsvis tidlig fravænning og fravænning ved 8 uger. **Composition of feeds for piglets with sow, for use in connection with early weaning and weaning at 8 weeks.**

12438 Madsen, A.; Nielsen, E.K. DK 010202/78/0001 N
Fodringsmetoder til slagtesvin. **Different feeding methods – dry or wet feeding – for growing–finishing pigs.**

12439 Madsen, A.; Nielsen, E.K.; Mortensen, H.P.; Larsen, A.E. DK 010202/78/0002 N
Vådfodring med alternative fodermidler til slagtesvin. **Alternative feeds for growing – finishing pigs using a liquid feeding system.**

12440 Hansen, V.; Andersen, I.–L.E. DK 010202/78/0003 N
Fiskeensilage med et lavt indhold af fedt til slagtesvin. **Fish silage with a low content of crude fat for bacon pigs.**

12441 Nielsen, H.E.; Danielsen, V. DK 010202/78/0009 N
Fedt af forskellig oprindelse i foder til smågrise. **Various sources of fat in the feed for piglets.**

12442 Nielsen, H.E.; Danielsen, V.; Eggum, B.O.
  DK 010202/78/0010 N
Stigende mængder skummetmælkspulver til tidligt fravænnede grise. **Increasing amounts of skimmilk powder for early weaned pigs.**

12443 Nielsen, H.E.; Danielsen, V.; Larsen, A.E.; Kruse, P.E.; Linnemann, F. DK 010202/78/0011 N
Anvendelse af to proteinniveauer til drægtige søer. **Two levels of protein for pregnant sows.**

12444 Nielsen, H.E.; Danielsen, V. DK 010202/78/0012 N
Forskellige smagsstoffer i foder til smågrise. **Different flavour compounds in the feed for piglets.**

12445 Just, A.; Jørgensen, H.; Fernandeź, J.
  DK 010202/78/0021 N
Kødbenmels foderværdi til svin. **The feed value of meat and bone meal for pigs.**

12446 Mason, V.C. DK 010206/78/0005 N
Forgæringsstudier i tyktarmen hos svin med særlig henblik på kvælstofomsætningen. **Studies of fermentation in the hind–gut of pigs, with special reference to nitrogen metabolism.**

12447 Madsen, N.P. DK 010400/77/0001 N
Tekniske undersøgelser af automatiske fodringsanlæg til svin. **Technical investigations of automatic feeding systems for pigs.**

12448 Keller, P. DK 010400/78/0001 N
Arbejdsbehov ved vådfodring af slagtesvin. **Labour requirement using wet–feeding systems for bacon pigs.**

12449 Wegger, I.; Jørgensen, P.F.; Palludan, B.
  DK 030126/77/0006 R
Selenomsætning hos svin og kalve. **Selenium turnover in swine and calves.**

12450 Wegger, I.; Moustgaard, J. DK 030126/78/0001 N
Kolesterolomsætningen hos svin. **Cholesterol metabolism in swine.**

12451 Wegger, I.; Palludan, B.; Lund, C.
  DK 030126/79/0001 N
Askorbinsyres betydning hos svin. **The importance of ascorbic acid for swine.**

12452 Jakobsen, K. DK 030141/74/0002 N
Undersøgelse over grises behov for linolsyre. **Investigations on the requirement of linoleic acid in pigs.**

12453 Charlet–Lery, G. FR 010205/58/2725
Dépenses énergétiques prandiales et postprandiales du porc en croissance. **Heat production in growing pigs during ingestion and in post feeding conditions.** Publications.

12454 Vodovar, N. FR 010205/62/2702
Morphologie de l'intestin grêle du Porc et mécanismes de l'absorption intestinale des lipides. **Morphology of the small bowell of the pig and mecanisms of the intestinal absorption of lipids.** Publications.

12455 Rerat, A. FR 010205/65/2720
Etude des facteurs de variation du débit sanguin dans le système porte intestinal du porc. **Study of the variations of the flow rate in the digestive portal system in the pig.** Publications.

12456 Charlet–Lery, G. FR 010205/65/2724
Diminution des dépenses d'extrachaleur et des quotients

respiratoires induite par l'ingestion de repas très riches en protéines chez le porc en croissance: tentative de limitation de la lipogénèse par la séparation partielle des apports protéiques et énergétiques. **Lowering of heat increment and respiratory quotient caused by ingestion of meals with high protein concentration by growing pigs: reduction of lipogenesis by dissociation of energy and protein intake.** Publications.

12457 Corring, T.   FR 010205/66/2738
Physiologie de la sécrétion exocrine du pancréas chez le porc fistulé. Adaptation au régime alimentaire. **Physiology of the exocrine secretion of the fistulated pig's pancreas. Adaptation to the diet.** Publications.

12458 Laplace, J.P.; Fevrier, C.; Tomassone, T.; Seve, B.
                                   FR 010205/68/2732
Le transit digestif chez le Porc: Mécanismes de contrôle et facteurs de variation. **Gastro intestinal transit in the Pig: control mechanisms and sources of variation.** Publications.

12459 Laplace, J.P.   FR 010205/69/2728
Adaptations végétatives d'ordre nutritionnel: effets des changements de l'alimentation, de la gestation et de la lactation, et de la réduction de la capacité digestive fonctionnelle. **Adaptations in the nutrition's fields: effects of the feeding variations, of the gestation and lactation, and of the reduction of the functional digestive ability.** Publications.

12460 Corring, T.; Aumaitre, L.; Lebas, F. FR 010205/69/2739
Evolution de l'équipement enzymatique du pancréas du jeune animal entre la naissance et le sevrage. **Development of the enzyme apparatus of the exocrine pancreas of the young animal between birth and weaning.** Publications.

12461 Fremont, L.; Flanzy, J.   FR 010205/70/2713
Etude des lipides circulants chez le Porc. **Study of circulating lipids in the Pig.**

12462 Laplace, J.P.   FR 010205/70/2733
La motricité gastro–intestinale chez le Porc et le Porcelet. **Gastro–intestinal motility studies in the Pig and Piglet.** Publications.

12463 Remy, J.; Daburon, F.; Aigueperse, J.
                                   FR 010205/70/2759
Exploration fonctionnelle du tube digestif chez le porc. **Functional exploration of digestive system of pigs.**

12464 Laplace, J.P.   FR 010205/72/2731
Motricité des voies biliaires extra hépatiques du Porc et dynamique de l'excrétion de bile. **Motility of the extra hepatic biliary tract in the Pig and biliary dymanics studies.** Publications.

12465 Corring, T.   FR 010205/72/2737
Mécanismes de la régulation de la sécrétion pancréatique exocrine chez le Porc. **Mechanisms of the regulation of the pig's exocrine pancreatic secretion.** Publications.

12466 Meslin, J.C.; Daburon, F.   FR 010205/73/2703
Renouvellement cellulaire de la muqueuse de l'intestin grêle du porc holoxénique adulte. **Cell renewal of small intestinal mucosa in the adult holoxenic pig.**

12467 Rerat, A.; Corring, T.   FR 010205/74/2735
Rôle de la sécrétion exocrine du pancréas dans la digestion et l'absorption des protéines chez le Porc. **Rôle of the pancreatic exocrine secretion in digestion and absorption of proteins, in the Pig.**

12468 Corring, T.   FR 010205/74/2736
Etude de la sécrétion salivaire totale en réponse au repas chez le Porc. **Total salivary secretion related to the meal in the Pig.**

12469 Gueguen, L.; Pointillart, A. FR 010205/75/2705
Régulation hormonale du métabolisme du calcium, du phosphore et du magnésium chez le Porc. **Hormonal regulation of calcium, phosphorus and magnesium metabolism in the Pig.**

12470 Pointillart, A.; Gueguen, L.   FR 010205/75/9549 N
Régulation endocrinienne du métabolisme phosphocalcique chez le Porc. **Hormonal regulation of calcium–phosphorus metabolism in pigs.**

12471 Laplace, J.P.; Corring, T.   FR 010205/76/2729
Influence des secrétions digestives sur la motricité gastro–intestinale chez le Porc. **Effects of digestive secretions on the gastro intestinal motility in the Pig.**

12472 Laplace, J.P.; Daburon, F.   FR 010205/76/2734
Motricité et transit digestif chez le Porc après irradiation. **Gastro–intestinal motility and transit in the Pig after irradiation.**

12473 Pascal, G.; Durand, G.   FR 010205/77/9559
Détermination du taux maximum d'acides gras polyinsaturés des graisses de porc compatible avec leur utilisation en charcuterie. **Determination of the maximum level of polyinsaturated fatty acids in pig fats consistent with their technological utilization.**

12474 Henry, Y.; Bourdon, D.; Rerat, A.; Desmoulin, B.; Duee, P.   FR 010206/60/2915
Besoins en acides aminés indispensables du porc en croissance. **Essential amino acid requirements of the growing pig.**

12475 Aumaitre, L.   FR 010206/61/2900
Alimentation du porcelet sevré de plus en plus précocement. **Rearing of piglet weaned as early as possible.**

12476 Henry, Y.   FR 010206/62/2911
Relation entre le niveau d'ingestion alimentaire et l'état d'engraissement chez le porc. **Feed intake and carcass adiposity in the pig.**

12477 Aumaitre, L.; Seve, B.; Le Dividich, J.
                                   FR 010206/64/2905
Etude des principaux composants de la ration chez le porcelet. Formulation. **Basic feed for piglet starter rations. Formulation of diets.**

12478 Henry, Y.; Bourdon, D.; Perez, J.M.
                                   FR 010206/66/2913
Valeur énergétique des aliments pour le porc. **Energy value of feed ingredients for pigs.**

12479 Bourdon, D.; Etienne, M.; Seve, B.; Aumaitre, L.; Henry, Y.; Fevrier, C.   FR 010206/67/2906
Utilisation des nouvelles sources azotées de remplacement dans l'alimentation du porc. **Utilization of new protein sources in pig feeding.**

12480 Desmoulin, B.; Bourdon, D.; Henry, Y.
FR 010206/68/2901
Influence des plans de rationnement quantitatif et qualitatif suivant le sexe et après la castration du porc mâle sur la qualité des carcasses. **Limited level of nutrition (Energy, Proteins and Amino-acids) in young male, female and castrated male pigs. Effect on carcass quality.**

12481 Le Devidich, J.; Roustan, J.L.
FR 010206/69/2934
Valeur énergétique et conditions d'emploi dans l'alimentation du porc de produits tropicaux riches en glucides. **Tropical feedstuff with a high glucide content in pig nutrition. Energetic value and level of nutrition.** Publications.

12482 Henry, Y.; Rerat, A.; Bourdon, D. FR 010206/70/2914
Besoin global de matières azotées du porc en croissance. **Protein requirement of the growing pig (non essential nitrogen).**

12483 Aumaitre, L.; Thiry, M.; Ducluzeau, R.; Ravaud, H.
FR 010206/71/2904
Alimentation du porcelet axénique. **Rearing of germ-free piglet.**

12484 Etienne, M.; Henry, Y. FR 010206/71/2910
Evaluation des besoins en énergie de la truie en gestation. **Assessment of the energy requirement of the pregnant sow.**

12485 Duee, P. FR 010206/71/2936
Apport optimum de protéines à la truie en gestation et en lactation. Etude du besoin en acides aminés pendant cette période. **Optimum contribution of proteins to the pregnant and lactating sow. Study of amino acids requirement during the pregancy and the lactation.** Publications.

12486 Henry, Y. FR 010206/72/2312
Profil métabolique et état d'engraissement du porc. **Metabolic profile and carcass adiposity in the pig.**

12487 Etienne, M.; Duee, P. FR 010206/72/2908
Alimentation énergétique et azotée de la truie en croissance: conséquences sur les performances de reproduction. **Energy and protein feeding of the growing gilt: effects on breeding performances.**

12488 Seve, B.; Aumaitre, L. FR 010206/72/2917
Recherche de sources de protéines dans les aliments d'allaitement artificiel et de sevrage du porcelet. **New protein sources in milk-replacers and foods for early weaned piglets.**

12489 Etienne, M.; Aumaitre, L. FR 010206/73/2907
Alimentation de la truie sevrée précocement. **Feeding of the sow early weaned.**

12490 Etienne, M.; Duee, P. FR 010206/73/2909
Possibilité d'utilisation des différentes matières premières alimentaires par la truie en gestation et en lactation. **Utilization of different feeding stuffs by the pregnant or lactating sow.**

12491 Seve, B. FR 010206/73/2916
Effets du sevrage sur les paramètres des métabolismes énergétiques et azoté et leur variabilité. Définition d'un plan d'alimentation adéquat au cours de la période post sevrage chez le porcelet. **Effects of weaning upon energy and nitrogen metabolisms of the baby pig. Variability of their parameters. Assessment of a proper feeding plan during the post weaning period.**

12492 Seve, B.; Duee, P. FR 010206/75/2919
Besoin en acides aminés du porcelet à partir de 3 kg de poids vif (lysine tryptophane acides aminés soufrés). **Amino-acid requirements of the piglet from 3 kg liveweight (lysine tryptophane sulphur amino acids).**

12493 Perez, J.M. FR 010206/75/2933
Emploi d'additifs alimentaires chez le porc. **Feed additives in pig.**

12494 Ducluzeau, R.; Raibaud, P. FR 010216/77/9601 N
Ecologie microbienne : effet de barrière exercé contre Escherichia coli dans le tube digestif de souris gnotoxénique par des souches bactériennes provenant des fèces de porcelets holoxéniques. **Microbial ecology : Barrier effect exerted by holoxenic piglet fecal bacterial strains against the Escherichia coli in the gas trointestinal tract of gnotoxenic mice.**

12495 Ducluzeau, R.; Raibaud, P. FR 010216/77/9605
Ecologie microbienne : etablissement compare des premières bacteries dans le tube digestif de porcelets holoxeniques recevant ou non du colostrum. **Microbial ecology : Comparative establishment of the first bacteria into the gastrointestinal tract of holoxenic piglets receiving colostrum or not.**

12496 Charlet, G.; Ruckebusch, M.; Desmoulin, B.
FR 010217/56/9537
Variation de la production de chaleur du porc en croissance au cours de la journee en fonction de l'apport azote et du moment de son ingestion. **Thermogenesis variation in growing pig during the day in relation with nitrogen supply and the time of intake.**

12497 Auffray, P.; Felix, B.; Marcilloux, J.C.
FR 010217/67/9529 N
Neurophysiologie de la prise alimentaire chez le porc. **Regulation of feed intake in the pig : neurophysiological aspects and feeding pattern.**

12498 Rerat, A.; Roger; Vaissade; Vaugelade, P.
FR 010217/71/9592 N
Etude quantitative de la digestion et de l'absorption des glucides chez le porc. **Kinetics of the digestion and absorption of carbohydrates in the pig.**

12499 Rerat, A.; Vaugelade, P.; Jung, J.; Roger; Vaissade
FR 010217/71/9593 N
Etude quantitative de la digestion et de l'absorption des matières azotées chez le Porc (azoté endogène, diverses protéines alimentaires). **Kinetics of the digestion and absorption of nitrogenous matters in the pig (endogenous nitrogen, various feed proteins).**

12500 Laplace, J.P. FR 010217/72/9535 N
Motricité gastro-intestinale chez le porc : influence de l'alimentation. **Gastro intestinal motility in the Pig : Effects of feeding.**

12501 Rerat, A.; Roger; Vaissade; Pion, R.; Vaugelade, P.
FR 010217/73/9591 N
Etude qualitative de la digestion et de l'absorption des matières azotées chez le Porc (acides aminés libres, urée). **Kinetics of digestion and absorption of nitrogenous matters in**

the pig.

12502 Laplace, J.P.; Cuber, J.C.   FR 010217/76/9534 N
Transit digestif chez le Porc. **Gastro intestinal food passage in the Pig.**

12503 Corring, T.; Nunes Simoes, C.   FR 010217/76/9542
Adaptation de la secretion pancreatique exocrine au regime alimentaire chez le porc: role des produits de l'hydrolyse enzymatique. **Adaptation of the exocrine pancréatic secretion to the diet in the pig: Role of the enzyme hydrolysis products.**

12504 Laplace, J.P.   FR 010217/77/9531
Régulation nerveuse de la motricité digestive chez le porc. **Nervous control of G.I. tract mobility in the Pig.**

12505 Corring, T.; Juste, C.   FR 010217/77/9540
Physiologie de la secretion biliaire chez le porc, en relation avec l'alimentation. **Physiology of the bile secretion in the pig in relationship with feeding.**

12506 Corring, T.; Leger, C.; Mourot, J. FR 010217/77/9541
Relation entre la secretion pancreatique exocrine et la secretion biliaire chez le porc. **Relationship between the exocrine pancreatic secretion and the bile secretion in the pig.**

12507 Corring, T.; Simoes; Juste, C.; Bourdon, D.; Nunes, C.
        FR 010217/77/9543
Role de la bile dans la digestion d'un aliment chez le porc, effet du niveau intestinal de la reintroduction de bile. **Role of the bile in the digestion of a diet. Effect of the intestinal site of the bile reintroduction.**

12508 Stephens; Heron   GB 010301/00/0046 R
Water metabolism in the pig.

12509 Stephens   GB 010301/00/0053 R
Control of food intake in the pig.

12510 Close   GB 010301/00/0058 R
Studies on the energy metabolism of the sow before and after parturition.

12511 Close   GB 010301/00/0061
The utilization of protein and energy in the pig.

12512 Ash   GB 010301/00/0063 R
Metabolic studies on the parturient and lactating sow and agalactia.

12513 Close   GB 010301/75/0074
Energy metabolism studies of boars, castrates and gilts.

12514 Stanier; Close   GB 010301/77/0079
Factors influencing growth and carcass composition in the weaned pig.

12515 Smith; James   GB 010308/76/0001
Intestinal absorption during development and its relevance to the basic physiology of intestinal transport.

12516 Low   GB 011711/00/0002
Nutrient requirements and digestion in the pig.

12517 Braude; Mitchell   GB 011711/00/0003
Preservation and use of dairy products as feed.

12518 Braude; Mitchell   GB 011711/00/0004
Growth promoting substances (e.g. copper, Payzone, Grofas, etc).

12519 Braude; Mitchell   GB 011711/00/0005
Evaluate new feeds (e.g. hydrocarbon yeast, lucerne juice, etc) for pigs.

12520 Braude; Mitchell   GB 011711/00/0006
Comparison of feeding techniques.

12521 Fowler; Livingstone   GB 030611/00/0004 R
Value of leguminous crops as protein sources for pigs.

12522 Jones; Hovell   GB 030611/00/0007
Nutrient requirements of the baby pig.

12523 Greenhalg   GB 030611/00/0012
Co-ordinated sow trials:nutritional and management factors requiring large population samples for quantification.

12524 Fuller; Livingstn   GB 030611/00/0013 R
Assessing the amino acid needs of the sow.

12525 Jones; Howell   GB 030611/00/0014
Effect on subsequent performance of early breeding of gilts and value of once–bred gilt as producer of meat.

12526 Houseman; Fowler   GB 030611/00/0017
Voluntary feed intake and appetite regulation.

12527 Cadenhead; Jones   GB 030611/00/0031 R
Purine metabolism.

12528 Livingstn; Fowler   GB 030611/76/0037
Studies of sites of digestion in the pig given different feed stuffs.

12529 Fowler; MacPherson   GB 030611/76/0039
Nutrition of the sow (intensive experiments).

12530 Kay; Goodall   GB 030612/77/0023
Fermentative digestion in the pig.

12531 McCracken   GB 040401/00/0011
Alternative sources of protein and energy for growing pigs.

12532 McCracken   GB 040401/00/0012
Effect of environment and related factors on the energy metabolism of growing pigs.

12533 Jordan   GB 040401/78/0029
Critical temperature of the fasted and fed early–weaned pig.

12534 Mccracken; Pearce   GB 040401/79/0030 N
Added fat in rations for growing pigs.

12535 Researcher not indicated   GB 050122/00/0002 R
Pigs: nutrition; improvement of feed utilisation.

12536 Researcher not indicated   GB 050162/00/0002
Pigs: nutrition; improvement of feed utilisation.

12537 Hillyer   GB 060102/00/0019
Novel feeds for growing and finishing pigs.

12538 Whittemore GB 060102/00/0020
Optimal nutrient requirements for pigs determined by modelling techniques.

12539 Whittemore GB 060102/00/0027
Quantification of parameters controlling growth responses to nutrients by pigs.

12540 Peers GB 060103/00/0003
Evaluation of foods for pigs.

12541 English GB 060208/00/0014
Diet formulation for efficient feeding of growing and breeding pigs with reference to ad–lib systems.

12542 Robertson GB 060224/78/0011 N
The design of feed troughs for pigs.

12543 Laird GB 060315/00/0009
Feeding of sows during lactation.

12544 O'Grady, J.F. IE 060400/63/0973 R
Sow nutrition. Performance. Publications.

12545 Hanrahan, T.J.; Kearney, P.A. IE 060400/68/0976 R
Interchangeability of feeding ingredients. Publications.

12546 O'Grady, J.F. IE 060400/72/0971 R
Nutrition and the management of weaned pigs. Publications.

12547 Hanrahan, T.J. IE 060400/77/1346 R
A comparison of gilts and boars fed ad libitum or to a restricted scale. Publications.

12548 O'Grady, J.F. IE 060400/77/1358 R
Evaluation of feed additives in pig rations. Publications.

12549 Mordenti, A. IT 040218/73/1821
Ricerche sull'allattamento artificiale e sullo svezzamento dei suinetti. **Research on artificial feeding and weaning of suckling pigs.**

12550 Mordenti, A. IT 040236/78/1160 N
Utilizzazione di amidi parzialmente idrolizzati nell'alimentazione dei suini con particolare riferimento alla preparazione di mangimi per svezzamento precoce. **The use of partially hydrolysed starch in pig feeding with particular emphasis on feedstuff formulae used in precocious weaning.**

12551 Galvano, G.; Lanza, A.; Gallo, C. IT 040319/75/0001
Effetti dell'acido erucico della farina di colza in diete per suini. **Effects of the rapeseed erucic acid in diets for pigs.**

12552 Di Lella, T. IT 040709/77/0597 R
Indagini sulla posibilità di valorizzazione di alcune popolazioni suine nel Mezogiorno mediante la prevalente utilizzazione delle risorse alimentari locali. **Research on the possibility of developing existing pig breeding in southern Italy using locally available food predominantly.**

12553 Romboli, B. IT 041123/77/0581 R
Alimentazione idrica, salinità delle acque, inconvenienti sulle carni e sui prodotti di trasformazione, indagini sperimentali nella specie suina. **Water nutrition and the salt content of water, negative effects on the quality of meat and on meat processing products, experimental research on pigs.**

12554 Tartari, E.; Bianchi, M. IT 041216/79/0001 N
L'impiego di antibiotici nell'alimentazione dei suini. **The employ of antibiotic in swine feeding.**

12555 Giardini, A. IT 062400/74/0112
Confronto tra "pastoni" di granella di mais e sorgo,con e senza lisina,nell'ingrasso del suino leggero. **Comparison of high moisture corn and sorghum grain,with and without lysine,in fattening young swine.**

12556 Minkema, D. NL 010112/67/1185
Onderzoek naar de efficiëntie van prestatietoets en toomgenoten–onderzoek bij varkens bij gerantsoeneerde en bij onbeperkte voedering. **Experimental evaluation of the efficiency performance testing and sib testing of pigs on restricted and ad lib feeding.** Publications.

12557 Lenis, N.P. NL 010115/67/5447
Gebruikswaarde van bestaande en nieuwe voedermiddelen voor varkens (voederproeven met groepen). **Possible use and feeding value of existing and newly introduced feeds for swine.**

12558 Lenis, N.P. NL 010115/67/5448
Gebruik van actieve stoffen in de varkensvoeding (incidentele voederproeven). **The effect of feed additives in rations for swine.**

12559 Lenis, N.P. NL 010115/74/5449
De eiwit (aminozuren) behoefte bij varkens van verschillend type of ras in samenhang met het benutten van de compensatoire groei (voederproeven, verteringsproeven). **Protein (amino acids) requirements in pigs of different type or breed, also in connection with the utilization of compensatory growth.**

12560 Jongbloed, A.W. NL 010115/74/5450
De optimale P–behoefte bij varkens mede gelet op milieuaspecten. **P–requirements of pigs in connection with the environment pollution and leg weakness.** Publications.

12561 Lenis, N.P. NL 010115/76/7226
Vermindering van het Cu–gebruik in de mestvarkensvoeding en het wegnemen van ongunstige gevolgen daarvan voor de varkensmesterij. **Diminshing the use of copper in pig nutrition; preventing pig farming from unfavourable consequences.**

12562 Jongbloed, A.W. NL 010115/78/8613 N
Verbetering dierlijk welzijn via vermindering van biggensterfte door het terugdringen van slingerziekte en diarrhee o.m. met behulp van voedingsmaatregelen. **Improvement of animal wellbeing by reducing the mortality in piglets by forcing back the colienterotoxicosis (amongst others by means of feeding methods).**

12563 Jongbloed, A.W. NL 010115/78/8614 N
Verbetering van het welzijn van fokzeugen door onderzoek omtrent de opfokintensiteit van zeugjes en levensduur van fokzeugen. **Improvement of the wellbeing of breeding sows by research concerning the growth intensity of gilts and longevity of breeding sows.**

12564 Kempen, G.J.M. van NL 020059/76/7362
De voerfrequentie bij mestvarkens. **The feeding frequency in fattening pigs.**

D 3200 – Animal nutrition

12565 Kempen, G.J.M. van   NL 020059/76/7363
De voeding van varkens in verband met vruchtbaarheid.
Feeding of pigs in relation to fertility.

12566 Cornelisse, J.L.   NL 030002/71/8030
Decontaminatie van voeders voor mestvarkens en
slachtkuikens m.b.t. Salmonellae, fungi en mycotoxinen
d.m.v. toevoeging van organische zuren. **Decontamination of
feed for fattening pigs and broilers by organic acids with regard
to Salmonellae, fungi and mycotoxins.** Publications.

12567 Berende, P.L.M.   NL 050305/65/8011
Nutritionele en toxicologische evaluatie van gist gegroeid op
paraffine bij varkens. **Nutritional and toxicological evaluation
of yeast grown on paraffins in pigs.**

12568 Berende, P.L.M.   NL 050305/71/8030
Decontaminatie van voeders voor mestvarkens en
slachtkuikens m.b.t. Salmonellae, fungi en mycotoxinen
d.m.v. toevoeging van organische zuren. **Decontamination of
feed for fattening pigs and broilers by organic acids with regard
to Salmonellae, fungi and mycotoxins.** Publications.

12569 Schutte, J.B.   NL 050305/73/8009
Dierlijke en plantaardige eiwitten als substituut van
melkeiwitten in rantsoenen voor jonge biggen. **Replacement of
milk protein by animal and vegetable protein in rations for
piglets.**

12570 Terluin, R.W.   NL 050305/74/8002
Methionine en cystine behoefte van mestvarkens. **Methionine
and cystine requirements of fattening pigs.**

12571 Schutte, J.B.   NL 050305/74/8016
Nutritionele evaluatie van eiwitisolaten bereid uit veldbonen
(Vicia faba) bij pluimvee en varkens. **Nutritional evaluation of
protein isolates from field beans (Vicia faba) in poultry and
pigs.**

12572 Hellemond, K.K. van   NL 050305/74/8041
Het ontwikkelen van een methode voor vroegtijdige
onderkenning van effecten van contaminanten in het voedsel
van fokvarkens op de reproduktie en teratogene afwijkingen
bij biggen. **Development of a method for early detection of the
effects of contaminants in the feed of breeding pigs on
reproduction and teratogenic effects of the piglets.**

12573 Schutte, J.B.   NL 050305/75/8014
Nutritionele en toxicologische evaluatie van microorganismen
eiwit gegroeid op koolhydraatrijke substraten bij pluimvee en
varkens. **Nutritional and toxicological evaluation of single cell
proteins grown on carbohydrate-rich substrates in poultry and
pigs.**

12574 Schutte, J.B.   NL 050305/76/8035
Biologische beschikbaarheid van mineralen (o.a. fosfor) voor
kuikens en varkens. **Bioavailability of minerals a.o. phosphor
for chickens and pigs.**

12575 Huisman, J.   NL 050305/78/8005
De vertering van aminozuren in de verschillende gedeelten van
het maagdarmkanaal van varkens. **The digestion of the amino
acids in the different parts of the gastrointestinal tract of pigs.**

Poultry and domestic birds in general (B 4400)

See also 11308, 11575, 12264, 12271, 12273, 12274, 12275,
12566, 12568, 12571, 12573, 12804, 13358, 13359, 13361, 13364,
14301, 14828, 19403

12576 Krampitz, G.; Lesur, E.   DE 111401/75/0002
Resorption, Transport und Verteilung von Beryllium im
Huhn. **Absorption, transport and distribution of beryllium in
the hen.**

12577 Hartfiel, W.; Willms, G.   DE 111451/75/0001
Möglichkeiten einer Veränderung der Prüfzeiten bei der
Futterwertleistungsprüfung für Geflügel. **Variable test times in
the feed conversion tests for poultry.**

12578 Hartfiel, W.; Wasmund, K.D.   DE 111451/75/0002
Die umsetzbare Energie von Lecithin beim Geflügel. **The
metabolisable energy of lecithin in poultry.**

12579 Wegner, R.–M.; Flick, K.; Petersen, J.
        DE 111501/75/0002
Zur restriktiven Fütterung von Legehennen. **Restricted feeding
of laying hens.**

12580 Günther, K.–D.; Tekin, C.   DE 132300/77/0001
Untersuchungen zur Charakterisierung spezifischer
Substanzen mit anabolischer Wirksamkeit bei Geflügel.
**Studies concerning specific substances with anabolic effects in
poultry.**

12581 Härtel, H.; Scholtyssek, S.   DE 144685/75/0008
Einsatz von Proteasen im Hühnerfutter. **Utilization of
proteases in feed for hens.**

12582 Härtel, H.; Scholtyssek, S.   DE 144685/78/0001 N
Wirkstoffe in der Geflügelfütterung. **Active substances in fowl
feeds.**

12583 Kreuzer, W.; Unsinn, P.   DE 160733/70/0006 N
Resorption, Verteilung, Ausscheidung und intrazelluläre
Lokalisation von Zn–65 bzw. Zn im Körper von Hühnern.
**Resorption, distribution, excretion, and intracellular
localization of Zn–65 resp. of Zn in poultry.**

12584 Vogt, H.; Harnisch, S.   DE 201300/70/0009
Verwendung von einheimischen Hülsenfrüchten – Süsslupine,
Ackerbohne – als Futtermittel in der Geflügelfütterung.
**Domestic legumes – blue and yellow lupins, field beans – in
poultry rations.**

12585 Harnisch, S.; Vogt, H.   DE 201300/71/5002
Verbesserung der Ausnutzung der pflanzlichen
Gerüstsubstanzen durch das Geflügel. Prüfung verschiedener
Geflügelarten, Enzymzusatz, technologische Massnahmen.
**Improving the utilization of fibrous substances by poultry.
Investigations of various poultry races, additional enzymes,**

12586 Vogt, H.; Stute, K.; Torges, H.-G.; Harnisch, S.
        DE 201300/72/0007
Der Einfluss von Futtermitteln mit futtereigenen Schadstoffen
ın der Geflügelfütterung. **Feedstuffs with antinutritional factors
in poultry rations.**

12587 Vogt, H.; Harnisch, S.; Stute, K.   DE 201300/73/0008
Einsatz von Einzellerproteinen – Bakterieneiweiss, Hefen,
Algen –. **Application of single-cell proteins – bacterial protein,**

yeasts, algae –.

12588 Harnisch, S.; Vogt, H. DE 201300/74/0001
Der Einsatz von Proteasen im Geflügelfutter. **Proteases in poultry rations.**

12589 Vogt, H. DE 201300/75/0002
Einsatz von Lecithin im Geflügelfutter. **Lecithin in poultry rations.**

12590 Vogt, H. DE 201300/78/0001 N
Rezyklierung von Rest– und Abfallstoffen in der Geflügelfütterung. **Recycling of residual and waste matters in poultry feeding.**

12591 Vogt, H. DE 201300/78/0003 N
Senkung des Nährstoffaufwandes beim Geflügel durch bessere Quantifizierung des Nährstoffbedarfes. **Lowering of the nutrient expense for poultry by better quantification of the nutrient requirements.**

12592 Harnisch, S. DE 201300/78/0004 N
Klärung der Ursachen individueller Unterschiede in der Nährstoffverwertung, insbesondere in der Energieverwertung beim Geflügel. **Investigation of the reasons for individual differences in the nutrient efficiency, especially in the energy efficiency of poultry.**

12593 Vogt, H. DE 201300/78/0005 N
Einsatz neuer Futtermittel beziehungsweise Ersatzfuttermittel in der Geflügelfütterung. **Use of new feedstuffs, resp. substitute feedstuffs in poultry rations.**

12594 Nezel, K. DE 201300/78/0008 N
Einfluss von mit toxischen umweltrelevanten Schwermetallen– Blei, Cadmium, Quecksilber, Arsen unterschiedlicher Bindungsart – kontaminiertem Futter auf die Leistung der Tiere und auf Rückstandsgehalte in den Eiern und im Geflügelfleisch. **The effect of rations contaminated with toxic heavy meatals – lead, cadmium, mercury, arsenic with different kind of chemical bounding – on the performance of layers and on the residues in eggs and tissues.**

12595 Wegner, R.–M.; Rauch, H.–W.; Torges, H.–G.
DE 201300/78/0020 N
Mast– und Ausschlachtungsversuche von Geflügel – Jungmasthähnchen, Enten, Puten, Gänse –. **Fattening and carcass–quality of different species of poultry – young broilers, ducks, turkeys, geese.**

12596 Fuhrken, E. DE 511250/78/0004 N
Legeleistungsversuch mit Flavomycin. **Experiment on laying performance with flavomycin.**

12597 Fuhrken, E. DE 511250/78/0006 N
Versuch mit Luzernegrünmehl zur Prüfung von Eidotterfarbe und Geschmacksbeeinflussung. **Experiment with Lucerne green meal for testing the colour of egg yolk and for taking influence on flavour.**

12598 Fuhrken, E. DE 511250/78/0007 N
Legehennenversuch mit verschiedenen Energiegehalten im Futter. **Experiment with layers by different energy content in feeds.**

12599 Petersen, V.E. DK 010203/75/0001
Rationering af energi og/eller protein til opdræt af kyllinger af kødtype. **Rationing of energy and/or protein for slaughter chicken raising.**

12600 Petersen, V.E. DK 010203/77/0001
Æglæggende høners behov for kalcium. **The need for calcium by egglaying hens.**

12601 Petersen, V.E. DK 010203/77/0002
Praktiske forsøg over æglægningsfoderets protein– og vitaminindhold. **Practical experiments concerning the protein and vitamin contents of egglaying feed.**

12602 Ambrosen, T. DK 010203/77/0003 N
Slagtekyllingers individuelle foderudnyttelse og sammensætning af kropvæv. **Feed utilization and body tissue composition of individual slaughter chickens.**

12603 Fris Jensen, J. DK 010203/77/0007
Den fysiske tilstand af foder til slagtekyllinger. **The physical condition of slaughter chicken feed.**

12604 Petersen, V.E. DK 010203/77/0015
Rapsskrå som proteinkilde til kyllinger. **Crushed rape as a protein source for chickens.**

12605 Petersen, V.E.; Jensen, O. DK 010203/77/0016 R
Foderværdi af tapiokamel og majsglutenfoder til slagtekyllinger. **The feeding value of tapioca meal and maize–gluten–feed for broilers.**

12606 Petersen, V.E. DK 010203/77/0018
Praktiske forsøg over indflydelsen af foderets struktur på kyllingers vækst. **Practical experiments concerning the influence of feed structure on chicken growth.**

12607 Petersen, V.E.; Høj, F.; Thomsen, M.G.; Munck, L.
DK 010203/78/0002 N
Foderværdi til æglæggende høner af majs og majsbiprodukter. **The feeding value of maize and maize byproducts for egglaying hens.**

12608 Petersen, V.E.; Høj, F.; Thomsen, M.G.; Munck, L.
DK 010203/78/0003 N
Foderværdi af byg og bygbiprodukter til rugeægproducerende Hvid Plymouth Rock–høner. **The feeding value of barley and barley byproducts for White Plymouth Rock breeding hens.**

12609 Petersen, V.E. DK 010203/78/0005 N
Flyvehavres spireevne efter formaling og passage gennem høners fordøjelsessystem. **The germinating power of wild oats after grinding and passage through the digestive tract of hens.**

12610 Mason, V.C. DK 010206/77/0001 R
Sand omsættelig energi målt i forsøg med fjerkræ. **True Metabolizable energy measured in experiments with poultry.**

12611 Mason, V.C.; Rotenberg, S. DK 010206/78/0004 N
Undersøgelse af æg– og blodparametre hos høns ved henholdsvis højt og lavt indhold af protein i foderet. **Egg and blood parameters in hens fed a high or low level of protein.**

12612 Jensen, A.T.; Ranvig, H. DK 030106/78/0003 N
Sammenligning af reaktiviteten af østersskaller, hjertemuslinger og hårde kalksten med henblik på anvendelse til æglæggende høns. **A comparison of reactivity profiles for**

oyster and cockle shells, soft and hard limestones with special reference to their effect in the feeding of egg–laying hens.

12613 Ranvig, H.   DK 030142/79/0001 N
Calciumkilder til æglæggende høner. **The reactivity of calcium sources used as mineral additives to poultry feed.**

12614 Whitehead   GB 010707/00/0034 R
Metabolism and deposition of fat.

12615 Wells   GB 010708/00/0007 R
Role of steroid hormones in the differentiation and function of the oviduct.

12616 Jackson; Stevenson   GB 040401/79/0033 N
Dried skim milk in poultry diets.

12617 Jackson; Stevenson   GB 040601/78/0033 N
Dried skim milk in poultry diets.

12618 D'Mello   GB 060101/00/0001 R
Biochemical aspects of food intake regulation in poultry.

12619 D'Mello   GB 060101/00/0002
New protein sources for poultry.

12620 Dun   GB 060305/78/0005
Nutrient utilisation in feeding systems for fowls.

12621 Giavarini, I.   IT 040212/73/1816
Ricerche sull'impiego di alcuni prodotti ad azione auxinica e di taluni chemioterapici nell'alimentazione delle specie avicole. **Research on the use of some auxinic products and chemotherapeutants in poultry feeding.** Publications.

12622 Giavarini, I.   IT 040212/74/0563
Zincobacitracina, moenomicina e virginiamicina nella alimentazione avicola. **Zinc bacitracin, moenomycin and virginiamycin in poultry feeding.**

12623 Ruffini–Castrovilli, C.M.   IT 040602/77/0290 R
Indagini sul metabolismo lipidico nel pollo ed in altri monogastrici alimentati con lieviti coltivati su N. paraffine. **Research on the oestral metabolism of the chicken and other monogastric birds fed on yeasts cultured on N. paraffin media.**

12624 Janssen, W.M.M.A.; Terpstra, K.   NL 010109/65/7871
Het onderzoek ter bepaling van de omzetbare energie van voedermiddelen voor pluimvee. **The metabolizable energy of feedstuffs for poultry.**

12625 Janssen, W.M.M.A.; Terpstra, K.   NL 010109/65/7873
Onderzoek ter bepaling van de omzetbare energie en de verteerbaarheid van voedervetten voor pluimvee. **Determination of the metabolizable energy and the digestibility of fats for poultry.**

12626 Helder, J.F.   NL 010109/70/3130
Onderzoek naar de voederwaarde van pluimveevoeder grondstoffen. **Research on the feeding value of raw materials for poultry feedstuffs.** Publications.

12627 Helder, J.F.   NL 010109/70/3131 R
De landbouwkundige betekenis van additieven in pluimvee voeders. **The agricultural effects of additives in poultry feedstuffs.** Publications.

12628 Terpstra, K.; Janssen, W.M.M.A.   NL 010109/70/7870
Onderzoek ter bepaling van de verteerbaarheid van eiwit en aminozuren in voedermiddelen voor pluimvee. **Determination of the digestibility of protein and amino acids in feedstuffs for poultry.**

12629 Kan, C.A.   NL 010109/72/3912
Het voorkomen van schadelijke stoffen in pluimveeprodukten via de voeding. **The occurrence of noxious compounds in poultry products from the feed.** Publications.

12630 Holsheimer, J.P.   NL 010109/72/3915 R
Het opbouwen van een databank t.b.v. het samenstellen van pluimvee voeders. **Collecting figures for a data bank for the formulation of poultry feeds.**

12631 Terpstra, K.; Janssen, W.M.M.A.   NL 010109/73/7872
Onderzoek ter bepaling van de OE en van de verteerbaarheid van eiwit en aminozuren voor pluimvee in voedermiddelen afkomstig van ontwikkelingslanden. **The determination of metabolizable energy and of digestibility of protein and amino acids in poultry feedstuffs from developing countries.**

12632 Kan, C.A.   NL 010109/75/6068
Toxische effecten van milieukritische stoffen in pluimveevoeders op pluimvee. **Toxic effects of environmentally hazardous compounds in poultry feed on poultry.** Publications.

12633 Scheele, C.W.   NL 010109/76/7229
De stofwisseling en de voeding van pluimvee onder tropische klimaatomstandigheden. **The metabolism and the nutrition of poultry kept under tropical conditions.**

12634 Kan, C.A.   NL 010109/77/7868
Mycotoxinen en pluimvee; residuen en effecten. **Mycotoxins and Poultry; residues and effects.**

12635 EL Boushy, A.R.   NL 020047/73/5073
Onderzoek naar de beschikbaarheid van aminozuren in voedermiddelen voor pluimvee. **Investigation on availability for poultry of amino acids in feedstuffs.** Publications.

12636 Schutte, J.B.   NL 050305/65/8010
Nutritionele en toxicologische evaluatie bij pluimvee van gist gegroeid op paraffine. **Nutritional and toxicological evaluation in poultry of yeast grown on paraffins.**

Chickens (B 4410)

See also 11340, 11341, 11342, 11343, 11555, 11556, 11557, 11558, 11559, 11986, 12574, 12845, 12846, 12854, 13404, 14887

12637 Vanbelle, M.; Fockedey, J.; Arnould, R.   BE 020601/76/0012
Le rôle des protéines dans le contrôle de l'appétit chez le poussin en croissance. **Protein action in the control of appetite by growing chickens.** Publications.

12638 De Groote, G.; Van Wambeke, F.   BE 070200/76/0040 R
Onderzoekingen over de energiebehoeften en voederbeperkingsmethoden tijdens de legperiode bij slachtkuikenmoederdieren. **Investigations on the energy requirements and feed restriction methods during the laying period of broiler breeder hens.** Publications.

12639 De Groote, G.; Fontaine, G.   BE 070200/76/0045
Energiebalans studies met lichte– en halfzware leghennen.
Energy balance studies with light– and medium weight laying hens.

12640 De Groote, G.; Fontaine, G.   BE 070200/78/0054 R
Bepaling van de energiebehoeften voor onderhoud en productie van zware slachtkuikenmoederdieren. **Evaluation of the energetic requirements for maintenance and production of meat type laying hens.**

12641 De Groote, G.; Fontaine, G.   BE 070200/79/0055 N
Studie van de factoren die de voederefficiëntie bij leghennen beïnvloeden. **Study of the factors affecting feed efficiency in laying hens.**

12642 De Groote, G.; Huyghebaert, G.   BE 070200/79/0056 N
Het gebruik van graanvervangende afvalstoffen in meel– en korrelrantsoenen bij lichte– en halfzware leghennen. **The use of cereal replacing offal ingredients in mash and pelleted diets for light and medium weight laying hens.**

12643 Van Aelten, G.; Hens, J.   BE 140000/78/0061 N
Nieuwe samengestelde voeders voor leghennen. **New concentrates for chickens.**

12644 Krampitz, G.; Vetter, G.   DE 111401/77/0001
Einfluss des Berylliums auf den Knochenstoffwechsel des Huhnes. **Influence of beryllium on bone metabolism of the hen.**

12645 Krampitz, G.; Mathiszik, P.   DE 111401/77/0002
Einfluss des Berylliums auf die Reproduktionsorgane des Huhnes. **Influence of beryllium on the reproductive tract of the hen.**

12646 Krampitz, G.; Weisse, E.   DE 111401/77/0003
Einfluss des Berylliums auf den Gehirnstoffwechsel beim Huhn. **Influence of beryllium on brain metabolism of poultry.**

12647 Krampitz, G.; Sauerwald, N.   DE 111401/78/0001 N
Einfluss von Beryllium auf den Leberstoffwechsel des Huhnes. **Influence of beryllium on the liver metabolism of chicken.**

12648 Niess, E.   DE 111450/71/0002
Wirkungsmechanismus von rohen Sojabohnen bzw. Trypsininhibitoren bei der Aufnahme durch Küken und Ratten. **Influences of unextracted soy beans and soy trypsin inhibitors in the intestines of chicken and rats.**

12649 Müller, R.; Boye, H.P.   DE 111450/74/0001
Biologische Futterbewertung im Kükentest. **Biological evaluation of feedstuff by a chick bioassay.**

12650 Günther, K.–D.; Mohme, H.; Tekin, C.; Strohschneider, R.   DE 132300/77/0003
Untersuchungen zum Protein– und Aminosäurenansatz beim Geflügel. **Investigations on protein and amino acid metabolism in chicken.**

12651 Greife, H.; Molnar, S.   DE 132300/78/0004 N
Untersuchungen zum Nucleinsäurestoffwechsel mit Hilfe von C–14–markierten Purin– und Pyrimidinbasen bei der Ratte und beim Küken. **Investigations of nucleic acid metabolism with C–14 labelled purine and pyrimidine bases in rat and chick.**

12652 Greife, H.; Badawy, N.; Molnar, S.   DE 132300/78/0006 N
Vergleichende Untersuchungen über die Grösse der N–Fraktionen im Harn nach unterschiedlicher Nucleinsäurezufuhr an Ratten und Küken. **Comparative investigations on the N–fractions in urine of rats and chicken after different supply of nucleid acids.**

12653 Abel, H.; Rosenow, H.; Günther, K.–D.   DE 132303/75/0002
Einfluss verschiedener Futterinhalts– und Zusatzstoffe auf die Phosphorkinetik des wachsenden Geflügels. **Influence of different feed constituents and additives on kinetic parameters of phosphorus metabolism in growing chicks.**

12654 Härtel, H.   DE 144685/75/0009
Der Einsatz neuerer Futtermittel in der Geflügelfütterung. **Utilization of more novel feedstuffs in poultry feeding.**

12655 Vogt, H.; Nezel, K.; Torges, H.–G.   DE 201300/73/0009
Beeinflussung der Eischalenqualität durch die Fütterung. **The influence of feeding on egg shell strength.**

12656 Vogt, H.   DE 201300/73/0010
Überprüfung von Substanzen, die die Futterverwertung beim Geflügel verbessern. **Testing of substances improving the feed utilization of poultry.**

12657 Fuhrken, E.   DE 511250/78/0002 N
Sojabohnen–Vollmehl im Broilermastfutter. **Whole meal of soya bean in broiler fattening feed.**

12658 Fuhrken, E.   DE 511250/78/0003 N
Rapsschrot im Broilermastfutter. **Coarse meal of rape in broiler fattening feed.**

12659 Petersen, V.E.   DK 010203/77/8001 N
Kyllingers natriumbehov og–indhold i relation til foderets natrium/kaliumforhold. **The sodium requirement of 0–3 weeks old chickens in relation to the sodium: potassium ratio of the feed.**

12660 Petersen, V.E.; Thomsen, M.G.   DK 010203/77/8003 N
Virkningen af stigende mængder fedt i foderet til slagtekyllinger på produktionsøkonomien under praktiske forhold. **The effect on production economy of increasing level of dietary fat to broilers in field trials.**

12661 Petersen, V.E.; Jensen, O.   DK 010203/77/8004 N
Virkningen af foderfedts smeltepunkt på kyllingers vækst og foderomsætning. **The influence of the melting–point of dietary animal fat on gain and feed conversion in broilers.**

12662 Jensen, J.F.   DK 010203/78/0001 N
Stigende mængder tapiokamel i foder til slagtekyllinger. **Increasing amounts of tapioca meal in the feed for broilers.**

12663 Ranvig, H.   DK 030142/77/0015 N
Slagtekyllingers udnyttelse af fosfor fra fosforkilder med forskellig pH statisk reaktivitet. **The utilization in slaughter chickens of phosphorus from phosphorus sources with different pH–static reactivity.**

12664 Szylit, O.; Raibaud, P.; Ducluzeau, R.   FR 010205/72/2748
Digestion des glucides chez le poulet gnotoxénique. **Digestion**

of glucides in the gnotoxenic chicken.

12665 Charlet–Lery, G.; Ducluzeau, R.; Szylit, O.; Raibaud, P.   FR 010205/74/2727
Rétention de l'énergie chez les poulets axéniques et gnotoxéniques en fonction de la qualité de l'amidon et de la flore (analyse des carcasses). **Retention of energy in germfree and inoculated chickens according to the quality of starch and of flora (slaughter techniques).**

12666 Szylit, O.; Charlet, G.   FR 010216/70/9538 N
Interrelation entre le régime et la flore intestinale du poulet (axénique, holoxénique et monoxénique). **Relationship between diet and intestinal microflora in the chicken (axenic, holoxenic and monoxenic animals).**

12667 Szylit, O.; Galpin, G.V.   FR 010216/70/9595 N
Ecologie microbienne : rôle de souches bactériennes amylolytiques dans la digestion de l'amidon chez le poulet gnotoxénique. **Microbial ecology : the role of amylolytic bacterial strains on starch breakdown by gnotoxenic chicken.**

12668 Szylit, O.; Charlet, G.   FR 010216/75/9596
Ecologie microbienne : bilans nutritionnels et analyse de carcasses chez des poulets holoxeniques, axéniques et gnotoxéniques. **Microbial ecology : nutritional balance and analytical studies on the carcass of axenic, holoxenic and gnotoxenic chickens.**

12669 Szylit, O.; Charlet, G.; Charbonniere
                                        FR 010216/75/9597
Ecologie microbienne : effet de la structure de l'amidon sur sa degradation dans le tube digestif du poulet holo– et axénique. **Microbial ecology : the effect of the structure of starch on its degradation in gastrointestinal tract of axenic and holoxenic chicken.**

12670 Szylit, O.; Galpin, J.V.   FR 010216/76/9598
Ecologie microbienne : comparaison entre les amylases bactériennes de Lactobacillus et les amylases salivaires et pancréatiques, in vivo et in vitro, dans le tube digestif de poulets gnotoxéniques. **Microbial ecology : Comparative studies in vivo and in vitro of bacteria amylases produced by Lactobacillus and salivary and pancréatic amylases in the gastrointestinal tract of gnotoxenic chickens.**

12671 Savory   GB 010704/00/0003 R
Physiological and environmental factors that influence feeding and drinking behaviour.

12672 Shannon   GB 010707/00/0001
Utilisation of energy by chickens.

12673 McNab   GB 010707/00/0004
Protein utilisation by chickens.

12674 Dewar   GB 010707/00/0007
Effect of dietary fats and other compounds on mineral requirement.

12675 Whitehead   GB 010707/00/0010
Fatty acid requirement of chickens.

12676 Lee   GB 010707/00/0012
Metabolism of nitrogenous compounds in chickens.

12677 Shannon   GB 010707/00/0013
Metabolism of carbohydrates in chickens and effect of food treatment on utilisation efficiency.

12678 McNab   GB 010707/00/0016
The value of new foods for broilers.

12679 McNab   GB 010707/00/0017
The value of new foods for layers.

12680 Wilson   GB 010707/00/0020
Dietary regimes for maximum profit from broilers.

12681 Shannon   GB 010707/00/0021
Dietary regimes for maximum profit from layers.

12682 Pearson   GB 010707/00/0022
Dietary regimes for maximal profit from breeding chickens.

12683 Whitehead   GB 010707/00/0025
Antibiotics and antibiotic–like substances as yield promoters for broilers.

12684 Whitehead   GB 010707/00/0026
Assess claims made for yield promoter for layers in terms of food use, egg number and weight.

12685 Whitehead   GB 010707/00/0027
Effect of pesticides and antinutritive factors on broilers.

12686 Whitehead   GB 010707/00/0028
Effect of pesticides and antinutritive factors on layers.

12687 Fisher   GB 010707/00/0029 R
Variations in composition and digestibility of poultry for food.

12688 Wilson   GB 010707/00/0035
Amino acid requirements of broilers.

12689 Shannon   GB 010707/00/0036
Amino acid requirements of layers.

12690 Lee   GB 010707/00/0039
Vitamin requirement of chickens in relation to replacement of dried grass by yolk colorants.

12691 Coates   GB 011708/00/0011
Effects of dietary copper on chick growth.

12692 Davidson   GB 030610/00/0005 R
The value of new or improved sources of feed for the laying hen.

12693 Jackson   GB 040401/00/0013 R
Effect of restriction of dietry nutrients for the laying hen.

12694 Researcher not indicated   GB 040401/76/0025 R
The effects of copper on the laying domestic fowl.

12695 Pearce   GB 040403/00/0002
Effects of dietary manipulation on enzyme activity in the domestic fowl.

12696 Pearce   GB 040403/00/0013
Interrelationships of carbohydrate and lipid in the nutrition of the laying hen.

12697 Foster GB 041305/00/0002 R
Value of feed additives in broiler production.

12698 Researcher not indicated GB 050129/00/0001 R
Laying hens: nutrition.

12699 Researcher not indicated GB 050169/00/0001
Laying hens: nutrition.

12700 Emmans GB 060102/00/0029
Growth of chickens.

12701 Michie GB 060209/00/0002
Feed utilisation studies in egg production.

12702 Baldissera Nordio, C. IT 040602/73/1806
Indagine calorimetrica sulla diversa utilizzazione energetica della dieta in maschi e femmine di polli in accrescimento. Calorimetric survey of the different energetic utilization of diet in male and female growing chicks. Publications.

12703 Baldissera Nordio, C. IT 040602/74/0506
Indagine calorimetrica sulla diversa utilizzazione energetica della dieta di polli in accrescimento, alimentati con proteine convenzionali e non convenzionali. Calorimetric survey of the different energetic utilization of diet by growing broilers fed with conventional and non conventional proteins.

12704 Olivetti, A. IT 041313/77/0249 R
Indagini sull'alimentazione dei polli e delle faraone, riflessi produttivi ed igienico–sanitari. Research on the feeding of chickens and guinea–fowls; relevance on output, health and hygiene.

12705 Quarantelli, A. IT 041521/78/1094 N
L'impiego del Saccharomyces cerevisiae e del Kluyveromyces fragilis, in qualità di lieviti vivi, nell'alimentazione delle galline ovaiole. The use of Saccharomyces cerevisiae and of Kluyveromyces fragilis in the feeding of laying hens.

12706 Canale, A. IT 062500/74/0195
La digeribilità apparente degli aminoacidi di diverse farine di estrazione di semi oleosi (colza, sesamo, girasole, ecc.) nelle ovaiole in ovideposizione. The apparent digestibility of aminoacids of a few oil seed–meals (rapeseed, sesame, sunflower, etc.) in laying hens. Publications.

12707 Canale, A. IT 062500/74/0197
Rilievi sull'energia metabolizzabile, sulla digeribilità dei principi immediati e degli aminoacidi e sulla utilizzazione nutritiva delle farine di origine animale (farina di carne e ossa di bovino, di suino, farina di pesce) nei polli in accrescimento. Investigation on metabolizable energy, on digestibility of nutrients and amino–acids and on the nutritive utilization of animal meals (meat and bones meals from calves and pigs, fishmeals) in growing chicken.

12708 Sarra, C. IT 062500/74/0200
Gli effetti trofici di grassi con differente"punto di fumo" nei pulcini in accrescimento. The trophic effects of fats with different"smoke point"in growing chicks. Publications.

12709 Maletto, S. IT 062500/77/0973
La disponibilità degli aminoacidi nei polli in accrescimento: la valutazione della digeribilità determinata mediante raccolta degli escreti nei confronti di quella ottenuta attraverso esame del contenuto ileale. Amino–acid availability in growing chicks: evaluation of digestibility through the comparison of collected faeces and ileal content.

12710 Janssen, W.M.M.A. NL 010109/70/3129
Onderzoek naar de voederbenutting bij legdieren. Research on the feed utilization of laying–hens. Publications.

12711 Scheele, C.W. NL 010109/73/5406
De beschikbaarheid van omzetbare energie van eiwitten, vetten en koolhydraten uit voeders voor eiwit– en vetaanzet en voor onderhoud bij pluimvee. Utilisable energy from proteins, fats and carbohydrates in feed, for energy and fat retention and for maintenance of poultry. Publications.

12712 Holsheimer, J.P. NL 010109/75/7869 R
Onderzoek naar de relatie voeding–kwaliteit van slachtkuikens – fasenvoeding, energie/eiwit/aminozuurverhouding. The relation between nutrition and quality of broilers – Phasefeeding, Energy/protein/ amino–acid ratio.

12713 Schutte, J.b. NL 050305/74/8001
Aminozuurbehoefte van legkippen. Amino acid requirements of laying hens.

12714 Schutte, J.B. NL 050305/77/8000
Aminozurenbehoefte bij slachtkuikens. Amino acid requirements of broilers.

Geese, turkeys and other domestic birds (B 4490)

See also 11361, 11362, 12704

12715 Wegner, R.–M.; Böttcher, J.; Petersen, J.
DE 111501/75/0001
Erzeugung von Fleischtauben unter Berücksichtigung von Futterzusammensetzung und Rassenkreuzungen. Production of meat pigeons with different feed ration composition and different breed crosses.

12716 Auffray, P.; Felix, B.; Marcilloux, J.C.
FR 010217/69/9530 N
Régulation nerveuse du comportement alimentaire de l'oie. Central control of food intake in goose.

12717 Savory; Gentle GB 010704/00/0010 R
Diet induced hypertrophy, effect on feeding behaviour and gut motility in quail.

12718 Shannon GB 010707/00/0003
Utilisation of energy by ducks.

12719 McNab GB 010707/00/0006
Protein utilisation by ducks.

12720 Dewar GB 010707/00/0009
Requirements for, and absorbability from food of, minerals by ducks.

12721 Lee; Hutcheon GB 010707/00/0015
Vitamin requirements of ducks.

12722 McNab GB 010707/00/0019
The value of new foods for ducks.

D 3200 – Animal nutrition

12723 Wilson   GB 010707/00/0024
Dietary regimes for maximum profit from ducks.

12724 Bianchi, M.   IT 041217/73/1808
L'integrazione proteica delle razioni impiegate per
l'allevamento del tacchino. **Protein supplementation of feed
rations used in turkey breeding.** Publications.

12725 Janssen, W.M.M.A.   NL 010109/78/8717 N
Onderzoek naar de invloed van de struktuur van het voer op de
groei, de voederconversie en de uitval bij slachtkalkoenen
gedurende de gehele mestperiode. **Studies on the effect of the
physical form of the feed on the performance of commercial
turkeys during the whole growing period.**

Fishes, crustacea, shell fish and frogs in general (B 4500)

See also 12440

12726 Elster, H.–J.   DE 126800/72/0003
Untersuchungen über limnische Nahrungsketten Quantitative
Untersuchungen zur Ingestion verschiedener Futterarten
durch Daphnia. **Investigations on limnological food chains.
Quantitative studies on the ingestion of different feeds by
Daphnia.**

12727 Koops, H.   DE 208020/77/0007
Untersuchungen über die Fischernährung und den
Nährstoffbedarf bei Fischen. **Studies on nutrition and nutrient
requirement of fish.**

12728 Deufel, J.; Löffler, H.   DE 501805/78/0005 N
Futter für Coregonenbrut. **Food for fry of coregonids.**

12729 Luquet, P.   FR 010204/70/5513
Etude des besoins en protéines des poissons. **Protein
requirement of fishes.**

12730 Luquet, P.; Kaushik   FR 010204/72/5518
Etude des besoins en acides aminés des poissons. **Amino acids
requirement of fishes.**

12731 Gatesoupe; Luquet, P.   FR 010204/74/5514
Recherche d'une alimentation artificielle adaptée à l'élevage
des stades larvaires des poissons. **Research on the artificial
feeding in the culture of fish larvae.**

12732 Luquet, P.; Bergot; Choubert, G.   FR 010204/76/5519
Etude du devenir des hydrocarbures paraffiniques et
naphténiques après ingestion par la truite. **Effects of
hydrocarbure intake on trout.**

12733 Fauconneau; Luquet, P.; Bergot   FR 010204/77/5515
Influence de la température et des variations thermiques sur le
métabolisme. **Effects of thermics levels and thermics variations
on fish metabolism.**

12734 Forneris, G.   IT 041216/77/0184 R
Valutazione della digeribilità degli alimenti nei pesci.
Confronto tra differenti procedimenti sperimentali.
**Evalutation of the digestibility of fish nutrients. Comparison
between different experimental procedures.**

Carp (B 4510)

See also 2333, 11396

12735 Elster, H.–J.; Sternik, K.H.   DE 126800/73/0001
Phosphatabgabe junger Karpfen – Cyprinus carpio L. – im
Hunger und bei Fütterung. **Release of phosphates by young
carp – Cyprinus carpio L. – before and after feeding.**

12736 Pfeffer, E.; Meske, C.   DE 132302/72/0003
Bedeutung des Eiweissgehaltes im Karpfenfutter. **Importance
of protein content in carp feed.**

12737 Pieper, A.; Pfeffer, E.; Meske, C.   DE 132302/77/0001
Krill–Mehl als Proteinträger im Futter für Forellen und
Karpfen. **Crill–meal as source of protein in trout and carp feed.**

12738 Zeitler, M.; Kirchgessner, M.   DE 161280/78/0002 N
Protein– und Energiestoffwechsel bei Karpfen. **Protein and
energy metabolism of carps.**

12739 Huisman, E.A.   NL 020058/69/7361
Voedselbehoefte van de karper (Cyprinus carpio). **Feeding
requirement of Carp (Cyprinus carpio).** Publications.

12740 Davina,   NL 020071/77/7327
Afweerreactie in de darm van karperachtigen in relatie tot de
aard van zijn voedsel. **Defense mechanisms in the intestine of
Cyprinids in relation with the kind of food.**

Salmon (B 4520)

See also 12750

Trout (B 4530)

See also 1407, 11425, 11429, 12737

12741 Langholz, H.–J.; Reinhardt, U.; Keesen, H.   DE 132273/75/0004
Produktionsleistung der Regenbogenforelle auf verschiedenen
Stufen der Intensivhaltung. **Fattening of rainbow trouts in
different confined management systems.**

12742 Pfeffer, E.; Pieper, A.   DE 132302/75/0002
Untersuchungen zur Verwertung von Energie aus
Kohlenhydraten, Proteinen und Fetten bei wachsenden
Forellen. **Utilization of energy from carbohydrates, proteins,
and fats in growing trouts.**

12743 Pfeffer, E.; Frenzel, E.   DE 132302/78/0002 N
Mineralstoff–Bedarf wachsender Forellen. **Mineral
requirments in growing trout.**

12744 Lillelund, K.; Gütter, W.–H.   DE 135251/77/0007
Untersuchungen über Wachstum und Futterverwertung von
Regenbogenforellen–Setzlingen bei Zugabe zweier
unterschiedlicher Futter unter variierten Temperaturen und
Rationen. **Investigations on growth and utilization of food of
rainbow trout fry by supplementation of two different feeds
under varied temperatures and rations conditions.**

12745 Researcher not indicated   DE 160000/77/0001
Rückstandsbildung und Ausscheidungsbeschleunigung von
Hexachlorbenzol bei schlachtbaren Nutztieren. **Residue
formation and acceleration of excretion of hexachlorobenzene in
livestock–for–slaughter.**

12746 Researcher not indicated   DE 160000/77/0003 N
Energiebewertung von Forellenfutter.
Stoffwechselphysiologische Untersuchung zur Abfindung eines
geeigneten Parameters. **Valuation of energy in feeds for trouts.
Metabolic–physiological analysis for finding of adequate
parameter.**

12747 Gropp, J.; Koops, H.; Tiews, K.   DE 160600/73/0003
Zur Optimierung von Forellenrationen. **Optimum rations for
trouts.**

12748 Gropp, J.; Schwalb, A.; Bodecker, J.
                                     DE 160600/75/0011
Nährstoffbedarfsuntersuchungen an Forellen. **Nutritional
requirements of trouts.**

12749 Bergot; Fremont; Luquet, P.; Leger   FR 010204/67/5511
Mécanismes d'absorption des lipides chez la truite. **Lipid
absorption in rainbow trout.**

12750 Lesel, R.   FR 010204/71/5507
Microbiologie du tube digestif de salmonidés. **Microbiology of
the digestive tract of salmonids.**

12751 Bergot; Chevassus; Luquet, P.; Blanc
                                     FR 010204/72/5512
Physiologie des caeca pyloriques chez la truite. **Physiology of
pyloric caeca in trout.**

12752 Kaushik; Luquet, P.   FR 010204/73/5517
Adaptation des truites en eau de mer. Conséquences sur le
métabolisme azoté. **Influence of salinity, changes on
nitrogenous metabolism on trout.**

12753 Bergot, F.   FR 010204/74/5510
Utilisation des glucides par la truite. **Carbohydrate utilisation
by trout.**

12754 Luquet, P.   FR 010204/77/5520
Utilisation de l'urée par la truite. **Urea utilisation by trout.**

12755 Leger, C.; Flanzy, J.; Bauchart, D.   FR 010205/69/2714
Etude de la lipase pancréatique de la Truite. **Study of the
pancreatic lipase in the Trout.**

12756 Léger, C.   FR 010205/69/9552 N
La lipase pancréatique de la Truite arc–en–ciel. **Pancreatic
lipase in the Rainbow trout.**

12757 Léger, C.; Luquet, P.   FR 010205/72/9551 N
Différents aspects de stockage des acides gras chez la Truite
arc–en–ciel (Salmo gairdneri R). **Some aspects of fatty acid
storage in rainbow trout.**

12758 Flanzy, J.; Bergot, P.; Leger, C.; Buclon, M.; Luquet,
P.   FR 010205/73/2715
Stockage des lipides chez la Truite. **The lipid storage in the
Trout.**

Mullet (B 4540)

12759 Ravagnan, G.   IT 121700/78/1150 N
Studio dei fabbisogni nutritivi dei cefali in allevamento. **A
study of the food requirements of mullets bred in fish farms.**

Eel (B 4550)

See also 11396, 11433

12760 Greuel, E.; Schilling, U.   DE 111404/75/0001
Untersuchung zur Fütterung von Aalen mit Fetten unter
besonderer Berücksichtigung verschiedener Fettsäuren.
**Studies on feeding eels with fats with special reference to
different fatty acids.**

12761 Greuel, E.; Schilling, U.   DE 111404/78/0004 N
Einfluss von Licht auf den Fressrhythmus von Aalen. **Influence
of illumination on rhythmic feed intake of eel.**

12762 Greuel, E.; Schilling, U.   DE 111404/78/0005 N
Verfahren zur Durchführung von Stoffwechseluntersuchungen
am Aal. **Procedures of metabolic investigations in eels.**

12763 Polesello, A.; Pizzocaro, F.   IT 021900/76/0006 N
Influenza della dieta sulla qualità delle anguille. **Dietary
influence on eel meat quality.**

Crustacea, shell fish, frogs (B 4560)

See also 11444

12764 Scalera Liaci, L.   IT 040121/78/1151 N
Alimentazione naturale di Penaeus kerathurus ed istologia
delle gonadi. **Natural diet of Penaeus kerathurus and gonad
histology.**

12765 Stagno d'Alcontres, G.   IT 041715/78/1152 N
Indagine chimica qualitativa e quantitativa su alcuni scarti di
pesca da utilizzare come alimento di Penaeus kerathurus.
**Chemical qualitative and quantitative study of certain fish
scraps to be used for feeding Penaeus kerathurus.**

Other fishes (B 4590)

See also 11396

12766 Gatesoupe; Boudon; Luquet, P.; Leger
                                     FR 010204/75/5516
Alimentation lipidique du turbot. Etude des besoins en acide
gras essentiel. **Lipid feeding of turbot. Essential fatty acids
requirements.**

12767 Luquet, P.; Léger, C.   FR 010205/76/9550 N
Acides gras essentiels du Turbot (Scophthalmus maximus).
Essential fatty acids in Turbot.

12768 Hoogendoorn, H.   NL 020058/78/8810 N
Voeding en groei van de Afrikaanse meerval, Clarias lazera.
Feeding and growth of the African catfish, Clarias lazera.

Invertebrates (bees, silk–worm) (B 4600)

See also 2832

12769 Weiss, K.   DE 502350/77/0004
Einsatz von künstlichem Bienenfutter. **Use of artificial bee
food.**

12770 Pain, J.; Roger, R.; Douault, Ph.   FR 010114/73/5144
Echanges alimentaires dans la colonie d'abeilles. **Food
exchanges in the honeybee colony.**

12771 Louveaux, J.; Albisetti, J.   FR 010114/73/5145
Influence des méthodes sylvicoles sur la productivité mellifère du sous–bois en forêt landaise. **Effects of forestry methods on the honey yield of the Landes forest underwood.**

12772 Louveaux, J.; Theurkauff, J.; Douault, P.
    FR 010114/74/5149
Influence des nourrissements sur la composition des miels récoltés. **Effects of feeding on the composition of extracted honeys.**

12773 Pouvreau, A.; Marilleau, R.   FR 010114/76/5147
Nutrition de l'abeille. Aliments de complément. **Honeybee nutrition. Substitute foods.**

12774 Reali, G.; Meneghini, A.; Cappezzolla, M.
    IT 020400/71/0001
Alimentazione del filugello con foglia di gelso variamente trattata. **Treated mulberry–leaf in silkworm food.** Publications.

12775 Reali, G.   IT 020400/75/0008
Ricerche sulla fisiologia alimentare del Bombyx mori. **Studies on the alimentary physiology of Bombyx mori.** Publications.

12776 Bonsempiante, M.; Bittante, G.   IT 040810/79/0002 N
Studio degli alimenti utilizzabili nell'allevamento della Helix Pomatia. **Studies on feedstuffs employing in Helix Pomatia breeding.**

Rabbits (B 4910)

See also 11308, 11362, 11503, 11530, 11553, 11554, 11799, 12460, 16853

12777 Jensen, N.E.   DK 010203/76/0012
Forskellige foderblandingers foderværdi til kaniner. **The feeding value of various feed mixes for rabbits.**

12778 Jensen, N.E.   DK 010203/77/0011
Ludet halm i foderblandingen til kaniner. **Lye treated straw in the feed mix for rabbits.**

12779 Jensen, N.E.   DK 010203/78/0013 N
Rapsskrå i foderblandinger til kaniner. **Rapeseed meal in feed mixtures for rabbits.**

12780 Jensen, N.E.   DK 010203/78/0014 N
Byg kontra havre i foderblandinger til kaniner. **Barley compared with oats in feed mixtures for rabbits.**

12781 Jensen, N.E.   DK 010203/78/0017 N
Tapiokamel i foderblandinger til kaniner. **Tapioca meal in feed mixtures for rabbits.**

12782 Jørgensen, G.   DK 010204/77/0002
Bestemmelse af protein og energiomsætning hos mink. **Calculation of protein and energy conversion in mink.**

12783 Mason, V.C.; Just, A.   DK 010206/75/0005
Sammenlignende undersøgelser (rotter og svin) vedrørende proteinkvalitet (SF, BV, NPU), fordøjelig energi samt omsættelig energi. **Comparative investigation (rats and pigs) concerning protein quality (SF, BV, NPU) and digestible and convertable energy.**

12784 Laplace, J.P.; Lebas, F.; Jolivet, E.   FR 010205/73/2730

Le transit digestif chez le Lapin: description, mécanismes et facteurs de variation. **Digestive transit in the Rabbit: descriptive studies, control mechanisms and sources of variation.** Publications.

12785 Corring, T.; Lebas, F.   FR 010206/67/2926
Rôle de la sécrétion exocrine du pancréas chez le lapin. **Part played by the pancreas in the digestion in the rabbit.**

12786 Lebas, F.; Colin, L.   FR 010206/70/2923
Etude des matières premières pour l'alimentation du lapin. **Utilization of different feedstuff in rabbit nutrition.**

12787 Laplace, J.P.; Lebas, F.   FR 010206/70/2927
Etude du transit digestif chez le lapin. **Digestive transit by the rabbit.**

12788 Colin, M.   FR 010206/72/2920
Etude du besoin azoté du lapin en croissance. **Nitrogen requirement of the growing rabbit.**

12789 Colin, M.   FR 010206/74/2921
Etude du besoin en énergie du lapin en croissance. **Energy requirement of the growing rabbit.**

12790 Lebas, F.   FR 010206/74/2924
Etude du besoin en énergie de la lapine reproductrice. **Energy requirement of the rabbit doe.**

12791 Colin, M.; Lebas, F.   FR 010206/75/2922
Etude du besoin en lest du lapin en croissance. **Feed ballast requirement of the growing rabbit.**

12792 Lebas, F.; Colin, M.   FR 010206/75/2925
Etude du besoin en azote de la lapine reproductrice. **Nitrogen requirement of the rabbit doe.**

12793 Colin, M.; Rougeot, J.   FR 010206/75/2928
Alimentation rationnelle du lapin Angora. **Rational alimentation of the Angora rabbit.**

12794 Laplace, J.P.; Lebas, F.   FR 010217/73/9532 N
Transit digestif chez le lapin. **Digestive transit in the Rabbit.**

12795 Gouet, P.   FR 010809/72/9526 N
La microflore digestive du lapin. **Digestive microflora of rabbit.**

12796 Le Bars, H.; Guemon, L.; Gallouin, F.; Demaux, G.
    FR 011702/65/2768
Nutrition et comportement alimentaire du lapin. **Nutritiae and alimentary behavior of rabbit.**

12797 Demaux Melle, G.; Guemon, L.   FR 011702/66/9512 N
Comportement alimentaire et digestion chez le lapin. **Feeding behavior and digestion in the rabbit.**

12798 Fuller; Partridge   GB 030611/79/0045 N
Nutrition and husbandry of rabbit.

12799 Auxilia, M.T.   IT 020700/73/1805
Effetto della grassatura del mangime sulla produzione della carne di coniglio. **Effect of fat supplementation of feedstuff on rabbit meat production.** Publications.

12800 Auxilia, M.T.   IT 020700/74/0503

Integrazione con metionina e lisina di una dieta grassata per conigli da carne. **Methionine and lysine supplementation of a fat–enriched diet for meat rabbits.**

12801 Auxilia, M.T.; Emaldi, G.C.; Terramoccia, S.
IT 020700/78/0005
Alimentazione di conigli all'ingrasso con pellettati contenenti polvere di siero addizionata o meno di fermenti lattici. **Feeding growing rabbits by pellets with whey powder and with or without lactobacilli.**

12802 Auxilia, M.T. IT 020700/78/1026 N
Impiego di farine di mais, di orzo e di frumento disidratati nell'alimentazione di conigli all'ingrasso. **Use of dehydrated maize, barley and wheat flour in the feeding of rabbits reared for fattening.**

12803 Auxilia, M.T.; Masoero, G.; Terramoccia, S.
IT 020700/79/0007 N
Impiego di mais disidratato integrale nella dieta per conigli in accrescimento. **Use of dehydrated whole maize plant in growing rabbits diets.**

12804 Auxilia, M.T.; Masoero, G.; Terramoccia, S.
IT 020700/79/0008 N
Ricerche sull'impiego di pollina essiccata nell'alimentazione dei conigli. **Use of dry poultry wastes in rabbits diets.**

12805 Matteuzzi, D. IT 040210/78/1079 N
Microbiologia dell'apparato intestinale del coniglio. **Microbiology of the rabbit intestinal tract.**

12806 Gallarati Scotti, G.C. IT 040613/72/0465
Ricerche sulla digeribilità ed esperimenti polifattoriali d'alimentazione nel coniglio. **Research on digestibility of the rabbit and polyfactorial experiments on feeding.** Publications.

12807 Gallarati–Scotti, G. IT 040613/77/0189 R
Ricerche sulle fonti alimentari del coniglio. **Research on the sources of food for rabbits.**

12808 Rigoni, M. IT 040626/78/1098 N
Digeribilità dei principi alimentari e bilancio materiale ed energetico in conigli ad alimentazione dissociata. **Digestibility of essential dietary elements; and energetic balance in rabbits on a dissociated diet.**

12809 Baldissera Nordio, C. IT 040638/78/1157 N
Indagini sull'alimentazione del coniglio da carne con l'impiego della virginiamicina istofisiologiche e di bilancio materiale ed energetico. **Rabbits reared for meat : research on feeding integrating virginiamycin, histological – physiological studies, material and energetical profiles.**

12810 Proto, V. IT 040722/72/0122
Funzione del cieco e significato nutrizionale del ciecotrofo nel coniglio. **Function of the caecum and nutritive significance of "ciecotrifo" in the rabbit.** Publications.

12811 Parigi Bini, R. IT 040810/73/1823
Ricerca sulla nutrizione e sui fabbisogni azotati del coniglie in accrescimento. **Research on the nutrition and the nitrogen requirements of growing rabbit.** Publications.

12812 Parigi–Bini, R. IT 040810/77/0256 R
Ricerche sui fabbisogni nutritivi energetici e proteici del coniglio. **Research on the energetic and protein requirements of the rabbit.**

12813 Finzi, A. IT 040907/77/0181 R
Svezzamento precoce e piani alimentari post svezzamento nell'allevamento cunicolo. Digeribilità delle razioni a diverso livello in fibra e inizio dell'attacco microbico della cellulosa in coniglietti svezzati precocemente. **Precocius weaning and post–weaning nutritional programs in rabbit breeding. Digestibility of rations with different fibre content and initial bacterial degradation of celulose in precociusly weaned baby rabbits.**

12814 Battaglini, M. IT 041017/73/1807
Utilizzazione di alcuni concentrati proteici e glucidici nella alimentazione del coniglio in funzione della razza e dell'età. **Use of some protein and glucide concentrates in rabbit feeding according to age and breed.**

12815 Battaglini, M. IT 041017/77/0110 R
Utilizzazione di alcuni sottoprodotti dell'industria alimentare nelle diete per conigli da carne. **Utilization of some by–products of the food industry in diets for rabbits bred for their meat.**

12816 Finzi, A. IT 041113/74/0553
Svezzamento precoce e piani alimentari post–svezzamento nell'allevamento cunicolo. Effetto sulle caratteristiche chimico–fisiche ed organolettiche delle carni. **Early weaning and post–weaning feeding programs in rabbit breeding. Effects on chemical, physical and organoleptic characteristics of meat.**

12817 Fedeli Avanzi, C. IT 041116/77/0178 R
Svezzamento precoce e piani alimentari post–svezzamento nell'allevamento cunicolo. **Precocious weaning and post–weaning feeding programs in rabbit breeding.**

12818 Cenni, B. IT 041118/73/1811
Svezzamento precoce e piani alimentari post–svezzamento nell'allevamento cunicolo. Appetibilità delle razioni, tempi e modi di assunzione dell'alimento. **Early weaning and post–weaning feeding programs in rabbit farming Palatability of feed rations, times and ways of feed utilization.**

12819 Cenni, B. IT 041127/77/0142 R
Svezzamento precoce e piani alimentari post svezzamento nell'allevamento cunicolo. **Premature weaning and post–weaning feeding schemes in brawit breeding.**

12820 Verità, P. IT 041127/78/1118 N
Svezzamento precoce e piani alimentari post–svezzamento nell' allevamento cunicolo. Appetibilità dei mangimi di svezzamento modificazioni della curva circadiana di consumo degli alimenti nei conigli in seguito a fenomeni di stress. **Early weaning and post weaning feeding programs in rabbit breeding. Appetitive qualities of weaning foodstuffs; changes in the circadian curve of food intake in stressed rabbits.**

12821 Pagano, Toscano, G. IT 041216/73/1822
Contribute allo studio del razionamento dei conigli impiegando nuovi sistemi per la valutazione del valore energetico degli alimenti. **Contribution to the study of rabbit feed rationing using new methods of evaluating the energetic value of feeds.** Publications.

12822 Pagano Toscano, G. IT 041216/78/1082 N
Contributo allo studio del razionamento dei conigli

impiegando nuovi sistemi per la valutazione del valore energetico degli alimenti. **A contribution to the study of rabbit food rationing using new systems to evaluate the energetical value of foodstuffs.**

12823 Ladetto, G.   IT 041313/77/0211 R
La digeribilità dei principo nutritivi nel coniglio. Influenza dell'età e dello stato fisiologico sull'utilizzazione digestiva degli alimenti con particolare riferimento alla componente fibrosa. **Digestibility of nutritional requirements in rabbits. Influence of age and of the physiological condition on the digestive utilization of foods with particular reference to roughage.**

12824 Schreurs, V.V.A.M.   NL 020017/76/7307
Metabolisme van weefseleiwitten bij het konijn. **Metabolism of tissue proteins in the rabbit.** Publications.

Domestic pets and zoo animals (B 4920)

12825 Engelhardt, W.von; Hinderer, H.; Ali, K.; Wipper, E.
                                        DE 144142/77/0001
Ausnutzung von Körperharnstoff beim Lama bei proteinarmen Diäten. **Utilization of body urea in llamas at low protein diets.**

12826 Gropp, J.; Beck, H.   DE 160600/73/0001
Zur Calcium/Phosphor–Versorgung schnell wachsender Junghunde. **The Ca/P–supply of rapidly growing puppies.**

Fur animals (B 4930)

See also 11530

12827 Jørgensen, G.; Hansen, N.G.   DK 010204/73/0008
Undersøgelse over forskellige forhold vedrørende fedt og kulhydraters fordøjeligbed hos mink. **Examination of various problems concerning digestibility of fat and carbohydrate in mink.**

12828 Jørgensen, G.; Hansen, N.G.   DK 010204/73/0009
Diverse fordøjeligheds– og balanceforsøg med mink. **Various balance and digestibility trials with mink.**

12829 Jørgensen, G.   DK 010204/76/0001 N
Undersøgelser over minks syre–base ligevægt og mineralstofbalance ved fodring med syrekonserveret fisk. **Investigations into the acid–alkali equilibrium and mineral balance in mink following feeding with acid–preserved fish.**

12830 Glem–Hansen, N.; Hansen, N.E. DK 010204/78/0001 N
Tilvækstens sammensætning hos mink ved fodring med forskellige mængder syrekonserveret fisk og ved forskelligt pH i foderet. **Body composition in mink fed diets with different amounts of acid preserved fish and with different pH.**

12831 Thorbek, G.   DK 010206/77/0005 N
Måling af protein– og energiomsætningen hos mink. **Measurement of protein and energi turnover in mink.**

12832 Hansen, N.E.; Glem–Hansen, N. DK 030125/78/0001 N
Tilvækstens sammensætning hos mink ved fodring med forskellige mængder syrekonserveret fisk og ved forskelligt pH i foderet. **Body composition in mink fed diets with different amounts of acid preserved fish and with different pH.**

12833 Poulsen, J.S.D.; Jørgensen, G. DK 030130/79/0003 N
Undersøgelser over variation i transketolase aktiviteter hos

mink ved fodring med ensilerede fodermidler. **Activity of transketolase in mink fed with acidified feedstuffs.**

12834 Charlet–Lery, G.; Rougeot, J. FR 010205/71/2726
Alimentation du vison (gestation, lactation, croissance). Choix des sources d'amidon, utilisation d'aggloméré. **Nutrition of mink.** Publications.

12835 Charlet, M.G.; Rougeot, J.   FR 010217/70/9536 N
Problêmes nutritionnels du vison. **Nutrition of mink.**

Other domestic animals (B 4990)

See also 12376

Laboratory animals (B 9120)

See also 11647, 11703, 12308, 12309, 12390, 12391, 12404, 12460, 12648, 12651, 12652, 14887, 15119, 15120, 18899

12836 Hiller, H.H.   DE 104351/72/0001
Protein– und Aminosäuren–Bedarfsermittlung für Versuchstiere und Bedarfsdeckung bei SPF– und gnotobiotischen Tieren Entwicklung von Futtertypen. **Determination of protein and amino acid requirement of experimental animals and supply in SPF and gnotobiotic animals. Development of types of feeds.**

12837 Molnar, S.; Ridwan, F.; Rochus, W.; Formanek, H.
                                        DE 132300/77/0006
Wechselwirkungen zwischen Schwermetallen und Huminsäuren im Verdauungstrakt der Ratte. **Interactions between heavy metals and humic acids in the digestive tract of rats.**

12838 Molnar, S.; Ridwan, F.   DE 132300/78/0005 N
Untersuchungen zur Huminsäureabsorption bei der Ratte mit Hilfe von C–14–uniform–markierten Huminsäuren. **Investigations of humic acid absorption in rat with C–14 uniform labelled humic acids.**

12839 Schlierf, G.   DE 142450/75/0001 N
Ermittlung der wünschenswerten Fett– und Kohlenhydratzufuhr am Kriterium optimaler Tagesprofile der Lipide, des Blutzuckers und des Insulinspiegels. **Determination of desirable fat and carbohydrate supply by the criteria of daily profiles of lipids, blood sugar and insulin level.**

12840 Kirchgessner, M.; Grassmann, E.; Kim, J.; Mader, H.
                                        DE 161280/71/0002
Interaktion bei der Verwertung von Eisen und Kupfer im Stoffwechsel der Ratte. **Interrelationship between iron and copper in rat metabolism.**

12841 Ochsenfahrt, H.   DE 173150/78/0001 N
Der Einfluss der Mukosadurchblutung auf die enterale Resorption. **The influence of mucosal blood flow the intestinal resorption.**

12842 Hoffmann, N.   DE 211040/78/0011 N
Anreicherung von Protein aus Abfallstoffen durch mechanische Verfahren. **Protein enrichment from waste products by mechanical techniques.**

12843 Mason, V.C.; Eggum, B.O.   DK 010206/78/0001 N
In vitro fordøjelighed af protein (rotter og svin). **In vitro**

digestibility of protein compared with in vivo in rats and pigs.

12844 Mason, V.C.; Jakobsen, P.E.; Rotenberg, S.
DK 010206/78/0002 N
Lipidstofskifte hos rotter ved højt indhold af citruspektin i
foderet. **Lipidmetabolism in rats fed a diet with high citrus
pectin content.**

12845 Raibaud, P.; Ducluzeau, R.; Jalpin, G.V.
FR 010205/55/2743
Analyse différentielle quantitative des populations
microbiennes du tube digestif chez le monogastrique et le
poulet holoxénique et gnotoxénique. **Differential and
quantitative analysis of the microbial populations of the
digestive tract in the holoxenic and gnotoxenic monogastrics and
chicken.** Publications.

12846 Ducluzeau, R.; Raibaud, P.; Dubos, F.
FR 010205/65/2758
Interactions entre bactéries dans le tube digestif d'animaux
gnotoxéniques. **Interactions between bacteria in the digestive
tract of gnotoxenic animals.** Publications.

12847 Duval, Y.; Raibaud, P.   FR 010205/67/2744
Variation des caractères sous l'influence des bactériophages in
vitro et in vivo dans le tube digestif d'animaux gnotoxéniques.
**Variation of the characteristics of the bacteria by
bacteriophages in vitro and in vivo in the digestive tract of
gnotoxenic animals.** Publications.

12848 Meslin, J.C.; Sacquet, E.; Raibaud, P.
FR 010205/68/2701
Action de la flore microbienne sur la morphologie et le
renouvellement cellulaire de la muqueuse de l'intestin grêle du
rat. **Action of microbial flora on the morphology and cell
renewal of rat small intestinal mucosa.**

12849 Sacquet, E.; Raibaud, P.   FR 010205/70/2749
Métabolisme des sels biliaires chez l'animal gnotoxénique.
Metabolism of bile salts in the gnotoxenic animal. Publications.

12850 Ducluzeau, R.; Raibaud, P.; Dubos, F.
FR 010205/70/2750
Effet du régime alimentaire sur l'écologie microbienne du tube
digestif. **Effect of the diet on the microbial ecology of the
digestive tract.** Publications.

12851 Demame, Y.; Flanzy, J.   FR 010205/70/9544 N
Effets de la flore du tractus digestif sur les mécanismes de
digestion et d'absorption des matières grasses alimentaires
chez le Rat. **Effects of G.I. flora on digestion and absorption of
dietary fats by the Rat.**

12852 Moreau, M.C.; Ducluzeau, R.; Raibaud, P.
FR 010205/71/2746
Inhibition de l'hydrolyse de l'urée dans le tube digestif
d'animaux gnotoxéniques par la vaccination. **Inhibition of
urealysis in the digestive tract of gnotoxenic animals by
immunization.** Publications.

12853 Ducluzeau, R.; Dubos, F.; Raibaud, P.
FR 010205/71/2751
Production in situ d'antibiotiques par les bactéries intestinales
chez des animaux gnotoxéniques. **In situ production of
antibiotics by the intestinal bacteria in the gnotoxenic animals.**

12854 Abrams, G.D.; Moreau, C.; Ducluzeau, R.; Raibaud,
P.   FR 010205/72/2753
Localisation des bactéries sur la muqueuse du tube digestif
d'animaux gnotoxéniques. **Localisation of bacteries on the
intestinal mucosa in gnotoxenic animals.**

12855 Moreau, C.; Ducluzeau, R.; Griscelli, J.C.
FR 010205/74/2747
Interaction entre la microflore du tube digestif et l'état
immunitaire de la muqueuse chez des animaux gnotoxéniques.
**Interaction between the microflora of the digestif tract and the
immunological state of the intestinal mucosa in gnotoxenic
animals.**

12856 Corring, T.; Raibaud, P.; Ducluzeau, R.
FR 010205/75/2740
Rôle de la flore bactérienne intestinale dans la digestion des
protéines alimentaires chez le rat. **Role of the intestinal flora in
digestion of alimentary proteins in the rat.**

12857 Ducluzeau, R.; Aumaitre, L.; Saint–Lebe, L.
FR 010205/75/2756
Radicidation et Radappertisation des provendes pour rats et
souris axéniques et hétéroxéniques. **Radicidation and
radappertisation of the diets for axenic and heteroxenic rats and
mice.**

12858 Hudault, S.; Ducluzeau, R.; Raibaud, P.
FR 010216/70/9599 N
Ecologie microbienne : effet de barrière exercé par certains
clostridia contre Clostridium perfringens dans le tube digestif
de souris gnotoxéniques. **Microbial ecology : Barrier effect
exerted against Clostridium perfringens by other clostridial
strains in the gastrointestinal tract of gnotoxenic mice.**

12859 Dubos, F.; Pelissier, J.   FR 010216/75/9608 N
Ecologie microbienne : influence de la composition du régime
alimentaire sur l'établissement de Acuformis perennis dans le
tube digestif de souris holoxéniques. **Microbial ecology : influence
of diet composition on the establishment of Acuformis perennis
in the gastrointestinal tract of axenic mice.**

12860 Moreau, M.C.; Ducluzeau, R.; Meslin, J.C.
FR 010216/75/9609 N
Ecologie microbienne : augmentation du nombre de
plasmocytes à IGA dans le duodénum de souris axéniques
associées à différentes souches bactériennes isolées du tube
digestif de souris holoxéniques. **Microbial ecology : increasing
of IGA plasmocyte number in the duodenum of axenic mice
associated with different bacterial strains isolated from the
gastrointestinal tract of the holoxenic mouse.**

12861 Corpet, D.; Ducluzeau, R.   FR 010216/76/9600 N
Ecologie microbienne : effet de barrière exercé par certaines
souches de bactéries anaérobies strictes contre Clostridium
perfringens dans le tube digestif de souris et de porcelets
gnotoxéniques. **Microbial ecology : Barrier effect exerced by
strictly anaerobic bacterial strains against Clostridium
perfringens in the gastrointestinal tract of gnotoxenic mice and
piglets.**

12862 Ducluzeau, R.; Raibaud, P.   FR 010216/76/9604
Ecologie microbienne : utilisation de la souris axenique dans
l'etude de la flore microbienne du tube digestif du porc.
**Microbial ecology : Use of axenic mouse for the study of the
gastrointestinal tract microflora of pigs.**

12863 Ducluzeau, R.; Demarne, Y.   FR 010216/76/9610 N
Ecologie microbienne: influence de la composition du lait sur le développement d'une souche de Clostridium dans le tube digestif de souris axéniques. **Microbial ecology: influence of milk composition on the development of a Clostridium strain in the gastrointestinal tract of axenic mice.**

12864 Corring, T.; Raibaud, P.; Moreau, C.; Ducluzeau, R.
     FR 010217/76/9539
Role de la microflore dans l'utilisation digestive de la proteine alimentaire, chez le rat. **Role of the microflora in the digestive utilization of the dietary protein, in the rat.**

12865 Pion, R.; Mendes Pereira, E.; Prugnaud, J.
     FR 010815/71/9571 N
Etude de la valeur nutritive de concentrés, d'isolats protéiques, et de protéines texturées réalisés à partir de ces derniers, mesure chez le rat. **Nutritive value of protein concentrates, protein isolates and textured proteins.**

12866 Grizard, J.; Pion, R.; Prugnaud, J.
     FR 010815/72/9573 N
Régulation hormonale de l'utilisation des acides aminés chez le rat en croissance soumis ou non à des restrictions énergétiques et azotées. **Hormonal regulation of amino acid metabolism in growing rats, fed a control diet or subjected to energy or nitrogen restriction.**

12867 Mendes Pereira, E.; Pion, R.; Prugnaud, J.
     FR 010815/74/9584 N
Sélection des légumineuses en fonction de leur valeur nutritive pour l'alimentation animale. Expérience chez le rat. **Nutritive value of reeds in proteins and amino acids contents.**

12868 Vermorel, M.; Fayet, J.C.; Tollier, Mme.
     FR 010816/76/9513 N
Valeur nutritive des tourteaux de colza à faible teneur en glucosinolates : influence du dépelliculage et de l'extraction des alpha galactosides ; études chez le rat en croissance. **Nutritive value of low glucosinolate rapeseed meal ; effects of dehulling and solvent extraction of galactosides ; studies in the growing rat.**

12869 Logten, M.J. van   NL 040011/73/7515
Bepaling van contaminanten in proefdiervoeders. **Determination of contaminants in experimental animal feeds.**

D 3300 – Animal breeding

See also 13509

12870 Hanset, R.; Michaux, C.   BE 060003/79/0003 N
Recherches sur la viabilité–fertilité en race blanc–bleu belge. **Viability and fertility in the blue belgian cattle breed.**

12871 Van Opdenbosch, E.; Wellemans, G.
     BE 110000/78/0048 N
Rôle d'un adjuvant huileux sur la sécrétion d'un haut titre en anticorps dans le lait de la vache. **Role of oleaginous additive on high quantity of antibodies in milk.** Publications.

12872 De Cueninck, B.   BE 110000/79/0050 N
Invloed van een adjuvans behandeling op colostrale secretie van immunoglobine bij rund. **Effect of additive administration on the colostral secretion of immunoglobins by cattle.**

12873 Orban; Ruwet, J.Cl.; Philippart   BE 140000/77/0041
Récupération des eaux de refroidissement de centrales électriques à des fins piscicoles. **Utilize refrigeration water of electric centrals from pisciculture.** Publications.

12874 Winner, C.; Westing, A.   DE 907000/75/0001
Morphologische Merkmale verschiedener Zuckerrübensorten unter dem Aspekt ihrer Eignung zur maschinellen Ernte. **Morphological characteristics of different sugar–beet varieties with regard to their suitability for mechanical harvest.**

12875 Roulund, H.; Søegaard, B.   DK 030102/74/0002 N
Forædling af abiesarter. **The improvement of Abies.**

12876 Robertson; Hill   GB 012502/00/0001 R
Quantitative genetics in relation to selection responses.

12877 Griffith; Banks   GB 030201/75/0032
The amylase system of bovine serum as a potential genetic indicator of milk production.

12878 Dalgleish   GB 030203/00/0008 R
Alterations in alpha–casein structure caused by the binding of calcium.

12879 Dalgleish   GB 030203/00/0010 R
Properties of particles formed from alpha–casein and calcium in various solvent conditions.

12880 Dalgleish   GB 030203/00/0013 R
Formation and properties of aggregates formed by interaction between alpha–casein, kappa casein and calcium.

12881 Rossi, J.; Costamagna, L.   IT 041023/70/0002 N
Ecologia Microbica. **Microbic Ecology.**

Animals and parts of their bodies (B 2300)

See also 13528

12882 Weniger, J.H.; Horst, P.; Steinhauf, D.; Major, F.; Tawfik, E.S.   DE 105550/70/0004
Modellversuche zur Selektion auf Eiweissansatz und Adaptationsfähigkeit. **Model trials on selection in protein store and adaptation.**

Domestic animals in general (B 4000)

See also 10451, 10477, 10480, 10523, 10558, 11715, 11726, 11727, 11728, 13724, 13727, 13748

12883 Petersen, J.; Gerken, M.   DE 111501/78/0001 N
Selektion auf Verhaltensparameter bei Japanischen Wachteln. **Selection for parameters of behaviour with Japanese quail.**

12884 Simon, D.; Schulte–Coerne, H.   DE 111502/77/0005
Berücksichtigung genetischer Unterschiede zwischen Vergleichswerten bei der Zuchtwertschätzung. **Estimation of breeding values considering genetic differences among group means.**

12885 Fischer, H.   DE 129540/71/0002
Zytogenetische Untersuchungen an Wild– und Haustieren tropischer Regionen. **Contribution to the knowledge of indigenous, wild and domestic animals of the tropics with the**

aid of chromosome analysis.

12886 Glodek, P.; Bartels, S.   DE 132274/77/0003
Möglichkeiten der Anwendung von Stufenselektion in der Nutztierzucht. **Possibility of using multiple step selection in farm animal breeding.**

12887 Wegner, W.; Reetz, I.; Dausch, D.   DE 139350/73/0003
Genetische Augendefekte bei Mensch und Tier. Untersuchungen zur Klärung der Heritabilität und Pathogenese genetisch determinierter Augenleiden bei Mensch und Tier. Ein Gemeinschaftsprojekt der Haustiergenetik und der Ophthalmologie. **Genetic eye defects of man and animal. Studies on the clarification of hereditability and pathogenesis of genetically determined ophthalmopathies in man and animal. Joint project of domestic animal genetics and ophthalmology.**

12888 Rundfeldt, H.   DE 139960/72/0001 R
Weiterentwicklung von biometrisch fundierten Verfahren zur Objektivierung von Entscheidungen zur Sortenwahl 1972. **Further development of biometric methods for objectivation of decisions on varietal selection.**

12889 Bakels, F.; Storhas, R.   DE 160710/75/0001
Untersuchungen über Erbe–Umwelt–Interaktionen. **Studies on interrelations between heritage and environment.**

12890 Dempfle, L.   DE 161300/78/0003 N
Untersuchungen über die Effizienz von extensiven Zuchtprogrammen. **Investigations on the efficiency of "low–cost" extensive breeding programmes.**

12891 Greve, T.; Lehn–Jensen, H.   DK 030128/76/0005
Undersøgelser over FSH og superovulation. **Investigations into FSH and superovulation.**

12892 Rudemo, M.; Petersen, P.H.; Andersen, S.
                    DK 030142/78/0002 N
Statistisk metodik inden for husdyravl. **Statistical methods applied in animal breeding.**

12893 Chevalet, C.; Flamant, J.C.; Rouvier, R.; Tchamitchian, L.   FR 011406/70/2523
Analyse et gestion des généalogies dans les troupeaux de faible effectif génétique. **Analysis and management of pedigrees in flocks with a small effective population size.** Publications.

12894 Smith   GB 010101/00/0017
Applied genetics theory.

12895 Hall   GB 010103/00/0008
Parentage and twin diagnosis in farm animals.

12896 Wilmut   GB 010106/00/0006 R
The manipulation and preservation of gametes and embryos.

12897 Ryder   GB 010106/00/0014
Growth cycles in mammalian skin follicle.

12898 Ryder   GB 010106/00/0015
Coat structure and evolution in livestock.

12899 Wilmut   GB 010106/79/0017 N
Genetic and environmental factors influencing fertilisation, embryo development and implantation.

12900 Alliston; Barker   GB 010107/76/0002
Assessment of carcass composition of live animals using a Danscan ultrasonic machine.

12901 Dain   GB 010301/00/0014
Cytogenics of domestic animals.

12902 Ingram   GB 010301/77/0081 R
Effects of environmental temperature, food intake and stress on hormone balance in pigs.

12903 Setchell   GB 010302/00/0013 R
Fluid secretion by the testis and the transport of spermatozoa out of the testis.

12904 Setchell; Jacks   GB 010302/00/0015 R
Effect of heat on sperm production by the testis.

12905 Setchell   GB 010302/00/0016 R
The effects of hormones on the testis and the production of hormones by the testis.

12906 Setchell; Hinton   GB 010302/76/0014 R
Analysis of epididymal luminal contents collected by micropuncture techniques.

12907 Wakerley; Cross   GB 010304/19/0058 N
Neurohormonal effects of suckling.

12908 Heap   GB 010305/00/0022 R
Mechanism of action of ovarian steroid hormones.

12909 Heap; Harrison   GB 010305/00/0047 R
Role of progesterone and oestrogens in pregnancy maintenance; onset of paturition; secretion prostaglandin F2a.

12910 Perry   GB 010305/00/0048 R
Endocrine control of maintenance of pregnancy and onset of paturition in sheep, pig, cow and guinea–pig.

12911 Heap   GB 010305/00/0049 R
Embryonic mortality.

12912 Peaker   GB 010305/00/0051 R
Physiological factors controlling the number and activity of secretory cells in the mammary gland.

12913 Deanesley   GB 010305/76/0057 R
Ovarian development and function.

12914 Peaker   GB 010305/76/0058 R
The onset of milk secretion.

12915 Maulewalker; Peaker   GB 010305/77/0062 R
Prostaglandins and mammary function.

12916 Flint   GB 010305/77/0064 R
Placental steroid synthesis in relation to maintenance of pregnancy and parturition.

12917 Flint   GB 010305/77/0065 R
Role of oxytocin in prostaglandin synthesis and oestrous cycle control.

12918 Flint   GB 010305/77/0066 R

Maternal recognition of pregnancy.

12919 Peaker; Maulewalker   GB 010305/77/0069 R
Mammary physiology and cell biology in small mammals.

12920 Parker; White   GB 010310/18/0013 N
Molecular aspects of reproductive hormones.

12921 Rowlands   GB 010404/00/0816 R
Selection of superior animals by metabolic profile.

12922 Rowlands   GB 010408/00/0816 R
Selection of superior animals by metabolic profile.

12923 Falconer; Roberts   GB 012501/00/0001 R
Cellular and physiological variables through which genetic controls of growth operate.

12924 Falconer   GB 012501/00/0002 R
Formal genetics and gene action.

12925 Robertson   GB 012502/00/0003
Advisory work and committees on farm animals.

12926 Beatty   GB 012505/00/0002 R
Genetics of spermatozoa and eggs.

12927 Beatty   GB 012505/00/0003 R
Genetics of spermatozoa. Sex ratio control in animals and man.

12928 Beatty   GB 012505/00/0007 R
Analysis of causes of chromosome aberration in mammals.

12929 Yudilevich   GB 022705/79/0001 N
Transport at blood tissue interfaces in placenta studied by single–circulation paired–tracer dilution.

12930 williams   GB 030604/00/0009 R
Role of trace elements in reproduction.

12931 Williams   GB 030604/77/0021 R
Effects of copper status on foetal and postnatal development in the rat.

12932 Lawson; Sharman   GB 030607/00/0002 R
The presence of fungal oestrogens in Scottish grain related to infertility in rats, poultry and ruminants.

12933 Campbell; Fell   GB 030608/00/0007 R
Effect of pregnancy and progesterone on intestinal enzymes, pancreas islet tissue and liver DNA in rats.

12934 McCaughey   GB 041608/75/0002 R
Pregnancy diagnosis in farm animals.

12935 Mathieson   GB 060116/00/0008
Reproductive disorders.

12936 Petchey; Downie   GB 060208/00/0016
Development of a cytogenic programme for farm animals.

12937 Raimondi, R.   IT 010500/77/0602 R
Marcatori genetici in popolazioni animali scarsamente valorizzate o in via di estinzione. Genetic markers in poorly developed or disappearing breeds.

12938 Minkema, D.   NL 010112/78/8715 N
Conservering van genen van landbouwhuisdieren. Conservation of domestic animal genetic resources.

12939 Bosma, A.A.   NL 030001/73/6127
Chromosomale afwijkingen bij huisdieren. Chromosomal disorders in domestic animals.

Equines (B 4100)

12940 Glodek, P.; Klatt, M.; Bruns, E.   DE 132274/77/0002
Nachkommenprüfung von Reitpferdehengsten anhand von Turnierergebnissen. Progeny testing of stallions in riding horses on competition results.

12941 Kräusslich, H.; Katona, Ö.   DE 160705/73/0002
Züchterische Auswertung der Trabrennleistung. Estimation of breeding values of trotters by racing performance.

12942 Grosclaude, F.; Nguyen, T.C.   FR 010202/73/2503
Mise en évidence du polymorphisme biochimique au niveau des groupes sanguins et de certaines protéines sanguines du cheval. Blood groups and blood protein polymorphism in horses.

12943 Langlois, B.; Legault, C.; Sellier, P.   FR 010202/73/2571
Etude du déterminisme génétique des performances en course au galop chez le pur sang anglais. Genetic aspects of racing ability in thoroughbred horse.

12944 Langlois, B.; Legault, C.   FR 010202/73/2572
Etude du déterminisme génétique de l'aptitude au saut chez le cheval. Genetic aspects of jumping ability in the horse.

12945 Flint   GB 010305/77/0063 R
Foeto–maternal endocrine relationships in the horse.

12946 Lewis, C.A.   IE 120502/75/7973 R
Horse breeding in Ireland, spatial patterns in the half–bred breeding industry, 1886–1976. Publications.

12947 Crimella, C.; Casati, M.; Carenzi, C.; Rognoni, G.; Campitelli, S.; Guella, P.   IT 040638/76/0001
Studio della struttura genetica delle popolazioni equine italiane a livello di polimorfismi ematici con particolare riguardo agli aspetti applicativi (controllo della parentela e modelli di accoppiamento). Researches on the genetic structure of equine populations in Italy studied by means of haematic polymorphisms with particolar emphasis on practical aspects, as parentage control and mating programs. Publications.

12948 Romagnoli, A.   IT 041126/77/0604 R
Polimorfismi ematici rilevabili mediante elettroforesi negli equini. Blood polymorphism screened through electrophoresis in horses.

12949 Minkema, D.; Dommerholt, J.   NL 010112/68/1203
Erfelijkheid van snelheid bij Nederlandse dravers. Heredity of speed in Dutch trotters. Publications.

12950 Meij, G.J.W. van der   NL 030009/67/5695 R
De erfelijke aanleg voor podotrochleitis bij het paard. The hereditary tendency for navicular disease in the horse.

12951 Meij, G.J.W. van der   NL 030009/77/8960 N
Een onderzoek naar de erfelijkheid van enkele afwijkingen

aan benen en mond bij rijpaarden. (erfelijkheid, hazehak, afwijkend kniegewricht, varkensmond, rijpaard). **An investigation into the hereditary of some defects of legs and mouth of saddle–horses. (hereditary, curb, defects of the stifle–joint, parrot mouth, saddle–horse).**

12952 Numans, S.R.　　　　　　　NL 030010/60/5826 R
Erfelijke aspecten van aangeboren knieafwijkingen bij Shetland ponies. **Investigation on hereditary stifle joint problems in Shetland ponies.** Publications.

Ruminants in general (B 4200)

See also 11892

12953 Schmid, D.O.　　　　　　DE 160760/75/0003
Erforschung der Leukozytenantigene bei landwirtschaftlichen Nutztieren mit dem Ziel einer Markierung von Immunitäts und Resistenzgenen. **Research on antigens of leucocytes in productive livestock for the purpose of labelling genes for immunity and resistance.**

12954 Poutous, M.; Mocquot, J.C.; Ricordeau, G.; Flamant, J.C.　　　　　　　　　FR 010202/55/2541
Méthodes de calcul des index de production laitière bovine, ovine et caprine. **Methods for calculating milk production indexes, in cattle, sheep and goat.** Publications.

12955 Lauvergne, J.J.; Lefebvre, J.; Ricordeau, G.
　　　　　　　　　　　　　FR 010202/66/2510
Génétique de la coloration du pelage chez les bovins (brune des alpes, charolais, gasconne——), les ovins et les caprins. **Genetics of coat colour in cattle (brown swiss, charolais, gasconne——), sheep and goat.** Publications.

12956 Wiener; Herbert　　　　　GB 010106/00/0010
Genetic control of mineral metabolism.

12957 Paterson; Hills　　　　　GB 010302/77/0069 R
Adrenal cortical and other endocrine responses to lactation (in goats).

12958 Peaker; Maulewalker　　　GB 010305/77/0067 R
Milk secretion and mammary physiology in cows.

12959 Wooding; Morgan　　　　GB 010308/19/0015 N
Ultrastructural histochemical and autoradiographic studies on implantation and placental growth in ruminants.

12960 Tindal; Hart　　　　　　GB 011710/00/0001 R
Neural factors affecting lactation.

12961 Forsyth; Cowie　　　　　GB 011710/00/0002 R
Hormonal factors affecting lactation.

12962 Jones; Forsyth　　　　　GB 011710/00/0003 R
Biochemical studies related to mammary gland metabolism and function.

12963 Pope; Senior　　　　　　GB 011710/00/0005 R
Endocrinology of reproduction.

12964 Smith; Walsh, R.W.　　　　GB 011712/00/0007 R
Metabolic adaptation to pregnancy and lactation.

12965 Kay; Goodall　　　　　　GB 030612/00/0019 R

Effects of day length on reproductive cycles and endocrine activity of red deer and sheep.

12966 MacLaren　　　　　　　GB 060312/00/0005
Reproductive disorders.

Cattle (B 4210)

See also 10644, 10645, 10716, 10739, 10741, 10744, 10759, 10770, 10821, 10822, 10867, 10890, 10896, 10919, 12025, 12153, 12221, 12870, 12871, 12872, 13344, 14102, 14172, 14211

12967 Bouquet, Y.; Van de Weghe, A.　　BE 050200/58/0001 R
Onderzoek van bloedgroepen en biochemische merkersystemen van bloedbestanddelen bij huisdieren. **Study of bloodgroups and biochemical markersystems of bloodsubstances in domestic animals.** Publications.

12968 Bouters, R.; Vandeplassche, M.; Geldhof, A.; Moyaert, I.　　　　　　　　BE 050300/75/0004 R
Superovulatie, Recuperatie en Transplantatie van runderembryo's. **Superovulation, recuperation en transplantation of cattle embryo's.** Publications.

12969 Hanset, R.; Michaux, C.　　BE 060003/68/0001 R
Recherches sur le déterminisme génétique de l'hypertrophie musculaire dans l'espèce bovine. **Research on genetical determinism of muscular hypertrophy in cattle.** Publications.

12970 Hanset, R.; Leroy, P.　　　BE 060003/77/0002
Méthodes de progeny–test des taureaux laitiers.
Progeny–testing methods of dairy bulls. Publications.

12971 Boucqué, Ch.　　　　　BE 070700/79/0038 N
Vleesproduktievermogen van kruisingsprodukten van beefalo met tweeledige melkveerassen. **Beef production potential of F 1 crossings between beefalo and dual purpose dairy breeds.**

12972 Hanset, R.; Michaux, C.　　BE 140000/78/0074 N
Evaluation des géniteurs pour productions laitières en race pie–noire de Herve. **Best linear unbased production (BLUP) by black–white dairy bulls of east Belgium.**

12973 Tijskens, R.; Vandepitte, W.　　BE 140000/79/0060 N
Verbetering van het Rood–Bonte melkras. **Breeding of the Red and White dairy cattle.**

12974 Weniger, J.H.; Bayer, W.; Hippen, H.
　　　　　　　　　　　　DE 105550/72/0004
Untersuchungen zur Reaktion eineiiger Rinderzwillinge auf Wärmebelastung. **Studies on reaction of monozygotic twins of cattle to heat stress.**

12975 Schmitten, F.　　　　　DE 111500/70/0007 N
Kreuzungsversuch mit Mastrindern. **Crossing experiment on fattening cattle.**

12976 Schmitten, F.; Schneider, J.; Birker, F.
　　　　　　　　　　　　DE 111500/74/0006
Untersuchungen zur Reduzierung des Aufwandes der Milchleistungsprüfung und zur Abschätzung von Korrekturfaktoren für die Zuchtwertschätzung von Bullen. **Studies on reducing the input in milk yield control and on valuating the conditions of correction in the estimation of the breeding value of bulls.**

12977 Schmitten, F.; Lütgemüller, F.–W.; Birker, F.
DE 111500/75/0003
Untersuchungen zur Nutzbarmachung von Teilerstlaktationen zur Optimalisierung der Zuchtwertschätzung beim Rind. **Studies on the utilization of partial first lactations for optimizing the estimation of the breeding value of cattle.**

12978 Simon, D.; Schulte–Coerne, H.; Birker, F.
DE 111502/77/0002
Anpassung der Zuchtwertschätzmethoden beim Milchrind an veränderte Populationsstrukturen. **Adaptation of breeding value estimation to modified population structures in dairy cattle.**

12979 Simon, D.; Meisterjahn, R.; Schulte–Coerne, H.
DE 111502/77/0004
Schätzung genetischer Parameter für den Eiweiss– und Laktosegehalt der Milch. **Estimation of genetic parameters for protein and lactose content of milk.**

12980 Simon, D.; Schulte–Coerne, H.; Romberg, F.–J.
DE 111502/78/0002 N
Zuchtwertschätzung von Jungbullen. **Estimation of breeding values of young bulls.**

12981 Wassmuth, R.; Tripp, H.; Diakite, B.; Steidl, T.; Knell, H.
DE 129250/77/0001
Färsenvornutzung in Reinzucht und Gebrauchskreuzung. **Pre–use of heifers in pure breeding and commercial cross.** Publications.

12982 Senft, B.; Rudolphi, K.; Meyer, F.   DE 129251/73/0002
Untersuchungen über genetisch–bedingte Einflüsse auf die Milcheiweissleistung bei Kühen. **Genetic influence on production of milk protein in cows.**

12983 Senft, B.; Erhardt, G.; Meyer, F.   DE 129251/78/0003 N
Genetische Aspekte des natürlichen Abwehrsystems im Euter. **Genetic aspects of the natural defence mechanism in the mammary gland.**

12984 Scheurmann, E.; Marx, W.   DE 129540/78/0001 N
Zytogenetische Untersuchungen an autochthonen Rinderpopulationen Marokkos. **Cytogenetic investigations on indigenous cattle populations in Morocco.**

12985 Rieck, G.W.; Kleine–Brörmann, B.
DE 129680/78/0001 N
Genetische Grundlagen des Schizosomie–Syndroms beim Rind. **Genetical background of schizosoma reflexum in cattle.**

12986 Smidt, D.; Jüttner, B.; Langholz, H.–J.
DE 132271/71/0001
Fruchtbarkeitsuntersuchungen beim Rind in Abhängigkeit von Kreuzungs– und Reinzuchtpaarung. **Studies on the fertility in cattle as a consequence of cross–breeding and pure breeding.**

12987 Langholz, H.–J.; Kräusslich, H.; Ernst, E.
DE 132273/72/0001
Rindfleischerzeugung mit Hilfe der Einfachgebrauchskreuzung – überregionale Experimentalstudie unter Verwendung von Deutschen Schwarzbunten und Deutschem Braunvieh als Mutterrassen und Deutschen Rotbunten, Deutschem Fleckvieh, Deut– schem Gelbvieh und Charolais als Vaterrassen –. **Beef production using commercial single cross breeding – a supraregional experimental study using German Frisian and German brown cattle as dam breeds, and German Holstein, German spotted cattle, German yellow and Charolais cattle as sire breeds.** Publications.

12988 Langholz, H.–J.   DE 132273/73/0002
Die Verwendung von Einfachkreuzungen in der Mutterkuhhaltung an marginalen Grünlandstandorten in Mittelgebirgslagen. **Use of single crosses in suckler cow keeping on marginal grassland in the uplands.**

12989 Langholz, H.–J.   DE 132273/74/0003
Milcherzeugung mit Rassen unterschiedlicher Nutzungsrichtung am Grünlandstandort Niedersachsens. **Milk production with breeds of different specialization on grassland in Lower Saxony.**

12990 Langholz, H.–J.; Happ, J.; Jongeling, C.
DE 132273/75/0002
Nachkommenprüfung von KB–Bullen auf Gewichtsentwicklung im Feld. **Field testing of A.I. bulls progeny for growth rate.**

12991 Langholz, H.–J.; Pabst, W.   DE 132273/77/0002
Einfachkreuzungen grosswüchsiger italienischer Vaterrassen mit schwarzbunten Kühen zur Erhöhung der Rindfleischerzeugung. **Commercial crossbreeding of large–framed Italian sire breeds with German Frisians aiming at increase in beef production.**

12992 Stephan, E.; Sasu, M.B.   DE 139260/72/0002
Zur Frage der Verwendbarkeit der Verlaufskontrolle von Schilddrüsenfunktion und Blut–Säure–Basen–Status bei Nachkommengruppen von Rind und Schwein zur Erkennung temperaturunempfindlicher oder anpassungsfähiger Populationen. **The use of the controlled course of the function of the thyroid gland and of the acid–base–status on progeny groups of cattle and pigs in order to identify temperature tolerant or more adaptable populations.**

12993 Geldermann, H.   DE 139352/77/0001
Untersuchung der Milchleistungsvererbung beim Deutschen Schwarzbunten Rind mit Hilfe von Markergenen. **Investigation on inheritance of milk production in German Friesian cattle by gene markers.**

12994 Lotthammer, K.–H.   DE 139800/70/0002
Beziehungen zwischen Milchleistungs– und Fruchtbarkeitsvererbung von Besamungsbullen. **Correlations between heredity of milk yield and fertility in insemination bulls.**

12995 Lotthammer, K.–H.; Gondesen, F.
DE 139800/78/0008 N
Untersuchungen über die Erblichkeit verschiedener Blutparameter beim Rind mit Beziehung zur Gesundheit und Fruchtbarkeit. **Investigations on the heredity of some blood parameters of dairy cattle with relation to health and fertility.**

12996 Haussmann, H.; Karras, K.; Graser, H.U.
DE 144680/73/0006
Weiterentwicklung der Methoden zur Zuchtwertschätzung beim Rind in Baden–Württemberg. **Improvement of methods of estimating breeding values of dairy cattle in Baden–Wuerttemberg.**

12997 Fewson, D.; Schlote, W.; Hässig, H.

DE 144680/75/0002

Untersuchungen über die Beziehungen von Körpermassen und Gewichten an Färse und Kalb zur Leichtkalbigkeit beim Deutschen Fleckvieh. **Investigations of the relations between body measurements and weights of heifers and calves and the ease of calving in German Fleckvieh.**

12998 Schlote, W.; Wenzler, A.   DE 144680/77/0002
Selektionsindices für mehrere Merkmale beim Zweinutzungsrind Schätzung von Populationsparametern. **Selection indices for several traits in dual–purpose cattle Estimation of population parameters.**

12999 Paizs, L.; Aksen, T.   DE 144690/72/0002
Über den Einfluss der Variation relevanter Nutzleistungen auf den Milchproduktionsprozess. **Some investigations into the influence of the variability of performance of cows on milk production.**

13000 Ernst, E.; Schubert, U.   DE 148350/71/0005
Nachkommenschaftsprüfung und Eigenleistungsprüfung beim Rind in Schleswig–Holstein. **Progeny and performance test of cattle in Sleswick–Holstein.**

13001 Meyer, J.; Radzikowski, A.; Graf, F.; Miesel, G.; Osterkorn, K.   DE 160705/70/0003
Vererbung physiologischer Merkmale bei Mäusen, Rindern und Schweinen. **Heredity of physiological characteristics in mice, cattle and swine.**

13002 Graf, F.; Frahm, K.; Furtmayr, L.; Osterkorn, K.
DE 160705/72/0001
Biochemische Parameter im Blutserum als Hilfsmerkmal für die Selektion beim Rind. **Biochemical parameters in blood serum as selection aid in cattle breeding.**

13003 Kräusslich, H.; Osterkorn, K.   DE 160705/73/0001
Untersuchungen von Fruchtbarkeitsparametern in Besamungspopulationen beim Rind. **Estimation of breeding values by fertility parameters in insemination populations of cattle.**

13004 Kräusslich, H.; Osterkorn, K.; Averdunk, G.; Gottschalk, A.   DE 160705/77/0002
Beziehungen zwischen den Eigenleistungsergebnissen von Prüfbullen und den Abkalbeergebnissen aus dem Testeinsatz. **Relationship between performance test data and calving performance of test bulls.** Publications.

13005 Kräusslich, H.; Bar–Anan, R.; Osterkorn, K.
DE 160705/78/0002 N
Genetische Einflüsse auf die Zwischenbesamungszeit. **Genetic components affecting the interval between consecutive inseminations.**

13006 Herz, J.; Frahm, K.   DE 160705/78/0003 N
Einfluss der Milchleistung auf die Fruchtbarkeit von Hochleistungskühen. **Correlations between milk yield and fertility of high yielding dairy cows.** Publications.

13007 Pirchner, F.   DE 161300/72/0006
Interaktionen zwischen Genotyp und Mastverfahren bei Rindern. **Interactions between genotypes and fattening methods in cattle.**

13008 Pirchner, F.; Graml, J.   DE 161300/73/0005

Milchleistung von Kreuzungstieren im Vergleich zu ihren reinrassigen Stallgefährtinnen. **Milk performance of crossbred cows compared to that of their purebred contemporaries.**

13009 Förster, M.   DE 161300/74/0017
Chromosomenuntersuchungen an Bullen und Ebern der bayerischen Besamungsstationen. **Chromosomal investigations on bulls and boars of the Bavarian A.I.–stations.**

13010 Pirchner, F.; El–Hakim, A.; Eichinger, H.
DE 161300/75/0002
Unterschiede in der Körperzusammensetzung zwischen und innerhalb von Rinderrassen. **Differences in body composition among and within cattle breeds.**

13011 Pirchner, F.; Clement, A.   DE 161300/75/0004
Ausmass und Ursachen von Heterosis bei Kreuzungen zwischen Braunvieh und Brown–Swiss. **Degree and causes of heterosis in crosses of Braunvieh and Brown Swiss.**

13012 Pirchner, F.; Khalil, H.   DE 161300/75/0006
Genotyp 'Rassen' – Umwelt Interaktion bei Körpermassen, Gewichten und Futterverwertung bei Rindern. **Interaction between genotype breeds and environment in body measurements, weight and feed efficiency in cattle.**

13013 Förster, M.; Zwiauer, D.   DE 161300/75/0007
Populationsuntersuchungen an Nachkommen von Bullen mit Zentromerfusionen. **Cytogenetic investigations in a population of offspring from sires with different centric fusions.**

13014 Pirchner, F.; Zwiauer, D.   DE 161300/75/0013
Koppelungsbeziehungen zwischen genetischen Markern und Leistungsgenen bei Höhenvieh. **Correlations between genetic markers and performance genes in highland cattle.**

13015 Dempfle, L.   DE 161300/77/0001
Untersuchungen über verschiedene Zuchtwertschätzungsmethoden bei Milchkühen unter Berücksichtigung des genetischen Trends der Selektion. **Investigations on the estimation of breeding values of dairy cows in consideration of genetic trend of selection.**

13016 Willeke, H.; Wörle, L.   DE 161300/77/0005
Schätzung der genetischen Parameter des Haupt– und Nachgemelkes mit Hilfe eines modifizierten Truestestes. **Estimation of the genetic parameters of milking and stripping with a modified true–tester.**

13017 Huth, F.W.   DE 201200/77/0028
Überregionale Experimentalstudie zur Verbesserung des Rindfleischaufkommens mit Hilfe der Einfach–Gebrauchskreuzungen auf der Mutterunterlage Deutsche Schwarzbunte in der Bundesrepublik Deutschland. **Supraregional experimental study on the increase in beef supply by means of single–commercial crossing basing on suckling cow stock of Deutsche Schwarzbunte in the Federal Republic of Germany.**

13018 Gravert, H.O.; Pabst, K.; Kordts, E.
DE 207010/77/0004
Programmierte Rinderzucht. **Programmed cattle breeding.**

13019 Schön, L.   DE 210010/75/0018
Untersuchungen über den Schlachtwert von Rindern verschiedener Nutzungsrichtungen und Kreuzungen. **Studies**

on the slaughter value of cattle of different use systems and crosses.

13020 Kögel, S.; Gottschalk, A.; Averdunk, G.
DE 502303/75/0001
Einfluss der Inzucht auf Wachstum, Fruchtbarkeit, Milchleistung und Langlebigkeit beim Deutschen Fleckvieh. **The influence of inbreeding on growth, fertility, milk production and longevity of the German Fleckvieh breed.**

13021 Kögel, S.; Alps, H.; Gottschalk, A.; Ferstl, R.
DE 502303/75/0003
Mast– und Schlachtleistung von Kälbern und Bullen mit 75 % Brown Swiss– Genanteil im Vergleich zu Deutschem Braunvieh. **Fattening ability and carcass quality of calves and bulls of 3/4 Brown Swiss in comparison with German Braunvieh.**

13022 Kögel, S.; Mager, A.
DE 502303/75/0004
Einfluss der Einkreuzung von Red Holstein in das Deutsche Fleckvieh auf Milch– und Fleischleistung. **The influence of crossing German Fleckvieh with Red Holstein on milk and beef production.**

13023 Christensen, L.G.; Hansen, M.; Neimann–Sørensen, A.
DK 010201/70/0003
Avlsplanlægning hos kvæg og specielle populationsgenetiske undersøgelser. **Breeding plans for cattle and special studies of population genetics.**

13024 Andersen, B.B.
DK 010201/71/0005
Race– og produktionstypeforsøg med kvæg af europæiske kødracer. **Cross–breeding and production–type studies with European beef and dual purpose breeds.**

13025 Christensen, L.G.
DK 010201/72/0007
Race– og krydsningsforsøg med Rød Dansk Malkerace, Holstein–Friesian og Finsk Ayrshire. **Pure– and cross–breeding studies with Red Danish, Holstein–Friesian and Finnish Ayrshire cattle.**

13026 Hansen, M.; Neimann–Sørensen, A.
DK 010201/72/0008
Import af arveanlæg til Rød Dansk Malkerace. (RDM). Sammenlignende raceforsøg med RDM, svensk rød og hvid boskap, finsk ayrshire og Maas Rhijn–Ijssen. **Importation of genes for Red Danish Cattle. (RDM). Comparative breed studies with RDM, Swedish Red and White Boskap, Finnish Ayrshire and Maas Rhijn–Ijssen.**

13027 Christensen, L.G.; Vesth, B.
DK 010201/73/0002
Selektionsforsøg med RDM. Stærkt udvalg for smørfedt ydelse i henholdsvis op– og nedadgående retning. **Selection studies with RDM. Strong selection for butterfat yield in a positive and negative direction respectively.**

13028 Nielsen, E.; Neimann–Sørensen, A.
DK 010201/74/0013
Undersøgelser vedr. mælke– og kødproduktion m. v. hos SDM og Holstein–Friesian samt hos krydsninger mellem disse racer. **Studies of milk and meat production etc. in SDM and Holstein–Friesian cattle and crosses between these breeds.**

13029 Nielsen, E.; Jørgensen, J.
DK 010201/74/0014
Undersøgelser vedr. ydelsesnedgangen hos Jerseykøer ikælvede ved henholdsvis Charolaistyre og Jerseytyre. **Studies of the decline in milk yield of Jersey cows mated to respectively**

Charolais and Jersey bulls.

13030 Lykke, T.; Andersen, B.B.
DK 010201/74/0017
Selektionsforsøg for vækstevne og slagtekvalitet hos kvæg. **Selection for growth potential and slaughter quality in cattle.**

13031 Bech Andersen, B.
DK 010201/75/0001
Forskellige kødracekrydsningers tilvækst, foderudnyttelse, slagtekvalitet og kødkvalitet ved forskellig slagtevægt, foderstyrke og proteinniveau. **Growth, feed utilization, slaughter and carcass quality at different slaughter weights, feeding intensities and protein levels of different beef cattle crosses.**

13032 Nielsen, S.M.
DK 010201/75/0010
Malkbarheds– og yversundhedsundersøgelser i selektions–forsøget for vækstevne og slagtekvalitet. **Ease of milking and udder health investigations in a carcass quality and growth rate selection experiment.**

13033 Elleby, F.
DK 010702/73/0001
Undersøgelser af kvægets frugtbarhed i relation til insemineringsstatistik, ydelseshøjde og kælvningsstatistik. **Investigations of the fertility of cattle in relation to their insemination, yield and calving records.**

13034 Elleby, F.
DK 010702/74/0001
Undersøgelser af bekæmpelsesforanstaltninger og kontrol med arvelige defekter og negative egenskaber i kvægbestanden. **Investigation of the prevention and control of genetical defects and negative traits in the cattle herd.**

13035 Elleby, F.
DK 010702/74/0002
Ydelsesundersøgelser på de kontrollerede køers datamateriale sat i forhold til avl– og miljømæssige forhold. **Yield studies on controlled cows set in relation to genetic and environmental conditions.**

13036 Elleby, F.
DK 010702/75/0001
Undersøgelser over faktorer, som påvirker en selektion for mælkeprotein. **Investigation of factors which influence a selection for milk protein.**

13037 Jensen, P.T.
DK 020100/79/5101 N
Genetiske studier over immunglobulinkoncentrationer i kvægserum og den eventuelle sammenhæng med resistens mod mastitis. **The genetic relation between immunoglobulinconcentrations in cattle serum and the resistance to mastitis.**

13038 Koefoed–Johnsen, H.
DK 030109/76/0006
Morfologiske undersøgelser af tyresperma med dag–defekt. **Morphological investigations of bull sperm with the day–defect.**

13039 Larsen, B.; Agergaard, N.; Wegger, I.
DK 030126/77/9020 R
Biokemiske–genetiske markørsystemer (blod– og proteintyper) og disses relationer til produktionsegenskaber hos kvæg. **Biochemical–genetic marker systems (blood and protein types) in relation to production characteristics in cattle.**

13040 Christiansen, I.J.; Greve, T.
DK 030128/76/0004
Undersøgelse af muligheden for kønsbestemmelse af kalvefostre in vivo. **An investigation of the possibilities for the sex determination of calf embryos "in vivo".**

13041 Petersen, P.H.   DK 030142/74/0002
Avlsværdivurdering af tyre og køer for
mælkeproduktionsevne. **An estimation of the breeding value of
bulls and cows with reference to milk producing ability.**

13042 Petersen, P.H.   DK 030142/77/0005
Undersøgelser over biokemiske–genetiske markøregenskaber
og disses relationer til produktionsegenskaber hos kalve.
**Investigations into biochemical and genetic marker properties
and their relations to production characteristics in calves.**

13043 Petersen, P.H.   DK 030142/77/0006
Undersøgelser vedrørende metodikken ved
avlsværdivurderingen af tyre, der individafprøves for
kødproduktionsegenskaber. **Investigations into the
methodology of breed evaluation in bulls, including that of the
individual tests indicative of meat producing characteristics.**

13044 Kragelund, K.   DK 030142/77/0007
Genetiske undersøgelser vedrørende kvægets frugtbarhed.
Genetic investigations concerning the fertility of cattle.

13045 Ipsen, E.J.   DK 030142/77/0014
Principper for bedømmelse af malkekvægets eksteriør.
Principles for judging the external appearance of dairy cattle.

13046 Sørensen, S.E.   DK 030191/77/0002 N
Undersøgelse af arveligt betinget bindevævssejghed i okse– og
kalvekød. **The influence of genetic factors on the connective
tissue component of meat tenderness in beef.**

13047 Lefebvre, J.   FR 010202/52/2508
Etude par les analyses multidimensionnelles des données
généalogiques, pour déterminer les critères de choix des
Taureaux à soumettre au testage. **Utilization of multivariate
analysis to genealogical data for sampling of bulls.** Publications.

13048 Lefebvre, J.; Bocquet, G.; Dupuy, G.
                    FR 010202/52/2509
Etude des relations entre la conformation, les caracteres de
production (viande, lait, la fécondité, la longévité), chez les
bovins normands et montbéliards par les analyses
multidimensionnelles. **Relationships between conformation and
production traits (meat, milk, fertility, longevity) in norman
and montbéliard cattle by multivariate analysis.** Publications.

13049 Foully, J.L.; Bibé, B.; Menissier, F.; Gaillard, J.
                    FR 010202/55/2531 R
Schémas de sélection des taureaux de race à viande en vue du
croisement terminal pour la production de jeunes bovins.
Selection schemes of French beef breeds for terminal crossing.
Publications.

13050 Grosclaude, F.; Mercier, J.C.; Ribadeau–Dumas, B.
                    FR 010202/64/2505
Analyse génétique et biochimique du polymorphisme des
caséines bovines. **Biochemical genetics of bovine casein
polymorphism.** Publications.

13051 Grosclaude, F.; Houlier, G.; Lefebvre, J.
                    FR 010202/66/2500
Relations de parenté entre les races bovines françaises et
situation génétique actuelle de ces races. **Genetic relationships
between French cattle breeds and genetic status of these breeds
at present time.** Publications.

13052 Menissier, F.; Bibé, B.; Foulley, J.L.
                    FR 010202/66/2537
Variations d'origine génétique de l'aptitude au vêlage et de ses
composantes. **Calving ability: genetic variations of anatomical
and physiological components.** Publications.

13053 Colleau, J.J.   FR 010202/66/2546
Comparaison de races bovines mixtes pour la production
laitière et l'efficacité alimentaire. **Comparison of dual purpose
cattle breeds for milk production and food efficiency.**

13054 Lauvergne, J.J.; Theret, M.   FR 010202/67/2511
Déterminisme et étude au niveau des populations des
anomalies héréditaires bovines, arthrogripose et palatoschizis
en race charollaise, alopécie en race normande. Analyse des
fratries de 1/2 germains. **Population genetics of mendelian
defects in cattle (syndrome of arthrogryposis with palatoschizis
in charollais, alopecia in norman breed). Behavidur and
frequency of the genes by analysis of half – sib families.**
Publications.

13055 Menissier, F.; Bibé, B.; Fabre, G.P.   FR 010202/68/2533
Production, comparaison et sélection de lignées de bovins à
musculature hypertrophiée en vue du croisement terminal.
**Breeding and comparison of double muscled cattle lines for
terminal crossing.** Publications.

13056 Menissier, F.; Foulley, J.L.; Frebling, J.
                    FR 010202/68/2535
Schémas de sélection des taureaux de races à viande françaises
en vue d'une utilisation en race pure. **Selection schemes of
French beef breeds for purebreeding.** Publications.

13057 Colleau, J.J.   FR 010202/68/2544
Sélection sur la vitesse de traite des vaches. **Selection on
milking rate in cows.** Publications.

13058 Colleau, J.J.   FR 010202/68/2545
Comparaison de races bovines spécialisées et leurs croisements
pour la production de lait et de viande. **Comparison of
specialized cattle breeds and their crosses for milk and meat
production.** Publications.

13059 Bibé, B.; Menissier, F.; Frebling, J.; Perreau, B.
                    FR 010202/70/2534
Analyse de la variabilité génétique entre races et intra–races
des races à viande bovines françaises. **Analysis of genetic
variability between breeds and within French beef breeds.**
Publications.

13060 Chesnais, J.; Colleau, J.J.; Mocquot, J.C.
                    FR 010202/70/2543
Estimation des variations génétiques intra–races bovines dans
le temps et dans l'espace. **Estimation of genetic trend of
characters between years and areas within cattle breeds.**

13061 Popescu, P.C.; Parez, M.; Menissier, F.
                    FR 010202/71/2514
Etude d' anomalies chromosomiques chez les bovins et de leurs
relations avec la fertilité. **Chromosome abnormalities in cattle
and their effects on fertility.** Publications.

13062 Menissier, F.; Frebling, J.   FR 010202/71/2536
Constitution et sélection d'un troupeau de bovins sur l'aptitude
à la gémellité. **Breeding beef cattle for twinning ability.**

Publications.

13063 Bibé, B. FR 010202/71/2538
Variations génétiques de l'efficacité alimentaire et de ses
composantes liées à l'activité métabolique ou au
comportement chez les bovins à viande. **Feed efficiency of beef
cattle: genetic variations and components.** Publications.

13064 Colleau, J.J.; Bibé, B. FR 010202/71/2539
Variations génétiques du comportement des bovins soumis à
un stress thermique. **Tolerance to thermic stress: genetic
variation and components.** Publications.

13065 Mocquot, J.C.; Elsen, J.M. FR 010202/71/2548
Rentabilité de la sélection bovine et ovine. **Economic efficiency
of cattle and sheep improvement schemes.** Publications.

13066 Grosclaude, F.; Guérin, G. FR 010202/72/2506
Incidence de la recombinaison génétique dans les systèmes de
groupes sanguins et de protéines polymorphes chez les bovins
et les ovins. **Estimation of genetic recombination in blood group
and protein polymorphic system in bovine and sheep.**

13067 Popescu, P.C. FR 010202/72/2513
Etude du caryotype bovin par les nouvelles méthodes
cytogénétiques. **Studies of bovine caryotype by recent
cytogenetic methods.** Publications.

13068 Poutous, M. FR 010202/73/2542
Comparaisons de souches bovines pie–noires pour leurs
performances de production et de reproduction. **Comparison
of black and white friesian strains for production and
reproduction performance.**

13069 Guibert, P.; Poutous, M; Guinot, J.P.
FR 012224/64/3016
Etude des possibilités de testage de taureaux Montbéliard en
station. **Studies on the possibility of testing progenies of
Montbéliard bulls in testing station.** Publications.

13070 Guibert, P.; Guinot, J.P.; Faivre, P. FR 012224/65/3018
Etude des possibilités d'utilisation des mâles de la race
Montbéliard pour la production de veaux de boucherie et de
taurillons. **Study of the possibility of producing veal and baby
beef with the males of the Montbéliard breed.** Publications.

13071 Mocquot, J.C.; Parrassin, P.; Colleau, J.J.; Guinot,
J.P. FR 012224/72/9003
Progrès génétique dû à la voie paternelle. **Measuring genetic
cattle improvement induced by the choice of the male.**

13072 Guibert, P.; Poutous, M.; Guinot, J.P.
FR 012224/73/3017
Essai de mesure du progrès génétique dû à l'utilisation des
meilleurs taureaux Montbéliard dans un troupeau de vaches
laitières. **Estimating the genetical progress due to the utilization
of the best bulls of Montbéliard breed through a herd of dairy
cows.** Publications.

13073 Hinks GB 010101/00/0001
Develop national breeding policies for beef and dairy cattle.

13074 Hinks GB 010101/00/0002
Identification and utilization of genetic superiority.

13075 Smith; Other GB 010101/76/0019

Genetic improvement of efficiency of lean meat production in
beef cattle.

13076 Taylor GB 010104/00/0001 R
**Productive efficiency in Friesian and Jersey cattle fed a
standard complete diet.**

13077 Thiessen GB 010104/00/0002
**Multibreed comparisons of productive efficiency in cattle fed a
standard diet.**

13078 Taylor; Shaw GB 010104/00/0003
Genetic and non–genetic variation between cattle twins.

13079 Wiener GB 010106/00/0011
Lactation disorders.

13080 Land GB 010106/75/0016 R
Physiological prediction of the genetic merit of dairy cattle.

13081 Linzell; Peaker GB 010305/00/0054 R
**The effect of hormones and of local factors on the yield and
composition of cow milk.**

13082 Reid; Manston GB 010404/18/0837 N
**Infertility in cattle in relation to liver function, lipid infiltration
and hormone metabolism.**

13083 Rowlands; Russell GB 010408/76/0836 R
Factors affecting fertility of cattle.

13084 Williams GB 010601/00/0020 R
**Relating milk and meat production potentials by carcass
dissection of male offspring of friesian and jersey bulls.**

13085 Leaver GB 011704/00/0003 R
Reproduction in dairy cattle.

13086 Manning; Price GB 011709/00/0004 R
Analysis of odours in relation to oestrus in dairy cattle.

13087 Welch; Stead GB 011712/00/0002 R
Transport of fat and its utilization for milk fat synthesis.

13088 Beatty; Spooner GB 012505/00/0001
Assess male fertility by mixed insemination.

13089 Ross GB 022802/79/0001 N
**Motility of bovine spermatozoa using the fibre optical doppler
anemoneter (foda).**

13090 Clegg GB 030202/76/0021 R
**Lipoprotein lipase activity in milk and in adipose and mammary
tissues.**

13091 Davies GB 030203/00/0006 R
**Natural variation in composition of casein micelles and the
effect of udder disease.**

13092 Phillippo; Denerley GB 030612/00/0011 R
Twinning in cattle.

13093 McCaughey GB 041608/75/0001
Control of reproduction in ruminants.

13094 McCaughey GB 041608/77/0003

Predictions of reproductive fitness in cattle.

13095 Researcher not indicated   GB 050432/00/0001 R
A study of biochemical parameters in stud bulls.

13096 Researcher not indicated   GB 050463/00/0001 R
Detection and synchronisation of oestrus in cattle.

13097 Researcher not indicated   GB 050473/00/0003 R
Special abortion investigations; bovine foetal immunology.

13098 Wijeratne; Hinks   GB 050509/00/0002
Conception rate in cattle and relationship of production
performance with pre– and perinatal mortality.

13099 Foulkes; Saunders   GB 050511/00/0001 R
Detection of oestrus in cattle.

13100 Saunders   GB 050511/00/0002
Breeding efficiency in cattle.

13101 Foulkes   GB 050511/00/0003 R
The characteristics of bull semen.

13102 Saunders; Sauer   GB 050511/00/0004 R
Embryonic development in cattle.

13103 Foulkes; Hartley   GB 050511/00/0005 R
Parturition in cattle and the post–parturient period.

13104 Foulkes   GB 050511/00/0007
The preservation of bull semen.

13105 Lamont; Goodey   GB 050511/00/0008 R
Disease agents and bull semen.

13106 Lamont   GB 050511/00/0009
The fertility of bulls and the production of semen.

13107 Norman   GB 050511/78/0011
Conception in cattle.

13108 Foulkes; Norman   GB 050511/78/0012
Insemination techniques in cattle.

13109 Saunders; Norman   GB 050511/78/0014 R
The inheritance of fertility in female cattle.

13110 Pollock   GB 060102/00/0002
Genetic improvement of dairy cows.

13111 Lowman   GB 060102/00/0009
Improving the fertility of suckler herds.

13112 Pollock   GB 060102/00/0010
Galloway cattle: tibial hemimelia evaluation.

13113 Chesworth   GB 060219/00/0005 R
The effect of plane of nutrition post–partum on oestrus and
conception in beef cows.

13114 Cunningham, E.P.; More O'Ferrall, G.J.
     IE 060100/72/0541 R
Evaluation of new breeds of beef cattle. Publications.

13115 Cunningham, E.P.   IE 060100/72/0549 R

Development of efficient dairy cow selection methods.
Publications.

13116 Cunningham, E.P.   IE 060100/73/0542 R
Comparison of international strains of friesian for milk and beef
production. Publications.

13117 Cunningham, E.P.   IE 060100/73/0543 R
Gene pool development of an experimental beef herd.
Publications.

13118 Cunningham, E.P.   IE 060100/73/0548 N
Studies on cost–effectiveness in cattle breeding. Publications.

13119 Cunningham, E.P.; More O'Ferrall, G.J.
     IE 060100/75/1175 R
Comparison of beef sire breeds. Publications.

13120 Cunningham, E.P.   IE 060100/75/1202 R
Study of breeding methods and population structure in
European cattle populations using computer simulation.
Publications.

13121 More O'Ferrall, G.J.; Cunningham, E.P.
     IE 060100/75/1206 R
Comparison of friesian strains for beef production.
Publications.

13122 Cunningham, E.P.; More O'Ferrall, G.J.
     IE 060100/77/1266 R
Study of the effect of crossing with beef breed bulls on the milk
production of friesian cows. Publications.

13123 Drennan, M.J.; Jennings, J.; Harte, F.J.; Cunningham,
E.P.   IE 060103/75/1185 R
Evaluation of different breed types as dams in single suckling.
Publications.

13124 Dassat, P.   IT 010500/77/0596 R
Programma di selezione sperimentale per l'addomesticamento
del carattere coscia in bovini. **Experimental selection program
to develop and maintain the characteristics of the round of beef.**

13125 Romita, A.   IT 020700/77/0582 R
Incrocio industriale chianina per frisona, macellazione dei
maschi a tre pessi differenti ed utilizzazione delle femmine per
un parto precoce. **Industrial crossbreeding of the Chianina and
Friesian breeds, male slaughtering at three different stages and
the use of dams for premature calving.**

13126 Masoero, G.; Auxilia, M.T.; Terramoccia, S.
     IT 020700/79/0001 N
Valutazione del valore di allevamento delle bovine di razza
Piemontese ai fini della conservazione dei caratteri materni.
**Breeding evaluation of Piemontese cows in order to maintain
maternal characters.**

13127 Santoro, P.   IT 040236/74/0626
Prove sull'incrocio industriale nella produzione della carne
bovina. **Industrial cross breeding trials for beef production.**

13128 Meregalli, A.   IT 040520/72/0110
Ricerche sulla produzione della carne bovina mediante
l'incrocio industriale fra razze da latte e da carne etc. **Research
on beef production through industrial cross–breeding of beef
cattle and dairy cattle breeds.** Publications.

13129 Meregalli, A. IT 040520/74/0587
Ricerche sulla produzione della carne bovina mediante l'incrocio industriale fra razze da carne e razze in allevamento brado. **Research on beef production by industrial cross–breeding of beef breeds and breeds reared in the wild state.**

13130 Meregalli, A. IT 040520/77/0239 R
Ricerche sulla produzione della carne bovina mediante l'incrocio industriale fra razze da carne e razze in allevamento brado. **Research on beef production through the industrial crossing of meat races and range cattle.**

13131 Meregalli, A. IT 040523/78/1161 N
Ricerche sulla produzione della carne bovina mediante l'incrocio industriale fra razze di carne in allevamento brado. Indagini comparative su vitelloni Chian.Xmaremm., Charol.Xmaremm., Chian.XCharol. maremm. e XChian. Maremm. **Research on beef production based on the industrial crossing of beef races reared in the wild state. Comparative study on weaned calves Chian.Xmaremm., Charol.Xmaremm., Chian.XCharol. maremm. and XChian. maremm..**

13132 Rognoni, G. IT 040613/74/0613
Miglioramento genetico–quantitativo della produzione lattea nella specie bovina mediante studi sui polimorfismi del sangue e del latte. **Genetic–quantitative improvement of milk yields in cattle through research on blood and milk polymorphisms.** Publications.

13133 Succi, G. IT 040613/77/0608 R
Indagini car–iologiche su razze bovine e suine scarsamente valorizzate o in via di estinzione. **Carvological research on undervalued or disappearing bovine and pig breeds.**

13134 Gallarati Scotti, G.C. IT 040613/78/1058 N
Ricerche biometriche su bovini di incrocio intra–raziale Brown swiss x Bruno alpina. **Biometrical research on Brown swiss x Bruno alpino inter–racial crossbreeds.**

13135 Rognoni, G. IT 040613/78/1099 N
Miglioramento genetico quali–quantitativo della produzione lattea nella specie bovina mediante studi sui polimorfismi caseinici ed enzimatici del latte, sui rapporti tra produzione lattea e fertilità bovina. **Qualitative and quantitative genetic improvement of milk production in the bovine race based on research on casein and enzymatic polymorphism in milk and on the relation between milk production and bovine fertility.**

13136 Aureli, G. IT 040626/77/0534 R
Ricerche sull'infertilità maschile nel bovino e nel suino con particolare riguardo al comportamento del complesso DNA proteine nello spermatozoo. **Research on male sterility in bulls and pigs with special regard to the behaviour of the DNA–protein compound in the spermatozoon.**

13137 Rognoni, G.; Dell'Orto, V.; Crimella, C.; Casati, Marta; Carenzi, C.; Pasi, Anna IT 040638/74/0002
Studio della struttura genetica delle razze bovine italiane a livello anagrafico e di polimorfismi immunologici e biochimici per una migliore conoscenza delle differenze genetiche utili per i piani di accoppiamento miranti ad una intensificazione della produzione di carne bovina. **Study on genetic structure of Italian cattle breeds by means of pedigree data, and immunological and biochemical polymorphisms in order to**

point out the genetic differences usable in breeding plane and by them intensify bovine meat production. Publications.

13138 Baglioni, T. IT 040641/77/0593 R
Polimorfismi enzimatici nei bovini. Studio attività enzimatiche. **Enzymatic polymorphism in bovine cattle. Study of enzymatic activity.**

13139 Iannelli, D. IT 040722/77/0599 R
Allotipi nei bovini e bufalini. **Allotypes in the bovine and buffalo breeds.**

13140 Salerno, A. IT 040722/77/0605 R
Polimorfismo cromosomico nei bovini e nei bufali. **Chromosomic polymorphism in bovine cattle and buffaloes.**

13141 Bonsempiante, M.; Rioni, M.; Bittante, G.; Guidetti, G. IT 040810/73/0001 N
Allevamento confinato di manze meticce per la produzione del vitello: effetto della combinazione razziale materna e cause di distocia. **Calves production from confinated rearing of heifers crosses: effect of heifers genetic type and causes of dystocia.** Publications.

13142 Bittante, G.; Guidetti, G. IT 040810/77/0002 N
Selezione dei bovini di razza Pezzata Rossa Friulana per la attitudine alla produzione della carne: elaborazione dei risultati dei primi cicli di prove di progenie. **Selection for meat production in Friuli Simmental cattle: elaboration of the results of progeny test.**

13143 Rioni, M.; Bittante, G.; Susmel, P.
IT 040810/77/0003 N
Produzione del vitellone: confronto fra tipi genetici diversi (Limousine, Charolaise, Guascone, Pezzata Rossa, Normanna, Bruna Alpina e Frisona). **Feedlot and slaugther performances of store calves of different breeds (Limousin, Charolais, Gascony, Simmental, Normandy, Brown Swiss and Friesian).** Publications.

13144 Bittante, G. IT 040810/78/0001 N
Comparazione delle prestazioni tecniche ed economiche fornite da vitelloni appartenenti a tipi genetici differenti. **Comparison of technical and economical performances of bulls of different breeds and crosses.**

13145 Lucifero, M.; Secchiari, P. IT 041113/76/0001
Studio dell'efficienza riprodultiva di bovine Maremmane e prove di incrocio contori da carne (Charollais e Chianini). **Reproductive efficiency of Maremmana cattle breed and cross–breeding with Charollaise and Chianina bulls.**

13146 Bosticco, A. IT 041216/73/0913
Studio del problema della fecondità nei comprensori di allevamento della razza bovina piemontese e delle razze bovine da latte utilizzate per l'incrocio F1 con il toro piemontese da carne. **Study on the problem of fecundity in rearing of Piemontese cattle breed and of the dairy cattle breeds used for F1 crossbreeding with the Piemontese beef bull.**

13147 Bosticco, A. IT 041216/77/0120 R
Studio del problema delle fecondità nei comprensori di allevamento della razza bovina piemontese e delle razze bovine da latte utilizzate per l'incrocio F1 con il toro piemontese da carne. **A study of fertility in breeding faels for Piedmont cattle and dairy cattle intended for F1 cross–breeding with the**

Piedmont bull.

13148 Mussa, P.P. IT 041216/77/0600 R
Trasmissibilità ed ereditabilità dei caratteri relativi alla produzione quantitativa e qualitativa delle carne in bovini di razza piemontese. **Transmissibility and hereditability of characters regarding the quality and quantity of meat production in Piedmont beef cattle.**

13149 Mussa, P.P. IT 041216/78/1156 N
Il comportamento dell'eterosi in alcune razze bovine utilizzate nell'incrocio di prima generazione. **Heterosis behaviour in some bovine races used in first generation cross–breeding.**

13150 Pagano Toscano, G. IT 041216/79/0002 N
Contributo allo studio, ai fini del miglioramento, della razza bovina Piemontese mediante indagini zoometriche. **Contribution to the study, for breeding improvement purposes, of cattle of the Piedmontese bred by means of zoometric researches.**

13151 Maletto, S. IT 041217/74/0580
Produzione della carne bovina attraverso l'incrocio, dimensione dell'eterosi e trasmissibilità dei caratteri legati alla produzione della carne relativi alla razza bovina piemontese. **Beef production through crossbreeding, size of heterosis and transmissibility of genetic characters relating to beef yields in Piemontese cattle breed.**

13152 Sartore, G. IT 041231/77/0607 R
Polimorfismi biochimici negli spermatozoi e nelle secrezioni utero–cervicali dei bovini e loro connesione con la fisiologia della riproduzione. **Biochemical polymorphism in spermatozoons, in uterine and cervical secretions in cows, its interaction with reproductive physiology.**

13153 Russo, V. IT 041501/74/0622
Ricerche sul polimorfismo genetico delle proteine del latte. Struttura delle razze bovine allevate in Italia e relazione tra varianti genetiche, produzione e qualità del latte. **Research on genetic polymorphism of milk proteins. Structure of cattle breeds raised in Italy and relationship between milk genetic variability, yields and quality.**

13154 Bonadonna, T. IT 050100/77/0594 R
Inventario delle popolazioni bovine e suine allevate in Italia variazioni della consistenza nell'ultimo decennio, caratteristiche morfologiche e funzionali ed eventuali iniziative in atto per il miglioramento. **Census of bovine cattle and pigs bred in Italy, variations in numbers in the last decade, morphological and functional characteristics and eventual measures to improve them.**

13155 Dommerholt, J. NL 010112/63/1171 R
Ontwikkeling van efficiente selectiemethoden in de rundvee–fokkerij. **Development of efficient selection methods in cattle.** Publications.

13156 Bergström, P.L. NL 010112/67/1198
Selektie op vleesproduktie–eigenschappen bij de Nederlandse runderrassen. **Selection on beef production characteristic in dual purpose cattle.** Publications.

13157 Oldenbroek, J.K. NL 010112/69/1207
Evaluatie van fokrichtingen bij melk/vleesrassen. **Evaluation of breeding purposes in dual purpose cattle breeds.** Publications.

13158 Oldenbroek, J.K.; Minkema, D.; Rooy, J. de; Laurijsen, H.A.J. NL 010112/70/3425
Kruisingsproef met Noordamerikaanse zwartbonten. **Cross breeding experiment with Holstein–Friesians.**

13159 Oldenbroek, J.K. NL 010112/71/3472
De effectiviteit van een gericht gebruik van K.I–stieren die geselecteerd zijn op melkgift of op melkgift en bevleesdheid. **The effect of using A.I bulls selected on milk yield and on a combination of milk yield and muscling.** Publications.

13160 Oldenbroek, J.K. NL 010112/73/5398
Het effect van een rotatiekruising bij rundvee gericht op melkproduktie, respectievelijk op melk- en vleesproduktie. **A rotation cross in cattle aiming at milk production, respectively at a combination of milk and beef production.**

13161 Dommerholt, J.; Kooper, H. NL 010112/75/6148
Onderzoek naar nauwkeuriger en in de praktijk toepasbare schattingen van de fokwaarde van stieren en koeien. **A study on a more reliable estimation of breeding value for bulls and cows and its practcal application.** Publications.

13162 Meijering, A. NL 010112/77/7900
Geboortemoeilijkheden en perinatale kalversterfte bij rundvee. **Calving difficulties and perinatal calf mortality in cattle.** Publications.

13163 Verboon, M.C. NL 010208/71/3472
De effectiviteit van een gericht gebruik van K.I–stieren die geselecteerd zijn op melkgift of op melkgift en bevleesdheid. **The effect of using A.I bulls selected on milk yield and on a combination of milk yield and muscling.** Publications.

13164 Snijders, P.J.M.; Horstink, A.R.M. NL 010208/73/5398
Het effect van een rotatiekruising bij rundvee gericht op melkproduktie, respectievelijk op melk- en vleesproduktie. **A rotation cross in cattle aiming at milk production, respectively at a combination of milk and beef production.**

13165 Oostendorp, D. NL 010208/76/8740 N
Technische en economische mogelijkheden van Piemontese–kruislingen voor de rundvleesproduktie. **Technical and economical possibilities of using Piemontese–crosses for beef production.**

13166 Politiek, R. NL 020058/70/3425
Kruisingsproef met Noordamerikaanse zwartbonten. **Cross breeding experiment with Holstein–Friesians.** Publications.

13167 Bakker, H.; Wallinga, J.H. NL 020058/75/6148
Onderzoek naar nauwkeuriger en in de praktijk toepasbare schattingen van de fokwaarde van stieren en koeien. **A study on a more reliable estimation of breeding value for bulls and cows and its practical application.** Publications.

13168 Albers, G.A.A. NL 020058/75/6853
De gastheer–parasiet relatie tussen kalveren en de darmworm cooperia oncophora. **Host–parasite relationship between calves and the intestinal worm cooperia oncophora.** Publications.

13169 Korver, S. NL 020058/78/8549
Ruwvoeropnamevermogen en melkproduktie bij melkkoeien in afhankelijkheid van het genotype voor melkproduktie en het krachtvoerniveau. **Roughage intake and milk production in**

dairy cows dependent on the genotype for milk production.

13170 Loo, J. van; Coelingh, J.P.   NL 030001/74/6046 R
Cellulaire achtergronden van een erfelijke malabsortie voor
zink bij het rund (lethal trait A46: Adema disease). **Cellular
aspects of lethal trait A46 in cattle (hereditary malabsorbtion of
zinc).**

13171 Mey, G.J.W. van der   NL 030009/70/3425
Kruisingsproef met noordamerikaanse zwartbonten. **Cross
breeding experiment with Holstein–Friesians.** Publications.

13172 Bakker, Ij.T.   NL 060004/70/3425
Kruisingsproef met Noordamerikaanse zwartbonten. **Cross
breeding experiment with Holstein–Friesians.** Publications.

Sheep (B 4220)

See also 10972, 10976, 11038, 11050, 11051, 11062, 12317,
12327, 12328, 12345, 13065, 13066, 14440, 14462, 14478

13173 Wassmuth, R.; Luft, B.   DE 129250/71/0021
Untersuchungen über Karyotypänderungen als mögliche
Ursache von Fruchtbarkeitsstörungen beim Schaf.
**Investigations on changes in karyotype of sheep as potential
causes of fertility disorders.**

13174 Luft, B.; Wassmuth, R.   DE 129250/72/0003
Untersuchungen über das Tetraploidie–Mosaik beim Schaf
und dessen Auswirkungen auf die Fruchtbarkeit. **Investigation
on the tetraploid mosaic in sheep and effects on fertility.**

13175 Wassmuth, R.; Jatsch, O.; Hartmann, W.; Popp, T.;
Wolanis, M.   DE 129250/72/0004
Grundlagen der Steigerung der Produktivität bei Schafen unter
Berücksichtigung züchterischer, hormonaler und
haltungstechnischer Massnahmen. **Conditions of rise in
productivity of sheep considering breeding, hormonal and
keeping measures.**

13176 Wassmuth, R.; Meinecke–Tillmann, S.; Meinecke, B.;
Goller, H.; Tillmann, H.   DE 129250/75/0001
Untersuchungen über Möglichkeiten der Erstellung
monozygoter Mehrlinge beim Schaf. **Investigations on
possibilities of producing monocygotes in sheep.**

13177 Wassmuth, R.; Kellner, P.   DE 129383/70/0001
Nutzung von Gebrauchskreuzungen der Schafrassen zur
Steigerung von Fruchtbarkeit, Mast- und Wolleistung sowie
der Fleischqualität. **Utilization of commercial crossbreeding for
rise in fertility, in fattening performance and wool yield and in
meat quality.**

13178 Langholz, H.–J.   DE 132273/77/0001
Weiterentwicklung des verbesserten Leineschafes als
synthetische Mutterrasse durch Einkreuzung von Bergschafen.
**Improving the breeding flock of "Leineschaf" as synthetic breed
by hybridization with Bergschaf.**

13179 Nitter, G.   DE 144680/73/0003
Selektion von Fruchtbarkeitslinien in Reinzucht bei Schafen.
Selection of prolific lines in pure breeding of sheep.

13180 Nitter, G.   DE 144680/73/0004
Prüfung und Vorausschätzung geeigneter
Zuchtlinienkombinationen bei Schafen unter intensiven

Nutzungsformen. **Test and estimation of suitable sheep line
crosses in intensive production systems.**

13181 Smidt, D.   DE 201200/77/0007
Züchterisch–genetische Untersuchungen zur spezifischen
Immunreaktion bei Schafen verschiedener Rassen und
Kreuzungen sowie bei Schweinen. **Breeding genetic studies on
specific immunoreaction of sheep of different breed and cross as
well as of pigs.**

13182 Kallweit, E.   DE 201200/77/0031
Steigerung der Fruchtbarkeit durch diskontinuierliche
Kreuzungen und Selektion beim Schaf. **Increase in fertility by
discontinuous crossing and selection of sheep.**

13183 Jensen, N.E.   DK 010201/78/0010 N
Individprøvning af vædderlam. **Performance testing of ram
lamb.**

13184 Petersen, P.H.; Ranvig, H.   DK 030142/78/0003 N
Registrering og analyse af data fra avls– og tilsynsbesætninger
under dansk fåreavl. **Registration and analysis of data from
registered flocks in Danish society for sheep breeding.**

13185 Nguyen, T. C.   FR 010202/65/2504
Mise en évidence du polymorphisme biochimique au niveau
des groupes sanguins et de certaines protéines sanguines des
ovins. **Blood groups and blood protein polymorphism in sheep.**
Publications.

13186 Lauvergne, J.J.; Casu, S.; Boyazoglu, J.G.
      FR 010202/70/2512
Etude de la structure génétique de la race ovine sarde et de
quelques caractères morphologiques externes (pendeloques,
pendants d'oreille) à déterminisme mendelien. **Genetical
studies in sardinian sheep: mendelian factors (wattle, ear
pendants) and genetical structure of the population.**
Publications.

13187 Millot, P.; Vaiman, M.   FR 010202/71/2502
Antigènes lymphocytaires des ovins, mise en évidence et mode
d'hérédité. **Lymphocyte antigenes in sheep – control and mode
of inheritance.** Publications.

13188 Nguyen, T.C.; Guérin, G.; Vaiman, M.
      FR 010202/73/2501
Recherche de liaison entre certains locus marqueurs
(polymorphismes biochimiques) des ovins et des porcins et la
fertilité. **Relationships between some ovine and porcine gene
markers (biochemical polymorphisms) and fertility.**

13189 Poujardieu, B.; Matheron, G.   FR 011404/68/2583
Méethodologie statistique et génétique et de traitement des
donnés par le calcul automatique appliqué à la sélection (lapin,
oie, lièvre, ovins). **Statistical and genetical methodology.
Utilization of computers for data processing in selection (rabbit,
goose, hare, sheep).** Publications.

13190 Ricordeau, G.; Tchamitchian, L.   FR 011405/64/2551
Expérience de sélection sur la prolificité en race pure chez le
mouton et croisement avec des races améliorées. **Selection on
prolificacy in purebred sheep and crossing with improved
breeds.** Publications.

13191 Flamant, J.C.   FR 011405/65/2556
Comparaison de la production laitière ovine en races pures et

utilisation de races étrangères en croisement. **Milk production in dairy sheep = comparison between pure bred animals and crosses with exotic breeds.** Publications.

13192 Flamant, J.C.   FR 011405/70/2555
Efficacité de la sélection sur la production laitiére et l'aptitude à la traite en race pure ovine laitière. **Efficiency of selection for milk production and milk ability in purebred milking sheep.** Publications.

13193 Ricordeau, G.; Tchamitchian, L.   FR 011405/72/2550
Déterminisme héréditaire des composantes de la prolificité chez la brebis. **Hereditary determinism of the components of prolificacy in the ewe.** Publications.

13194 Tchamitchian, L.; Ricordeau, G.   FR 011405/72/2553
Etude des facteurs de variation de la fertilité et de la prolificité en rythme accéléré de reproduction chez la brebis. **Variation factors of fertility and prolificacy under an intensive reproductive system in the ewe.** Publications.

13195 Bonaiti, B.; Flamant, J.C.   FR 011405/72/2554
Efficacité des méthodes de sélection sur la production de viande de mouton. **Efficiency of methods used in selection for meat production in the sheep.** Publications.

13196 Razungles, J.   FR 011405/73/2549
Aspects théoriques et méthodologiques de l'efficacité et de la précision de la sélection chez les ovins à viande. **Theoretical and methodological aspects of efficiency and accuracy in selection of sheep for meat production.** Publications.

13197 Smith   GB 010101/00/0013
Increase fertility by crossbreeding.

13198 Smith   GB 010101/00/0014
Compare sires for fat lamb production.

13199 Bateman; Purser   GB 010101/00/0016
Value of crossbreeding in severe hill environment.

13200 Smith; Roberts   GB 010101/76/0020
Welsh mountain group breeding scheme.

13201 Taylor   GB 010104/00/0006
Between–breed differences in growth, development, food utilisation and meat characteristics.

13202 Purser   GB 010105/00/0001
Genetic variation in performance of Scottish Blackface sheep.

13203 Purser   GB 010105/00/0002
Genetic variation in performance of Welsh Mountain sheep.

13204 Purser   GB 010105/00/0003
Heterosis in performance of Welsh x Blackface sheep.

13205 Purser   GB 010105/00/0004
Genetic improvement in the British sheep industry.

13206 Land; Carr   GB 010106/00/0001
Attempt to increase the frequency of lambing in Finn–Dorset ewes.

13207 Land; Carr   GB 010106/00/0002
Genetic and environmental sources of variation in reproductive

performance.

13208 Slee; Purser   GB 010106/00/0008
Cold resistance and metabolic efficiency in hill sheep.

13209 Wiener; Herbert   GB 010106/00/0012
Effect of crossing and inbreeding on performance and production.

13210 Wiener   GB 010106/00/0013
Factors affecting survival.

13211 Dain   GB 010301/00/0039
Sexing of embryos for transplantation.

13212 Walser   GB 010301/00/0070 R
Sensory involvement in maternal behaviour in sheep and its relation to survival in lambs.

13213 Heap   GB 010305/00/0031 R
Pituitary gonadotrophins and control of breeding in sheep.

13214 Tucker; Kilgour   GB 010308/76/0006
Blood groups and other polymorphic characters in physiology and immunology of sheep, and husbandry.

13215 Slater   GB 030101/00/0024 R
Factors affecting foetal nitrogen metabolism in the pregnant sheep.

13216 Wright; Smith   GB 030101/78/0028 N
Pregnancy associated substances and perinatal mortality in sheep.

13217 Mitchell; Williams   GB 030112/76/0011 R
Pregnancy diagnosis.

13218 Gunn; Doney   GB 030301/00/0001 R
Environment and genetic factors affecting reproductive rates of hill sheep.

13219 Doney   GB 030301/00/0004 R
Effectiveness of new genotypes in utilising better hill resources.

13220 McGaughey   GB 041102/76/0009
Selection for economic traits in the Scottish Blackface.

13221 Foster   GB 041306/79/0004 N
Selection of dorset horn sheep for increased length of breeding season.

13222 Pollock   GB 060102/00/0015
Group breeding scheme for hill sheep.

13223 Speedy   GB 060102/00/0016
Practical frequent lambing systems.

13224 Owen   GB 060208/00/0009
Development of low cost grass based systems to maximise lamb output:(2) use of lambs of high growth rate.

13225 Chesworth   GB 060219/00/0006 R
Factors affecting the control of oestrus in the breeding ewe.

13226 Hanrahan, S.P.; Timon, V.   IE 060100/63/0797 R
Genetic studies of reproductive performance in specialised

fertility flocks. Publications.

13227 Hanrahan, S.P.; More O'Ferrall, G.J.; Carew, J.
IE 060100/70/0534 R
Galway sheep – breed improvement scheme. Publications.

13228 More O'Ferrall, G.J.   IE 060100/71/0536 R
Suffolk sheep breed improvement scheme. Publications.

13229 More O'Ferrall, G.J.; Timon, V.   IE 060100/73/0796 R
Development of fast growing fat lamb sire lines based on (1) suffolk (2) galway and texel (3) synthetic or mixture of breeds.
Publications.

13230 More O'Ferrall, G.J.; Timon, V.   IE 060100/73/0798 R
Selection of findorset ewes to breed three times in two years.
Publications.

13231 Hanrahan, S.P.   IE 060700/72/1040 N
Genetic studies with Finnish landrace sheep. Publications.

13232 Hanrahan, S.P.   IE 060700/73/1042 R
Genetic analysis of ovulation rate in sheep. Publications.

13233 Hanrahan, S.P.; Quirke, J.F.   IE 060700/74/1045 R
Genetic variation in endocrine activity and its relationship with fecundity in sheep. Publications.

13234 Hanrahan, S.P.   IE 060700/74/1046 R
On–farm development of a superior ewe breed. Publications.

13235 Hanrahan, S.P.; Timon, V.   IE 060702/72/0436 N
Genetic improvement of galway sheep with respect to fertility and growth. Publications.

13236 Gordon, I.; McDonnell, H.; Boland, M.P.; Crosby, F.
IE 120105/77/9034 R
Artificial insemination in suffolk sheep improvement programmes. Publications.

13237 Gordon, I.; Kelleher, D.L.   IE 120105/79/9213 N
A method of progeny testing texel rams under Irish conditions.

13238 Fabbri, G.   IT 012400/77/0598
Razze e popolazioni ovine e caprine nel territorio nazionale, consistenza caratteristiche morfologiche e funzionali. **Sheep and goat races and herds in the national territory, persistance of functional and morphological characteristics.**

13239 Carena, A.; Costa; Mazziotti Di Celso, P.
IT 020700/76/0029
Indagini sulla possibilita di miglioramento degli allevamenti ovini della basilicata mediante l'introduzione di razze estere ed il miglioramento dell'ambiente. **Improvement of sheep population in Basilicata by introducing foreign breeds and by improving the invironment.**

13240 Pilla, A.M.; Dell'Aquila, S.; Pelosi, A.; Taibi, L.; Di Taranto, F.P.   IT 020700/77/0011 N
Costituzione di una nuova razza ovina tramite l'incrocio a tre vie tra la Gentile di Puglia, l'Ile de France e Ürtthenberg. **Costitution of a new race of sheeps by the crossbreed of three races: "Gentile di Puglia, Ile de France and Württhenberg..**

13241 Pilla, A.M.   IT 020700/78/0001
Arieti sintetici per la produzione della carne. **Terminal rams**

for meat production.

13242 Romita, A.; Borghese, A.; Malossini, F.; Gigli, S.
IT 020700/78/0004
Incrocio di pecore sopravissane con arieti da carne (Suffolk–Ile de France – Bergamasca–Dorset horn); due sistemi di allevamento degli agnelli e macellazione a tre differenti età–. **Crossbreeding of Sopravissana ewes with meat rams (Suffolk–Ile de France–Bergamasca–Dorset horn); two systems of breeding and slaghtering of lambs at 3 different live weights.** Publications.

13243 Pelosi, A.; Dell'Aquila, S.; Taibi, L.
IT 020700/79/0002 N
Studio di selezione della pecora Comisana in purezza e possibilità d'incrementare la produzione del latte mediante l'incrocio con la razza della Frisia. **Selection of Comisana sheep and possibility of improving milk production by crosses with Frisian breed.**

13244 Bellitti, E.   IT 040111/77/0537 R
Studio della combinabilità genetica delle razze ovine per il miglioramento delle caratteristiche produttive nei soggetti da macello e della prolificità delle femmine meticce. **A study of the genetic possibilities of crossing sheep races so as to improve the productive qualities of sheep for slaughter and the fertility of crossbred ewes.**

13245 Matassino, D.; Cosentino, E.; Girolami, A.; Bordi, A.; Colatruglio, P.; Grasso, F.   IT 040722/72/0003 R
Parametri ematici in tipi genetici ovini e tacchini. **Some hematochemical parameters in sheep and turkey.** Publications.

13246 Fratteggiani Bianchi, R.   IT 041020/77/0187 R
Ricerche e rilievi dei caratteri morfologici e funzionali, allo scopo di definire uno standard per la popolazione ovina umbra indicata come razza appenninica. **Research on functional and morphological characteristics, in order to establish a standard for the Umbrian (Apennine race) sheep population.**

13247 Fratteggiani Bianchi, R.   IT 041020/78/1158 N
Ricerca sulla razza–popolazione ovina appenninica al fine di potenziarne le caratteristiche della carne sia con la pratica selettiva come con l'incrocio. **Apennine sheep : research on race populations with a view to improving meat quality by selection and crossing.**

13248 Lucifero, M.; Secchiari, P.; Ferruzzi, G.
IT 041113/75/0001
Ricerche sulla produzione della carne ovina. **Researches on the sheep breeding for meat production.** Publications.

13249 Lucifero, M.   IT 041113/77/0562 R
Prove di incrocio a due e tre vie per la produzione di meticci da macello nella specie ovina. **Trials of two–breed and three–breed crossing of sheep for mutton production.**

13250 Visscher, A.H.   NL 010112/71/8723 N
Opvoering van worpgrootte en frequency der werpen middels kruising bij schapen. **Crossbreeding sheep to increase litter size and frequency of lambing.** Publications.

13251 Visscher, A.H.; Diepen, H. van   NL 010112/76/6147
Verhoging van de lamsvleesproduktie van het heideschap in marginale gebieden d.m.v. kruising met vleesrassen. **Improvement of the fat lamb production of the heather sheep**

in fallow regions by crossing with meatbreeds.

13252 Bekendam, M.   NL 020058/70/4636
Selectie van schapenrassen en –lijnen op vruchtbaarheid, snelle groei en goede slachteigenschappen en geschiktheid voor kruising. **Selection of sheep–breeds and sheep–lines in the field of fertility, fast growth and good slaughter qualities and capacibility for crossing.** Publications.

13253 Grommers, F.J.   NL 030009/69/5715 R
Onderzoek naar de mogelijkheid het oestrusseizoen bij schapen langs genetische weg te verlengen. **An attempt to extend the breeding season of sheep by selection within breed.**

13254 Migo, F.J.   NL 060006/76/6147
Verhoging van de lamsvleesproduktie van het heideschaap in marginale gebieden d.m.v. kruising met vleesrassen. **Improvement of the fat lamb production of the heather sheep in fallow regions by crossing with meatbreeds.**

13255 Hemminga, H.   NL 060009/71/5595 N
Onderzoek naar de mogelijkheden van het Friese Melkschaap als grootouderras voor slachtlammeren in Nederland. **Investigations on the possibilities of the Friesian Milksheep as grand parent–breed for fattening lambs in the Netherlands.**

Goats, farm deer and other ruminants (B 4290)

See also 12957, 13139, 13140, 13238, 14587

13256 Sambraus, H.H.; Sander, P.   DE 160705/75/0011
Prägung auf die eigene Rasse bei Tauben. **Imprinting on the own race in pigeons.**

13257 Ricordeau, G.; Mocqudt, J.C.; Razungles, J.   FR 011405/65/2557
Estimation du progrès génétique réalisé en station et en fermes sur les performances laitières de la chèvre. **Estimation of genetic progress in station and farms on milk performances in the goat.** Publications.

13258 Ricordeau, G.   FR 011405/72/2558
Etude génétique des performances de reproduction chez la chèvre. **Genetic study on fertility in the goat.** Publications.

13259 Peaker; Maulewalker   GB 010305/77/0068 R
Mechanism and control of milk secretion ,physiology of mammary glands and cells in goats.

13260 Carena, A.; Maiorana, M.   IT 020700/79/0003 N
Prova di meticciamento tra le razze caprine Saanen e Maltese. **Crosses trials between goat Saanen and Maltese breeds.**

13261 De Vincentiis, M.   IT 040744/73/0194
Ricerche su alcuni polimorfismi enzimatici nelle popolazioni bufaline dell'Italia meridionale con particolare riguardo al miglioramento animale. **Research on some enzymatic polymorphisms in buffalo populations of southern Italy with specific reference to animal breeding.** Publications.

Pigs (B 4300)

See also 11170, 11190, 11210, 11211, 11214, 11232, 11242, 11253, 11264, 12556, 12559, 12902, 12992, 13001, 13009, 13133, 13136, 13154, 13181, 13188, 14647, 14755, 14777, 19256

13262 Vandeplassche, M.; Spincemaille, J.; Bonte, P.; Dossche, L.   BE 050300/75/0007 R
Morfologische afwijkingen van spermatozoiden bij laag vruchtbare beren. **Morphological abnormalities of spermatozoa in low fertility boars.** Publications.

13263 Tijskens, R.; Matthijs   BE 140000/77/0008 R
Simulatie van de selectie en van epidemiën bij het Belgisch landvarken. **Simulation of selection and epidemics of the Belgium landpig.** Publications.

13264 Schmitten, F.; Finke, K.   DE 111500/71/0001
Untersuchungen über Leistung und Nutzungsdauer von Zuchtsauen verschiedener Rassen und Kreuzungen bei Intensiv– und Extensivhaltung. **Studies on performance and service life of breeding sows of different races and crosses in intensive and/or extensive husbandry.**

13265 Schmitten, F.   DE 111500/78/0003 N
Untersuchungen zur Vererbung der Halothanreaktion beim Schwein. **Investigations on the heredity of holothane–reaction in pigs.**

13266 Schmitten, F.; Düx, A.; Schepers, K.H.   DE 111500/78/0004 N
Ermittlung von physiologischen Parametern zur Selektion auf Fleischqualität beim Schwein. **Determination of physiological parameters for the selection on meat quality in pigs.**

13267 Trappmann, W.   DE 111500/78/0005 N
Möglichkeiten der züchterischen Leistungsverbesserung beim Schwein unter Berücksichtigung ökonomischer Gesichtspunkte. **Possibilities of increasing breeding performance in pigs considering economic aspects.**

13268 Researcher not indicated   DE 111500/78/0006 N
Entwicklung einer pigmentfreien Eberlinie zur Kreuzungszucht beim Schwein. **Development of pigment–free line of boar for hybridization of swine.**

13269 Simon, D.; Harbeck, J.; Schulte–Coerne, H.   DE 111502/78/0001 N
Eigenleistung aus Feldprüfungen für die Zuchtwertschätzung von Jungebern. **Performance tests under field conditions as basis for breeding value estimation of young boars.**

13270 Wassmuth, R.; Dzapo, V.; Herzog, A.; Mütze, P.; Finger, K.W.   DE 129250/74/0001
Vergleichende Untersuchungen über Reinzucht– und Kreuzungstiere unter besonderer Berücksichtigung der Erfassung von Heterosiseffekten auf der Ebene des mitochondrialen Stoffwechsels. **Comparative investigations on purebred and crossbred pigs with special regard to heterosis on the level of mitochondrial metabolism.**

13271 Wassmuth, R.; Kellner, P.   DE 129383/70/0002
Sowjetische Forschungsergebnisse auf dem Gebiet der Gebrauchskreuzungen und Heterosiszucht bei Schweinen. **Soviet research results on commercial crossbreeding and heterozygotic breeding of pigs.**

13272 Glodek, P.; Meyer, J.–N.   DE 132274/72/0002
Beziehungen zwischen geschätztem Heterozygotiegrad und Heterosiseffekten in Schweinekreuzungen. **Relations between estimated heterozygoty level and heterosis effects in pig crosses.**

13273 Glodek, P.; Frese, D.; Bruns, E.   DE 132274/75/0003
Untersuchungen zur selektiven Anpaarung von
Herdbuchsauen an Eber und Berücksichtigung dieses Effektes
bei der Zuchtwertschätzung von Ebern. **Investigations of
selective màting of pedigree sows to boars and the effect on
estimated breeding values of boars.**

13274 Glodek, P.; Bohnenkemper, O.; Groeneveld, E.
DE 132274/77/0001
Schätzung von Kreuzungsparametern in
Zuchtliniengebrauchskreuzungen beim Schwein. **Estimation of
crossbreeding parameters in commercial line crosses of pigs.**

13275 Fewson, D.; Faber, H.von; Rogdakis, E.
DE 144680/71/0002
Stressempfindlichkeit und Fleischqualität bei verschiedenen
Schweinepopulationen und deren Kreuzungsprodukten.
**Sensitivity to stress and meat quality in different populations
and crosses of pigs.**

13276 Fewson, D.; Rogdakis, E.; Fender, M.
DE 144680/75/0001
Selektion zur Verminderung des Fettansatzes beim Schwein
nach der Aktivität NADPH–liefernder Enzyme im Fettgewebe
und nach der Rückenspeckdicke. **Selection for lowering the
degree of fatness in swine by use of NADPH–generating enzyme
activities in adipose tissue as well as backfat thickness as
selection criteria.**

13277 Fewson, D.; Niebel, E.   DE 144680/75/0003
Optimierung der Zuchtplanung für die Reinzucht beim
Schwein. **Optimum planning for purebreeding of swine.**

13278 Ernst, E.; Wandhoff, H.E.   DE 148350/77/0002
Die züchterische Entwicklung des Pietrainschweines in
Schleswig–Holstein. **The development of the breed of Pietrain
in SchleswigHolstein.**

13279 Kräusslich, H.; Buschmann, H.; Meyer, J.; Osterkorn,
K.   DE 160705/70/0002
Vererbung Resistenz bestimmender Faktoren bei Mäusen und
Schweinen. **Heredity of resistance determining factors in mice
and swine.**

13280 Pirchner, F.; Claus, R.; Willeke, H. DE 161300/77/0002
Selektionsversuch auf Ebergeruch. **Selection experiment on
boar taint.**

13281 Willeke, H.; Stein, L.   DE 161300/77/0008
Genetischer Zusammenhang zwischen
Jungsaueneigenleistungsdaten aus Ferkelerzeugerbetrieben
und Verwandtenleistungen in Mastprüfanstalten. **Genetic
relationship between the performance test of gilts in the field
and their ancestors in the test station.**

13282 Meinhold, K.; Hinrichs, P.   DE 201100/78/0009 N
Wirtschaftlichkeitsrechnungen zum
Bundeshybridzuchtprogramm für Schweine aus der Sicht
verschiedener Entscheidungsträger. **The profitableness of the
German Federal hybrid pig breeding program as seen by the
different participants.**

13283 Pfleiderer, U.–E.   DE 201200/77/0032
Kombination der Information aus der Eigenleistungsprüfung
im Feld mit der aus der Nachkommenprüfung zu einem
Gesamtindex und Populationsanalysen der Deutschen
Landrasse beim Schwein. **Combination of information from
performance testing in the field with that from progeny testing
to an overall index and to population analyses of the German
Land Race pig.**

13284 Scheper, J.   DE 210010/75/0004
Untersuchungen über genetische Einflüsse auf die
Gewebebeschaffenheit beim Schwein. **Studies on genetic
influences on the tissue quality of swine.**

13285 Blendl, H.M.; Puff, H.; Härtl, J.   DE 502300/75/0004
Genetische und ökonomische Aspekte einer
Dreirassenkreuzung beim Schwein. **Genetic and economic
aspects of three–breed crossing in pigs.**

13286 Burgstaller, G.; Kögel, J.   DE 502302/78/0004 N
Untersuchungen zum Protein– und Energieansatz bei
Schweinen aus dem Bundeshybrid–Zuchtprogramm. **Studies
on accumulation of protein and energy in pigs of the Federal
hybrid breeding programme.**

13287 Jonsson, P.   DK 010202/72/0002
Metodestudier ved selektionsforsøg med mus. **Method studies
in selection experiments with mice.**

13288 Staun, H.   DK 010202/72/0003
Krydsningsforsøg med svin af Dansk Landrace, Norsk
Landrace og Yorkshirerace – herunder renavl med
Yorkshireracen. **Cross–breeding experiments with Danish
Landrace, Nordwegian Landrace and British Large White pigs
and pure–breeding with British Large White pigs.**

13289 Staun, H.; Just, A.   DK 010202/72/0024
Heritabiliteten af forskellige blodparametre samt relationerne
mellem disse og forskellige slagtekvalitetsegenskaber. **The
heritability of various blood parameters, and the relationships
between these and various carcass quality characteristics.**

13290 Jonsson, P.   DK 010202/74/0025
Selektionsforsøg med svin. **Selection experiments with pigs.**

13291 Jonsson, P.   DK 010202/75/0015
Sammenligning mellem to svineracer i Skotland og Danmark.
Comparison between two pig races in Scotland and Denmark.

13292 Meding, J.H.   DK 010202/75/0016
Dybfrysning af ornesæd. **Deep frezing of boar semen.**

13293 Meding, J.H.   DK 010202/76/0013
Spermiemorfologiske undersøgelser af ornesæd.
Spermatium–morphological investigations of boar semen.

13294 Staun, H.   DK 010202/76/0015
Genetiske undersøgelser vedrørende kødkvalitet hos svin.
Genetical investigations concerning the meat quality of pigs.

13295 Pedersen, O.K.   DK 010202/76/0016
Beregning af avlsindeks for svin af Dansk Landrace. **Calculation of the breeding index for Danish Landrace pigs.**

13296 Pedersen, O.K.   DK 010202/76/0018
Undersøgelser i forbindelse med individprøve af avlssvin,
herunder beregning af indeks. **Investigations in connection with
performance testing of breeding pigs, including index
calculations.**

13297 Meding, J.H.   DK 010202/77/0013
Befrugtningseffektivitet ved anvendelse af
Hetero–inseminering hos søer. **Fertilization effectivity of
Hetero–insemination of sows.**

13298 Pedersen, O.K.   DK 010202/77/0014
Supplering af databanksystem for dansk svineavl.
Supplementation of data bank system for Danish pig breeding.

13299 Moustgaard, J.; Nielsen, P.B.; Agergaard, N.
    DK 030126/76/0005 N
Biokemisk genetik og kødkvalitet hos svin. **Biochemical
genetics and meat quality in swine.**

13300 Andresen, E.; Jensen, P.   DK 030127/76/0001 N
Undersøgelser over det genetiske grundlag for kødkvalitet hos
svin. **Investigations of the genetic basis of porcine meat quality.**

13301 Staun, H.; Barton–Gade, P.; Jensen, P.; Jonsson, P.;
Laursen, B.; Andresen, E.   DK 030127/77/0001 N
Undersøgelser over specifik avlsværdi hos svin. **Investigations
of specific breeding value of swine.**

13302 Jensen, P.; Langballe, H.E.   DK 030142/75/0016 R
Krydsningsforsøg med fem svineracer. **Cross breeding
experiments with five breeds of swine.**

13303 Jensen, P.   DK 030142/76/0015
Undersøgelse af arveligheden af kødkvalitetsegenskaber hos
svin. **An investigation of the inheritability of meat quality
characteristics in swine.**

13304 Staun, H.; Jensen, P.; Andresen, E.; Christensen, A.;
Barton, P.   DK 030142/78/0004 N
Undersøgelse af heterosis ved HAL–locus hos svin.
Investigations on heterotic effects at the HAL–locus in pigs.

13305 Ollivier, L.   FR 010202/65/2561
Expérience de sélection sur la prolificité des truies dans un
troupeau fermé de race large white. **Selection experiment for
sow prolificacy in a closed large white heard.** Publications.

13306 Legault, C.   FR 010202/66/2560
Etude du déterminisme génétique de l'aptitude à la
reproduction des jeunes truies. **Genetic study of reproductive
ability in gilts.** Publications.

13307 Molenat, M.; Ollivier, L.   FR 010202/66/2564
Estimation du progrès génétique réalisé dans le cadre des
stations de contrôle des performances porcines. **Estimation of
genetic progress realized through the use of testing stations in
pigs.** Publications.

13308 Sellier, P.   FR 010202/70/2565
Recherche sur le choix d'une lignée mâle porcine spécialisée.
**Research on the choice of a specialized terminal sire line in the
pig.** Publications.

13309 Legault, C.; Molenat, M.   FR 010202/70/2566
Etude de quelques facteurs de variation de la productivité de la
truie dans les élevages. **Study of some variation factors of sow
productivity on farms.** Publications.

13310 Sellier, P.; Ollivier, L.   FR 010202/70/2567
Evaluation en stations des performances d'engraissement et de
carcasse de "Produits Terminaux" des programmes agréés de
sélection et de croisement chez le porc. **Random sample test for
growth and carcass on "Hybrid pigs".** Publications.

13311 Ollivier, L.; Legault, C.   FR 010202/70/2570
Recherches d'indices de sélection adaptés aux différents types
de production chez le porc. **Study of selection indices adapted to
various types of production in the pig.** Publications.

13312 Ollivier, L.   FR 010202/72/2562
Etude de la prédisposition héréditaire à la rhinite atrophique
chez les porcins. **Genetic aspects of atrophic rhinitis in pigs.**
Publications.

13313 Legault, C.   FR 010202/72/2568
Evaluation en fermes des performances de reproduction de
"truies hybrides". **Field comparisons between reproductive
performances of "hybrid sows".**

13314 Sellier, P.; Ollivier, L.   FR 010202/73/2569
Recherches sur les méthodes de sélection de la race de
piétrain: intérêt d'une lignée à très fort développement
musculaire. **Research on specific selection methods for the
pietrain breed: advantages of a "double muscled" line.**

13315 Ollivier, L.   FR 011405/65/2559
Expérience de sélection sur un indice d'engraissement et de
carcasse dans le cadre d'un centre d'insémination artificielle en
race Large White. **Selection experiment on a performance
test–index including growth and carcass measurements applied
to large white boars used in artificial insemination.**
Publications.

13316 Echard, G.   FR 011406/69/2519
Etude des bandes chromosomiques du porc et de trois
différentes souches de cellules de rein de porc en culture (PK
15, F et RP). **Chromosomal banding patterns and karyotype
evolution in three pig kidney cell strains (PK 15, F and RP).**
Publications.

13317 Mulsant, Ph.; Caboche, M.   FR 011406/70/2524
Induction et caractérisation de mutants résistants à des drogues
sur souches cellulaires de porc et de hamster. **Induction and
characterization of drug. Resistant mutants from pig and baby
hamster kidney cell lines.** Publications.

13318 Mulsant, Ph.; Echard, G.   FR 011406/72/2525
Analyse génétique du porc au moyen d'hybrides somatiques
entre cellules de porc en culture. **Genetic analysis of the pig
with somatic cell hybrids.**

13319 Mulsant, Ph.; Sellier, P.   FR 011406/73/2526
Comparaison des besoins nutritionnels de souches cellulaires
en culture provenant de porcs Piétrain et de porcs Landrace
Français. **Comparison of the nutritional needs of primary cell
cultures derived from Piétrain and French Landrace pigs.**

13320 Webb   GB 010101/00/0007
Development of sire–lines in pigs.

13321 King   GB 010101/00/0008
Breed comparisons in pigs.

13322 Webb   GB 010101/00/0009
Crossbred comparisons in pigs.

13323 King; Webb   GB 010101/00/0010

D 3300 – Animal breeding

Compare crossing systems in pigs.

13324 King; Webb   GB 010101/00/0011
Pig industry consultation.

13325 Webb   GB 010101/00/0012
Conformation and leg weakness.

13326 Webb   GB 010101/00/0015
Methods of measuring and improving meat quality.

13327 Ash   GB 010301/00/0060 R
Induction and control of farrowing by prostaglandins.

13328 Fowler; MacPherson   GB 030611/76/0040 R
Management of the sow for concurrent lactation and
pregnancy.

13329 O'Neill   GB 050509/00/0005
Gestation periods, farrowing time, milk flow, mummified
foetuses and related breeding problems in sows.

13330 O'Neill   GB 050509/00/0023
Use of prostaglandin for the induction of parturition in sows.

13331 Miller   GB 050510/00/0011
Pig fertility recording and management aids.

13332 Saunders   GB 050511/00/0006
The preservation of boar semen.

13333 Norman   GB 050511/00/0010
Parturition in the pig.

13334 Hunter   GB 060102/00/0024 R
Ovarian physiology of sexually mature pigs.

13335 Hunter   GB 060102/00/0025 R
Gamete maturation, fertilisation and embryonic development in
pigs.   .

13336 Robertson   GB 060224/78/0012 N
The design and layout of farrowing pen components.

13337 Baxter   GB 060224/79/0015 N
Parturition in the sow: the effect of environment constraints
imposed by housing.

13338 Baxter   GB 060224/79/0016 N
The feeding environment of the pig.

13339 Laird   GB 060315/00/0008
The selection of pigs for higher lean meat content and food
conversion efficiency.

13340 McGloughlin, P.   IE 060100/00/1478 N
Establishment of a stress susceptible landrace herd.
Publications.

13341 McGloughlin, P.; Cunningham, E.P.
          IE 060100/70/0531 N
Efficiency of hybrid pig breeding operations. Publications.

13342 McGloughlin, P.   IE 060100/71/0530 N
Analyses of pig breeding data. Publications.

13343 Semprini, P.   IT 040212/73/0308
Indagine genetica su alcuni caratteri morfologici e funzionali in
linee diverse di suini Large White. **Genetic studies of some
morphological and functional characteristics in different lines of
Large White pigs.**

13344 Santoro, P.   IT 040236/77/0606 R
Qualità delle carcasse e delle carni suine e bovine in relazione
alla razza ed al tipo di incrocio. **Carcass and meat quality in
pigs and beef cattle depending on race and type of cross–breed.**

13345 Quadri, G.   IT 040245/77/0273
Confronto tra le prestazioni zootecniche, le caratteristiche
della carcassa, la qualità della carne e del prosciutto in suini
pesanti di razza pura e ibridi. **Comparison of zootechnical
performances, characteristics of carcasses, quality of the meat
and ham in heavyweight pure–bred swine and in hybrids.**

13346 De Franciscis, G.   IT 040709/72/0446
Indagini sulla produzione carnea del suino di razza casertana
allevato in purezza e dei prodotti derivati dall'incrocio con
verri di razza pie train. **Survey on the production of Caserta
pure–bred pigs and experiments of crossbreeding with other
breeds having greater meat–producing characteristics.**
Publications.

13347 Brascamp, E.W.   NL 010112/67/1183
Ontwikkeling en toetsing van efficiënte selectie methoden bij
varkens. **Development and evaluation of efficient methods of
selections in pigbreeding.** Publications.

13348 Minkema, D.   NL 010112/69/2316
Interaktie tussen erfelijke aanleg en voederniveau
(gerantsoeneerd/ad lib.) bij varkens. **Interaction between
genotype and level of feeding (restricted/ad lib.) in pigs.**
Publications.

13349 Walstra, P.; Mateman, O.   NL 010112/69/2847
Internationale vergelijking van de produktiviteit en slacht
kwaliteit van enige West–europese varkens rassen.
**International comparison of the productivity and
slaughtering–quality of some West–European pig breeds.**
Publications.

13350 Brascamp, E.W.   NL 010112/72/3470
Evaluatie van buitenlandse varkensrassen ten behoeve van
kruising. **Evaluation of foreign pig breeds for crossing purposes.**
Publications.

13351 Eikelenboom, G.; Eldik, P. van; Wal, P.G. van de;
Minkema, D.   NL 010112/73/5396
Bepalingsmethoden voor PSE–gevoeligheid bij het levende
varken voor selectiedoeleinden. **Development of methods for
detection of PSE–susceptibility in the living animal and their
application in the selection of breeding pigs.** Publications.

13352 Wal, P.G. van der   NL 010112/76/5809 N
Onderzoek naar erfelijke en milieuinvloeden op
locomotiestoornissen bij varkens o.a. klinische en
pathologische parameters voor osteochondropathieën. **Genetic
and environmental influences on locomotion disturbances in
pigs a.o. clinical and pathological parameters for
osteochondrosis.** Publications.

13353 Eikelenboom, G.; Minkema, D.   NL 010112/76/6997
De betekenis van erfelijke factoren voor het ontstaan van

atrofische rhinitis bij varkens. **The significance of genetic factors for the development of atrophic rhinitis in pigs.** Publications.

13354 Brascamp, E.W. NL 010112/78/8714 N
Vergelijkende toets van reproduktie– en mesterij–fase van (merk) varkens van fokkerij–instellingen en van een experimentele kruisingscombinatie. **Comparative test of the reproductive and fattening phase of pigs from breeding firms, including an experimental crossing combination.**

13355 Van der Steen, H.A.M. NL 020058/75/6856
De methodiek van en respons op selectie op toomgrootte. **Maternal influences on littersize in pigs in relation to the direct genetic influence.**

Poultry and domestic birds in general (B 4400)

See also 11296, 14858

13356 Reyntens, N.; Okerman, F. BE 070200/54/0009 R
Behoud van het genetisch patrimonium van pluimveerassen. **Preservation of the genetic properties of poultry breeds.**

13357 Scholtyssek, S. DE 144685/75/0013
Modellmässige Zuchtversuche an Wachteln zur Klärung wichtiger Probleme in der Geflügelzucht. **Model breeding experimentation on quails for clearing up important problems in poultry breeding.**

13358 Pirchner, F.; Heil, G. DE 161300/75/0003
Selektion zur Verbesserung der Futterverwertung bei Legehennen. **Selection for improving feed efficiency in layers.**

13359 Pirchner, F.; Schild, H.–J. DE 161300/75/0005
Schätzung genetischer Parameter für Futterverwertung und andere Merkmale bei Legehennen in der 2. Legeperiode. **Estimates of genetic parameters of feed efficiency and of other traits of layers in the 2nd laying period.**

13360 Hartmann, W.; Heil, G. DE 201300/77/0005
Untersuchungen zur Methodik der Leistungsermittlungen vom Standpunkt der Maximierung der Unterschiede zwischen kommerziellen Legehybridherkünften. **Studies on methods of performance determination in view of maximum of differences between commercial hybrid layer proveniences.**

13361 Sørensen, P. DK 010203/73/0005
Selektionsforsøg med 3 linier af Hvid Plymouth Rock for øget tilvækstevne. Som opdrætningsfoder anvendes i en linie normalt broiler–foder, i en anden foder med lavt proteinindhold, og i den tredie anvendes restriktiv fodertildeling. **Selection studies for improved growth efficiency involving three stains of White Plymouth Rock, reared on a normal broiler diet, a low protein diet and restricted quantities of the normal broiler diet, respectively.**

13362 Ambrosen, T. DK 010203/76/0004
Haners reproduktionsevne. Parringsvillighed. Spermakvalitet. **Cock fertility. Mating willingness. Sperm quality.**

13363 Ambrosen, T. DK 010203/76/0005
Statistiske undersøgelser hos æglæggende høner og slagtekyllinger over heritabiliteter og genetiske korrelationer. **Statistical investigations with egg laying hens, and slaughter chickens concerning heritabilities and genetical correlations.**

13364 Petersen, V.E. DK 010203/77/0010
Avls– og fodringsforsøg med ænder, gæs og kalkuner. **Breeding and feeding experiments with ducks, geese and turkeys.**

13365 Perramon, A.; Bocquet, G. FR 010202/65/2515
Corrélations entre caractères antigéniques cellulaires sanguins et caractères économiques chez la volaille. Signification physiologique de la variabilité antigénique. **Correlations between cellular antigenic blood factors and economic traits in fowl physiological significance of antigenic variability.** Publications.

13366 Laughlin GB 010703/00/0001 R
Effects of genotype, pre–incubation storage and incubation environment on embryonic heart rate.

13367 Laughlin GB 010703/00/0007 R
Effects on hatching eggs of genotype and environment before and during incubation.

13368 Duncan GB 010704/00/0001 R
Role of ovarian hormones and CNS in control of nesting. relation between nesting and ovulation.

13369 McIndoe GB 010708/00/0001 R
Physiology, biochemistry and structure of seminal plasma and spermatoza.

13370 Sharp GB 010708/00/0005 R
Radio–immuno assay for follicle–stimulating hormone.

13371 Sharp; Davidson GB 010708/00/0006 R
Define area of hypothalamus producing gonadotrophin releasing factors and its regulation of reproduction.

13372 Sharp GB 010708/00/0010 R
Neuroendocrine factors and male reproductive activities.

13373 Gilbert GB 010708/00/0013 R
Physiology of ovary and oviduct activity, with reference to high egg yield.

13374 Sharp GB 010708/00/0015 R
Hormonal factors involved in breeding success in grouse.

13375 Lake GB 010708/78/0002 R
Storage of semen: factors affecting survival of spermatozoa in–vitro and their fertilisation properties.

13376 Follet GB 020606/79/0001 N
Environmental control of seasonal breeding cycles–with special reference to photoperiodism in birds.

13377 Whittle GB 060305/00/0001 R
Variety trials of egg laying strains.

13378 Lindsay GB 060305/78/0004
Fertility in broiler breeders.

13379 Kirk GB 060315/00/0010
The effects of production,storage and incubation conditions on hatchability of eggs.

13380 Brantas, G.C.; Kuit, A.R. NL 010109/70/7886
Verandering in gedrag van pluimvee door genetische selectie.

D 3300 – Animal breeding

Changes in behaviour of poultry by genetic selection. Publications.

13381 Hoogerbrugge, A.　　　NL 030009/69/5691 R
Genetische resistentie van pluimvee tegen leucose. **Genetic resistance to lymphoid leucosis in poultry. Publications.**

Chickens (B 4410)

See also 11346

13382 De Groote, G.; Okerman, F.　　BE 070200/70/0008 R
Vergelijkende proeven met kommerciële – en experimentele stammen slachtkuikenouderdieren. **Comparative experiments with commercial and experimental strains of heavy broiler breeders. Publications.**

13383 De Groote, G.; Keppens, L.　　BE 070200/72/0006 R
Vergelijkende studie van de kommerciële leghennenrassen (lichte– en halfzware) in België (nationale random sample test). **A comparative study of the commercial laying strains (light and medium weight) in Belgium (national random sample test). Publications.**

13384 De Groote, G.; Keppens, L.　　BE 070200/73/0007 R
Vergelijkende studie van de kommerciële slachtkuikenrassen in België (nationale random sample test). **A comparative study of the commercial broiler strains in Belgium (national random sample test). Publications.**

13385 De Groote, G.; Van Wambeke, F.　　BE 070200/77/0051
Onderzoek omtrent de reproduktieresultaten en het lichaamsgewicht van de afstammelingen van zware fokhanen geselekteerd op vroege groeisnelheid. **Research concerning reproduction results and body weight of offspring from broiler breeder males which have been selected on early growth rate.**

13386 Horst, P.; Petersen, J.; Tawfik, E.S.　DE 105550/70/0001
Genetische Untersuchungen beim Legehuhn unter besonderer Berücksichtigung der Eiqualität. **Investigations on genetics in layers with special regard to egg quality.**

13387 Petersen, J.; Schaten, M.　　DE 111501/78/0005 N
Untersuchungen über die Bedeutung von Herkunft x Aufzuchtform – Interaktionen beim Legehuhn. **Investigations on the signification of strain x rearingmethods – interactions with laying hens.**

13388 Hartmann, W.; Löliger, H.–C.; Hagen, D. von dem
　　　　　　　　　　　　　　　DE 201300/72/5002
Untersuchungen erblicher Einflüsse auf die Widerstandsfähigkeit gegen aviäre Tumorkrankheiten – Leukose, Rous Sarkom, Marek'sche Krankheit – bei Leghornlinien und ihren Kreuzungen. **Investigations in genetic influences on resistance to tumorous diseases – leukosis, Rous sarcoma, Marek's disease – of Leghorn lines and their crosses.**

13389 Hartmann, W.; Hagen, D. von dem; Löliger, H.–C.
　　　　　　　　　　　　　　　DE 201300/73/5005
Untersuchung der züchterischen Möglichkeiten zur Verbesserung der Widerstandsfähigkeit von Hühnern gegen Darmkokzidiosen. **On the effectiveness of breeding selection for improved resistance of chicken to coccidiosis.**

13390 Hartmann, W.　　　　　DE 201300/74/5003
Einfluss des geschlechtsgebundenen Verzwergungsfaktors auf Leistungseigenschaften und Wirtschaftlichkeit des Mastgeflügels. **Influence of sex–linked dwarfism on performance quality and economy of broiler.**

13391 Löliger, H.–C.; Hagen, D. von dem; Hartmann, W.
　　　　　　　　　　　　　　　DE 201300/75/0006
Untersuchungen über Veränderungen an lymphoretikulären Organen – Thymus, Bursa, Milz – von Hühnern verschiedener Linien mit unterschiedlicher Anfälligkeit für die Marek'sche Krankheit. **Investigations into the changes of lymphoretical organs – thymus, bursa, spleen – of chicks of various lines with different susceptibility to Marek's disease.**

13392 Hartmann, W.; Krieg, R.; Heil, G.; Löliger, H.–C.
　　　　　　　　　　　　　　　DE 201300/77/0001
Untersuchungen zur Frage der Erfassung erblicher Unterschiede in der Wirksamkeit des Immunsystems von Hühnern. **Studies on the problem of determination of hereditary differences in the action of the immunosystem in chicken.**

13393 Hartmann, W.; Heil, G.; Rauch, H.–W.
　　　　　　　　　　　　　　　DE 201300/77/0002
Erbliche und umweltbedingte Einflüsse auf die Bruchfestigkeit der Eischalen und Zuverlässigkeit verschiedener Messverfahren für deren züchterische Verbesserung. **Influences of heredity and environmental conditions on the stability of egg shells and on the reliability of different measuring methods for their breeding improvement.**

13394 Hartmann, W.; Heil, G.　　DE 201300/77/0006
Zusammenfassende Auswertung der amtlichen Legeleistungsprüfungen für Hühner. **Summarizing evaluation of official laying tests.**

13395 Fuhrken, E.　　　　　DE 511250/77/0001
8. Herkunftsprüfung verschiedener Legehybriden für Schleswig–Holstein. **8. Provenance testing of different layer hybrids in Sleswick Holstein.**

13396 Jensen, J.F.; Sørensen, P.; Ambrosen, T.
　　　　　　　　　　　　　　　DK 010203/72/0004
Selektionsforsøg med høns af æglægningstype. Specialiseret selektion for henholdsvis æglægning og ægkvalitet sammenlignes med indeksselektion. **Selection experiments with hens of laying type. Specialised selections for egg laying in one strain, and egg quality in another strain are compared to index selection for both of the traits.**

13397 Sørensen, P.　　　　　DK 010203/75/9039
Fodringsmiljøets betydning ved selektion for høj tilvækstevne hos slagtekyllinger. **Importance of the feeding environment in selection for rapid growth rate in broiler chicken.**

13398 Ambrosen, T.　　　　　DK 010203/78/9060
Måling af ændringer i æggets kvalitetsegenskaber i relation til specialiseret selektion og hønealder. **Measurement of changes in quality characteristics of eggs in relation to specialized selection and hen age.**

13399 Mason, V.C.; Rotenberg, S.　DK 010206/78/0003 N
Måling af ændringer i æggets kvalitetsegenskaber i relation til specialiseret selektion og hønealder. **Measurement of changes in quality characteristics of eggs in relation to specialized selection and hen age.**

13400 Merat, P. FR 010202/54/2516
Relations entre gènes connus affectant la morphologie ou la coloration et les performances de production (croissance, consommation alimentaire, ponte——) chez la poule. **Relationships between identified genes determining morphological or feather color traits and production performance (growth, feed intake, egg production ——) in the fowl.** Publications.

13401 Merat, P. FR 010202/65/2518
Relation entre variants génétiques de protéines polymorphes (gène HI protéines de l'oeuf) et les performances de production (ponte, croissance, fertilité——) chez la poule. **Relationships between genetic variants of proteins (HI gene, egg albumen proteins) and production traits (egg laying, growth, fertility ——) in the fowl.** Publications.

13402 Merat, P. FR 010202/66/2517
Recherches sur un gène de nanisme (dw) chez la poule: interactions avec d'autres gènes connus et certains facteurs ambiants pour les performances de production. **Research on a dwarf gene (dw) in the fowl: interaction with other known genes and with certain environmental factors pertaining to production traits.** Publications.

13403 Duncan GB 010704/00/0002 R
Stimuli controlling laying behaviour in pens and battery cages.

13404 Gilbert GB 010708/00/0012 R
Use of calcium restricting diets to regulate reproductive activity in the hen.

13405 Foster GB 041305/00/0003
Selection of laying hens under ahemeral light–dark cycles.

13406 Costantini, F. IT 041017/74/0539
Miglioramento genetico del pollo domestico. **Genetic improvement of domestic chicken.**

13407 Costantini, F. IT 041017/77/0154
Miglioramento genetico del pollo domestico. **Genetic improvement of broilers.**

13408 Tijen, W.F. van; Gerritsen, G.; Kuit, A.R.
NL 010109/71/7730
Onderzoek naar selektiekriteria voor de eiproduktie van leghennen. **Research into criteria for selection on egg production in layers.** Publications.

13409 Kuit, A.R. NL 010109/74/7731 R
Gebruik van kleine kippen voor de eiproduktie. **Aspects of mini layers.** Publications.

13410 Kuit, A.R. NL 010109/75/7862 R
Kwaliteit en efficiëntie van de vleesproduktie bij kippen. **Quality and efficiency of poultry meat production.**

13411 Simons, P.C.M.; Tijen, W.F. van; Oosterwoud, A.; Teunis, G.P.; Japing, H.M. NL 010109/77/7861
Breukpreventie door verbetering van schaalkwaliteit. **Prevention of shell damage by improvement of shell quality.** Publications.

13412 Van der Zijpp, A.J. NL 020058/76/6858
Onderzoek naar de genetische bijdrage aan en de invloed van het milieu op de immuunresponse bij kippen. **Research project

regarding the genetic contribution to and the influence of the environment on the immune response of chickens.** Publications.

13413 Oosterlee, C.C. NL 020058/78/8548
Het typeren van de B–locus (major histocompatibility locus) van kippen, in relatie tot het resistentie–onderzoek. **B–locus genotyping for resistance research in chickens.**

13414 Middelkoop, J.H. van NL 060007/55/5092
Foktechnische verbetering van slachtkuikens. **Genetic improvement of broilers.**

13415 Heyboer, D.C. NL 060007/55/5652
Foktechnische verbetering van legkippen. **Genetic improvement of laying hens.**

Geese, turkeys and other domestic birds (B 4490)

See also 11363, 11365, 12715, 13189, 13245

13416 Petersen, J.; Orlovins, I.; Wegner, R.–M.
DE 111501/74/0006
Leistungsmerkmale von drei Linien der japanischen Wachtel. **Performance characteristics of three different lines of the Japanese quail.**

13417 Romboli, I. IT 041116/74/0614
Selezione e prove di rendimento zootecnico di nuove varietà di anatra muschiata. **Selection and testing of breeding efficiency of new species of musky duck.** Publications.

13418 Romboli, I. IT 041116/77/0284 R
Selezione e prove di rendimento zootecnico di nuove varietà di anatra muschiata–cairina moschiata L.–. **Selection and testing of breeding rentability of new varieties of cairina moschiata L.–.**

Fishes, crustacea, shell fish and frogs in general (B 4500)

See also 12873

13419 Meske, C.; Kuhlmann, H. DE 208020/77/0006
Entwicklung von Fischzuchtverfahren in offenen und geschlossenen Süss– und Salzwassersystemen. **Development of methods for fish breeding in open and closed fresh–water and salt–water systems.**

Salmon (B 4520)

See also 13425

13420 Researcher not indicated DE 132000/77/0001
Eignung salmonider Artkreuzungen für die intensive Fischproduktion. **Suitability of Salmonidae crosses for intensive fish production.**

13421 Chevassus, B.; Leblanc, J.M. FR 010203/73/5537
Etudes de l'hybridation chez les salmonidés. **Studies on hybridization in salmonids.**

Trout (B 4530)

See also 13421

13422 Reizer, C.; Dupont, E. BE 140000/77/0053

Intensification des productions piscicoles en eau douce. **Intensification of inland water fisch culture.**

13423 Researcher not indicated   DE 502650/78/0022 N
Züchtung einer umwelttoleranten, standorttreuen Regenbogenforelle. **Breeding of a rainbow trout tolerant of environmental conditions and adhering to certain site.**

13424 Blanc, J.M.   FR 010204/74/5505
Génétique quantitative de la truite commune en élevage. **Quantitative genetics of hatchery brown trout.**

13425 Blanc, J.M.; Chevassus, B.   FR 010204/77/5504
Hybridations interspécifiques chez les salmonidés. **Interspecific hybridizations among salmonids.**

13426 Heland, M.   FR 010711/73/5527
Ontogénèse du comportement territorial chez la truite commune. **Ontogeny of territorial behaviour in brown trout.**

Crustacea, shell fish, frogs (B 4560)

13427 Meixner, R.; Neudecker, T.   DE 208020/77/0005
Entwicklung von Zuchtverfahren für Krebs– und Muscheltiere sowie Überwachung der Nutz–Muschelbestände im deutschen Wattenmeer. **Development of methods for breeding crustaceans and shell–fish.**

Other fishes (B 4590)

See also 13422

Invertebrates (bees, silk–worm) (B 4600)

13428 Drescher, W.; Böger, K.   DE 111201/70/0001
Selektion auf Sammelleistung bei der Honigbiene. **Selection on collecting performance of honeybee.**

13429 Drescher, W.   DE 111201/75/0002
Selektion von Bienenstämmen mit geringer und hoher Schwarmneigung. **Selection of genetic lines of honeybee with low and high swarming tendency.**

13430 Weiss, K.   DE 502350/77/0006
Versuche zur Hybridisation der Honigbiene. **Experiments with hybrid bees.**

13431 Holm, S.N.   DK 030145/73/0009
Forædling af honningbier. **Breeding of honeybees.**

13432 Holm, S.N.   DK 030145/75/0012
Udvikling af honning–linier med resistens mod bipest. **Development of honeybee lines resistant to foul brood.**

13433 Lavie, P.; Fresnaye, J.   FR 010608/68/1751
Hybridation d'abeille. **Honey bee hybridization.**

13434 Lavie, P.; Fresnaye, J.   FR 010608/70/5277
Obtention et utilisation des hybrides de races géographiques d'abeilles. **Getting and using hybrides of honeybee geographic races.**

13435 Reali, G.   IT 020400/70/0003
Costituzione di nuovi poliibridi di baco da seta. **Formation of' new polyhybrids of silkworms.**

Rabbits (B 4910)

See also 11508, 13189

13436 De Groote, G.; Okerman, F.   BE 070200/76/0030 R
Selektie bij twee slachtkonijnenrassen (wit van Dendermonde, Witte Nieuw Zeelander). **Selection within two meat rabbit breeds (Termonder white, New Zealand white).**

13437 De Groote, G.; Bombeke, A.; Okerman, F.   BE 070200/76/0032 R
Studie van de kunstmatige inseminatie bij konijnen. **Study of artifical insemination with rabbits.**

13438 Jensen, N.E.   DK 010203/74/0002 N
Avlsforsøg med kaniner. **Progeny tests with rabbits.**

13439 Jensen, N.E.   DK 010203/78/0015 N
Daglængdens indflydelse på avlsresultatet i kaninstalden. **The influence of day length on breeding results in rabbits.**

13440 Ouhayoun, J.; Mue Delmas   FR 011404/70/2576
Variations génétiques au cours de la croissance, du métabolisme énergétique du tissu musculaire chez le lapin; relations avec le degré de maturité. **Genetic variations during growth of energetic metabolism of muscular tissue in the rabbit; relationships with the maturing state.** Publications.

13441 Matheron, G.; Poujardieu, B.; Vrillon, J.L.; Rouvier, R.   FR 011404/71/2573
Etude des croisements de souches femelles de lapins et recherche de la combinaison optimum pour accroître la productivité numérique. **Crossbreeding between rabbit dam lines and research for optimum combination to improve litter size.** Publications.

13442 Rouvier, R.; Poujardieu, B.; Vrillon, J.L.   FR 011404/71/2581
Sélection pour les aptitudes de production (croissance, engraissement, qualités bouchères——) de souches mâles chair de lapins pour le croisement industriel du terminal. **Selection on productive traits (growth, fattening, carcass quality——) of rabbit terminal sire lines.** Publications.

13443 Ouhayoun, J.; Rouvier, R.   FR 011404/72/2577
Etude de la variabilité génétique et recherche des critères objectifs de qualité de la viande chez le lapin. **Genetic variability and research on objective criteria for meat quality in the rabbit.** Publications.

13444 Ouhayoun, J.; Rouvier, R.; Vrillon, J.L.   FR 011404/73/2578
Sélection massale des lapins sur la vitesse de croissance pendant la phase d'engraissement. Etude des réponses corrélées des caractères économiques et de qualité de la viande. **Mass selection of rabbits on growth rate during fattening period. Correlative responses in economic traits and meat quality.**

13445 Hulot, F.; Poujardieu, B.; Vrillon, J.L.   FR 011404/74/2579
Etude de la variabilité génétique des caractères biologiques de reproduction chez la lapine en vue d'améliorer sa fécondité. **Genetic variability and improvement of reproduction characters. Rabbits in the doe.** Publications.

13446 Echard, G.　　　　　　　　FR 011406/73/2520
Etude des bandes chromosomiques de type G chez le lapin domestique (oryctolagus cuniculus). **G. band pattern of rabbit chromosomes (oryctolagus cuniculus).** Publications.

13447 Masoero, G.; Auxilia, M.T.　　　IT 020700/76/0014
Formazione di un ceppo specializzato di conigli da carne in vista di una ulteriore selezione per i caratteri produttivi nella fase post–svezzamento. **Selection of a strain of rabbit for meat with high performances after weaning.**

13448 Matassino, D.; Gioffre', F.; Proto, V.; Cosentino, E.; Bordi, A.; Gargano, D.　　　　　IT 040722/64/0002
La ciecotrofia nel coniglio. **Rabbit cecotrophy.** Publications.

Domestic pets and zoo animals (B 4920)

See also 15010, 15056, 15066

13449 De Groote, G.; Waegeman, D.　BE 070200/76/0046 R
Studie van de kweek van de botvink (Fringilla coelebs) in gevangschap. **Study of the breeding of the finch (Fringilla coelebs) in captivity.** Publications.

13450 Herzog, A.; Kluge, A.　　　　DE 129680/75/0007
Untersuchung der Karyotypen von Caniden mit verschiedenen Färbmethoden. **Banding patterns of chromosomes in different species of Canidae.**

13451 Herzog, A.; Krämer, O.　　　DE 129680/78/0006 N
Untersuchungen zur Leistungsvererbung beim Deutschen drahthaarigen Vorstehhund. **Performance genetics of German wire–haired pointers.**

13452 Herzog, A.; Kuhn, P.　　　　DE 129680/78/0007 N
Untersuchungen zur Vererbung und Eugenik der Hüftgelenksdysplasie beim Deutschen Wachtel. **Genetics and eugenics of hip dysplasia of German spaniel.**

13453 Wegner, W.; Reetz, I.; Rudorf, B.; Zielonka, C.
　　　　　　　　　　　　　　　DE 139350/72/0002
Vergleichende medizinische Untersuchungen über die Erblichkeit von Augen– und Ohrenanomalien – Versuchsobjekt: Hund –. **Comparative medical examinations of hereditary abnormities of eyes and ears – objects of trials: dogs –.**

13454 Christiansen, I.J.　　　　　DK 030128/74/0001 N
Undersøgelse over dybfrysning af hundesæd. **An investigation into the deep freezing of canine spermatozoa.**

13455 Groot, E.C.B.M.　　　　　NL 030005/76/7760
Hereditaire doofheid bij de hond. **Genetic hearing impairment in the dog.**

13456 Velden, N.A. van der　　　NL 030009/52/6025 N
Genetische bepaalde afwijkingen bij de hond (oorstand, premolaren, doofheid, aortas :enose, hond). **Hereditary abnormalities in dogs (ear–carriage, premolars, deafness, aortastenosis, dog).**

13457 Stades, F.C.　　　　　　NL 030009/72/5865 R
Progressieve Retina Atrofie (PRA) bij de hond in Nederland (hond, progressieve retina atrofie, staafjes, kegeltjes, degeneratie, erfelijke oogafwijkingen). **Progressive Retinal Atrophy (PRA) in dogs in the Netherlands (dogs, progressive retinal atrophy, rods–cones degeneration, inherited eye–disease).** Publications.

13458 Velden, N.A. van de　　　NL 030009/72/6025
Aorta stenose bij Dalmatische honden (erfelijke afwijking). **Aorta stenosis in Dalmatian dogs (hereditary defect).**

13459 Velden, N.A. van der　　　NL 030009/72/6063 R
Abnormaal gedrag bij Berner Senner honden (hond, gedrag, agressie, erfelijk). **An abnormal behaviour trait in Bernese Mountain dogs (dog, behaviour, aggression, heredity).**

13460 Velden, N.A. van der　　　NL 030009/76/7760
Hereditaire doofheid bij de hond. **Genetic hearing impairment in the dog.**

Fur animals (B 4930)

See also 15073, 15075

Other domestic animals (B 4990)

See also 15081

Laboratory animals (B 9120)

See also 12883, 13001, 13279, 13287

13461 Weniger, J.H.; Horst, P.; Steinhauf, D.
　　　　　　　　　　　　　　　DE 105550/72/0002
Enzymaktivitäten und Enzympolymorphismen in Populationen, die auf Adaptationsfähigkeit und Eiweissansatz selektiert wurden – Modellversuche an Mäusen –. **Activities and polymorphisms of enzymes in populations selected on adaptation performance and protein store – trials with mice –.**

13462 Buschmann, H.; Kräusslich, H.; Meyer, J.; Osterkorn, K.; Radzikowski, A.　　　　DE 160765/73/0004
Ursachen für die Variation der Phagozytoseaktivität bei Mäusen und die Bedeutung genetischer Faktoren. **Causes of the variation of the phagocytic activity in mice and the role of genetic influence.**

13463 Pirchner, F.; Willeke, H.; Butler, I. von
　　　　　　　　　　　　　　　DE 161300/77/0004
Selektionsexperiment auf Veränderung der Wachstumskurven bei der Maus. **Selection experiment in changing the growth curves in mice.**

13464 Förster, M.　　　　　　　DE 161300/78/0005 N
Mitotische Chiasmata. **Mitotic chiasmas.**

13465 Bakker, H.　　　　　　　NL 020058/75/6854
Vergelijking van muizenlijnen, waarin is geselekteerd op groeikenmerken. **Comparison of lines of mouse selected for growth traits.**

13466 Bakker, H.　　　　　　　NL 020058/75/6855
Analyse van het effect van selektie op worpgrootte in muizen. **Evaluation of effects of selection for litter size in mice.**

13467 Bouw, J.　　　　　　　　NL 030009/49/5719 R
Ontwikkeling van een ingeteelde konijnenstam (konijn, inteelt, normaalwaarden). **Development of an inbred strain of rabbits (rabbit, inbred strain, strain characteristics).**

13468 Zutphen, L.F.M. van   NL 030009/70/5720 R
Genetische analyse van elektroforetisch aantoonbare
biochemische varianten bij laboratorium dieren. **Genetic
analysis of electrophoretically detectable polymorphisms in
laboratory animals.** Publications.

13469 Kremer, A.K.   NL 030009/74/6023 R
Verschillen in milieu–adaptatie bij muizenstammen en
stamkruisingen (genetica, milieu, muis, dag/nacht ritme,
aanpassing). **Differences between inbred mouse–strains and
crosses in adaptability to environment (genetics, environment,
mouse, circadian rythm, adaptation).**

13470 Zutphen, L.F.M. van   NL 030009/77/7750 R
Onderzoek naar de oorzaken van de genetische variatie iń
gevoeligheid voor dietair cholesterol bij konijnen: correlatie
met esterase patronen. **Genetic variation of dietary cholesterol
response in rabbits: correlation with esterase patterns.**
Publications.

D 3400 – Animal diseases, veterinary medicine

See also 313, 2113, 2114, 2115, 3341, 8250, 8252, 8253, 10415,
15137, 15665, 16226, 19559, 19767, 19768, 20145, 20190

13471 Van den Bruel, W.   BE 010017/67/0002
Etude éthologique et écologique de Lymnea Truncatula en vue
de la lutte contre cette limmée hôte intermédiaire de la
Fasciola Hépatica dans prairies humides. **Ethological and
ecological study of Lymnea Truncatula in order to control this
snail intermedial host of Fasciola Hépatica in moist pastures.**
Publications.

13472 Devos, A.; Devriese, L.; Viaene, N.; Spanoghe, L.
    BE 050600/71/0004
Onderzoek naar de modaliteiten van vaccinaties tegenover
Pseudovogelpest. **Investigations on vaccinations against
Newcastle Disease in poultry.** Publications.

13473 Kaekenbeek, A.; Josse, M.; Pastoret, P.P.
    BE 060002/67/0001 R
Recherches sur les entérites colibacillaires et virales du veau.
Research on the colibacillary and viral enteritis of calf.
Publications.

13474 Pastoret, P.P.   BE 060002/74/0002 R
Etude de la structure du virus I.B.R. **Study on the structure of
I.B.R. virus.** Publications.

13475 Pouplard, L.; Pêcheur, M.; Detry, M.
    BE 060004/71/0001
Etude de l'épidémiologie et de la lutte contre la verminose
gastro–intestinale du bétail. **Study of the epidemiology and
action against gastro–intestinal worms in cattle.** Publications.

13476 Moens, R.   BE 081100/61/0002
Etude de l'écologie de Lymnaea truncatula, hôte intermédiaire
de Fasciola hepatica L et de l'incidence économique de la
Fasciolose en Belgique. **Study of the ecology of Lymnaea
truncatula, intermediate host of Fasciola hepatica L and of the
economic incidence of Fascioliasis in Belgium.** Publications.

13477 Strobbe, R.; Debecg, J.   BE 110000/72/0002 R
Dénaturation des entigènes du vaccin antiaphteux par certains
composants en cours de conservation. **Denaturation of foot and
mouth disease antigens of some of the components during
vaccine storage .** Publications.

13478 Pohl, P.; Thomas, J.   BE 110000/73/0011
Classification des plasmides de résistance bactériens aux
antibiotiques. **Classification of bacterial plasmid resistance
against the antibiotica.** Publications.

13479 Halen, P.; Meulemans, G.   BE 110000/76/0028
Recherches épidémiologiques sur les virus de la bronchite
infectieuse, les adéno et réovirus aviaires. **Epidemiological
researchs on avian infective bronchitis, adeno and reoviruses.**
Publications.

13480 Famerée, L.; Cotteleer, C.   BE 110000/78/0054 N
Enquête et recherches épidémiologiques sur la trichinose en
Belgique. **Survey and epidemiological research on trichinosis in
Belgium.** Publications.

13481 Cotteleer, C.; Famerée, L.   BE 110000/78/0056 N
Détermination et fréquence des ixodides en Belgique.
Determination and frequency of ixodideae in Belgium.

13482 Cottelcer, C.; Famerée, L.   BE 110000/78/0058 N
Identification des différentes coccidies infestant les animaux.
**Identification of various protozoa species in animals (coccidae
sarcosporidae – toxoplasma).** Publications.

13483 Cotteleer, C.; Famerée, L.   BE 110000/78/0060 N
Recherche des kystes de protozoaires dans les matières fécales.
Research on protozoa cysts in faeces.

13484 De Cueninck, B.   BE 110000/79/0049 N
Bereiding van een oppervlakte eiwit van Streplococcus
agalactiae. **Preparation of a surface protein of streptococcus
agalactiae.**

13485 Biront, P.   BE 110000/79/0051 N
Betekenis van Parvo–virus in beren sperma. **Role of
Parvo–virus in boar sperm.**

13486 Strobbe, R.; Debecq, J.   BE 110000/79/0053 N
Conservation d'antigènes aphteux concentrés en vue de la
préparation de vaccins. **Storage of concentrated foot and mouth
disease antigens for vaccine preparation.**

13487 Geissler, H.; Busche, R.   DE 129800/75/0005
Behandlungsversuche der Capillariasis bei Greifvögeln.
Attempt of Capillariasis treatment in birds of prey.

13488 Siegmann, O.; Kaleta, E.F.; Hinz, K.–H.; Neumann,
U.; Lüders, H.   DE 139700/75/0002
Einfluss aviärer Mykoplasmen auf die Interferoninduktion.
**The influence of avian mycoplasma on the induced interferon
production of Marek's disease virus 'MDV'.** Publications.

13489 Büttner, K.   DE 176051/75/0002
Untersuchungen zur Parasitierung des Rehwildes bei
abnehmbarer Wilddichte. **Investigations into the parasitic
infestation of roe deer under decreasing population density.**
Publications.

13490 Honikel, K.   DE 210040/75/0011
Biochemische Untersuchungen zur Ursache des Auftretens
von wässrigem, blassem Schweinefleisch – PSE–Fleisch –.
Biochemical studies on the causes of wateriness and paleness of

PSE–pork.

13491 Pietzsch, O. DE 305030/75/0030
Pathogenese und Immunologie der Salmonella–Infektionen–
zur Zeit: bei Tauben –. **Pathogenesis and immunology of
salmonella infections – at present in pigeons –.**

13492 Pedersen, K.B. DK 020100/75/5161
Undersøgelse af immunmekanismen og patogenesen ved
infektiøs atrofisk rhinitis og tarmbrand. **Investigation of the
immunity mechanism and pathogenesis of infectious atrophic
rhinitis and necrotising enteritis.**

13493 Meyling, A. DK 020100/77/8047
Virusbetingede enteritter hos kalve, svin og børn.
Virus-conditioned enteritis in calves, pigs and children.

13494 Henriksen, S.Aa. DK 020100/78/9026
Udbredelsen af løbe–tarm infektioner med Cooperia spp. hos
dansk kvæg og deres betydning. **Frequency of abomasum
infections by Cooperia spp. in Danish cattle and their
importance.**

13495 Klastrup, N.O. DK 020202/78/9000
Genetisk resistens mod mastitis belyst ved resistensmarkører
som somatisk celletælling, laktoglobulinfænotyper,
malkbarhed samt yver patteformer. **Genetic resistance to
mastitis elucidated by resistance markers such as somatic cell
counts, lactoglobulin phenotypes, milkability and udder teat
form.**

13496 Bisgaard, M. DK 020300/78/8170
Biokemisk og serologisk karakterisering af Pasteurella
anatipestifer, species incertae sedis hos ænder. **Biochemical
and serological characterisation of Pasteurella anatipestifer,
species incertae sedis in ducks.**

13497 Olsen, C.E.; Hansen, A. DK 030106/78/0007 N
Bestemmelse af det extracellulære væskevolumen i hjernen.
Determination of brain extracellular space.

13498 Christensen, N.O. DK 030121/75/0001
Sårsygdom hos torsk og marine vibriopopulationers forhold til
forureningskomponenter, især kulhydratforurening i marine
bioteper. **Wound disease in cod and a comparison of marine
Vibrio populations to pollutants, especially carbohydrate
contamination in marine biotopes.**

13499 Aalund, O. DK 030129/72/0006
Radioimmunanalyser til kvantitering af bl.a. mykotoksiner og
hormoner. **Radio–immune analysis for the quantification of
mycotoxins and hormones.**

13500 Poulsen, J.S.D.; Smith, M.; Deckert, T.
 DK 030130/79/0004 N
Undersøgelser over intraperitoneal insulininfusion. **Absorption
of insulin applicated intraperitoneally.**

13501 Fries, A.S. DK 030133/73/0006
Undersøgelser over Tyzzer's Disease. **Investigations into
Tyzzer's Disease.**

13502 Christensen, N.O.; Larsen, J.L.; Jensen, N.J.; Guildal,
J.A.; Dalsgaard, I. DK 030137/75/0001 R
Mikrobiologisk–økologiske virkninger af kulhydratforurening
gennem spildevandsforurening i marine recipienter. Betydning

for marine vibrioarter og relation til infektioner hos fisk og
bundinvertebrater. **The microbiological and ecological effects of
carbohydrate contamination through waste water pollution in
marine organisms. The significance of the marine bacteria of
the genus Vibrio and their relationship to infections in fish and
bottom invertebrates.**

13503 Larsen, H.E. DK 030137/76/0005
Sygdoms– og miljømæssige problemer i forbindelse med
behandling og spredning af gylle. 1. Bakteriologiske
undersøgelser. **Disease and environmental problems in
connection with the treatment and spreading of ammoniated
manure. (1) Bacteriological investigations.**

13504 Jørgensen, R.J. DK 030137/78/8149
Epidemiologiske undersøgelser vedrørende kvægets lungeorm,
med henblik på forebyggelse af verminøs brochitis.
**Epidemiological investigations of cattle lung worm with
reference to prevention of verminous bronchitis.**

13505 Lund, E. DK 030138/76/0009
Sygdoms– og miljømæssige problemer i forbindelse med
behandling og spredning af gylle. **Disease and environmental
problems in connection with the treatment and spreading of
ammoniated manure.**

13506 Bendixen, P.H. DK 030138/77/0001
Undersøgelse af kvægmakrofagers lyserende kapacitet. **An
investigation of the lysogenic capacity of cattle macrophages.**

13507 Rønsholt, L.J.V. DK 030138/77/9061
Udvikling af test til bestemmelse af chlamydia infektion hos
husdyr, specielt kvæg. **Development of test for determination of
Chlamydia infection in livestock, particularly cattle.**

13508 Lacey; Hill GB 012009/00/0009
Medical and veterinary implications of storage moulds.

13509 Reeve GB 012504/00/0001 R
**Genetics of antibiotic resistance in bacteria. Genes controlling
continuous variation.**

13510 Ratledge GB 021703/79/0003 N
**Iron metabolism in mycobastin–dependent myco bacteria of
veterinary importance.**

13511 Sayers GB 022604/79/0001 N
**Analysis of fox rabies propagation in relation to geographic and
seasonal factors.**

13512 Pusztai GB 030601/00/0009 R
Isolation of proteolytic enzymes from bean seeds.

13513 Pusztai GB 030601/00/0010 R
**Cellular location in germinating seeds – development of
methods.**

13514 Mann; Hobson GB 030605/00/0005
**Survival of anaerobes and other bacteria of rumen and faecal
origin in air and other media.**

13515 Muttrie GB 030903/00/0313 R
**Behaviour and ecology of Dermesters peruvianus in Glasgow
and elsewhere in Scotland.**

13516 Damoglou GB 040103/76/0008 R

Mycotoxins in feedingstuffs.

13517 Researcher not indicated   GB 050484/00/0001 R
Clostridium oedematiens epidemiological survey.

13518 Lindsay   GB 051101/79/0006 N
Cadmium duplicate – diet study on farms in the Heathrow area.

13519 Robb   GB 060113/00/0005 R
Microbiology and biochemistry of Fusarium toxin production.

13520 O'Riordan, F.   IE 060300/75/1190 R
Control of diseases of nursery stocks and ornamentals.
Publications.

13521 Hope Cawdery, M.J.   IE 060706/72/0459 R
Snail population studies. Publications.

Animals and parts of their bodies (B 2300)

See also 11631, 13478, 13479, 14069

13522 Kjærsgaard, P.   DK 030132/70/0003
Undersøgelser over tværstribet skeletmuskulaturs histokemi og
finstruktur. Investigations into the histochemistry and fine
structure of crossstriated skeletal muscle.

13523 Vodovar, N.; Desnoyers, F.   FR 010205/71/2716
Etude morphologique de l'action physiopathologique de
différentes matières grasses et hydrocarbures sur l'organisme.
Morphological study of the physiopathological action of
various fats and hydrocarbons on the organism. Publications.

13524 Remesy, C.; Demigne, C.   FR 010817/74/8040
Etude du métabolisme hépatique. Studies of hepatic
metabolism.

13525 Galtier, P.; Alvinerie, M.; Eeckhoutte, C.
    FR 011407/78/8053
Devenir de la zéaralénone dans l'organisme animal. Fate of
zearalenone in animal organism.

13526 Wal, J.M.   FR 011412/74/2772
Dosage radioimmunologique de la pénicilline et de ses résidus
allergènes (groupes penicilloyl) dans les milieux biologiques.
Radioimmunoassay of penicillin and its allergen residues
(penicilloyl groups) in biological samples.

13527 Guarda, F.; Cornaglia, E.; Cravero, G.; Gennaro
Soffietti, M.; Valenza, F.; Galloni, M.   IT 041222/75/0001 R
– Patologia cardiaca e muscolare – Neuropatologia – Chimica
dei residui nell'organismo animale. – Cardiac and muscular
pathology – Neuropathology – Chemistry of residues in animal
organism. Publications.

13528 Baccetti, B.   IT 041401/78/1179 N
Struttura e metabolismo r patologia delle cellule germinali
maschili, conservazione, selezione, azione di farmaci sugli
spermatozoi. Structure and metabolism concerning the
pathology of male germinal cells; conservation, selection, drug
action on spermatozoa.

13529 Bercken, J. van den   NL 030003/73/5889 R
Ototoxiciteit van een aantal antibiotica en diuretica.
Ototoxicity of antibiotics and diuretics. Publications.

13530 Bercken, J. van den   NL 030003/75/3662 R
De invloed van ACTH en corticosteroi den op de synaptische
transmissie. The effects of ACTH and corticosteroids on
synaptic transmission. Publications.

Animal communities as ecological systems (B 2400)

13531 Devos, A.; Devriese, L.   BE 050600/71/0005
Onderzoek naar de biochemische en fysiologische
eigenschappen van staphylococcus aureus geïsoleerd bij dieren
en naar de ecologie van S. aureus bij dieren. Investigations on
the biochemical and physiological characteristics of
staphylococcus aureus strains isolated from animals and on the
ecology of S. aureus in animals. Publications.

13532 Gray, J.S.; Strickland, K.L.   IE 120101/75/9070 N
Studies on the ecology and life cycles of the tick, ixodes r icinus
in ireland. Publications.

Domestic animals in general (B 4000)

See also 1943, 5079, 5616, 8107, 10444, 10455, 10457, 10479,
11668, 11669, 11694, 11706, 11707, 11721, 11738, 11749, 11765,
13482, 13486, 13501, 13507, 13531, 16347, 19163, 19199, 19633,
19634, 19769, 19771, 19860, 20326, 20327

13533 Vercauteren, R.; Vanneste–Ijsebeert, M.; Vaneste,
W.; Heyneman, R.   BE 050900/61/0001 R
Studie van de zuurstof overdragende enzymen bij leucocyten.
Study of oxygentransferring enzymes in leucocytes.
Publications.

13534 Halen, P.   BE 110000/76/0043
Identification et caractérisation des mycoplasmes chez les
animaux domestiques. Identification and caracterisation of
mycoplasma from domestic animals. Publications.

13535 Risse, H.J.; Rogge, H.; Arnold, D.; Rössler, H.
    DE 104100/77/0001
Biosynthese von Glykoproteinen in differenzierenden
Systemen. Biosynthesis of glycoproteins under development.
Publications.

13536 Risse, H.J.; Reinwald, E.; Rautenberg, P.; Camara,
J.J.   DE 104100/77/0002
Biochemie von Trypanosomen Antigenen. The biochemistry of
Trypanosoma antigens.

13537 Kühn, D.; Janitschke, K.; Warnecke, M.; Oppermann,
W.H.; Rödel, H.; Centurier, H.   DE 104200/72/0004 N
Untersuchungen über die Epidemiologie und Biologie der
Toxoplsasma–Infektion bei Haustieren. Studies on
epidemiology and life cycle of Toxoplasma gondii in domestic
animals.

13538 Schein, E.; Warnecke, M.   DE 104201/73/0001
Entwicklungszyklus von Theilerien in den Überträgerzecken.
Life cycle of Theileria in vector ticks.

13539 Schein, E.; Müller, M.; Warnecke, M.; Voigt, P.;
Sälker, R.; Zweygarth, P.   DE 104201/77/0001
Entwicklung, Pathogenität und Immunogenität von
Arthropoden übertragener Blutprotozoen. Development,
pathogenicity and immunogenicity of arthropode–born blood
protozoa. Publications.

13540 Hörchner, F.; Grase; Oguz, T. DE 104202/73/0004
Helminthenbefall und Möglichkeit der galaktogenen
Übertragung bei Gebärenden aus der Türkei. **Helminthism and
the possibility of galactogenous transmission in parturients from
Turkey.**

13541 Hörchner, F.; Zander, B. DE 104202/74/0001
Antigenstruktur von Fasciola hepatica. **Antigen structure of
Fasciola hepatica.**

13542 Hörchner, F.; Albert, H.; Edokwe, G.; Gerber, H.C.;
Grelck, H.; Zander, B. DE 104202/77/0001
Epidemiologie, Pathologie und Immunität von Helminthen bei
Haus– und Nutztieren sowie des Menschen. **Epidemiology,
pathogenicity and immunity of helminths of domestic animals,
livestock and man.** Publications.

13543 Heydorn, A.–O.; Fischer, G.; Gebelhoff, E.
DE 104203/77/0001
Untersuchungen zur Epidemiologie und Pathogenität
isosporoider Kokzidien 'Isospora, Toxoplasma, Sarcocystis'
von Haus– und Nutztieren sowie des Menschen. **Epidemiology
and pathogenicity of isosporial coccidia 'Isospora, Toxoplasma,
Sarcocystis' of domestic animals, livestock and man.**

13544 Heidrich, H.J.; Berger, M.; Brattig, B.
DE 104400/74/0003
Kreislaufüberwachung nach Gaben verschiedener Narkotika.
Circulation check after application of diverse narcotics.

13545 Opitz, M. DE 104500/72/0001
Serumlipiduntersuchungen beim spontanen Diabetes mellitus.
Serum lipid tests in spontaneous Diabetes mellitus.

13546 Saar, C.; Grund, S.; Kasbohm, C. DE 104500/77/0005
Klinische Hämatologie und Zytologie. **Clinical hematology and
cytology.** Publications.

13547 Opitz, M.; Kasbohm, C.; Lettow, E.; Loppnow, H.;
Schwartz–Porsche, D.; Weiss, J. DE 104500/77/0006
Klinische Endokrinologie. **Clinical endocrinology.**
Publications.

13548 Opitz, M.; Kasbohm, C.; Lettow, E.; Loppnow, H.;
Schwartz–Porsche, D. DE 104500/77/0008
Erkrankungen des Magen–Darm–Trakts sowie der
Bauchspeicheldrüse. **Gastroenterological diseases, incl.
pancreatic diseases.** Publications.

13549 Greuel, E. DE 111404/70/0003
Die Wirkung verschiedener neuer Coccidiostatica. **Effect of
several new coccidiostatics.**

13550 Lampert, W.; Pott, E.; Schober, U.; Lemcke, H.–W.
DE 126803/75/0001
Untersuchungen der Wirkungen und Anreicherung von
Herbiziden auf der Nahrungskettenstufe Primärproduzent–
Filtrierender Primärkonsument. **Studies on effects and
accumulation of herbicides on the food chain step primary
producer – filtering primary consumer.**

13551 Meyer, F.; Erhardt, G.; Senft, B. DE 129251/75/0002
Genetische Aspekte der natürlichen Abwehrmechanismen –
Lactoferrin – der Milchdrüse. **Genetic aspects of the natural
defence mechanisms – lactoferrin – of the mammary gland.**

13552 Schliesser, T.; Thiel, N. DE 129385/77/0001
Tierhygienische Aspekte der industriemässigen
Tierproduktion. **Animal hygienic aspects of large–scale
livestock production.** Publications.

13553 Schliesser, T.; Thiel, N. DE 129385/77/0003
Das Vorkommen von Zoonosen in den ost– und
südosteuropäischen Ländern. **The distribution of zoonoses in
the countries of East and Southeast Europe.** Publications.

13554 Schliesser, T.; Thiel, N. DE 129385/78/0001 N
Staatliche Tierseuchenbekämpfung und das Veterinärwesen in
den RGW–Ländern. **Infectious disease control and veterinary
public health in the countries of the Comecon.**

13555 Schliesser, T.; Thiel, N. DE 129385/78/0002 N
Die veterinärmedizinische Ausbildung und Forschung in den
ost– und südosteuropäischen Ländern. **Veterinary education
and research in the countries of East and Southeast Europe.**

13556 Fischer, H.; Scheurmann, E. DE 129540/75/0001
Jungtierkrankheiten am tropischen Standort. **Diseases of young
animals in the tropics.**

13557 Weiss, E.; Käufer, I.; Reinacher, M.; Burkhardt, E.;
Teredesai, A.; Weikel, J. DE 129620/70/0002
Pathogenese der Virusinfektion im Organismus. **Pathogenesis
of infection by virus in the organism.**

13558 Weiss, E.; Frese, K.; Rudolph, R.; Frank, H.; Käufer,
I.; Reinacher, M. DE 129620/78/0003 N
Kasuistische Berichte in der Veterinär–Pathologie aufgrund
wissenschaftlicher Bearbeitung von Obduktionsgut. **Case
reports in veterinary pathology based on post mortem findings.**
Publications.

13559 Frimmer, M.; Petzinger, E.; Rufeger, U.
DE 129660/78/0001 N
Vorübergehende Desensibilisierung von isolierten
Hepatozyten gegen Phalloidin durch Behandlung mit
Phospholipase A. **Transient desensibilization of isolated
hepatocytes against Phalloidin by treatment with Phospholipase
A.** Publications.

13560 Frimmer, M.; Petzinger, E.; Rufeger, U.; Veil, L.B.
DE 129660/78/0002 N
Die Rolle von Gallensäuren bei Phalloidinvergiftung. **The role
of bile acids in Phalloidin poisoning.** Publications.

13561 Frimmer, M.; Rufeger, U. DE 129660/78/0003 N
Temperaturabhängigkeit einer Reaktion von Phalloidin in
isolierten Hepatozyten von Ratten. **Temperature dependence
of Phalloidin response in isolated rat hepatocytes.** Publications.

13562 Frimmer, M.; Petzinger, E.; Rufeger, U.; Veil, L.B.
DE 129660/78/0004 N
Schutz der Hepatozyten gegen Phalloidin durch Trypsin.
Trypsin protection of hepatocytes against Phalloidin.
Publications.

13563 Frimmer, M.; Scharmann, W. DE 129660/78/0005 N
Toxizität eines weitgehend gereinigten Leukocidins von
Pseudomonas aeruginosa in perfundierter Rattenleber.
**Toxicity of a highly purified Leukocidin from Pseudomonas
aeruginosa in perfused rat liver.** Publications.

13564 Frimmer, M.; Lutz, F.　　　DE 129660/78/0006 N
Schwellung und Kaliumverlust bei perfundierten Lebern nach
Einwirkung von dampfförmigem Tetrachlorkohlenstoff,
Chloroform und Halothan auf das Perfusionsmedium. **Swelling
and loss of potassium of perfused livers after action of vaporized
carbon tetrachloride, chloroform and halothane on perfusion
medium.** Publications.

13565 Frimmer, M.　　　DE 129660/78/0007 N
Phalloidin, ein membran–spezifisches Toxin. **Phalloidin a
membrane specific toxin.** Publications.

13566 Rieck, G.W.; Höhn, H.; Schmidt, I.; Gräf, L.
　　　DE 129680/75/0002
Erkennung chromosomaler Strukturveränderungen als
Ursachen pathologischer Zustände bei Haustieren mittels der
RasterElektronenmikroskopie. **Identification of structural
chromosome anomalies causing pathological conditions in
domestic animals by means of scanning electron microscopy.**

13567 Blobel, H.; Schaeg, W.　　　DE 129740/77/0001
Anwendung Protein A–positiver Staphylokokken im
Radioimmunoassay. **Use of protein A–positive staphylococci in
radioimmunoassay.** Publications.

13568 Sernetz, M.; Hannibal, O.　　　DE 129762/77/0001
Mikrofluorometrie der Kinetik immobilisierter Enzyme und
zellulärer Enzym– und Bindungsreaktionen. **Microfluorometry
of the kinetics of immobilized enzymes and of cellular enzyme
and binding reactions.**

13569 Balke, E.; Kammerer, D.　　　DE 129820/77/0004
Differenzierung schnellwachsender Mycobakterien anhand der
Lipide. **Differentiation of fast growing Mycobacteria by their
lipids.**

13570 Schliesser, T.; Schichowski, H.–D.
　　　DE 129820/78/0001 N
Untersuchungen zur Immunisierung über den
Respirationstrakt mit Clostridium botulinum–Toxoid.
**Investigations on immunization with Clostridium
botulinumtoxoid via the respiratory tract.**

13571 Krauss, H.; Meissler, M.　　　DE 129820/78/0002 N
Untersuchungen zur Vermehrung von Chlamydien in
Zellkulturen. **Investigations on propagation of Chlamydiae in
tissue cultures.**

13572 Krauss, H.; Arenz, M.　　　DE 129820/78/0003 N
Untersuchungen zur Charakterisierung der Phasenantigene
von Coxiella burnetii. **Investigations on characterization of the
phase antigens of Coxiella burnetii.**

13573 Krauss, H.; Knab, S.　　　DE 129820/78/0004 N
Nachweisbarkeitsgrenzen von Coxiella burnetii bei
verschiedenen diagnostischen Verfahren. **Limits of detection of
Coxiella burnetii in different diagnostic procedures.**

13574 Krauss, H.; Hammes, H.; Haenseler, J.
　　　DE 129820/78/0005 N
Radio– und enzymimmunologischer Nachweis von
Chlamydieninfektionen. **Radio– and enzyme immuno–assay for
infections with Chlamydiae.**

13575 Eikmeier, H.; Kraft, W.　　　DE 129881/74/0003

Schilddrüsenfunktionsstörungen bei Haustieren. **Thyroid
dysfunctions in domestic animals.**

13576 Eikmeier, H.; Kraft, W.; Gerbig, T.　DE 129881/75/0001
Blutgerinnungsstörungen bei Haustieren. **Disorders of blood
coagulation in domestic animals.** Publications.

13577 Eikmeier, H.　　　DE 129881/75/0003
Probleme der Ankaufsuntersuchung. **Problems of examination
for purchase purposes.** Publications.

13578 Bitsch, I.　　　DE 129900/74/0003
Untersuchungen über Zusammenhänge zwischen
Bleiintoxikationen und Verhaltensstörungen. **Investigations on
correlations between lead poisoning and disturbances of
behaviour.**

13579 Seifert, H.S.H.　　　DE 132331/77/0001
Untersuchungen zur Differenzierung und Charakterisierung
pathogener Clostridia mit Hilfe der Gaschromatographie.
**Investigations for differentiation and characterisation of
pathogenic clostridia by means of gas chromatography.**

13580 Seifert, H.S.H.; Vogler, H.　　　DE 132331/78/0001 N
Untersuchungen zur Bestimmung der Fettreserve von
Tsetse–Puppen und teneralen Fliegen. Versuche zur
Ermittlung von Parametern, die auf die Überlebensfähigkeit
gezüchteter Tsetse–Fliegen Einfluss haben. **Analysis of
fat–reserves in tsetse–pupae and teneral flies. Trials to
determine parameters with influence on viability of flies from
artificial breeding programs.**

13581 Seifert, H.S.H.; Böhnel, H.　　　DE 132331/78/0002 N
Untersuchungen zur Bestimmung von Bodenseuchenerregern
in Madagaskar. **Investigations for determination of agents of
soil–borne epidemics in Madagascar.**

13582 Scupin, E.　　　DE 132337/78/0001 N
Prüfung verschiedener parasiticider Präparate zur Abtötung
von Kokzidienoocysten und Spulwurmeiern. **Testing of
different parasiticidal preparations for killing Coccidia oocysts
and Ascaris ova.**

13583 Ueberschär, S.　　　DE 139100/74/0004
Experimentelle Infektion mit Erysipelothrix insidiosa in vitro
Beeinflussung des Fibroblasten–, Kollagen– und
Glycosaminoglycanstoffwechsels. **Experimental infection with
Erysipelothrix insidiosa in vitro modification of fibroblast,
collagen, and glycosaminoglycan metabolism.**

13584 Messow, C.　　　DE 139102/73/0007
Wundheilung bei Tieren. **Healing of wounds in animals.**

13585 Hapke, H.–J.　　　DE 139151/74/0003
Biochemische Untersuchungen über Kombinationswirkungen
von Blei und Zink. **Biochemical analyses on the combination
effects of lead and zinc.**

13586 Hapke, H.–J.; Kühl, U.; Glaser, U.　DE 139151/74/0004
Toxikologische und biochemische Untersuchungen zur
Feststellung subklinischer Cadmiumwirkungen zur Ermittlung
der tolerierten Cadmiummenge für Nutztiere. **Toxicological
and biochemical analyses on determining subclinical effects of
cadmium and the quantum of Cd tolerated by productive
livestock.**

13587 Schole, J.   DE 139250/74/0003
Untersuchungen über die Resistenz des Makroorganismus gegen bakterielle und parasitäre Infektionen. **Investigations on the resistance of macroorganism to bacterial and parasitic infections.**

13588 Bisping, W.; Bügel, G.; Sonnenschein, B.
DE 139450/71/0004
Nachweis von Botulinum–Toxinen mit Hilfe von in–vitroReaktionen. **Detection of Botulinum toxins by means of in vitro reactions.**

13589 Bisping, W.; Kirpal, G.   DE 139450/71/0006
Erstellung von Richtlinien zur Prüfung chemischer Desinfektionsmittel in der Veterinärmedizin. **Setup of instructions for the examination of chemical disinfectants in veterinary medicine.**

13590 Bisping, W.; Sonnenschein, B.; Bringewatt, W.
DE 139450/74/0001
Hygienische Kontrollen über neuzeitliche Verfahren der Tierkörperbeseitigung. **Hygienic control of modern rendering systems.**

13591 Bisping, W.   DE 139450/77/0001
Untersuchungen zur Ätiologie und Pathogenese der Rhinitis atrophicans. **Investigations on etioligiy and pathogenesis of atrophic rhinitis.**

13592 Kirchhoff, H.; Heitmann, J.   DE 139450/78/0005 N
Mykoplasmenarthritis. **Mycoplasma–arthritis.**

13593 Petzoldt, K.; Raetzmann, U.   DE 139450/78/0006 N
Nachweis der Immunantwort auf Erythrozytenantigene mittels der Hämolyse in Gel–Technik und der Hämagglutination beim Gerbil 'Meriones unguiculatus'. **Proof of immune response of erythrocyte antigens by means of hemolysis in gel–technique and of hemagglutination in gerbil 'Meriones unguiculatus'.**

13594 Liebisch, A.   DE 139500/78/0002 N
Empirische Felduntersuchungen zur geographischen Verbreitung und zur Ökologie von Zecken als Krankheitsüberträger bei landwirtschaftlichen Nutztieren im Nahen Osten. **Field vector studies on geographical distribution and ecology of ticks and tick–borne diseases in farm animals in the Near East.**

13595 Liebisch, A.   DE 139500/78/0003 N
Zeckenfauna Deutschlands. **Tick fauna of Germany.**

13596 Liebisch, A.; Gillani, S.   DE 139500/78/0004 N
Die Möglichkeit der Übertragung von importierten Stämmen der Babesia canis durch deutsche Zeckenstämme der Arten Rhipicephalus sanguineus und Dermacentor reticulatus.) **The possible transmission of imported Babesia canis by German tick strains of the species Rhipicephalus sanguineus and Dermacentor reticulatus.**

13597 Liebisch, A.; Walter, G.   DE 139500/78/0005 N
Untersuchungen zur Ökologie und Biologie der Zeckenart Ixodes ricinus in einem Norddeutschen Moorgebiet. **Studies on the ecology and biology of the tick species Ixodes ricinus in a North German swamp forest.**

13598 Rommel, M.; Pötters, U.   DE 139500/78/0008 N
Untersuchungen über das Wirtsspektrum und über die Verbreitung von Hammondien in Deutschland. **Investigations into the host range and frequency of Hammondia in Germany.**

13599 Stoye, M.; Herschel, A.   DE 139500/78/0009 N
Die Bedeutung paratenischer Wirte für die Ausbildung patenter Infektionen mit Toxocara canis. **The importance of paratenic hosts for the development of patent infections with Toxocara canis.**

13600 Stoye, M.; Manhardt, J.   DE 139500/78/0010 N
Untersuchungen über die Wanderung und das Verhalten der Larven von Toxocara canis in definitiven und paratenischen Wirten. **Studies on the migration and behaviour of Toxocara canis larvae in definitive and paratenic hosts.**

13601 Stoye, M.; Sonnen, P.; Chatziannastassiu, B.
DE 139500/78/0011 N
Die Wirkung neuerer Anthelminthika auf inhibierte Larven von Ancylostoma caninum und Toxocara canis in paratenischen und definitiven Wirten. **Chemotherapeutic effect of new anthelmintics on inhibited larvae of Ancylostoma caninum and Toxocara canis in paratenic and definitive hosts.**

13602 Kunstyr, I.; Friedhoff, K.T.   DE 139500/78/0014 N
Kultur und Cytologie von Spironucleus muris. **Culture and cytology of Spironucleus muris.**

13603 Friedhoff, K.T.   DE 139502/78/0001 N
Sexuelle Stadien von Piroplasmen: Entwicklung und in vitro Kultur. **Sexual stages of piroplasms: development and in vitro culture.**

13604 Friedhoff, K.T.; Petrich, J.   DE 139502/78/0002 N
Entwicklung von Serotests zur Diagnose von Babesia equi und Babesia caballi Infektionen. **Serology for diagnosis of infections with Babesia equi and Babesia caballi.**

13605 Weber, G.   DE 139502/78/0003 N
Enzym–ultracytochemische Untersuchungen an Entwicklungsstadien von Babesia sp. und Theileria sp. in Überträgerzecken und Vertebratenwirten. **Enzyme–ultracytochemical investigations on developmental stages of Babesia sp. and Theileria sp. in ticks and vertebrate hosts.**

13606 Weber, G.   DE 139502/78/0004 N
Licht– und elektronenmikroskopisch–immunocytochemische Untersuchungen an Babesia sp. und Theileria sp.. **Light and electron microscopic immunocytochemical studies on Babesia sp. and Theileria sp..**

13607 Moennig, V.; Riffelmann, B.   DE 139551/74/0001
Isolierung und Charakterisierung der Glycoproteine von verschiedenen RNS–Tumorviren –C–Typ–Viren. **Isolation and characterization of glycoproteins of different RNA tumor viruses –C–type viruses–.** Publications.

13608 Schulze, W.; Schulz, L.–C.; Hertrampf, B.
DE 139750/74/0030
Rheumatoide Erkrankungen bei Mensch und Tier. **Rheumatoid diseases in man and animal.**

13609 Diesfeld, H.J.   DE 142150/73/0001
Die Immunreaktion des Wirtsorganismus auf Filarieninfektionen – epidemiologische und tierexperimentelle Untersuchungen zum Infektionsverlauf und zum Problem der

Diagnose der Filariose. **The immunoreaction of host organism to filariases – epidemiological experimentation on animals concerning course of infection and problematic diagnosis of filariasis.**

13610 Frank, W.; Bosch, D. DE 144130/78/0004 N
Untersuchungen zur Entwicklung der Oncosphären von Echinococcus multilocularis im Zwischenwirt 'Microtus arvalis'. **Studies on the development of oncospheres of Echinococcus multilocularis in the intermediate host Microtus arvalis.**

13611 Müller, W.; Woiwode, J.; Wieser, P.
DE 144610/77/0001
Lebensfähigkeit von Keimen in der Stalluft. **Survival of airborne bacteria in stables.** Publications.

13612 Müller, W.; Wieser, P.; Leimeister, R.; Herdlitschka, P. DE 144610/77/0002
Modelluntersuchungen an tierischen Luftkeimquellen. **A model of sources of airborne bacteria in stables.**

13613 Müller, W.; Hörsten, H.von DE 144610/77/0005
Flug–, See– und Eisenbahntransport von Nutztieren.
Transport of animals by aircraft, ship and railway.
Publications.

13614 Walter, P. DE 160460/77/0001
Untersuchungen zur Verwendbarkeit biologischer Gewebe in der rekonstruktiven Chirurgie. **Investigations on biological tissues for reconstructive surgery.**

13615 Sandersleben, J.von; Pospischil, A.; Elling, H.; Hänichen, T. DE 160491/78/0001 N
Untersuchungen zur Histogenese und Ätiologie tierischer Tumoren. **Histogenetical and etiological studies on tumours in domesticated animals.** Publications.

13616 Stavrou, D. DE 160495/74/0001
Immunologische Aspekte des Wachstums und der Differenzierung spontaner und experimenteller Tumoren des Nervensystems. **Immunological aspects of the growth and development of spontaneous and experimental neurogenic tumors.**

13617 Tempel, K. DE 160550/72/0006
Haustierartliche Unterschiede im Ablauf der Strahlenkrankheit. **Species differences with respect to the effects of external and internal X–irradiation on domestic animals.**

13618 Schmid, A. DE 160550/75/0008
Lipidperoxidation als pathogenetischer Faktor bei der Organschädigung durch Chloroform. **Lipid peroxidization as pathogenetic factor in organic lesions caused by chloroform.**

13619 Schmid, A.; Bauer, S. DE 160550/78/0001 N
Untersuchungen über die Konzentrationsverhältnisse von Hexachlorbenzol im Blut und in verschiedenen Geweben von schlachtbaren Nutztieren. **Investigations on the ratio of concentration of hexachlorobenzene in blood and different tissues in animals–for–slaughter.**

13620 Schmid, A. DE 160550/78/0002 N
Ursachen der medikamentösen Eisenvergiftung in der Tiermedizin: Wirkungsmechanismus des Fe–2–Ions. **Causes of medicamentous siderism in veterinary medicine: action mechanism of Fe–2–ion.**

13621 Hegner, D.; Kroker, R.; Nohl, H.; Breuninger, V.; Ungemach, F.; Anwer, M.S. DE 160552/77/0001
Leberschadstoffe und Pharmaka, deren Einfluss auf Lipidperoxydation und Gallensäuretransport. **Influence of drugs and toxins on lipid peroxidation and bile acid transport.** Publications.

13622 Lösch, U.; Hoffmann–Fezer, G. DE 160600/72/0028
Charakterisierung einer erblichen Dysgammaglobulinämie. **Characterization of a hereditary dysgammaglobulinemia.**

13623 Mayr, A.; Schaller, M.; Baljer, G. DE 160760/74/0002
Lokale Immunisierung mit Tetanustoxoid bei strahlenbelasteten Tieren. **Local immunization of x–rayed animals with tetanus toxoid.**

13624 Gedek, B.; Weber, A. DE 160761/70/0001
Beteiligung von Prototheca–Arten bei Krankheiten von Mensch und Tier. **Presence of Prototheca species in diseases of man and animal.** Publications.

13625 Gedek, B.; Baljer, G. DE 160761/71/0001
Orale Immunisierung von landwirtschaftlichen Nutztieren während Aufzucht. **Oral immunization of livestock during raising.**

13626 Buschmann, H. DE 160765/73/0002
Fortschritte bei der medikamentellen Steigerung der Resistenz. **Advances in the medicamentous raising of resistance.**

13627 Weiland, G.; Rommel, M. DE 160820/77/0003
Vergleichende serologische Untersuchungen an Labor– und Haustieren nach Infektion mit Toxoplasma gondii und Hammondia hammondi. **Comparative serological investigations on laboratory and domestic animals experimentally infected with Toxoplasma gondii and Hammondia hammondi.** Publications.

13628 Patzik, F.; Boch, J. DE 160820/77/0004
Biologie und Pathologie von Paramphistomum Cervi. **Biology, pathogenicity and pathology of Paramphistomum Cervi infection.**

13629 Erber, M.; Boch, J. DE 160820/77/0005
Untersuchungen über Vorkommen und Pathogenität von Sarcocystis suicanis. **Studies on occurrence and pathogenicity of Sarcocystis suicanis.**

13630 Centurier, C.; Klima, R. DE 160820/77/0011
Untersuchungen über die Biologie von Amblyomma variegatum 'Fabricius, 1974' unter neun verschiedenen Mikroklimaten im Labor. **Investigations into the biology of Amblyomma variegatum 'Fabricius, 1794' under 9 different microclimates in the laboratory.**

13631 Centurier, C. DE 160820/77/0012
Untersuchungen zur Immunität verschiedener Wirtstiere gegen Amblyomma variegatum. **Investigations into the immunity of different host animals against Amblyomma variegatum.**

13632 Weiland, G.; Umbach, U.; Boch, J.

DE 160820/78/0003 N
Serologie der Sarkosporidiose der Haustiere. **Serological methods for Sarcocystis–infection of domestic animals.**

13633 Boch, J.; Bruse, H.   DE 160820/78/0006 N
Erzeugung von Hammondia–Zysten mit Immunsuppressiva. **Stimulation of Hammondia–cysts with immunosuppressiva.** Publications.

13634 Dennig, H.K.   DE 160820/78/0008 N
Virulenzveränderung von Trypanosoma evansi nach Behandlung mit trypanoziden Verbindungen. **Change of virulence of Trypanosoma evansi after treatment with trypanocides.**

13635 Göbel, E.; Krampitz, H.E.   DE 160820/78/0012 N
Mikromorphologische Untersuchungen zum Lebenszyklus von Hepatozoon erhardovae. **Micromorphological investigations on the life cycle of Hepatozoon erhardovae.**

13636 Göbel, E.; Patzik, F.; Krampitz, H.E.
DE 160820/78/0013 N
Licht– und elektronmikroskopische Untersuchungen zur Morphologie, Vermehrung und Ernährung von Babesia microti 'Stamm München und Thun'. **Light and electron microscopic studies on the morphology, multiplication and feeding mechanism of Babesia microti 'Strains Muenchen and Thun'.**

13637 Centurier, C.; Wöhrle, W.   DE 160820/78/0015 N
Die Übertragung von Babesia galagolata durch Schild– und Lederzecken. **The transmission of Babesia galagolata by ixodid and argasid ticks.**

13638 Centurier, C.; Ogedegbe, E.   DE 160820/78/0016 N
Untersuchungen zur Biologie von Hyalomma impressum unter Laborbedingungen. **Investigations on the biology of Hyalomma impressum under laboratory conditions.**

13639 Dennig, H.K.   DE 160822/73/0005
Untersuchungen zur Wirtsspezifität von Trypanosoma evansi. **Investigations on the host specificity of Trypanosoma evansi.**

13640 Forstner, M.J.; Kopp, H.   DE 160823/75/0001
Untersuchungen über Protostrongylidenlarven in Zwischenwirtsschnecken. **Investigations on larvae of protostrongyles in snails as intermediate hosts.**

13641 Krampitz, H.E.; Bäumler, W.; Centurier, C.
DE 160825/78/0001 N
Vorkommen, jahreszeitliche Prävalenz und Wirtsbindung von Babesia microti in Bayern. **Occurrence, seasonal prevalence and host range of Babesia microti in Bavaria.** Publications.

13642 Rolf, J.; Kienzle, J.   DE 160855/77/0007
Klinisch–chemische Parameter zur Nierendiagnostik. **On the diagnostics of kidney function by clinical and chemical parameters.**

13643 Schebitz, H.; Matis, U.; Brunnberg, L.; Köstlin, R.G.
DE 160940/70/0001
Osteosynthese beim Kleintier. **Osteosynthesis in small animals.**

13644 Fritsch, R.; Endres, B.; Funk, K.   DE 160940/72/0001
Resektion des Klauensesambeines. **Resection of sesamoid**

coffin bone.

13645 Schebitz, H.; Brunnberg, L.; Matis, U.
DE 160940/77/0002
Schock beim traumatisierten Patienten. **Shock in traumatised patient.**

13646 Reissig, F.   DE 161360/78/0002 N
Der Einfluss des Stallklimas auf Gehalt und Grösse von luftgetragenen Partikeln wie Staub und Bakterien hinsichtlich der Tiergesundheit. **The influence of stall–climate on content and size of air–borne particles like dust and bacteria with regard to the health of animals.**

13647 Wenk, P.; Grunewald, J.; Wirtz, H.P.
DE 173200/73/0001
Die hydrochemischen Lebensbedingungen der Larvenstadien von Simulium damnosum. **Hydrochemical life conditions for Simulium damnosum larval stages.**

13648 Wenk, P.; Loubier, C.   DE 173200/77/0001
Orientierungsverhalten von Onchocerca–Mikrofilarien. **Orientation behaviour of Onchocerca–microfilariae.**

13649 Löliger, H.–C.; Matthes, S.   DE 201300/78/0012 N
Untersuchungen über Ursache und Bekämpfungsmöglichkeit von Embryopathien und Jungtiersterblichkeit. **Investigations of cause and control of embryopathies and mortality of young animals.**

13650 Löliger, H.–C.; Hagen, D.von dem
DE 201300/78/0014 N
Untersuchungen über die wirksamen Resistenzmechanismen bei der Leukose und der Marek'schen Krankheit. **Investigations of the effective resistance mechanisms against leucosis and Marek's disease.**

13651 Löliger, H.–C.; Matthes, S.; Hagen, D.von dem
DE 201300/78/0015 N
Untersuchungen über den Einfluss verschiedener Haltungsmethoden auf die Gesundheit von Kleintieren. **Influence of different management systems on the state of health of small animals.**

13652 Schwöbel, W.; Streissle, G.   DE 216010/75/0009
Chemotherapie von Virusinfektionen. **Chemotherapy of virus infections.** Publications.

13653 Mussgay, M.   DE 216010/77/0003
Immunbiologie virusinduzierter Tumoren. **Immunobiology of virus–induced tumors.**

13654 Weiland, F.   DE 216010/77/0004 N
Elektronenmikroskopische Studien. **Electron microscopic studies.**

13655 Matheka, M.D.   DE 216010/77/0006 R
Diagnose der infektiösen Anämie und Entwicklung eines Impfstoffes. **Diagnosis of infectious anemia and development of a vaccine.**

13656 Schneider, L.   DE 216020/77/0001 N
Herstellung einer Tollwutvirus–Spaltvakzine. **Production of a rabies virus fissuring vaccine.**

13657 Cox, J.   DE 216020/77/0002

Epidemiologie der Tollwut und Biologie des Tollwutvirus.
Epidemiology of rabies and biology of rabies virus.

13658 Mussgay, M.; Doeller, G.　　　DE 216020/78/0001 N
Sicherheitsstudie Insektenviren als
Schädlingsbekämpfungsmittel. **Safety study on insect viruses used as pesticides.**

13659 Mussgay, M.; Huebschle, O.　　　DE 216030/77/0006
Optimierung zur Probeentnahme von hochinfektiösen
Virus–Aerosolen. **Optimization of sampling of highly infectious virus aerosols.**

13660 Ahl, R.　　　DE 216030/77/0008 N
Interferonisierung von Tieren. **Interferonization of animals.**

13661 Jakubik, J.　　　DE 216030/77/0011 N
Impfstoffprophylaxe bei der Aujeszkyschen Krankheit.
Vaccine prophylaxis in Aujeszky's disease.

13662 Mussgay, M.; Rziha, H.–J.　　　DE 216030/78/0001 N
Virus der Marekschen Krankheit. **Marek disease virus.**

13663 Scheibner, E.　　　DE 305030/75/0026
Herstellung, Standardisierung, Prüfung und Erfassung
tierseuchendiagnostischer Mittel in der BRD. **Production, standardization, testing, collection of data, and evaluation of diagnostic agents for epizootic diseases in the Federal Republic of Germany.**

13664 Pietzsch, O.　　　DE 305030/75/0028
Salmonellose – Forschung im Veterinärbereich. **Salmonellosis – Research in the veterinary field.** Publications.

13665 Weinhold, E.; Triemer, B.　　　DE 305030/75/0039
Prüfung von Desinfektionsmitteln für die staatliche
Tierseuchenbekämpfung. **Testing of disinfectants for epizootics control by government agencies.**

13666 Levetzow, R.　　　DE 305030/75/0045
Früherkennung von Zoonosen durch
Bestandsuntersuchungen. **Early detection of zoonoses by examinations on the feed lot.**

13667 Grossklaus, D.; Walther, M.　　　DE 305030/75/0050
Feststellung der Cysticercose und Echinokokkose bei
Schlachttieren mittels serologischer Verfahren und deren
Bekämpfung. **Detection of cysticercosis and echinococcosis in animals for slaughter by means of serological methods and control of these diseases.**

13668 Staak, C.　　　DE 305030/77/0002
Chromatographische Auftrennung von Antigenen mit
anschliessender serologischer Untersuchung der einzelnen
Fraktionen. **Chromatographic fractionation of antigens and serological investigation of the resulting fractions.**

13669 Staak, C.　　　DE 305030/77/0003
Blutmahlzeitbestimmungen bei Tsetsefliegen. **Blood meal identification in tsetse flies.**

13670 Staak, C.; Schönberg, A.　　　DE 305030/77/0005
Massenkultivierung von Leptospiren. **Mass cultures of leptospira.**

13671 Hancock, M.　　　DK 030106/75/0037 N

Platin (II) komplexer med anti–tumor virkning. **Platinum (II) complexes with anti–tumor effect.**

13672 Ladefoged, O.　　　DK 030123/76/0004
Ændringer i lægemidlers farmakokinetik hos dyr med
patologiske tilstande. **Changes in medicine pharmacokinetics in animals with pathological conditions.**

13673 Christensen, K.　　　DK 030127/71/0004
Cytogenetiske studier. **Cytogenetic studies.**

13674 Hoff–Jørgensen, R.; Christiansen, I.J.; Greve, T.;
Lehn–Jensen, H.; Jensen, A.M.; Schmidt, M.H.
　　　DK 030128/78/0002 N
Undersøgelse over Maedi–infektionens smitteveje.
Transmission of Maedi–visna virus.

13675 Andersen, S.; Eriksen, L.; Nielsen, K.
　　　DK 030129/71/0001
Ascaris–suum. Immunologi og vært–parasitrelationer.
Ascaris–suum. Immunology and host–parasite relations.

13676 Aalund, O.　　　DK 030129/75/0007
Programmer for sundhedsstyring i husdyrproduktionen.
Programmes for health control in domestic animal production.

13677 Aalund, O.　　　DK 030129/76/0010
Initiativet: Paratuberkulose. **The initiative: Paratuberculosis.**

13678 Sønnichsen, H.V.　　　DK 030130/76/0015
Undersøgelser over anvendelse af myografi i
halthedsdiagnostikken. **Investigations into the application of myography in the diagnosis of lameness.**

13679 Willeberg, P.　　　DK 030135/74/0001
Epidemiologiske analyser under anvendelse af elektronisk
databehandling. **Epidemiological analysis using electronic data systems.**

13680 Adler, H.C.　　　DK 030135/74/0003
Etologiske undersøgelser. b. Metodestudier. **Ethological investigations. (b) Study methods.**

13681 Frandsen, F.; Nansen, P.; Christensen, N.Ø.
　　　DK 030137/78/0002 N
Trematodinfektioner hos husdyr i udviklingslandene.
Undersøgelser med henblik på belysning af immunologiske
mekanismer, herunder krydsresistensforhold mellem
trematodarter. **Trematode infections of domestic animals in developing countries. Studies on immunological mechanisms with special reference to cross–resistance.**

13682 Jørgensen, K.　　　DK 030137/79/0002 N
Forekomst af "related" campylobacter hos husdyr samt
belysning af den mulige smittevej til mennesker gennem
fødekæden eller ved kontaktsmitte. **The occurrence of "related" Campylobacter in farm animals and pets, and investigations of possible infection routes to human beeings via food and/or direct contact.**

13683 Barnouin, J.; Brochart, M.　　　FR 010811/78/8058
Enquête éco–pathologique continue. **Continuous eco–pathological survey.**

13684 Théodosiadis, G.　　　FR 010817/72/8037
Météorisation. **Bloat.**

D 3400 – Animal diseases, veterinary medicine

13685 Escoula, G. FR 011407/70/8045
Moisissures et mycotoxines des ensilages. **Fungi and mycotoxins in silages.**

13686 Dantzer, R.; Arnone, M.; Mormede, P.
FR 011407/72/8042
Efficacité biologique et pratique des psychotropes en médecine vétérinaire. **Biological and practical effectiveness of psychotropic drugs in veterinary medicine.**

13687 More, J.; Bories, G.; Camguilhem, R.; Soual, C.; Brunel, N. FR 011407/73/8055
Toxicité de l'ochratoxine A sur la reproduction. **Toxicity of ochratoxine A on reproduction.**

13688 Hatey, F. FR 011407/75/8048
Etude du mécanisme d'action de la Patuline, Intéraction Patuline – Synthèse nucléoprotéique. **Study of the mechanism of toxicity of Patulin, Interaction with translation and transcription.**

13689 Dantzer, R.; Camguilhem, R.; Hachet, T.
FR 011407/77/8043
Toxicité comportementale du plomb. **Behavioral toxicology of lead.**

13690 Le Bars, J.; Larrien, G. FR 011407/77/8050 N
Mycotoxines dans les denrées alimentaires – Moisissures et oxinogenèse: Elaboration d'acide pénicillique et d'acide cyclopiazonique par le Penicillium Cyclopium, et de zéaraléone par le Fusarium Roseum Graminearum.. **Mycotoxins in feedstuffs – fungi and toxinogenesis: Bioproduction of pencillic acid and cyclopiazonic acid by P. cyclopium and zearalenone by Fusarium.**

13691 Hatey, F. FR 011407/78/8047
Etude du mécanisme d'action de la zearaléone : propriétés oestrogène et anabolisante. **Study of the mechanism of action of Zearalenone. Oestrogenic and anabolic properties.**

13692 Le Bars, J. FR 011407/78/8051
Moisissures et mycotoxines des denrées alimentaires : prospection. **Fungi and mycotoxins in feedstuffs : prospecting.**

13693 More, J.; Bories, G.; Camguilhem, R.; Soual, C.; Brunel, N. FR 011407/78/8052
Toxicité de la zéaraléone sur la reproduction. **Toxicity of zearalenone on reproduction.**

13694 Tulliez, J. FR 011412/73/2769
Etude du bilan métabolique, de la rétention apparente et de la rétention vraie des différentes classes d'hydrocarbures aliphatiques (n–paraffines, paraffines ramifiées, cycloparaffines). **Study of the metabolic balance, apparent retention and real retention of different classes of aliphatic hydrocarbons (n–paraffins, branched paraffins and cycloparaffins).**

13695 Tulliez, J.; Durand, P.; Peleran, E. FR 011412/73/9502
Absorption, transport et métabolisation des hydrocarbures saturés chez les oiseaux et les mammifères. **Absorption, transport and metabolism of saturated hydrocarbons in birds and mammals.**

13696 Verger, J.M. FR 011503/74/8090
Typage épidémiologique des Brucella. **Epidemiological typing of Brucella.**

13697 Dubray, G.; Charriaut, C.; Le Louedec, C.
FR 011503/77/8087
Etudes ultrastructurale et biochimique des antigènes des Brucella. **Ultrastructural and biochemical studies on Brucella antigens.**

13698 Verger, J.M.; Simon, F. FR 011503/77/8088
Les bactériophages des Brucella. **Bacteriophages of Brucella.**

13699 Fensterbank, R.; Dubray, G. FR 011503/77/8089
Diagnostic de la Brucellose par la réaction d'hypersensibilité de type retardé au moyen d'un allergène brucellique (Brucelline). **Skin test with allergen as a diagnostic method in animal and human Brucellosi.**

13700 Bosseray, N.; Plommet, M. FR 011503/77/8091
Méthodes de contrôle des vaccins antibrucelliques. **Control of activity of vaccines against Brucellosis.**

13701 Fuensalida, E.; Rodolakis, A. FR 011503/77/8099
Mécanismes immunologiques dans le contrôle de l'infection chlamydienne. **Immunological mechanisms of control of the chlamydial infection.**

13702 Verger, J.M.; Pardon, P. FR 011503/77/8102
Etude bactériologique de Salmonella abortus ovis. **Bacteriological study of Salmonella abortus ovis.**

13703 Rodolakis, A.; Fuenzalida, E. FR 011503/78/8098
Pathologie de la Chlamydiose. **Studies on Epidemiology and pathogeny of Chlamydiosis in farm animals.**

13704 Charriaut, C.; Rodolakis, A.; Dubray, G.; Fuensalida, E. FR 011503/78/8100
Etude analytique des différents composés antigéniques de la paroi des Chlamydia abortives. **Analytical study of chlamydia cell–wall antigens.**

13705 Rodolakis, A. FR 011503/78/8101
Virulence des Chlamydia. **Virulence of chlamydia determined in vitro and in vivo.**

13706 Guillot, J.F.; Chaslus–Dancla, E.; Lafont, J.P.
FR 011504/74/8080
Epidémiologie de la résistance bactérienne aux antibiotiques chez les animaux d'élevage – Etude expérimentale. **Experimental study of the Epidemiology of bacterial antibio–resistance in animal flocks.**

13707 Lafont, J.P.; Guillot, J.F. FR 011504/78/8084
Recherche des causes d'agglutinations non spécifiques dans le dépistage de la Pullorose. **Origin of non–specific reactions in the serological diagnosis of Pullorum disease.**

13708 Jolivet, G.; Lesage, M.C.; Kerboeuf, D.; Pelletier, G.
FR 011505/78/8070
Incidence des traitements anthelminthiques sur la dynamique des réinfestations au cours des Strongyloses gastro–intestinales. **The effect of anthelmintic treatments on the dynamic of reinfections with Strongyles.**

13709 Kerboeuf, D.; Pelletier, G.; Lesage, M.C.
FR 011505/78/8071

Etude de la ponte chez les Trichostrongylidés. Relations avec la physiologie des stades larvaires. **The eggoutput of the Trichostrongylidae. Relationships with the physiology of the larval stages.**

13710 Janet, C.; Gorse, P.   FR 012205/76/8519
La consommation des médicaments vétérinaires dans l'élevage intensif en France. **Veterinary medicine use in French intensive breeding.**

13711 Luffau, G.; Bernard, S.; Petit, A.; Pery, P.; Charley, J.
                                                   FR 012225/66/8014
Réactions immunitaires au cours des affections parasitaires. Immunité générale. **Immune response in parasitic disease. General Immunity.**

13712 Pery, P.; Petit, A.; Luffau, G.; Bernard, S.
                                                   FR 012225/72/8016
Antigènes de parasites. **Parasite antigens.**

13713 Pery, P.; Charley, J.; Rouze, P.; Luffau, G.
                                                   FR 012225/74/8012
Essais de prophylaxie médicale antiparasitaire par ionisations à l'aide d'antigènes de parasites purifiés ou de composés synthétiques. **Anti–parasite vaccination trials with purified parasite antigens or synthetic compounds.**

13714 Scherrer, R.; Laporte, J.; Vautherot, J.F.; L'haridon, R.; Cohen, J.   FR 012225/75/8026
Entérites néonatales à rotavirus et à coronavirus : épidémiologie, pathologie, diagnostic. **Neonatal enteritis caused by rotaviruses and coronaviruses : epidemiology, pathology, diagnosis.**

13715 La Bonnardiere, C.   FR 012225/75/8028
Association d'interféron avec des liposomes, utilisation des complexes pour les essais cliniques et pour l'obtention de sérums anti–interféron. **Association of interferon with liposomes. Use of the complexes in clinical trials and for the production of anti–interferon sera.**

13716 Paraf, A.; Aubry, J.; Zachowski, A.; Charlemagne, D.; Simonin, G.; Beny, G.   FR 012225/76/8016
Membranes et adjuvants de l'immunité. **Membranes and immune adjuvants.**

13717 Charlemagne, D.; Geny, B.   FR 012225/76/8019
Analyse des protéines détachées par L'EDTA de la face cytoplasmique de la membrane plasmique et impliquées dans la sensibilité à l'ouabaine de l'atpase Na + /K +. **Analysis of proteins removed by EDTA from cytoplasmic face of the plasma membrane and involved in the sensitivity to ouabaine of NA + / K + AT pase.**

13718 Paraf, A.; Simonin, G.   FR 012225/76/8020
Membranes et adjuvants de l'immunite. **Membranes and immune adjuvants.**

13719 La Bonnardiere, C.; L'haridon, R.; Scherrer, R.
                                                   FR 012225/77/8027
Facteurs non spécifiques de la résistance aux infections à rotavirus : interféron et interférence. **Non specific factors involved in resistance against Rotavirus infections : interferon and interference.**

13720 Aubry, J.   FR 012225/78/8021

Membranes et adjuvants de l'immunité. **Plasma membranes and immune adjuvants.**

13721 Asso, J.   FR 012225/78/8025
Sélection de mutants utilisables comme vaccins vivants contre la fièvre aphteuse. **Foot and Mouth disease virus mutants as live vaccines.**

13722 Taylor   GB 010102/00/0005
Etiology and pathogenesis of renal infections.

13723 Fraser   GB 010102/00/0006
Ageing and neoplasia of central nervous system.

13724 Halliday; Spooner   GB 010103/00/0003 R
Immune responses, their heritability and association with disease.

13725 Halliday   GB 010103/00/0004 R
Factors affecting immunology of the new born.

13726 Spooner; Oliver   GB 010103/76/0012 R
Lymphocyte antigens, definition and role in disease.

13727 Rowlands   GB 010103/77/0013 R
An immunological study of embryo development and mortality in farm animals.

13728 Sharman   GB 010301/00/0068 R
Cerebral metabolism of biogenic amines in relation to animal behaviour.

13729 Munn   GB 010302/00/0006 R
Correlated electron microscopic and biochemical studies of structure of immune globulins (IgM, IgM, and IgA) and alpha 2–macroglobulins.

13730 Dawson   GB 010302/00/0054 R
A study of proteins, glycoproteins and lipids in the myelin sheath during disease processes.

13731 Feinstein; Milstein   GB 010303/00/0007 R
Comparison, structure and function of human, murine, porcine and ruminant IgM and IgA antibodies.

13732 Kerry   GB 010303/00/0058 R
Production of prostaglandins by blood leucocytes in response to inflammation.

13733 Howard   GB 010303/00/0060 R
Distribution of specific reactivity among T cells.

13734 Milstein   GB 010303/00/0063 R
Structural studies on human immunoglobulins.

13735 Feinstein; Richard   GB 010303/00/0065 R
Biosynthesis of murine IgM and IgA antibody.

13736 Howard; Corvalan   GB 010303/75/0068 R
Maturation of T lymphocytes.

13737 Ramasamy; Freeman   GB 010303/75/0070 R
Receptors for immunoglobulins.

13738 Warley   GB 010303/75/0072 R
Investigation into the biosynthesis of the carbohydrate moiety of

IgM and the metabolism of CII lymphocytes.

13739 Taussing; Holliman   GB 010303/77/0073
Immune response genes of different species mechanism of cell interaction in the immune response.

13740 Feinstein; Wright   GB 010303/77/0074
Generation by cell fusion of clonal cell lines secreting antibody.

13741 Howard; Milstein   GB 010303/78/0075 R
Structural studies on rat histocompatibility antigens.

13742 Fuenmayor; Vogt   GB 010304/75/0052 R
Monoamines in the brain : their role in brain function and in the effect of centrally acting drugs.

13743 Laser; Miller   GB 010307/00/0012 R
In vitro research on the action mechanism of antimalarial drugs.

13744 Gordon; Hutchings   GB 010308/76/0013 R
Cellular reactions in early inflamation.

13745 Reid   GB 010403/00/0820 R
Pathogenesis of fatty liver in cows and its effect on metabolic performance.

13746 Hall; Parsons   GB 010403/78/0058 N
Structure and function of pig and calf intestine in unthrifty animals and specific enteropathies.

13747 Sansom   GB 010404/00/0022 R
Production disease associated with mineral and trace element metabolism.

13748 Allen   GB 010404/00/0026 R
The hazards of excessive iron intake either by oral or parenteral routes.

13749 Allen   GB 010404/00/0027
Metabolic diseases of muscle associated with selection for superior performance.

13750 McDiarmid; Matthew   GB 010405/00/0012
Atypical acidfast organisms in farm livestock and wildlife.

13751 Jones   GB 010405/00/0037
Role of 'slurry' in the epidemiology of salmonellosis.

13752 Jones   GB 010405/00/0038
Survival of pathogens in farm waste.

13753 McDiarmid; Matthew   GB 010405/00/0040
Diseases of hares, especially leptospirosis, yersiniosis and mycobacterial infections.

13754 McDiarmid; Matthew   GB 010405/00/0041
Diseases of other species of free–living animals.

13755 Lemcke; Burrows   GB 010405/76/0053
The role of potential pathogens other than E. coli and viruses in enteric disease in young calves and pigs.

13756 Brown   GB 010901/00/0001
Viral proteins.

13757 Newman   GB 010901/00/0002
Viral RNA.

13758 Newman   GB 010901/00/0003
Correlation of serological type differences in foot–and–mouth disease with chemical constitution.

13759 Crick   GB 010901/00/0004
Rhabdovirus structure.

13760 Black   GB 010901/00/0006
Viral replication.

13761 Brown; Underwood   GB 010901/00/0007
Structure function relationships in rinderpest, measles and canine distemper.

13762 Brown; Crick   GB 010901/76/0009
Rabies glycoprotein– special study.

13763 Buckley   GB 010902/00/0001
World reference typing of virus.

13764 Pereira; Hedger   GB 010902/00/0007
Ad hoc testing diagnostic and epidemiological investigations.

13765 Hedger; Rowe   GB 010902/00/0010
The serology of foot–and–mouth disease and swine vesicular disease.

13766 Bruce; Breame   GB 010903/00/0001
Develop screening equipment to test air filters used in large animal units, laminar flow cabinets, etc.

13767 Bruce   GB 010903/00/0002
Transmission of virus through air trunking systems. Develop test–bed for filters.

13768 Bruce   GB 010903/00/0003
Efficiency and practicality of viral disinfection by fumigation.

13769 Burrows   GB 010904/00/0001
Pathogenesis of vesicular disease following natural and simulated natural infection.

13770 Mann   GB 010904/00/0002
Properties of local antibodies during disease and convalecense; their relation to humoral defence mechanisms.

13771 Burrows; Goodridge   GB 010904/00/0004
Cultural characters and pathogenesis of equine herpes virus. Aetiology of respiratory infections.

13772 Chapman; Hamilton   GB 010904/76/0005
Developmental work on cultural, seriological and microscopical tests for the diagnosis of viral diseases.

13773 Boorman   GB 010905/00/0001 R
Culcoides as possible vectors of arboviruses. Susceptibility to virus diseases as models for bluetongue.

13774 Parker   GB 010905/00/0003
Multiplication and assay of AHS virus, neutralisation in culture and immunogenicity in rabbit, cavy and horse.

13775 Wilkinson; Ellis   GB 010905/00/0007

Methods to detect strain differences in African swine fever virus pathogenesis and immunology.

13776 McCahon   GB 010906/00/0001 R
Genetic analysis of the structural proteins of FMD virus.

13777 McCahon   GB 010906/00/0002 R
Experiment on recombination of foot and mouth virus mutants. Investigate homogenicity and field evolution.

13778 Skinner; Knight   GB 010907/00/0001
Epidemiology and control of murine lymphocytic coriomeningitis and other latent viruses in laboratory animals.

13779 Mowat   GB 010908/00/0001
Evaluate strains of foot and mouth virus for vaccine. Study properties leading to good antigenicity.

13780 Mowat   GB 010908/00/0002
Dose response relation for cattle, pigs and laboratory animals of inactivated foot and mouth disease virus vaccines.

13781 Mowat; Prince   GB 010908/00/0003
Compare adjuvants for foot and mouth vaccines for different species.

13782 Morrow   GB 010908/00/0004 R
Methods to concentrate and purify FMD antigens, including tangential flowfiltration and chemical processes.

13783 Spiev   GB 010908/00/0005 R
Factors for optimum growth of mammalian cells in submerged culture. Conditions for virus growth in such cells.

13784 Lacey; Hill   GB 012009/00/0007 R
Development of moulds on forages and grain.

13785 Lacey; Hill   GB 012009/00/0008 R
Biology and systematics of thermophilic actinomycetes and fungi.

13786 Barlow; Buxton   GB 030106/00/0010
Diagnosis of miscellaneous neuropathological disease.

13787 Buxton; Gardiner   GB 030106/78/0028 N
Toxoplasnosis, its pathogenesis and epidemiology.

13788 Martin   GB 030109/78/0003 N
Pathogenicity of herpes mammillitis.

13789 Martin   GB 030109/78/0005 N
Causes epidemiology and transmission of pulmonary adenomatosis.

13790 Smith   GB 030601/00/0023 R
Role of s–methyl cysteine sulphoxide and dimethyl disulphide in Brassica poisoning.

13791 Davies   GB 030604/00/0008
Metabolic antagonism involving the elements copper, zinc, cadmium, molybdenum and sulphur.

13792 Campbell; Mills   GB 030604/77/0025
Role of cadmium in induction of osteomalacia.

13793 Sharman; Hunter   GB 030607/00/0005
Toxoplasma infection; epidemiological studies particulary related to the housing of ruminants.

13794 Corrigall; May   GB 030607/00/0022
Causes of mortality in rabbits.

13795 Fell; Dinsdale   GB 030608/00/0001
Histological observations on animals deficient in copper or zinc. Rats, ruminants and pigs.

13796 Fell; Dinsdale   GB 030608/00/0004
Cell kinetics in the alimentary canal.

13797 Leigh; Fell   GB 030608/76/0021
Nephrosis in multiparous pigs and sheep.

13798 Newson   GB 030903/75/0402 R
Predation and scavenging by foxes on a hill sheep flock.

13799 McFerran   GB 041601/00/0005
Development of an Aujeszkys disease vaccine.

13800 Adair   GB 041601/00/0006
Adenoviruses of mammals and birds.

13801 McMurray   GB 041604/00/0001
Role of vitamin E and selenium.

13802 Logan   GB 041606/75/0001
Neonatal immunity.

13803 Researcher not indicated   GB 050411/00/0001
Epidemiology and diagnosis of salmonellosis.

13804 Researcher not indicated   GB 050432/00/0002 R
Enquires into the extent of lead pollution in north Derbyshire.

13805 Researcher not indicated   GB 050432/00/0004 R
Monitory of larvae of ostertagia species on permanent pasture.

13806 Researcher not indicated   GB 050432/00/0007 R
Studies on animal health on land restored with pulverised fuel ash.

13807 Researcher not indicated   GB 050435/00/0001
Develop serological test for erysipelas in pigs and sheep.

13808 Researcher not indicated   GB 050441/00/0001
Effects of thiamine and thiaminase on cerebral cortical necrosis.

13809 Researcher not indicated   GB 050454/00/0003
E. Coli vaccine trial.

13810 Researcher not indicated   GB 050455/00/0003
Transmissable gastro–enteritis, diagnosis and epidemiology.

13811 Researcher not indicated   GB 050463/00/0007
Serological diagram.

13812 Researcher not indicated   GB 050471/00/0002 R
Monitoring of field hatching of nematodirus battus in relation to meteorological conditions.

13813 Researcher not indicated   GB 050474/00/0001
Tuberculosis in wildlife.

13814 Researcher not indicated   GB 050474/00/0002
Fungal antibodies present in sera of farm animals.

13815 Sojka   GB 050501/00/0001
Classification of salmonella and monitoring for drug resistant strains in farm livestock.

13816 Boughton; Pritchard   GB 050501/00/0014
Serology of listeria monocytogenes.

13817 Boughton   GB 050501/00/0015
Classification and pathogenicity of mycobacteria.

13818 Burn   GB 050501/00/0017
Tuberculosis in badgers and ticks from cattle/badgers.

13819 Little   GB 050501/00/0018
Examine sera for leptospiral antibodies; isolate and maintain cultures.

13820 Morris   GB 050501/00/0026
Immunoglobulin classes active in bacerial infections of farm animals 1 salmonellosis; 2 leptospirosis.

13821 Morris   GB 050501/00/0027
Studies on cell mediated immunity in bacterial infections of farm animals : salmonellosis.

13822 Shreeve; Pritchard   GB 050501/00/0031
Studies on the genus Haemophilus.

13823 Patterson   GB 050502/00/0001
Neurochemistry of congenital central nervous disorders.

13824 Machin   GB 050502/00/0004
Toxicology, metabolism, residues and diagnostic studies of organophosphorus pesticides in animals.

13825 Parr   GB 050502/00/0008
Vitamin E and selenium deficiency.

13826 Saba   GB 050502/00/0011
Pituitary and other hormones in relation to animal problems.

13827 Drane; Saba   GB 050502/00/0012
Effects and mechanisms in grazing animals of plant oestrogens.

13828 Patterson   GB 050502/00/0014
Mycotoxicoses.

13829 Machin   GB 050502/75/0018
Development of analytical methods.

13830 Matthews; Patterson   GB 050502/77/0021
Studies on haemorrhagic syndromes of cattle and pigs.

13831 Lee   GB 050503/00/0008
Tuberculins–assay methods and stability and production techniques.

13832 Gray   GB 050503/00/0009
Develop production of quality control methods for clostridial vaccines and test toxins.

13833 Thomson   GB 050503/76/0016
Safety and potency test for enteric bacterial vaccines.

13834 Frerichs; Evans   GB 050503/77/0018
Quality control methods for canine vaccines.

13835 Frerichs   GB 050503/77/0019
Sterility testing of biological substances.

13836 Frerichs; Chandler   GB 050503/77/0024
Determination of preservatives in biological products.

13837 Frerichs; Woods   GB 050503/77/0026
Development of potency tests for Leptospira vaccines.

13838 Corbel; Thomas   GB 050504/00/0010
Methods for brucellosis classification and identification including phage typing and electrophoresis.

13839 Patterson   GB 050504/00/0015
Mycotoxicoses.

13840 Tarry; Kirkwood   GB 050505/00/0015
Study and control of ectoparasites.

13841 Tarry   GB 050505/00/0016
Black light attraction for fly control.

13842 Tarry   GB 050505/00/0020
Transmission of viruses by arthropods (cockroaches).

13843 Higgins   GB 050508/00/0019
Immunology of viral diseases.

13844 Parker; Little   GB 050509/77/0021
Disease surveillance at Ripley farms. Leptospirosis.

13845 Miller; Richards   GB 050510/00/0016
The identification and recording of abnormal resrpiratory sounds.

13846 Ross; Halliday   GB 050512/77/0021
Extended research and development investigations arising from diagnostic and consultancy services.

13847 Mathieson   GB 060116/00/0006
Veterinary diagnostic service.

13848 Mathieson   GB 060116/00/0009
Salmonellae – occurrence and control.

13849 Mathieson   GB 060116/00/0011
Veterinary investigation and advisory service.

13850 Donald   GB 060212/00/0005
Veterinary diagnostic service.

13851 Donald   GB 060212/00/0006
Veterinary investigation and advisory service.

13852 Halliday   GB 060212/00/0009
Evaluation of biochemical tests as a laboratory aid to diagnosis in veterinary medicine.

13853 Ross   GB 060212/00/0010
Radiographic studies of pathological changes in the foetus and neonate of farm animals.

13854 Fenlon   GB 060220/79/0009 N
An investigation into the incidence of salmonella in seagulls in
agricultural land.

13855 Webb   GB 060224/79/0021 N
Injury to livestock in buildings.

13856 Titchener; Newbold   GB 060309/00/0001
The ecology and control of ectoparasites of economic
significance in the West of Scotland.

13857 Wright   GB 060312/00/0006
Veterinary diagnostic service.

13858 Wright   GB 060312/00/0007
Veterinary investigation and advisory service.

13859 Dolan, L.   IE 060400/75/2046
Brucellosis control. Publications.

13860 Collins, J.K.; O'Donoghue, M.; Scannell, C.M.G.;
Cullinane, D.; Vaughan, A.   IE 110102/78/9141 N
A study of the mechanism of animal cell killing by lytic viruses.

13861 Gray, J.S.   IE 120101/77/9177 N
The epidemiology of babesiosis in County Meath, Ireland.

13862 Cunningham, B.; Walsh, J.; Chukwu, C.
                                    IE 120205/79/9206 N
Investigation of factors affecting the delayed hypersensitivity
test.

13863 Grainger, J.N.R.; Gibson, M.   IE 140202/76/9190 N
Prediction of larval development rate under changing
temperature conditions in ostertagia circumcincta and o.
ostertagi.

13864 Morganti, L.; Mantovani, A.; Tampieri, M.P.; Battelli,
G.; Bianchedi, M.; Baldelli, R.   IT 040229/70/0002
Ricerche sull'epidemiologia delle micosi animali.
Investigations on the epidemiology of animal mycoses.
Publications.

13865 Restani, R.; Widenhorn, O.; Poglayen, G.; Tampieri,
P.; Tassi, P.; Pavoncelli, R.   IT 040229/70/0003
Ricerca sulla diffusione dei piu' importanti parassiti degli
animali domestici in italia. Survey of diffusion of the most
important parasites of domestic animals in Italy. Publications.

13866 Pampiglione, S.; Morganti, L.; Caporale, V.;
Sanguinetti, V.; Prosperi, S.; Baldelli, R.   IT 040229/70/0004
Patologia esotica degli animali domestici e dell'uomo. Exotic
pathology of domestic animals and man. Publications.

13867 Pampiglione, S.; Merlanti, M.; Prosperi, S.; Battelli,
G.; Canestri–Trotti, G.; Poglajen, G.   IT 040229/71/0001
Ricerche sugli animali selvatici come portatori di malattie degli
animali domestici e dell'uomo. Investigations on wild–life
animals as carriers of diseases of domestic animals and man.
Publications.

13868 Mantovani, A.; Gagliardi, G.; Prosperi, S.; Magagnoli,
P.; Benazzi, P.   IT 040229/71/0002
Richerche sulla epidemiologia della rabbia in Italia.
Investigations on the epidemiology of rabies in Italy.

Publications.

13869 Mantovani, A.; Canestri Trotti, G.; Battelli, G.;
Pampiglione, S.; Tassi, P.; Zanetti, R.   IT 040229/76/0001
Indagini sulle zoonosi in ambiente urbano in Italia. Survey of
zoonoses in urban areas in Italy. Publications.

13870 Montanaro, N.   IT 040246/77/0516
Tossicita acuta e cronica di nuovi fitofarmaci e fitoregolatori.
Acute and chronic toxicity of new pesticides and growth
regulators.

13871 Aureli, G.   IT 040626/78/1181 N
Comportamento morfofunzionale delle gonadi dei mammiferi
domestici con particolare riguardo all'infecondità ed all'
Embryo trasfert. Domestic mammals: morphological and
functional behaviour of their gonads, with particular regard to
infertility and embryo transfer.

13872 Genchi, C.; Agnes, F.; Simonic, T.; Arrigoni, C.; De
Luca, A.   IT 040641/77/0001 N
Elaborazione in vivo di "tossine" epatotrope da parte di
Fasciola hepatica. In vivo production of hepatotropic "toxins"
by Fasciola hepatica. Publications.

13873 Mandelli, G.   IT 040642/77/0565 R
Incidenza delle caratteristiche comportamentali di alcune
specie animali di allevamento intensivo sulla efficacia dei
trattamenti di massa–vaccinali, terapeutici, ecc., parametri
produttivi e sanitari in funzione della densità delle popolazioni
allev. The influence of behavioural characteristics of certain
intensively bred animal species on the efficiency of
mass–vaccination, therapeutical interventions, etc. Production
and health parameters related to the population density of
reared animals.

13874 Chiesara, E.   IT 040647/78/1122 N
Ricerca di attività mutogena delle nuove preparazioni.
Modificazioni biochimico–funzionali a livello epatico, renale e
polmonare dopo trattamento con le nuove preparazioni.
Ricerche di tipo tossicologico tradizionale. Research on the
mutagenic action of new products. Biochemical and functional
modifications in the liver, kidney and lungs after treatment with
the new products. Traditional toxicological research.

13875 Ceretto, F.   IT 041236/77/0546
Problemi igienico–sanitari conseguenti ad intossicazioni da
mercurio in animali da carne e da uova. Health and hygiene
problems due to mercury intoxication in meat and egg
producing animals.

13876 Galassi, D.   IT 050800/77/0554 R
Controllo delle malattie perinatali condizionate. Control of
mediated perinatal diseases.

13877 Oliviero, G.; Padula, P.; Montemurro, N.; Quesada,
A.   IT 051000/78/0006 N
Indagini sull'azione inquinante svolta dalle acque di scarico dei
macelli. Research on the polluting action of filthy water from
slaughter houses.

13878 Contini, A.   IT 051100/77/0001
Isolamento e coltura del micobatterio paratubercolare su
embrione di pollo. Mycobacterium paratubercolosis : the
chicken embryos for isolation and cultivation.

13879 Maletto, S.　　　　　　　　IT 062500/77/0975
Gli effetti metabolici della somministrazione di piombo negli animali in produzione zootecnica: l'assorbimento del piombo in funzione della concentrazione di etanolo nel sangue provocata nei conigli mediante adatta ingestione di alcool. **Metabolic reactions to lead administration in farm animals: lead absorption according to blood ethanol concentration in rabbits to which adequate doses of alcohol were administered per os.**

13880 Haagsma, J.　　　　　　　　NL 010401/52/1650
Mycobacteriële infecties. Type–determinatie van mycobacteriën. **Determination of the different types of mycobacteriae.** Publications.

13881 Wirahadiredja, R.M.S.　　　　NL 010401/63/1631
Diagnostiek van diverse ziekteverwekkers met behulp van immuno–fluorescentie. **The use of immuno fluorescense in the diagnosis of several infectious diseases.** Publications.

13882 Bokhout, B.A.　　　　　　　NL 010401/70/2726 R
Isolatie van antigenen en antilichamen en delen daarvan. **Isolation of antigens and antibodies and their fractions.** Publications.

13883 Haagsma, J.　　　　　　　　NL 010401/70/2727
Onderzoek in verband met verbetering van bestaande en ontwikkeling van nieuwe biologische produkten. **Investigation on the improvement of existing biological products respectively on the development of new biological products for the control of animal diseases.** Publications.

13884 Lensing, H.H.　　　　　　　NL 010401/70/6905
Kwaliteitscontrole van zowel middelen ter onderkenning, voorkoming en genezing van dierziekten, als van proefdieren. **Quality control of means for diagnosis, prevention and curing of animal diseases, as well as quality control of laboratory animals.** Publications.

13885 Haagsma, J.　　　　　　　　NL 010401/75/6527
Differentiatie van streptococcen en faagtypering van staphylococcen t.b.v. dierziekte problemen. **Differentiation of streptococci and phage typing of staphylococci concerning animal disesse problems.**

13886 Haagsma, J.; Laak, E.A. ter　　NL 010401/75/6528
Algemeen bacteriologisch en taxonomisch onderzoek t.b.v. dierziekte problemen. **General bacteriological and taxonomic investigations concerning animal disease problems.**

13887 Haagsma, J.　　　　　　　　NL 010401/76/6999
Rabiesonderzoek bij dieren. **Investigations on rabies in animals.** Publications.

13888 Dorsman, W.　　　　　　　　NL 020013/72/4406
Oecologie van larvenstadia van parasieten. **Ecology of larval stages of parasites.** Publications.

13889 Hagens, F.M.　　　　　　　　NL 030002/74/5668 R
Voorkomen en bestrijdingsmogelijkheden van huidschimmelinfecties bij landbouwhuisdieren. **Mycotic infections in animals.**

13890 Bercken, J. van den　　　　　NL 030003/73/5888 R
Werking van chloorkoolwaterstoffen en pyrethroïden (pyrethroïden, DDT–analogen, zenuwmembraan, insnoering

van Ranvier, 'voltage clamp', ionen–kanalen). **Mechanism of action of chlorinated hydrocarbon and pyrethroid insecticides (pyrethroids, DDT–analogues nerve membrane, node of Ranvier, voltage clamp, ionic channels).** Publications.

13891 Woutsersen, R.; Wit, J.G.; Holsteyn, C.W.M. van
　　　　　　　　　　　　　　　　NL 030003/75/6164
Experimentele erythropoietische porfyrie bij warmbloedige diersoorten. **Experimental erythropoietic porphyria in warm–blooded animals.** Publications.

13892 Frens, J.　　　　　　　　　NL 030003/76/7756 R
Dopamine als centrale neurotransmitter in thermoregulatie en koorts. **Dopamine as central neurotransmitter in thermoregulation and fever.** Publications.

13893 Eysker, M.; Jansen, J.　　　　NL 030004/68/5841 R
Trichostrongylideninfekties bij dieren. **Epidemiology of trichostrongylosis in sheep; inhibition os the development of gastro–intestinal nematodes of ruminants; influence of wormburdens on the production of sheep.** Publications.

13894 Danse, L.H.J.C.　　　　　　NL 030005/72/5784 R
Etiologisch en pathogenetisch onderzoek van geelvetziekte. **Etiological and pathogenetic studies of yellow fat disease.** Publications.

13895 Gruys, E.　　　　　　　　　NL 030005/72/6107
Aangeboren afwijkingen van het centraal zenuwstelsel. **Teratology of the central nervous system.** Publications.

13896 Seinen, W.　　　　　　　　NL 030005/73/6115 R
Invloed xenobiotica op het immuunsysteem. **Immunosuppression by xenobiotics.** Publications.

13897 Linde–Sipman, J.S. van de　　NL 030005/76/7761
Oogafwijkingen bij huisdieren. **Pathology of the eye in domestic animals.** Publications.

13898 Danse, L.H.J.C.; Verschuren, P.　NL 030005/76/7762
Funktie van het reticulo–endotheliale systeem tijdens de ontwikkeling van geelvetziekte. **Fish oil induced Yellow Fat Disease; Functional changes in the Reticuloendothelial system.**

13899 Danse, L.H.J.C.　　　　　　NL 030005/76/7764 R
Invloed van poly onverzadigde vetzuren en vitamine E op de aktiviteit van makrofagen in vitro. **Effect of unsaturated fatty acids and vitamin E on the activity of macrophages in vitro.**

13900 Seinen, W.　　　　　　　　NL 030005/76/7766
Pathogenese van Babesia–infekties. **Pathogenesis of Babesia infections.**

13901 Seinen, W.　　　　　　　　NL 030005/77/7831
Organotin–verbindingen als anti–tumor agentia. **Organotin compounds; a new class of anti–tumour agents.**

13902 Seinen, W.　　　　　　　　NL 030005/77/7832
Invloed van di–alkyltin verbindingen op het energie metabolisme van thymus lymphocyten. **Interactions of di–alkyltin compounds with the energy metabolism of thymus lymphocytes.**

13903 Overdulve, J.P.　　　　　　NL 030006/76/6962 R
Haplo–, di– en polyploiditeit van de ontwikkelingsstadia, gametogonie–inducerende en sexe–determinerende faktoren

bij Eimerine (Toxoplasma). **Haplo-, di– en polyploidity of life cycle stages, gametogony inducing and sex determining factors in Eimerina (Toxoplasma).** Publications.

13904 Kuil, H.　　　　　　　　NL 030006/76/7766
Pathogenese van Babesia infekties. **Pathogenesis of Babesia infections.**

13905 Horzinek, M.C.　　　　　NL 030007/73/5728 R
Struktuur, replicatie en persistentie van het lactaatdehydrogenase virus. **Structure, replication and persistence of lactic dehydrogenase virus.** Publications.

13906 Schotman, A.J.H.; Wensing, Th.; Franken, P.
　　　　　　　　　　　　　　　　NL 030011/58/7824
Ontwikkeling nieuwe bepalingen, methoden enz. klinische biochemie en hematologie. **Development of new estimations, methods etc. clinical biochemistry and haematology.**

13907 Gunnik, J.W.　　　　　　NL 030013/68/5482
Afweermechanisme van de uterus bij verschillende diersoorten. **Defence mechanism of the uterus in various domestic animals.** Publications.

13908 Donk, J.A.W.M. van der　　NL 030018/76/7837 N
Ectopisch hormoon–producerende tumoren (peptide hormonen, prohormoon, enzymen, tumoren). **Ectopically hormone–producing tumours (peptide, hormones, prohormones, enzymes, tumours).** Publications.

13909 Schothorst, M. van　　　　NL 040011/60/7435
Salmonella–onderzoekingen bij grote huisdieren. **Salmonella–investigations in large animals.** Publications.

Equines (B 4100)

See also 10568, 11034, 14164

13910 Wintzer, H.–J.; Hartung, K.; Jaeschke, G.; Keller, H.
　　　　　　　　　　　　　　　　DE 104450/71/0001 N
Laboratoriumsdiagnostische Kriterien zur Bestimmung von Trainingsbereitschaft und Trainingsfortschritten bei Trabrennpferden. **Criteria of laboratory diagnostic for determination of readiness to and progress in training of trotters.**

13911 Hartung, K.; Münzer, B.　　DE 104451/77/0001
Radiologische Untersuchung verschiedener Gelenke beim Pferd. **Radiological examinations of different joints in horses.**

13912 Keller, H.; Fries, I.　　　　DE 104452/75/0001
Statistische Erhebungen über den Endoparasitenbefall in Berliner Pferdebeständen. **Statistical observations on endoparasites in Berlin horse stables.**

13913 Keller, H.; Stelter, U.　　　DE 104452/78/0001 N
Untersuchungen über Sulfaphenazol 'Eftolon' beim Pferd. **Studies on sulfaphenazol 'Eftolon' in horses.**

13914 Keller, H.; Jördens, C.P.　　DE 104452/78/0002 N
Statistische Auswertungen von Sehnenerkrankungen bei Sportpferden. **Statistical evaluations of tendon lesions in horses.**

13915 Wintzer, H.–J.; Schulz, S.　　DE 104452/78/0003 N
Blutgasanalyse während der Narkose des Pferdes. **Blood gas analysis during anaesthesia in horses.**

13916 Schliesser, T.　　　　　　DE 129820/75/0003
Deckhygienische Überwachung bei Pferden. **Cover hygienic observations on horses.** Publications.

13917 Weiss, R.; Böhm, K.H.　　DE 139450/73/0004 N
Vorkommen und Bedeutung von Klebsiellen bei Warmund Vollblutpferden. **Incidence and importance of Klebsiella in warm–blood and thoroughbred horses.**

13918 Zeller, R.; Hertsch, B.; Lieske, R.; Ehard, H.
　　　　　　　　　　　　　　　　DE 139850/71/0002
Fohlenkrankheiten. **Diseases of foals.**

13919 Zeller, R.; Jensen, W.; Messow, C.;
Neumann–Kleinpaul, K.H.　　　　DE 139850/71/0004
Wundheilung beim Pferd. **Healing of wounds in horse.**

13920 Zeller, R.; Eidt, E.; Froehner, H.; Stadie, U.; Anhalt,
G.　　　　　　　　　　　　　　　DE 139850/77/0002
Antibiotika–Therapie beim Pferd. **Treatment of horses with antibiotics.** Publications.

13921 Hertsch, B.; Ehard, H.; Pohlmeyer, K.
　　　　　　　　　　　　　　　　DE 139850/77/0003
a. Angiographische Untersuchungen beim Pferd b. Zervikale Myelographie. **a. Angiographical studies on horse b. Cervical myelography.**

13922 Hertsch, B.　　　　　　　DE 139850/77/0004
Röntgenologische Untersuchung der Ossifikationsvorgänge beim Fohlen. **X–ray examination of ossification in foal.**

13923 Zeller, R.; Schlichting, K.; Lieske, R.; Ehard, H.
　　　　　　　　　　　　　　　　DE 139850/77/0005
Thrombophlebitis der Vena jugularis ext. des Pferdes. **Thrombophlebitis of Vena jugularis ext. in horse.** Publications.

13924 Zeller, R.; Herken, A.; Behrens, D.　DE 139850/77/0008
Narkose beim Pferd. **Narcosis of horse.**

13925 Schels, H.　　　　　　　DE 160761/72/0003
Streptococcus zooepidemicus als Deckinfektionserreger des Pferdes. **Streptococcus zooepidemicus as an agent for venereal infections in horses.**

13926 Thein, P.　　　　　　　　DE 160763/72/0001
Untersuchungen zum Vorkommen von Reo–Virus–Infektionen bei Pferden. **Studies on the occurrence of infections with reovirus I, II, III in horses.**

13927 Boch, J.　　　　　　　　DE 160820/77/0001 N
Biologie von Eumeria leuckarti des Pferdes. **Biology of horse coccid Eumeria leuckarti.**

13928 Boch, J.; Erber, M.　　　　DE 160822/78/0001 N
Untersuchungen zur Biologie der Sarkosporidien des Pferdes. **Studies on the biology of Sarcosporidia of horses.**

13929 Hasslinger, M.–A.　　　　DE 160823/77/0001
Parasitenbekämpfung beim Pferd. **Control of parasites in horse.** Publications.

13930 Hasslinger, M.–A.　　　　DE 160823/77/0003
Epidemiologische Untersuchungen über Pferde–Strongyliden.

Epidemiological studies on strongylides in horses.

13931 Schebitz, H.; Mohamed, O.　　DE 160940/77/0006
Atmung und Blutgasanalyse beim Pferd während der
Halothan–Narkose. **Respiration and blood gas analysis in horse
during halothane narcosis.**

13932 Rasmussen, F.; Gelså, H.　　DK 030123/78/0001 N
Farmakokinetik for trimethoprim og sulfadoxin hos heste.
Pharmacokinetics of trimethoprim and sulphadoxine in horses.

13933 Nielsen, P.　　DK 030123/78/0002 N
Metabolisme af trimethoprim hos heste. **Metabolism of
trimethoprim in horses.**

13934 Nielsen, K.; Vibe–Petersen, G.　　DK 030129/77/0015 N
Kroniske luftvejslidelser hos hest. **Chronic diseases of the
respiratory tract in horses.**

13935 Arnbjerg, J.　　DK 030129/79/0003 N
Bivirkninger af steroidbehandling af hostepatienter (heste).
Laminitis in horses treated with steroids.

13936 Espersen, G.; Bülow–Olsen, A.　　DK 030130/76/0017 N
Undersøgelser vedr. optræden af hestens græssyge i Danmark
og Sverige. **Grass sickness in horses in Denmark and Sweden.**

13937 Smith, M.　　DK 030130/77/0011
EKG–ændringer under anæstesi af hest, konditionsmåling på
grundlag af kredsløbsændringer på heste. **ECG changes in the
horse under anaesthesia monitored by circulatory changes
within the animal.**

13938 Kristoffersen, J.; Falk–Rønne, J.; Sønnichsen, H.V.
　　DK 030130/78/0002 N
Undersøgelser over forekomsten af osteochondrose i
haseleddet hos 2– og 3–årige travheste. **Investigations on
frequency of osteochondrosis in the tarsal joints of 2 and 3 years
old standardbred horses.**

13939 Gilmour; Johnson　　GB 030106/77/0027
Biochemical studies on grass sickness neurotoxin.

13940 Frerichs; G C　　GB 050503/00/0007
**Quality control methods for vaccines and standardisation of
serological diagnostic tests –equine influenza.**

13941 Lamont; Chapman　　GB 050508/00/0017 R
Viral diseases of horses. Equine infectious anaemia.

13942 Conway, D.A.　　IE 120201/79/9170 N
Effects of antibiotic adjuvants on muscular tissue of horse.
Publications.

13943 Glazier, D.B.; Littledike, E.T.　　IE 120203/76/9203 N
**The effects of hyperkalaemia, hypercalcaemia and hyporal
caemia on the equine electrocardiogram in the anaesthetised
and unaesthetised horse.** Publications.

13944 Glazier, D.B.; Littledike, E.T.　　IE 120203/76/9204 N
**An investigation of possible factors in the genesis of epistaxis in
race horses in Ireland.** Publications.

13945 Hatch, C.　　IE 120207/78/9138 N
Epidemiology of strongylus vulgaris infection of the horse in

Ireland.

13946 Baker, K.P.; Quinn, P.J.; Morrow, A.
　　IE 120208/76/9200 N
**A study of dermal reactivity in infectious and allergic dise ase of
the horse.** Publications.

13947 Aleandri, M.; Zardi, O.; Piragino, S.; Adorisio, E.;
Lillini, E.　　IT 050700/78/0002 N
Isolamento di Toxoplasma gondii da feto equino. **Isolation of
Toxoplasma gondii from equine foetus.** Publications.

13948 Leori, G.; Lepori, S.; Muszetto, P.; Scarano, C.
　　IT 051100/76/0005
Ricerche batteriologiche sull'apparato genitale di cavalle in
rapporto a episodi di infertilità. **Careful considerations about a
bacteriological and clinical research of the genital apparatus in
mares in relation to infertility.**

13949 Bekkum, J.G. van　　NL 010402/67/1217 R
Virusinfecties van paarden. **Virus infections of horses.**
Publications.

13950 Mirck, M.H.　　NL 030004/72/5804 R
Epidemiologie van strongylidose bij shetlandponies in
Nederland. **Epidemiology of strongylidosis in shetlandponies in
the Netherlands.**

13951 Boersema, J.H.　　NL 030004/74/5850 R
Dictyocaulus arnfieldi bij het paard en de ezel. **Dictyocaulus
arnfieldi infections in horses and donkeys.** Publications.

13952 Goedegebure, S.A.　　NL 030005/74/6037 R
Aetiologie, pathologie en behandelingsmogelijkheden van
polyarthritis (groeirafels) bij veulens. **Etiology, pathology and
therapy of polyarthritis (growth irregularities) in foals.**

13953 Zeijst, B.A.M. van der　　NL 030007/76/6959 R
Opwekking en karakterisering van ts–mutanten van het
paardearteritis virus. **Induction and characterization of
ts–mutants of Equine arteritis virus.**

13954 Numans, S.R.　　NL 030010/71/5829
Klinische en röntgenologische beoordeling van de hoefkatrol
bij dekhengsten. **Clinical and radiological aspects of
podotrochleitis in horses.**

13955 Kersjes, A.W.　　NL 030010/73/5823 R
Verbetering van operatieve koliekbehandeling bij het paard.
Surgical treatment in colic horses. Publications.

13956 Numans, S.R.　　NL 030010/73/5825 R
Evaluatie van verschillende technieken bij de operatieve
behandeling van cornage bij het paard (cornage,
arykraakbeen, verlamming, paard). **Surgical treatment of
laryngeal hemiplegia in the horse (hemiplegin laryngis,
arytenoid, paresis, horse).**

13957 Kersjes, A.W.　　NL 030010/74/6037 R
Aetiologie, pathologie en behandelingsmogelijkheden van
polyarthritis (groeirafels) bij veulens. **Etiology, pathology and
therapy of polyarthritis (growth irregularities) in foals.**

13958 Nemeth, F.　　NL 030010/75/5833 R
Het spatkreupelheidsprobleem bij het paard. **Spavin in horses.**

13959 Lagerweij, E.   NL 030010/77/8964 N
Farmakokinetisch en klinisch onderzoek van
Guayacol–Glycerine–Ether (GGE) bij huisdieren, in het
bijzonder het paard. (GGE, farmakokinetiek, klinisch
onderzoek). **Farmacocinetic and clinical studies on the use of
GGE in domestic animals, especially in horses (GGE,
Farmacocinetics, clinical studies).**

13960 Mirck, M.H.   NL 030011/72/5804 N
Epidemiologie van strongylidose bij shetlandponies in
Nederland. **Epidemiology of strongylidosis in shetlandponies in
the Netherlands.** Publications.

13961 Wagenaar, G.   NL 030011/74/5801 R
Onderzoek naar neussecretum, sputum en serum van paarden
i.v.m. betere diagnostiek van aandoeningen voorste
luchtwegen. **The testing of nasal discharge, sputum and sera of
horses in order to improve diagnosis of disorders of respiratory
tract.**

13962 Schotman, A.J.H.   NL 030011/74/5805 R
Erythropoësis bij het paard i.v.m. het voorkomen van anemie.
Erythropoësis in the horse. Publications.

13963 Kroneman, J.   NL 030011/75/5812 R
Vectorcardiografie bij paarden, een poging om te komen tot
electrisch orthogonale afleidingen. **Vectorcardiography in
horses, an approach to electrically orthogonal derivations.**

13964 Binkhorst, G.J.   NL 030011/76/7818
Voortgezet onderzoek coördinatiestoornissen bij het paard.
**Locomotion disorders in horses due to central nervous
disturbances.**

13965 Schotman, A.J.H.   NL 030011/76/7820 R
De mobilisatie van depotvet bij ponies; fysiologische,
pathofysiologische, prognostische en therapeutische aspecten.
**The mobilisation of body–fat in ponies; physiological,
pathophysiological, prognostical and therapeutical aspects.**
Publications.

13966 Kalsbeek, H.C.   NL 030011/77/7819 R
Diarrhee bij het paard. **Diarrhoea in horses.**

13967 Watering, C.C. van de; Dik, K.J.   NL 030016/71/5829
Klinische en röntgenologische beoordeling van de hoefkatrol
bij dekhengsten. **Clinical and radiological aspects of
podotrochleitis in horses.**

13968 Dik, K.J.   NL 030016/74/6037 R
Aetiologie, pathologie en behandelingsmogelijkheden van
polyarthritis (groeirafels) bij veulens. **Etiology, pathology and
therapy of polyarthritis (growth irregularities) in foals.**

13969 Dik, K.J.   NL 030016/75/5833 R
Spatkreupelheidsprobleem bij het paard. **Spavin in horses.**

13970 Dik, K.J.   NL 030016/76/7834
Röntgenkontrastonderzoek van gewrichten bij honden en
paarden. **Arthrografic studies in dogs and horses.**

13971 Goudswaard, J.   NL 030018/77/8987 N
De immunoglobulinen van het paard (immunoglobulinen,
paard, isolatie, zuivering). **Equine immunoglobulins
(immunoglobulins, horse, isolation, purification).** Publications.

Ruminants in general (B 4200)

See also 11909, 13471, 13474, 13477, 14702, 15008, 15036,
20153

13972 De Moor, A.; De Ley, G.   BE 050100/71/0002
Studie van de congenitale of erfelijke afwijkingen aan de
ledematen bij jonge runderen; Spastische Parese, congenitale
articulaire Rigiditeit en aanverwante aandoeningen. **Research
on the congenital and hereditary abnormalities of the limbs of
young cattle: Spastic Paralysis, congenital articular Rigidity
and related conditions.** Publications.

13973 Hörchner, F.; Gerber, H.C.; Karrasch, A.; Oguz, T.
DE 104202/73/0003
Epidemiologie und Bekämpfung der Gigantica–Fasciolose in
Madagascar. **Epidemiology and control of Fascioliasis gigantica
in Madagascar.**

13974 Merck, C.C.   DE 104400/70/0011
Beurteilung der Euterverträglichkeit von einigen
Mastitispräparaten nach intrazisternaler Applikation.
**Determination of udder tolerance of some mastitis
preparations after intracisternal application.**

13975 Heidrich, H.J.; Zeller, U.; Merck, C.C.
DE 104400/74/0002
Die Vakzinierung als prophylaktische Massnahme zur
Bekämpfung der Pyogenesmastitis. **Prophylactic vaccination
for the control of pyogenic mastitis.**

13976 Wenk, P.; Winkhardt, H.J.   DE 173200/77/0002
Überträger der Onchozerkose bei Cerviden. **Vectors of
onchocerciasis in Cervids.**

13977 Weinhold, E.   DE 305030/75/0038
Ätiologie der Rinderleukose. **Etiology of bovine leukosis.**
Publications.

13978 Weisser, W.   DE 501342/78/0001 N
Isolierung, Bestimmung und Auswertung bei Tieren
vorkommender Streptokokken, ausgenommen von
Isolierungen aus der Milch. **Isolation, identification and
evaluation of streptococci occurring in livestock, excepting
streptococci isolated from milk.** Publications.

13979 Reuss, U.; Kittsteiner, H.   DE 507600/78/0001 N
Wirksamkeit vorbeugender Impfungen gegen die
Parainfluenza–3 der Rinder. **Efficiency of prophylactic
vaccination against bovine para–influenza–3.** Publications.

13980 Reuss, U.; Bechmann, G.; Neumann, W.; Plöger, W.
DE 507600/78/0002 N
Der Erregernachweis der Bovinen Virusdiarrhoe – Mucosal
Disease – BVD/MD – im Vergleich zwischen der
OrganFluoreszenz–Gefrierschnittmethode und der
Direktanzüchtung in der Gewebekultur. **Proof of the virus of
bovine virus diarrhea – mucosal disease in comparison of
organ–fluorescence–frozen section–method and direct
cultivation in tissue culture.** Publications.

13981 Hesselholt, M.; Møller, D.; Hvelplund, T.; Mason, V.
DK 030130/73/0001
Eksperimentelkirurgiske indgreb i forbindelse med
stofskiftefysiologiske undersøgelser på drøvtyggere.
Experimental surgery in connection with metabolic and

physiological investigations on ruminants.

13982 Lund, E.; Have, P. DK 030138/77/0014 N
Studier af metoder til påvirkning af virusantigen og cellemedieret immunitet inden for området bovin leukose. **Studies of methods for the detection of viral antigens and cell mediated immune responses in cennection with bovine leukosis.**

13983 Brochart, M. FR 010811/77/8059
Pathologie podale des ruminants. **Foot diseases in ruminants.**

13984 Escoula, G. FR 011407/77/8046
Toxiques et flores digestives – Action sur l'activité métabolique de la flore du rumen et des principales espèces microbiennes isolées de tractus digestifs. **Drugs and digestive flora – Studies of the effect of toxic molecules on different metabolic activities of the rumen flora and of some specific microbial species isolated of digestive tracts.**

13985 Poutrel, B.; Lerondelle, C.; Rainard, P.
FR 011503/77/8095
Prophylaxie et traitements des mammites. **Experimental model of staphylococcal mastitis used to define the value of treatments and control schemas.**

13986 Kerboeuf, D.; Pelletier, G.; Lesage, M.C.
FR 011505/78/8072
Emploi du dosage du pepsinogéne plasmatique pour le diagnostic des Strongyloses des ruminants. **The use of the plasma pepsinogen for the diagnosis of the Strongylosis of Ruminants.**

13987 Camus, L.; Ricou, G. Mme FR 012220/73/5285
Traitement de la Faschiolose. **Treatment of Fasciolosis.**

13988 Ward; Huskisson GB 010302/00/0053 R
Carbohydrate metabolism of Ostertagia circumcincta.

13989 Munn; Greenwood GB 010302/75/0071
Development of a vaccine against haemonchosis.

13990 Symons; Binns GB 010303/00/0031 R
Properties of lymphoid cell populations in pigs sheep and cow.

13991 Aitken; Hall GB 010405/75/0827
Subclinical carriers of salmonellosis among cattle.

13992 Arrowsmth GB 010902/00/0002
Standard collection of subtype strains.

13993 Hedger; Barnett GB 010902/00/0004
Relation between type and subtype differences of foot and mouth disease and vaccination problems.

13994 Hedger GB 010902/00/0005
Trials of foot and mouth vaccine in Africa and relation of serum antibody to protection.

13995 Hedger GB 010902/00/0006
Importance of carriers of foot and mouth among livestock and game.

13996 Pereira GB 010902/00/0009
Fundamental studies on the parameters of serological tests for foot–and–mouth disease.

13997 Gibbs GB 010905/00/0002
Bluetongue diagnosis, detection, pathogenesis and vaccine development.

13998 Donaldson GB 010905/00/0005
Factors affecting survival of virus in aerosol, including humidity, pollutants and suspending media.

13999 Mccahon; Slade GB 010906/75/0004
Vaccine strains of SVD and FMD viruses.

14000 Austin GB 011211/76/0001
Bloat : investigations into causes and prevention.

14001 Austin GB 011211/77/0002
Mineral deficiencies of ruminants : investigations into causes and prevention.

14002 Field GB 030101/00/0001
Genetic control of mineral metabolism.

14003 Field; Munro GB 030101/00/0002
Aetiology of hypomagnesaemic tetany.

14004 Moon; Field GB 030101/00/0004
Chemical pathology of domestic animals.

14005 Mould; Dawson GB 030102/00/0012
Isolation of bacterial antigens associated with pulmonary infections.

14006 Mould; Dawson GB 030102/00/0015
High resolution preparative techniques for isolation of biologically active material.

14007 Smith GB 030103/00/0013
Diagnosis of viruses.

14008 Smith; Gray, W. GB 030103/00/0014
Ultrastructural studies on various animal tissues.

14009 Smith; Gray GB 030103/00/0016
Respiratory infections.

14010 Gray GB 030103/76/0020
Mycoplasma.

14011 Smith; Gray GB 030103/76/0023
Enteric disease in young livestock.

14012 Coop GB 030104/00/0013
Damage caused by gut worms.

14013 Thompson; Gilmour GB 030105/00/0005
Pathogenesis of pasteurellosis.

14014 Gilmour; Thompson GB 030105/00/0007
Bacteriological diagnostic service.

14015 Jones; Rae GB 030105/00/0008
Isolation, identification and pathogenicity of types of mycoplasmas.

14016 Snodgrass; Herring GB 030105/00/0020
Isolation and diagnosis of viruses.

14017 Snodgrass; Herring   GB 030105/00/0021
Serological diagnosis of virus infections.

14018 Gilmour; Fraser   GB 030105/77/0025
Moraxella and neisseria.

14019 Vantsis; Wells   GB 030105/77/0026
Border disease and mucosal disease.

14020 Angus; Rushton   GB 030106/00/0020
Morphology and pathogenesis of host reactions in
gastro–intestinal nematodiasis.

14021 Angus; Gardiner   GB 030106/77/0022
Enteric disease in young livestock.

14022 Angus   GB 030106/77/0025
CO MO and S inter–relationships in ruminants.

14023 Gilmour   GB 030106/77/0026
Infectious keratoconjunctivitis.

14024 Mitchell; Williams   GB 030112/00/0004
Aetiology of hypo–magnesaemic tetany.

14025 Mitchell; Williams   GB 030112/00/0005
Availability of copper in ruminant diet.

14026 Mitchell; Williams   GB 030112/00/0006
Distribution of plasma copper in sheep.

14027 Mitchell; Williams   GB 030112/76/0013
Liver biopsy under general anasthetic.

14028 cuthbertson; Clerihew   GB 030112/76/0017
Clinical and epidemiological studies of respiratory infections.

14029 Kadir; Sharman   GB 030607/78/0023
Relationships between nutritional deficiencies and infections in
rats and ruminants.

14030 Fell   GB 030608/00/0011
Ruminal lesions of sheep and cattle fed diets based on barley
and maize.

14031 Fell; Dinsdale   GB 030608/78/0023
Aetiology and pathology of molybdenum and thiomolybdate
poisoning in rats and ruminants.

14032 Phillippo   GB 030612/00/0010
Hormonal changes in parturient cows and sheep.

14033 Ball; Bryson   GB 041601/00/0024
Mycoplasma species in respiratory disease.

14034 Pearson; Mackie   GB 041607/00/0002
Studies on eradication of streproccus agalactiae mastitis
infection.

14035 Researcher not indicated   GB 050443/00/0001
Epidemiology of border disease, association of disease in sheep
and cattle.

14036 Researcher not indicated   GB 050454/00/0002
Diagnosis and control of brucellosis in sheep and cattle.

14037 Researcher not indicated   GB 050473/00/0001
Liver fluke in cattle and sheep.

14038 Researcher not indicated   GB 050484/00/0003
Epidemiology and pathology of gastro–intestinal disease in
cattle and sheep.

14039 Sojka   GB 050501/00/0003
Immunoelectrophoretic and conventional studies on E. coli
enteropathogenic for calves and lambs.

14040 Shreeve; Edwin   GB 050501/00/0008
Microbiology and biochemistry of cerebrocortical necrosis in
calves and lambs.

14041 Little   GB 050501/00/0016
Develop serological tests for mycobacteria infections with
particular reference to Johnes disease.

14042 Sojka   GB 050501/00/0028
Enteritic colibacillosis in lambs and calves.

14043 Ivins   GB 050502/00/0003
Johnes disease vaccine and improvement of specificity of johnin.

14044 Edwin   GB 050502/00/0005
Chemical study on pathogenesis of cerebrocortical necrosis and
mechanism of thiamine depletion.

14045 Lewis   GB 050502/00/0009
Methods of giving copper to prevent the onset of delayed
swayback.

14046 Ivins   GB 050502/77/0022
Immunosuppressant effect of bracken.

14047 Lee   GB 050503/00/0006
Johnes disease vaccine and johnin.

14048 Lesslie   GB 050503/77/0025
Johnes disease: quality control methods for vaccines.

14049 Corbel   GB 050504/00/0004
Mechanisms of resistance to brucellosis including responses to
vaccination.

14050 Kendall   GB 050505/00/0001
Rate of development and therapy of fascioliasis.

14051 Ollernshaw   GB 050505/00/0006
Incidence and control of fascioliasis.

14052 Ollernshaw   GB 050505/00/0008
Forecasting incidence of parasitic gastroenteritis in cattle sheep
from climatic data.

14053 Sinclair; Wassall   GB 050505/00/0009
Serology of helminth infection and relations with resistance and
development of diagnostic tests.

14054 Afshar; Lucas   GB 050508/00/0018
Other viral diseases of sheep and goats.

14055 Mathieson   GB 060116/00/0003

Tick–borne fever.

14056 Porter   GB 060218/00/0007
Major helminth parasitic infections of cattle and sheep in the north of Scotland.

14057 Murray   GB 060219/00/0008
Livestock fluorosis resulting from pollution by atmospheric fluorides from industrial sources.

14058 Murray   GB 060219/78/0013
Factors affecting fluoride pollution of herbage causing livestock fluorosis.

14059 Roche, J.; Boland, M.; Mcgeady, T.A.
         IE 120201/78/9117 N
Studies in embryonic death in the bovine.

14060 Greene, H.J.; Bakheit, H.; Walsh, J.
         IE 120205/76/9085 N
Bovine perinatal and neonatal morbidity and mortality; a study of causes, pathology and prevention of mortality. Publications.

14061 Guarda, F.   IT 041222/77/0559 R
Cause di mortalità pre e post natale fino allo svezzamento con particolare riferimento all' etiologia e patologia degli aborti nei bovini, suini, ovini e caprini. Produzione sperimentale di sindromi neuropatologiche in ruminanti Patologia aviare. **Pre and post natal causes of death up to the weaning period with particular regard to the aetiology and pathology of bovine, swine, sheep and goat abortions. Experimental induction of neuro–pathological syndromes in ruminants. Avien pathology.**

14062 Quesada, A.; Roperto, F.; Galati, P.; Guarino, C.
         IT 051000/78/0001 N
Grave episodio di Paranfistomosi intestinale in grandi e piccoli ruminanti domestici. **A very serious case of Paramphistomosis in domestic ovines and cattle.**

14063 Bekkum, J.G. van   NL 010402/67/1211 R
Onderzoek met betrekking tot productie van mond–en klauwzeervaccins en vaccincontrole. **Research on foot–and mouth disease vaccine production and control.** Publications.

14064 Mulder, I.   NL 030015/64/5761 R
Acetonaemie bij herkauwers (acetonaemie, slepende melkziekte thyroxine). **Ruminant ketosis (acetonaemia, bovine ketosis, thyroxine).** Publications.

14065 Bergh, S.G. van den   NL 030015/73/5758 R
Vergelijkend onderzoek van het metabolisme van parasitaire helminten en hun gastheren. (leverbot, helminten, metabolisme, excystatie). **Comparative biochemistry of helminth parasites and their hosts. (liver fluks, helminths, metabolism, excystation).** Publications.

Cattle (B 4210)

See also 5083, 10691, 10711, 10732, 10848, 10850, 10854,
10889, 10911, 11035, 12017, 12040, 12077, 12151, 12201, 12253,
13032, 13037, 13091, 13097, 13473, 13475, 13476, 13484, 13493,
13494, 13495, 13504, 13506, 13507, 14580, 14631, 14758, 14766,
15112, 15445, 15538, 15664, 15685, 20154

14066 Burnay, A.; Ghysdael, J.; Kettmann, R.; Portetelle, D.
         BE 010003/73/0014 R

Etude biochimique du virus de la leucémie bovine.
Biochemistry of bovine leukemia Virus. Publications.

14067 De Moor, A.; De Ley, G.; Cockelbergh, D.
         BE 050100/71/0001
Onderzoek naar de etiologie, de pathogenese en de erfelijke grondslagen van de Spastische Parese bij het rund. **Research on the ethiology, the pathogenesis and genetical aspects of Spastic Paralysis in Cattle.**

14068 De Moor, A.; De Kesel, A.; Cockelbergh, D.
         BE 050100/79/0003 N
Studie van congenitale en/of erfelijke gewrichtsdeviaties (arthrogryposis, peesretraktie, spierhypotonie) bij jonge runderen. **Study of congenital and/or hereditary joint deformations (arthrogryposis, tendonretraction, muscle hypotonia) in calves.**

14069 Vercauteren, R.; Bruyninckx, W.; Vanneste, W.
         BE 050900/78/0002 N
Biochemische studie van de morfologische en metabole veranderingen gedurende de fagocytose, bactericidie en digestie van microorganismen door mononucleaire fagocyten. **Cell physiological study of the morphology and metabolic events accompanying phagocytosis, bactericidy and digestion of micro organisms by mononuclear phagocytes.**

14070 Pouplard, L.; Pêcheur, M.; Detry, M.
         BE 060004/76/0002
Etude de l'influence du parasitisme sur la production laitière et sa prophylaxie. **Study of the influence of parasitism in dairy cows and prophylaxis.** Publications.

14071 Pouplard, L.; Pêcheur, M.; Detry, M.
         BE 060004/76/0004
Importance du lisier de porc dans l'infestation parasitaire du bétail. **Importance of liquid manure of pigs in the parasitic infestation of cattle.** Publications.

14072 Pouplard, L.; Pêcheur, M.; Detry, M.
         BE 060004/79/0005 N
Prophylaxie et traitement de la gale du bétail. **Prophylaxis and treatment of mange in cattle.**

14073 Deriveaux, J.; Ectors, F.; Beckers, J.
         BE 060006/72/0001 R
Etudes sur la stérilité hormonale chez la vache. **Studies on hormonal sterility in cows.** Publications.

14074 Mammerickx, M.   BE 110000/66/0004 R
Etude sur le diagnostic, l'épizootiologie et l'étiologie de leucose bovine. **Study of the diagnosis, epizootiology and etiology of bovine leukosis.** Publications.

14075 Famerée, L.; Cotteleer, C.   BE 110000/75/0025
Incidence et épidémiologie de la babésiellose bovine en Belgique. **Prevalence and epidemiology survey on babesiosis (Redwater) on the cattle in Belgium.** Publications.

14076 Wellemans, G.; Van Opdenbosch.
         BE 110000/77/0041 R
Influence des virus Rota, Corona et BVD dans la pathologie digestive du jeune veau. **Influence of the Rota, Corona and BVD virusses in the digestive pathology of the young calves.** Publications.

14077 Mortelmans, J.; Geerts, S.; Kumar, V.; De Deken, R.
BE 140000/74/0010 R
Diagnose– en behandelingsmethoden van Dictyocaulus viviparus en van cysticercose bij het rund. **Diagnosis and treatment of Dictyocaulus viviparus and cysticercose.** Publications.

14078 Thomas, R.; Bollen, A.; Bex, F.; Herzog, R.;
Couturier, M.; Janssens, J.   BE 140000/78/0048
Mise au point d'un test immunologique pour identification des résistances aux antibiotiques. **Immunological testing experiment to identification antibiotical resistance by cattle.**

14079 Depelchin, A.   BE 140000/79/0068 N
Etude in vitro de tests immunologiques de résistance des bovins aux maladies virales et bactériennes. **Study in vitro of immunological tests of cattle resistance against virus and bacterial diseases.**

14080 Schein, E.; Warnecke, M.; Gebelhoff, E.
DE 104201/72/0002
1. Entwicklung von subtropischen Zeckenarten in Mitteleuropa
2. Morphologie u. Entwicklungszyklus von Hyal. schulzei
3. Einfluss von Zeckeninfestationen auf latent mit Piroplasmen infizierte Wirtstiere 4. Veränderungen im Blutbild des Rindes nach Besatz mit Hyalommaund Boophiluszecken.
**1. Development of subtropical ticks in Central Europe
2. Morphology and growth cycle of Hyalomma schulzei
3. Influence of tick infestation on hosts infected latently with piroplasms 4. Changes in blood picture of cattle after infestation with Hyalomma and Boophilus.**

14081 Heydorn, A.–O.; Gestrich, R.   DE 104203/73/0002
Entwicklung und Pathogenität der Sarkosporidien der Kälber.
Development and pathogenity of Sarcosporidia in calves.

14082 Merck, C.C.; Dannemann, R.   DE 104400/70/0010
Mastitisprophylaxe und Bestandsanierungen durch Trockenstellen der Kühe mit halbsynthetischen Penicillinen.
Mastitis prophylaxis and stock sanitation by drying of cows with half–synthetic penicillins.

14083 Mülling, M.; Hoffmann, R.   DE 104400/72/0002
Hypoxie des Kalbes. **Hypoxia in calves.**

14084 Mülling, M.; Harth, K.   DE 104400/77/0001
Systemische Behandlung der Retentio secundinarum des Rindes mit Chloromycetin. **Systemic treatment of bovine Retentio secundinarum with Chloromycetin.**

14085 Mülling, M.; Gross, W.   DE 104400/77/0002
Therapie von Kälberdurchfällen mit ferment– und milchsäurebakterienhaltigen Präparaten. **Therapy of enteritis in calves with preparations containing ferments and Lactobacillaceae.**

14086 Heidrich, H.J.; Edzards, H.   DE 104400/77/0004
Biometeorologische Beobachtungen in Zusammenhang mit spezifischen Kälberkrankheiten. **Biometeorological observations in relation to specific diseases of calves.**

14087 Sommer, H.; Sonneck, R.   DE 111403/75/0003
Untersuchungen zur Früherkennung der Mastitis des Rindes.
Studies on early diagnosis of mastitis in cows.

14088 Sommer, H.; Voss, G.; Kowertz, D.

DE 111403/78/0001 N
Ökonomik von Programmen zur Gesundheitsüberwachung bei Milchkühen. **Economy of health control programs in dairy cattle.**

14089 Senft, B.; Meyer, F.; Erhardt, G.   DE 129251/78/0001 N
Wechselwirkungen zwischen Lysozym und Mastitis.
Correlations between lysozyme and mastitis.

14090 Senft, B.; Erhardt, G.   DE 129251/78/0002 N
Wirkungsmechanismen zur Aktivierung bakteriostatischer Effekte in der Milchdrüse. **Mechanisms on activation of bacteriostatic effects in the udder of cows.**

14091 Senft, B.; Wilhelm, H.   DE 129251/78/0004 N
Veränderungen der Mikroflora im Euter in Abhängigkeit bakteriostatischer Komponenten. **Changes in microflora of the udder caused by bacteriostatic components.**

14092 Rieck, G.W.; Herzog, A.; Höhn, H.; Rieke, H.
DE 129680/70/0002
Embryonal–, Prae– und Perinatalpathologie beim Rind. Ätiologie angeborener Missbildungen beim Rind. Verbreitung angeborener Missbildungen beim Rind in Hessen. **Embryonic, pre– and perinatal pathology in cattle. Etiology of congenital malformations in cattle. Frequencies and control of congenital malformations in cattle in Hesse.**

14093 Rieck, G.W.; Herzog, A.   DE 129680/74/0003
Statistische Arbeiten zur Koordinierung von Symptomen embryonalpathologischer Prozesse zur Aufstellung von Missbildungssyndromen beim Rind. **Statistic survey to coordinate the symptoms of embryonic pathological processes for specification of bovine malformation syndromes.**

14094 Herzog, A.; Kopp, U.   DE 129680/75/0003
Chromosomenanomalien bei der erblichen Parakeratose des Rindes. **Structural anomalies of chromosomes in hereditary parakeratosis in cattle.** Publications.

14095 Rieck, G.W.; Lindemann, M.   DE 129680/75/0005
Untersuchungen zur Syndromatologie der Atrichie, bzw. Hypotrichie und zur Ätiologie der Behaarungsdefekte beim Rind. **Investigations of congenital malformation syndromes connected with atrichia 'hypotrichia' in calves and their etiology.**

14096 Rieck, G.W.; Vainas, E.   DE 129680/78/0002 N
Untersuchungen zur Syndromatologie, Pathogenese und Ätiologie der Rachimyeloschisis 'Spina bifida' beim Rind.
Investigations on syndromatology, pathogenesis and etiology of spina bifida in cattle.

14097 Rieck, G.W.; Turkalj, K.   DE 129680/78/0004 N
Untersuchungen zur Ätiologie hydropischer Zustände beim neugeborenen Kalb mit besonderer Berücksichtigung der fetalen Leberdystrophien. **Etiology of hydrops in newborn calves with special consideration of fetal dystrophia of liver.**

14098 Rieck, G.W.; Stix, K.A.   DE 129680/78/0005 N
Chromosomenanomalien bei angeborenen Missbildungen des Zentralnervensystems des Rindes mit besonderer Berücksichtigung des Auftretens von Polyploiden in Zellkulturen. **Chromosome anomalies connected with congenital malformations of the CNS in cattle with special consideration of polyploidies in lymphocyte cultures.**

14099 Paulsen, J. DE 129820/70/0001
Leukose bei Rind und Schaf. **Leukosis in cattle and sheep.**

14100 Schmidt, F.–W.; Mitscherlich, E. DE 132330/77/0001
Untersuchungen zum Auftreten der tumorösen Rinderleukose und ihrer Differenzierung. **Occurrence of tumorous bovine leukosis and differentiation of tumor–forms.**

14101 Seifert, H.S.H.; Greiling, J.; Sy, O.; Chavarrya, F.
DE 132331/77/0002
Vergleichende Untersuchungen der Resistenzfaktoren Lysozym, Komplement und der Phagozytoseaktivität bei autochthonen afrikanischen und südamerikanischen und europäischen Leistungsrindern unter unterschiedlicher Umweltbelastung zur Beurteilung der relativen Resistenz gegenüber Infektionskrankheiten. **Comparative analysis of resistance factors lysozym, complement and phagocytosis activity in native cattle of Africa and South America and high–productive European stock under different conditions of environmental stress to determine relative resistance – inherited – to infectious diseases.**

14102 Schmidt, F.–W.; Mitscherlich, E. DE 132332/72/0001
Epidemiologie und Diagnose der Rinderleukose.
Epidemiology and diagnosis of bovine leucosis.

14103 Bürger, H.–J.; Steiner, A. DE 139500/78/0001 N
Untersuchungen über Formen der Weidehaltung von Kälbern zwecks Verminderung von Infektionen mit Magen–Darm-Strongyliden. **Investigations of pasture management systems in order to reduce infections of calves with trichostrongyles.** Publications.

14104 Liebisch, A.; Zielasko, B. DE 139500/78/0006 N
Untersuchungen zur Epizootologie und Bekämpfung der Psoroptesräude bei Schaf und Rind im Hinblick auf die Tierseuchengesetzgebung. **Studies on the epizootology and control of psoroptic mange in sheep and cattle with view to the animal health regulation.**

14105 Bürger, H.–J.; Bünke, V. DE 139500/78/0007 N
Epizootologie und Ökologie der Dictyocaulose beim Rind.
Epizootology and ecology of infections of cattle with Dictyocaulus.

14106 Liess, B.; Frey, H.R.; Marschall, H.–J.; Schnaedter, R.
DE 139550/78/0001 N
Isolierung zytopathogener Rotavirusstämme aus Kälber– und Ferkelfäces. **Isolation of cytopathogenic strains of Rotavirus from the feces of calves and piglets.**

14107 Kaaden, O.–R.; Frenzel, B. DE 139552/78/0001 N
Wechselwirkungen des Rinderleukosevirus in infizierten und transformierten Zellen. **Interactions of bovine leukosis virus in infected and transformed cells.**

14108 Nogai, K.; Wiesner, H.–U.; Döring, G.
DE 139650/78/0001 N
Pyruvat zur Einschätzung der Produktionshygiene und Beeinflussung des Pyruvatgehaltes durch Peroxide. **Pyruvate for taxation of production hygiene and influence of peroxides on pyruvate content.** Publications.

14109 Wiesner, H.–U.; Rottscheidt, W. DE 139650/78/0002 N
Laktose als Parameter zur Einschätzung der Eutergesundheit.
Lactose as parameter for taxation of hygienic condition of udder.

14110 Wiesner, H.–U.; Röttger, B. DE 139651/75/0002
Eutergesundheitsdienst: Nachweis von B–Streptokokken in Herdensammelmilch als Informationssignal zur Vervollständigung der zytologischen Information. **Udder health service: identification of B–streptococci in milk collected from herds as an information signal for completing cytological information.**

14111 Frerking, H. DE 139800/70/0008 N
Untersuchungen über die Eihautwassersucht beim Rind. **Investigations on hydrops of egg membrane in cattle.**

14112 Grunert, E.; Schulz, L.–C.; Ahlers, D.
DE 139800/73/0001
Untersuchungen über die Pathogenese der Retentio secundinarum beim Rind nach corticoinduzierter Geburt. **Studies on the pathogenesis of placental retention in cattle after cortico–induced labour.**

14113 Grunert, E.; Andresen, P. DE 139800/74/0004 N
Untersuchungen über die Brunstsynchronisation beim Rind mit Prostaglandin und Gonadotropin–Freigabehormon. **Studies on heat synchronization in cattle by using prostaglandin and Gn–RH.**

14114 Grunert, E. DE 139800/74/0005
Untersuchung zur Ätiologie und Pathogenese der Ovarialzysten des Rindes. **Studies on the etiology and pathogenesis of ovarian cysts in cattle.**

14115 Grunert, E.; Hartmann, R. DE 139800/78/0002 N
Untersuchungen über die Brauchbarkeit des Uterusabstriches für die Endometritisdiagnose. **Uterine biopsy a useful trial on diagnosis of endometritis.**

14116 Grunert, E.; Steiner, J. DE 139800/78/0005 N
Untersuchungen über die Brauchbarkeit der Beckenmessung zur Diagnose von Schwergebieten. **Can determination of the pelvic diameter predict obstetrical problems?.**

14117 Grunert, E.; Ziegler, U. DE 139800/78/0006 N
Untersuchungen über die Ursachen der Nachgeburtsverhaltung unter Berücksichtigung des Reifegrades der Plazentome. **On causes of retained placenta and maturation of placentomas.**

14118 Weigt, U.; Bleckmann, E. DE 139804/73/0002
Untersuchungen zur Sommermastitis der Rinder. **Research on pyogenic mastitis in heifers.**

14119 Weigt, U.; Stute, C. DE 139805/78/0001 N
Untersuchungen zur Ausbreitung der Mastitiden in Kuhbeständen und Versuche zur Mastitisbekämpfung unter Vermeidung übermässiger Chemotherapie. **Studies on spreading of mastitis in bovine herds and trials for mastitis control without excessive chemotherapy.**

14120 Weigt, U.; Stute, C. DE 139805/78/0002 N
Einfluss häufigen Melkens auf die Heilungsquoten bei der Mastitistherapie. **Influence of frequent milking on the success of mastitis treatment.**

14121 Weigt, U.; Bleckmann, E. DE 139805/78/0003 N

Untersuchungen zur Ätiologie und Pathogenese der Sommermastitis des Rindes. **Studies on the etiology and pathogenesis of summermastitis in heifers.**

14122 Weigt, U.; Ahlers, D. DE 139805/78/0004 N
Untersuchungen zur phlegmonösen Staphylokokkenmastitis. **Studies on the phlegmonic staphylococcal mastitis.**

14123 Rosenberger, G.; Fischer, W. DE 139900/72/0009
Untersuchungen über die Ätiologie und Therapie von Kälberinfektionen. **Investigations on etiolgy and therapy of infections in calves.**

14124 Gründer, H.D.; Martens, H.H. DE 139900/78/0001 N
Untersuchungen mit der Glutaraldehydprobe nach Sandholm im Vollblut gesunder und kranker Rinder. **Examinations with the glutaraldehyde test according to Sandholm by healthy and sick whole–blood cattle.**

14125 Stöber, M.; Hauck–Bauer, R. DE 139900/78/0002 N
Untersuchungen über den therapeutischen Nutzen der regionalen intravenösen Verabreichung von Oxytetrazyklin in die Vv. Digitalis Dorsalis communis III und IV bei Klauenerkrankungen des Rindes. **Evaluation of the therapeutic effect of regional intravenous administration of oxytetracyclin into the Vv. digitalis dorsalis communis III and IV in affection of the claws in cattle.**

14126 Stöber, M.; Weber–Kirchner, C. DE 139900/78/0003 N
Beitrag zur Eichelvergiftung des Rindes – Beobachtungen an spontan erkrankten Klinikpatienten sowie an zwei Versuchstieren –. **Contribution to bovine balanic infection– observations of spontaneous infected clinical patients and of two experimental animals –.**

14127 Stöber, M.; Krusic, L. DE 139900/78/0004 N
Physikalisch–chemische Untersuchungen des Kotes gesunder und kranker Rinder – unter Berücksichtigung der diagnostischen Verwertbarkeit der Befunde –. **Physico–chemical examinations of faeces of healthy and sick cattle – in consideration of diagnostic utilization of findings –.**

14128 Rosenberger, G.; Rosenberger, V. DE 139900/78/0005 N
Beitrag zur Messung des intraokulären Druckes beim Rind– Prüfung einiger Tonometer auf ihre Brauchbarkeit. **Contribution to measurement of the intraocular pressure in cattle – testing of some tonometers for their usefulness.**

14129 Stöber, M.; Meyer, J.–M. DE 139900/78/0006 N
Untersuchungen über die diagnostische Verwertbarkeit des rektalen Palpationsbefundes der Lnn.ruminales dextri 'caudales' beim Rind. **Studies on the diagnostic usefulness of rectal palpation finding of bovine Lnn. ruminales dextri 'caudales'.**

14130 Stöber, M.; Metzger, U. DE 139900/78/0007 N
Synopsis der Symptome der Infektionskrankheiten des Rindes. **Synopsis of symptoms of bovine infectious diseases.**

14131 Stöber, M.; Hänke–Petersen, W. DE 139900/78/0008 N
Beitrag zum Strabismus convergens cum exophthalmo beim Rind – klinische und histomorphologische Untersuchungen–. **Contribution to Strabismus convergens cum exophthalmo in cattle – clinical and histomorphological examinations –.**

14132 Stöber, M.; Baackmann, W. DE 139900/78/0009 N
Untersuchungen über die Brauchbarkeit eines aus dem Maulkeil nach Drinkwater entwickelten Instrumentes zum Offenhalten des Maules sowie zur Inspektion von Maulhöhle, Rachen und Kehlkopfeingang beim Rind. **Studies on the usefulness of an instrument developed from mouth wedge by Drinkwater for keeping the mouth open and for inspection of mouth cavity, jaws, and larynx orifice in cattle.**

14133 Loeffler, K.; Walla, L. DE 144605/77/0002
Synovialgruben beim Rind. **Synovial fossae in cattle.**

14134 Rabold, K.; Pichler, O. DE 144690/78/0002 N
Zur Lokalisation von Mastitiden im Kuheuter. **A contribution to the localisation of mastitis in the udder of cows.**

14135 Zucker, H.; Gropp, J.; Schulz, V.; Busch, L. DE 160600/75/0003
Pestizid–Carry–over bei Kalb, Schwein, Geflügel, Forelle. **Carry–over of pesticides in veal calves, swine, poultry and trouts.**

14136 Kalich, J.; Specker, R. DE 160701/77/0001
Einfluss der verschiedenen Aufstallungssysteme auf die Gesundheit und Leistung des Rindes unter besonderer Berücksichtigung der Beinschäden. **Influence of different housing systems on health and performance of cattle with special regard to injuries to legs.**

14137 Graf, F.; Osterkorn, K. DE 160705/71/0004
Hypocalcaemie und Hypophosphorämie des Rindes im Zusammenhang mit der Geburt. **Parturient hypocalcemia and hypophosphoremia in cows.**

14138 Terplan, G.; Grove, H.–H. DE 160731/75/0005
Zur ökonomischen Effektivität der Mastitisprophylaxe. **On the economic effectivity of the mastitis prophylaxis.**

14139 Gedek, W. DE 160731/75/0015
Verweildauer von Antibiotika in Trockensekret und in Körperflüssigkeiten nach Trockenzeitbehandlung beim Rind. **Persistence of antibiotics in the dry secretion and in body fluids of cows after dry–period treatment.**

14140 Gedek, W. DE 160731/75/0016
Zufuhr antibakteriell wirksamer Arzneimittel beim Kalb und Nachweis von Rückständen in Körpergeweben. **Application of antibacterial drugs to calves and detection of residues in tissues.** Publications.

14141 Grove, H.–H. DE 160731/77/0004
Einsatz von Resistenz stimulierenden Mitteln in der Mastitisbekämpfung. **Use of resistance stimulating agents in mastitis control.**

14142 Terplan, G.; Grove, H.–H. DE 160731/77/0006
Betriebswirtschaftliche Bedeutung der Mastitisprophylaxe in bayerischen Milcherzeugerbetrieben. **Economic value of mastitis control for dairy farms in Bavaria.**

14143 Mayr, A.; Wizigmann, G. DE 160763/75/0001
Bekämpfung infektiöser Kälberkrankheiten nach crowding. **Control of infectious diseases in calves after crowding.**

14144 Weiland, G. DE 160820/77/0002
Serologische Untersuchungen über das Vorkommen von

Rinderbabesien in Bayern. **Serological investigations on the occurrence of Babesia species in cattle in Bavaria.**

14145 Boch, J.; Laupheimer, K.-E.; Erber, M.
DE 160820/78/0002 N
Das Vorkommen von Sarcocystis bovicanis, Sarcocystis bovifelis und Sarcocystis bovihominis bei Schlachtrindern in Süddeutschland. **The incidence of Sarcocystis bovicanis, Sarcocystis bovifelis and Sarcocystis bovihominis in slaughter cattle in South Germany.** Publications.

14146 Dirksen, G.; Plank, P.; Simon, U.; Hänichen, T.; Spiess, A.
DE 160882/74/0001
Erforschung der enzootischen Kalzinose des Rindes. **Research on enzootic calcinosis in cattle.**

14147 Leidl, W.; Hundschell, C.; Stolla, R.; Rockel, P.; Bostedt, H.
DE 160910/75/0002
Ätiologie, Diagnose und Therapie von ovariellen Dysfunktionen beim Rind. **Etiology, diagnosis and treatment of ovarian dysfunctions in cows.**

14148 Walser, K.; Maurer-Schweizer, H.
DE 160910/75/0005
Acidose bei neugeborenen Kälbern. **Acidosis in newborn calves.**

14149 Walser, K.; Saile, R.
DE 160910/75/0006
Erfolgskontrolle nach Mastitisbehandlung beim Rind. **Control of success of mastitis treatment in cows.**

14150 Schams, D.
DE 161320/78/0001 N
Gonadotropine, vornehmlich beim Rind. **Gonadotropin activity especially in cattle.**

14151 Schams, D.; Schmidt-Polex, B.; Prokopp, A.
DE 161320/78/0004 N
Entwicklung eines Radioimmunotests für Oxytocin als Parameter für den maschinellen Milchentzug beim Rind.
Development of radio-immuno-assay for oxytocin as parameter of machine milking.

14152 Hoffmann, B.; Arnstadt, K.-I.; Schopper, D.
DE 161320/78/0005 N
Entwicklung eines Enzym-Immuno-Tests für Diethylstilböstrol und Nachweis von Protein gebundenen Anabolika im Rahmen des Rückstandproblems. **Development of an enzyme-immuno-assay for diethylstilbesterol and identification of protein-bound-anabolic agents in connection with problems of residues.**

14153 Lamina, J.; Bernhard, D.
DE 161361/78/0005 N
Die Bedeutung des Magen-Darmnematodenbefalls bei Milchkühen. **Significance of the attack of gastrointestinal nematodes in dairy cattle.** Publications.

14154 Schlünsen, D.
DE 201090/75/0016
Beziehungen zwischen Zellgehalt und Milchleistung. **Relations between cell content and milk yield.**

14155 Heeschen, W.; Hamann, J.; Tolle, A.; Hübler, K.; Hahn, G.
DE 207020/72/5005 N
Experimentelle Untersuchungen zur Immunisierung der Milchdrüse des Rindes. **Experimental studies on the immunization of the bovine mammary gland.**

14156 Strohmaier, K.
DE 216010/77/0002

Proteine des Maul- und Klauenseuche-Virus. **Proteins of foot-and-mouth disease virus.**

14157 Straub, O.C.
DE 216020/77/0005
Impfprophylaxe gegen die infektiöse bovine Rhinotracheitis-IBR-. **Prophylactic vaccination against infectious bovine rhinotracheitis.**

14158 Straub, O.C.
DE 216020/77/0009
Epidemiologie der Rinderleukose. **Epidemiology of bovine leukosis.**

14159 Bauer, K.
DE 216030/77/0001
Kälberaufzuchtkrankheiten: Immunisierung über den Respirationstrakt. **Diseases in calf raising: immunization via respiratory tract.**

14160 Frenzel, B.
DE 216030/77/0007
Antigene des Erregers der Rinderleukose. **Antigens of the agent of bovine leukosis.**

14161 Beinhauer, R.
DE 301060/77/0001
Einfluss von Witterungsparametern auf Ausbreitung von Leberegelzwischenwirten. **Influence of weather parameters on circulation by intermediate hosts of liver flukes.**

14162 Weinhold, E.
DE 305030/75/0001
Untersuchungen über die Ätiologie der Rinderleukose. Steigerung der Virulenz des infektiösen Agens. **Investigations into the etiology of bovine leucosis. Increasing the virulence of the infectious agent.**

14163 Pietzsch, O.; Staak, C.
DE 305030/77/0001
Immunität bei Kälber-Salmonellose. **Immunity in calf salmonellosis.**

14164 Reuss, U.
DE 507600/78/0003 N
Behandlungsmöglichkeiten der Trichophytie bei Rind und Pferd. **Possibilities of treating trichophytia in cattle and horses.** Publications.

14165 Nielsen, S.M.; Neimann-Sørensen, A.
DK 010201/69/0009
Undersøgelser af faktorer, der påvirker køernes mastitisforhold. **Studies of factors influencing the incidence of mastitis in dairy cows.**

14166 Larsen, J.B.; Sejrsen, K.; Neimann-Sørensen, A.
DK 010201/74/0006
Løbetarmparasitters betydning for tilvæksten hos kalve på græs samt effekten af forskellige kontrolforanstaltninger. **The significance of intestinal parasites for the growth of calves on grass, and the effect of various control measures.**

14167 Nielsen, S.M.; Madsen, P.
DK 010201/78/0009 N
Genetisk resistens mod mastitis hos kvæg. **Genetic resistance to mastitis in dairy cows.**

14168 Thorbek, G.
DK 010206/75/0012
Stofskiftemålinger hos kalve inficeret med løbeorm.
Measurements of metabolism in calves infested with worms.

14169 Thorbek, G.
DK 010206/75/0013
Stofskiftemålinger hos kalve inficeret med leverikter.
Measurements of metabolism in calves infested with liverfluke.

14170 Jørgensen, J.B. DK 020100/79/9172 N
Patogenitetsbestemmelse og måling af cellemedieret og
humoralt immunrespons ved podning med atypiske
mykobakterier på kalve. **The pathogenic effect and
cell–mediated and humoral immunity in calves inoculated with
atypical mycobacteria.**

14171 Sørensen, G.H. DK 020400/79/0263 N
Sommermastitis. Undersøgelser vedrørende
sommermastiternes forløb. **Investigations of the development of
summer mastitis.**

14172 Larsen, B.; Hyldgaard–Jensen, J.; Moustgaard, J.
DK 030126/79/0002 N
Genetiske markører og mastitisresistens hos kvæg. **Genetic
markers and resistance against mastitis in cattle.**

14173 Jørgensen, S.T. DK 030127/79/0001 N
Epidemiologiske undersøgelser af
antibiotikaresistensplasmider fortrinsvis i patogene bakterier
fra kalve og svin. **Epidemiological investigations of R plasmids
in primarily pathogenic bacteria from calves and piglets.**

14174 Philipsen, H. DK 030128/72/0016 R
Andrologiske undersøgelser af ungtyre på
individprøvestationerne "Egtved", Aalestrup" og
"Stradebrogård". **Andrological investigations of young bulls at
the individual testing stations of Egtved, Aalestrup and
Stradebrogård.**

14175 Koefoed–Johnsen, H.H. DK 030128/74/0013
Undersøgelser over et frugtbarhedsnedsættende og muligvis
arveligt betinget kompleks af spermiehaledefekter hos tyre af
jerseyrace. **Investigations of reduced fertility and a possible
inherited condition complex of sperm tail defects in bulls of the
jersey race.**

14176 Rasbech, N.O. DK 030128/74/0018
Bovine ægtransplantationsforsøg. **Bovine egg transplantation
studies.**

14177 Christiansen, I.J. DK 030128/75/0002
Undersøgelse over prostaglandiners anvendelighed til
afbrydelse af drægtighed, induktion af fødsel samt udtømning
af uterus for patologisk indhold hos kvæg. **An investigation in
cattle into the use of prostaglandins to terminate pregnancy,
induce birth and empty the uterus of any pathological matter.**

14178 Philipsen, H. DK 030128/76/0017
Releasinghormoners kliniske anvendelse. **The clinical
application of releasing hormones.**

14179 Rasbech, N.O. DK 030128/76/0019
Undersøgelse af mælkeprogesteron i forbindelse med
superovulation af køer. **An investigation of milk progesterone
in connection with super–ovulation in cows.**

14180 Pedersen, K.M. DK 030128/77/0015
Kvantitering af IgG i sædplasma fra tyre. **The quantification of
IgG in sperm plasma from bulls.**

14181 Smedegaard, H.H. DK 030130/65/0010
Nydannelser i klovspalten hos kvæg med særlig henblik på
ætiologien. **Regeneration in the interdigital cleft of cattle with
particular reference to the aetiology.**

14182 Poulsen, J.S.D. DK 030130/75/0005
Undersøgelser over forebyggelse af traumatisk indigestion hos
kvæg. **Investigations into the prevention of traumatic
indigestion in cattle.**

14183 Sønnichsen, H.V. DK 030130/75/0014
Undersøgelser over hofteledslidelser hos kvæg. **Investigations
into hip joint complaints in cattle.**

14184 Hesselholt, M.; Grymer, J. DK 030130/75/0015 N
Ætiologi og epidemiologi ved gastro–intestinal atoni og
laminitis hos kvæg. **Gastro–intestinal atony and laminitis in
cattle. Studies on aetiology and epidemiology.**

14185 Sonnichsen, H.V. DK 030130/76/0012
Undersøgelser vedr. aseptiske haseledslidelser hos hest.
Investigations concerning aseptic hock complaints in the horse.

14186 Smedegaard, H.H. DK 030130/77/0009
Klovlidelser hos kvæg med særlig henblik på lidelsernes
ætiologi (på 5 herregårde). **Hoof complaints in cattle with
particular attention to their aetiology (on 5 manors).**

14187 Hesselholt, M.; Agger, J.F. DK 030130/78/0001 N
Pattelæsion hos kvæg, epidemiologi og terapi. **Teat injury in
cattle. Epidemiology and therapy.**

14188 Brummerstedt, E.; Sørensen, G.H.
DK 030133/79/0001 N
Immunologiske og immunpatologiske forhold i forbindelse
med sommermastitis. **Immunologic and immunopathologic
conditions related to summer mastitis.**

14189 Nansen, P. DK 030137/76/0006
Fællesnordisk projekt vedrørende kvægets
mave–tarmparasitter. Koordinerede metodologiske og
epidemiologiske undersøgelser med henblik på praktiske
bekæmpelsesforanstaltninger. **Joint Nordic project on stomach
and intestinal parasites in cattle. Coordinated methological and
epidemiological investigations with reference to practical
measures for combating the problem.**

14190 Jørgensen, R.J. DK 030137/78/0001 N
Post mortem diagnosticering af bovin dictyocaulose. **Post
mortem diagnosis of bovine dictyocaulosis.**

14191 Jørgensen, R.J. DK 030137/79/0003 N
Pilobulus' rolle for spredning af bovin dictyocaulose. **The role
of Pilobulus in spreading bovine dictyocaulosis.**

14192 Larsen, H.E.; Nansen, P.; Aalbæk, B.; Hansen, J.;
Foldager, J.; Pedersen, J. DK 030137/79/0004 N
Bakteriologiske, immunologiske, immunpatologiske,
entomologiske og epidemiologiske forhold samt
kontrolforanstaltning vedrørende sommermastitis.
**Summermastitis in cattle. (Bacteriology, immunology,
immunopathology, entomology, epidemiology and control).**

14193 Bendixen, P.H.; Jensen, P.T. DK 030138/78/0001 N
Undersøgelse af kvægmakrofagers funktion som initiatorcelle i
det cellemedierede immunsvar. **An investigation on the role of
bovine macrophages as initiatorcells in the cell mediated
immune response.**

14194 Bendixen, P.H.; Aasted, B.　　DK 030138/79/0001 N
Undersøgelse af kvægseras indhold af makrofag–deriverede enzymer. **A study on the contents of macrophage derived enzymes in bovine sera.**

14195 Nielsen, B.O.　　DK 030603/79/0262 N
Sommermastitis. Økologiske undersøgelser over insektfaunaen på græssende kvæg med særligt henblik på belysning af insekternes rolle i spredningen af sommermastitis. **Ecological studies of insects on grassing cattle with special reference to elucidate the role of insects in spreading summer mastitis.**

14196 Levieux, D.　　FR 010807/77/8009
Mesure de l'immunité des bovins et ovins. **Immune responsiveness measure in cattle and sheep.**

14197 Gouet, Ph.; Girardeau, J.P.; Contrepois, M.; Dubourguier, H.C.　　FR 010809/72/9522 N
Diarrhée néo–natale du veau d'étiologie infectieuse – Etude de la pathogénie du syndrome et recherche d'une prophylaxie. **Infections etiology of neonatal calf diarrhoea – Pathogeny and prophylaxis.**

14198 Barnouin, J.　　FR 010811/78/8057
Exploration de la fonction hépatique chez les bovins. **Hepatic function survey in bovine.**

14199 Cabello, G.; Larvor, P.　　FR 010817/76/8035
Pathologie du veau nouveauné : facteurs endocriniens au cours de la période périnatale. **Pathology of the newborn calf : endocrine factors during the perinatal period.**

14200 WAL Jean–Michel.　　FR 011412/75/9506 N
Résidus de produits médicamenteux et de contaminants dans l'environnement. Etude d'un modèle de recyclage des fientes par ensilage. **Drugs residues in environment. Influence of silage as a waste recycling process for cattle feeding.**

14201 Fensterbank, R.; Plommet, M.　　FR 011503/76/8094
Vaccination antibrucellique des bovins avec le B.19 administré par voie conjonctivale. **Vaccination against bovine brucellosis with strain 19 administered by the conjunctival route.**

14202 Poutrel, B.; Rainard, P.; Caffin, J.P.　FR 011503/77/8096
Etude préliminaire sur l'immunité de la glande mammaire bovine. **Preliminary studies of the immunological status of the bovine mammary gland.**

14203 Roguinsky, M.　　FR 011503/78/8105
Epidémiologie des avortements des bovins. **Surveys and Epidemiology of bovine infectivus abortions.**

14204 Boulard, C.; Plat, M.; Faublee, V.; Villejoubert, C.; Mallet, S.　　FR 011505/64/8065
Définition d'une prophylaxie de l'hypodermose bovine. Réponse immunitaire au cours des traitements. **Reflexion on a programm for bovine cattle–grubs control in France.**

14205 Faublee, V.; Plat, M.; Boulard, C.; Villejoubert, C.; Mallet, S.　　FR 011505/77/8064
Définition d'une prophylaxie de l'hypodermose bovine : la réponse immunitaire de nature réaginique. **Reflexion on a programm for bovine cattle–grubs control in France.**

14206 Le Jan, C.; Asso, J.　　FR 012225/72/8024
Immunité dans les maladies respiratoires à virus du veau. **Calf viral respiratory disease immunity.**

14207 Cohen, J.; Laporte, J.; Scherrer, R.　　FR 012225/76/8030
Propriétés physicochimiques et antigéniques des Rotavirus et Coronavirus bovins. **Physicochemical and antigenic properties of bovins rotaviruses and Coronaviruses.**

14208 Vautherot, J.F.; Scherrer, R.; Cohen, J.　　FR 012225/77/8029
Immunité dans les infections à rotavirus du veau et prophylaxie. **Immunity in rotavirus infections of calves and prophylaxis.**

14209 Spooner　　GB 010103/00/0002
Association of blood type with disease and production.

14210 Spooner　　GB 010103/76/0011 R
Survey of factors contributing to longevity and disease in East Anglian dairy herds.

14211 Young　　GB 010103/79/0014 N
Genetic diseases with reference to A. I. of cattle.

14212 Beale; Kent　　GB 010303/00/0064 R
Comparative study of bovine immunoglobulins.

14213 MacIlhinney　　GB 010303/75/0071 R
The characterisation of membrane bovine IgM: and a study of its mode of attachment to lymphocyte membranes.

14214 Payne; Dew　　GB 010401/00/0808
Aging as a limiting factor in production.

14215 Rutter; Gibbons　　GB 010402/75/0825
Virulence determinants in E. coli infection in calves.

14216 Sansom; Gibbons　　GB 010402/76/0835
Diseases associated with a deficient dietary intake and poisioning assocated with an excessive intake of Se.

14217 Payne; Dew　　GB 010403/00/0808
Aging as a limiting factor in production.

14218 Hall　　GB 010403/00/0819
Pathogenesis of Salmonella dublin infection in cattle.

14219 Chandler; Mackenzie　　GB 010403/74/0823
Host pathogen relationships in mastitis due to bacteria.

14220 Aitken; Hall　　GB 010403/75/0827
Subclinical carriers of salmonellosis among cattle.

14221 Dhandler; Turfrey　　GB 010403/77/0056
Infectious bovine keratoconjunctivitis:host–pathogen relationships,prophlaxis, treatment;associated studies.

14222 Treacher.　　GB 010404/00/0024 R
Production disease associated with variations in protein and amino acid supply in dairy cattle.

14223 Little　　GB 010404/00/0807
Production disease associated with new systems of feeding and management.

14224 Hughes　　GB 010404/00/0817

Biological, immunological and chemotherapeutic control of liver fluke.

14225 Reid   GB 010404/00/0820 R
Pathogenesis of fatty liver in cows and its effect on metabolic performance.

14226 Rowlands; Allen   GB 010404/75/0826
Use of mathematical models in defining limiting factors to production.

14227 Allen; Woode   GB 010404/75/0828
Longterm recovery from enteritis with particular respect to calf scours.

14228 Sansom; Hoare   GB 010404/75/0830
New aspects of the physiology and treatment of milk fever.

14229 Aitken; Hall   GB 010404/76/0827
Subclinical carriers of salmonellosis among cattle.

14230 Rowlands; Russell   GB 010404/76/0836
Factors affecting fertility.

14231 Baggott; Russell   GB 010404/79/0838 N
The aetiology pathogenesis and control of foot lameness in cattle.

14232 Woode   GB 010405/00/0004
Aetiological studies of enteric viral infections in calves.

14233 Gourlay   GB 010405/00/0029
Aetiology of calf pneumonia.

14234 Gourlay   GB 010405/00/0810
Role of mycoplasmas in calf pneumonia and other diseases of farm animals.

14235 Stott; Thomas   GB 010405/00/0811
Role of animal viruses in calf respiratory diseases.

14236 Rowlands   GB 010405/00/0818
Epidemiology of calf diseases, especially respiratory and enteric infections.

14237 Hall   GB 010405/00/0819
Pathogenesis of Salmonella dublin infection in cattle.

14238 Rutter; Gibbons   GB 010405/75/0825
Virulence determinants in E. coli infection in calves.

14239 Allen; Woode   GB 010405/75/0828
Longterm recovery from enteritis with particular respect to calf scours.

14240 Jones   GB 010405/76/0047
The occurrence and survival of bacterial pathogens in sewage sludge.

14241 Brownlie; Stott   GB 010405/76/0833
Cellular immune reactions in cattle following infection with immunosuppressants and pathogens.

14242 Rowlands; Russell   GB 010405/76/0836
Factors affecting fertility.

14243 Brocklsby   GB 010406/00/0015
Taxonomy, epidemiology and pathogenesis of Babesia major and Babesia divergens.

14244 Brocklsby   GB 010406/00/0016
Epidemiology and pathogenesis of Theileria species in British cattle.

14245 Brocklsby; Young E   GB 010406/00/0017
Biology of British ticks and their role in parasite transmission.

14246 Hughes   GB 010406/00/0817
Biological, immunological and chemotherapeutic control of liver fluke.

14247 Brownlie; Stott   GB 010406/76/0833
Cellular immune reactions in cattle following infection with immunosuppressants and pathogens.

14248 Little   GB 010408/00/0807
Production disease associated with new systems of feeding and management.

14249 Rowlands   GB 010408/00/0818
Epidemiology of calf diseases, especially respiratory and enteric infections.

14250 Rowlands; Allen   GB 010408/75/0826
Use of mathematical models in defining limiting factors to production.

14251 Russell   GB 010408/76/0055
Cattle lameness survey.

14252 Hibbitt; Rowlands   GB 010408/76/0831
The measurement of non–specific resistance to infection in dairy herds.

14253 Hibbitt; Hill   GB 010410/00/0001
The role of nonspecific resistance factors in cattle with special refefence to mastitis.

14254 Brownlie; Gleed   GB 010410/00/0003
Specific immune proteins at the local level.

14255 Gourlay; Howard   GB 010410/00/0810
Role of mycoplasmas in calf pneumonia and other diseases of farm animals.

14256 Stott; Thomas   GB 010410/00/0811
Role of animal viruses in calf respiratory diseases.

14257 Hughes   GB 010410/00/0817
Biological, immunological and chemotherapeutic control of liver fluke.

14258 Anderson; Hill   GB 010410/74/0823 R
Host pathogen relationships in mastitis due to bacteria.

14259 Hibbit; Rowlands   GB 010410/76/0831
The measurement of non–specific resistance to infection in dairy herds.

14260 Brownlie; Stott   GB 010410/76/0833
Cellular immune reactions in cattle following infection with immunosuppressants and pathogens.

14261 Bramley; King   GB 011701/00/0008
Effect of hygiene at milking on rate of new mastitis infections.

14262 Bramley; Higgs   GB 011701/00/0009
Effect of milking machine factors on rate of new mastitis infections.

14263 Bramley   GB 011701/00/0010
Conditions giving rise to coliform mastitis infections.

14264 Reiter; Bramley   GB 011701/00/0011
Virulence of strains of mastitis Streptococci and Staphylococcus aureus in the udder, and udder defences.

14265 Reiter; Marshall   GB 011701/00/0012
Bactericidal and bacteriostatic systems in the intestinal tract of the neonate in relation to scouring.

14266 Jayne–Williams   GB 011701/78/0028
Microflora of the calf gut in relation to host health.

14267 Dodd; Kingwill   GB 011704/00/0015
Develop and test system for the control of udder diseases.

14268 Kingwill   GB 011704/00/0016
Effect of hygiene at milking on rate of new mastitis infections.

14269 Griffin; Kingwill   GB 011704/00/0017
Effect of milking machine factors on rate of new mastitis infections.

14270 Griffin; Kingwill   GB 011704/00/0018
Economics of udder disease, and its effects on milk yield.

14271 Kingwill   GB 011704/00/0019
Antibiotic therapy and control of udder disease.

14272 Smith   GB 030103/00/0006
Pathogenicity of bovine herpes virus.

14273 Martin; Scott   GB 030105/00/0019
Pathogenicity and epidemiology of and immunity to infections of bovine herpesvirus.

14274 Barlow   GB 030106/00/0008
Diagnosis, pathology and pathogenesis of bovine cerebellar ataxia.

14275 Gilmour   GB 030106/77/0023
Pathogenesis of herpes mammillitus.

14276 Martin   GB 030109/78/0004 N
Pathogenicity and epidemiology of and immunity to infections of bovine herpes virus.

14277 Cuthbrtsn   GB 030112/77/0018
Epidemiological investigation of infectious bovine keratoconjunctivitis.

14278 Mills; Dalgarno   GB 030604/75/0014
Quantitative relationships between Cu, Mo and S intake in the development of Cu deficiency in growing cattle.

14279 Siddons; Clews   GB 030604/75/0016
Selenium and vitamin e interrelationships in the aetiology of myopathus and ill thrift systems.

14280 Bryson   GB 041602/75/0001
Respiratory disease in young cattle.

14281 Ellis   GB 041603/75/0001
Studies on the causes of bovine abortion.

14282 McMurray   GB 041604/76/0002
Copper deficiency in ruminants.

14283 Taylor; Cawthorne   GB 041605/00/0001
Arthropod borne haematozoal diseases of cattle in Nothern Ireland.

14284 Pearson; Mackie   GB 041607/00/0001
Clinical mastitis the study and documentation of factors related.

14285 Pearson   GB 041607/00/0003
Mechanisms of immunity in the bovine udder.

14286 Pearson; Mackie   GB 041607/79/0004 N
The epidemiology of Streptococcus agalactie.

14287 Pearson; Ellis   GB 041607/79/0005 N
Leptospiral and mycoplasmal mastitis.

14288 Researcher not indicated   GB 050461/00/0001
Listeria agglutinins in the sera of apparently normal cattle.

14289 Researcher not indicated   GB 050462/00/0002
Enzyme variants in bovine serum in relation to disease.

14290 Researcher not indicated   GB 050463/00/0002
The use of the cf test for the detection of bovine adenovirus antibodies.

14291 Researcher not indicated   GB 050463/00/0003
Production and conjugation of a specific brucella abortus antiserum for the F.A.T.

14292 Researcher not indicated   GB 050463/00/0004
Inoculation proceedures.

14293 Researcher not indicated   GB 050463/00/0005
Antibody levels in blood samples against viruses in calves with low gamma globulin levels.

14294 Researcher not indicated   GB 050463/00/0006
Production of antibody to bovine Igm and Igg, development of a radial immuno–diffusion technique.

14295 Researcher not indicated   GB 050463/00/0008
Association of bulk milk cell counts with sub–clinical mastitis.

14296 Researcher not indicated   GB 050471/00/0001
Investigation into the effects on health of intensification of dairy farming.

14297 Researcher not indicated   GB 050471/00/0004
Thyroid dysfunction: bovine foetal goitre related to stillbirths and non–viable calves.

14298 Researcher not indicated   GB 050471/00/0005
Effects of dietary imbalance on bovine fertility.

14299 Researcher not indicated   GB 050471/00/0006
Myopathy in young calves.

14300 Researcher not indicated   GB 050471/00/0008
Pyrexia of unknown origin in dairy cattle in Devon.

14301 Researcher not indicated   GB 050473/00/0002 R
Microbiological examination of poultry waste intended as cattle feed.

14302 Researcher not indicated   GB 050483/00/0002
Bovine hypocuprosis.

14303 Researcher not indicated   GB 050484/00/0002
Epidemiology and pathogenises of respiratory diseases of housed cattle.

14304 Wray   GB 050501/00/0006
Antibody response of calves to salmonella vaccines.

14305 Boughton; Pritchard   GB 050501/00/0009
Bacteriological investigations into respiratory disease.

14306 Boughton   GB 050501/00/0010
Isolation and characterisation of mycoplasmas and of L forms.

14307 Boughton   GB 050501/00/0012
Transmission of respiratory disease by direct contact. Improve diagnostic tests.

14308 Wilson   GB 050501/00/0013
Relate milk cell counts to sub–clinical mastitis; monitor awareness scheme; study response to therapy.

14309 Pritchard   GB 050501/76/0029
Study of bovine mycoplasma mastitis.

14310 Tarry   GB 050501/77/0030
Study of summer mastitis.

14311 Anderson   GB 050502/00/0002
Chemical pathology of muscle disorders in pigs and cattle.

14312 Patterson   GB 050502/75/0019
Chemical pathology of liver injury in farm animals.

14313 Thornton   GB 050503/00/0005
Production and quality control methods for brucellosis vaccines and antigens.

14314 Shreeve   GB 050504/00/0001
Mycotic abortion.

14315 Bracewell; Corbel   GB 050504/00/0002
Diagnosis, vaccination and treatment of Vibrio foetus infection.

14316 Bracewell   GB 050504/00/0003
Studies of brucellosis related to incentives and eradication schemes.

14317 Corbel   GB 050504/00/0008
Susceptibility of brucella to antibiotic and other therapeutic agents.

14318 Davies; Bell   GB 050504/00/0009
Abortion statistics–BES vetinary research computer tape.

14319 Michel   GB 050505/00/0004
Epidemiology of parasitic gastroenteritis in cattle.

14320 Donnelly; Joyner   GB 050505/00/0013
Epidemiology of babesiasis.

14321 Bradley   GB 050506/00/0059
The development of foetal bovine muscle.

14322 Shaw   GB 050506/00/0062
Reproductive failure in cattle. Pathogenicity of bovine enteroviruses for the foetal calf.

14323 Terlecki; Richardscn   GB 050506/75/0027
Border disease : pathogenicity for bovine foetus.

14324 Richardson; Terleck   GB 050506/75/0043
Morphological study of bovine foetal development.

14325 Markson   GB 050506/75/0048
Definitive and differential pathology of naturally occurring diseases of cattle.

14326 Terlecki   GB 050506/75/0051
Pathogenicity of BVD virus to bovine foetus. Diagnostic criteria.

14327 Markson   GB 050506/75/0053
The relationship of juvenile sporadic bovine leukosis to enzootic bovine leukosis (EBL).

14328 Richardson   GB 050506/77/0061
Osteochondrosis in cattle.

14329 Harkness   GB 050508/00/0004 R
Morphology of bovine virus diarrhoea by immune electron microscopy.

14330 Lamont   GB 050508/00/0006
Study direct contact transmission of respiratory disease of cattle and improve diagnostic tests.

14331 Lucas; Chasey   GB 050508/00/0008 R
Rotaviruses and enteric diseases of calves.

14332 Lamont; Chapman   GB 050508/00/0016 R
Parvovirus infections of cattle.

14333 Harkness   GB 050508/00/0020 R
Enteroviruses of cattle.

14334 Roberts; Stagg   GB 050508/75/0015 R
Bovine leukosis and virus leucocyte interactions : diagnostic tests and serum surveys.

14335 Richards   GB 050510/00/0012
Environment recording in calf houses.

14336 Hebert   GB 050510/00/0015
Collaborative studies on EEC tuberculin.

14337 Wilesmith; Scott   GB 050510/00/0018
Johnes disease survey.

14338 Wilson; Richards   GB 050510/00/0019
National survey of mastitis.

14339 Wilesmith   GB 050510/77/0022
Johnes disease. Investigation of vaccinated herds to evaluate the combined efficacy of the vaccine.

14340 Wilesmith; Wilson   GB 050510/77/0023
Mastitis control. The effect of practitioners advice on the adoption of mastitis control methods.

14341 Ross   GB 050512/00/0007
Liver fluke epidemiology (Scotland).

14342 Hunter   GB 050512/00/0020
Bovine nephritis.

14343 Mathieson   GB 060116/00/0001
Mastitis control in dairy herds.

14344 Mathieson   GB 060116/00/0007
Brucellosis eradication.

14345 Johnston   GB 060212/00/0001
Alimentary conditions in the housed suckler calf and their association with diet.

14346 Donald   GB 060212/00/0007
Brucellosis eradication.

14347 Halliday   GB 060212/00/0008
Aids to the diagnosis of liver disfunction in ruminants.

14348 Wood   GB 060212/78/0011 N
Maintaining a low incidence of subclinical, mastitis in the absence of dry cow therapy.

14349 Porter   GB 060218/00/0008
Study of ticks in relation to redwater fever and its incidence in the Dee valley.

14350 Hunter   GB 060220/00/0001
Mastitis control : effect of automatic cluster removal.

14351 Hunter   GB 060220/78/0008 N
A survey of udder washing techniques and water supplies.

14352 Robinson   GB 060220/79/0011 N
Examination of rapid methods for identification of bacteria responsible for bovine mastitis.

14353 Wright   GB 060312/00/0001
Bovine mastitis.

14354 Wright   GB 060312/00/0004
Brucellosis eradication.

14355 Downey, N.E.; O'Shea, J.   IE 060100/72/0326 R
Grazing management in relation to infestation of calves by flukeworm and gastro–intestinal worms. (1)effect of the ratio of adults to calves. (2)Low–level anthelmintic in drinking water. Publications.

14356 Maguire, M.F.; Roche, J.F.   IE 060103/77/1392 N
Post–partum anoestrus in beef suckler cows. Publications.

14357 Arkins, S.   IE 060400/00/2093 N
A survey of lameness in dairy cattle. Publications.

14358 O'Shea, J.; O'Callaghan, E.J.; Meaney, W.J.
     IE 060400/73/2064 R
The effect of liner design on milking characteristics and the effect of milking machine factors on the incidence of mastitis. Publications.

14359 Langley, O.   IE 060400/75/1145 R
Evaluation of treatments for postpartum uterine infection therapy but also its timing and repetition. Publications.

14360 Langley, O.; O'Farrell, K.J.   IE 060400/75/1151 R
Examination and treatment of postpartum anoestrus and repeat breeder syndromes in dairy cows. Publications.

14361 Langley, O.   IE 060400/75/1152 R
Investigation of management components in bovine dystokia. Publications.

14362 Meaney, W.J.   IE 060400/76/2062 R
Mastitis in in–calf heifers and dairy cows. Publications.

14363 Walsh, J.P.   IE 060400/76/2078 R
Causes of calf mortality.

14364 O'Dowd, M.; Walsh, J.P.   IE 060400/77/2081 R
Summer mastitis.

14365 Walsh, J.P.   IE 060400/77/2082 R
Bacterial infection and reproductive efficiency in cows.

14366 Hope Cawdery, M.J.   IE 060701/74/1032 N
Evaluation of a fluke control system based on individual dairy farm survey in north central Ireland. Publications.

14367 Conway, D.A.   IE 120201/78/9169 N
Survey of respiratory diseases of calves in County Cork and County Meath, Ireland. Publications.

14368 Hilton, G.; Fitzpatrick, E.   IE 120201/79/9167 N
Histochemical and histological examination of bovine muscle after certain drugs.

14369 McGeady, T.A.; Alias, A.M.   IE 120201/79/9168 N
Histological and histochemical studies on the bovine uterus during early pregnancy.

14370 Cunningham, B.; Walsh, J.; Dolan, L.
     IE 120205/75/9086 N
Immunological studies of bovine brucellosis in large commerc ial dairy herds. The effects of management and vaccination i n its control. Publications.

14371 Collins, J.D.; Brophy, P.O.; Dunne, C.; York, A.;
O'Reilly, L.M.   IE 120206/77/9236 N
Control and eradication of mycobacterium bovis from a dairy herd.

14372 Hannan, J.; Walsh, J.; Arkins, S.   IE 120206/79/9240 N
The aetiology, effects on production and the prevention of lameness in dairy cattle.

14373 Monaghan, M.L.M.; Hannan, J.; Sheahan, B.J.
     IE 120206/79/9241 N

Effects of sub–clinical nephritis on cattle.

14374 De Maria, C.; Puppo, S.   IT 020700/79/0013 N
Indagini sulla presenza di residui di antibiotici nel colostro e
nel latte di bovine trattate all'inizio del periodo di asciutta.
**Studies of antibiotic residues in colostrum and milk of cows
treated at the begining of drought period.**

14375 Gentile, G.   IT 040232/77/0555 R
Ricerca dei fattori atti a rendere di particolare gravità e
frequenza le sindromi dismetaboliche nelle bovine ad alta
produzione ed eventuali rapporti con la crescente ipofecondità.
**Research of factors likely to increase the severity and frequency
of dysmetabolic syndromes in intensively bred cows and their
eventual connection with increasing hypo–fecundity.**

14376 Cappa, V.   IT 040411/78/1042 N
Studio di talune anomalie del latte e relazione con il profilo
metabolico della lattifere. Effetto dell'impiego di quantità
elevate di insilati. **a study of certain anomalies of milk and their
relation to the metabolic picture in milch–cows. Effects of using
ensilage in large quantities.**

14377 Farnaroli, D.   IT 040613/77/0183 R
Attività aglutinante di farine di soia sugli eritrociti di vitelli.
**Aglutination action of soya fluor on the red blood cells of
calves.**

14378 Pesce, A.   IT 040635/77/0844
Studio dei rapport fra bovid herpesvirus e herpes simplex.
**Study on the relationship between bovine herpesvirus and
herpes simplex.**

14379 Castrucci, G.   IT 041029/77/0842 R
Studio sulle possibilità di uno stato di latenza virale in vitelli
infettati con Bovid herpesvirus 2 per via venosa. **A study on a
possible latent virus stage in calves infected intravenously with
Bovid herpesvirus 2.**

14380 Salutini, E.   IT 041126/77/0585 R
I profili metabolici come metodo di controllo della patologia da
produttività nel bovino. **Metabolic profiles as a method of
checking productivity induced pathology in bovine cattle.**

14381 Scatozza, F.   IT 041505/77/0846 R
Virosi respiratorie ed enteriche degli animali. Etiologia delle
sindromi respiratorie ed enteriche dei bovini in allevamento
intensivo. **Respiratory and enteric virus diseases in animals.
The etiology of respiratory and enteric syndromes in bovine
cattle on intensive breeding farms.**

14382 Gianelli, F.; Pesce, A.; Cattabiani, F.; Freschi, E.;
Brindani, F.   IT 041507/79/0001 N
Diffusione dei plasmidi Ent, Col, Hly e R in popolazioni di E.
coli isolati da vitelli e suinetti affetti da diarrea colibacillare.
**Incidence of Ent, Col, Hly and R plasmids in strains of E. coli
isolated from calves and piglets with neonatal diarrhoea.**
Publications.

14383 Panebianco, F.; Muscarella, A.; Galofaro, V.; Macri,
B.; Filoramo, C.   IT 041703/79/0001 N
I fosfolipidi nel polmone bovino. Indagini cromatografiche
quali–quantitative su focolai di enfisema e di atepectasia.
**Phospholipids in the lung of the bovines. Researches quantity
and quality–wise by thin layer chromatography upon
emphysematous and atelectatics foci.**

14384 Carlotto, F.   IT 050400/77/0542 R
Ricerca sulla eziologia, epidemiologia, mortalità e profilassi
nei confronti delle malattie respiratorie del bovino. **Research
on the entiology, epidemiology, mortality and prophylaxis of
respiratory diseases in bovine cattle.**

14385 Corrias, A.   IT 050500/77/0655
Studio dei tassi sierici degli ormoni ovarici e ipofisari nella
specie bovina in varie condizioni fisiologiche e patologiche. **A
study of the serum values of ovarian and hypophysis hormones
in the bovine race under physiological and pathological
conditions.**

14386 Rossi, C.   IT 050500/77/0845
Virosi enteriche nei vitelli. **Enteric virus diseases in calves.**

14387 Nachtimann, C.   IT 050500/78/1177 N
Studio dei tassi sierici degli ormoni ovarici e ipofisari nella
specie bovina in varie condizioni fisiologiche e patologiche.
**Study of the serum level of ovarian and pituitary hormones in
the bovine species under various physiological and pathological
conditions.**

14388 Orfei, Z.; Piragino, S.; Lillini, E.; Di Trani, L.;
Amaddeo, D.; Zitelli, P.   IT 050700/78/0001 N
Primi rilievi serologici sulla incidenza e sulla diffusione di
alcune virosi dei bovini nell'Agro Romano. **First serologic
remarks on the occurence and diffusion of some viral diseases of
bovine in the roman country.** Publications.

14389 Evenhuis, H.H.   NL 010108/74/6385 R
Onderzoek naar de levenswijze en bestrijdingsmogelijkheden
van mest– en veevliegen. **Investigations on the life habits and
control of dung and cattle flies.**

14390 Brandsma, S.; Maatje, K.   NL 010112/75/6179
De invloed van de vacuüm condities tijdens het machinaal
melken op de infectiekansen van de uier van het rund. **The
influence of the vacuum conditions during machine milking on
the chance for udder infections in the dairy cow.**

14391 Maatje, K.; Dekker, T.   NL 010112/75/6180
De waarde van de elektrische geleiding van melk, gemeten
tijdens het melken voor het onderkennen van mastitis. **The
possibilities of electrical conductivity of milk for mastitis
detection during milking.**

14392 Kommerij, R.   NL 010208/72/8732 N
Bestrijden en voorkomen van klauwgebreken bij rundvee.
Control and prevention of lameness in cattle. Publications.

14393 Kommerij, R.   NL 010208/72/8733 N
Bestrijden en voorkomen van long– en luchtweginfecties bij
jongvee. **Control and prevention of respiratory infections in
young–stock.**

14394 Kommerij, R.   NL 010208/72/8735 N
Bestrijden en voorkomen van diarree bij kalveren. **Control and
prevention of diarrhoea in calves.**

14395 Kommerij, R.   NL 010208/73/8734 N
Bestrijding uitwendige parasieten bij rundvee en schapen.
Control of ectoparasites in cattle and sheep. Publications.

14396 Seinhorst, J.W.   NL 010208/77/8755 N

Hygiënische en preventieve maatregelen ter verbetering van de gezondheidstoestand van het vee. **Improving the health status of cattle and sheep by hygienic and preventive measures.**

14397 Kommerij, P. NL 010208/78/7959 R
Relatie tussen huisvesting en diergezondheid in moderne grupstallen en boxenstallen. **Relation between housing and animal health in modern tying stalls and cubic stalls.**

14398 Oostendorp, D. NL 010208/79/8765 N
Preventie van parasitaire infecties bij rundvee en schapen. **Controlling parasites in calves and sheep.** Publications.

14399 Schipper, C.J.; Dijkman, A.J.; Brouwer, J. NL 010213/62/4168
Onderzoek naar de hygiënische aspecten bij het optreden van uierontstekingen (o.a. bruikbaarheid speendipmiddelen, oorzaken lage produktie en matige uiergezondheid koeien Waiboerhoeve). **Hygienic aspects of the occurrence of udder infections (a.o. usefulness teatdips, cause of lowproduction and bad udder health of cattle at the experimental farm "Waiboerhoeve").** Publications.

14400 Ressang, A.A. NL 010401/64/1648
Enzoötische leucose bij het rund. **Enzootic leucosis in cattle.** Publications.

14401 Grootenhuis, G. NL 010401/68/1662
Onderzoek vatbaarheid mastitis in verband met afstamming. **Susceptibility to mastitis in relation to heredity of cattle.** Publications.

14402 Over, H.J. NL 010401/69/5538 R
Transmissie van helminthen bij rund en schaap. **Transmission of helminths in cattle and sheep.** Publications.

14403 Vliet, G. van NL 010401/69/5539 R
Infecties van rund en schaap met helminthen. **Infections of cattle and sheep by helminths.** Publications.

14404 Jong, M.F. de NL 010401/71/3012 R
Onderzoek naar het voorkomen van Chlamydia–infecties bij het rund en schaap. **Investigations on the incidence of Chlamydia infections in cattle and sheep in the Netherlands.** Publications.

14405 Over, H.J. NL 010401/71/3014 R
Immunologisch onderzoek van het rund bij leverbotinfecties. **Immunological investigations on liverfluke infested cattle.**

14406 Akkermans, J.P.W.M. NL 010401/72/4783
Ziekte van Aujeszky; diagnostiek, epizoötiologie, pathogenese, vaccinatie. **Aujeszky's disease; diagnosis, epidemiology, vaccination, pathogenesis.** Publications.

14407 Grootenhuis, G. NL 010401/75/6179
De invloed van de vacuüm condities tijdens het machinaal melken op de infectiekansen van de uier van het rund. **The influence of the vacuum conditions during machine milking on the risk of udder infections in the dairy cow.**

14408 Grootenhuis, G. NL 010401/75/6526
Diagnostiek, oorzaak en bestrijding van mastitis bij het rund. **Diagnosis, causes and control of mastitis in cattle.** Publications.

14409 Bekkum, J.G. van NL 010402/67/1212
Epidemiologisch onderzoek over mond– en klauwzeer. **Epidemiology of foot– and mouth disease.** Publications.

14410 Bekkum, J.G. van NL 010402/67/1215
Virusinfecties van runderen. **Virus infections of cattle.** Publications.

14411 Bekkum, J.G. van NL 010402/72/4783 N
Ziekte van Aujeszky; diagnostiek, epizoötiologie, pathogenese, vaccinatie. **Aujeszky's disease; diagnosis, epidemiology, vaccination, pathogenese.** Publications.

14412 Bekkum, J.G. van NL 010402/73/6901
Onderzoek met betrekking tot het "Infectious Bovine Rhino trachetis" (I.B.R.) Virus bij rundvee. **Investigations on "Infectious Bovine Rhino trachetis" (I.B.R.) virus in cattle.** Publications.

14413 Bekkum, J.G. van NL 010402/75/6902 R
Virale oorzaken van diarree bij kalveren en biggen. **Viral diarrhoea in calves and baby–pigs.** Publications.

14414 Vorstenbosch, C.J.A.H.V. NL 030001/77/7784 R
Theileria soorten bij het rund (rund, theileriosis, immunologie, iso–enzymen, epidemiologie). **Theileria species in cattle (cattle, theileriosis, immunology, iso–enzymes, epidemiology).** Publications.

14415 Bijlsma, I.G.W. NL 030002/73/5663 R
Escherichia coli–infecties bij kalveren. **Escherichia coli infections in calves.**

14416 Frik, J.F. NL 030002/75/5670 R
Diagnostiek van Mycobacterium johneïnfecties bij runderen in een preklinisch stadium met behulp van immunologische technieken. **The diagnosis of Johne's disease in a preclinical stage by different immunological techniques.**

14417 Zijderveld, F.G. van NL 030002/75/5897 R
Salmonella–infecties bij kalveren. **Salmonella infections in calves.**

14418 Hartman, E.G. NL 030002/76/6971 R
Mycoplasma–infecties bij het rund. **Mycoplasma infections in cattle.**

14419 Groothuis, D.G. NL 030002/76/8966 N
De farmakokinetiek van antibiotica bij mestkalveren en de antibakteriële aktiviteit van antibiotica en chemoterapeutica met betrekking tot salmonellose (S. dublin). **The pharmacinetics of antimicrobial drugs in veal calves and their antibacterial activity in relation to salmonellosis (S. dublin).**

14420 Gruys, E. NL 030005/73/5776
Etiologie en pathogenese van nieramyloidose bij het rund. **Ethiology and pathogenesis of bovine renal amyloidosis.** Publications.

14421 Ingh, I.G.A.M. van den NL 030005/75/7808
Atypische pneumonie bij het rund. **Atypical pneumonia in cattle.**

14422 Gruys, E. NL 030005/77/7828 R
Proteinurie bij de huisdieren (proteinurie, glomerulus, tubulus, hond, rund). **Proteinuria in domestic animals**

(proteinuria, glomerulus, tubule, dog, cattle).

14423 Uilenberg, G.   NL 030006/77/7784 R
Theileria soorten bij het rund (rund, theileriosis, immunologie, iso–enzymen, epidemiologie). **Theileria species in cattle (cattle, theileriosis, immunology, iso–enzymes, epidemiology).** Publications.

14424 Grommers, F.J.   NL 030009/73/5745 R
Mastitispreventie (mastitis, rund, ziektepreventie). **Mastitisprevention (mastitis, dairy cattle, disease prevention).** Publications.

14425 Peterse, D.J.   NL 030009/76/6160 R
Stalklimaat en longaandoeningen bij kalveren. **Relation between indoor climate and respiratory diseases in calves.**

14426 Kersjes, A.W.   NL 030010/72/5834 R
Operatieve en postoperatieve behandeling van runderen lijdende aan een lebmaagdislokatie naar rechts c.q. lebmaagtorsie. (lebmaag, pyloromyotomie, omentopecie, duodenum, alkalose, infuustherapie). **Clinical and therapeutical aspects of Abomasum Displacements (abomasum, displacements, torsions, pyloromyotomy, alkalosis, cattle).**

14427 Numans, S.R.   NL 030010/76/7765 R
Bestudering van het effect van intra–tumoraal toegediend BCG–vaccin op de ontwikkeling van oogcarcinomen bij het rund. **Studies on effect of intra–lesional BCG and surgical therapy on primary squamous cellcarcinoma of the eye in cattle.**

14428 Breukink, H.J.   NL 030011/71/5807 R
Pathogenese van de lebmaagdislokatie; invloed van rantsoen op lebmaagmotiliteit bij runderen. **Pathogenesis of abomasal displacement in cattle; influence of ration on abomasal motility.** Publications.

14429 Breukink, H.J.   NL 030011/74/5806 R
Het vóórkomen van abomasal reflux bij melkkoeien. **The occurence of abomasal reflux in dairycows.** Publications.

14430 Breukink, H.J.   NL 030011/77/7821 R
Evaluatie van de behandeling van nitraatvergiftiging bij het rund. **Evaluation of the treatment of nitrate poisoning in cattle.**

14431 Breukink, H.J.   NL 030011/77/7823
Etiologie en pathogenese van het ziektebeeld, dat optreedt bij de zogenaamde bostelvergiftiging bij rundvee. **Etiology and pathogenesis of the so–called brewers–yeast poisoning of cattle.** Publications.

14432 Breukink, H.J.   NL 030011/77/8962 N
Pyrexia, dermatitis en hemorrhagische diathese bij runderen na voedering met DUIB (di–ureo–iso–boterzuur) houdend krachtvoer. **Pyrexia, dermatitis and haemorrhagis syndrome in cattle fed with DUIB (di–ureo–iso–butyric acid) concentrates.** Publications.

14433 Biewenga, W.J.   NL 030012/77/7828 R
Proteïnurie bij de huisdieren (proteïnurie, glomerulus, tubulus, hond, rund). **Proteinuria in domestic animals (proteinuria, glomerulus, tubule, dog, cattle).**

14434 Bergh, S.G. van den   NL 030015/77/7784 R
Theileria soorten bij het rund (rund, theileriosis, immunologie,

iso–enzymen, epidemiologie). **Theileria species in cattle (cattle, theileriosis, immunology, iso–enzymes, epidemiology).** Publications.

14435 Dik, K.J.   NL 030016/76/7833
Middenrifmyopathie bij runderen. **Myo–pathology of the diaphragm in cattle.**

14436 Verhoeff, J.   NL 030017/76/6144 R
Het bovine serumalbumine en het celgetal in de diagnostiek van uierinfekties. **Bovine serumalbumine and cellcount in the diagnosis of udderinfections.**

14437 Helle, W.   NL 040001/74/6740 R
Resistentie tegen pesticiden bij runderteken, Rhipicephalus spp.. **Resistance to pesticides in Cattle ticks, Rhipicephalus spp.. Publications.**

14438 Knapen, F. van   NL 040011/73/7504
Ontwikkeling van detectiemethoden van cysticercose bij het rund, mede i.v.m. besmettingsgevaar voor de mens. **Development of detection methods of cysticercosis in cattle, also in connection with contamination danger for humans.**

14439 Ruitenberg, E.J.; Sirks, J.L.; Kreeftenberg, J.G.
    NL 040011/76/7765 R
Bestudering van het effect van intra–tumoraal toegediend BCG–vaccin op de ontwikkeling van oogcarcinomen bij het rund. **Studies on effect of intra–lesional BCG and surgical therapy on primary squamous cellcarcinoma of the eye in cattle.**

Sheep (B 4220)

See also 10911, 10939, 11034, 11035, 11036, 11047, 12315, 13216, 14099, 14104, 14161, 14196, 14395, 14396, 14398, 14402, 14403, 14404

14440 Rudolph, R.; Weiss, E.   DE 129620/73/0002
Untersuchungen zur Ätiologie und Pathogenese der Schafleukose. **Investigations into the etiology and pathogenesis of sheep leukosis.**

14441 Rieck, G.W.; Mayer, K.   DE 129680/78/0003 N
Typen und Vorkommen von Spontanmissbildungen beim Schaf. **Types and frequencies of spontaneous malformations in sheep.**

14442 Loeffler, K.; Fluhr, R.   DE 144605/77/0001
Synovialgruben beim Schaf. **Synovial fossae in sheep.**

14443 Dennig, H.K.   DE 160820/74/0003
Vergleichende Untersuchungen zur Trypanosoma evansiInfektion bei Laboratoriumstieren, Chinchillas, Schafen und Schweinen. **Comparative studies on the infection of laboratory animals, chinchillas, sheep and pigs with Trypanosoma evansi.**

14444 Munz, E.; Munderloh, U.   DE 160821/77/0001
Die Nairobi Sheep Disease – eine synoptische Darstellung der Erkrankung sowie Untersuchungen zum Verhalten des Erregers in vivo und in vitro. **Nairobi sheep disease – a synoptic review about the disease and in vivo and in vitro experiments with the virus.**

14445 Munz, E.   DE 160821/78/0001 N

Untersuchungen zur biologischen Charakterisierung des Virus der Nairobi–Schafkrankheit. **Investigations on biological characteristics of Nairobi sheep disease virus.**

14446 Forstner, M.J.; Kopp, H.　　　　DE 160823/75/0002
Untersuchungen über Entwicklung und Pathogenität kleiner Lungenwürmer – Cystocaulus;Neostrongylus – im Schaf. **Investigations of development and pathogenicity of small lungworms – Cystocaulus;Neostrongylus – in sheep.**

14447 Forstner, M.J.; Kopp, H.　　　　DE 160823/78/0001 N
Untersuchungen über die jahreszeitlichen Schwankungen in der Ausscheidung von Protostrongylidenlarven bei Schafherden. **Investigations of the seasonal fluctuations in the excretion of protostrongyle larvae by flocks of sheep.**

14448 Dirksen, G.; Damaris, E.　　　　DE 502300/77/0006
Über Osteopathien bei Mastlämmern. **On osteopathies of store lambs.**

14449 Researcher not indicated　　　　DE 502400/74/0001
Die Beeinflussung einer Infektion mit Rickettsia burneti –Q–Fieber– in Schafherden durch Einsatz von Organ–Vakzinen. **The effect of organ vaccines on flocks of sheep infected with Ricksettsia burneti –Q fever–.**

14450 Lund, E.　　　　DK 030138/76/0007
Fællesnordiske undersøgelser angående den langsomme virusinfektion maedi–visna hos får. **Collaborative Scandinavian studies of the slow virus infection of sheep caused by Maedi visna.**

14451 Remesy, C.; Demigne, C.　　　　FR 010817/73/8038
Problèmes de la néoglucogénèse et de cétogénèse chez la brebis gestante : Toxémie de gestation. **Problems of gluconeogenesis and ketogenesis in pregnant ewes : Pregnancy toxemia.**

14452 Pardon, P.; Fensterbank, R.; Verger, J.M.
　　　　FR 011503/78/8103
Salmonellose ovine, naturelle et expérimentale. **Natural and experimental ovine salmonellosis.**

14453 Gruner, L.; Mauleon, P.　　　　FR 011505/76/5175
Ecologie des strongles parasites du mouton dans le Limousin. **Ecology of the sheep thread–worms in "Limousin".**

14454 Bories, G.　　　　FR 011912/74/2770
Etude d'un modèle de contamination de la chaîne alimentaire: transfert d'un antibiotique (tétracycline – ³H) et d'un pesticide (lindane) chez le Mouton consommateur de fientes de poules pondeuses ayant reçu ces substances dans leur alimentation. **Study of a food chain contamination model: transfer of an antibiotic (³H – tetracycline) and a pesticide (lindane or –HCH) in sheep fed on droppings of laying hens that have received these substances in their diet.**

14455 Asso, J.; L'haridon, R.; Le Jan, C.　　FR 012225/70/8023
Immunité dans l'ecthyma du mouton et de la chèvre. **Orf immunity in goat and sheep.**

14456 Dickinson; Stamp　　　　GB 010102/00/0001
Epidemiology and pathogenesis of scrapie.

14457 Dickinson; Stamp　　　　GB 010102/00/0002
Genetics of scrapie susceptibility.

14458 Dickinson　　　　GB 010102/00/0003
Pathogenesis of scrapie.

14459 Dickinson　　　　GB 010102/00/0004 R
Nature and variation of scrapie agents.

14460 Nind　　　　GB 010102/76/0008
Cell chemotaxis changes in disease.

14461 Dickinson; Taylor　　　　GB 010102/79/0009 N
Development of scrapie decontamination procedures.

14462 Sales　　　　GB 010103/75/0010 R
Genetic aspects of correlated immune responses in sheep.

14463 Ward; Huskisson　　　　GB 010302/00/0037 R
Metabolism of adult Haemonchus contortus from sheep.

14464 Ward; Huskisson　　　　GB 010302/00/0049 R
In vitro culture of Haemonchus contortus from egg to adult.

14465 Hunter; Kimberlin　　　　GB 010402/00/0030 R
Interference with the development of scrapie.

14466 Haig; Kimberlin　　　　GB 010402/00/0812
Epidemiological studies of scrapie.

14467 Hunter; Kimberlin　　　　GB 010402/00/0813
Nature of the scrapie agent and pathogenesis of disease.

14468 Kimberlin　　　　GB 010402/00/0814
Genetic control of susceptibility of sheep to experimental scrapie.

14469 Hunter; Kimberlin　　　　GB 010402/76/0051
Long term transmission experiments with scrapie and related nervous disorders.

14470 Hunter; Kimberlin　　　　GB 010403/00/0813
Nature of the scrapie agent and pathogenesis of disease.

14471 Pattison　　　　GB 010404/78/0031
Development of scrapie resistant Swaledale sheep.

14472 Hunter; Kimberlin　　　　GB 010404/78/0813
Nature of the scrapie agent and pathogenesis of disease.

14473 Kimberlin　　　　GB 010404/78/0814
Genetic control of susceptibility of sheep to experimental scrapie.

14474 Haig　　　　GB 010405/00/0812
Epidemiological studies of scrapie.

14475 Hunter; Kimberlin　　　　GB 010405/00/0813
Nature of the scrapie agent and pathogenesis of disease.

14476 Brown; Newman　　　　GB 010901/78/0010
Structure function relationships in bluetongue virus.

14477 Austin　　　　GB 011211/77/0003
The health of ewes and lambs during the perinatal period.

14478 Clarkson　　　　GB 022207/79/0002 N
Cultural and immunological studies on enzootic abortion of

ewes.

14479 Sykes; Robinson   GB 030101/00/0014
Broken mouth.

14480 Smith; Wright   GB 030101/00/0022
Vitamin d status of sheep.

14481 Suttle   GB 030101/76/0027
Effect of parasitism on metabolism.

14482 Mould   GB 030102/00/0006
Nature of antigen and antibody in inactivated virus
encephalomyelitis (louping–ill).

14483 Dawson; Mould   GB 030102/00/0011
Secretory immunoglobulins in pneumonia.

14484 Mould   GB 030102/00/0013
Development of foetal immune response.

14485 Mould; Dawson   GB 030102/00/0014
Isolation and characterisation of Border Disease Virus.

14486 Smith; Gray, W.   GB 030103/00/0001
Pulmonary adenomatosis.

14487 Smith; Gray, W.   GB 030103/00/0003
Ultrastructure of small intestine and nematodirus battus
infection.

14488 Smith   GB 030103/00/0005
Electron microscopy of louping–ill virus.

14489 Smith   GB 030103/00/0008
Border disease.

14490 Smith; Gray   GB 030103/76/0019
Contagious pustular dermatitis ORF.

14491 Smith; Gray   GB 030103/76/0021
Pasteurella.

14492 Smith   GB 030103/76/0022
Moraxella.

14493 Christie   GB 030104/00/0001
Size of dose to produce self–cure from Haemonchus contortus.

14494 Christie; Patterson   GB 030104/00/0002
Physiological changes in sheep during development of resistance
to Haemonchus contortus.

14495 Christie; Patterson   GB 030104/00/0003
Immunity developed on prolonged high intake of larvae of
Haemonchus contortus.

14496 Christie; Jackson   GB 030104/00/0008
Development of immunity to Tricholstrongylus colubriformis.

14497 Christie; Patterson   GB 030104/00/0011
Nematode physiology.

14498 Jackson   GB 030104/00/0012
Egg counting method for studying immunity in pure and mixed
worm infections.

14499 Robinson   GB 030105/00/0009
Identification and pathogenicity of Chlamydia.

14500 Snodgrass   GB 030105/00/0010
Diagnostic service for tick–borne fever.

14501 Vantsis   GB 030105/00/0012
Aetiology and pathology of border disease.

14502 Martin; Scott   GB 030105/00/0013
Causes, epidemiology and transmission of pulmonary
adenomatosis.

14503 Martin; Scott   GB 030105/00/0014
Biological, physical and ultrastructural characteristics of the
herpesvirus in pulmonary adenomatosis.

14504 Martin; Scott   GB 030105/00/0015
Distribution of tumor antigens in pulmonary adenomatosis.

14505 Snodgrass; Sharp   GB 030105/00/0016
Isolate and characterise viral agents in respiratory infections.

14506 Burrells; Wells   GB 030105/00/0017
Local and serological immune reactions to respiratory
infections.

14507 Wells; Burrells   GB 030105/00/0018
Study of cellular immune mechanisms.

14508 Reid; Boyce   GB 030105/00/0022 R
Epidemiology and control of louping ill.

14509 Jones; Rae   GB 030105/00/0023
Sheep mycoplasma –pathogenicity and immunity studies.

14510 Reid; Boyce   GB 030105/77/0024
Contagious pustular dermatitis ORF.

14511 Snodgrass; Gilmour   GB 030105/77/0027
Lamb enteritis.

14512 Barlow; Gardiner   GB 030106/00/0001
Pathogenesis and aetiology of border disease.

14513 Buxton   GB 030106/00/0012
Pathology, histochemistry and biochemistry of focal
symmetrical encepalomalacia.

14514 Rushton; Gilmour   GB 030106/00/0016
Pathology, pathogenesis and immunity in non–viral sheep
pneumonias.

14515 Rushton   GB 030106/00/0017
Viral pneumonias and respiratory tract infections of
sheep; aetiology, pathogenesis, pathology and immunity.

14516 Spence; Aitchison   GB 030106/00/0019
Clinical study of broken mouth and comparative morphology
and biochemistry of bone.

14517 Angus; Gardiner   GB 030106/77/0021
Pulmonary adenomatosis of sheep.

14518 Barlow; Gardiner   GB 030106/77/0024

Reproductive loss.

14519 Stamp — GB 030109/00/0001
Etiology and pathogenesis of scrapie.

14520 Mellor; Matheson — GB 030111/00/0002
Self regulation of foetal development in utero and its association
with lamb mortality.

14521 Mitchell; Williams — GB 030112/00/0002
Causes, epidemiology and transmission of pulmonary
adenomatosis.

14522 Cuthbertson — GB 030112/76/0012
Causes of embryonic and perinatal deaths in sheep.

14523 Clenhew — GB 030112/76/0015
Prevalence and aetiology of sheep infertility.

14524 Clerihew — GB 030112/77/0016
Clinical and epidemiological studies on scrapie.

14525 Cuthbertson — GB 030112/78/0019
Sheep disease surveillance.

14526 Quarterman; Morrison — GB 030604/00/0007
Influence of dietary composition on the absorption, retention
and toxicity of lead in farm animals.

14527 King — GB 030608/75/0019
Cytology of copper poisoning.

14528 Fell; Wilson — GB 030608/78/0022
Pathology of cobalamin and thiamin deficiency in sheep.

14529 Bowen; Cuthbert — GB 030903/69/0409 R
Use of stupefacients for control of hooded crows.

14530 Thompson; Todd — GB 040403/79/0016 N
Studies of chronic copper poisoning in sheep.

14531 Researcher not indicated — GB 050404/00/0002
Causes of sheep tumors including bracken.

14532 Researcher not indicated — GB 050422/00/0004
Listeriosis in sheep.

14533 Researcher not indicated — GB 050422/00/0006
Study of experimental ovine toxoalasmosis.

14534 Researcher not indicated — GB 050434/00/0001
Sheep health project, parasite control.

14535 Researcher not indicated — GB 050434/00/0002
Ovine hypocalcaemia in association with osteomalacia.

14536 Researcher not indicated — GB 050435/00/0002
Epidemiology of transmission of toxoplasmosis.

14537 Researcher not indicated — GB 050443/00/0003
Studies on wastage of adult sheep, with reference to dental
defects (VLP 6/30).

14538 Researcher not indicated — GB 050471/00/0010
National survey of lungworms in sheep.

14539 Researcher not indicated — GB 050481/00/0001
Eradication of foot rot.

14540 Researcher not indicated — GB 050483/00/0007
Seasonal variations in metabolic disorders and twinning rates.

14541 Ollernshaw — GB 050502/00/0015
Forecasting the incidence of swayback.

14542 Machin; Quick — GB 050502/76/0020
Sheep dip studies.

14543 Gray — GB 050503/00/0011
Development of a potency test for Fusiformis nodusus vaccines.

14544 Frerichs; Evans — GB 050503/00/0012
Development of the potency tests for ovine enzootic abortion
vaccine.

14545 Frerichs; Evans — GB 050503/00/0013
Development of the potency tests for contagious pustular
dermatitis vaccine.

14546 O'Neill — GB 050504/00/0016
Sheep dermatophilus infection.

14547 Everett — GB 050505/00/0003
Epidemiology of parasitic gastro–enteritis in sheep.

14548 Ollernshaw — GB 050505/00/0007
Forecasting the incidence of swayback.

14549 Joyner — GB 050505/00/0011
Experimental coccidiosis in lambs.

14550 Tarry; Kirkwood — GB 050505/00/0014
Efficacy, persistance and safe disposal of sheep dips.

14551 Kirkwood — GB 050505/00/0018
Sheep scab and mange.

14552 Tarry — GB 050505/00/0019
Biology and vectors of Dicrocoelium dendriticum.

14553 Richardson — GB 050506/75/0030
Ovine mandibular osteopathy.

14554 Markson — GB 050506/75/0049
Definitive and differential pathology of naturally occurring
diseases of sheep.

14555 Terlecki — GB 050506/75/0054
Reproductive failure in sheep. Pathogenicity of BVD virus for
the sheep foetus.

14556 Harkness — GB 050508/00/0002 R
Border disease of sheep: transmission, virus isolation, electron
microscopy, serological relationships.

14557 Brown; Lapraik — GB 050512/00/0008
Salmonella typhimurium infections in lambs.

14558 Ross; Halliday — GB 050512/00/0018
Trichostrongylus axei : immunology.

14559 Miller — GB 060116/00/0002

An epidemiological approach to the control of ovine toxoplasmosis.

14560 Linklater GB 060116/00/0004
Experimental salmonella infection in sheep.

14561 Dyson GB 060116/00/0005
Studies on respiratory infection in sheep.

14562 Johnston GB 060212/00/0003
Investigations into neonatal deaths in Caithness lambs.

14563 Walker GB 060219/00/0009
Cerebrocortical necrosis.

14564 Knox GB 060226/00/0004 R
Investigation of causes of acceleration of broken mouth condition in sheep.

14565 Knox GB 060226/79/0008 N
Investigation of the condition of broken mouth in sheep.

14566 Bannatyne GB 060312/00/0002
The epidemiology, diagnosis and control of louping ill.

14567 Maddox GB 060312/00/0003
Fluke control and forecasting.

14568 Barber; MacPherson GB 060312/78/0009
Survey of blood copper and cobalt levels in sheep flocks in the West of Scotland.

14569 Kearney, A. IE 060700/74/1011 R
Effect of anelthelmintic treatment at mating on lambing performance. Publications.

14570 Hope Cawdery, M.J. IE 060701/71/0698 R
Evaluation of mid–season fat lamb production on drained drumlin soil with emphasis on control of liver fluke. Publications.

14571 Hope Cawdery, M.J. IE 060706/69/0460 R
Control of fascioliosis (fluke and sheep) 1. Study of the epizootiologe of fascioliosis and the effects of various control measures on it. Publications.

14572 Leek, B.F.; Kisauzi, D.N. IE 120203/79/9202 N
Liver blood flow and metabolism in healthy and diseased sheep.

14573 Hirsch, E.A.; Abouswa, M. IE 120205/79/9205 N
A study of the pathology of lameness in lambs and sheep under intensive management.

14574 Pelosi, A.; Di Taranto, F.; Taibi, L.; Dell'Aquila, S. IT 020700/79/0015 N
Controllo del passaggio e del metabolismo delle sostanze utilizzate per la sincronizzazione dei calori nelle pecore. **Metabolism of the substances used in sheep oestrum synchronisation.**

14575 Goffredo, G. IT 050900/77/0558 R
Cause di mortalità pre e post–natale fino allo svezzamento degli ovini. Ricerche su portatori di enterobatteri–ovini. **Sheep: pre and post natal causes of death up to the weaning period. Research on entero–bacteria carriers.**

14576 Sobrero, L. IT 050900/77/0587 R
Ricerca sulla incidenza delle malattie degli ovini da ectoparassiti e riflessi negativi sulle produzioni. **Research on the frequency of ecto–parasitosis in sheep and its negative consequences on production.**

14577 Bekkum, J.G. van NL 010402/67/1216 R
Zwoegerziekte bij schapen. **Chronic interstitial pneumonia of sheep.** Publications.

14578 Bekkum, J.G. van NL 010402/75/6903 R
Virusinfecties bij schapen (Border disease, Ecthyma). **Virus infections of sheep (Border disease, Ecthyma).** Publications.

14579 Cornelisse, J.L. NL 030002/73/5669 R
Onderzoek naar het effect van een vaccin tegen rotkreupel bij schapen. **Results of a vaccination against footrot in sheep.** Publications.

14580 Cremers, H.J.W.M. NL 030004/74/5842 R
Vookomen, epidemiologie en pathofysiologie van de kleine longworm, in het bijzonder Muellerius capillaris bij het schaap in Nederland. **Incidence, epidemiology and pathophysiologie of small lungworms in sheep, especially Muellerius capillaris, in the Netherlands.** Publications.

14581 Uilenberg, G. NL 030006/77/8965 N
Bloedparasieten bij schapen in Nederland (schaap, Babesia, Anaplasma, Cytoecetes, Nederland). **Blood parasites of sheep in the Netherlands (sheep, Babesia, Anaplasma, Cytoecetes, Netherlands).** Publications.

14582 Grommers, F.J. NL 030009/70/5714
De oorzaak van abnormale liggingen van lammeren bij de partus i.v.m. perinatale lammersterfte. **Perinatal lambmortality: Causes of abnormal presentation of lambs at birth.**

14583 Peterse, D.J. NL 030009/73/5669 R
Onderzoek naar het effect van een vaccin tegen rotkreupel bij schapen. **Results of a vaccination against footrot in sheep.** Publications.

14584 Toussaint, E. NL 030010/73/5669 R
Onderzoek naar het effect van een vaccin tegen rotkreupel bij schapen. **Results of a vaccination against footrot in sheep.** Publications.

14585 Buitelaar, J.W. NL 030017/73/5669 R
Onderzoek naar het effect van een vaccin tegen rotkreupel bij schapen. **Results of a vaccination against footrot in sheep.** Publications.

14586 Herweijer, C.H. NL 060011/57/4350
Oorzaken van ziekte en sterfte onder schapen en methoden tot preventie en behandeling van ziekten. **Causes of morbidity and mortality in sheep and methods for prevention and treatment of diseases.** Publications.

Goats, farm deer and other ruminants (B 4290)

See also 1888, 14455, 14670, 14671

14587 Fischer, H.; Berger, W. DE 129540/71/0007
Untersuchungen über die Gesundheit, Haltung, Zucht und Nutzung von Dromedaren. **Investigations on health,**

husbandry, breeding and utilization of dromedaries.

14588 Loeffler, K.; Marx, D.; Rieck, G.W.
DE 144605/75/0003
Sexualaktivität, Spermaqualität und zytogenetische Befunde von Nachkommen eines Ziegenbockes mit Gynäkomastie. **Sexual activity, quality of sperm and cytogenetic status of the offsprings of a goat with gynaecomastia.**

14589 Yvore, P.; Guillimin, P.; Naciri, M.; Hubert, J.
FR 011505/78/8069
Coccidiose caprine. **Coccidiosis of goats.**

14590 McDiarmid; Matthew
GB 010405/00/0039
Diseases of deer, especially those associated with mycobacteria.

14591 Sharman; Corrigall
GB 030607/00/0014
Susceptibility of red deer to parasitic and other diseases.

14592 Hunter
GB 050512/00/0019
Diseases of red deer. Susceptibility to Mycobacterium avium.

14593 Bannatyne; Maddox
GB 060312/78/0008
The health of farmed red deer on Rahoy estate, Morvern.

14594 Izzi, R.
IT 051000/77/0560 R
Cause di mortalita pre e post–natale ivi comprese le malattie neonatali dei bufalini. **Pre– and post–natal causes of death in buffalo calves including neo–natal diseases.**

14595 Rania, U.; Izzi, R.; Aprea, M.
IT 051000/78/0002 N
Ulteriori indagini sulle mastiti della specie bufalina. **Further research on the mastitis in Buffaloes.**

14596 Miert, A.S.J.P.A.M. van
NL 030003/78/8988 N
Invloed van tryponasome infekties bij de geit en het konijn op stollingsfaktoren. De beïnvloeding hiervan door anti–pyretica (geit, T.vivax, bloed–coagulatie, anti–pyretica, konijn, T.brucei). **The influence of trypanosomal infection in the goat and rabbit on coagulation factors and the effect of anti–pyretics (goat, T.vivax, bloodcoagulation factors, anti–pyretics, T.brucei). Publications.**

14597 Dijk, J.E. van
NL 030005/73/5777 R
Congenitaal struma bij geiten (congenitaal, struma, geit, eiwitsynthese defekt, hypothyreoidie). **Congenital goitre in goats (congenital, goitre, protein synthesis defect, hypothyroidism).**

14598 Ingh, Th.S.G.A.M. van den
NL 030005/78/8988 N
Invloed van tryponasome infekties bij de geit en het konijn op stollingsfaktoren. De beïnvloeding hiervan door anti–pyretica (geit, T.vivax, bloed–coagulatie, anti–pyretica, konijn, T.brucei). **The influence of trypanosomal infection in the goat and rabbit on coagulation factors and the effect of anti–pyretics (goat, T.vivax, bloodcoagulation factors, anti–pyretics, T.brucei). Publications.**

14599 Zwart, D.
NL 030006/78/8988 N
Invloed van tryponasome infekties bij de geit en het konijn op stollingsfaktoren. De beïnvloeding hiervan door anti–pyretica (geit, T.vivax, bloed–coagulatie, anti–pyretica, konijn, T.brucei). **The influence of trypanosomal infection in the goat and rabbit on coagulation factors and the effect of anti–pyretics (goat, T.vivax, bloodcoagulation factors, anti–pyretics, T.brucei). Publications.**

14600 Slappendel, R.J.
NL 030012/78/8988 N
Invloed van tryponasome infekties bij de geit en het konijn op stollingsfaktoren. De beïnvloeding hiervan door anti–pyretica (geit, T.vivax, bloed–coagulatie, anti–pyretica, konijn, T.brucei). **The influence of trypanosomal infection in the goat and rabbit on coagulation factors and the effect of anti–pyretics (goat, T.vivax, bloodcoagulation factors, anti–pyretics, T.brucei). Publications.**

14601 Dam, R.H. van
NL 030018/74/6974 N
Histocompatibiliteitssystemen bij herkauwers (geit) (weefselantigenen, immunogenetica, regulatie van de immuunrespons, resistentie, MHC). **Histocompatibility systems in ruminants (goat) (tissue antigens, immunogenetics, regulation of the immune response, disease resistance, MHC). Publications.**

Pigs (B 4300)

See also 10911, 11107, 11214, 11264, 12427, 12494, 12562, 12861, 13263, 13352, 13477, 13485, 13490, 13493, 14063, 14106, 14135, 14156, 14173, 14382, 14406, 14409, 14411, 14413, 14443, 15125

14602 Hoorens, J.; De Rijcke, R.
BE 050500/69/0001 R
Studie van enteritis bij varkens. **Study of enteritis in swine.** Publications.

14603 Hoorens, J.; Thoonen, F.
BE 050500/72/0002 R
Klinisch anatomo pathologische studie voor de diagnostiek van vomiting en wasting disease bij varkens. **Clinica anatomo–pathological study to establish a diagnose of vomiting and wasting disease in swine (viral encephalitides). Publications.**

14604 Hoorens, J.; Thoonen, F.; Ducatelle, R.
BE 050500/76/0003 R
Viral encephalitis bij varkens. **Viral encephalitis in pigs.**

14605 Hoorens, J.; Coussement, W.; Van Den Berghe, J.
BE 050500/76/0004 R
Bloederig Bowel syndroom en adematosis bij varkens. **Haemorrhagic bowel syndrome and adematosis by pigs.**

14606 Pensaert, M.; Andries, K.
BE 050600/69/0001 R
Studie van de immunisatie tegen transmissibele gastroenteritis (TGE) bij varkens. **Study on immunisation against transmissible gastroenteritis (TGE) in swine.** Publications.

14607 Pensaert, M.; Callebaut, P.; Vandeputte, J.
BE 050600/72/0002 R
Studie van virale encephalitiden bij varkens (Vomiting and wasting: ziekte van Aujeszky). **Study of viral encephalitides in swine (Vomiting and wasting disease Aujeszky disease).**

14608 Pensaert, M.; Debouck, P.
BE 050600/77/0007 R
Virale diarrhee bij varkens: rotavirus en epizoötisch coronavirus. **Viral diarrhea in swines: rotavirus and epizootic diarrhea virus.** Publications.

14609 Dewaele, A.; Martineau, G.
BE 060007/69/0001
Recherches sur les maladies respiratoires chez le porc. **Research on respiratory diseases in pigs.**

14610 Thomas, J.; Pohl, P.
BE 110000/72/0010
Etude des colibacilles entéropathogènes du porcelet. **Study of**

E. coli pathogenic for baby pigs. Publications.

14611 Famerée, L.; Cotteleer, C.; De Meuter, F.
BE 110000/72/0012
Enquête épidémiologique sur la toxoplasmose et étude de la maladie chez le porc. **Epidemiologic survey on toxoplasmosis and study of the disease in pig.** Publications.

14612 Biront, P.
BE 110000/78/0052 N
Rol van intrauteriene virale besmetting bij de zeug. **Role of intra–uterine virusinfection in sow.** Publications.

14613 Mortelmans, J.; Geerts, S.; Kumar, V.; De Deken, R.
BE 140000/74/0065 N
Interne en externe parasieten bij varkens. **Internal and external parasites of pigs.** Publications.

14614 Hörchner, F.; Langnes, A.
DE 104202/74/0003
Therapie der larvalen Bandwürmer beim Schwein und des Echinococcus granulosus bei Maus und Kaninchen. **Therapy of larval stages of cestodes in pigs and of Echinococcus granulosus in mice and rabbits.**

14615 Mülling, M.; Krauss, D.
DE 104400/75/0003
Über den Einfluss verschiedener zur Schnittentbindung bei Schweinen benutzter Anästhetika auf das Verhalten von pHWerten und Blutgasen bei Ferkeln und Sauen. **The influence of different anaesthetics employed in cesarean section in swine on the behaviour of pH values and blood gases in piglets and sows.**

14616 Schimmelpfennig, H.H.; Ferstl, T.
DE 132330/71/0004
Untersuchungen zur Ätiologie der Rhinitis atrophicans der Schweine. **Studies on the etiology of atrophic rhinitis of pig.** Publications.

14617 Schulz, L.–C.
DE 139100/73/0001
Experimenteller Rotlauf bei verschiedenen Spezies als Modell einer systemischen Bindegewebskrankheit. **Experimental erysipelas in different swine species as model of systemic connective tissue disease.**

14618 Trautwein, G.
DE 139101/73/0001
Immunpathogenese der chronischen Rotlauf–Polyarthritis des Schweines. **Immunopathogenesis of chronic erysipelas polyarthritis in pigs.**

14619 Trautwein, G.
DE 139101/73/0002
Fetale Virusinfektionen – Schweinepest – und Ontogenese der Antikörperbildung beim Schwein. **Fetal virus infections – hog cholera – and ontogenesis of antibody formation in pigs.**

14620 Trautwein, G.; Winkelmann, J.
DE 139101/74/0001
Enzymbestimmung der experimentellen Rotlaufpolyarthritis des Schweines. **Enzyme determination in experimental polyarthritis of pig –Erysipelothrix rhusiopathiae–.**

14621 Trautwein, G.; Müller–Peddinghaus, R.
DE 139101/75/0001
Complementbestimmung 'CH 50' bei 1.experimentellem Rotlauf des Schweines 2.Aleutenkrankheit der Nerze 3.spontaner Glomerulonephritis des Hundes. **Complement determination 'CH 50' in 1.experimental erysipelas of pig 2.Aleutian disease of minks 3.spontaneous glomerulonephritis of dog.**

14622 Drommer, W.
DE 139103/74/0001
Experimenteller Coli– und Neurotoxinschock beim Schwein Transmissions– und Rasterelektronenmikroskopie. **Experimental Coli– and neurotoxin shock of pig transmission electron microscopy and raster electron microscopy.**

14623 Drommer, W.
DE 139103/74/0003
Transmissions– und raster–elektronenmikroskopische Untersuchungen beim experimentellen Rotlauf des Schweines. **Transmission electron microscopy and raster electron microscopy in experimental erysipelas of pig.**

14624 Drommer, W.; Veltmann, E.
DE 139103/75/0001
Nierenalterationen beim Schwein nach experimentellem Schock und Rotlauf. **Morphological alterations in the pig kidney due to experimental shock and esysipelas.**

14625 Harmeyer, J.; Grabe, C.von
DE 139200/73/0004
Klinisch ätiologische Untersuchungen bei Schweinen mit erblicher Rachitis. **Etiological studies on pigs with hereditary rickets.**

14626 Wegner, W.; Reetz, I.; Rudorf, B.
DE 139350/75/0001
Endo– und Exogenese der elastischen Eigenschaften von Aorta und Herzkranzgefässen in einer grossen Schweinepopulation. **Endogenesis and exogenesis of characteristics related with the elasticity of the aorta and the coronary vessels of the heart in a big pig population.**

14627 Böhm, K.H.; Weiss, R.; Ross, R.F.; Bollwahn, W.; Mumme, J.
DE 139450/70/0001
Untersuchungen zur Pathogenese des chronischen Rotlaufs beim Schwein sowie des Aborts durch Rotlaufbakterien. **Investigations of the pathogenesis of chronic erysipelas infection of swine and of abort caused by these bacteria.**

14628 Böhm, K.H.; Mumme, J.
DE 139450/72/0002
Untersuchungen über toxische Bestandteile von Rotlaufbakterien. **Investigations into toxic factors of erysipelas bacteria.**

14629 Kirchhoff, H.; Ross, R.F.
DE 139450/75/0002
Mykoplasmenarthritis des Schweines. **Mycoplasma arthritis in swine.**

14630 Kirchhoff, H.; Bisping, W.; Bugel, G.; Meyer, H.; Markquardt, J.; Schulze, W.
DE 139450/75/0003
Untersuchungen zu Ätiologie und Diagnose der Rhinitis athrophicans des Schweines. **Studies on etiology and diagnosis of atrophic rhinitis of swine.**

14631 Amtsberg, G.
DE 139450/78/0002 N
Untersuchungen zur Bakteriologie, Pathogenese und Immunprophylaxe der Staphylococcus–hyicus–Infektion des Schweines und der Staphylococcus epidermitis Biotyp–2–Infektion des Rindes. **Investigations on bacteriology, pathogenesis and immunoprophylaxis of infection of swine with staphylococcus hyicus and of infection of cattle with Staphylococcus epidermitis biotype 2.**

14632 Petzoldt, K.
DE 139450/78/0003 N
Untersuchungen zur aerogenen Immunisierung gegen bakterielle Infektionskrankheiten insbesondere am Modell der Rotlaufinfektion von gnotobiotischen Schweinen und Mäusen. **Investigations on aerogenic immunization against bacterial infectious deseases, especially against infection with erysipelas**

in gnotobiotic swine and mice.

14633 Liess, B.; Marquardt, J.; Hafez, S. DE 139550/77/0001
Übertragung von Cytomegalovirus auf gnotobiotische
Schweine. **Transmission of cytomegalovirus into gnotobiotic
piglets.**

14634 Liess, B.; Frey, H.R.; Meyer, H. DE 139550/78/0003 N
Bestimmung von neutralisierenden Antikörpertitern gegen
Stämme des Virus der Europäischen Schweinepest 'ESP' und
des Virus der Bovinen Virusdiarrhoe 'BVD' in Feldseren aus
Schweinepestverdächtigen Ferkelerzeugerbetrieben. **Titration
of neutralizing antibodies against SF and BVD strains in swine
sera collected from SF suspected piglet breeding farms.**

14635 Liess, B.; Marquardt, J.; Hafez, S.
DE 139550/78/0004 N
Virologische und serologische Untersuchungen zur Ätiologie
der Rhinitis atrophicans des Schweines. **Virological and
serological investigations for the etiology of the atrophic rhinitis
in pigs.**

14636 Liess, B.; Hermanns, W.; Meyer, H.; Trautwein, G.
DE 139550/78/0005 N
Immunologische Reaktion und persistierende Virämie bei
Europäischer Schweinepest. **Immunological reaction and
persistent virusinfection in European swine fever.** Publications.

14637 Moennig, V.; Busse, C.; Riffelmann, B.
DE 139551/75/0001
Analyse der Polypeptidzusammensetzung eines C–Virus vom
Schwein und Herstellung eines komplexen Antiserums
dagegen. **Analysis of the polypeptide composition of a porcine
c–type virus 'PLCP' and production of a complex antiserum
against it.** Publications.

14638 Plonait, H. DE 139750/78/0002 N
Beeinträchtigung von Futterverwertung und täglicher
Zunahme von Mastschweinen durch chronische Krankheiten.
**Effect of chronic diseases on feed conversion and daily gain in
fattening pigs.** Publications.

14639 Schulze, W.; Raebel, R. DE 139750/78/0005 N
Behandlung der puerperalen Septicämie und Toxämie der
Sauen mit Lotagen. **Treatment of puerperal septicemia and
toxemia in sows using Lotagen.**

14640 Schulze, W.; Warnecke, W. DE 139750/78/0007 N
Behandlungsversuche bei der puerperalen Septikämie und
Toxämie der Sauen 'MMA–Syndrom' mit Trimethoprim '24%'
unter Zusatz von Glucocorticoid und Antihistaminikum in
alternierender Reihe vergleichend mit einer praxisüblichen
Therapie. **Treatment trials in puerperal septicemia and toxemia
in sows 'MMA–syndrome' using trimethoprime '24%' with the
addition of glucocorticoid and antihistamine alternating with a
treatment customary in practice.**

14641 Schulze, W.; Herbst, M. DE 139750/78/0008 N
Versuche zur Steigerung der Galaktopoese mit
Diphenylbutylamin 'Pimozide' bei Sauen mit puerperalen
Störungen. **Trials for increase of galactopoesis using
diphenylbutylamine 'pimocide' in sows with puerperal
disorders.**

14642 Schulze, W.; Carstens, W. DE 139750/78/0009 N
Konzentrationsbestimmung von Totocillin im Vergleich zu

Ampicillin und Oxacillin in Blut und Milch von gesunden und
kranken Muttersauen im Puerperium. **Estimation of the
concentration of totocilline in blood and milk of healthy and
diseased sows during puerperium as compared to ampicillin and
oxacilline.**

14643 Schulze, W.; Kroeger, E.–A. DE 139750/78/0010 N
Untersuchungen zur Therapie der Lactatacidose beim
Schwein. **Therapeutic trials in lactate acidosis in pigs.**

14644 Schulze, W.; Habermalz, G. DE 139750/78/0013 N
Die Escherichia–coli bedingten Darmerkrankungen des
Schweines mit besonderer Berücksichtigung der Ätiologie und
Immunologie. **Enteral diseases in pigs caused by Escherichia
coli with special reference to etiology and immunology.**

14645 Schulze, W.; Pferdmenges, D. DE 139750/78/0014 N
Versuche zur Prophylaxe der Puerperalen Septikämie und
Toxämie der Sau mit Oxytocin und einer
TrimethoprimSulfonamid–Kombination. **Trials on prophylaxis
of puerperal septicemia and toxemia of sows using oxytocin and
a trimethoprime– sulfonamide combination.**

14646 Schulze, W.; Haimberger, B. DE 139750/78/0022 N
Klinische und bakteriologische Untersuchungen von Sauen im
Puerperium mit besonderer Berücksichtigung des
Keimgehaltes in Genitaltrakt, Harnapparat und Milch. **Clinical
and bacteriological examinations of sows post partum with
special reference to the germ content of the genital tract,
urinary tract and milk.**

14647 Loeffler, K.; Brosi, C. DE 144605/75/0005
Einfluss moderner Zucht– und Haltungsverfahren auf die
Entwicklung und die Erkrankungshäufigkeit der Gliedmassen
beim Schwein. **Influence of modern breeding and keeping
techniques on the development and frequency of leg diseases in
pigs.** Publications.

14648 Buchenauer, D. DE 144675/78/0001 N
Analyse von Ferkelverlusten. **Analysis of piglet losses.**

14649 Erbersdobler, H.; Husstedt, W. DE 160600/77/0002
Versuche zur intraamnialen Ernährung der Feten bei
Meerschweinchen. **Experiments on intraamnial nutrition of
fetus in guinea pigs.**

14650 Kräusslich, H.; Schmid, D.O.; Cwik, S.; Osterkorn, K.
DE 160705/75/0002
Untersuchungen von Lymphozyten–Antigenen als
Markierungssubstanzen bei Schweinen. **Studies on lymphocytes
antigenes as labelling substances in swine.**

14651 Bachmann, P.A. DE 160760/73/0001
Untersuchung zur Entwicklung einer Immunprophylaxe gegen
die übertragbare Gastroenteritis –TGE– beim Schwein.
**Studies on the development of an immunoprophylaxis against
transmissible gastro–enteritis –TGE– in pigs.**

14652 Buschmann, H. DE 160760/74/0001
Immunglobulinklassen beim Schwein. **Immunoglobulins in
pigs.**

14653 Buschmann, H. DE 160765/70/0001
Untersuchungen über die Vererbung der Antikörperbildung
gegenüber Hapten–Bakteriophagen–Konjugaten bei Schwein
und Maus. **Investigations on the heredity of antibody formation**

in pigs and mice against hapten bacteriophages conjugates.

14654 Boch, J.; Mannewitz, U.; Erber, M.
DE 160820/78/0001 N
Vorkommen von Sarcocystis suihominis und Sarcocystis
suicanis bei Schlachtschweinen in Süddeutschland. **The
existence of Sarcocystis suihominis and Sarcocystis suicanis in
slaughter pigs in South Germany.** Publications.

14655 Boch, J.
DE 160820/78/0005 N
Toxoplasmose bei Schlachtschweinen. **Toxoplasmosis in pigs
for slaughter.**

14656 Göbel, E.; Katz, M.; Erber, M.
DE 160820/78/0011 N
Licht- und elektronenmikroskopische Untersuchungen zur
Entwicklung von Muskelzysten von Sarcocystis suicanis in
Hausschweinen nach experimenteller Infektion. **Light and
electron microscopic studies on the development of muscle cysts
of Sarcocystis suicanis in experimentally infected pigs.**
Publications.

14657 Centurier, C.; Seubert, S.
DE 160820/78/0014 N
Auswirkungen mehrfachen Besatzes von Maus, Kaninchen
und Schwein mit Ornithodorus moubata. **Effects of repeated
infestations of mice, rabbits and pigs with Ornithodoros
moubata.**

14658 Matthaeus, W.
DE 216010/77/0001 R
Virus der europäischen Schweinepest und der Mucosal
Disease. **Virus of European swine fever and of Mucosal disease.**

14659 Lorenz, R.J.
DE 216010/78/0002 N
Simulationsstudie zur Epizootologie der Schweinepest.
Simulation studies on the epizootiology of hog cholera.

14660 Korn, G.
DE 216030/77/0004
Pathogenese der europäischen Schweinepest. **Pathogenesis of
European swine fever.**

14661 Blendl, H.M.; Matzke; Hoffmann, R.
DE 502304/78/0001 N
Früherkennung der Rhinitis atrophicans infectiosa –
Schnüffelkrankheit – beim Schwein mittels Röntgendiagnostik.
**Early recognition of Rhinitis atrophicans infectiosa in pigs by
x–ray diagnosis.**

14662 Blendl, H.M.; Hollwich, W.; Puff, H.; Härtl, J.
DE 502304/78/0002 N
Frühdiagnose einer möglichen Stressresistenz am lebenden
Schwein mittels Halothan–Test. **Early diagnosis of possible
stress resistance in living pigs by the halothane–test.**

14663 Reuss, U.; Schöss, P.; Oberwalder, U.
DE 507600/75/0007
Ätiologie und Diagnose der Rhinitis atrophicans des
Schweines. **Etiology and diagnosis of Rhinitis atrophicans in
pigs.** Publications.

14664 Reuss, U.; Neumann, W.; Plöger, W.; Neubacher,
H.–J.
DE 507600/78/0004 N
Vorkommen der Aujeszkyschen Krankheit bei Schweinen im
nordwestdeutschen Küstengebiet und Möglichkeiten ihrer
Bekämpfung. **Occurrence of Aujeszky's disease in pigs in the
coastal region of Northwest Germany and possibilities of
control.** Publications.

14665 Reuss, U.; Schöss, P.
DE 507600/78/0005 N
Einschlusskörperchen–Rhinitis der Schweine und Rhinitis
atrophicans. **Inclusion–bodies–rhinitis in pigs and Rhinitis
atrophicans.** Publications.

14666 Researcher not indicated
DE 508240/77/0001 N
Untersuchungen über Aufnahmen und Rückstandsbildung von
mit Futter aufgenommenen Schwermetallen – Cadmium,
Quecksilber, Arsen – bei Mastschweinen. **Examination of
uptake and residue formation of heavy metals – Cd, Hg, As–
taken in via feeds in fattening pigs.**

14667 Witte, K.
DE 508452/78/0001 N
Klärung der Ursachen einer neuen Darmerkrankung bei
Schweinen – Pseudo–TGE –. **Elucidation of the cause of an
intestinal disease – pseudo–TGE – unknown so far in pigs.**

14668 Meding, J.H.
DK 010202/76/0014
Forekomst af entero– og parvovirus i ornesæd. **Occurance of
entero– and parvovirus in boar semen.**

14669 Møller–Madsen, Aa.
DK 010300/71/0601
Undersøgelser vedr. fodring af svin med kulturer af
Lactobacillus acidophilus. **Studies on the feeding of pigs with
cultures of Lactobacillus acidophilus.**

14670 Nielsen, P.; Lee, J.–N.
DK 030123/78/0003 N
Farmakokinetik for levamisol hos geder og svin.
Pharmacokinetics of le**vamisol in goats and swine.**

14671 Nielsen, P.
DK 030123/79/0002 N
Metabolisme af levamisol hos geder og svin. **Metabolism of
levamisol in goats and swine.**

14672 Jørgensen, P.F.; Hyldgaard–Jensen, J.; Palludan, B.
DK 030126/76/0003
Halothanfølsomhed hos svin af Dansk Landrace. **Halothane
sensitivity in swine of Danish Landrace.**

14673 Hyldgaard–Jensen, J.; Wegger, I.
DK 030126/77/0005
Infektionsresistens og enzymkonstitution hos svin. **Immunity
and enzyme constitution in swine.**

14674 Christiansen, I.J.
DK 030128/75/0003
Undersøgelse af forskellige anæstesimidlers anvendelighed til
svin i forbindelse med operativ forløsning. **An investigation of
the usefulness of different anaesthetics to swine in connection
with surgical delivery.**

14675 Hansen, L.H.; Christiansen, I.J.
DK 030128/76/0010
Undersøgelse af muligheder for opbevaring af befrugtede æg
isoleret fra slagtesøer. **An investigation of the possibilities for
the live storage of fertilised eggs isolated from slaughter sows.**

14676 Simesen, M.G.
DK 030129/77/0005
Effekten af selen og vitamin E på biokemiske og histologiske
parametre hos svin. **The effect of selenium and vitamin E on the
biochemical and histological parametres in swine.**

14677 Nielsen, N.C.; Eskildsen, M.
DK 030129/77/0012
Epidemiologiske undersøgelser af parvovirusinfektionen i
sohold. **Epidemilogical investigations of the Parvo virus
infection amongst sows.**

14678 Nielsen, N.C.; Nielsen, D.H.
DK 030129/79/0002 N

Undersøgelse af bensvaghed hos voksende grise.
Leg–weakness in growing pigs.

14679 Dantzer, V.; Hesseldahl, H. DK 030132/73/0004 R
Undersøgelser over blodøer i blommesækken hos svin.
Investigations of the blood islands found in the chorionic sack of swine.

14680 Hasselager, E. DK 030132/74/0002
Elektronmikroskopiske undersøgelser af leverskader hos svin induceret af levnedsmiddelfarvestoffer. **Electron–microscopic investigations of liver injures in swine induced by food colouring agents.**

14681 Björkman, N. DK 030132/77/0001
Finstrukturen af svinets hunkønsorganer med særlig henblik på placenta. **Fine structure of the female reproductive organs in swine with particular reference to the placenta.**

14682 Basse, A.; Nielsen, H.E. DK 030133/77/0001 N
Patologiske undersøgelser i forbindelse med selen og vitamin E til søer og pattegrise. **Studies of the pathology related to deficiency of vitamin E and selenium.**

14683 Bille, N. DK 030133/77/0002 N
Strøelsens indflydelse på forekomst af navleblødning hos pattegrise. **The influence of the type of bedding on the occurrence of navel cord bleeding in suckling pigs.**

14684 Bille, N.; Smedegård, K. DK 030133/78/0001 N
Organforandringer hos svin fodret med rapskager. **Organ changes in pigs due to the feeding of rape seed cake.**

14685 Bindseil, E.; Andreassen, J. DK 030133/78/0002 N
Undersøgelser over den mulige immunosuppressive virkning af svinets spolorm, Ascaris suum. **The immunosuppressive effect of Ascaris suum, the large round–worm of pigs.**

14686 Biering–Sørensen, U.; Hansen, O.
DK 030134/74/0001 N
Palpation og inspektion som alternativ til den kødkontrolmæssige opbladning af krøslymfekirtlerne hos svin. **Investigation on palpation and visual inspection procedures as possible substitutes for meat inspection routine incisions into the mesenterial lymph nodes in swine.**

14687 Ducluzeau, R.; Raibaud, P. FR 010205/74/2755
Décontamination post–natale immédiate comme moyen d'obtenir des porcelets axéniques. **Immediate post–natal decontamination as a means of obtaining axenic piglets.** Publications.

14688 Chardon, P. Renard, C. FR 010215/70/9511 N
Recherches pathogéniques et thérapeutiques chez le porc après irradiation externe aiguüe supralétale. **Pathogenic and therapeutic studies on the pig after acute external supralethal irradiation.**

14689 Mormede, P.; Dantzer, R. FR 011407/76/8041
Intéractions entre le fonctionnement du système nerveux central et l'activité neuro–endocrinienne au cours du stress chez le porc. **Interactions between endocrine and nervous systems during stress in pigs.**

14690 Charley, B.; Salmon, H.; Corthier, G.
FR 011809/74/8002

Immunologie et mécanismes pathogéniques du tractus respiratoire du porc. **Pig respiratory tract : immunology and pathogenic mechanisms.**

14691 Salmon, H.; Metzger, J.J.; Aynaud, J.M.; Asso, J.; Charley, B.; Laude, H. FR 011809/75/8006
Physiologie des sous–populations lymphocytaires du porc. **Lymphocyte sub–populations.**

14692 Laude, H.; Corthier, G. FR 011809/76/8005
Pestivirus porcins : relations physicochimiques et antigéniques avec les autres pestivirus. **Pig Pestiviruses : Relationships with other Pestiviruses.**

14693 Aynaud, J.M.; Laude, H.; Corthier, G.
FR 011809/77/8001
Gastroentérite transmissible du porcelet : mise au point d'un vaccin à virus vivant. **Transmissible Gastroenteritis of swine : Preparation of a live virus vaccine.**

14694 Aynaud, J.M.; Corthier, G.; Laude, H.
FR 011809/77/8003
Gastroentérite transmissible du porcelet : marqueurs génétiques du virus en relation avec le pouvoir pathogène. **Transmissible Gastroenteritis of swine. Genetic markers of the virus.**

14695 Corthier, G. FR 011809/78/8004
Incidence des infections à rotavirus dans les cas de gastroentérites infectieuses du porcelet. **Newborn pig gastroenteritis : incidence of rotavirus infection.**

14696 Houdayer, M.; Milon, A.; Metzger, J.J.
FR 012225/76/8017
Les adjuvantes de l'immunite et réactions immunitaires dans l'espèce porcine. **Adjuvants and immune response in pigs.**

14697 Milon, A.; Metzger, J.J. FR 012225/77/8015
Protection des porcelets durant la période périnatale. Mécanismes immunitaires. **Immune protection in the pig around birth. Immune mechanisms.**

14698 Binns GB 010303/00/0019 R
Cellular immunology in the pig; functions of thymus, lymphocyte and lymph node.

14699 White GB 010303/00/0024 R
Major histocompatibility complex of the pig.

14700 Davies GB 010303/00/0053 R
Antigens of the major histocompatibility complex in the pig.

14701 Beale; Kent GB 010303/00/0066 R
Structure and function of porcine immunoglobulins.

14702 Feinstein; Richard GB 010303/00/0067 R
Biosynthesis of different antibody classes by pig and ruminant lymphoid tissues.

14703 Smith; Burton GB 010308/76/0003
Intestinal transmission of immune proteins in neo–natal animals.

14704 Gibbons GB 010402/00/0801
Mucus and the epithelial cell surface in enteric infection in young pigs.

14705 Gibbons   GB 010402/00/0802
E. coli infection in piglets and genetics involved in natural resistance.

14706 Hall   GB 010403/00/0824
Aetiological studies of enteritic viral infections in pigs.

14707 Garwes; Bridger   GB 010405/00/0005
Transmissible gastroenteritis of pigs: virological and comparative studies.

14708 Rutter   GB 010405/00/0006
Porcine enteric infections of unknown aetiology.

14709 Gibbons   GB 010405/00/0801
Mucus and the epithelial cell surface in enteric infection in young pigs.

14710 Rutter   GB 010405/00/0802
E.Coli infection in piglets and genetics involved in natural resistance.

14711 Woode   GB 010405/00/0824
Aetiological studies of enteric viral infections in pigs.

14712 Lysons; Lemcke   GB 010405/76/0052
Swine dysentry; the aetiological agents, pathogenesis and control.

14713 Rutter; Plowright   GB 010405/79/0839 N
Aetiology pathogenesis and control of atrophic rhinitis of pigs.

14714 Burden   GB 010406/00/0014
Epidemiology and pathogenesis of Trichuris suis in pigs.

14715 Anderson; Chandler   GB 010410/00/0020
Immunopathological aspects of the host–pathogen relationship.

14716 Pereira; Dawe   GB 010902/75/0011
Studies on porcine enteroviruses.

14717 Fuller; Reiter   GB 011701/78/0026
Microflora of the pig gut in relation to host health.

14718 Silver   GB 020709/79/0002 N
Metabolism, circulation and endocrine environment of the foetal piglet.

14719 Imlah   GB 021005/79/0001 N
Relationships between blood groups, halothane sensitivity and porcine stress syndrome.

14720 Rattray; Sharman   GB 030607/00/0010
Antibiotic therapy: development of drug resistance with reference to post–weaning scour of pigs.

14721 Cushnie   GB 030607/00/0018
Factors causing cerebro–cortical necrosis in ruminants.

14722 Corrigall   GB 030607/78/0025 N
Microbiological monitoring of the health status of pigs.

14723 Wilson; Mackie   GB 030608/00/0014
Maturation of skeletal muscle and neuro–muscular diseases of neonatal pigs.

14724 Jones; Hovell   GB 030611/00/0008
Development of immunological competence in the baby pig.

14725 Rayner   GB 030612/00/0009 R
Gastrointestinal physiology of normal and diarrhoeic pigs.

14726 Researcher not indicated   GB 050422/00/0003
Swine dysentery vaccination trials.

14727 Researcher not indicated   GB 050422/00/0005
Navel bleeding in pigs, determine hereditability.

14728 Researcher not indicated   GB 050454/00/0004
Miliary tuberculosis in pigs.

14729 Researcher not indicated   GB 050471/00/0007
Porcine abortions in devon.

14730 Researcher not indicated   GB 050471/00/0011
National survey to confirm absence of trichinosis.

14731 Sojka; Wray   GB 050501/00/0002
Immunoelectrophoretic and conventional studies on E. coli enteropathogenic for pigs.

14732 Kendall   GB 050505/00/0002
Internal parasites of pigs.

14733 O'Neill; Parfitt   GB 050505/00/0021
Observation of Isospora suis infestation in a minimal disease pig herd.

14734 Wells   GB 050506/00/0057
Pietrain creeper syndrome (PCS) in pigs.

14735 Wells; Bradley   GB 050506/00/0058
Haloxon neurotoxicity in the pig.

14736 Done; Wrathall   GB 050506/00/0064
Congenital nervous diseases in pigs radiomimetic cerebellar teratogens.

14737 Ward   GB 050506/75/0037
Disorders of muscle development in pigs. Congenital splayleg.

14738 Wrathall; Done   GB 050506/75/0045
Porcine cytomegalovirus infection in the sow.

14739 Done   GB 050506/75/0046
Neuropathology of swine vesicular disease.

14740 Wells   GB 050506/75/0050
Definitive and differential pathology of naturally occurring diseases of pigs.

14741 Wells   GB 050506/77/0005
Congenital tremour of pigs, type A ii.

14742 Wrathall   GB 050506/77/0060
Virus infection of the very early pig embryo.

14743 Cartwright   GB 050508/00/0001 R
Transmissible gastroenteritis.

14744 Lamont   GB 050508/00/0005 R

Interaction between viruses and bacteria in respiratory disease.
Cultivate inclusion body rhinitis virus.

14745 Lucas; Chasey   GB 050508/00/0007 R
Rotaviruses and enteric diseases of pigs.

14746 Cartwright   GB 050508/00/0010 R
Parvovirus infections of pigs : pathogenesis, isolation and vaccine trials.

14747 Cartwright   GB 050508/75/0011 R
Picornavirus infections. Teschen group and encephalomyocarditis viruses.

14748 Cartwright   GB 050508/75/0012 R
Aujeskys disease: epidemiology pathogenesis and diagnostic tests.

14749 Cartwrigt   GB 050508/75/0013 R
Isolation and characterisation of causative agent of epidemic diarrhoea of pigs.

14750 Roberts   GB 050508/75/0014 R
Swine fever and serological cross reactions.

14751 Cartwright   GB 050508/77/0009 R
Porcine congenital disease.

14752 Wijeratne   GB 050509/77/0022 R
Renal cysts in pigs.

14753 Harris   GB 050512/00/0016
Pathogenesis of Chlamydia infections.

14754 Smith   GB 060212/00/0004
Trial of a vaccine designed to control necrotic enteritis in pigs.

14755 Robertson   GB 060224/79/0018 N
The reduction of piglet mortality using a farrowing box.

14756 McGloughlin   IE 060100/76/1256
Testing for pse muscle in the live pig using the halothane test. Publications.

14757 Lynch, P.B.; O'Grady, J.F.   IE 060400/78/1412 N
Factors influencing perinatal mortality in pigs. Publications.

14758 Evans, J.; Boland, M.   IE 120201/80/9166 N
Study on placental function on the domestic pig and cow. Publications.

14759 Ahern, C.P.; McLoughlin, J.V.; McGloughlin, P.
    IE 120203/75/9201 N
Studies on the procine stress syndrome so as to identify the factors which make pigs susceptible or resistant to stress. Publications.

14760 Keenan, L.R.J.   IE 120204/77/9020
Studies of genital abnormalities in female swine.

14761 Lee, R.P.; Dooge, D.J.   IE 120207/79/9225 N
Evaluation of the efficacy of acaricides against sarcoptes scabiei in pigs.

14762 Kelly, W.R.; Barragry, T.B.M.   IE 120208/77/9199 N
Antibiotic induced malabsorption in piglets.

14763 Mura, D.; Coni, V.; Cossu, P.; Leori, G.; Scarano, C.; Serra, U.   IT 051100/78/0001
Osservazioni su alcuni focolai di Peste Suina Africana nella Sardegna merioionale (Italia). **Some outbreaks of East African swine fever in South Sardinia (Italy) are reported.**

14764 Jong, M.F. de   NL 010401/33/1626
Ademhalingsziekten bij varkens. **Respiratory diseases in pigs.** Publications.

14765 Akkermans, J.P.W.M.   NL 010401/52/1624
Enteritiden bij het varken. **Some aspects of enteritis in pigs.** Publications.

14766 Nabuurs, M.J.A.   NL 010401/68/1665 R
Colibacillose van big en kalf. **Colibacillosis in pigs and calves.** Publications.

14767 Akkermans, J.P.W.M.; Jong, M.F. de; Rondhuis, P.R.
    NL 010401/72/6524
Atrophische rhinitis bij het varken. **Atrophic rhinitis in pigs.**

14768 Akkermans, J.P.W.M.   NL 010401/75/6522 R
Transmissible gastro–enteritis bij varkens. **Transmissible gastro–enteritis in pigs.**

14769 Bekkum, J.G. van   NL 010402/67/1213 R
De vaccinatie van varkens tegen mond– en klauwzeer. **Vaccination of pigs against foot and mouth disease.** Publications.

14770 Bekkum, J.G. van   NL 010402/67/1214 R
Varkenspest (inclusief diagnostiek t.d.v. de praktijk). **Hog cholera virus of pigs.** Publications.

14771 Bekkum, J.G. van; Boer, G.F. de   NL 010402/70/3399
Virusinfecties bij varkens. **Virus infections of pigs.**

14772 Smit, H.F.   NL 030002/76/6970 R
Diagnostiek van subklinische varkensdysenterie (dragers). **Diagnosis of swine–dysentery; detection of carrier animals.**

14773 Frik, J.F.   NL 030002/77/7749 R
Serologische diagnostiek van Erysipelothrix rhesiopathiae infekties bij het varken. **Serological diagnosis of E.rhesiopathiae infections in pigs.**

14774 Bijlsma, I.G.W.   NL 030002/77/8967 N
E. coli infekties bij biggen (enterotoxicose, K88–antigeen, enteropathogene E. coli, big). **E. coli infections in piglets (enterotoxicose, adherence antigen, K88–antigen, enteropathogenic E. coli, piglet).**

14775 Linde–Sipman, J.S. van de   NL 030005/71/5775
Het links hypoplastisch hart bij de minipig; Een morfogenetisch onderzoek. **The left hypoplastic heart in the minipig; A morphogenetic investigation.**

14776 Valk, P.C. van der   NL 030011/73/5808 R
Resorbtie en "malabsorption" in de digestietraktus van biggen. **Absorption and malabsorption in the intestinal tract of piglets.**

14777 Valk, P.C. van der   NL 030011/76/5809 N
Onderzoek naar erfelijke en milieuinvloeden op locomotiestoornissen bij varkens o.a. klinische en

pathologische parameters voor osteochondropathieën. **Genetic and environmental influences on locomotion disturbances in pigs a.o. clinical and pathological parameters for osteochondrosis.** Publications.

14778 Valk, P.C. van der   NL 030011/76/6524
Atrophische rhinitis bij het varken. **Atrophic rhinitis in pigs.**

14779 Kortbeek, J.M.C.   NL 030018/75/5665 N
Immunologische aspekten van neonatale infekties bij het varken (immunoglobulinen, vaccinaties, K88, colostrumcellen). **Immunological aspects of neonatal infections of the pig (immunoglobulins, vaccination, K88, colostral cells).** Publications.

14780 Schothorst, M. van   NL 040011/71/7436
Onderzoek naar de mogelijkheden tot doorbraak van de Salmonella kringloop bij varkens op het eiland Walcheren. **Investigation on the breaking through the Salmonella cycle in pigs on the isle of Walcheren.** Publications.

14781 Knapen, F. van; Teppema, J.S.; Ruitenberg, E.J.
                                              NL 040011/71/7501
Onderzoek naar het voorkomen van Trichinella spiralis bij varkens, mede in verband met besmettingsgevaar voor de mens. **Development of detection methods and epidemiological surveys on Trichinella spiralis in pigs, also in connection with contamination danger for humans.** Publications.

Poultry and domestic birds in general (B 4400)

See also 2185, 14061, 14135, 14301

14782 Halen, P.   BE 110000/73/0020
Identification des mycoplasmes aviaires. **Identification of avian mycoplasmas.** Publications.

14783 Meulemans, G.   BE 110000/77/0044
Recherches sur le syndrome proventriculite en pathologie aviaire. **Research on proventriculitis syndrom in avian pathology.**

14784 Meulemans, G.   BE 110000/78/0045
Application des méthodes immuno enzymologiques au titrage des anticorps dans les affections virales aviaires et recherche des virus aviaires. **Application of immuno enzymological methods on titration of antibodies in viral diseases of poultry and on research of antigens.**

14785 Meulemans, G.   BE 110000/78/0055 N
Epidémiologie des virus Influenza chez la volaille. **Epidemiology of Influenza viruses in chickens.** Publications.

14786 Monreal, G.; Dorn, R.; Maichle, I.
                                              DE 104252/78/0001 N
Aviäre Adenovirusinfektionen und Adenovirusantigene. **Avian adenovirus infections and antigens of adenoviruses.**

14787 Monreal, G.; Maichle, I.   DE 104252/78/0002 N
Virusspezifische Antigene beim Virus der Marek'schen Krankheit. **Virus specific antigens of the virus of Marek's disease.**

14788 Weiss, E.; Käufer, I.; Burkhardt, E.; Reinacher, M.; Marquard, H.; Friederici, I.   DE 129620/74/0001 R
Immunstatus und infektiöse Bursitis des Huhnes.

Immunocompetence and infectious bursitis of chickens.

14789 Geissler, H.; Goepel, A.; Kösters, J.
                                              DE 129800/78/0002 N
Aerosol–Desinfektion nicht homogenisierbarer Keimträger. **Aerosol disinfection of germ carriers not to homogenize.**

14790 Speck, J.; Täubert, K.   DE 132333/77/0002
Einfluss von aktiver Interferonisierung auf Viruskrankheiten beim Geflügel. **Control of virus diseases of poultry by active interferonisation.**

14791 Speck, J.; Täubert, K.   DE 132333/78/0001 N
Einfluss von aktiver Interferonisierung auf Viruskankheiten beim Geflügel. **Control of virus diseases of poultry by active interferonisation.** Publications.

14792 Sallmann, H.-P.; Schole, J.   DE 139250/75/0003
Untersuchungen zum Fettlebersyndrom der Legehenne. **Experiments on the fatty liver syndrome of laying hens.**

14793 Kaaden, O.-R.; Lange, S.   DE 139552/78/0002 N
Die Antigene des Virus der Marekschen Krankheit. **The antigens of Marek's disease virus.**

14794 Lüders, H.   DE 139700/70/0005
Massentherapie beim Geflügel. **Mass therapy of poultry.**

14795 Lüders, H.; Hinz, K.-H.   DE 139700/70/0006
Pharmakotherapeutische Untersuchungen von Arzneimitteln beim Geflügel nach Applikation über das Trinkwasser und Futter. **Parmacotherapeutical research on drugs applied in drinking water and feed of poultry.**

14796 Bessei, W.; Gschwindt, B.   DE 144685/75/0004
Erfassung und Quantifizierung möglicher Stressituationen bei Hühnern durch biochemische Parameter. **Survey and quantification of possible stress situations in hens by means of biochemical parameters.**

14797 Schmid, A.; Christoph, M.   DE 160550/75/0006 R
Versuche zur Ausscheidungsbeschleunigung von Hexachlorbenzol bei Legehennen. **Experiments on accelerating the excretion of hexachlorobenzene in layers.**

14798 Schmid, A.   DE 160550/75/0007
Metabolisierung von Hexachlorbenzol beim Huhn. **Metabolization of hexachlorobenzene in fowls.**

14799 Lösch, U.; Bohner, K.-J.   DE 160600/75/0015
Präparation von Immunglobulinen aus Hühnersera. **Preparation of chicken–immunoglobulins.** Publications.

14800 Gylstorff, I.   DE 160855/71/0008
Arzneimittelversorgung von Geflügel. **Supply of medicaments to poultry.**

14801 Winteroll, G.; Mousa, S.; Akreae, M.
                                              DE 160855/77/0001
Untersuchungen über zwischenartliche Verwandtschaft von aviären Pockenviren. **Studies on interspecies relations between avian pox viruses.**

14802 Gylstorff, I.; Kleber, H.-D.   DE 160855/77/0003
Histopathologie der Pankreas bei verschiedenen Vogelarten. **Histopathology of the pancreas in various bird species.**

14803 Gylstorff, I.; Reiss, W.   DE 160855/77/0004
Histopathologie der Schilddrüse bei verschiedenen
Vogelspezies. **Histopathology of the thyreoidea in various bird species.**

14804 Radzikowski, H.-P.; Wedemeyer, D.von
                   DE 160855/77/0005
Veränderungen von Blutstatus und Elektrolyten nach
Glucocorticoidgabe bei Vögeln. **Changes of the different glucose corticoides on status of blood and electrolytes in birds.**

14805 Rolf, J.; Heilmeier, A.   DE 160855/77/0006
Wirkung verschiedener Corticoide auf Entzündungen und
Glucoseblutspiegel beim Vogel. **Efficacy of different corticoides on inflammation and glucose blood levels in birds.**

14806 Matthes, S.   DE 201300/75/0011
Untersuchungen über die Kinetik der Ei– und
Fleischinfektionen bei Legehennen und Broilern.
Investigations on the kinetics of infections of eggs and meat of layers and broilers.

14807 Hagen, D.von dem   DE 201300/78/0016 N
Bildung von Antikörpern gegen aviäre Tumorviren und
Störfaktoren. **Development of antibodies against avian tumor viruses and their inhibition.**

14808 Bülow, V.von   DE 216030/77/0002
Pathogenese und Diagnose der Marekschen Krankheit.
Pathogenesis and diagnosis of Marek's disease.

14809 Dambrine, G.; Cauchy, L.   FR 011504/73/8075
Tumeurs à virus des oiseaux : Antigènes de surface des cellules
de poulet infectées ou transformées par des virus à leucoses et
sarcomes aviaires. **Virus–induced tumours of birds: Cell surface antigens on avian cells infected or transformed with avian leucosis.**

14810 Chaslus–Dancla, E.; Lafont, J.P.; Guillot, J.F.
                   FR 011504/74/8085
Etude épidémiologique des plasmides d'antibiorésistance chez
les bactéries d'origine aviaire : Evolution dans les élevages et
analyse des supports plasmidiques. **Epidemiological study of resistance plasmids in enteric bacteria of poultry : evolution in poultry flocks and genetical analysis of the plasmids.**

14811 Cauchy, L.; Coudert, F.; Alamargot, J.
                   FR 011504/75/8078
Tumeurs à virus des oiseaux. Mesures qualitatives et
quantitatives du développement des tumeurs. **Virus–induced tumours of birds : qualitative and quantitative data of the growth of tumours.**

14812 Lafont, J.P.; Guillot, J.F.; Chaslus–Dancla, E.
                   FR 011504/75/8083
Méthodes d'obtention et de maintien d'animaux indemnes de
bactéries porteuses de plasmides d'antibiorésistance.
Obtention of poultry flocks free from enteric bacteria harboning R–factors.

14813 Coudert, F.; Dambrine, G.; Cauchy, L.
                   FR 011504/76/8076
Tumeurs à virus des oiseaux = corrélation entre les
phénomènes immunitaires et la formation des tumeurs.
Virus–induced tumours of birds = relationship between immunity and growth of the tumour.

14814 Coudert, F.; Dambrine, G.; Cauchy, L.
                   FR 011504/76/8077
Tumeurs à virus des oiseaux = mécanismes de résistance à la
formation des tumeurs. **Virus–induced tumours of birds = Mechanisms of resistance to the growth of tumours.**

14815 Dho, M.; Lafont, J.P.; Guillot, J.F.   FR 011504/77/8086
Escherichia coli pathogènes aviaires : épidémiologie,
déterminisme de la pathogénicité. **Pathogenic E. coli in Poultry.**

14816 Lafont, J.P.; Guillot, J.F.; Chaslus–Dancla, E.
                   FR 011504/78/8082
Lutte contre la contamination des volailles par les Salmonella.
Prevention of Salmonella infection in poultry.

14817 Naciri, M.; Conan, J.; Yvore, P.; Balancon, M.
                   FR 011505/78/8066
Mise au point d'une technique d'évaluation du pouvoir
anticoccidien de nouvelles substances pour la
chimioprévention des coccidioses aviaires. **Research for a new method of evaluation of chemicals as chemopreventive agents in avian coccidiosis.**

14818 Yvore, P.; Naciri, M.; Faure, P.   FR 011505/78/8068
Pathogénie des coccidioses aviaires. **Pathogenesis of avian coccidiosis.**

14819 Wight   GB 010701/00/0009
Histopathology in avian metabolic diseases.

14820 Martindale   GB 010701/00/0011 R
Renal function in normal and diseased poultry.

14821 Burns   GB 010701/00/0013 R
Immune processes in poultry.

14822 McDougall; Briggs   GB 011301/00/0009
Field studies of poultry diseases.

14823 Cooper   GB 011303/00/0006 R
Disinfection procedures for hatcheries and hatching eggs.

14824 Cooper   GB 011303/00/0009 R
Effect of stress in conventionally and isolator maintained birds.

14825 Cooper   GB 011303/78/0010 R
Methyl bromide gas for disinfection in poultry production.

14826 Butler   GB 011307/00/0001 R
Metabolic disturbances produced by microbial toxins.

14827 Pearson; Butler   GB 011307/00/0002 R
Aetiology and pathogenesis of fatty liver syndrome.

14828 Davison; Misson   GB 011307/00/0005 R
Effects of temperature stress on metabolism.

14829 Freeman; Manning   GB 011307/00/0006 R
Measurement of response to stress.

14830 Freeman; Manning   GB 011307/00/0007 R
Factors affecting response to stress.

14831 Freeman; Manning GB 011307/00/0008
Effect of stress on susceptibility to and course of infection.

14832 Harry GB 011308/00/0017 R
Methyl bromide gas for disinfection in poultry production.

14833 Barling GB 011308/76/0021
Respiratory disease of racing pigeons.

14834 Holmes; Darbyshir GB 011308/77/0022
Studies of avian enteric viruses.

14835 Brackenbury GB 026201/79/0001 N
Respiratory responses of domestic birds to hyperthermia and carbon dioxide.

14836 Tucker; Cutler GB 030903/77/0112 R
Survey of pesticide usage in poultry enterprises.

14837 McFerran GB 041601/00/0011
The pathogenesis and control of Newcastle Disease.

14838 Thornton GB 050503/00/0002
Develop quality control methods and standardise serological diagnostic tests for Newcastle disease.

14839 Muskett GB 050503/00/0003
Avian viral vaccines; methods for detecting contaminants; effects of interactions of vaccines.

14840 Thornton; Muskett GB 050503/76/0017
Avian reovirus infections–quality control methods for vaccines.

14841 Hopkins GB 050503/77/0021
Avian pox quality control methods for vaccines.

14842 Kirkwood GB 050505/00/0017
Biology and control of poultry mite (Dermanyssus gallinae).

14843 Cullen GB 050507/00/0001
Pathology, serology and transmission of mycoplasmosis in chickens.

14844 Cullen GB 050507/00/0003
Diagnosis and serology of psittacosis in cage birds and domestic poultry.

14845 Allan GB 050507/00/0004
Newcastle disease in chickens, including pathology, serology, transmission and prevention with vaccines.

14846 Asplin GB 050507/00/0006
Diseases of ducks and geese.

14847 Cullen GB 050507/00/0008
Minor diseases of domestic poultry.

14848 Alexander GB 050507/00/0009
Structure and cytopathogenicity of various strains of Newcastle disease virus.

14849 Cullen GB 050507/00/0010
Aetiology, pathology transmission of infectious bursal disease and its immunosuppressive effects.

14850 Allen GB 050507/00/0012
Avian vaccine production and test methods.

14851 Allan; Alexander GB 050507/75/0017
Avian influenzas, trials of inactivated vaccines and monitoring of new field isolates.

14852 Thain GB 050507/75/0020
Avian salmonellosis.

14853 Cullen; Thain GB 050507/77/0021
Immune responses to Pastucrella. multocida in poultry.

14854 Cullen; Wyeth GB 050507/77/0022
Application of the Elisa test to diseases of poultry.

14855 Researcher not indicated GB 050507/77/0024
Comparison of the properties of avian paramyxoviruses.

14856 Ross; Christie GB 050512/00/0001
Clinical profiles (metabolic, immunological and disease status) in broilers in relation to production.

14857 Brown GB 050512/00/0006
Avian salmonellosis; bacteriology, clinical pathology and histopathology of S. Infantis and S. Typhimurium.

14858 Bruce GB 060308/00/0003 R
Relationships between the bacterial contamination of incubated eggs and their hatchability.

14859 Papparella, V. IT 040743/77/0847 R
Infezioni da adenovirus negli allevamenti avicoli intensivi. Adenovirus infections in birds on intensive breeding farms.

14860 Compagnucci, M.; Izzi, R.; Di Modugno, G.
IT 051000/77/0008 N
Metodi di controllo delle salmonellosi aviarie. Methods of control of avian Salmonellosis.

14861 Yadin, H. NL 010401/71/3637
Vaccinatie tegen Pseudovogelpest. Vaccination against Newcastle disease. Publications.

14862 Yadin, H.; Yadin, H. NL 010401/72/5577
Ziekte van Gumboro bij pluimvee. Gumboro disease of poultry.

14863 Yadin, H. NL 010401/74/6525
Aviaire Pasteurellose. Avian pasteurellosis. Publications.

14864 Boer, G.F. de NL 010402/63/1636
Aviare leukose bij pluimvee. Avian leucosis in poultry. Publications.

14865 Boer, G.F. de NL 010402/68/1664
Ziekte van Marek bij pluimvee. Marek's disease in poultry. Publications.

14866 Walsum, J. van NL 030017/75/5820 N
Niet infectieuze factoren in de aetiologie van Synovitis bij pluimvee. The aetiology of synovitis in chickens with special reference to non–infective factors. Publications.

14867 Davelaar, F.G. NL 030017/75/6985 N
De betekenis van adenovirussen als ziekteverwekkers bij pluimvee. Adenovirus as pathogenic agent in poultry.

Publications.

14868 Goudswaard, J. NL 030018/74/5667 N
De immunoglobinen van pluimvee (immunoglobinen, kalkoen, kip). **Poultry immunoglobulins (immunoglobulins, turkey, chicken).** Publications.

14869 Schothorst, M. van; Notermans, S.H.W.
NL 040011/77/7295
Het salmonella–vrijhouden van pluimvee. **Eradication of Salmonella in poultry.**

14870 Vertommen, M.H. NL 060010/75/5820 R
Niet infectieuze factoren in de aetiologie van Synovitis bij pluimvee. **The aetiology of synovitis in chickens with special reference to non–infective factors.** Publications.

14871 Goren, E. NL 060010/75/7291 R
De betekenis van mycoplasmose synoviae, Mycoplasmose meleagridis en Mycoplasmose iners als ziekteverwekkers bij pluimvee. **The significance of Mycoplasmosis synoviae, Mycoplasmosis meleagridis and Mycoplasmosis iners as pathogenic agents to poultry.**

14872 Goren, E. NL 060010/77/7295
Het Salmonella–vrijhouden van pluimvee. **Eradication of Salmonella in poultry.**

Chickens (B 4410)

See also 11327, 12704, 13391, 13472

14873 Devos, A.; Viaene, N.; Spanoghe, L.; Bynens, B.
BE 050600/78/0008 N
Onderzoek van vaccinaties bij pluimvee. **Investigations on vaccinations in poultry.** Publications.

14874 Heidrich, H.J.; Roters, H. DE 104400/75/0004
Beitrag zur Therapie der akuten Mastitis beim Rind. **A contribution to the therapy of acute mastitis in cows.**

14875 Geissler, H.; Schmidt, E. DE 129800/77/0001
Einfluss von CO2 auf einige Blutparameter und Leistung bei Legehennen im Langzeitversuch. **Influence of carbon dioxide on some blood parameters and egg position in laying hens in longtime–experiment.**

14876 Kösters, J.; Ulloa, J. DE 129800/78/0003 N
Serologische Kontrolle der aviären Enzephalomyelitis der Hühner. **Serological control of avian encephalo–myelitis in chicks.**

14877 Speck, J.; Kuhn, B.; Flock, D. DE 132333/77/0001
Untersuchungen über unspezifische Resistenzfaktoren bei verschiedenen Hühnerrassen. **Studies on unspecific resistance factors in different chicken lines.**

14878 Speck, J. DE 132333/77/0003
Serologische Diagnose der Hühnerleukose. **Serology of avian leukosis.**

14879 Speck, J.; Flock, D. DE 132333/78/0002 N
Untersuchungen über unspezifische Resistenzfaktoren bei verschiedenen Hühnerrassen. **Studies on unspecific resistance–factors in different chicken lines.**

14880 Kaleta, E.F. DE 139700/70/0001
Kinetik der NDV–spezifischen Antikörper im Huhn. **Kinetics of NDV–specific antibodies in chickens.**

14881 Kaleta, E.F. DE 139700/70/0004
Kontrolle des Impferfolges nach Massenvakzinationen gegen die Newcastle Disease mit serologischen Methoden. **Control of the results of mass vaccination of chickens against Newcastle disease with serological methods.**

14882 Hinz, K.-H. DE 139700/72/0001
Kulturelle, biochemische und serologische Untersuchungen zur Differenzierung von aus Hühnern isolierten Bakterienstämmen der Gattung Haemophilus. **Cultural, biochemical and serological investigations of differentiation of bacteria of the species Haemophilus isolated from chickens.**

14883 Siegmann, O. DE 139700/78/0001 N
Quantitative Bestimmung zur Kinetik von Therapeutika in Huhn, Ei und Embryo. **Quantitative assays of the kinetics of therapeutics in the chicken, egg and chicken embryo.**

14884 Dennig, H.K.; Dierig, B. DE 160820/78/0009 N
Untersuchungen zur Züchtung von Trypanosema evansi auf embryonierten Eiern. **Cultivation of Trypanosoma evansi in developping chick–embryos.**

14885 Löliger, H.–C.; Matthes, S.; Füllgraf
DE 201300/71/0016
Untersuchungen über die Pathogenese der Dünndarmkokzidiose der Hühner. **Pathogenesis of small intestinal coccidiosis in fowl.**

14886 Löliger, H.–C.; Hagen, D.von dem; Hartmann, W.
DE 201300/75/0008
Untersuchungen über den Einfluss RSV–neutralisierender Antikörper auf die Entwicklung der Leukose beim Huhn. **Investigations into the influence of RSV–neutralizing antibodies on the development of leucosis in chicks.** Publications.

14887 Tulliez, J. FR 011412/73/2771
Métabolisation de l'heptadécane– ^{14}C et du dodecylcyclohexane–^{3}H chez le Rat et le Poulet. **Metabolic study of heptadecane– ^{14}C and dodecylcyclohexane–^{3}H in the Rat and Chicken.**

14888 Guillot, J.F. FR 011504/76/8081
Etude de l'implantation précoce des entérobactéries dans le tube digestif du poulet. **Early implantation of enteric bacteria in the digestive tract of poultry.**

14889 Chaslus–Dancla, E.; Guillot, J.F. FR 011504/78/8079
Etude expérimentale de l'implantation de souches bactériennes dans le tube digestif de poulets adultes. **Late implantation of enteric bacteria in digestive tract of Hens.**

14890 Hobson–Frohock GB 010205/79/0047 N
Determination of residues of cocciodiostats in poultry excreta.

14891 Siller GB 010701/00/0001
Histology of healthy and diseased avian kidneys.

14892 Duncan GB 010704/00/0006 R
Effects of physiology, environment and genotype on feather pecking and cannibalism.

14893 Goodchild; Briggs   GB 011301/00/0005
Neoplasia of the avian oviduct.

14894 Biggs; McDougall   GB 011301/00/0011
Field studies on vaccination against mareks disease.

14895 Cooper; Timms   GB 011303/00/0001 R
Studies of management of specific–pathogen–free flocks in isolators.

14896 Cooper   GB 011303/00/0003 R
Special hygiene required in use of isolators.

14897 Cooper   GB 011303/00/0005
Mortality in isolator maintained birds.

14898 Ross   GB 011304/00/0002
Antigens of Mareks disease and related herpes viruses and their role in pathogenesis and immunity.

14899 Payne; Rennie   GB 011304/00/0005
Immunopathology of Mareks disease.

14900 Lawn   GB 011304/00/0006
Ultrastructural changes in Mareks disease.

14901 Powell   GB 011304/00/0007
Role of cell–mediated and humoral immunity in Mareks disease.

14902 Payne; Rennie   GB 011304/00/0008
Mechanism of vaccinal immunity in Mareks disease.

14903 Pani   GB 011304/00/0011
Genetic control of response to leukosis–sarcoma viruses by experimental lines of fowl.

14904 Pani   GB 011304/00/0012
Genetic control of response to leukosis–sarcoma viruses by commercial fowl.

14905 Payne; Howes   GB 011304/00/0018
Prevalence of different sub–groups of lymphoid leukosis virus in commercial populations.

14906 Long   GB 011305/00/0001
Site and host specificity of Eimeria.

14907 Long   GB 011305/00/0002
Pathenogenicity and immunogenicity of embryo passaged strains of Eimeria.

14908 Shirley; Long   GB 011305/00/0005
Pathogenicity of Eimeria.

14909 Rose; Long   GB 011305/00/0008
Immune response of host to coccidia.

14910 Rose   GB 011305/00/0009
Immunisation with non–infectious coccidial antigens.

14911 Rose   GB 011305/00/0012
Immunoglobins of the fowl.

14912 Chapman   GB 011305/00/0013 R
Resistance of coccidia to drugs.

14913 Long; Millard   GB 011305/00/0014 R
Incidence of coccidia in broiler house litter.

14914 Smith; Page   GB 011308/00/0001 R
Produce autogenous vaccine from Newcastle disease virus Essex 70.

14915 Darbyshre; Cook   GB 011308/00/0002 R
Interaction between bacteria and viruses in respiratory diseases.

14916 Holmes   GB 011308/00/0003 R
Immune response to viruses causing respiratory disease.

14917 Cook   GB 011308/00/0008 R
Interaction between different viruses and viral vaccines in respiratory infections.

14918 Cook   GB 011308/00/0009 R
Avian adenoviruses and their role as pathogens.

14919 Smith; Tucker   GB 011308/00/0010
Factors influencing Salmonella excretion in poultry.

14920 Smith   GB 011308/00/0011 R
Transmissable plasmids in Escherishia coli.

14921 Darbyshre; Cook   GB 011308/75/0020 R
Laboratory studies on the pathogenesis and serology of respiratory viruses.

14922 Williams; Fuller   GB 011701/78/0027
Microflora of the chick gut in relation to host health.

14923 Thornton   GB 050503/00/0001
Develop quality control methods for Mareks disease vaccines.

14924 Armitage; Evans   GB 050503/77/0020
Infectious bronchitis: quality control methods for vaccines.

14925 Hopkins   GB 050503/77/0022
Infectious laryngotracheitis: quality control methods for vaccines.

14926 Thornton; Muskett   GB 050503/77/0023
Infectious bursal disease: quality control methods for vaccines.

14927 Joyner; Norton   GB 050505/00/0010
Coccidiosis with reference to immunity factors affecting pathogenicity.

14928 Allan   GB 050507/00/0007
Serological studies on infectious bronchitis in chickens with special reference to diagnosis and classification.

14929 Cullen   GB 050507/75/0018
Studies on inclusion body hepatitis in chickens.

14930 Allan   GB 050507/77/0023
Studies on the egg drop syndrome.

14931 McMartin   GB 050512/00/0004
Surveys of avian nephritis and arthritic syndromes.

14932 McMartin GB 050512/00/0005
Avian respiratory disease (infectious bronchitis virus, celo virus and M.Gallisepticum.

14933 Guarda, F.; Cornaglia, E.; Galloni, M.
IT 041223/75/0001
Patologia cardio–vascolare Salpingo–peritoniti delle galline. Cardio–vascular pathology Salpingo–peritonitis in fowl. Publications.

14934 Simons, P.C.M.; Haye, U. NL 010109/72/3918
Skeletafwijkingen bij slachtpluimvee. Skeletal deviations in broilers. Publications.

14935 Kuil, H. NL 030006/74/7783 R
Immunologie van Eimeria infekties van de kip. Immunology of Eimeria infections of the fowl. Publications.

14936 Davelaar, F.G. NL 030017/75/6152 R
Betekenis van infectieuze bronchitus bij respiratoire aandoeningen en produktiedalingen bij de kip. Significance of infectious bronchitis in respiratory diseases and production problems in chickens. Publications.

14937 Guinee, P.A.M. NL 040011/76/7290
Ontwikkeling van een bruikbaar vaccin tegen colibacillose bij kuikens. Development of a useful vaccin against colibacillosis in chickens. Publications.

14938 Kouwenhoven, B. NL 060010/74/7783
Immunologie van Eimeria infekties van de kip. Immunology of Eimeria infections of the fowl. Publications.

14939 Kouwenhoven, B. NL 060010/75/6152 R
Betekenis van infectieuze bronchitus bij respiratoire aandoeningen en produktiedalingen bij de kip. Significance of infectious bronchitis in respiratory diseases and production problems in chickens. Publications.

14940 Eck, J.H.H. van NL 060010/75/6985 R
De betekenis van adenovirussen als ziekteverwekkers bij pluimvee. Adenivirus as pathogenic agent in poultry. Publications.

14941 Goren, E. NL 060010/76/7290
Ontwikkeling van een bruikbaar vaccin tegen Colibacillose bij kuikens. Development of a useful vaccin against Colibacillosis in chickens. Publications.

14942 Vertommen, M. NL 060010/77/8972 N
Achterblijven in groei gepaard gaande met beengebreken bij slachtkuikens. Stunting associated with leg weakness in broilers.

Geese, turkeys and other domestic birds (B 4490)

See also 12704, 13496

14943 Geissler, H.; Busche, R. DE 129800/74/0004
Untersuchungen über den Verseuchungsgrad von Ornithose und Salmonellose in Taubenbeständen. Investigations on the level of infection with ornithosis and salmonellosis in pigeonries.

14944 Geissler, H.; Hafez, H.M. DE 129800/77/0002
Entwicklung und Funktion der Bursa fabricii der Pute.

Development and function of Bursa fabricii of turkey.

14945 Gerlach, H. DE 160855/72/0002
Charakteristik von Mykoplasmenstämmen aus Tauben. Characteristics of mycoplasma strains isolated from pigeons.

14946 Löliger, H.–C.; Hagen, D.von dem; Hartmann, W.
DE 201300/75/0007
Untersuchungen zum Vorkommen Putenherpes–Virus–neutralisierender Antikörper und ihre Rolle in der Pathogenese der Marek'schen Krankheit. Studies on the occurrence of antibodies neutralizing the turkey herpes virus and on their role in the pathogenesis of Marek's disease.

14947 Gianelli, F.; Cabassi, E.; Brindani, F.; Cattabiani, F.
IT 041507/77/0003 N
Presenza di plasmidi R e Col in enterobatteri isolati dal contenuto intestinale di tacchini allevati industrialmente.. Presence of R and Col plasmids in Enterobacteriaceae isolated from intestinal contents of turkey's intensive breedings.

14948 Poelma, F.G. NL 030005/76/7769
Cochlosomose bij Japanse meeuwtjes. Cochlosomose in Japanese finches.

14949 Dorrestein, G.M. NL 030005/77/7767 R
Atoxoplasmose bij de kanarie (Serinus canaria), epidemiologie en pathogenese. Atoxoplasmosis in canary–birds (Serinus canarius), epidemiology and pathogenesis.

14950 Dorrestein, G.M. NL 030005/77/7768 R
Bloedspiegels bij kanaries na het toedienen van antibiotica via het drinkwater. Blood–serum levels of antibiotics applied via the drinkingwater to canaries.

Fishes, crustacea, shell fish and frogs in general (B 4500)

See also 1934, 2042, 2062, 2165, 2285, 12732

14951 Greuel, E.; Skorupka, A. DE 111404/78/0006 N
Staatliche Massnahmen zur Bekämpfung von Fischkrankheiten. Legal procedures in control of fish diseases. Publications.

14952 Neukirch, M.; Liess, B. DE 139550/78/0002 N
Viruserkrankungen der Fische: Untersuchungen über neutralisierende Antikörper. Virus diseases of fish: investigations on neutralizing antibodies.

14953 Researcher not indicated DE 160000/77/0002
Untersuchungen über die Verbreitung fischpathogener Viren und deren Tenazität ausserhalb des Wirtsorganismus. Investigations on distribution of fish–pathogenic viruses and their tenacity outside of the host organism.

14954 Reichenbach–Klinke, H.H.; Ahne, W.
DE 160771/73/0002 N
Viruskrankheiten bei Fischen. Virus diseases in fish.

14955 Reichenbach–Klinke, H.H. DE 160771/73/0004 N
Rückstandsuntersuchungen bei Fischen. Analyses of residues in fish.

14956 Ollenschläger, B.; Marzouk, M. DE 160771/78/0001 N
Histologische Untersuchungen zur Wirkung des Molluscizids

Bayluscid auf Fische. **Investigations on the effect of the molluscicide Bayluscid on fish.**

14957 Ahne, W.; Hussein, M. DE 160771/78/0002 N
Untersuchungen zur Diagnostik fischpathogener Rhabdoviren.
Investigations on fish pathogenic rhabdoviruses.

14958 Enzmann, P.-J. DE 216010/78/0001 N
Virusbedingte Fischkrankheiten. **Viral fish diseases.**

14959 Schulz, D. DE 305030/75/0034
Fischseuchen. **Infectious diseases of fish.**

14960 Researcher not indicated DE 502650/78/0024 N
Bakterielle Infektion als Ursache von Fischkrankheiten
Artendifferenzierung fischpathogener Aeromonaden. **Fish diseases caused by bacterial infection. Differentiation of species of fish–pathogenic Aeromonads.**

14961 Banning, P. van NL 010702/69/7131
Onderzoek naar het voorkomen en de betekenis van
parasieten in vissen, schaal– en schelpdieren. **Investigation into the occurrence and the significance of parasites in fish and shellfish.** Publications.

14962 Helder, Th. NL 030005/76/8969 N
Toxische effekten van 2, 3, 7, 8 tetrachlordibenzo–p–dio::in
(TCDD) op viseieren en visbroed. **Toxic effects of 2, 3, 7, 8 tetrachlorodibenzo–p–dioxin (TCDD) on fish eggs and fish fry.**

Carp (B 4510)

14963 Reichenbach–Klinke, H.–H.; Burzynski, H.
DE 160771/73/0005
Untersuchungen zur Blutgerinnung beim Karpfen.
Investigations into blood coagulation in carp.

14964 Deufel, J.; Euringer, H.; Hille, S. DE 501805/78/0001 N
Haematologische Untersuchungen zur Diagnose von
Fischkrankheiten bei Forelle und Karpfen. **Haematological investigations on diagnosis of fish diseases of trout and carp.** Publications.

14965 Rijkers, G.T. NL 020071/77/7328
De bouw en functie van het immuunsysteem bij de karper
(Cyprinus carpio). **Structure and function of the immune system of carp (Cyprinus carpio).** Publications.

14966 Bootsma, R. NL 030005/78/8968 N
De aeteologie van haemorrhagische septicaemie bij
graskarperbroed. **The etiology of haemorrhagic septicaemia in grass carp fry.**

14967 Bootsma, R. NL 030005/78/8970 N
Het nerveus syndroom bij de karper: identiteit en aetiologie.
Nervous syndrom in carp: identity and etiology.

14968 Vos–Maas, M.G. NL 030005/78/8971 N
Immunisatie van de karper tegen columnaris ziekte (karper,
immunisatie, Flexibaxter, columnaris). **Immunization of carp against columnaris disease (carp, immunization, Flexibacter, columnaris).**

Salmon (B 4520)

See also 14964

14969 Researcher not indicated DE 502650/78/0017 N
Bekämpfung der Verpilzung von Salmonidenlaichfischen.
Control of fungus infestation of Salmonidae spawn fish.

14970 Michel, M.C. FR 012225/75/5503
Etude des relations hôte–bactérie dans la Furonculose des
Salmonidés. **Relation between fish and bacteria in furunculosis of Salmonids.**

14971 Michel, M.C. FR 012225/75/8061
Etude des relations hôte–bactérie dans la Furonculose des
Salmonidés. **Relation between fish and bacteria in furunculosis of Salmonids.**

14972 Adair; Fergusson GB 041601/77/0025 R
Infectious Pancreatic Necrosis in salmonids.

Trout (B 4530)

See also 14135, 14964, 14970

14973 Tulliez, J.; Luquet, P.; Durand, E. FR 011412/77/9501
Devenir des hydrocarbures paraffiniques et naphténiques chez
le poisson. Intéractions métaboliques, effets
physiopathologiques. **Fate of paraffinic and naphtenic hydrocarbons in trout. Metabolic interaction and physiopathological effects.**

14974 de Kinkelin; Le Berre; Dorson; Torchy; Chilmonczyk;
Gerard FR 012225/70/5501
Protection de la truite contre les Septicémies Hémorragiques
Virales (S.H.V.). **Reaction of Trout against Viral Hemorragic Septicemiae Viruses.**

14975 de Kinkelin; Le Berre, M.; Dorson, M.; Torchy;
Chilmonczyk, S.; Gerard, J.P. FR 012225/70/8062
Protection de la truite contre les Septicémies Hémorragiques
Virales (S.H.V.). **Reaction of Trout against Hemorragic Septicemiae viruses.**

14976 Dorson; Torchy FR 012225/74/5502 N
Protection des alevins de Truite Arc–en–Ciel contre la Nécrose
Pancréatique. **Protection of Rainbow Trout Fry against Infectious Pancreatic Necrosis.**

14977 Dorson, M.; Torchy FR 012225/74/8063
Protection des alevins de truite Arc–en–Ciel contre la Nécrose
Pancréatique Infectieuse. **Protection of Rainbow Trout Fry against Infectious Pancreatic Necrosis.**

14978 Ferguson GB 041602/00/0002 R
An investigation of Proliferative Kidney Disease (PKD) in rainbow trout.

Eel (B 4550)

14979 Greuel, E. DE 111404/78/0007 N
Dermocystidium branchialis – Leger, 1914 – in den Kiemen des
Aals – Anguilla anguilla L. –. **Dermocystidium branchialis– Leger, 1914 – in the gills of eel – Anguilla anguilla L. –.**

14980 Peters, G. DE 135250/78/0004 N
Die Papillomatose des Aals. Experimentell–pathologische
Untersuchungen zum Krankheitsverlauf. **The papillomatosis of eel: experimental–pathological studies on the process of disease.**

Publications.

14981 Peters, G.   DE 135251/75/0007
Ätiologie der epidermalen Tumoren des europäischen Aals, Anguilla anguilla L.. **Studies on the etiology of epidermal papillomas in the European eel, Anguilla anguilla L.**. Publications.

Crustacea, shell fish, frogs (B 4560)

14982 Vey, A.; Meynadier, G.; Vago, C.; Fosset, J.; Boemare, N.   FR 010612/68/5189
Pathologie des Ecrevisses. **Pathology of crayfish.**

14983 Pierotti, P.   IT 041123/78/1149 N
Ricerche sulla patologia del Penaeus kerathurus. **Research on Penaeus kerathurus pathology.**

Invertebrates (bees, silk–worm) (B 4600)

See also 2050, 11487, 11488

14984 Ruttner, F.; Ritter, W.   DE 123100/78/0001 N
Entwicklung einer Therapie der Varroatose in Honigbienenvölkern. **Development of a therapy against varroatosis in honey–bee colonies.**

14985 Wahl, O.   DE 157100/73/0001
Untersuchungen über den Einfluss der Eiweiss– und Vitaminernährung auf die Giftempfindlichkeit der Honigbiene – Apis mellifica L. –. **Investigations into the influence of protein and vitamin supply on the susceptibility of honey bee – Apis mellifica L. – to toxins.**

14986 Mautz, D.   DE 502350/73/0001
Methoden zur Bekämpfung der Bösartigen Faulbrut. **Methods of American foulbrood control.**

14987 Mautz, D.   DE 502350/74/0001
Eine neue Nosema sp. –Microsporidia als Darmparasit von Apis florea –Hymenoptera–?. **A new nosema sp. –Microsporidia– infesting the midgut of Apis florea –Hymenoptera–?.**

14988 Mautz, D.   DE 502350/77/0007
Beeinflussung der Nosemainfektion bei der Honigbiene. **Influence on nosema infection of the honeybee.**

14989 Rasmussen, P.; Svendsen, O.   DK 010106/44/0007 N
Pesticiders og andre giftes virkning på bier samt mulighederne for at begrænse giftens evt skadevirkning. **The effect of pesticides and other poisons on bees and the possibilities of limiting the damaging effect.**

14990 Rasmussen, P.; Svendsen, O.   DK 010106/78/0001 N
Undersøgelser over sygdomme hos honningbien. **Investigations of diseases of honey bees.**

14991 Albisetti, J.; Vago, C.   FR 010114/62/5138
Méthodes de lutte contre les maladies des abeilles dans le Sud–Ouest de la France. **Control methods against honeybee diseases in southwestern France.**

14992 Bailey   GB 012004/78/0044 R
Diseases of honeybees.

14993 Findlay   GB 030903/74/0204 R
Monitoring the occurrence of pesticide residues in bees.

14994 Couston   GB 060104/00/0002
Bees, disease crop sprays and pollination.

14995 Persano, L.; Intoppa, F.   IT 020400/74/0004
Tossicità dei fitofarmaci nei confronti delle api (Apis mellifera ligustica L.). **Toxicity of several pesticides to honeybees (Apis mellifera ligustica L.).**

Rabbits (B 4910)

See also 11107, 14614, 14657, 15125

14996 Devos, A.; Spanoghe, L.; Okerman, G.   BE 050600/74/0006
Pathologisch onderzoek betreffende het mestkonijn. **Pathological research on broiler rabbits. Publications.**

14997 Peeters, J.; Halen, P.   BE 110000/71/0021 N
Onderzoek naar de profylaxie van Konijnen coccidiose met coccidiostatica. **Research on prevention of Coccidiosis in rabbit by the use of coccidiostatics.**

14998 Peeters, J.   BE 110000/78/0059 N
Identificatie en frekwentie der coccidiose specii in industriële konijnenbedrijven. **Identification of coccidiosis on industrial rabbit farms. Publications.**

14999 Frese, K.; Risch, W.   DE 129620/77/0001
Pathogenese der Bornainfektion beim Kaninchen. **Pathogenesis of Borna virus infection in rabbits.**

15000 Wenk, P.; Kleist, R. von; Illgen, B.; Haas, B.   DE 173200/74/0002
Experimentelle Untersuchungen an Nagetier Filariosen. **Experiments on filariases in rodents.**

15001 Löliger, H.–C.; Matthes, S.   DE 201300/70/5020
Ätiologie und Bekämpfung der Dysenterien bei Kaninchen. **Etiology and control of dysenteries in rabbit.**

15002 Gyrd–Hansen, N.   DK 030123/79/0003 N
Tetracykliners effekt på hjertefunktionen hos kaniner. **The effect of tetracyclines on the rabbit heart.**

15003 Martinet, L.; Ducluzeau, R.; Dabard, J.; Dubos, F.   FR 010205/73/2754
Etablissement d'une colonie de lièvres S P F pour éliminer la diarrhée néo–natale du levreau. **Establishment of a colony of S P F hares for the elimination of the diarrhoea in the new bornhares. Publications.**

15004 Coudert, P.; Licois, D.   FR 011504/70/8073
Physiopathologie du lapin. **Rabbit physiopathology.**

15005 Coudert, P.; Balencon   FR 011504/78/8074
Physiopathologie du lapin. **Rabbit physiopathology.**

15006 Fenizia, D.; Zicarelli, L.; De Anseris, P.   IT 051000/78/0004 N
Risultati sperimentali e pratici di cura in alcune micosi spontanee dei conigli. **Sperimental and pratical results in the treatment of spontaneous mycosis in rabbits.**

15007 Fenizia, D.; Bordi, B.; De Anseris, P.
IT 051000/78/0005 N
Grave episodio di aflatossicosi in un allevamento cunicolo. **A serious case of aflatoxicosis from fungi in a rabbit stock–farm.**

15008 Canale, A. IT 062500/74/0199
Studio degli effetti del piombo su alcuni fenomeni metabolici nei conigli e nei ruminanti. **A study on the effects of Pb on certain metabolic aspects, determined in rabbits and ruminants.** Publications.

Domestic pets and zoo animals (B 4920)

See also 1978, 1979, 13457, 13682, 13970, 14422, 14433, 14621, 15099

15009 Schwartz–Porsche, D. DE 104500/73/0001 N
Klinische Nierenfunktionsprüfungen beim Hund mit direktem und indirekten Clearanceverfahren. **Clinical renal function tests of dog with direct and indirect clearance methods.**

15010 Trautvetter, E.; Pagel, B.; Werner, J.
DE 104500/77/0002
Klinische, genetische und vergleichend medizinische Aspekte angeborenen Herzfehler beim Hund. Derzeitiger Schwerpunkt: Subvalvuläre Aortenstenose. **Clinical, genetical and comparative aspects of congenital cardiovascular anomalies in dogs. Current point of main interest: subvalvular aortic stenosis.**

15011 Schwartz–Porsche, D.; Lettow, E.; Opitz, M.; Siegert, M. DE 104500/77/0003
Nierenerkrankungen bei Hund und Katze. **Renal diseases of dog and cat.**

15012 Lettow, E.; Kasbohm, C.; Loppnow, H.; Opitz, M.; Schwartz–Porsche, D. DE 104500/77/0004
Lebererkrankungen bei Hund und Katze. **Liver diseases in dogs and cats.**

15013 Opitz, M.; Lettow, E.; Schwartz–Porsche, D.; Siegert, M. DE 104500/77/0009
Symptomatische Hyperlipidämien bei Spontanerkrankungen des Hundes und der Katze 'Diabetes mellitus, Nephropathien, Hepatopathien, Endokrinopathien'. **Symptomatic hyperlipidemias in spontaneously occuring canine and feline disease conditions 'Diabetes mellitus nephropathia, hepatopathia, endocrinopathia'.**

15014 Frank, H. DE 129620/78/0002 N
Pathologie der Wild– und Zootierkrankheiten. **Pathology of wild animals and animals in zoo.** Publications.

15015 Kösters, J.; Rendemann, S. DE 129800/78/0001 N
Immunprophylaxe bei Psittaciden. **Immunoprophylaxis of Psittacidae.**

15016 Paulsen, J.; Knecht, E. DE 129820/77/0003
Virusinfektionen bei Katze und Hund. **Virus infections in cats and dogs.**

15017 Eikmeier, H.; Kraft, W. DE 129881/75/0004
Erkrankungen katzenartiger Raubtiere. **Diseases of feline predacious animals.** Publications.

15018 Eikmeier, H.; Schumann, W. DE 129881/77/0001

Wirkung extern und peroral applizierter Organophosphate auf die Serum–Cholinesterasen beim Hund Wirkung extern und peroral applizierter Organophosphate auf die Erythrozyten–Cholinesterasen beim Hund. **Serum cholinesterases and erythrocyte cholinesterases in dogs as affected by external and peroral application of organophosphates.**

15019 Eikmeier, H.; Muto, S. DE 129881/78/0001 N
Einfluss der Lagerung von Hunde–Blutkonserven auf Zellen und Plasma. **Influence of storage of stored dog blood on cells and plasma.**

15020 Trautwein, G.; Müller–Peddinghaus, R.
DE 139101/74/0002
Immunpathologie der Nierenerkrankungen des Hundes. **Immunopathology of kidney diseases in dog.**

15021 Reetz, I. DE 139350/75/0002
Untersuchungen über erbliche, polymorphe Protein– und Enzymtypen im Blut bei Hunden. **Investigations on hereditary polymorphic protein and enzyme types in the blood of dogs.**

15022 Kirchhoff, H.; Amtsberg, G.; Eberle, G.; Trautwein, G.; Kersten, U. DE 139450/70/0002
Untersuchungen zur Ätiologie und Pathogenese der Klappenendocarditis des Hundes. **Investigation on the etiology and pathogenesis of valvular endocarditis in dogs.**

15023 Amtsberg, G.; Stäcker, W. DE 139450/78/0001 N
Untersuchungen zur experimentellen Erzeugung von bakteriellen Harnblasenentzündungen bei Ratten und Hunden unter Berücksichtigung der Wirksamkeitsprüfung von Methenaminhippurat. **Investigations on experimental generation of bacterial cystitis in rats and dogs with special regard to efficiency testing of methenamine hippurate.**

15024 Brass, W.; Amtsberg, G.; Bisping, W.; Kersten, U.; Kirchhoff, H.; Kirpal, G. DE 139450/78/0004 N
Untersuchungen rheumatoider Erkrankungen des Hundes. **Investigations on rheumatoid diseases in dogs.**

15025 Stoye, M. DE 139500/75/0002 N
Untersuchungen über den Umfang pränataler und galaktogener Toxocara canis–Infektionen beim Hund. **Studies on the extent of prenatal and galactogenous infections with Toxocara canis in dogs.**

15026 Petrich, J.; Stoye, M. DE 139500/78/0012 N
Prüfung verschiedener serologischer Methoden zum Nachweis impatenter Helmintheninfektionen beim Hund. **Testing of different serological techniques for the detection of impatent helminth infections of dog.**

15027 Liess, B.; Diederichsen, U.; Thiel, W.
DE 139550/78/0006 N
Untersuchungen über die diagnostische Brauchbarkeit des Neutralisations–Immuno–Fluoreszenz–NIF–Tests–zum Nachweis neutralisierender Antikörper gegen das Virus der Hundestaupe im CCSC–cell culture and staining chamber–System. **Investigations on the diagnostic utility of neutralization immuno–fluorescence assay for identification of neutralizing antibodies against canine distemper virus in cell culture and staining chamber system.**

15028 Brass, W.; Schütt, I. DE 139950/77/0002

Experimentelle rheumatische Polyarthritis beim Beagle durch Infektion mit Rotlaufbakterien. **Experimental rheumatoid polyarthritis in beagle by infection with erysipelothrix rhusiopathiae.**

15029 Frank, W.; Liebchen, S.   DE 144130/75/0008
Untersuchungen an Helminthen der Reptilien – systematische Zuordnung der bei ca 8.000 Sektionen gefundenen Nematoden. **Investigations of helminths of reptiles – systematic classification of nematodes found in about 8,000 dissections.**

15030 Schubert, G.   DE 144151/70/0001
Krankheiten von Aquarienfischen. **Diseases in aquarium fish.**

15031 Loeffler, K.; König, W.   DE 144605/74/0003
Bakteriologische Befunderhebungen an Kleintierpatienten und im Stallbereich. **Bacteriological studies on small animal patients and on clinic kennel.**

15032 Loeffler, K.; Nowak, B.   DE 144605/77/0003
Bestimmung des Öffnungswinkels am Acetabulum von Hunden mit und ohne Hüftgelenksdysplasie. **Determination of the opening–angle in the acetabulum of dogs with and without hip dysplasia.** Publications.

15033 Loeffler, K.; Niedermeyer, R.   DE 144605/78/0001 N
Verlaufsuntersuchungen bei Hunden mit Hüftgelenksdysplasie. **Sequential studies on dogs with hip dysplasia.**

15034 Boch, J.; Walter, D.   DE 160820/78/0004 N
Die Bedeutung der Katze für die Übertragung der Toxoplasmose. **The significance of cat for the transmission of Toxoplasmosis.**

15035 Boch, J.; Böhm, A.   DE 160820/78/0007 N
Zystenbildende Kokzidien des Hundes. **Cyst–forming coccidia of dogs.**

15036 Forstner, M.J.; Wiesner, H.; Kopp, H.   DE 160823/75/0003
Untersuchungen über die Herdenbehandlung zur Entwurmung von Zootieren mit modernen Medikamenten. **Investigations on herd therapy for dehelminthisation of zoo ruminants with modern anthelmintics.** Publications.

15037 Hasslinger, M.–A.   DE 160823/77/0002
Zur Verbreitung von Ollulanus tricuspis bei Katzen. **Investigations on the spreading of Ollulanus tricuspis in cats.** Publications.

15038 Grimm, F.   DE 160855/71/0006
Therapie bei Infektionskrankheiten von Zier– und Zoovögeln. **Therapy of infectious diseases of pet and zoo birds.**

15039 Rüsse, M.W.   DE 160910/75/0003
Die Behandlung der Laktomanie der Hündin mit L–Dopa und 2Br–alpha–Ergocryptin. **Treatment of lactomania in the bitch with L–Dopa and 2Br–alpha–Ergocryptin.**

15040 Schebitz, H.; Euler, B.   DE 160940/77/0003
Nierenfunktionsprüfungen bei mehrfach verletzten Hunden unter besonderer Berücksichtigung der Elektrolytbestimmung und Kreatininclearance. **Renal function test in dogs with several hurts in special consideration of electrolyte determination and creatinine clearance.**

15041 Fritsch, R.; Franzusky, D.   DE 160940/77/0007
Die Metomedat–Narkose beim Hund. **Metomedat narcosis in dog.**

15042 Schebitz, H.; Schröder, M.; Widmer, W.   DE 160940/77/0008
Zur Osteogenese beim wachsenden Hund. **Osteogenesis of growing puppy.**

15043 Andresen, E.; Christensen, K.   DK 030127/73/0002 N
Undersøgelse af genetiske polymorfier hos hunde. **An investigation of genetical polymorphs in dogs.**

15044 Venge, O.   DK 030127/74/0008 N
Afkomsstudier over genetisk betingede sygdomme hos hund (progressiv retinal atrofi og Collie eye anomali). **Progeny studies of genetically conditioned diseases in dogs (progressive atrophy and Collie eye anomally).**

15045 Andresen, E.   DK 030127/75/0001 N
Undersøgelser over anæmi hos hunde. **Investigations of anaemia in dogs.**

15046 Hasholt, J.   DK 030136/74/0006 N
Knælidelser hos hund. **Knee complaints in dogs.**

15047 Flagstad, A.   DK 030136/78/0001 N
Undersøgelse vedrørende diagnosticering af felin infektiøs peritonitis. **Diagnostic studies of feline infectious peritonitis.**

15048 Nielsen, B.   DK 030136/78/0002 N
Undersøgelse over malabsorption hos hund og kat. **Studies of the malabsorption syndrome in dogs and cats.**

15049 Hartman, E.G.; Dam, R.H. van; Dam–Knubben, G.M.S. van   NL 030002/73/5671 R
Epidemiologie en immunologie van infekties met leptospieren bij de hond. **Epidemiology and immunology of leptospirosis in dogs.** Publications.

15050 Hendrix, W.M.L.   NL 030004/73/5846 R
Onderzoek van parasieten bij amphibieën. **Parasites of Amphibians.**

15051 Gaag, I. van der   NL 030005/72/5768 R
Gastro–duodenale funktiestoornissen en afwijkingen bij de hond. **Gastro–duodenal functional disorders and diseases in the dog.** Publications.

15052 Ingh, T.S.G.A.M. van den   NL 030005/76/6946 R
Leverziekten bij kleine huisdieren (leverziekten, hond, kat). **Diseases of the liver in small animals (liver diseases, dog, cat).**

15053 Wouda, W.   NL 030005/77/7759
Pathomorfologisch onderzoek van honden en katten met neurologische verschijnselen. **Pathomorphological investigation of dogs and cats with neurological symptoms.** Publications.

15054 Horzinek, M.C.   NL 030007/76/6961 R
Infektieuze peritonitis: etiologie en immunopathogenese. **Feline infectious peritonitis: etiology and immune pathogenesis.** Publications.

15055 Happé, R.H.   NL 030012/72/5768 R

Gastro–duodenale funktiestoornissen en afwijkingen bij de hond. **Gastro–duodenal functional disorders and diseases in the dog.** Publications.

15056 Stades, F.C.　　　　　NL 030012/72/5865
Vóórkomen, erfelijkheidspatroon en therapie van progressieve retina atrofie bij de hond. **Incidence, heredity and therapy of progressive retinal atrophy in dogs.**

15057 Zimmerman, A.N.E.　　　NL 030012/72/8985 N
Klinische en experimentele fysiologie van circulatie en respiratie bij kleine huisdieren. **Clinical and experimental physiology of circulation and respiration in small domestic animals.** Publications.

15058 Venker, A.J.　　　　　NL 030012/74/6154 R
Spontaan optredende larynxparalyse bij de jonge bouvier. **Spontaneous laryngeal paralysis in young bouviers.** Publications.

15059 Bruyne, J.J. de　　　　NL 030012/75/5869 R
Onderzoek naar de vetstofwisseling bij de vastende hond. **Lipid–metabolism in fasting dogs.** Publications.

15060 Meijer, J.C.　　　　　NL 030012/76/5682 R
Onderzoek naar de pathogenese van het hypofyse–afhankelijk hyperadrenocortisisme bij de hond. **Pathogenesis of pituary–dependent hyperadrenocortisism in the dog.**

15061 Belshaw, B.E.; Rijnberk, A.　　NL 030012/76/5867
Primaire hypothyroidie bij honden, o.a. radio–immuno–assays van plasma T4 en T3. **Primary hypothyroidism in dogs, a.o. radio immuno assays of plasma T4 en T3.**

15062 Rothuizen, J.　　　　　NL 030012/76/6946 R
Leverziekten bij kleine huisdieren (leverziekten, hond, kat). **Diseases of the liver in small animals (liver diseases, dog, cat).**

15063 Nes, J.J. van　　　　　NL 030012/76/8982 N
Cytologisch en biochemisch onderzoek van liquor cerebrospinalis van normale honden en honden met neurologische afwijkingen. **Cytological and biochemical examination of cerebrospinal fluid of normal dogs and dogs with neurological conditions.**

15064 Hendriks, H.J.　　　　　NL 030012/76/8984 N
Onderzoek naar de waarde van de duitse en scandinavische methode bij de bepaling van SGPT met een "short interval analyzer". **Investigations of the merits of the German and Scandinavian method for determination of SGPT with a "short interval analyzer".** Publications.

15065 Willemse, A.　　　　　NL 030012/78/8983 N
Atoptie bij de hond: evaluatie van diagnostiek en hyposensibilisatie (diagnostiek van atopie, hond, hyposensibilisatie). **Atopy in dogs: evaluation of diagnostic methods and hyposensitization (diagnosis of atopy, dogs, hyposensitization).**

15066 Watering, C.C. van de　　　NL 030016/65/7809
Genetische aspecten van en milieu–invloeden op heupdysplasie bij de hond. **Genetic aspects and environmental influences on hipdysplasia in dogs.**

15067 Wolvenkamp, W.Th.C.　　　NL 030016/72/5768 R
Gastro–duodenale funktiestoornissen en afwijkingen bij de

hond. **Gastro–duodenal functional disorders and diseases in the dog.** Publications.

Fur animals (B 4930)

See also 14443, 14621

15068 Trautwein, G.　　　　　DE 139101/70/0001 N
Untersuchungen über die Pathogenese der Aleutenkrankheit der Nerze. **Studies on the pathogenesis of Aleutian disease in mink.**

15069 Venge, O.; Hansen, N.G.　　DK 010204/75/0019
Selektion på grundlag af immunelektroosmoforese med henblik på eliminering af plasmacytose hos mink. **Selection of breeding stock on the basis of immunelektroosmoforese with a view to elimination of plasmacytosis in mink.**

15070 Venge, O.; Larsen, A.S.; Christensen, K.;
Glem–Hansen, N.; Sørensen, H.　　DK 010204/78/0002 N
Undersøgelser over genetisk betinget tyrosinæmi hos mink. **Syndrome of heditary Tyrosinemia in mink.**

15071 Sørensen, H.　　　　　DK 030106/77/0001 N
Studier over den biokemiske årsag til en arvelig minksygdom; sygdomskompleks svarende til Tyrosinemia. **Biochemical investigations in relation to Tyrosinemia in mink.**

15072 Christensen, K.; Glem–Hansen, N.; Møller, T.; Venge, O.　　　　　　　　DK 030127/75/0006 N
Arvelig sygdom hos mink. **Heredity disorders in mink.**

15073 Venge, O.; Jørgensen, G.　　DK 030127/77/0002 N
Arvens betydning for bekæmpelse af plasmacytose hos mink. **Genetic basis of eradication of plasmacytosis in mink.**

15074 Poulsen, J.S.D.; Jepsen, R.Ø.; Jørgensen, G.
　　　　　　　　　　　　DK 030130/78/0003 N
Undersøgelse over hæmatologiske og klinisk–kemiske ændringer ved bloddudtagning hos mink. **Hematological and clinical–chemical changes during blood sampling in mink.**

15075 Larsen, S.; Christensen, K.; Sørensen, H.; Henriksen, P.S.　　　　　　　　DK 030133/79/0002 N
Undersøgelser over arveligt betinget tyrosinæmi hos mink. **Studies on hereditary tyrosinemia in mink.**

15076 Gierløff, B.C.H.　　　　DK 030136/74/0003 N
Undersøgelse vedrørende diagnosticering af aleutiansyge hos mink gennem påvisning af specifikt antistof ved hjælp af modstrømselektroforese. **An investigation into the diagnosis of Aleutian sickness in mink through demonstrating the existence of specific antibodies with the aid of A.C. electrophoresis.**

15077 Lund, E.　　　　　　　DK 030138/76/0010 N
Distempervirus betinget encephalit hos mink. **Distemper virus conditioned encephalitis in mink.**

15078 Lund, E.; Hansen, M.　　　DK 030138/79/0003 N
In vitro undersøgelser af mink virus. **The detection of various mink viruses in cell cultures.**

15079 Aasted, B.; Hansen, M.　　DK 030138/79/0004 N
Metode til diagnosticering af plasmacystose hos mink. **Studies on improved methods for the detection of plasmacystosis in mink.**

15080 Haagsma, J.   NL 010401/63/1628
Mink Aleutian disease. **Mink Aleutian disease.** Publications.

Other domestic animals (B 4990)

15081 Frese, K.   DE 129620/70/0003
Untersuchungen zur Klassifikation und Histogenese der
Melanome des Hundes. **Studies on classification and
histogenesis of melanoma in dog.**

15082 Dobos, F.; Martinet, L.   FR 010216/74/9607 N
Ecologie microbienne : rôle de Clostridium difficile associé à
C. periringens et C. tertium dans l'étiologie de la diarrhée
néo–natale chez le levraut gnotoxénique. **Microbial ecology :
the role of Clostridium difficile associated with C. perfringens
and C. terium in the aetiology of neonatal diarrhoea in the
gnotoxenic young hare.**

Laboratory animals (B 9120)

See also 12858, 12861, 13561, 13563, 13627, 13878, 13884,
14126, 14443, 14632, 14633, 14653, 14657, 14887, 15009, 15023

15083 Gerber, H.C.; Schmitt, M.; Dorn, R.; Oguz, T.;
Hörchner, F.   DE 104200/72/0005 N
1. Modellinfektion an kleinen Versuchstieren mit F. gigantica.
2. Beeinflussung von Zwischenwirtsschnecken durch
Umweltfaktoren und larvale Trematodeninfektionen mit F.
gigantica. 3. Kreuzimmunität zwischen F. hepatica und F.
gigantica bei Meerschweinchen und Kaninchen. 4.
Wirtstierantigene im Tegument von F. hepatica. **1. Model
infection of small experimental animals with F. gigantica. 2.
Intermediate host snails as affected by environmental conditions
and larval trematode infections by F. gigantica. 3. Cross
immunity between F. hepatica and F. gigantica in guinea–pig
and rabbit. 4. Host antigens in the tegument of F. hepatica.**

15084 Hörchner, F.   DE 104200/72/0007 N
Immunmechanismus der Ratte gegen Nippostrongylus
brasiliensis in vitro. **Mechanism of immunity in rat against
Nippostrongylus brasiliensis.**

15085 Beuthner, U.; Zander, B.   DE 104201/75/0002
Antigenstruktur von Trypanosomen. **Antigen structure of
Trypanosoma.**

15086 Krampitz, G.; Resch, N.   DE 111401/75/0001
Einfluss von Beryllium auf Calcifizierungsvorgänge. **Influence
of beryllium on calcification processes.**

15087 Rudolph, R.; Thiel, W.; Reinacher, M.; Müller, H.
DE 129620/74/0002
Untersuchungen zur Morphologie, Ätiologie und Pathogenese
epithelialer Hauttumoren von Mastomys natalensis.
**Investigations of the morphology, etiology and pathogenesis of
epithelial skin tumors of Mastomys natalensis.**

15088 Rehner, G.; Koopmann, M.   DE 129900/74/0002
Wirkungen einer chronischen Blei–Intoxikation auf die
physiologische und biochemische Funktion der Niere. **Effects
of chronic lead poisoning on physiological and biochemical renal
functions.**

15089 Leitzmann, C.; Cremer, H.–D.   DE 129900/74/0005
Der Einfluss von Tryptophanmangel auf Enzymaktivität und

Nervenfunktion der Ratte. **The influence of tryptophan
deficiency on enzyme activity and nerve action in rats.**

15090 Schulz, L.–C.; Ehard, H.   DE 139100/74/0001
Experimenteller Rotlauf der Ratte 1.Standardisierung einer
rheumatoiden Modellkrankheit mit besonderer
Berücksichtigung morphologischer Veränderungen im Bereich
der Gelenke und der Aorta 2.Inhibition mit Antirheumatika.
**Experimental Erysipelas in rats 1.Standardization of a
rheumatoid disease model in animals with special reference to
morphological alterations in joints and aorta 2.Inhibition with
antirheumatic drugs.**

15091 Schulz, L.–C.; Ehard, H.; Weiss, R.; Böhm, K.H.
DE 139100/75/0002
Rotlaufinfektion bei Ratten und Mäusen 'Rheuma–Modell'.
**Erysipelas infection in rats and mice 'model for rheumatoid
arthritis in man'.** Publications.

15092 Drommer, W.; Ehard, H.   DE 139103/74/0002
Experimenteller Rotlauf der Ratte Transmissions– und
Rasterelektronenmikroskopie an Gelenken und der Aorta.
**Experimental erysipelas in rats transmission electron
microscopy and raster electron microscopy in joints and aorta.**

15093 Hapke, H.–J.; Tachampa, S.   DE 139151/74/0005
Einfluss einer chronischen Bleikontamination auf den Ablauf
einer akuten Hepatose, Nephrose und eines Diabetes mellitus
bei Ratten. **The influence of a chronic lead contamination on
the process of acute hepatosis, nephrosis and Diabetes mellitus
in rats.**

15094 Hapke, H.–J.; Youssef, S.   DE 139151/74/0006
Einfluss einer chronischen Bleikontamination auf Aktivierung
und Inaktivierung von Alkylphosphaten –Parathion und
Paraoxon– bei Ratten. **The influence of chronic lead
contamination on activation and inactivation of alkyl
phosphates –Parathion and Paraoxon– in rats.**

15095 Schole, J.; Sallmann, H.–P.   DE 139250/75/0002
Synthesekapazität des Bindegewebes in verschiedenen
Organen der rotlaufinfizierten Ratte. **Connective tissue
synthesis in various organs of rats infected with Erysipelothrix
rhusopathiae.**

15096 Kirchhoff, H.; Amtsberg, G.; Kersten, U.; Trautwein,
G.   DE 139450/75/0001
Erzeugung der Endocarditis durch experimentelle Infektion.
Production of endocarditis by experimental infection.

15097 Böhm, K.H.; Weiss, R.; El–Sayed, M.T.
DE 139451/75/0001
Experimentelle Untersuchungen über Immunitätsverhältnisse
bei kleinen Nagern nach
Trichophyton–verrucosum–Infektionen. **Experimental
investigations into immunity in small rodents after infection
with Trichophyton verrucosum.**

15098 Stoye, M.   DE 139500/73/0001 N
Untersuchungen über die Wanderung und das Verhalten der
Larven von Ancylostoma caninum in definitiven und
paratenischen Wirten. **Studies on migration and behavior of
Ancylostoma caninum Larvae in definitive and secondary hosts.**

15099 Frank, W.; Zeyhle, E.   DE 144130/75/0004

D 3400 – Animal diseases, veterinary medicine

Untersuchungen über die Entwicklung von Echinococcus multilocularis LEUCKART, 1863 in verschiedenen Nagetieren nach oraler Verabreichung von Eiern; zugleich ein Beitrag zur Epidemiologie der Echinococcose – natürliche Infektionen beim Fuchs und experimentelle bei der Katze –. **Investigations of the development of Echinococcus multilocularis LEUCKART, 1863 in various rodents after oral application of eggs: a contribution to the epidemiology of echinococcosis – natural infections of foxes 'Vulpes vulpes' and experimental ones of domestic cats – Felis domestica –.**

15100 Frank, W.; Mitlacher, A.   DE 144130/75/0010
Licht– und elektronenmikroskopische Untersuchungen des "Hirnwurms" von Dicrocoelium dendriticum in Ameisen der Gattung Formica. **Light and electromicroscopic investigations into "Hirnwurm" of Dicrocoelium dendriticum of ants of the genus Formica.**

15101 Tempel, K.; Schmerold, I.   DE 160551/75/0001
Untersuchungen zur Induktion einer Zellkern–Desoxyribonuclease II der Rattenleber nach akuter Schädigung durch Diäthylnitrosamin. **Investigations on the induction of a nuclear desoxyribonuclease II of rat liver under the influence of toxic diethylnitrosamine doses.** Publications.

15102 Tempel, K.   DE 160551/78/0001 N
DNA–Reparatur in Lymphozyten der Ratte unter dem Einfluss von ionisierenden Strahlen und Radiomimetika. **DNA–repair of lymphocytes of the rat under the influence of ionizing radiation and radiomimetics.** Publications.

15103 Hegner, D.; Kroker, R.; Breuninger, V.; Nohl, H.; Heckers   DE 160552/75/0002
Die Wirkung von essentiellen Glycerinphosphatiden auf die Eigenschaften der ATPasen in isolierten Leberplasmamembranen bei jungen und alten Ratten. **Effect of essential phospholipids on the properties of ATP–ases of isolated rat liver plasma membranes of young and old animals.** Publications.

15104 Lösch, U.; Fiedler, H.–H.; Starker; Herlyn, D.; Hoffmann–Fezer, G.   DE 160600/75/0014
Stimulierung bzw. Unterdrückung – Phythämoglobin, Dextransulfat bzw. Cyclophosphamid – von B–Zellen in vivo und in vitro. **Stimulation resp. suppression – phythaemoglobin, dextransulphate resp. cyclophosphamide – of B–cells in vivo and in vitro.** Publications.

15105 Munz, E.; Kaufmann, R.   DE 160821/77/0002 R
Experimentelle Untersuchungen zur Belastbarkeit einer maternalen Immunität von Saugmäusen gegen infektiöse Ektromelie – ein Beitrag zur Immunprophylaxe der Krankheit mit Orthopoxviren. **The resistance of a maternally–derived immunity of babymice against mousepox – experiments regarding a special possibility of immunization with orthopox viruses.**

15106 Krampitz, H.E.; Weber, B.; Scheffer, K.   DE 160825/78/0002 N
Organotropie und Gewebeverhalten von menschenpathogenen Leishmania–Stämmen im Infektionsexperiment am kleinen Versuchstier. **Organotropism and tissue relationship of human infective Leishmania strains in experiments with small animals.** Publications.

15107 Krampitz, H.E.   DE 160825/78/0003 N

Die Züchtung von Nagetierflöhen unter Laboratoriumsbedingungen und Prüfung ihrer Vektorfunktion für Blutprotozoen. **Rodent fleas reared under laboratory conditions and determination of their vector capacity for blood protozoa.** Publications.

15108 Kaiser, W.   DE 160960/74/0001 N
Regulation der Cholesterinsynthese und deren Beeinflussung. **Regulation of cholesterol synthesis and factors of influence.**

15109 Kirchgessner, M.; Schneider, U.   DE 161280/75/0001
Zum Trächtigkeitsanabolismus von Spurenelementen. **Anabolic effects of trace elements on pregnant rats.**

15110 Wenk, P.; Kleist, R. von   DE 173200/78/0001 N
Immunstimulation neonataler Mastomys gegen Mikrofilarien von Litomosoides carinii – Nematoda, Filarioidea –. **Immunological stimulation of neonatal Mastomys against Microfilariae of Litomosoides carinii – Nematoda, Filarioidea –**

15111 Dönges, J.   DE 176250/72/0001 N
Physiologische Untersuchungen zum Parasit–Zwischenwirtsverhältnis, zum Parasito–Coenose–Problem und zur Morphologie von Echinostomatiden. **Physiological studies on interrelations between parasite and intermediate host, on the problem of parasitico–coenosis, and on the morphology of Echinostomatidae.**

15112 Heeschen, W.; Kaiser, M.; Blüthgen, A.; Tolle, A.   DE 207020/74/5010 N
Tierexperimentelle Untersuchungen zur biologischen Wirkung von Fascioliziden auf Physiologie und Biochemie der Laktation. **Experiments with laboratory animals to study the biological effect of fasciolocides on physiology and biochemistry of lactation.**

15113 Schönberg, A.   DE 305030/75/0033
Verbesserung der Leptospirose–Listeriose–Diagnostik. **Improvement of the diagnosis of leptospirosis–listeriosis.**

15114 Rasmussen, F.   DK 030123/79/0001 N
Udvikling af metoder til in vivo bestemmelse af den lokalbeskadigende effekt af lægemidler injiceret intramuskulært. **Development of methods for in vivo determination of the tissue damaging effect after intramuscular injection of drugs.**

15115 Poulsen, J.S.D.; Bjældager, P.   DK 030130/78/0004 N
Undersøgelser over myoglobins renale toxicitet. **The renal toxicity of myoglobin.**

15116 Kjærsgaard, P.; Chang, A.; Dellman, H.D.   DK 030132/78/0001 N
Morfologiske ændringer i tværstribet skeletmuskulatur inficeret med Trichinella spiralis og Trichinella pseudospiralis. **Morphological alterations in striated skeleton muscles infected with Trichinella spiralis and Trichinella pseudospiralis.**

15117 Jørgensen, K.; Turnbull, P.C.P.; Kramer, J.M.; Mellins, J.   DK 030137/74/0001 N
Bacillus toksiner. **Bacillus toxins.**

15118 Aasted, B.   DK 030138/77/0016 N
Immunologisk karakteristik af plasminogen aktivatorer.

Immunological characterisation of plasminogen activators.

15119 Ducluzeau, R.; Dufresne, S.　　FR 010205/70/2757
Production de produits toxiques par la flore du tube digestif à partir du régime alimentaire. **Production of toxic metabolites by the flora of digestif tract from the diet.**

15120 Ducluzeau, R.; Dufresne, S.　　FR 010205/73/2745
Ensemencement du tube digestif de souris axéniques par les bactéries de l'eau minérale. **Inoculation of the digestive tract of axenic mice by the bacteria of the mineral water.** Publications.

15121 Ducluzeau, R.; Raibaud, P.　　FR 010205/73/2753
Effet de barrière microbiologique à l'encontre de bactéries potentiellement pathogène (entérobactéries, staphylocoques, clostridium, chez des animaux gnotoxéniques. **Effect of microbiological barrier against potentially pathogenic (Enterobacteria, Staphylococcus, Clostridium) in the gnotoxenic animals.**

15122 Duval, Y.; Rousseau, M.; Denarie, J.
　　　　　　　　　　FR 010216/75/9603 N
Ecologie microbienne : transferts d'informations génétiques in vivo, dans le tube digestif de souris gnotoxéniques, entre souches de Staphyloccus et souches d'entérobactéries. **Microbial ecology : genetic information transfer in vivo between Staphylococcus and enterobacteria strains in the gastrointestinal tract of gnotoxenic mice.**

15123 Duval, Y.; Raibaud, P.　　FR 010216/78/9602
Ecologie microbienne : interaction entre souches de escherichia coli sensibles et reststantes aux antibiotiques dans le tube digestif de souris gnotoxeniques. **Microbial ecology ; interaction between antibiotic sensitive and resistant strains of Escherichia coli in the gastrointestinal tract of gnotoxenic mice.**

15124 Fayet, J.C.; Genest, M.　　FR 010800/77/8056
Thyroïde et réponse immunitaire chez la souris. **Thyroid and immunitary response in mice.**

15125 Galtier, P.; Charpenteau, J.L.; Alvinerie, M.;
Eeckhoutte, C.　　FR 011407/76/8054
Etude pharmacocinétique de l'ochratoxine a chez le rat, le lapin et le porc. **Pharmacokinetics of ochratoxin a in rat, rabbit and pig.**

15126 Bosseray, N.　　FR 011503/77/8093
Mécanismes de la colonisation foetale transplacentaire par Brucella chez l'animal de laboratoire. **Transplacental foetal colonization by Brucella in laboratory animals.**

15127 Pardon, P.　　FR 011503/78/8104
Salmonellose expérimentale murine : immunité locale et systématique. **Local and systematic immunity to Salmonella infection in mice.**

15128 Pelt, F.L.　　NL 020019/77/7319
Blijvende effecten van fysische milieufactoren op het gedrag van proefdieren. **Persistent behavioural effects of physical environmental factors in experimental animals.**

15129 Donk, J.A.W.M. van der　　NL 030018/78/8986 N
Makrofagen in verband met de immuunrespons bij de rat (makrofagen, monokines, gen–expressie, rat, lymfocyten). **The role of macrophages in the immune response of the rat (macrophages, monokines, gene–expression, rat,**

lymphocytes).

15130 Steenis, G. van　　NL 040011/76/7488
Detectie van virussen bij proefdieren. **Detection of viruses in experimental animals.**

D 4100 – Engineering – equipments

See also 1471, 15787

15131 Nisen, A.   BE 010002/76/0008
Etude des possibilités de culture maraîchère et ornementale en serres chauffées par des systèmes enterrés. **Study of the possibilities of vegetable and ornemental culture in glasshouses heated with buried systems.**

15132 Maton, A.; Lips, J.   BE 070300/78/0047 R
Het rooien van witloofwortelen. **Harvesting of Brussels endive roots. Publications.**

15133 Andries, A.; Carlier, L.   BE 070400/78/0028 R
Techniek van herinzaai van grasland.

15134 Martens, M.; Van Steyvoort, L.; Roussel, N.; Vigoureux, A.; Vanstallen, R.   BE 140000/74/0027 R
Studie van de mechanisatie van de teelttechnieken en onderzoek op het zaad van suikerbieten. **Study of the mechanization of the cultivation technics and research on the seed of sugarbeets. Publications.**

15135 Salje, E.; Thomas, D.   DE 114502/75/0004
Bandschleifen von Holz– und Holzwerkstoffen. **Belt–sanding of wood and wood materials.**

15136 Konggaard, S.P.   DK 010201/77/0010
Tekniske vandsystemer til småkalve. **Technical watering systems for young calves.**

15137 Weidner, K.   DK 010206/76/0001
Gyllebehandlingsmetoders smitte– og miljømæssige konsekvenser. **The environmental consequences and disease risks associated with slurry treatment methods.**

15138 Klausen, K.G.   DK 010400/76/0002
Reduktion af anvendte mængder af svampe– og skadedyrsmidler ved benyttelse af ULV (Ultra Low Volume) – sprøjteteknik. **Reduction of fungicide and insecticide dosages by the use of ULV (Ultra Low Volume) spraying technique.**

15139 Chappell   GB 011004/00/0007
Construction, instrumentation and operation of fruit stores.

15140 Knapp   GB 011102/00/0026
Systems for monitoring temperature,humidity and light.

15141 Knapp   GB 011102/77/0028
Weighing machine for groups of plants in controlled–environment cabinets.

15142 Sheard   GB 011106/76/0018
Use of reject heat as an energy source for heating glasshouses.

15143 Egan; Butler   GB 011307/00/0009
Commercial applications of unidirectional air flow isolators.

15144 Patterson; Collins   GB 011601/00/0008
The improvement of performance of cereal drills.

15145 Harral; Patterson   GB 011601/75/0009
Perennial cultivation experiments with cereals and studies of cultivation implement development.

15146 Stayner; Dale   GB 011602/00/0005
Ride vibration studies.

15147 Klinner; Hale   GB 011603/00/0001 R
The performance of crop mowing and conditioning equipment.

15148 Harries; Ambler   GB 011604/00/0001
Automatic guidance for primary cultivations.

15149 Turner; Filby   GB 011604/00/0005
Automation of cattle feeding.

15150 Dawson; Filby   GB 011604/00/0006
Livestock weighing and handling.

15151 Bowman; Hooper   GB 011604/00/0017 R
Moisture measurement in forage.

15152 Turner; Barlow   GB 011604/00/0018
Dairy parlour engineering.

15153 Harries; Ambler   GB 011604/00/0019
ADAS greenhouse controller experiments.

15154 Chisholm   GB 011605/00/0001 R
Wear of metallic materials by soil.

15155 Chestney; Manby   GB 011605/00/0005
Design and performance of overload protection devices.

15156 Hilton   GB 011606/00/0001 R
Sugar beet topping mechanisms.

15157 Richardson; Bufton   GB 011606/00/0002
Seed drills for rowcrops (vegetables).

15158 Richardsn; Bufton   GB 011606/00/0003
Seed drills for rowcrops (sugar beet).

15159 O'Dogherty; Wayman   GB 011606/00/0006
Rotary plough assessment.

15160 Chittey   GB 011606/00/0007
B.S.C. demonstration seed drill.

15161 Miller   GB 011606/75/0009 R
Sugar beet lifting mechanisms.

15162 Shepperson; Holden   GB 011607/00/0004
Application of preservatives during hay harvesting.

15163 Chaplin; Klinner   GB 011607/00/0008
Investigations of machines for compacting and transporting straw.

15164 Klinner; Knight   GB 011607/76/0009
Research and development in forage chopping.

15165 Marchant Shepperson   GB 011607/78/0011
Comminution and processing of animal feeds.

15166 Holt; Sharp   GB 011608/00/0003 R
Materials handling and allied operations in glasshouses.

15167 Byass   GB 011609/00/0002
Spraying of plantation crops.

15168 Lake; Frost   GB 011609/00/0003
Formation and use of sprays with controlled properties.

15169 Byass   GB 011609/00/0005
Improved performance of sprayers used on large farms.

15170 Hepherd   GB 011610/00/0001
Slurry handling, treatment and recycling to land.

15171 Hepherd; Davis   GB 011610/00/0002
Mechanical feeding of livestock; concentrates for pigs.

15172 Lindsay   GB 011610/00/0005
Buildings and equipment for vegetable storage.

15173 Marchant   GB 011610/75/0007 R
The pressure of agricultural materials on retaining walls.

15174 Connell   GB 011704/00/0014
Forage fractionation to provide dietary protein and energy for
both monogastric and ruminant animals.

15175 Clough   GB 011704/00/0020
Design and performance of rotary milking installations.

15176 Clough   GB 011704/00/0021
Mechanisation and automation in milking parlour.

15177 Dawkins; Hoyle   GB 011705/00/0010
Methods for automatic cleaning and disinfection of dairy
equipment.

15178 Hoyle; Dawkins   GB 011705/00/0016
Sediment in milk and milk filtration.

15179 Belcher; Dawkins   GB 011705/76/0033
Cost reduction, and utilisation of extracted heat, in on–farm
milk cooling.

15180 Shea   GB 012201/00/0019
Increase reliability and cheapen maintenance of wire work.
Measure response to wind.

15181 Shea   GB 012201/00/0020
Thin–layer and deep–bed drying. Develop automatic control of
commercial continuous hop drier.

15182 Shea; Armstrong   GB 012201/76/0028
Mechanisation of hop production.

15183 Butson; MacIntyre   GB 030501/00/0001
Design data for power–driven rotary mouldboards on one and
two–way ploughs.

15184 Butson; MacIntyre   GB 030501/00/0002
Construct one and two–way ploughs to compare rotary and
conventional mouldboards.

15185 Butson; MacIntyre   GB 030501/00/0003
Relation between frequency and amplitude of vibration and
draught in soil working tools.

15186 Butson; MacIntyre   GB 030501/00/0004
Optimum vibration of soil working tools.

15187 Butson; MacIntyre   GB 030501/00/0005
Field studies of equipment with vibrated components.

15188 Butson; Lock   GB 030501/00/0006
Problems of introducing seeds, plants and materials into the
soil.

15189 Butson; MacIntyre   GB 030501/77/0007
Study of sheep shower.

15190 Lockhart; Hamilton   GB 030501/77/0008
An investigation of some aspects of rotary cultivator
performance.

15191 Butson; Hamilton   GB 030502/00/0001
Field studies of powered 2–wheel trailer. Compare with
unpowered trailer.

15192 Butson; Hamilton   GB 030502/00/0002
Wheel arrangement on multiple–wheeled powered trailer.

15193 Butson; Hamilton   GB 030502/00/0003
Farm application of fluidised conveying.

15194 Soane   GB 030503/00/0001
Develop hand–held soil density probes designed for extensive
field investigations.

15195 Soane   GB 030503/00/0002
Use two sources of radiation of different energy levels for
moisture and density.

15196 Spencer; Hunter   GB 030504/00/0001
Study of factors affecting safety of tractors and field machines
for use on sloping ground.

15197 Spencer   GB 030504/00/0002
Measure forces on wheels moving across a slope which affect
stability and steering.

15198 Spencer; Owen   GB 030504/00/0003
Study of handling behaviour of tractors and field machines on
sloping ground.

15199 Hamilton; Butson   GB 030504/68/0004
An investigation of various ways of reducing the grain loss from
combine harvesters on sloping ground.

15200 Spencer; Owen   GB 030504/76/0005
Measurement of behaviour of different tractor/implement
combinations.

15201 McRae; Carruthers   GB 030505/00/0001
Develop mechanism capable of accurate distribution of fertilizer
at high forward speeds.

15202 Bailey   GB 030506/00/0001
Acquire data for use in design of herbage dryers.

15203 Bailey   GB 030506/00/0002
Acquire data for use in design of grain dryers.

15204 Bailey; Lamond   GB 030506/00/0003
Air distribution patterns from various duct arrangements in

on–floor drying of cereals.

15205 Bailey; Ingram   GB 030506/00/0004
Theory of drying process for cereals.

15206 Bailey   GB 030506/00/0005
Design and construct heated bed dryer for cereals.

15207 Ingram; Bailey   GB 030506/75/0006
Use of solar energy for crop drying.

15208 McRae; Carruthers   GB 030507/00/0001
Design and construct high speed planter for chitted seed.

15209 Palmer; Mcgechan   GB 030507/00/0002
Factors affecting primary sifting operations on potato harvester.

15210 Mcrae; Hutchison   GB 030507/00/0004
Self–propelled tool carrier.

15211 Mcrae; Hutchison   GB 030507/00/0006
Develop multiple–row harvesting equipment.

15212 Mcrae; Carruthers   GB 030507/00/0007
Sources and severity of mechanical damage to potato tubers.

15213 Mcrae   GB 030507/00/0008
Design trailer to reduce tuber damage for bulk handling.

15214 Mcrae; Carruthrs   GB 030507/00/0009
Automatic control of discharge height of conveyors used to handle potatoes.

15215 MacRae; Carruthrs   GB 030507/00/0010
Fractionating web digger. Effect on separation of grading the potato–stone–clod mixture into two sizes.

15216 Mcrae; Carlow   GB 030508/00/0001
Weight grading of potatoes.

15217 Mcrae; Carlow   GB 030508/00/0002
Sorting potatoes for quality.

15218 Palmer   GB 030509/00/0001
Radio–linked automatic survey of machine performance.

15219 Palmer   GB 030509/00/0002
Automatic control of harvester to optimise efficiency of separator.

15220 Palmer   GB 030509/00/0003
Use of proprioceptive controls on agricultural machinery.

15221 Palmer   GB 030509/00/0004
Simplify tractor controls.

15222 Palmer; Tillson   GB 030509/75/0006
Automatic combine control.

15223 Gillfilln; Ramsay   GB 030510/00/0001
Test and modify American harvester for British use.

15224 Gilfillan   GB 030510/00/0002
Factors affecting removal of ripe fruit by shaking.

15225 Pascal   GB 030511/00/0001
Liason and collaboration with Scottish agricultural colleges.

15226 Porteous; Brown   GB 030515/00/0001
Spectral properties of soil, stones, produce, as a tool in the identification of produce,disease,damage.

15227 Porteous   GB 030515/00/0002
Investigate feasibility of single–ended phase–contrast techniques in visualising airflow in potato stores.

15228 Porteous   GB 030515/00/0003
Applications of photogrammetry.

15229 Porteous; Brown   GB 030515/00/0004
Development of acoustic imaging systems operating by refexion.

15230 Porteous   GB 030515/00/0005
Multivariate analysis of physical properties of fruit,soil, etc to define factors for identification.

15231 Gilmour   GB 040101/00/0009
Relative efficiencies of cold circulation and acid boiling water cleaning systems for milking equipment.

15232 Researcher not indicated   GB 050102/00/0016 R
Design, construction and orientation of glasshouses and structures.

15233 Researcher not indicated   GB 050102/00/0017 R
Control of aerial environment in glasshouses and structures by light modulation.

15234 Ff   GB 050102/75/0018
Fuel saving by use of insulating materials.

15235 Researcher not indicated   GB 050126/00/0001 R
Farm waste: treatment systems and techniques.

15236 Researcher not indicated   GB 050129/00/0002 R
Poultry: equipment.

15237 Researcher not indicated   GB 050142/75/0014
Design, construction and orientation of glasshouses and structures.

15238 Researcher not indicated   GB 050166/00/0001
Farm waste: treatment systems and techniques.

15239 Researcher not indicated   GB 050169/00/0002
Poultry equipment.

15240 Smith; Thomson   GB 051002/67/0002
The handling and processing of plentiful but underutilised species especially blue whiting and norway pout.

15241 Graham; Johnston   GB 051006/00/0020
Development of machine for removal of backbone etc from small white fish.

15242 Graham; Mair   GB 051006/00/0028
Design and development of small continuous air blast freezers.

15243 Graham; Johnston   GB 051006/00/0030
Size grading of small pelagic and demersal species including

vibrating methods.

15244 Graham; Johnston   GB 051006/00/0032
Development of new gutting machine for round fish.

15245 Graham; Kelman   GB 051006/00/0033
Bulk refrigerated sea water road tanker (fish).

15246 Langley   GB 060109/00/0001
Mechanisation of hay making.

15247 Tradd   GB 060109/00/0002
The climatic environment in agricultural buildings.

15248 Witney   GB 060109/00/0003
Mechanisation systems selection.

15249 Witney   GB 060109/00/0004
Cost benefits of stone treatment for crop production.

15250 Harper   GB 060110/00/0001 R
Appraisal of recent building designs and layouts for cattle and crop storage.

15251 Harper   GB 060110/00/0002 R
Analysis of design elements in cattle buildings and associated steading layouts.

15252 Shaw   GB 060218/00/0009
Adaption of granule disseminating equipment for crofter use.

15253 Shiach   GB 060221/00/0003
Grass fractionation pretreatments before pressing and preservation of pulp.

15254 Philip   GB 060221/00/0004
Machine assessment of grain cleaners and graders.

15255 Elliot   GB 060221/78/0005
Ventilated winter storage of swedes.

15256 Kelly   GB 060222/00/0001
An evaluation of accommodation for the weaned pig.

15257 Gerrie   GB 060222/00/0002
Work in connection with building projects on college farms.

15258 Mitchell   GB 060224/00/0001
Housing requirements of fattening cattle.

15259 Mitchell   GB 060224/00/0002
An examination of animal cleanliness and performance in a topless beef building on three floor types.

15260 Cermak   GB 060224/00/0005
Gravity flow slurry channels.

15261 Robertson   GB 060224/00/0006
Influence of animal zoometry and behaviour on building design.

15262 Cermak   GB 060224/00/0007
Ergonomic aspects of building and equipment design.

15263 Briggs   GB 060302/00/0001
A comparative evaluation of mower–coditioners for hay and

silage making.

15264 Davidson   GB 060324/00/0001
Machinery assessment survey.

15265 McNulty, P.B.; McRandal, D.   IE 120301/69/7958
Design and performance parameters for grass cutting machines. Publications.

15266 Manfredi, E.   IT 040209/74/0582
Ricerche su macchina per la raccolta di pomacee con particolare riguardo ai problemi relativi all'intercettamento e convogliamento dei frutti. **Research on pome fruit harvesting machine with particular reference to problems related to fruit detection and conveyance.**

15267 Paschino, F.   IT 041306/74/0597
Trattamento procascola e raccolta meccanica delle olive mediante l'impiego di macchine scuottrici. **Treatment by phyto–hormones and mechanical harvesting of olives using automatic shakers.**

15268 Piccarolo, P.   IT 041306/77/0705 R
Meccanizzazione della raccolta degli agrumi, raccolta integrata, aspetti meccanici ed operativi. **Mechanization of citrus fruit harvesting, integrated harvesting, mechanical and operational aspects.**

15269 Dullemen, E. van   NL 010106/70/2934 R
Mechanisatie van de oogst van champignons. **Mechanization of mushroom picking.** Publications.

15270 Telle, M.G.   NL 010106/74/6399 R
Mechanisatie van de opkweek van chrysantenstek.
Mechanisation in raising of chrysanthemum cuttings.

Implements, tools and machinery in general (B 6100)

See also 965, 2811, 2835, 15725, 17427, 19644, 19653

15271 Abeels, P.; Baudewijns, J.M.   BE 020400/72/0002 R
Etude des relations entre machines, outils et les sols en mécanisation rurale et forestière. **Study of interaction between machinery, tools and the soil in land and forest mechanization.** Publications.

15272 Dufey, V.; Depoorter, J.; Prade, J.   BE 080400/72/0001
Essais et observations de machines agricoles. **Tests and observations of agricultural machinery.** Publications.

15273 Dufey, V.; Legrand, E.; Prade, J.   BE 080400/76/0011
Techniques et outillages susceptibles d'améliorer là productivité. **Technics and equipment capable to improve the productivity.**

15274 Dufey, V.; Vitlox, O.; Depoorter, J.; Prade, J.
    BE 080400/77/0012 R
Economie d'énergie et de matière. **Economy of energy and materials.** Publications.

15275 Matthies, H.J.; Petersen, H.   DE 114201/71/0001
Energieverluste bei der Wurfförderung im Krümmer. **Energy losses of air supported throwing conveyance in bows.**

15276 Matthies, H.J.; Hoffmann, D.; Böinghoff, O.

DE 114203/73/0002
Untersuchung zur Schwingungs- und Geräuschdämpfung an hydrostatischen Antrieben. **Investigations into damping of vibrations and noises of hydrostatic gears.**

15277 Matthies, H.J.; Renius, K.T. DE 114206/73/0001 N
Untersuchungen zum Reibungsverhalten zwischen Kolben und Zylinder bei Schrägscheiben–Axialkolbenmaschinen. **Investigations into the friction between piston and cylinder in axial piston pumps with swash plates.**

15278 Matthies, H.J.; Harms, H.H. DE 114206/75/0001
Untersuchungen an Radialkolbenmaschinen. **Investigations of radial piston pumps.**

15279 Matthies, H.J.; Höfflinger, W. DE 114206/75/0002
Thermodynamische Wirkungsgradmessung in der Ölhydraulik nach dem Drossel–Drucktopf–Verfahren. **Thermodynamic measurement of efficiency in oil hydraulics according to the throttle–pressure box method.**

15280 Matthies, H.J.; Höfflinger, W. DE 114206/75/0003
Theoretische und experimentelle Untersuchungen der Förderstrompulsation von Zahnradpumpen. **Theoretical and experimental studies of the delivery current pulsation of gear water pumps.**

15281 Kutzbach, H.–D.; Wacker, P. DE 144701/73/0006
Energiewirtschaft in der landwirtschaftlichen Verfahrenstechnik. **Energy efficiency in farming methods.**

15282 Kutzbach, H.–D.; Wacker, P. DE 144701/74/0002
Ergonomie bei Schleppern und Landmaschinen. **Ergonomics of tractors and other farm machinery.**

15283 Segler, G. DE 144701/78/0001 N
Mechanisierung der Agrarproduktion in tropischen und subtropischen Ländern. **Mechanization of agricultural production in tropical and subtropical countries.** Publications.

15284 Hanf, C.H. DE 148400/75/0001
Möglichkeiten des Einsatzes moderner Planungsverfahren zur Koordinierung von Investitionen und zur Koordinierung des Maschineneinsatzes in Maschinenringen. **Possibilities of applying modern planning methods to investment coordination and to coordination of machinery employment in machinery–co–operatives.**

15285 Wessel, J.; Nied, R. DE 161500/77/0002
Theoretische und experimentelle Untersuchungen zu Staubabscheidung in Schüttschichten. **Theoretical and experimental investigations on dust collection in layers of dry granular materials.** Publications.

15286 Batel, W. DE 201060/77/0001
Verbesserung der Arbeitsbedingungen z.B. durch Fahrerkabinen. **Improvement of working conditions e.g. by driver's cabin.**

15287 Biller, R.H. DE 201090/75/0001
Alternativen der Koppelung oder Kombination von Geräten zu Gerätesystemen. **Alternatives to couple or combine agricultural aggregates to systems of aggregates.**

15288 Biller, R.H. DE 201090/75/0002
Beanspruchungskollektive von Schlepperantriebselementen

durch Geräte und Arbeitsmaschinen bei unterschiedlichen Einsatzbedingungen. **Load spectra of tractor driving elements by agricultural aggregates and machines at different working conditions.**

15289 Sourell, H. DE 201090/75/0010
Ermittlung des Arbeitszeitbedarfes von Geräten und Maschinen bei ihrem Einsatz in der Feldwirtschaft. **Determination of working time requirements for tools and machines utilized in field production.**

15290 Klausen, K.G.; Olsen, V.; Tønnesen, Å.; Madsen, N.P.; Thellesen, H.; Johnsen, J.H. DK 010400/50/0001
Prøvevirksomhed vedrørende maskintekniske hjælpemidler og kontrol af beskyttelsesforanstaltninger m.v. indenfor jordbruget. **Testing and control of protection arrangements, etc., for machinery in agriculture and horticulture.**

15291 Klausen, K.G.; Guul–Simonsen, F. DK 010400/50/0002
Udviklingsarbejder vedrørende måle– og prøvemetoder for undersøgelse af tekniske hjælpemidler indenfor jordbruget med henblik på at tilgodese de krav, som den tekniske udvikling medfører. **Development of measuring and testing methods for agricultural and horticultural machinery in order to meet the demands of technical development.**

15292 Clough GB 011601/00/0002 R
The tractive performance of tyres and other ground drive systems.

15293 Soane; Kenworthy GB 030503/00/0008 R
Effect of load, slip and spacing of wheels on soil compaction.

15294 Colzani, G.; Marsili, A.; Nuccitelli, G.
IT 020600/77/0003 N
Ricerca sulla affidabilità delle macchine motrici ed operatrici agricole più rappresentative operanti in Italia.. **About the security of the most representative and operative machines working in Italy..**

15295 Godini, A. IT 040112/72/0476
Ricerca interdisciplinare coordinata sulla meccanizzazione della vendemmia. **Coordinated interdisciplinary research on the mechanization of vintage.** Publications.

15296 Robertig. IT 040725/75/0003
Ricerca sperimentale sull'accoppiamento pneumatico terreno. **Experimental research on tyre–soil coupling.**

15297 Rossing, W. NL 010106/49/0321
Ontwikkeling van de meettechniek t.b.v. het landbouw–werktuigenonderzoek. **Development of measuring techniques for the research of agricultural machines and equipment.** Publications.

15298 Brands, J.T. NL 010106/65/6458 R
Mechanisatie en technische ontwikkeling bij de groenteteelt onder glas. **Mechanization and technical development of vegetable production in greenhouses.** Publications.

15299 Straelen, B.C.P.M. van NL 010106/66/0282
De hydraulische aandrijftechniek in de land– en tuinbouwmechanisatie. **The hydraulic driving technique in agricultural and horticultural engineering.** Publications.

15300 Werken, J. van de NL 010106/68/9022 N

Mechanisatie van de fruitteelt. **Mechanization of fruit growing.** Publications.

15301 Maring, J.   NL 010106/69/8341
Onderzoek naar de ergonomische aspecten van de geluidsproduktie van landbouwtrekkers, werktuigen en apparatuur en de mogelijkheden het akoestisch klimaat op de werkplek te verbeteren. **Ergonomic aspects of noise of agricultural tractors and equipment, reducing noise for the improvement of the workplace.** Publications.

15302 Maring, J.   NL 010106/69/8342
Onderzoek naar de milieuhygiënische aspecten van de geluidhinder, veroorzaakt door apparatuur en/of werkzaamheden in de landbouw en het treffen van lawaaiwerende maatregelen. **Environmental aspects of noise of agricultural machinery and measures to reduce annoying noise levels.** Publications.

15303 Porskamp, H.A.J.   NL 010106/70/2683
Wiskundige verwerking en –analyse van de bij het merkenonderzoek van werktuigen verkregen gegevens. **Mathematical processing and analysing of data obtained during comparative research of agricultural machinery.** Publications.

15304 Kuiken, J.C.J.   NL 010106/70/8343 R
De mechanisatie en technische uitrusting van de teelt van sier- en groentegewassen zonder grond. **Mechanization and technical equipment for growing ornamental and vegetable crops with soilless culture systems.**

15305 Straelen, B.C.P.M.   NL 010106/72/3846
Veiligheids aspecten van landbouwwerktuigen. **Safety aspects of farm machinery.** Publications.

15306 Dullemen, E. van   NL 010106/73/5357
Mechanisatie van nieuwe teeltsystemen in de champignonteelt. **Mechanisation of new growing techniques for mushrooms.**

15307 Werken, J. van de   NL 010106/73/9023 N
Mechanisatie van de potplantenteelt in kassen. **Mechanization of pot plant growing in greenhouses.** Publications.

15308 Lange, J.M.   NL 010106/74/5188
Onderzoek naar de mogelijkheden voor een doelmatig en verantwoord energie verbruik op landbouwbedrijven. **Research into the possibilities of an efficient and responsible consumption of energy on agricultural enterprises.** Publications.

15309 Werkhoven, C.   NL 010106/75/6395 R
Signalerinsapparatuur voor landbouwwerktuigen ter controle op de voortgang en de kwaliteit van het werk. **Signalling apparatus for agricultural equipment with regard to the progress and the quality of the work.**

15310 Brands, J.T.   NL 010106/76/6630
Het technisch uitrusten van revisie werkplaatsen voor het agrarisch bedrijf in ontwikkelingslanden. **The technical fitting out of repair workshops for agricultural machinery in developing countries.** Publications.

15311 Perdok, U.D.   NL 010106/76/6637
Het ontwikkelen van een teeltsysteem voor de verbouw van gewassen op niet bereden grond. **Development of a cropping system for the cultivation of crops on controlled traffic systems.**

Publications.

15312 Huizing, J.A.   NL 010106/77/7573 R
Mechanisatie van de boomteelt. **Mechanization in nursery stock.** Publications.

15313 Terpstra, J.   NL 010106/78/8344
Onderzoek naar de insporing van getrokken banden. **Research into the sinkage of trailed tyres.**

15314 Ravensberg, K.   NL 010203/66/2574
Ontwikkeling van apparatuur ten behoeve van de boomkwekerij. **Research on apparatus, which can be used in the nursery.** Publications.

15315 Heijning, J.J.; Vries, H.C.P.   NL 020026/72/4477
Ontwikkeling van landbouwwerktuigen voor ontwikkelingslanden (o.a. een rijstdorser en een trekvoertuig). **Development of agricultural implements for developing countries (rice–threshing machine, tractor).** Publications.

15316 Quast, G.J.   NL 020026/76/8795 N
Ontwikkeling van een verantwoorde mechanisatie van de (klein)–landbouw in Indonesië. **Appropriate mechanization of agriculture (for small farming) in Indonesia.**

15317 Baarveld, W.C.   NL 040007/74/8563
Bruikbaarheid en toepassingsmogelijkheden van luchtbanden op landbouwtrekkers en werktuigen. **Utility and possibility for application of pneumatic tyres on agricultural machinery.**

Soil working, tilling and fertilization equipment (B 6110)

See also 558, 15270, 15462

15318 Balligand, E.; Nachtergeal, J.   BE 010013/73/0001
Etude d'un véhicule dynamométrique. **Study of a dynamometrical vehicle.**

15319 Maton, A.; Priem, R.   BE 070300/73/0006 R
Studie van een bodeminjektor voor het toedienen van mengmest rekening gehouden met de reukhinder, de arbeidsbehoefte, de trekkracht, en kostprijs. **Research on the spreading of liquid manure by means of soil injectors take into account with annoying gasses, labourtime requirement tractive power and cost price.**

15320 Dufey, V.; Depoorter, J.; Pletinckx, A.; Van Camp, R.; Vitlox, O.   BE 080400/76/0010
Essais dynamométriques d'outils de travail du sol, stabilité et sécurité des machines. **Dynamometrical trials of soilworking equipment, stability and security of machines.**

15321 Heege, H.J.; Schöley, W.   DE 111850/73/0003
Einfluss von Witterungsfaktoren auf den Energiebedarf für die Sekundärbodenbearbeitung. **The influence of atmospheric conditions on the energy requirement in secondary soil cultivation.**

15322 Brinkmann, W.; Schöley, W.   DE 111850/78/0001 N
Entwicklung eines mechanischen Bodenprobenehmers. **Development of mechanical soil sampler.**

15323 Tietjen, C.; El–Bassam, N.   DE 201040/75/0007
Technische Verfahren der Anwendung organischer Reststoffe

auf landwirtschaftliche Nutzflächen. **Technical processes for application of organic residual substances to agricultural areas.**

15324 Borchert, H.   DE 502055/73/0006
Untersuchung der Bodenaggregatstabilität bei verschiedener Humuszufuhr, Kalkmelioration und Bodenbearbeitung. **Investigations on the stability of aggregates as influenced by organic matter, liming and cultivation.**

15325 Frenz, F.–W.; Andresen, F.   DE 502104/75/0001
Feldversuch über die Auswirkung verschiedener Tiefenbodenbearbeitungsgeräte. **Field trial on the effect of different types of deep tillage–equipment.**

15326 Rühling, W.; Bäcker, G.   DE 506113/77/0003
Druckluftanwendung beim Roden und der Neuanlage von Rebflächen. **Pneumatic devices for clearing and renewing of vineyards.**

15327 Klausen, K.G.; Tønnesen, Å.   DK 010400/69/0001
Spredning af handelsgødning omfattende undersøgelser over de vigtigste gødningers spredbarhed og undersøgelse over hvorledes de forskellige spredetyper reagerer overfor variationer i gødningernes fysiske egenskaber. **Distribution of artificial fertilizers, including studies of the spreadability of the most important fertilizers and the sensitivity of different spreader types to variation in the physical characteristics of the fertilizer.**

15328 Andersen, S.Aa.   DK 010900/67/0001
Undersøgelse af forskellige dræningsmaskiners egnethed under varierende jordbundsforhold og ved anvendelse af forskellige rør– og pakningsmaterialer. **Investigation of the suitability of different drainage machines under different soil conditions and with the use of different pipe and packing materials.**

15329 Fortune, A.   IE 060500/73/0856 N
Fertilizer distributor tests.

15330 Cunney, M.B.; O'Donoghue, T.   IE 060500/73/0865 R
Test of equipment for handling liquid manure. Publications.

15331 Grubb, L.   IE 060706/77/1303 R
Pilot testing of blanket bog reclamation machinery for commercial purposes. Publications.

15332 Colzani, G.   IT 020600/77/0006 N
Macchine e meccanizzazione della redenzione dei litosuoli. **On the mechanical ways of recovering the stony soils..**

15333 Potecchi, S.   IT 063300/72/0069
L'impiego di acciai antiusura negli organi lavoranti delle macchine per la lavorazione del terreno. **Use of wear–resisting steel in the working parts of implements for soil tillage.** Publications.

15334 Speelman, L.   NL 020026/70/4979
Verdeeltechniek van pesticiden, graanzaad en kunstmeststoffen. **Distribution techniques of pesticides, seed of cereals and fertilizers.** Publications.

Equipment for sowing, planting and setting (B 6120)

See also 558, 2834, 4767, 15133, 15134, 15334

15335 Heege, H.J.; Metzner, C.   DE 111852/78/0001 N
Verstopfung bei Säscharen. **Stoppage of sowing shares.**

15336 Meijer, E.N.C.   NL 010106/77/7576
Onderzoek en ontwikkeling van nieuwe zaaitechnieken. **Research into new drilling techniques.**

Equipment and implements for crop husbandry and crop protection (B 6130)

See also 2753, 3868, 4767, 7390, 7792, 7857, 7954, 8098, 9877, 15131, 15270, 15334, 15590

15337 Göhlich, H.; Jegatheeswaran, P.   DE 105601/73/0006
Technisch–physikalische Voraussetzungen und Bewertungsmassstäbe für den Einsatz von Grossgeräten im Pflanzenschutz. **Large–scale machinery in plant protection – technophysical conditions of use.**

15338 Göhlich, H.   DE 105601/78/0002 N
Ermittlung von Grenzdaten für Flugzeug- und Driftsprühgeräte–Einsatz im Pflanzenschutz. **Determination of marginal data of drift by aeroplane and large–scale sprayers for plant protection.**

15339 Brinkmann, W.; Flake, E.; Gehlen, W.
                                           DE 111850/78/0003 N
Sicherung des Feldaufganges bei Zuckerrüben. **Securing the coming up of sugar beets.**

15340 Kohsiek, H.; Rietz, S.   DE 215110/77/0001
Entwicklung eines Parzellenspritzgerätes. **Development of a plot sprayer.**

15341 Mackroth, K.   DE 506113/73/0003
Die Reissfestigkeit verschiedener Kunststoff–Schattiergewebe nach 2, 4, 6, 8 oder 10 Jahren natürlicher Bewitterung. **Tearproof test of divers plastic shading tissues after 2, 4, 6, 8 or 10 years natural weathering.**

15342 Mackroth, K.; Bambach, G.   DE 506113/77/0005
Untersuchungen über die Eigenschaften von Giessmatten. **Investigations into the attributes of capillary–mattings.**

15343 Klausen, K.G.   DK 010400/76/0003
Udvikling af ny sprøjteteknik for marksprøjter til reduktion af kemikalie– og vædskemængder til landbrugsafgrøder. **Development of new spraying technique for field sprayers to reduce the quantities of chemical and liquid carrier applied to agricultural crops.**

15344 Bruno, J.F.   FR 010112/74/9096
Utilisation des eaux de refroidissement d'une centrale nucléaire pour le chauffage des serres. **Utilization of the cooling water effluents of ab electronuclear power station for the heating of glasshouses.**

15345 Byass; Nation   GB 011609/19/0006 N
Design of field sprayers.

15346 Byass; Lake   GB 011609/79/0007 N
Spray physics.

15347 Byass; Sharp   GB 011609/79/0008 N
Air carried sparying.

D 4100 – Engineering – equipments

15348 Colzani, G.; Santoro, G.; Ferri, E.

IT 020600/79/0002 N

Ricerche sulla distribuzione a basso e bassissimo volume. **Research on high and low volume distribution.**

15349 Petralia, S.; Perella, C.; D'Amore, R.

IT 021000/75/0007 R

Influenza di coperture plastiche sulla produttività e precocità di alcune ortive in ambiente protetto. **Plastic covering influence on productivity and earliness of some horticultural plants in protected cultures.** Publications.

15350 D'Amore, R.; Petralia, S.; Perella, C.

IT 021000/79/0014 N

Studio dell'influenza di vari materiali plastici pacciamanti su diverse specie orticole in pieno campo e in coltura protetta. **Study of effects of different mulching plastic films on different horticultural species in open air and protected cultures.**

15351 Spaink, G.N.
NL 010106/69/6397

Onderzoek en ontwikkeling van spuitapparatuur voor de landbouw; van uit milieuhygiënisch oogmerk. **Research and development of agricultural spraying equipment from a milieu–hygienic point of view.**

15352 Os, E.A. van
NL 010106/70/6641 R

Onderzoek naar de mechanisering en automatisering van de grondloze teelt van planten in kassen. **Research into the mechanization and automation of soilless cultivation of plants in greenhouses.**

15353 Hartmans, D.
NL 010106/75/9027 N

Onderzoek naar nieuwe mechanische toepassingsmogelijkheden van brede polytheenfolie in de akkerbouw en vollegrondsgroenteelt. **Research into the possibilities of mechanical covering of arable crops with polythene film.**

15354 Werkhoven, C.
NL 010106/76/6629

Onderzoek naar de technische aspecten van het gebruik van water in de akker– en tuinbouw. **Research on the technical aspects of the use of water in agriculture and horticulture.**

15355 Frederiks, J.
NL 010106/76/6635

Mechanisatie van de snoei van fruitbomen. **Mechanization of pruning fruit trees.**

15356 Klomp, G.
NL 010106/76/6636

Waterzuivering ten behoeve van tuinbouw bedrijven. **Waterpurification for the irrigation in horticulture.**

15357 Weel, P.A. van
NL 010106/77/7220

Onderzoek naar de toepassingsmogelijkheden van nieuwe produktiesystemen voor potplantenbedrijven. **Research into the applications of new production systems for pot plant nurseries.** Publications.

15358 Telle, M.G.
NL 010106/79/9020 N

Automatisering en regeling van de voedingsstoffenverzorging voor grondloze teelten. **Automated and controlled supply of nutrient solution for soilless culture.**

15359 Weel, P.A. van; Goorts, A.J.C.
NL 010201/77/7220

Onderzoek naar de toepassingsmogelijkheden van nieuwe produktiesystemen voor potplantenbedrijven. **Research into the applications of new production systems for pot plant**

nurseries. Publications.

15360 Hey, W.
NL 020010/73/5654

Simulatie van een veller/snoeier. **Simulation of a feller–limber.**

Implements and machinery for harvesting crop products (B 6140)

See also 3282, 3964, 4356, 4461, 10185, 15132, 15265, 15266, 15268, 15269, 15360, 17251

15361 Monin, A.
BE 080200/72/0003 R

Récolte mécanique de fruits à noyaux. **Mechanical harvesting of stone fruits.** Publications.

15362 Brinkmann, W.
DE 111850/78/0002 N

Faktoren, die die Köpfqualität beeinflussen – Zuckerrübenernte –. **Determinants of topping quality – sugar beets –.**

15363 Tebrügge, F.
DE 129401/78/0001 N

Hangmähdrescher im Vergleich zu Standardmaschinen im Blickfeld von Kosten und Nutzen. **Combine harvester with height adjustment compared with standard combine harvester in view of expenditure and output.** Publications.

15364 Segler, G.; Freye, T.
DE 144700/78/0001 N

Die Kornabtrennung im Mähdrescher mittels der dem Dreschwerk nachgeschalteten Trennelemente. **Grain separation in a combine harvester by elements placed behind the threshing drum.** Publications.

15365 Moser, E.; Kleisinger, N.
DE 144720/75/0001

Theoretische und experimentelle Untersuchungen an Kernobst–Aufsammelmaschinen. **Theoretical and experimental studies on stone fruit pick–up machines.**

15366 Guglhör, W.; Plettenberg, M.
DE 160310/74/0002

Leistung und Einflussfaktoren bei Gassendurchforstung von Fichtenjungbeständen mit der Ernte– maschine Timberjack RW 30. **Output and operating factors in row–thinning in young stands of Picea abies with Timberjack RW 30.**

15367 Auerhammer, H.; Schön, H.; Estler, M.
DE 161520/75/0001 N

Erstellung von Arbeitszeitfunktionen. Aufbereitung und Speicherung in EDV–Anlagen und Modellkalkulationen; Ermittlung des Arbeitszeitbedarfes bei Grossmaschinen und bei der Silomaisernte. Analyse des Arbeitsplatzes bei Grossmaschinen. **Establishment of labour functions. Preparation and storage in EDP machines and model calculations; determination of labour reqirements of great machines and in the harvesting of maize for ensilage. Analysis of the working place at great machines.**

15368 Schmidt, J.A.; Orbeck, K.
DE 501121/73/0001

Erprobung der vollautomatischen Tabakerntemaschine Roanoke aus USA in Verbindung mit dem speziellen bulk–curing–Verfahren im deutschen Virginanbau. **Testing of the American automatic tobacco harvester "Roanoke" in combination with a special bulk–curing–system in the growing area of flue cured tobacco in West Germany.**

15369 Grimm, K.
DE 502601/72/0001 R

Mechanisierung des Feldversuchswesens durch Weiterentwicklung spezieller Erntemaschinen und

Verarbeitungsgeräte 1970. **Mechanization of field experiments by further development of special harvesters and processing implements.**

15370 Rühling, W.; Bäcker, G.; Struck, W.

DE 506113/77/0002

Trennverfahren für die Ernte von Weintrauben. **Methods for separation of grapes from vine. Publications.**

15371 Klausen, K.G.; Madsen, N.P.; Olsen, V.

DK 010400/64/0001

Undersøgelse af mejetærskerens egnethed til direkte høst af frøafgrøder samt undersøgelse af frøspild ved forskellig modenhed med henblik på at fastslå gunstigste høsttidspunkt for de enkelte frøarter. **Studies of the suitability of the combine for direct harvesting of seed crops and studies of seed losses at different stages of ripeness with reference to establishing the most favourable time of harvest for different seed crops.**

15372 Elyakime, B.; Mouton, B.   FR 010308/75/3328
Enquête sur le matériel d'exploitation forestière en France. **Investigation on wood felling equipment in France.**

15373 Colzani, G.   IT 020600/77/0679 R
Meccanizzazione della raccolta del tabacco, criteri di raccolta, aspetti meccanici. **Mechanization of tobacco harvesting, harvesting standards, mechanical aspects.**

15374 Colzani, G.   IT 020600/77/0680 R
Meccanizzazione della raccolta dei foraggi per gli allevamenti vacca–vitello, utilizzazione paglia e deiezioni, aspetti meccanici della linea vacca–vitello. **Mechanization of fodder crops harvesting for brood–cow farms, utilization of litter and excreta, mechanical aspects of the cow–calf line.**

15375 Baraldi, G.   IT 040209/77/0672 R
Meccanizzazione della raccolta della barbabietola da zucchero e del pisello; controllo cantieri di raccolta, aspetti meccanici, barbabietola, controllo cantieri raccolta pisello. **Mechanization of sugar beet and pea harvesting; Control of harvesting yards, mechanical aspects, sugar beet, control of pea harvesting yards.**

15376 Blandini, G.   IT 040312/77/0673 R
Meccanizzazione della raccolta degli agrumi, raccolta integrata, aspetti meccanici ed operativi. **Mechanization of citrus fruit harvesting, integrated harvesting, mechanical and operational aspects.**

15377 Dallari, F.A.   IT 040512/77/0681 R
Meccanizzazione della raccolta delle olive di frutta e fragola, problemi meccanici, raccolta olive, prototipo raccolta frutta da mensa. **Mechanization of olive, fruit and strawberry harvesting, mechanical problems, olive harvesting, prototype of table–fruit harvesting.**

15378 Dallari, F.A.   IT 040512/77/0682 R
Meccanizzazione della raccolta di pomodoro, raccolta meccanica cernita fotoottica. **Mechanization of tomato harvesting, mechanised harvesting, photo–optical selection.**

15379 Stefanelli, G.   IT 040512/77/0713 R
Meccanizzazione della raccolta dell'uva, perfezionamento vendemmiatrici. **Mechanization of grape–gathering, development of vine harvesters.**

15380 Castelli, G.   IT 040610/77/0677 R
Meccanizzazione della raccolta dei foraggi per gli allevamenti vacca da latte, nuove macchine e nuove strutture. **Mechanization of fodder crops harvesting for dairy farms, new machinery and new structures.**

15381 Tine, G.   IT 040725/77/0716 R
Meccanizzazione della raccolta di pomodoro, raccolta meccanica cernita automatica colorimetrica. **Mechanization of tomato harvesting, mechanical harvesting, automatic colour grading.**

15382 Cera, M.   IT 040807/77/0678 R
Meccanizzazione della raccolta dei foraggi per gli allevamenti vacca–vitello, valutazione stocchi, recupero zone marginali, aspetti meccanici. **Mechanization of fodder crops harvesting for brood–cow farms, evaluation of the stalks, the reclaiming of marginal lands, mechanical aspects.**

15383 Di Ciolo, S.   IT 041112/77/0687 R
Meccanizzazione della raccolta del peperone, raccolta meccanica con prototipi. **Mechanization of Capsicum Grossum harvesting, mechanised harvesting with prototypes.**

15384 Di Ciolo, S.   IT 041112/77/0688 R
Meccanizzazione della raccolta di frutta e fragola, raccolta fragola, prove prototipi. **Mechanization of fruit and strawberry harvesting, strawberry harvesting, trials of prototypes.**

15385 Piccarolo, P.   IT 041306/77/0704 R
Meccanizzazione della raccolta dei foraggi per gli allevamenti ovini e caprini, raccolta prodotti; mungitura aspetti meccanici. **Mechanization of fodder crops harvesting for sheep and goat farms, collecting produce; mechanised milking.**

15386 Lisa, L.   IT 063300/67/0062
Costruzione e sperimentazione di vendemmiatrici a taglio e a taglio scuotimento combinati per la collina. **Construction and testing of various grape harvester proto–types able to operate in hillside regions, incorporating the cutter bar system and the combined cutting–shaking system. Publications.**

15387 Lisa, L.   IT 063300/77/0725
Perfezionamento vendemmiatrici. **Improvement of grape harvesters.**

15388 Elia, P.   IT 063300/77/0726
Raccolta meccanica del peperone con prototipi. **The mechanical harvesting of Capsicum using prototypes.**

15389 Bouman, A.   NL 010106/69/2284
Bestudering van de mogelijkheden van het machinaal loof verwijderen. **Study of the possibilities to remove the foliage mechanically.**

15390 Perdok, U.D.   NL 010106/71/6418
Onderzoek naar werktuigen en teelttechnieken voor het kluitvrij rooien van bol– en knolgewassen. **Research on implements and growing techniques for harvesting of bulbous and tuberous plants on cloddy clay soils.**

15391 Bosch, A.   NL 010106/73/5350
Mechanisatie van de oogst van radijs in kassen. **Mechanical harvesting of radish in greenhouses.**

15392 Bouman, A.   NL 010106/76/6639

Verlies en tarra bij de bietenoogst. **Research into the possibilities to decrease tare and losses of sugar beets.** Publications.

15393 Weerd, B. van der NL 010106/77/7578 R
Het onderzoeken van een nieuw dorsprincipe voor peulvruchten met minder dop– en beschadigingsverliezen. **Study of a new threshing system for pods with fewer shell and damage losses.**

15394 Bouman, A. NL 010106/78/8345
Onderzoek naar de mogelijkheden ter voorkoming van verliezen, tarra en beschadiging bij de aardappeloogst. **Research in to the possibilities of preventing losses, tare and damage at the potato harvest.**

15395 Weerd, B. van de NL 010106/78/8346 N
Mechanische oogst van vollegrondsgroenten. **Mechanization in vegetable production/harvest.**

15396 Bosch, A. NL 010106/79/9013 N
Het mechanisch oogsten en schonen van "Chufa" knolletjes. **Mechanical harvesting and cleaning of "Chufa" tubers.**

15397 Cappon, A. NL 010106/79/9019 N
Ontwikkeling van schoningsapparatuur voor bieten na de oogst en verbetering resp. nieuwe ontwikkeling van rooiprincipes voor minder verliezen en betere reiniging. **Development of cleaning mechanisms for beet after harvesting and the improvement, viz. new development of harvesting principles to get fewer losses and better cleaning.**

15398 Bosch, A. NL 010106/79/9024 N
Mechanisatie van de oogst van aardbeienstekplanten. **Mechanical harvest of strawberry plants.**

15399 Kuiken, J.C.J. NL 010106/79/9025 N
Mechanisatie van de oogst van snijchrysanten op de vaste grond. **Mechanization of the harvest of cut chrysantemums in soil.**

15400 Leek, N.A. NL 010601/73/4464
Houtoogst– en opwerkingsmachines. **Tree harvesting machines.** Publications.

15401 Huisman, W. NL 020026/70/4978
Oorzaken van schudderverliezen in de maaidorser en het automatisch regelen van deze verliezen. **Causes of walker loss of grain combine harvesters and automatic control of these loss.** Publications.

15402 Heijning, J.J.; Loo, J. van; Vries, H.C.P. de; Bergman, O.C.; Huisman, W. NL 020026/73/4474
Ontwikkeling van een geïntegreerd maai–, dors– en scheidingssysteem. **Development of an integrated mowing, threshing and separating system.** Publications.

15403 Meuleman, J. NL 020026/78/8650 N
Het maaien met onderaangedreven landbouwcirkelmaaiers. **The moving process of rotary mowers.**

15404 Sar, T. van der NL 020026/78/8797 N
De mechanisatie van de cassave–oogst. **The mechanization of the cassava harvest.**

Equipment for harvesting animal products and

raising of animals (B 6150)

See also 10894, 11102, 11391, 11622, 12447, 12448, 12542, 14151, 14390, 14391, 14407, 15374, 15385, 15654, 17280, 19720, 20074

15405 Hovart, P.; Van den Broucke, G.; Fonteyne, R.; Delanghe, F.; Van Hee, J. BE 070800/59/0002 R
Onderzoek van vistuig en visserijtechniek. **Research on fishing gear and fishing techniques.** Publications.

15406 Hovart, P.; Van den Broucke, G.; Fonteyne, R.; Delanghe, F.; Van Hee, J. BE 070800/59/0003 R
Studie van de technische uitrusting van visserijvaartuigen. **Research on the technical equipement of fishing vessels.** Publications.

15407 Kielwein, G.; Söngen, W. DE 129701/75/0006
Reinigung und Desinfektion milchwirtschaftlicher Geräteschaften besonders bei niederen Temperaturen. **Low temperature cleaning and disinfection of dairy equipment.**

15408 Rabold, K.; Buchholz, C. DE 144690/74/0002
Der Einfluss der Druckverhältnisse im MelkbecherInnenraum auf die Ausprägung des Maschinennachge– melks bei unterschiedlicher Form und Elastizität des Zitzengummis. **On the influence of pressure conditions inside a teat cup on stripping by machine with differences in form and elasticity of teat rubber.**

15409 Rabold, K.; Aksen, T. DE 144690/78/0001 N
Vergleiche von Zitzengummis hinsichtlich ihres Einflusses auf die Ausprägung von Melkbarkeitsmerkmalen. **Comparisons of teatcup liners referring to their influence on the distinctness of milkability characteristics.**

15410 Isensee, E.; Rix, J. DE 148150/74/0002
Erprobung und Weiterentwicklung eines automatischen Fütterungssystems auf elektronischer Basis für die individuelle Kraftfuttergabe an Milchkühe. **Testing and development of an automated electronic feeding system for individual dairy cow concentrate feeding.**

15411 Söhne, W.; Scholtysik, B. DE 161500/74/0001
Dosierverfahren für Futtermittel. **Processes of feed dosing.**

15412 Schön, H.; Worstorff, H. DE 161520/77/0001
Beeinflussung der Vor– und Nachmelkphase durch verschiedene technische Parameter. **Effects of different technical parameters on premilking and stripping.**

15413 Wenner, H.L.; Worstorff, H. DE 161520/77/0003
Experimentelle Untersuchungen zur Optimierung der Vakuumapplikation im Melkzeug. **Experiments on optimization of vacuum application in pail milking unit.**

15414 Worstorff, H.; Freiberger, F.; Stanzel, H. DE 161520/77/0004
Entwicklung und Einsatz von Geräten zur Erfassung des maschinellen Milchentzuges in Zuchtbetrieben. **Development and use of instruments for measuring of mechanical milking in breeding farms.**

15415 Stanzel, H. DE 161524/74/0001
Erprobung verschiedener elektronischer Geber und Entwicklung einer Melkanlage mit stufenloser Steuerung von

Pulsfrequenz, Taktverhältnis und Vakuum in Abhängigkeit vom Milchfluss. **Testing of different electronic transmitters and development of a milking plant with ungraduated control of pulse frequence, time ratio and vacuum in dependence on milk flow.**

15416 Schön, H.   DE 161524/75/0001
Untersuchungen zur optimalen Gestaltung des Melkarbeitsplatzes und Felduntersuchungen über programmgesteuerte Melkanlagen. **Investigations into optimal organization of the milking working place and field studies on program–controlled milking plants.**

15417 Schön, H.; Worstorff, H.   DE 161524/75/0002
Biotechnische Untersuchungen an Melksystemen. **Biotechnical investigations of milking systems.**

15418 Mejer, G.–J.   DE 201060/73/5001
Verbesserung und Automatisierung des maschinellen Milchentzuges. **Improvement and automatization of mechanical milking.**

15419 Paul, W.   DE 201060/74/0008
Steuerung der Tierleistung bei Wiederkäuern. **Automatic feeding of ruminants in dependence on their performance.**

15420 Paul, W.   DE 201060/77/0004
Verbessern und Automatisieren tierischer Versorgungs– und Entsorgungssysteme. **Improvement and automation of animal supply and cleaning system.**

15421 Artmann, R.   DE 201090/75/0003
Entwicklung und Erprobung neuer Fütterungsverfahren. **Development and test of new feeding systems.**

15422 Artmann, R.   DE 201090/75/0018
Entwicklung und Erprobung eines Erkennungssystems für freilaufende Rinder. **Development and testing of an electronic identification system for grazing cattle.**

15423 Tolle, A.; Hamann, J.   DE 207020/72/5001
Entwicklung einer neuen Technologie der Milchgewinnung. **Development of a new technology of milking.**

15424 Steinberg, R.   DE 208030/77/0002
Weiterentwicklung und Erprobung von Fanggeräten und –methoden für die See– und Binnenfischerei. **Further development and testing of fishing tool and fishing methods for deep–sea fishing and river and lake fishery.**

15425 Horn, W.   DE 208030/77/0003
Elektrifizierung von Fanggeräten. **Electrification of fishing tool.**

15426 Bohl, H.   DE 208030/77/0004
Untersuchungen über die Selektionseigenschaften fischereilicher Fanggeräte. **Studies on selection properties of fishing tool.**

15427 Dahm, E.   DE 208030/77/0005
Untersuchung neuer Netzmaterialien auf ihre fischereiliche Brauchbarkeit. **Examination of new network materials for their use in fishery.**

15428 Freytag, G.   DE 208030/77/0006
Weiterentwicklung der Nahbereichs– und Grossraumortung von Fangobjekten. **Further development of short–range and long–distance position finding of fishing objects.**

15429 Lange, K.   DE 208030/77/0007
Arbeiten auf dem Gebiet des Baues von Fischereifahrzeugen im Hinblick auf weitere Mechanisierung und Automatisierung sowie Untersuchungen zur funktionsgerechten Besetzung. **Operations on the construction of fishing boats with regard to further mechanization and automation and studies on functional occupation.**

15430 Mohr, H.   DE 208030/77/0008
Untersuchungen über das Verhalten von Fangobjekten gegenüber Fanggeräten. **Studies on the behaviour of fishing objects towards fishing tool.**

15431 Nielsen, S.M.   DK 010201/75/0008
Mælkerecorderbeholderes anvendelse ved ydelseskontrol. **The use of milk recorder containers in yield registration.**

15432 Klausen, K.G.; Madsen, N.P.   DK 010400/67/0001
Malketekniske undersøgelser over nye konstruktioners indflydelse på koens sundhedstilstand, mælkens kvalitet, malkeprocessen og vakuumstabiliteten. **Technical investigations of the influence of new milking equipment on the health of the cow, milk quality, the milking process and vacuum stability.**

15433 Le Du, J.   FR 011310/72/7562
Etude des facteurs qui conditionnent les caractéristiques de traite des manchons trayeurs pour vaches. **Milking charactéristics of milking liners.**

15434 Le Du, J.; Labussiere, J.   FR 011310/72/7564
Incidence de la hauteur d'élévation du lait (lactoduc) sur les caractéristiques de traite des brebis. **Effect of the milkpipeline height on milking characteristics of ewes.**

15435 Le Du, J.   FR 011310/75/7563
Appareil de mesure automatique de la production laitiére. **Device for automatic recording of milk production.**

15436 Le Du, J.; Labussiére, J.   FR 011310/76/7561
Etude et réalisation d'un transporteur linéaire pour la traite mécanique des brebis laitières. **Linear milking conveyor for milking ewes.**

15437 O'Callaghan, E.J.; O'Shea, J.   IE 060400/75/2063 R
Endurance testing of milking equipment. Publications.

15438 Meaney, R.A.; Lee, T.; Connaughton, J.   IE 180111/78/8758 R
Feasibility study of gill netting in Irish waters. Publications.

15439 Mennella, V.; Sediari, T.   IT 041016/77/0001
Fase di svezzamento per bovini, suini ed ovini in rapporto all'ambiente. Programmazione, moduli, attrezzature e costi. **Weaning stage for cattle, pigs and sheep with reference to environment. Principles for layout and design of building system and equipment.**

15440 De Montis, S.   IT 041304/78/0006 N
Sperimentazione su attrezzature modulari per l'allevamento ovino. **Experimentation on modular equipments for sheep breeding.**

15441 Rossing, W.   NL 010106/70/2848
Automatisering bij het machinaal melken, de krachtvoederverstrekking en de produktiecontrole in de draaimelkstal. **Automation of the milking performance and food distribution in rotating milking parlour.** Publications.

15442 Kerkhof, J.A.   NL 010106/70/8722 N
Onderzoek melkwinningsapparatuur. **Research into milking equipment.** Publications.

15443 Buitink, W.J.   NL 010106/71/6405 R
Het samenstellen en verstrekken vanuit meerdere componenten bestaande voederrantsoenen voor rundvee. **System for proportioning and distributing compound feed rations for dairy cattle.**

15444 Rossing, W.   NL 010106/71/8777 N
Automatische systemen voor de koeherkenning, de krachtvoer dosering, de verzameling en de reproduktie van diergegevens in de melkveehouderij. **Automatic systems for cow identification, concentrate feeding, the gathering and reproduction of animal data in dairying.** Publications.

15445 Rossing, W.   NL 010106/75/6180
De waarde van de elektrische geleiding van melk, gemeten tijdens het melken voor het onderkennen van mastitis. **The possibilities of electrical conductivity of milk for mastitis detection during milking.**

15446 Burema, H.J.   NL 010106/75/6423 R
Onderzoek en ontwikkeling van een automatisch bewakingssysteem voor grote melkstallen. **Research and evelopment of an automatic watch over system for big milking parlours.** Publications.

15447 Benders, G.A.   NL 010106/77/7581 R
Onderzoek naar technieken voor de voederverstrekking van diverse voedermiddelen aan daarvoor in aanmerking komende dieren bij rundvee. **Research into techniques for supplying feedstuffs to dairy cattle.**

15448 Rossing, W.   NL 010106/79/9026 N
Ontwikkeling managementsysteem voor grote melkveebedrijven. **Development of a management system for large dairies.**

15449 Brandsma, S.   NL 010112/70/2848
Automatisering bij het machinaal melken, de krachtvoederverstrekking en de produktie–controle in de draaimelkstal. **Automation of the milking procedure and food distribution in rotating milking parlour.**

15450 Snijders, P.J.M.   NL 010208/70/8743 N
Melkmethoden en hulpmiddelen bij het melken. **Milking methods and equipment for milking.** Publications.

15451 Snijders, P.J.M.   NL 010208/73/8757 N
Doelmatige methoden van ruwvoer– en krachtvoerverstrekking aan melkvee. **Efficient methods of feeding concentrates and roughage to dairy cows.** Publications.

15452 Schipper, C.J.; Vries, Tj. de; Brouwer, J.
                                    NL 010213/62/3381
Onderzoek naar de invloed van melkmachine installaties op de hygiënische hoedanigheid van boerderijmelk (invloed van melkafvoerleiding, voorkomen van water, automatische voorbehandeling van de koe, melkmeters en schuimvorming). **Research about the effect of pipeline–systems on the hygienic aspects of farm milk (influence of the milkoutlet, presence of water, automatic pre–treatment of the cow, milkmeters, skimming).** Publications.

15453 Boer, E.J. de   NL 010702/66/7150
Vermindering van de exploitatiekosten van visserijvaartuigen (mechanica van gesleepte vistuigen o.a. met behulp van modelonderzoek, beperking slijtage grondnetten, vermindering weerstand gesleepte vistuigen, constructieve vereenvoudiging en standaardisering van gesleepte vistuigen, verbetering van de selectiviteit van vistuigen). **Decreasing working–expenses of fishing vessels (mechanics of trawl a.o. by means of model research, reduction damage and wear of bottom trawls, constructive simplification and standardization of trawls, reduction of trawl resistance, improvement of trawl selectivity).** Publications.

15454 Boonstra, G.P.   NL 010702/68/7153
Onderzoek naar de toepassingsmogelijkheden van elektrische stimuleringsmethoden ter verbetering van de selektiviteit en verlaging van de bedrijfskosten bij de visserij op vis, schaal– en schelpdieren. **Research into the applicability of electrical stimulation to increase selectivity and decrease costs in the catch of fish, crustacea and shellfish.**

15455 Boer, E.J. de   NL 010702/75/7155 R
Toepassingsmogelijkheden spanzegenvisserij in de Nederlandse zeevisserij; vervanging van netwerk in het voornet van pelagische vistuigen door lijnen; ontwikkeling en mechanisatie van de visserij op rond– en platvis met warnetten. **Application Danish pair seining in the Dutch fishing industry; replacement of the meshed webbing in the front part of midwater trawls by ropes; development and mechanization of catching round– and flat fish species by bottom set entangling nets.** Publications.

Machines and equipment for processing of products (B 6160)

See also 15135, 15368, 15369, 15397, 15400, 15698, 15703, 15709, 15745, 15985, 16028, 16268, 16289, 16474, 16578, 16620, 16621, 17081, 17113, 17114, 17125, 17151, 17280, 18930, 19632, 19659

15456 Brinkmann, W.; Pingen, J.   DE 111850/75/0003
Untersuchungen über die Arbeitsqualität von mechanischen Granulatbandstreuern für Pflanzenschutzmittel unter verschiedenen Arbeitsbedingungen. **Studies on the working quality of mechanical spreaders of granulates for plant protection products under different working conditions.**

15457 Salje, E.; Bartsch, U.   DE 114502/75/0001
Geräuschminderung an Doppelendprofilern durch primäre und sekundäre Massnahmen. **Noise reduction on woodworking machines by primary and secondary measures.**

15458 Salje, E.; Thomas, D.   DE 114502/77/0003
Katalog für die ergonomisch und sicherheitstechnisch zweckmässige Gestaltung von Holzbearbeitungsmaschinen. **Ergonomical design of woodworking machines.**

15459 Salje, E.; Dubenkropp, G.   DE 114502/77/0004
Ermittlung optimaler Zahnformen zum Kreissägen von Spanplatten. **Investigations of optimum tooth form for circular**

sawing of fibre boards.

15460 Salje, E.; Redeker, W. DE 114502/77/0005
Flexible Handhabungssysteme für die holzverarbeitende
Industrie. **Flexible manipulators for woodworking industry.**

15461 Krüger, R.; Schweiger, F. DE 161480/75/0001
Planung der vorbeugenden Instandhaltung. **Planning of
preventive maintenance.**

15462 Krause, R. DE 201070/71/5009
Technische Verfahren der Anwendung organischer Reststoffe
auf landwirtschaftlichen Flächen. **Land–disposal of organic
wastes.**

15463 Orth, H.W.; Löwe, R. DE 201070/72/5002
Verdichtung von Halmgut in Strangpresseeinrichtungen.
Technical research on aggregating of roughage in extruders.

15464 Dernedde, W. DE 201070/75/0001
Verbesserung der Trocknung von Halmgut unter
Feldbedingungen durch mechanische Massnahmen.
**Improvement of drying roughage under field–conditions by
mechanical provisions.**

15465 Reuter, H.; Konietzko, M. DE 207060/74/5003 N
Ermittlung von Kriterien zur Beurteilung von
Ultra–Hocherhitzungsanlagen. **Elaboration of criteria for the
estimation of UHT plants.**

15466 Bolling, H.; Zwingelberg, H. DE 209020/75/0006
Möglichkeit zur Einsparung des Kraftbedarfes in Weizenund
Roggenmühlen. **Possibilities of saving energy in wheat and rye
mills.**

15467 Leistner, L.; Schmidt, U. DE 210030/78/0009 N
Überleben von Mikroorganismen auf Oberflächen in
fleischverarbeitenden Betrieben. **Survival of microorganisms
on surfaces in meat processing plants.**

15468 Schurig, M. DE 502600/75/0002
Einsatzversuche mit neuen Halmfutterbereitungsgeräten.
Testing new cereal feed preparing machinery.

15469 Klausen, K.G.; Madsen, N.P.; Thellesen, H.
DK 010400/69/0002
Foderblanding og foderhåndtering omfattende undersøgelse af
forskellige blandetypers blandeeffekt samt undersøgelse af
separationen ved transport af blandingen i forskellige
transportmidler. **Feed mixing and handling, including studies of
the mixing effect of different types of mixer and the degree of
separation in mixed feed during transport by different types of
equipment.**

15470 Fleming, M. IE 060400/78/2087 N
Field survey of farm refrigerated bulk milk coolers.
Publications.

15471 Colzani, G. IT 020600/77/0007 N
Meccanizzazione della distribuzione degli additivi e
conservativi ai trinciati. Conservazione.. **About the mechanical
assignment of the additive and conservative cut up substances
and their care.**

15472 Conte, L.; Castiglione, A.; Montanari, S.
IT 020600/79/0003 N

Meccanizzazione del trattamento dei sottoprodotti aziendali
per l'alimentazione dei bovini nell'ambito del piano agricolo
alimentare. **Mechanization of company by–products processing
for cattle feeding within the agricultural and alimentary
project.**

15473 Cucurachi, A.; Di Giovacchino, L.; Mascolo, A.;
Solinas, M. IT 022100/73/0008
Esame comparativo degli impianti per la lavorazione delle
olive. Parte1 : le rese. **Comparative studies of olive processing
equipment. Part one: the out–puts.** Publications.

15474 Finassi, A. IT 063300/72/0064
Automazione di impianti statici per l'essiccamento del risone.
Automation of deep bed driers. Publications.

15475 Bosma, A.H. NL 010106/75/6420 R
Onderzoek en ontwikkeling van apparatuur voor het vullen en
lossen van torensilo's. **Research and development of equipment
for filling and unloading of towersilos.** Publications.

15476 Poelma, H.R. NL 010106/75/6452
Het roeren van dunne mest onder roostervloeren in grote
opslag silo's en grondputten. **Agitating slurry under slatted
floors in large silos and ground pits.**

15477 Poelma, H.R. NL 010106/75/6454 R
Het op mechanische wijze scheiden van dunne mest.
Separating slurry mechanically. Publications.

15478 Weel, P.A. van NL 010106/76/6640
Intern transport en verwerking van rozen. **Internal transport
and processing of roses.**

15479 Koning, K. de NL 010106/77/7577
Het persen van hooi en stro tot grotere dichtheid. **Baling of hay
and straw with extra high density.**

15480 Bosma, A.H. NL 010106/77/7582 R
Onderzoek naar verdichtings– en mechanisatiemogelijkheden
van horizontale kuilvoeropslagsystemen. **Research into
densation and mechanization possibilities for special trench
silo's.**

15481 Telle, M.G. NL 010106/77/8381
Ontwikkeling van een elektronisch–mechanische apparatuur
voor het schouwen van broedeieren. **Development of an
electronic–mechanical candling equipment for hatching eggs.**

15482 Schoneveld, J.A. NL 010106/78/8354 R
Het oplossen van een aantal technische en arbeidskundige
problemen bij de witloftrek in containers. **The solution of a
number of technical and work management problems when
forcing witloof chicory in containers.**

15483 Kaltofen, R.S. NL 010109/77/8381
Ontwikkeling van een elektronisch mechanische apparatuur
voor het schouwen van broedeieren. **Development of
electronic–mechanical candling equipment for hatching eggs.**

15484 Weel, P.A. van NL 010201/76/6640 N
Intern transport en verwerking van rozen. **Internal transport
and processing of roses.**

15485 Schoneveld, J.A. NL 010207/78/8354 R
Het oplossen van een aantal technische en arbeidskundige

problemen bij de witloftrek in containers. **The solution of a number of technical and work management problems with the forcing of witloof chicory in containers.**

15486 Burg, W.J. van der   NL 010210/76/7753 R
Ontwikkeling van een betere methodiek c.q. machine voor het verwijderen van duist (Alopecurus myosuroides) uit raaigraszaad. **Development of an improved method or machine for the removal of slender fox–tail (Alopecurus myosuroides) from ray–grass seed.**

15487 Hoek, K.W. van de   NL 040010/75/6454
Het op mechanische wijze scheiden van dunne mest. **Separating slurry mechanically. Publications.**

Transport equipment, – installations and facilities (B 6170)

See also 15406, 15429, 15453, 15454, 15455, 15475, 15478, 15484, 16158, 17129, 17151, 17280, 20249

15488 Göhlich, H.; Magnus, L.   DE 105601/74/0001
Einfluss der Ackerschlepper–Konstruktion und der Kabinengestaltung auf die Sicht und die Arbeitsbedingungen des Fahrers. **Influence of farm tractor construction and cab–design on view conditions and tractor operation.**

15489 Göhlich, H.; Kauss, W.   DE 105601/75/0003
Aufhängung und Federung von Schlepperkabinen. **Suspension and damping tractor cabins.**

15490 Göhlich, H.; Mertins, K.–H.; Ulrich, A.
          DE 105601/77/0001
Das Fahr– und Lenkverhalten von Ackerschleppern bei höheren Fahrgeschwindigkeiten. **Manoeuvrability and road holding of farm tractors under street conditions.**

15491 Matthies, H.J.; Harms, H.H.   DE 114205/75/0001
Untersuchungen zur Minderung der Geräusche an Hydraulikanlagen für landwirtschaftliche Schlepper und Baumaschinen. **Studies on noise reduction of hydraulic systems for tractors and building machines.**

15492 Eichhorn, H.; Tebrügge, F.   DE 129400/77/0002
Zur relativen Vorzüglichkeit unterschiedlicher Schlepperbauarten. **Relative excellence of different types of tractor.**

15493 Kutzbach, H.–D.; Ngnyen, S.C.; Schrogl, H.
          DE 144701/74/0003
Technische Ausbildung von Transportketten. **Technical modelling of transporting chains.**

15494 Segler, G.; Hutt, W.   DE 144705/73/0003
Injektorschleusen für pneumatische Feststoff–Förderung. **Injector sluices for pneumatic transport of solid material.**

15495 Söhne, W.; Steiner, M.   DE 161500/71/0001 N
Kraftübertragung zwischen Reifen und Boden. Reifendeformationen. **Power transmission between tyre and soil. Tire deformatons.**

15496 Schwanghart, H.   DE 161500/71/0002 N
a. Berechung des Weiterrollverhaltens eines an einem Hang umstürzenden Fahrzeuges; b. Ermittlung und Berechnung der Festigkeit und Sicherheit von Schlepper–Umsturzbügel und Kabine. **a. Calculation of the roll–over performance for an over–turning vehicle on a slope; b. Investigation and calculation of strength and safety of tractor frames and cabs.**

15497 Söhne, W.; Bacher, R.   DE 161500/75/0001
Untersuchungen des Schlepperlärms und der Möglichkeiten der Lärmverringerung. **Investigations of tractor noise and of the possibilities of reduction.**

15498 Söhne, W.; Schwanghart, H.   DE 161500/77/0001
Untersuchung und Berechnung der statischen und dynamischen Kippsicherheit von Ackerschleppern. **Investigation and calculation of the static and dynamic safety against tipping.**

15499 Mejer, G.–J.   DE 201060/71/0010
Lageregelung grosser Massen an landwirtschaftlichen Fahrzeugen. **Automatic position control of large inertial loads mounted on agricultural vehicles.**

15500 Jahns, G.   DE 201060/74/0005
Untersuchung von Leitsystemen für eine automatische Fahrzeuglenkung. **Analysis of automatic vehicle guidance systems.**

15501 Janssen, J.   DE 201060/78/0006 N
Klimatechnische Gestaltung von Fahrerkabinen. **Climatic design of driver's cabs.**

15502 Janssen, J.   DE 201060/78/0007 N
Wärmebelastung in Kabinen landwirtschaftlicher Zug– und Arbeitsmaschinen. **Heat load in cabs of agricultural tractors and other working machines.**

15503 Steinkampf, H.   DE 201090/71/5007
Energiesparende Leistungsübertragung beim Schleppereinsatz in der Feldwirtschaft. **Energy saving performance transmission by field working tractors.**

15504 Rühling, W.; Bäcker, G.   DE 506113/77/0004
Untersuchungen zur Anwendung einer Einschienenbahn in nicht erschlossenen Steillagen. **Studies on the possibility of using a monorail in undeveloped slope–vineyards.**

15505 Bottoms; Barber   GB 011602/00/0001 R
Ergonomics in tractor design and operation monitoring and control.

15506 O'Neill   GB 011602/78/0010 N
Ergonomics of tractor design and operation thermal stress in tractor cabs.

15507 Holt   GB 011608/76/0004 R
Farm transport.

15508 Dumont; Owyer   GB 011611/79/0018 N
Determine the design requirements for agricultural vehicles an operational reseach study.

15509 Spencer   GB 030504/79/0006 N
DOI contract tractor implement dynamics stability studies.

15510 Spencer; Owen   GB 030504/79/0007 N
Tractor overturning on slopes using an unmanned full size tractor.

15511 Palmer GB 030509/79/0005 N
Department of industry survey of tractor use.

15512 Gioia, R. IT 063300/71/0072
Carro freno a frenatura idrostatica. **Braking car with hydrostatic transmission.**

15513 Gioia, R. IT 063300/72/0071
Telai e cabine di sicurezza per trattrici. **Tractor safety cabs and frames.** Publications.

15514 Gioco, M. IT 063300/73/0070
Cabine per trattrici, comfort del conducente. **Tractor cabs, driver's comfort.**

15515 Gioia, R. IT 063300/73/0073
Prove sui sedili delle trattrici. **Tests on tractor seats.**

15516 Telle, M.G. NL 010106/70/2666
Het verlichten van de arbeid en het verbeteren van de werkkwaliteit door het automatiseren van de trekkerbesturing. **The relief of labour and the improvement of the quality of work by automation of the tractor control.** Publications.

15517 Maanen, J. van NL 010106/71/6411
Onderzoek en ontwikkeling van een wagen met een groot laadvermogen en een lage wieldruk. **Research and development of an agricultural trailer with a high carrying capacity and a low wheel pressure.** Publications.

15518 Koning, K. de NL 010106/76/6638
Transport en hantering van losgestorte produkten. **Transport and handling of agricultural products in bulk.**

15519 Nieuwenhuizen, G.H. van NL 010118/77/7266
Verkorte testprocedures voor koelvoertuigen. **Quick check methods for testing of refrigerated vehicles.** Publications.

15520 Nieuwenhuizen, G.H. van NL 010118/77/7267
Doelmatige testmethoden voor koelvoertuigen. **Suitable methods for testing of refrigerated vehicles.**

15521 Lantau, T. NL 010702/67/7159
Modelonderzoek naar de dynamische stabiliteit van kotters; optimalisering van het ontwerp van kotters. **Model research into the dynamic stability of beam trawlers; optimalization of the design of fishing vessels.** Publications.

15522 Lantau, T. NL 010702/77/7160
Onderzoek naar de standaardisering en naar methoden en systemen ter verbetering van de onderhoudsstrategie van machinekamerinstallaties. **Research on the standardization and on improvement of the maintenance strategy of engine room equipment on board fishing vessels.**

Household equipment (B 6180)

15523 Piekarski, J.; Burkhart, P. DE 211100/78/0003 N
Technische Einrichtungen für die Schulverpflegung beim System "Mischküche". **Technical equipment fo school feeding programs. Combined systems.**

Other machinery and equipment (B 6190)

15524 Heege, H.J.; Balg, J.; Simons, D.
 DE 111852/78/0002 N

Einsatz von Wärmepumpen im Landbau. **Use of heat pumps in agriculture.**

15525 Tebrügge, F. DE 129400/77/0001
Möglichkeiten, Grenzen und Kosten der mechanischen Landschaftspflege unter Berücksichtigung unterschiedlicher Standorte und Vegetationsformen. **Possibilities, limits and charges of mechanical landscape husbandry for different stands and vegetations.** Publications.

15526 Isensee, E.; Schuster, J. DE 148150/77/0002
Verfahrenstechnik zur Beseitigung von Steinen auf landwirtschaftlichen Nutzflächen. **Methods for removing stones from farmland.**

15527 Bruce GB 060224/79/0023 N
Automatically controlled natural ventilation.

15528 Arts, W.B.M. NL 010106/76/6632
Onderzoek naar en ontwikkeling van apparatuur voor het onderhoud van natuurterreinen. **Research and development of machinery for the preservation of nature areas.** Publications.

15529 Wijk, A. van NL 010106/76/6642 R
Werktuigen voor het mechanisch onderhoud van sloten en wegbermen. **Implements for the mechanical upkeep of ditches and roadsides.** Publications.

15530 Boer, E.J. de NL 010702/78/7035 R
Onderzoek naar de mogelijkheden tot het weghouden van vis bij in–en uitlaatwerken van koelwatersystemen door middel van elektroschermen. **Research into the application of electrified barriers to prevent fish to enter intakes or aggregate round outlets of cooling water systems.**

D 4200 – Engineering – buildings

See also 6627, 6628, 11228, 11229, 11230, 11231, 11391, 13336, 13337, 15139, 15140, 15141, 15142, 15143, 15144, 15145, 15146, 15147, 15148, 15149, 15150, 15151, 15152, 15153, 15154, 15155, 15156, 15157, 15158, 15159, 15160, 15161, 15162, 15163, 15164, 15165, 15166, 15167, 15168, 15169, 15170, 15171, 15172, 15173, 15174, 15175, 15176, 15177, 15178, 15179, 15180, 15181, 15182, 15183, 15184, 15185, 15186, 15187, 15188, 15189, 15190, 15191, 15192, 15193, 15194, 15195, 15196, 15197, 15198, 15199, 15200, 15201, 15202, 15203, 15204, 15205, 15206, 15207, 15208, 15209, 15210, 15211, 15212, 15213, 15214, 15215, 15216, 15217, 15218, 15219, 15220, 15221, 15222, 15223, 15224, 15225, 15226, 15227, 15228, 15229, 15230, 15231, 15232, 15233, 15234, 15235, 15236, 15237, 15238, 15239, 15240, 15241, 15242, 15243, 15244, 15245, 15246, 15247, 15248, 15249, 15250, 15251, 15252, 15253, 15254...

15531 Nisen, A.; Deltour, J. BE 010002/57/0001
Etude de l'éclairement naturel des serres par la voie d'un modèle mathématique susceptible d'être appliqué par ordinateur. **Study of the natural illumination of greenhouse by a mathematical model suitable for ordinator application.** Publications.

15532 Debruyckere, M.; Dewilde, J. BE 030029/57/0003 R
Onderzoek naar de toepassingen van elektriciteit in de land– en tuinbouw en in het bijzonder op bodemverwarming, belichting, en groeiruimten in de tuinbouw en op bodemverwarming in stallen. **Research on applications of electricity in agriculture and horticulture with special attention**

to soil heating, lighting and growing rooms in horticulture and floor heating in animal houses. Publications.

15533 Maton, A.; Daelemans, J.   BE 070300/69/0016 R
Studie van de gedragingen van koeien in stallen met het oog op het bepalen van de optimale dimensies van de staluitrusting. **Study of animal behaviour in cowsheds with intent to find their optimum dimensions of their equipment.** Publications.

15534 Olesen, S.E.; Larsen, V.   DK 010900/78/0001 N
Rensning gennem jordfiltre af spildevand fra landbrugsejendomme. **Purification through sand filters of sewage water from farm buildings.**

15535 Pedersen, J.   DK 011000/74/0400
Analyse og udvalg af kombinationer af produktionsfaktorer i slagtesvinestalde. **Analysis and choice of combination of production factors in pig houses.**

15536 Strøm, J.S.   DK 011000/76/0002
Beregning af mulige energibesparelser ved anvendelse af alternative former for klimastyring under forudsætning af forskellige husdyrprodukter, staldbygninger, klimaforhold og klimaanlæg. **Calculation of possible energy savings with the use of alternative forms of climatic control assuming different animal products, stall buildings, climatic conditions and climate–control plant.**

15537 Feinstra, A.   DK 011000/77/0005
Fastlæggelse af de lavest tilladelige lufttemperaturer til tidligt fravænnede smågrise og udarbejdelse af et grundlag for udformning og dimensionering af strålevarmeanlæg til klimastalde. **Establishment of the lowest permissible air temperatures for early weaned piglets and the development of a basis for the design and dimensions of radiant–heating plant for controlled–climate stalls.**

15538 Nielsen, K.; Arnbjerg, J.; Blom, J.Y.
    DK 030129/78/0002 N
Staldtypers indflydelse på sundheden hos kvæg. **The influence of different production systems on cattle health.**

15539 Cooper; Timms   GB 011303/00/0002 R
Design and fabrication of isolators suitable for use with pathogens.

15540 Stayner; Talamo   GB 011602/00/0004 R
Noise in farm buildings and plant.

15541 Carpenter   GB 011610/00/0003 R
Ventilation of livestock buildings.

15542 Researcher not indicated   GB 050483/00/0003 R
Genetic factors in relation to the metabolic disorders of sheep.

15543 Baxter   GB 060224/00/0003 R
Farm buildings: costs and indices.

15544 Baxter   GB 060224/00/0004 R
Farm buildings: survey of building costs.

15545 Bruce   GB 060224/00/0008 R
Influence of climate on building design.

15546 Baxter   GB 060224/00/0009 R
Materials and structures for farm buildings.

15547 Maccormack   GB 060224/00/0010 R
Information service: farm buildings.

15548 Cermak   GB 060224/78/0014 N
Space standards for common animal housing task.

15549 Tasker   GB 060224/79/0024 N
Glass reinforced concrete as a flooring material in livestock buildings.

15550 Grierson   GB 060317/00/0001 R
Investigational work to obtain information required for preparation of farm buildings handbook.

15551 Comerford, P.J.   IE 060500/72/0169 R
Determination of the behaviour and performance of animals under various degrees of electric fence control. Publications.

Structures and other permanent installations in general (B 6200)

See also 15281, 15301, 15302, 15308

15552 Dufey, V.; Legrand, E.   BE 080400/69/0005
Etude et expérimentation des équipements d'intérieur de ferme. **Study and experimentation of interior equipment of farms.** Publications.

15553 Göhlich, H.; Jensen, U.   DE 105601/78/0001 N
Untersuchungen an hydraulischen Bauelementen, insbesondere an Servoventilen. **Functional analysis of hydraulic components, especially pilot valves.**

15554 Kratz, W.; Ziesel, J.   DE 114450/74/0017
Die Verwendbarkeit des Holzes nach geltenden und in Vorbereitung befindlichen Bauvorschriften. **Utilization of wood according to present building rules and those in preparation.**

15555 Kejwal, K.; Kindereit, E.   DE 138500/77/0001
Untersuchungen zur genaueren rechnerischen Erfassung des Kriech– und Relaxationsverhaltens von Bauholz und Holzverbindungen. **Investigations on the exact calculation of creep and relaxation behaviour of building timber and timber assemblings.**

15556 Kejwal, K.; Krause, U.   DE 138500/77/0002
Beitrag zur Berechnung und Optimierung von Faltwerken. **A contributory study on the computation and the optimization of folded–plate structures.**

15557 Bischoff, T.; Rubitschek, P.   DE 144710/75/0002
Entwicklung einer Bauplanungsmethode für landwirtschaftliche Wirtschaftsgebäude bei vorhandener Altgebäudesubstanz. **Development of a method for the planning of farm buildings considering available old structures.**

15558 Niebergall, H.; Seitz, H.   DE 145100/71/0004 N
Über die Gas– und Wasserdampfdurchlässigkeit chemisch vernetzter Zellglasfolien. **On gas and vapour permeability of chemically cross linked cellophan foil.**

15559 Niebergall, H.; Aydin, B.   DE 145100/72/0003 N
Einflüsse von Weichmachern auf Zellglas. **The influences of softeners on cellophane.**

15560 Möhler, K.; Ehlbeck, J.　　　DE 145400/74/0002
Untersuchungen über den Einfluss des LastZeitablaufes bei
Prüfversuchen für Holzver– bindungsmittel – vorwiegend
Nagelplatten – auf Traglast und Verformungsgrössen als
Grundlagen für die zulässige Belastung. **Experiments on the
effect of the time–load curve in testing wood connectors esp. of
nailed boards for strength and slip–behaviour as conditions of
safe load.**

15561 Möhler, K.; Rathfelder, M.　　　DE 145400/77/0001
Konstruktive Möglichkeiten zur Aufnahme von Schub– und
Querzugspannungen bei Brettschichtholz. **Constructive
possibilities for the reception of shear– and
transverse–tension–stresses at glulam.**

15562 Möhler, K.; Lautenschläger, R.　　　DE 145400/77/0002
Ausbildung von Queranschlüssen bei angehängten Lasten an
Brettschichtträger oder Vollholz. **Construction of transverse
joints for suspending loads on glulam or timber beams.**

15563 Möhler, K.; Herröder, W.　　　DE 145400/77/0003
Ersatz von Bolzen durch Holzschrauben und Schraubnägel bei
Dübelverbindungen. **Screws and screw nails instead of bolts at
joints, using dowels.**

15564 Möhler, K.; Hemmer, K.　　　DE 145400/77/0004
Zusammenwirken von Längs–, Quer– und Schubspannungen
'Torsionsspannungen' bei Brettschicht– und
Vollholzbauteilen. **Interaction of longitudinal, transverse and
shear stresses at glulam and timber elements.**

15565 Möhler, K.; Lautenschläger, R.　　　DE 145400/77/0005
Grossflächige Queranschlüsse bei Brettschichtholz. **Transverse
joints of big areas at glulam.**

15566 Möhler, K.; Mistler, L.　　　DE 145400/77/0006
Untersuchungen über den Einfluss von Ausklinkungen im
Auflagerbereich von Holzbiegeträgern auf die Tragfestigkeit.
Investigations of end–notched beams of wood.

15567 Möhler, K.; Hemmer, K.　　　DE 145400/78/0002 N
Hirnholzdübel–Verbindungen bei Brettschichtholz. **Timber
dowel connectors in the end face of glulam.**

15568 Möhler, K.; Herröder, W.; Brüninghoff
　　　　　　　　　DE 145400/78/0003 N
Knickaussteifung von Brettschichtträgern mit veränderlichem
Querschnitt. **Buckling support of glued laminated beams with
various profile.**

15569 Topf, P.　　　DE 160331/77/0002
Messung der Rauchentwicklung von Feuerschutztüren und
Wandelelementen. **Smoke development by fire doors and wall
elements.**

15570 Witte, E.　　　DE 201060/74/0001
Berechnung von Tragwerken. **Calculation of supporting
structures.**

15571 Witte, E.　　　DE 201060/74/0002
Betriebsfestigkeitsversuche an Bauteilen. **Spectrum loading
tests of construction at elements.**

15572 Schulz, H.; Rittel, L.　　　DE 502600/72/0001
Förderung der baulichen Selbsthilfe durch Entwicklung und

Erprobung neuer Konstruktionen, Erstellung statischer
Unterlagen und Durchführung von Baukursen 1972.
**Stimulation of do–it–yourself building work by developing and
testing new designs, by furnishing static data, and arranging
building courses.**

15573 Schulz, H.; Rittel, L.; Englert, G.
　　　　　　　　　DE 502603/71/0001 R
Untersuchungen an Leichtbauhallen und Flächentragwerken
zur Verbilligung des landwirtschaftlichen Bauwesens
Untersuchungen neuer Bau– und Werkstoffe unter
landwirtschaftlichen Bedingungen 1971. **Studies on
light–building halls and plane supporting structures for
cheapening agricultural building. Analysis of new building
materials under agricultural conditions.**

15574 Andersen, K.T.　　　DK 011000/76/0001
Toplagstykkelsen i isolerede staldgulve. **Top layer thickness in
isolated stall floors.**

15575 Wells　　　GB 011604/76/0024 R
Effect of wind on agricultural buildings.

15576 Stewart　　　GB 041101/00/0013 R
Disposal of silage effluent and its effect on concrete structures.

15577 Pratelli, G.　　　IT 040241/78/1089 N
Normative per fabbricati destinati alla produzione agricola in
funzione della ristrutturazione della dimensione aziendale e di
trasformazione territoriali in atto. **Norms to be applied to farm
outbuildings in connection with the re–dimensioning of farms
and the present territorial changes.**

15578 Spek, J.C.　　　NL 010106/63/1233
Bedrijfsgebouwen voor de tuinbouwkundige sector van het
agrarisch bouwen. **Horticultural buildings in the agricultural
building sector.**

15579 Stoffers, J.A.　　　NL 010106/65/1248 R
Ontwikkeling van meetapparatuur t.b.v. het
klimaatsonderzoek. **Development of measuring apparatus for
climate research.**

15580 Hangelbroek, P.B.　　　NL 010106/65/6707
Materiaaltechnische ontwikkeling en verbetering van
bouw–elementen in landbouwbedrijfsgebouwen. **Research on
application of modern building materials in the agricultural
field.**

15581 Ouwerkerk, E.N.J. van　　　NL 010106/65/6708 R
Warmte– en vochthuishouding in bouwconstructies in de
agrarische sector met het oog op rationele energiebenutting.
**Thermal and hygro behaviour in building materials for
agricultural buildings in view of rational energy utilization.**

15582 Spek, J.C.　　　NL 010106/70/3169 R
Het samenstellen van constructienormen en NPR's
(nederlandse praktijkrichtlijnen) voor agrarische
bedrijfsgebouwen en kassen. **The composition of building
standards and Dutch Practical Rules for agricultural buildings
and greenhouses.**

15583 Hart, C. 't　　　NL 010106/72/4730
Constructieve aspecten van agrarische bedrijfsgebouwen.
Construction aspects of agricultural buildings. Publications.

15584 Hangelbroek, P.B.   NL 010106/76/6709 R
De inpassing van agrarische gebouwen in het landschap.
**Architectural aspects of new agricultural buildings in relation
with the landscape.**

15585 Brabander, W.H. de   NL 010106/76/6710 R
De verlenging van de levensduur van bouwmaterialen in
verschillende expositie omstandigheden. **Durability of building
materials in agricultural exposure.**

15586 Swierstra, D.   NL 010106/79/9032 N
Standaardisatie van de uitgangspunten voor het ontwerpen van
huisvestingssystemen. **Standardization of (basic) starting points
for the design of housing systems.**

15587 Bouman–Sweers, M.J.M.   NL 020026/77/8796 N
Onderzoek inzake constructieve en planologische aspecten van
landbouw bedrijfsgebouwen. **Research on construction and
architechnical aspects of agricultural buildings.**

15588 Bargerbos, G.   NL 040007/67/8564
Ontwikkelingen in de boerderijbouw t.b.v. het ontwerp van
nieuwe bedrijfsgebouwen. **Developments in the farm building
sector in connection with the design of new buildings.**

Glasshouses, nurseries (B 6210)

See also 2753, 15531, 15532, 15660

15589 Nisen, A.   BE 010002/76/0009
Recherche de matériaux nouveaux pour la couverture des
serres: vitrages isolants, réfléchissants, diffusants. **Study of new
materials for glasshouses such as isolated, reflected, diffused
glazing, etc.**

15590 Maton, A.; Taverne, W.   BE 070300/73/0023 R
Studie van de eigenschappen van droge en vochtige lucht en
luchtbehandelingssystemen. **Research on the characteristics of
dry and humid air and methods of airconditioning.**

15591 Zabeltitz, C.von; Tantau, H.–J.   DE 138390/72/0002
Grundlagen der Typisierung von Regelorganen zur Steuerung
und Regelung der Klimatisierung von Gewächshäusern.
**Groundwork for standardization of controllers for
environmental control systems in greenhouses.**

15592 Zabeltitz, C.von; Tantau, H.–J.   DE 138390/73/0001
Ermittlung des Wärmebedarfes und der Klimafaktoren bei
doppelt verglasten Gewächshäusern. **Investigations into heat
consumption and climatic conditions in double–glazed
glasshouses.**

15593 Zabeltitz, C.von; Meyer, J.   DE 138390/73/0003
Entwicklung eines Growing–Rooms zur Jungpflanzenanzucht.
Development of a growing–room for seedlings.

15594 Damrath, J.   DE 138390/75/0001
Sonnenenergieausnutzung für die Beheizung von
Gewächshäusern. **The use of solar energy for
greenhouse–heating.**

15595 Schockert, K.   DE 138390/77/0001
Klima unter Doppelbedachungen. **Climate in double sheltered
greenhouses.**

15596 Tantau, H.–J.   DE 138390/77/0002

Einsatz und Programmierung von Mikrocomputern zur
Klimaregelung von Gewächshäusern. **Use and programming of
microcomputers for climate control in glasshouses.**

15597 Elsner, B.von   DE 138390/78/0001 N
Einsatz von Niedertemperaturwärme für die
Gewächshausheizung. **Utilization of low temperature energy
for the heating of greenhouses.**

15598 Zabeltitz, C.von; Elsner, B.von   DE 138390/78/0002 N
Mikroklima im Pflanzenbestand bei unterschiedlichen
Heizungssystemen. **Microclimate of plant canopies in regard of
different heating systems.** Publications.

15599 Hege, H.; Lecker, F.   DE 502110/77/0001
Messen und Regeln von CO2 im Gewächshaus. **Measuring and
adjustment of the CO2–concentration in greenhouses.**

15600 Hege, H.; Achatz, A.   DE 502110/78/0002 N
Energieeinsparung durch Rauchgasklappen in
Heizungsanlagen für Gewächshäuser. **Economizing of energy
in glasshouses by regulators for smoke.**

15601 Mackroth, K.   DE 506113/73/0004
Die Lichtdurchlässigkeit verschiedener Kunststoffe für
Gewächshauseinrichtungen nach 2, 4, 6, 8 oder 10 Jahren
natürlicher Bewitterung. **Light transmittance test of divers
plastics for glasshouses after 2, 4, 6, 8 or 10 years natural
weathering.**

15602 Strotmann, G.; Papenhagen, A.   DE 508201/75/0001
Untersuchungen über den Energieverbrauch von
Gewächshäusern mit verschiedenen Einrichtungen zur
Wärmedämmung. **Studies on energy consumption of
greenhouses with various equipments for heat insulation.**

15603 Amsen, M.G.   DK 010113/75/4209
Gardiner og andre isoleringsmaterialers anvendelse som
energibesparende foranstaltning i væksthus. **Use of curtains
and other insulation materials as energy–saving measures in
glasshouses.**

15604 Petersen, L.K.   DK 011000/77/0001
Udarbejdelse af anvisning vedr. indretning, materialer og
klimastyring for grorum. **Development of recommendations for
layout, materials and climatic control of growth rooms.**

15605 Traberg–Borup, S.   DK 011000/78/1813 N
Udvikling af let monterbare elementer til præfabrikerede
væksthuse. **Prefabricated greenhouses built with easy–to–erect
components.**

15606 Pedersen, L.K.   DK 011000/78/1814 N
Bygherreprogram for klargøringsafdelinger til
blomstergartnerier. **Construction management program for
packaging facilities in floricultural production.**

15607 Brun, R.; Peyriere, J.   FR 010610/71/3001
Etude de l'intérêt de différents films plastiques pour la
fabrication d'abris destinés à la production maraîchère. **Study
of the relative interest of plastic films for building shelters in
vegetable production.** Publications.

15608 Brun, R.   FR 010616/75/9090
Utilisation des eaux tempérées circulant dans des gaines posées
sur le sol pour le chauffage des serres. **Utilisation of warm

water circulating through plastic sheaths laid on the ground for glasshouse heating.

15609 Bailey; Cotton   GB 011604/00/0013 R
More efficient use of energy in greenhouses.

15610 Weaving   GB 011604/75/0020 R
Greenhouse monitoring and control systems.

15611 Wells   GB 011604/76/0025 R
Effect of wind on plastic greenhouses.

15612 Wells   GB 011604/79/0026 N
Methods of heating greenhouses.

15613 O'Flaherty, T.   IE 060300/74/0887 R
Evaluation of windbreaks for reduction of heat requirement of glasshouses and plastic greenhouses. Publications.

15614 Bianchi, A.   IT 040110/74/0517
Analisi dell'effetto delle radiazioni solari e della velocità del vento sul condizionamento di serre con differenti tipi di copertura. **Analysis of the effect of solar radiation and wind velocity on the conditioning of greenhouses having different types of cover.**

15615 Chiusoli, A.; Bazzocchi, R.   IT 040203/77/0001
Ricerche sulla climatizzazione nelle serre. **Research on acclimatization in glasshouses.** Publications.

15616 Spek, J.C.   NL 010106/60/1226
Constructie van kassen met verschillende omhullingsmaterialen. **Construction of glasshouses with various coating materials.** Publications.

15617 Weijerman, A.W.E.; Germing, G.H.
    NL 010106/64/6459
Installaties voor plantenbestraling. **Installations for plant illumination.** Publications.

15618 Breuer, J.G.G.   NL 010106/73/5354 R
Metingen warmteverlies van kasdekken. **Measurements of heat losses of greenhouse bays.** Publications.

15619 Kieboom, A.M.G. van de   NL 010106/73/5358 R
Lichtdoorlatendheidsbepalingen van kassen en kasmodellen. **Determination of light permeability (light transmission) in greenhouses and glasshouse models.** Publications.

15620 Zijlstra, J.A.   NL 010106/74/6716
Evaluatie van de gebruksmogelijkheden van een Total Energy installatie bij belichting en de verwarming van kassen. **Evaluation of the applications of a Total Energy plant for the illumination (irradiation) and heating of greenhouses.** Publications.

15621 Stoffers, J.A.   NL 010106/75/6455
Bepaling van energiestromen van geschermde kasdekken i.v.m. energiebesparing. **Measurement of energy flows in screened glasshouses in view of energy–savings.**

15622 Breuer, J.G.G.   NL 010106/75/6456 R
Ontwikkeling van een rekenmodel voor het kasklimaat. **Development of a simulation model for glasshouse climate.** Publications.

15623 Gieling, T.   NL 010106/76/6714
Onderzoek naar meetopnemers in kassen t.b.v. een economisch optimale klimaatregeling. **Research into set–points in greenhouses on behalf of an economic optimal climate–control.**

15624 Weijerman, A.W.E.   NL 010106/76/6715
Toetsing van meetapparatuur voor bepaling van bodemvochtigheid gericht op automatisering van de watertoediening. **Testing of measuring apparatus for the determination of the soil humidity aimed at the automation of water supply.**

15625 Kieboom, A.M.G. van de   NL 010106/76/8372
Energiebesparende schermen in kassen. **Screens for energy saving in greenhouses.**

15626 Meurs, W.T.M. van   NL 010106/77/7593
Centraal beheer van regelprogramma's voor het kasklimaat. **Central administration of developed algorithms for climate control in greenhouses.** Publications.

15627 Mulder, W.P.   NL 010106/78/8371
Doelmatig energiegebruik in kassen. **Optimal energy use in glasshouses.**

15628 Huizing, J.A.   NL 010106/79/9021 N
Onderzoek naar de mogelijkheden met betrekking tot de technische uitvoering van schermen in kassen. **Research into the possibilities with regard to the technical design of screens in greenhouses.**

15629 Vente, J.M.   NL 010106/79/9035 N
Alternatieve verwarmingsmethoden van kassen. **Low temperature heating of glasshouses; alternative heating methods.**

15630 Heyna, B.J.   NL 010106/79/9036 N
Afvalwarmte ten behoeve van kassen. **Application of reject heat for heating glasshouses.**

15631 Langers, R.A.   NL 010106/79/9037 N
Modelstudie verwarmingstechnieken in kassen. **Model study of heating systems in greenhouses.**

15632 Arkenbout, J.   NL 010106/79/9038 N
Energiebesparing bij de klimatisering van de champignonteelt. **Energy saving in air conditioned mushroom houses.**

15633 Bokhorst, D.   NL 010106/79/9039 N
Bepaling ventilatievouden voor kasgewassen. **Ventilation rates in glasshouses.**

15634 Berg, G.A. van den   NL 010201/76/8372
Energiebesparende schermen in kassen. **Screens for energy saving of greenhouses.**

15635 Holsteijn, G.P.A. van   NL 010206/76/8372
Energiebesparende schermen in kassen. **Screens for energy saving of greenhouses.**

15636 Bokhorst, D.   NL 010206/79/9039 N
Bepaling ventilatievouden voor kasgewassen. **Ventilation rates in glasshouses.**

Stables (B 6220)

D 4200 – Engineering – buildings

See also 10404, 10450, 10698, 10714, 10718, 10726, 10840, 10856, 10857, 10903, 10905, 11063, 11100, 11101, 11167, 11174, 11176, 11177, 11178, 11235, 11248, 11252, 11283, 11309, 11397, 11417, 11462, 14397, 15380, 15439, 15450, 15451, 15532, 15533, 15535, 15536, 15537, 15538, 15552, 16352, 17299, 19746

15637 Petit, K.; Debruyckere, M.; Nicolaus, A.

BE 030029/30/0001 R
Fundamentele studie van de boerderijgebouwen en hun uitrusting in het bijzonder de planning, de isolatie, de verluchting, de elektrificatie en de verwerking van dierlijke afvalstoffen. **Fundamental study of farm buildings and equipment especially planning insolation, ventilation problems and electrification and animal waste disposal.** Publications.

15638 Debruyckere, M.; Christiaens, J.; Neukermans, G.

BE 030029/61/0002 R
Studie van de klimatisatieproblemen in de veeteelt en in het bijzonder van de ventilatie, verwarming in stallen, klimatisatie in grote produktieeenheden, reukbestrijding en stalverlichting. **Study of climatisation problems of livestock accomodation especially ventilation, heating in animal house, climate problems in big production units odour abatement and lighting in animal houses.** Publications.

15639 Goedseels, V.; Berckmans, D.   BE 040401/70/0002 R
Bepaling en realisatie van intern en extern optimaal milieu in stallen. **Determination and realization of optimal climate in stables.** Publications.

15640 Maton, A.; Priem, R.   BE 070300/76/0046 R
Het gebruik van een statisch strofilter voor het scheiden van mengmest. **The use of a static straw–filter for the separation of liquid manure.** Publications.

15641 Seufert, H.; Pflug, R.   DE 129400/73/0008
Bemessung und Ausführung tiergerechter strohloser Bodenbeläge. **Measurement and finish of animal–adjusted strawless floor covering.**

15642 Lorenz, J.   DE 129400/75/0009
Untersuchungen zur Optimierung des Funktionsablaufes und der Klimaführung in einem Sauen–Deckzentrum. **Investigations into optimizing the functional process and the climatic conditions in a service station for sows.**

15643 Bischoff, T.; Heckmann, G.   DE 144710/75/0001
Erstellung und Systematisierung von Planungsunterlagen für die Vorentwurfsplanung in der Schweinehaltung. **Provision and systematization of planning data for projecting hog housings.**

15644 Bischoff, T.; Hatem, M.   DE 144710/77/0001
Untersuchungen über die Eignung von Baustoffen und Baukonstruktionen für Ställe der Geflügelmast unter ägyptischen Verhältnissen. **Investigations on the suitability of building materials and constructions for poultry housing under Egyptian conditions.**

15645 Isensee, E.; Leuschner, P.   DE 148150/75/0003
Untersuchungen über das Regelverhalten lüftungstechnischer Anlagen in Schweinemastställen. **Investigations of ventilation control systems in swine–fattening houses.**

15646 Schön, H.; Krinner, L.; Wenner, H.L.

DE 161520/77/0002
Entwicklung von Raumprogrammen und Standardgrundrissen für die Rinderhaltung. **Development of housing programs and standardized layouts for cattle husbandry.**

15647 Hagemann, D.   DE 201080/74/0005
Auswirkungen des Bau– und Planungsrechts auf das landwirtschaftliche Bauen. **Effect of building and planning law on building in agriculture.**

15648 Borchert, K.–L.   DE 201080/77/0002
Energiesparende Verfahren und Konstruktionen – Teilbereich: Energiesparende Formen der Raumklimatisierung von Ställen –. **Energy–saving methods and constructions – partial project: energy–saving air–conditioning of stalls.**

15649 Piotrowski, N.   DE 201080/77/0003
Kosten– und arbeitssparendes sowie tiergerechtes Bauen unter Berücksichtigung technischer wie struktueller Entwicklungen. **Costs– and energy–saving and animal–adjusted construction considering technical and structural trends.**

15650 Herms, A.   DE 201080/77/0004
Kriterien zur Standortbeurteilung für grössere Tierbestände. **Criteria for valuation of location of large–scale livestock.**

15651 Boxberger, J.; Metzner, R.   DE 502600/75/0003
Weiterentwicklung an Stalleinrichtungen für Rindvieh und Schweine. Ermittlung von Kennwerten für die optimale Stallhaltung von Rindern – Fütterungsanlagen für Mastschweine –. **Further development of stable installations for cattle and pigs.**

15652 Keller, P.   DK 010400/71/0004 N
Arbejdsbehov i løsdriftsstalde til kvæg. **Labour requirement in loose housing systems for cattle.**

15653 Klausen, K.G.; Guul–Simonsen, F. DK 010400/74/0003
Undersøgelse vedrørende materiel til staldventilation omfattende sammenlignende prøve af eksisterende materiel for at tilvejebringe et ensartet vurderingsgrundlag. **Studies of stall ventilation equipment, including comparative tests of existing equipment for the purpose of providing a uniform basis of evaluation.**

15654 Keller, P.; Madsen, N.P.; Nielsen, V.

DK 010400/74/0005 N
Tekniske og arbejdsmæssige konsekvenser ved anvendelse af forskellige arbejds– og maskinkæder til håndtering af grovfoder. **Technical and working consequences using various work and machine chains for handling roughage.**

15655 Pedersen, S.; Møller, F.   DK 010400/78/0002 N
Klimastyring i kalvestalde. **Control of climatic conditions in calfhouses.**

15656 Christensen, J.; Laursen, B.   DK 010500/78/0004 N
Udvikling af modeller til belysning af kvægstaldsystemers indbyrdes konkurrenceevne. **Development of models showing the economic competitiveness of different dairy–housing systems.**

15657 Sørensen, B.   DK 010500/78/0006 N
Undersøgelse af prisbillige svinestaldes konkurrenceevne overfor traditionelle stalde. **The competitiveness of low–costs**

pig stable–systems.

15658 Walter–Jørgensen, A.   DK 010500/78/0008 N
Leasing af svinestalde vurderet på baggrund af traditionelle staldinvesteringer. **Leasing of pig stables seen in relation to traditional investments.**

15659 Pedersen, S.   DK 011000/71/0330
Funktionskrav og ydeevnebeskrivelser for ventilationsanlæg til stalde. **Performance of ventilation systems for farm buildings.**

15660 Strøm, J.S.   DK 011000/76/0003
Inventarets skærmvirkning i slagtesvinestalde. Udarbejdelse af retningslinier for valg af gunstige kombinationer af ventilationsmateriel og inventar. **Shelter effect of stall equipment in bacon pig stalls. Development of recommendations for choice of suitable combinations of ventilation and stall equipment.**

15661 Illum, J.C.   DK 011000/77/0002
Udarbejdelse af koordinerede konstruktioner og konstruktionsdetaljer til landbrugsbygninger. **Development of co–ordinated constructions and construction details for agricultural buildings.**

15662 Mortensen, B.   DK 011000/77/0006
Opstilling af grundlag for udformning af planløsninger til bygningsanlæg til malkekvæg. **Development of basis for the elaboration of plan arrangements for dairy cattle buildings.**

15663 Krabbe, H.   DK 011000/77/0007
Udvikling af et edb–baseret priskalkulationssystem for landbrugsbyggeri. **Development of an edb–based price calculation system for agricultural building.**

15664 Østergaard, V.; Smedegaard, H.H.
    DK 030130/78/0005 N
Eksperimentelle staldtypesystemer. Klovlidelsers udbredelse, mulighed for forebyggelse af klovlidelser og klovlidelsers økonomiske betydning. **Experimental housing of cattle on pilot farms. The frequency of clawdiseases, the effect of treatment, the possibility of prevention and the economical importance of clawdiseases.**

15665 Petersen, P.H.; Møller–Madsen, Aa.; Jensen, H.; Konggaard, S.P.   DK 030142/78/0001 N
Undersøgelser over tre staldtypers indflydelse på mælkehygiejnen. **The influence of three housing systems on milk hygiene.**

15666 Brun, R.   FR 010616/72/9088
Utilisation des matériaux de couverture sur grands abris plastiques. **Utilisation of covering materials for large plastic shelters.**

15667 Kavanagh A.J.   IE 060600/76/0897 N
The design of buildings (other than milking sheds) for dairy herds. Publications.

15668 Chiappini, U.   IT 040223/72/0429
Ricerca sulla produzione di calore, di vapore acqueo e di gas nocivi in ricoveri per allevamenti zootecnici. **Research on the production of heat, water vapour and noxious gases in shelters used for animal breeding.** Publications.

15669 Satta, R.; Pisanu, M.; Porcu, C.   IT 041304/78/0001 N

Ristrutturazione dell'allevamento ovino su scala territoriale, in Sardegna: proposta di modello di organizzazione basata su una metodologia operativa coordinata con edifici di produzione a tipologia modulare. **Restructuration of sheep rearing on territorial scale, in Sardinia: proposal for organizing model based on coordinated methods with modular type buildings.** Publications.

15670 Satta, R.; Pisanu, M.; Porcu, C.   IT 041304/78/0002 N
Modulo di mantenimento di agnelli per produzione di carne in milk lots. **Modulus of lambs keeping for meat production in milk lots.** Publications.

15671 Pisanu, M.; Porcu, C.   IT 041304/78/0003 N
Analisi di differenti tipi di pavimentazione per ricoveri ovini. **Analysis of different flooring for sheep housing.**

15672 De Montis, S.   IT 041304/78/0004 N
Problematiche sperimentazioni e prospettive dell'allevamento ovino da carne in Sardegna. **Problematics experimentations and prospects of meat sheep breeding in Sardinia.** Publications.

15673 De Montis, S.   IT 041304/78/0005 N
Moduli e tipologie edilizie per l'allevamento ovino da carne. **Modulus and buildings typologies for meat sheep breeding.** Publications.

15674 Westendorp, Tj.   NL 010106/70/8779 N
Huisvesting van kalveren. **Housing of calves.** Publications.

15675 Poelma, H.R.   NL 010106/72/4728 R
Stankbestrijding bij mest en gier door middel van beluchting; mestafvoersystemen uit stallen. **Odour abatement by aerating manure and liquid manure; dung removal systems in stables.** Publications.

15676 Gels, J.A.   NL 010106/72/4745
Ontwikkeling en verbetering van plannen voor complete bedrijven met ligboxenstallen, voerligboxenstallen en verschillende voerstystemen. **Development and improvement of complete dairy farming enterprises with cubicle houses, feed cubicle houses and different feed systems.**

15677 Koomans, P.   NL 010106/72/4760
De huisvesting van fokvarkens. **Housing of breeding pigs.** Publications.

15678 Koomans, P.   NL 010106/72/4763
De huisvesting van mestvarkens (vnl. toetsing van goedkope huisvestingsvormen). **Housing systems for fattening pigs (especially testing of cheaper housing systems).** Publications.

15679 Westendorp, Tj.   NL 010106/72/8776 N
Huisvesting van schapen en lammeren. **Housing of sheep and lambs.** Publications.

15680 Poelma, H.R.   NL 010106/72/8780 N
Mest en gier afvoersystemen in melkveestallen. **Removal systems of dung and urine in houses for dairy cattle.** Publications.

15681 Westendorp, Tj.   NL 010106/72/8781 N
De inrichting van ligboxstallen en vloerligboxstallen voor melkvee. **The arrangement of cubicles and feed cubibles for dairy cattle.** Publications.

15682 Smits, A.C. NL 010106/73/8782 N
Bouwkundige voorzieningen voor de gezondheidszorg van melkvee. **Building supplies for the health care of dairy cattle.** Publications.

15683 Westendorp, Tj. NL 010106/75/6449
Aanpassing van grupstallen voor melkvee t.b.v. toepassing van moderne bedrijfsmethoden. **Adaption of tying stalls for dairy cattle for application of modern handling methods.**

15684 Mulder, W.P. NL 010106/76/6717
Energiebesparing in veestallen. **Energy savings in animal husbandry.**

15685 Gels, J.A. NL 010106/78/7959 R
Relatie tussen huisvesting en diergezondheid in moderne grupstallen en boxenstallen. **Relation between housing and animal health in modern tying stalls and cubic stalls.**

15686 Brabander, W.H. de NL 010106/78/8370
Huisvesting en verzorging van sportpaarden. **Housing and charge of sporting horses.**

15687 Brandsma, C. NL 010106/78/8373
Het verzorgen van minimale ventilatievouden in varkensstallen. **Study of minimal air change rates in piggeries.**

15688 Zijlstra, J.A. NL 010106/78/8374
Gebruik van melkwarmte op het veehouderijbedrijf. **The optimal use of the heat produced by milk cooling at dairy farms.**

15689 Smits, A.C. NL 010106/79/9033 N
Aanpassing van huisvesting en inrichting van stallen voor rundvee bestemd voor de vleesproduktie met het oog op een welzijnsverbetering. **Adaption of the housing systems of beef cattle and veal calves with the aim of better welfare for the animals.**

15690 Jongebreur, A.A. NL 010106/79/9034 N
Huisvesting van kalveren en jongvee in open en gesloten stallen in relatie tot de gezondheid en de technische resultaten. **Housing of calves and young stock in open and closed stalls in relation to health and the technical results.**

15691 Oosterwoud, A. NL 010109/78/8719 N
De relatie tussen de constructie van batterijkooien en het ontstaan van eischaalbeschadeging. **Battery–cage design and its relation to egg–shell damage.**

15692 Maatje, K. NL 010112/74/6185
Onderzoek naar de optimale afmetingen en inrichting van visgraatmelkstallen. **Investigation into the optimal size and design of herringbone milking parlours.** Publications.

15693 Snijders, P.J.M. NL 010208/73/8758 N
Inrichting ligboxenstallen voor melkvee in verband met gezondheid en welzijn. **Lay–out of buildings for dairy cattle with free stalls on behalf of animal health and well–being.** Publications.

15694 Kommerij, R. NL 010208/75/6167
Bouwkundige voorzieningen voor de gezondheidszorg van melkvee. **Building supplies for the health care of dairy cattle.** Publications.

15695 Snijders, P.J.M. NL 010208/78/8742 N
Oriënterend onderzoek naar energiebesparende werkmethoden en systemen in de rundveehouderij. **Orienting research into energy saving methods and systems for cattle husbandry.**

15696 Snijders, P.J.M. NL 010208/78/8756 N
Ontwikkeling en beproeving van een moderne grupstal. **Developing and testing of a modern stanchion barn.**

15697 Brouwer, J. NL 010213/74/6185
Onderzoek naar de optimale afmetingen en inrichting van visgraatmelkstallen. **Investigation into the optimal size and design of herringbone milking parlours.** Publications.

15698 Zijlstra, J.A. NL 010601/77/9040 N
Klimaatsonderzoek in de pluimveehouderij (stoombevochtiging in voorbroedmachines; energiebesparende verwarmingssystemen in slachtkuikenhokken). **Poultry environment research (steam moistening in incubators; energy saving heating systems in broiler housing).**

Accomodation for storing and processing of products (B 6230)

See also 15461, 15480, 15676, 15680, 15688, 15695, 15723, 16076, 16096

15699 Baumann, H. DE 111301/77/0001
Temperatur-, Feuchte- und Dichtigkeitsregulierungen in Lagerräumen. **Regulations of temperatures, humidity and density in storage rooms.**

15700 Heege, H.J.; Hellweg, W. DE 111852/78/0003 N
Mischstationen für Mineraldünger. **Mixing stations for mineral fertilizer.**

15701 Dernedde, W.; Peters, H. DE 201070/75/0003
Einfluss der Förderelemente von Befüll- und Entleereinrichtungen für Halmfutter–Lagerbehälter auf Leistungsbedarf, Durchsatz und Funktionssicherheit. **Research on filling and emptying systems of roughage stores with regard to requirement for energy, flow–rate, and functional security.**

15702 Møller, S. DK 011000/77/0004
Trykfordeling og vægbelastninger i plansiloer til korn. **Pressure distribution and wall loads in horizontal grain silos.**

15703 Bøgh–Sørensen, L. DK 030131/78/0001 N
Temperaturforholdene i danske kølediske. **Survey of product temperatures in chilled display cabinets in Denmark.**

15704 Bøgh–Sørensen, L. DK 030131/78/0002 N
Faktorer (emballage, natlåg, belysning m.m.) der indvirker på energiforbrug og varetemperatur i frostdiske. **Factors, e.g. packaging, materials, night cover, lighting etc., influencing energy consumption and product temperatures in freezer display cabinets.**

15705 Daly, O.G. IE 060600/72/1054 R
Precast concrete manure storage tank – varying capacities. Publications.

15706 Eck, G. van NL 010106/67/6447
Bouwkundige aspecten van de bewaarplaatsen voor de opslag van bol-, knol-, en wortelgewassen. **Building aspects of stores**

for storing of bulbs, tuberous plants and roots. Publications.

15707 Hart, C. 't   NL 010106/72/4725
Belastingnormen en berekeningswijzen van silo's voor de
opslag van kuilvoer. **Loads and calculation methods of silos for
silage.** Publications.

15708 Poelman, H.R.   NL 010106/72/4726 R
De opslag van mest en de mogelijkheden voor de verwerking
en afzet. **Possibilities for storage, processing and sale of
manure.** Publications.

15709 Geneijgen, J. van   NL 010208/73/8759 N
Opslag in kunststofsilo's en scheiden van rundveedrijfmest.
Storage in synthetic silos and separating cattle slurry.
Publications.

15710 Hoek, K.W. van de   NL 040010/72/4726 N
De opslag van mest en de mogelijkheden voor de verwerking
en afzet. **Possibilities for storage, processing and offtake of
manure.** Publications.

Houses and furniture (B 6240)

15711 Dimitrov, N.S.; Sengler, D.   DE 170350/72/0001 R
Entwicklung eines Bausystems demontierbarer Wohnzellen
1971. **Development of building system of disassembling
residential cells.**

Domestic and community water supply facilities and systems (B 6250)

See also 1335

Drainage and irrigation facilities and systems (B 6260)

See also 1395, 1441, 2699, 5181, 5186, 15624

15712 Maton, A.; Dierickx, W.   BE 070300/65/0026 R
Studie van de fysische vorm en waterstroming in en rond
plastieken draineerbuizen. **Research on the physical form and
the waterflow into and around the draintubes of plastic.**
Publications.

15713 Maton, A.; Dierickx, W.   BE 070300/65/0027 R
Vergelijkende studie van diverse kombinaties van
draineerbuizen en drainagematerialen. **A comparative study of
different combinations of draintubes and drainage materials.**
Publications.

15714 Maton, A.; Dierickx, W.   BE 070300/66/0025 R
Studie van de fysische en mechanische eigenschappen van
filtermaterialen bij drainage. **Research on the physical and
mechanical properties of drainage filtermaterials.** Publications.

15715 Maton, A.; Dierickx, W.   BE 070300/67/0030 R
Technische en economische studie over de verwerking van
drainagematerialen, nieuwe drainagemethoden en machines.
**Technical and economical research on the utilisation of
drainage materials, new drainage methods and machines.**
Publications.

15716 Maton, A.; Dierickx, W.   BE 070300/73/0028
Studie van de invloed van de afmetingen van drains op hun
weerstand tegen grondbelasting. **Research on the influence of**

the dimensions of draintubes, on their resistance against soil
load.

15717 Sourell, H.   DE 201090/75/0008
Arbeitswirtschaftliche Bewertung von Beregnungsverfahren.
Valuation of the working process of irrigation systems.

15718 Sourell, H.   DE 201090/75/0012
Ermittlung von Kenndaten von Tropfbewässerungsanlagen in
Feldversuchen. **Determination of characteristic data for drip
irrigation in field research.**

15719 Mackroth, K.; Bambach, G.   DE 506113/75/0006
Vergleich von Topfpflanzenbewässerungsanlagen und von
Geräten zu ihrer Automatisierung. **Comparison of irrigation
systems for potted plants and of automation devices.**

Sewage and waste disposal facilities and systems (B 6270)

See also 1356, 11374, 11397, 15534, 15680, 15708, 15710, 17159

15720 Bischofsberger, W.; Günthert, W.
                                DE 161861/78/0001 N
Untersuchungen über die Leistung von Nachklärbecken bei
Belebungsanlagen – Einfluss der Schlammräumung.
**Investigations of activated sludge final settling tanks influence
of sludge scrapers.**

15721 Bischofsberger, W.; Resch, H.   DE 161861/78/0002 N
Untersuchungen über die Leistung von Nachklärbecken bei
Belebungsanlagen – Vertikal durchströmte Becken.
**Investigations of activated sludge final settling tanks – basins
with vertical flow.**

15722 Poelma, H.R.   NL 010106/78/8369
Ontwikkeling van een installatie voor de anaërobe behandeling
van mest. **Development of an installation for anaerobic
digestion of manure.** Publications.

Roads, farm yards, fences (B 6280)

See also 5047, 15375, 15551

15723 Gels, J.A.   NL 010106/72/4739 R
Materialen en constructies voor erf– en kavelverharding en
horizontale opslag van kuilvoer. **Materials and constructions
for farm–yard and farm road pavements and for storage of
silage.** Publications.

Other structures and facilities (B 6290)

See also 15686

15724 Eck, G. van   NL 010106/78/8355
Aanvaardbare huisvestingssystemen in kinderboerderijen en
recreatieparken. **Acceptable housing systems in farms for
children and recreation parks.**

D 4300 – Civil engineering

See also 1554, 1586, 1590, 1693, 2485, 15542, 15723

15725 Abeels, P.; Reginster, J.; Losseau, L.
                                BE 020400/70/0003 R
Etude et conduite d'aménagements en génie rural. **Study and**

management in connection with agricultural engineering. Publications.

15726 Maton, A.; Dierickx, W.   BE 070300/66/0024 R
Studie van de mechanische eigenschappen bij verschillende types van drainbuizen. **Research on the mechanical properties by different construction of the drain tubes.** Publications.

15727 Maton, A.; Dierickx, W.   BE 070300/68/0029 R
Studie van het chemisch en mechanisch onderhoud van onbevaarbare waterlopen en sloten. **Study of the Chemical and mechanical maintenance of ditches and unnavigable watercourses.** Publications.

15728 Binns; Symons   GB 010303/00/0018 R
Immune reactions in foetal and neonatal pigs and sheep.

15729 Bakker, J.W.   NL 010501/73/5231 R
Bodemmilieu van straatbeplanting. **Root environment of trees in towns.**

15730 Smaalen, H. van   NL 020065/75/7349
Verkeersgedragonderzoek op plattelandswegen. **Research on drivers behaviour on rural roads.**

15731 Smaalen, H. van   NL 020065/76/7348
Sterkte en versterking van grond als funderingsmateriaal voor wegen in ontwikkelingslanden. **Strength and stabilisation of soil as a sub–base material for roads in developing countries.** Publications.

15732 Knaap, G.J.J. van der   NL 020065/78/8833 N
Onderzoek bijzondere constructies in de tropische cultuurtechniek. **Research for special structures in irrigation and drainage engineering, for developing countries.**

15733 Knaap, G.J.J. van der   NL 020065/78/8834 N
Onderzoek speciale bouwmaterialen voor de tropische cultuurtechniek. **Research for special construction materials in irrigation and drainage engineering for developing countries.**

D 4400 – Technology

See also 2998, 3293, 10849, 11040, 11190, 15134, 15680, 16056, 18968, 19024, 19100

15734 Mottet, A.; Fraipont, L.   BE 010001/64/0002
Etude de l'aptitude des essences indigènes pour la fabrication des panneaux de fibres ligno–cellulosiques durs, ainsi que les problèmes de fabrication et la mise au point de tests appropriés. **Research of the fitness of indigenous wood species for the fabrication of lignocellulosic hardboard and the problems of the fabrication of these fibreboard and elaboration of tests.** Publications.

15735 Mottet, A.   BE 010001/71/0004 R
Variabilité de diverses caractéristiques du bois parmi diverses provenances d'épicéa. **Variability of various wood characteritics among diverse spruce's provenances.**

15736 Roosen, P.; Sacré, E.   BE 081000/72/0001 R
Etude des propriétés anatomiques, physiques et mécaniques du bois d'Epicéa et du peuplier au stade juvénile et adulte. **Study of anatomical, physical and mechanical properties of spruce and poplar wood at the juvenile and adult stages.** Publications.

15737 Carré, J.; Lacroix, A.   BE 081000/72/0004 R
Qualification du panneau de particules en fonction de la matière première et des conditions de fabrication. **Particleboard qualifying related to raw materials and manufacture conditions.** Publications.

15738 Roosen, P.; Leclercq, A.   BE 081000/73/0002 R
Etude des propriétés anatomiques, physiques et mécaniques du bois de hêtre en fonction de la provenance. **Study of anatomical, physical and mechanical properties of beechwood related to provenance.**

15739 Carré, J.; Lacroix, A.   BE 081000/79/0008 N
Etude des propriétés mécaniques des matériaux à base de bois par une méthode non–destructive. **Study of the mechanical properties of wood–based materials by a non destructive method.**

15740 Carré, J.; Lacroix, A.   BE 081000/79/0009 N
Aptitude des dérivés du bois à la finition. **Suitability of wood derivatives for finishing.** Publications.

15741 Wasmund, R.   DE 105750/75/0003
Grundlagen der Energiebedarfsdeckung in Produktionsund Lagerstätten der Lebensmittelindustrie. **Basic research on the demand for energy in production equipments and stores of food industry.** Publications.

15742 Knigge, W.; Wenzel, V.   DE 132780/75/0002
Untersuchung der Holzeigenschaften verschiedener Provenienzen der Europäischen Lärche. **Analysis of the wood properties of various provenances of the European larch.**

15743 Kutzbach, H.–D.; Scherer, R.   DE 144701/73/0001
Thermische und mechanische Eigenschaften von Körnerfrüchten. **Thermal and mechanical properties of grain cereals.**

15744 Fengel, D.; Feckl, J.   DE 160332/78/0002 N
Untersuchungen zur Aufklärung der Bindung zwischen Lignin und Polysacchariden. **Studies on the bond between lignin and polysaccharides.**

15745 Kromer, K.–H.; Grimm, R.; Estler, M.
    DE 161520/71/0002 R
Gewinnung und Aufbereitung von Maiskorn–Spindel–Gemisch mit dem Feldhäcksler und Mähdrescher – Silieren und Füttern von Maiskolben – Entlieschvorrichtung zur Steuerung des Rohfaseranteiles selbstfahrender Futtervollernter – Produktion standartisierter Futtermittel – 1971. **Production and treatment of mixture of maize grains and spike with field chopper and combine harvester. Ensiling and feeding of maize cobs. Device for removal of husks for control of share of crude fibre in self–propelled complete forage harvesters – production of standardized feeds –.**

15746 Heimeshoff, B.; Baderschneider, F.
    DE 161582/78/0001 N
Ermittlung des Verhaltens von in Betonfundamenten eingegossenen und eingespannten Holzstützen sowie Ermittlung der statisch zulässigen Beiwerte Untersuchungsstufe I. **Determination of the behaviour of wood pillars cast and fixed into concrete base and determination of statically admissible coefficients – first stage of analysis.**

D 4400 – Technology

15747 Heimeshoff, B.; Glos, P.   DE 161582/78/0002 N
Ermittlung des Zusammenhangs zwischen der Zugfestigkeit und dem Biege–Elastizitätsmodul bei Brettlamellen aus Fichtenholz. **Determination of correlations between the tensile strength and the modules of elasticity in bending of laminated spruce boards.**

15748 Meinhold, K.; Kleinhanss, W.   DE 201100/78/0003 N
Die Wettbewerbsfähigkeit ausgewählter Technologien zur Energieerschliessung. **The competitiveness of selected technologies of utilizing agricultural energy resources.**

15749 Schulz, H.; Perwanger, A.; Strehler, A.
DE 919000/73/0001 R
Verfahren der Strohverwertung. Einarbeitung in den Boden, Energiegewinnung aus Stroh, Herstellung von Bauplatten aus Stroh, Einsatz von Grossballenketten. Entwicklung und Erprobung einfacher Lagerballen und Folienabdeckungen für Grossballen. **Methods of straw utilization. Bringing into soil, production of energy from straw, production of constructional plates of straw, use of large–bale chains. Development and testing of simple storing bales and film covers for large bales.**

15750 Klausen, K.G.   DK 010400/76/0001
Anvendelse af halm som brændsel til opvarmning af beboelser m.v. **Use of straw as fuel for domestic heating, etc.**

15751 Keller, R.; Thiercelin, F.   FR 010304/67/4200 N
Microdensitométrie du bois. **Wood microdensitometry.**

15752 Janin, G.; Letzelter, B.   FR 010304/74/4207 N
Classage – microclassage des fibres de bois. **Classifying – Microclassifying.**

15753 Normandin, D.   FR 010308/78/8531
Le liège brut et ses produits dérivés. **Raw Cork and derived products.**

15754 Larrieu, G.   FR 011407/78/8049
Conservation de souches fongiques – recherche et production de mycotoxines. **Preservation of toxic fungi ; mycotoxins : research and production.**

15755 Nellist   GB 011606/79/0010 N
Drying of agricultural crops.

15756 Evertsen, J.; Linehan, M.   IE 070200/75/9119 N
National survey of the density of home grown timber.

15757 McDarby, F.; Gallagher, L.   IE 070200/78/9120 N
National survey of the occurrence of spiral grain in home–grown timber.

15758 Zambonelli, C.   IT 040240/74/0651
Selezione genetica della microbiologia tecnologica. **Genetic selection in technological microbiology.**

15759 Resmini, P.; Albonico, F.; Volonterio, G.
IT 040609/68/0001
Chimica e tecnologia del latte e dei prodotti derivati. **Chemistry and technology of milk and dairy products.** Publications.

15760 Di Giacomo, A.; Calvarano, M.; Calvarano, I.; Mammi De Leo, M.; Bovalo, F.; Postorino, E.   IT 070600/77/0001 N
Olii essenziali. **Essential Oils.**

15761 Gorin, N.   NL 010118/73/4224
Chemische karakterisering van de appel. **Chemical characterization of the apple.** Publications.

15762 Gorin, N.   NL 010118/78/7846 R
De (bio) chemische/fysische kwaliteit van de tomaat. **(Bio) chemical/physical quality of tomatoes.**

15763 Knegt, E.   NL 020041/72/4875
De pectinestofwisseling van de rijpende tomaat. **Pectin metabolism of ripening tomato fruits.** Publications.

15764 Colon, F.J.   NL 050210/70/7684
Milieuverontreiniging door veehouderijbedrijven. **Environmental pollution by animal farms.** Publications.

15765 Beumer, H.   NL 050302/79/8993 N
Energiebesparing in de maalderij, bakkerij en veevoederindustrie. **Energy saving in milling business, bakery's business and feed industry.**

15766 Houwing, H.   NL 050303/78/2973 N
Onderzoek naar de mogelijkheden van optimale valorisatie van gequoteerde en andere, veelal nog niet volledig benutte, vissoorten. **Research on the possibilities of optimum valorization of quotated fish species and other fish species which are mostly not yet fully utilized.**

D 4410 – Harvesting

See also 1930, 3154, 3497, 3683, 4475, 13019, 15367

15767 Dufey, V.; Plétinckx, A.; Prade, J.; Legrand, E.
BE 080400/79/0013 N
Traitements des fourrages. **Forage treatment.**

15768 Isensee, E.; Guericke, W.   DE 148150/75/0007
Untersuchungen zum Einsatz selbstfahrender Arbeitsmaschinen. **Studies on the use of self–propelled machines.**

15769 Leistner, L.   DE 210030/75/0002
Verbesserung der Geflügelschlachthygiene. **Improvement of hygienic conditions of poultry slaughter.**

15770 Green   GB 011203/75/0016 R
The effect of weather factors and swath microclimate on the field drying of forage crops.

15771 Billington   GB 011603/00/0013 R
Reduction of losses and dirt tare in sugar beet harvesting.

15772 Arnold   GB 011607/79/0012 N
The separation of grain from straw and other materials.

15773 Soane; Campbell   GB 030503/00/0015 R
Incidence and persistence of clods in relation to mechanical harvesting.

15774 Mcrae; Carlow   GB 030507/00/0003 R
Use of radio–isotopes for discriminating between potatoes and stones and clods.

15775 Mcrae   GB 030507/00/0011 R

Harvesting of early potatoes.

15776 Lilwall   GB 060108/00/0005 R
Economics of harvesting and processing fruit and vegetable crops.

15777 Amaducci, M.T.   IT 040201/78/1170 N
Controllo degli aspetti agronomici dei vari cantieei di raccolta e degli effetti della lavorazione e della semina sull'efficienza delle macchine da raccolta. **A check on the agronomic aspect of different harvesting plants, on the effects of tilling and sowing on the efficiency of harvesting machines.**

Roughage (B 6320)

See also 3280, 3367, 3370, 3529, 11751, 15385, 15814

15778 Matthies, H.J.; Hesse, T.   DE 114204/75/0001
Dichteverteilung an Rollballen. **Distribution of density in pressed bales.**

15779 Honig, H.   DE 201030/77/0012
Analyse und Beeinflussung des Trocknungsverhaltens von Halmgut unter Feldbedingungen. **Analysis and dependence of drying behaviour of cereals under field conditions.**

15780 Chiappini, U.; Valli, L.   IT 040241/77/0001 N
Impiego di collettori solari nell'essicamento del fieno. **Solar collectors in hay drying.** Publications.

15781 Giardini, A.   IT 040242/77/0693
Meccanizzione della raccolta dei foraggi per gli allevamenti vacca da latte, disidratazione in campo dei foraggi. **Mechanization of fodder crops harvesting for milk–cow farms, fodder dehydration in the field.**

15782 Chiappini, U.   IT 040414/78/1044 N
Andamento della essiccazione del fieno in fienili a ventilazione forzata. **Hay drying by forced ventilation in hay–lofts.**

15783 Luppi, G.   IT 041201/78/1173 N
Meccanizzazione della raccolta dei foraggi linea vacca–vitello. **The mechanisation of forage harvesting for the cow–calf line.**

15784 Bianchi, M.   IT 041217/78/1172 N
Meccanizzazione della raccolta dei foraggi linea vacca–vitello. **The mechanisation of forage harvesting for the cow–calf line.**

15785 Bullitta, P.   IT 041302/78/1169 N
Meccanizzazione della raccolta dei foraggi nell'allevamento ovino e caprino, raccolta del foraggio e del seme, decespugliamento dei pascoli. **The mechanisation of forage harvesting on sheep and goat farms; the harvesting of forage and seed, de–shrubbing pastures.**

15786 Ciotti, A.   IT 063300/71/0059
Raccolta, essicamento per ventilazione e conservazione dei foraggi prativi. **Harvesting, aeration drying and conservation of meadow forage.** Publications.

15787 Ciotti, A.   IT 063300/77/0727
Fienagione e insilamento; aspetti meccanici linea vacca da latte. Utilizzazione sottoprodotti; recupero zone marginali. Aspetti meccanici – linea vacca–vitello. **Haymaking and ensilage; mechanical aspects of the dairy cow line. The use of by–products; marginal area recuperation. Mechanical aspects**

of the cow calf line.

15788 Schukking, S.   NL 010208/71/3063
Drogestofverliezen tijdens de veldperiode bij de hooiwinning en het inkuilen. **Drymatterlosses during the fieldperiode of haymaking and ensiling.** Publications.

Fibre materials and wood products (B 6700)

See also 2423, 4756, 4819, 17115, 17264, 17658

15789 Henne, A.; Riebeling, R.   DE 506401/77/0005 N
Holzaufkommensprognose aus Inventurdaten der Forsteinrichtung anstatt Grossrauminventuren. **Prognosis of wood supply from forest management inventories data instead of Large–area inventories.** Publications.

15790 Elyakime, B.   FR 010308/78/8530
Mobilisation des poteaux de ligne en bois. **Poles, harvesting of poles.**

Mill and bakery products (B 6810)

15791 Huss, W.; Reichl, J.R.; Koschnitzke, C.
                    DE 144625/73/0001
Mikroskopisch–morphologische Veränderungen an Körnerfrüchten bei Trocknung und Ernte. **Morphological–microscopical changes of cereals by combine harvesting and different drying conditions.**

15792 Isensee, E.; Lottmann, D.   DE 148150/75/0005
Rationelle und energiesparende Getreidekonservierung bei hoher Erntekapazität. **Rationalization and energy saving in grain drying with high–capacity harvesting.**

Oils, fats and related products (B 6820)

See also 15818

15793 Cucurachi, A.; Di Giovacchino, L.; Mascolo, A.;
Solinas, M.   IT 022100/73/0007
L'estrazione dell'olio dalle olive mediante centrifugazione. **Oil extraction from olives by means of centrifugation.**

15794 Cucurachi, Angelo.; Di Giovacchino, Luciano.;
Mascolo, Antonio.; Angerosa, Franca.; Solinas, Mario.
                  IT 022100/77/0002 N
Caratteristiche di qualità dell'olio di oliva in dipendenza dell'epoca di raccolta delle olive e della durata dello stoccaggio. **Quality characteristics of olive oil in relation to the harvest time and the storage period of olives before processing.**

15795 Gellini, R.   IT 040505/73/0218
Raccolta meccanica delle olive. **Mechanized harvesting of olives.** Publications.

Sugar and starch products (B 6830)

See also 3289, 3303, 12874

15796 Biston, L.; Nijs, R.   BE 080900/78/0011 R
L'irradiation aux rayons gamma des pommes de terre (traitement antigerminatif) et des productions maraîchères et fruitières (conservation). **Gamma irradiation of potatoes, market garden and fruit produce.** Publications.

D 4410 – Harvesting

15797 Panaro, V.   IT 040103/78/1175 N
Meccanizzazione della raccolta della barbabietola, del carciofo
e del cavolfiore. **The mechanisation of beetroot, artichoke and
cabbage harvesting.**

Fruit and vegetable products (B 6840)

See also 3703, 3815, 4199, 15796, 15797, 16096

15798 Fritz, D.; Michalsky, F.   DE 161260/77/0002
Ernteerträge, Feldabfälle, Marktverluste und Küchenabfälle
von Gemüse. **Yields and weight losses of vegetables found at
harvesting, during marketing, and handling at the consumers.**

15799 Colorio, G.   IT 021500/78/1168 N
Meccanizzazione della raccolta della frutta e della fragola. **The
mechanisation of fruit and strawberry harvesting.**

15800 Barone, L.   IT 040725/75/0004 R
Indagine sperimentale sulla possibilità di cernita delle patate
dalle zolle e dalle pietre in base alle proprietà ottiche.
**Experimental investigation on the possibility of selecting
potatoes from clods and stones, on the basis of optical
properties.** Publications.

15801 Alvisi, F.   IT 061000/77/0723 R
Meccanizzazione della raccolta della frutta. **The mechanisation**
of fruit harvesting.

15802 Zocca, A.   IT 063000/70/0015
Raccolta meccanica della frutta. **Fruits mechanical harvesting.**
Publications.

Meat, meat products and fish products in general (B 6850)

15803 Roberts   GB 010603/75/0020 N
**Identify abattoir operations for improved hygiene and test
methods for improving.**

15804 Dempster, J.F.   IE 060100/71/0524 R
Bacon curing with salt and nitrite only. Publications.

Meat and meat products (B 6851)

See also 10493, 10938, 15787, 19168, 19170

15805 Schön, L.; Fischer, K.; Augustini, C.
                                       DE 210010/75/0017 R
Zusammenhänge zwischen antemortaler Belastung,
physiologischer Reaktionslage und postmortaler Entwicklung
von Muskelstoffwechsel und Fleischbeschaffenheit bei
Schlachtrindern. **Relations between premortal stress,
physiological condition and post–mortal development of muscle
metabolism and meat quality of cattle.**

15806 Schön, L.   DE 210010/78/0001 N
Schlachtnebenprodukte – Menge und Güte. **Slaughter
by–products – quantity and quality.**

15807 Schön, L.; Sack, E.   DE 210010/78/0004 N
Schlachtausbeute und Kühlverluste bei schlachtbaren
Haustieren. **Dressing percentage and cooling loss on slaughter
animals.**

15808 Schön, L.; Sack, E.   DE 210010/78/0006 N

Referenz–Zerlegung von Schweinehälften. **Reference–cutting
of pigs.**

15809 Linke, H.   DE 210030/74/5014
Erarbeitung von Qualitätsnormen für mechanisch entknochtes
Fleisch. **Quality standardization for meat separated and boned
mechanically.**

15810 Lister   GB 010601/76/0062 N
**Study of the physiological basis of industrial practice
slaughtering to improve meat quality.**

15811 McKenna, B.M.; Joseph, R.L.; O'Leary, D.
                                       IE 120301/79/9235 N
**A study of parameters affecting weight loss in beef carcasses
during post slaughter chilling.**

Fish and marine food products (B 6852)

15812 Westbroek, L.   NL 010702/72/7158
Ontwikkeling van effectievere en minder schade
veroorzakende vangmethoden en transportbehandelingen van
mossels en kokkels. **Reduction of damage and improvement of
efficiency during the fishing and handling of mussels and
cockles.**

Dairy products, eggs, egg products, ice cream in general (B 6860)

15813 Bruce; Cruickshank   GB 060308/00/0002 R
**In–place cleaning of milking installations and hygiene measures
at milking on dairy farms.**

15814 Toppino, P.M.; Bossi, G.; Aliano, N.; Francani, R.
                                       IT 022200/79/0003 N
Stocchi di mais insilati con aggiunta di siero di caseificazione.
Corn stalks silage with added cheese whey.

Milk products (B 6861)

See also 3367, 11084, 15385, 15434, 15781, 15787

15815 Schlünsen, D.   DE 201090/75/0017
Einfluss der Melkroutinen auf die bakteriologische und
zytologische Wertigkeit der Milch. **Influence of the milking
routine on the bacteriological and cytological content of milk.**

15816 Heeschen, W.; Hübler, K.; Tolle, A.
                                       DE 207020/74/5005 N
Untersuchung zur sekretorischen und postsekretorischen
Bakterizidie der Milch. **Studies on secretory and postsecretory
bactericidia of milk.**

Alcoholic liquors, coffee, tea, tobacco and other table luxuries (B 6890)

See also 4450, 17006

15817 Rühling, W.   DE 506113/78/0001 N
Untersuchungen über die Eignung deutscher Rebsorten und
Erziehungssysteme für die Anwendung mechanischer
Ernteverfahren. **Investigations into the behaviour of German
vine varieties and training systems for using mechanical
harvesting techniques.**

15818 Arrivo, A.   IT 040103/78/1171 N

Meccanizzazione della vendemmia e della raccolta delle olive. **The mechanisation of grape and olive harvesting.**

15819 Magherini, R.   IT 040507/78/1174 N
Meccanizzazione della vendemmia. **The mechanisation of grape harvesting.**

15820 Quaglino, A.   IT 041203/78/1176 N
Meccanizzazione della vendemmia. **The mechanisation of grape harvesting.**

D 4420 – Storage and conservation

See also 3333, 3335, 3553, 3867, 8020, 11745, 12156, 15767, 15770, 16269, 19551

15821 Vanbelle, M.; Arnould, R.   BE 020601/64/0010 R
Etude des conservants pour ensilages. **Study of preserving products for silage conservation.** Publications.

15822 Vanbelle, M.; Moreels, A.; Arnould, R.
          BE 020601/75/0003
Conservation et valeur alimentaire du soya en plante entière cultivé en mélange avec du maïs fourrage. **Conservation and feeding value of entire soya plant cultivated with maize.**

15823 Maton, A.; Lips, j.   BE 070300/69/0036 R
Onderzoek op de bewaring van witloofwortelen in frigoruimten of geventileerde silo's. **Refrigerated storage and storage in ventilated silos for Belgian endive roots.** Publications.

15824 Maton, A.; Lips, J.   BE 070300/71/0035 R
Onderzoek op het voorkoelen van witloofwortelen. **Research on the pre–refrigeration of Belgian endive roots.**

15825 Maton, A.; Priem, R.   BE 070300/72/0011 R
Studie van de invloed van de droogtemperatuur op de kwaliteit van de hop. **Research of the influence of the drying temperature on the quality of hop.** Publications.

15826 Detroux, L.; Seutin, E.; Carré, J.
          BE 080700/79/0027 N
Etude de l'efficacité et persistance d'insecticides appliqués sur divers types de panneaux de particules. **Study of the effectiveness and persistence of insecticides applied on various kinds of particle board.**

15827 Cotteleer, C.; Famerée, L.   BE 110000/79/0057 N
Etude des acariens détriticoles dans les aliments et les poussières. **Study of acarii living in food products and dust.**

15828 Martens, M.; Van Steyvoort, L.; Roussel, N.; Vigoureux, A.; Vanstallen, R.   BE 140000/74/0024 R
Industriële kwaliteit en bewaring van suikerbieten. **Study of the industrial qualitiés and the storage of sugarbeets.** Publications.

15829 Antoine, H.; Leunen, J.E.; Grégoire, R.; Vanopdenbosch, E.; Pivont, P.; Wellemans, G.
          BE 140000/78/0069 N
Etudes de techniques de manipulation et d'administration de colostrum pour jeunes veaux. **Study of technics and manipulation of colostrum for young calves.** Publications.

15830 Franke, W.; Dohmes, G.   DE 111152/75/0002
Über den Vitamin–C–Gehalt in Gewürzkräutern nach Tiefkühllagerung. **On the content of vitamin C in spice plants**

after deep freezing storage.

15831 Kalich, J.; Schuh, W.   DE 160701/75/0002
Zur Problematik der Gülleverwertung in Schweinegrossbetrieben. **Problems of utilization of liquid manure in large pig managements.**

15832 Eckstein, D.; Liese, W.   DE 202040/77/0009
Holzanatomische Untersuchungen zur Verträglichkeit von Umwelteinflüssen. **Wood anatomic studies on environmental stress on trees.**

15833 Reichmuth, C.   DE 215030/77/0001
Ermittlung von Minimaldosen bei Phosphorwasserstoff– und Methylbromidbegasungen gegen Vorratsschädlinge. **Determination of minimum dosage of phosphoric hydrogen and methyl bromide fumigation against storage pests.**

15834 Rumberg; Becker; Weisheit; Gross
          DE 508651/78/0001 N
Lagerbeständigkeit ölartiger bindemittel– und pigmenthaltiger Holzschutzmittel. **Storage life of oily wood preservatives containing binders and pigments.**

15835 Poulsen, E.; Rasmussen, P.M.   DK 010102/64/3106
Opbevaring ved forskellige lagerforhold af æble og pære, der er behandlet forskelligt før lagring. **Storage under different store conditions of apples previously subjected to different treatments.**

15836 Hansen, S.E.; Bach, Aa.   DK 010111/74/4002
Forskellige opbevaringsmetoders indflydelse på udbytte og kvalitet af kartofler. **Influence of different storage methods on the yield and quality of potatoes.**

15837 Hallig, V.Aa.; Bacher, E.   DK 010113/75/0012 N
Produktudvikling med henblik på tomatfrugternes husholdningsmæssige egenskaber (fasthed, skæreegnethed, smag). **The influence of variety and storage conditions on firmness, slicing quality and flavour of tomatoes.**

15838 Hallig, V.A.   DK 010113/77/0013
Opbevaring og holdbarhed af væksthusprodukter. **Storage and keeping qualities of glasshouse products.**

15839 Mølle, K.G.; Møller, E.   DK 010114/70/4304
Marktørrings– og bjærgningsteknikkens indflydelse på tab og kvalitet ved høberedning og fortørringsensilering. **Influence of field drying and harvesting technique on losses and quality in the production of hay and pre–dried ensilage.**

15840 Mølle, K.G.; Møller, E.; Witt, N.   DK 010114/70/4305
Kvalitetsvurdering, sammensætning, foderværdi og andre egenskaber i friske og konserverede grovfoderafgrøder. **Quality estimates, composition, nutrient value and other factors in fresh and conserved forage crops.**

15841 Mølle, K.G.; Pedersen, E.J.N.; Witt, N.
          DK 010114/72/4302
Ensilering af grønmajs og lign. afgrøder med henblik på at undersøge virkningen af findelingsgrad samt tilsætning af syre, urea og ammoniak. **Ensiling of forage maize and similar crops with reference to the degree of shredding and the addition of acids, urea and ammonia.**

15842 Mølle, K.G.; Skovborg, E.B.; Witt, N.

D 4420 – Storage and conservation

DK 010114/72/4303
Udvikling og tilpasning af ensileringstekniske metoder for at
nedbringe tabet ved ensilering i praksis. **Development and
adaptation of ensiling techniques to reduce losses in practice.**

15843 Mølle, K.G.; Skovborg, E.B. DK 010114/74/4306
Produktion af kløvergræs og rene græsser ved afgræsning og
som konserveringsafgrøde samt kvægs udnyttelse af afgrøden.
**Production of clover–grass and pure grass mixtures for grazing
and conservation, and degree of crop utilization by cattle.**

15844 Jørgensen, M.B.; Rasmussen, P.M.
DK 010115/70/4506
Opbevaring af blomkål, issalat, kepaløg, porre, rosenkål,
hovedkål, og gulerødder dyrket på friland. **Storage of
cauliflower, lettuce, onion, leeks, brussel sprouts and carrots
grown outdoors.**

15845 Sørensen, C.; Kyllingsbæk, A. DK 010117/76/0009 R
Rapsfrøets fedtsyresammensætning ved varierende
modenhedsgrad, tørring og opbevaring. **Fatty acid composition
of rape seed under different maturity, drying and storage
conditions.**

15846 Madsen, A. DK 010202/75/0014
Iltning af svinegylle i ringkanal, temperatur, mængde og
sammensætning. **Oxidation of pigslurry in ring channels,
temperature, quantity and composition.**

15847 Klausen, K.G. DK 010400/76/0004
Undersøgelse af teknisk udstyr til kemisk behandling af halm
på gårdbrug. **Investigation of technical equipment for the
chemical treatment of straw on farms.**

15848 Rasmussen, R. DK 010800/76/0002
Betjening af kartoffelventilationsanlæg for at reducere
vægttabet, rådtabet og spireproblemerne. **Operation of potato
ventilation plant for the reduction of weight loss, rot loss and
germination problems.**

15849 Jakobsen, E. DK 010800/77/0002
Formalingstidspunktets og opbevaringsforholdenes indflydelse
på forskellige kvalitetsegenskaber i byg. **Influence of milling
time and storage conditions on different quality characters in
barley.**

15850 Nielsen, E.W. DK 030193/73/0003
Bakteriofager i forbindelse med syrningsvanskeligheder i
mejeribruget. **Bacteriophages in connection with acidification
difficulties in dairying.**

15851 Stow GB 011004/00/0005 R
**Determining the optimum orchard and storage conditions for
pears.**

15852 Jones; Tetlow GB 011202/19/0048 N
**Acceleration of water loss in the field during haymaking :
conservation, efficiency and feed value.**

15853 Shepperson GB 011607/00/0007 R
Reduction of energy use in forage conservation.

15854 Clark; Wilton GB 023706/79/0013 N
Solar heating for barn hay drying.

15855 Lupton GB 030903/00/0310 R

**Effect of mite infestation during storage on germination of
barley.**

15856 Jeffrey GB 030903/75/0309 R
Development of mite infestation in propionic acid treated grain.

15857 Jeffrey; McNeil GB 030903/75/0311 R
**Assessment of resistance in barley varieties to damage by
storage mites.**

15858 Tucker GB 030903/76/0109 R
Survey of pesticide usage on stored potatoes.

15859 Muttrie GB 030903/76/0111 R
Survey of pesticide usage in farm grain stores.

15860 Wylie GB 040401/79/0031 N
Alkali treatment of hay and straw using ammonia.

15861 Gault; Harper GB 040404/79/0007 N
**An investigation into the role played by nitrite in the
development of flavour in cured pork.**

15862 McCullough GB 041101/00/0006 R
Effect of fertilisers on silage fermentation.

15863 Frost; Easson GB 041304/79/0002 N
Sodium hydroxide treatment of hay.

15864 Wignall; Tatterson GB 051009/00/0007 R
The chemical preservation of industrial fish.

15865 Berridge GB 060215/79/0012 N
Storage of horticultural produce.

15866 Dunlop GB 060225/79/0002 N
Big bale silage.

15867 Jeffares, M. IE 060300/77/1291 R
**Storage of vegetables. An examination of problems and
practices in packaging and holding of vegetables for fresh
market and for processing. Publications.**

15868 Kampelmacher, E.H. NL 020031/72/3907
Radio resistentie van verschillende micro–organismen, in het
bijzonder Salmonella, in pluimveevlees. **Radiation resistance
among micro–organisms, especially Salmonellae, in poultry
meat. Publications.**

Ornamentals and ornamental products in general (B 3700)

See also 4493, 4501, 4502, 4503, 15838, 16092, 16167, 16168,
16170

Bulbs (B 3710)

See also 4559, 4560, 4565, 4566, 4567, 4568, 4570, 4572, 4574,
15878, 15879, 15880, 15881, 15882, 15883, 15941

15869 Vonk, C.R. NL 010102/72/7981
Endogene groeiregulatoren en assimilatenverdeling met
betrekking tot de bloemproduktie van bolgewassen.
**Endogenous growth regulators and distribution of assimilates
as related to flower production of bulbous plants. Publications.**

15870 Staden, O.L. NL 010118/73/4228
Invloed van het microklimaat tussen bloembollen in de verpakking op het optreden van bewaarziekten. **The microclimate of packaged flowerbulbs and its relation to storage diseases.** Publications.

15871 Rudolphij, J.W. NL 010118/74/5275 R
Ontwikkeling van een scrubber voor ethyleen verwijdering (vnl. m.b.t. bloembolbewaarplaatsen). **Design apparatus for removal of ethylene from flower bulbs.**

15872 Rudolphij, J.W. NL 010118/78/7849
Onderzoek naar de mogelijkheden tot verlaging van de normen voor luchtcirculatie en ventilatie in bloembollenbewaarplaatsen. **Air flow and ventilation in flower bulb stores.** Publications.

15873 Munk, W.J. de NL 010205/65/1493
Kernrot en bloemverdroging in tulpen, mede onder invloed van ethyleen. **Bud necrosis in tulips.** Publications.

15874 Swart, A. NL 010205/74/5909
Houdbaarheid bij bolbloemen. **Keeping quality of bulb flowers.** Publications.

Flowers and pot plants (B 3720)

See also 4598, 4613, 4617, 4627, 5893, 15944

15875 Huhnke, W.; Hoffmann, M.; Engelhardt, M.; Preil, W. DE 206000/73/5005
Kühllagerung von Chrysanthemen–Zuchtmaterial aus Meristemkultur zur Arbeitsersparnis bei der Erhaltungszüchtung. **Cold storage Chrysanthemum material bred in meristem culture for saving labour in preserving techniques.**

15876 Hobson GB 011103/75/0014 R
Enzyme changes in the senescent cut flower.

15877 Stigter, H.C.M. de NL 010102/72/7989 R
Vergelijkend fysiologisch onderzoek aan afgesneden en intacte rozen, in relatie tot de houdbaarheid van snijbloemen. **Comparative physiological research on cut and intact roses, as related to keeping quality of cut flowers.** Publications.

15878 Veen, B.W.; Kleinendorst, A. NL 010104/75/6221
De invloed van water en energiehuishouding op de houdbaarheid van snijbloemen. **The influence of the water and energy balance on the post–harvest development of cut flowers.** Publications.

15879 Boer, W.C. NL 010118/73/4202 R
Bewaarbaarheid van snijbloemen. **Storage methods for cut flowers.** Publications.

15880 Berkholst, C.E.M. NL 010118/73/4230
Knopsnee van bloemen. **Studies on flower development in excised buds.** Publications.

15881 Staden, O.L. NL 010118/74/5281
Oorzaken van vroegtijdige kwaliteitsachteruitgang van de snijbloem. **Causes of early loss of quality of cut–flowers.** Publications.

15882 Staden, O.L. NL 010118/75/6002

Oorzaken en bestrijding van bladvergeling bij enige snijbloemen. **Cause and control of leaf yellowing of some cut flowers.** Publications.

15883 Koek, P.C. NL 010118/76/6656
Standaardisering van werkwijzen bij het snijbloemenonderzoek (t.b.v. het vaasleven van bloemen). **Standardization of methods in the research of the vase life of cut flowers.**

15884 Sytsema, W.; Barendse, L. NL 010201/63/0946
De invloed van (chemische) middelen en methoden op de houdbaarheid van snijbloemen. **Influence of chemicals, packing and storage on the vase life of cut flowers.** Publications.

Ornamental shrubs (B 3730)

15885 Koek, P.C. NL 010118/77/7258
Invloed van de bewaarcondities op de hergroei van boomkwekerijprodukten. **Influence of storage – conditions on the re–growth of nursery stock (trees and shrubs).**

15886 Elk, B.C.M. van NL 010203/66/3757
Het gekoeld bewaren van boomkwekerijgewassen. **Cold storage of nursery products.** Publications.

Feeding stuffs and drinking water for animals in general (B 6300)

See also 2702, 3318, 15576, 15990, 15997, 16026

15887 Müller, H.–M.; Schröppel, E. DE 144625/74/0002
Einfluss von N–Gehalt und pH–Wert des Nährmediums auf die Produktion sekundärer Stoffwechselprodukte durch Aspergillus flavus. **Influence of nitrogen content and pH value of culture medium on the production of secondary metabolites by Aspergillus flavus.**

15888 Theune, H.H. DE 201030/77/0008 R
Untersuchungen zur Quantifizierung des Proteinstoffwechsels im Konservierungsprozess – Art und Ursache des Eiweissabbaues –. **Investigations on quantification of protein metabolism during preserving process – kind and cause of protein breakdown.**

15889 Seher, A. DE 213010/78/0011 N
Einfluss der Fette auf die Haltbarkeit von Futtermitteln und Übergang von Futterbestandteilen in tierische Lebensmittel. **Influence of lipids on the stability of feeds and carry–over of feed constituents into animal foods.**

15890 Woolford; Wilkinson GB 011202/76/0034 R
Microbiological screening of potential silage and hay additives.

Concentrates (B 6310)

See also 16043, 16323

15891 Müller, H.–M.; Thaler, M. DE 144625/74/0001
Einfluss von Propionsäurekonservierung und Kornwassergehalt auf die Entwicklung von Mycotoxin–Bildnern auf Körnermais. **The effects of propionic acid preservation and moisture content in grain–maize on the development of toxinogenic fungi.**

15892 Poisson, J. FR 012203/70/2243

Microflore des tourteaux de colza. Son évolution au cours du stockage. **Microflora of rape seed meal. Evolution during storage.** Publications.

15893 Gaspari, F.   IT 062400/71/0109
Variazioni quanti–qualitative nell'insilamento delle farine umide di granella di mais e sorgo. **Quanti–qualitative variations in storage in silo of moist grain meal of corn and sorghum.** Publications.

Roughage (B 6320)

See also 3280, 3367, 3391, 3661, 11571, 11701, 11723, 11771, 12084, 14200, 15786, 15787, 15821, 15822, 15839, 15840, 15841, 15842, 15843, 15854, 15966, 16044, 16323, 16340

15894 Vanbelle, M.; Arnould, R.; Meurens, M.
                    BE 020601/77/0013 R
L'emploi de cellulases comme conservateur des ensilages. **Utilization of cellulase for silage conservation.**

15895 Boucqué, C.; Cottyn, B.   BE 070700/72/0016 R
Testen van inkuilbewaarmiddelen (mierenzuur, formol...). **Testing of silage conservation products (formic acid, formaldehyde).** Publications.

15896 Biston, R.; Nijs, L.   BE 080900/75/0005 R
Etude des modalités de stockage, fermentation des ensilages et bilan de conservation des fourrages. **Stockage procedures of crops, ensilage fermentation and energy balance (nutritional value) of forage.**

15897 Wieneke, F.; Claus, H.G.   DE 132540/77/0002
Steuerung und Regelung von Heubelüftungsanlagen mit Aussen– und angewärmter Luft im Hinblick auf minimalen Energieaufwand. **Control and regulation of equipment for aeration of hay with outside air and heated air regarding minimum input of energy.**

15898 Voigtländer, G.; Züchner, S.   DE 161255/71/0002
Der Einfluss der Unterdachtrocknung mit starker Luftvorwärmung auf Trocknungsdauer, Qualität und Verluste von Gras und Mähweidefutter 1971–1978. **english title not indicated.**

15899 Honig, H.   DE 201030/77/0009
Gasaustauschvorgänge in randnahen Zonen von Futterstöcken und das Problem der Haltbarkeit. **Gas exchange process in marginal zones of silage piles and the problem of stability.**

15900 Honig, H.   DE 201030/77/0010
Einfluss der Zerkleinerung von Halmfutter auf die Konservierung und Futteraufnahme. Beitrag zum Problem der wiederkäuergerechten Struktur. **Influence of crushing of cereal forage on preservation and intake of forage. Contribution to the problem of structure adequate to ruminants.**

15901 Theune, H.H.   DE 201030/77/0020
Konservierung von mikrobiell zu Futterzwecken aufbereitetem Stroh. **Preservation of straw processed microbially for fodder purposes.**

15902 Dernedde, W.   DE 201070/75/0002
Dichtlagerung von Halmgut in Behältern. **Densely packed storage of roughage in bins.**

15903 Kaufmann, W.   DE 207010/77/0005
Futterkonservierung. **Forage preservation.**

15904 Beckhoff, J.   DE 508301/75/0003
Einfluss des Futteralters auf das Trocknungsverhalten unter Freilandbedingungen. **Influence of fodder age on outdoor drying behaviour.**

15905 Rasmussen, P.; Augustinussen, E.   DK 010106/70/3507
Opbevaringsmetoder til roer og gulerødder. **Storage methods for beet and carrots.**

15906 Olesen, J.   DK 010701/74/0003 R
Teknik ved ensilering af lucerne, kløvergræs, græs, majs, helsæd og roetop samt ammoniakbehandling af halm. **Ensiling techniques for lucerne, clover–grass, grass, maize, wholecrop cereals and beet–tops. Ammonia treatment of straw.**

15907 Perez, J.M.; Fevrier, C.   FR 010206/74/2943
Céréales humides (mode de conservation et utilisation). **Wet cereals (storage and utilization).**

15908 Demarquilly, C.; Michalet–Doreau, B.
                    FR 010814/74/6504
Etude de l'efficacité des conservateurs pour ensilage. **Study of the silage additives.**

15909 Woolford   GB 011202/00/0021 R
The disposal or utilisation of silage effluent.

15910 Wilson; Wilkinson   GB 011202/76/0032 R
Manipulation of silage fermentation with chemical additives.

15911 Woolford   GB 011202/76/0033 R
Microbiology of ensiling.

15912 Woolford; Cook   GB 011202/76/0035 R
The aerobic deterioration of silage.

15913 Henderson   GB 060101/00/0003 R
Biochemical changes during ensilage.

15914 McDonald   GB 060101/00/0004 R
Silage deterioration studies.

15915 Beveridge   GB 060102/00/0036 R
Economic assessment of silage making and feeding.

15916 Robb   GB 060113/00/0004 R
Microbiology and chemical properties of hay.

15917 Raftery, T.H.; O'Donavan, S.F.; Kett, J.J.
                    IE 110104/79/9223 N
The elimination of drying and grinding of barley for storage and feeding by treating green barley with NA⁵8000.

15918 Talamucci, P.   IT 040501/78/1114 N
Conservazione dei foraggi provenienti da nuovi tipi di prati mono e polifiti. **The storage of fodder harvested in the newer types of mono or polyphyte fields.**

15919 Giardini, A.   IT 062400/73/0108
Variazioni quanti–qualitative nell'insilamento del foraggio integrale di mais raccolto alla maturazione cerosa della granella e trattato all'entrata nel silo con diversi composti azotati e minerali. **Quanti–qualitative variations in integral**

fodder storage of corn harvested when grain reaches dough stage and treated before storage in silo with different nitrogen and mineral compounds.

15920 Gaspari, F.   IT 062400/73/0110
Impiego dei microsili sperimentali per lo studio dei processi fermentativi nella conservazione dei trinciati integrali di mais e delle farine umide dei cereali. **Use of experimental micro–silos in order to study fermentation processes in the storage of integral ground corn and of the moist feed grain meal.**

15921 Gaspari, F.   IT 062400/77/0728
Conservazioni stocchi di mais. **Maize stalks storage.**

15922 Baldoni, R.   IT 062400/77/0951
Valutazione degli effetti del trattamento con urea e carbonato di calcio sulla conservazione in silo del foraggio ceroso di mais. **Evaluation of the effects of urea and calcium carbonate treatment on silo consrvation of waxy maize fodder.**

15923 Ciotti, A.   IT 063300/72/0060
Tecniche di insilamento di foraggi prativi e di cereali foraggeri mediante pressainsilatrice. **Ensiling techniques of meadow forage and cereal fodder crops with the Silopress system.** Publications.

15924 Vreman, K.   NL 010115/77/7613
Conserveringsonderzoek; in eerste instantie met betrekking tot de ontwikkeling van boterzuurbacteriën. **Research on fodder conservation; in first instance relating to the development (growth) of butyric acid bacteria.**

15925 Schukking, S.; Hengeveld, A.G.   NL 010208/71/3070
Opslag en bewaring van ruwvoer m.i.v. het testen van nieuwe plastiekkwaliteiten. **Storage and preservation of roughage, including the testing of new plastic qualities.** Publications.

15926 Schukking, S.; Hengeveld, A.G.; Overvest, J.
                                NL 010208/74/6176
Konservering en bewaring van voor rundveevoeder bestemd bij– en afvalprodukten. **Storage and conservation of by–products and wastes intended for cattle feeding.** Publications.

15927 Schukking, S.   NL 010208/77/8768 N
Factoren die het aantal sporen van boterzuurbacteriën in voordroogkuil beïnvloeden. **Factors affecting spores of butyric acid bacteria in wilted silage.** Publications.

Other feeding stuffs (B 6390)

See also 16344, 16345

Fertilizers and water for plants in general (B 6400)

See also 15862

15928 Vanbelle, M.; Vervack, W.; Arnould, R.
                                BE 020601/66/0011 R
Etude de la protéolyse et de la redistribution de l'azote dans l'ensilage. **Study of the proteolysis and of the nitrogen redistribution in silage.** Publications.

Organic fertilizers (B 6410)

See also 15709, 16264

15929 Busse, M.; Hennlich, W.   DE 502551/77/0005
Zusammensetzung der Mikroflora von Flüssigmist als Parameter zur Beurteilung von Behandlungstechniken. **Composition of the microflora in liquid manure as a function of manure management.** Publications.

Mineral fertilizers (B 6420)

See also 3568, 3837, 4131

Propagation materials in general (B 6500)

15930 Tiemann, K.–H.; Blank, H.–G.   DE 507308/75/0001
Verbesserung und Weiterentwicklung von Lagerverfahren besonders für Neuzüchtungen. **Improvement and further development to storage procedures special for new varieties.**

Seed for sowing (B 6510)

See also 2697, 2858, 3095, 4598, 7812, 16059, 16060

15931 Bader, H.; Heuer, C.   DE 139400/78/0006 N
Tiefgefrierkonservierung von Büffelsperma. **Deep–freezing preservation of buffalo semen.**

15932 Krause, D.; Conrad, A.; Graser, A.; Günther, A.; Hellemann, C.; Möller–Holtkamp, P.   DE 139401/78/0001 N
Langzeitkonservierung des spermas von Versuchstieren. **Long–term storage of sperm of laboratory animals.** Publications.

15933 Hahn, J.; Heise, P.   DE 139803/78/0002 N
Tiefgefrierung von Mäuseeizellen. **Deepfreezing conservation of mouse ova.**

15934 Grahl, A.   DE 201040/75/0005
Langzeitlagerung von Genmaterial – Saatgut – bei tiefen Temperaturen und niedrigem Wassergehalt. **Long–term storage of gene material – seed – at low temperatures and low water content.**

15935 Sommer, C.; Dambroth, M.   DE 201040/75/0019 R
Modellversuche über die Auswirkung der Lagerungsdicte und Wasserspannung auf die Pflanzenentwicklung und die Entwicklung von Bodenorganismen. **Model trials on the effects of storage density and moisture tension on plant growth and on development of soil organisms.**

15936 Foschi, S.   IT 061800/77/1015
Efficacia di trattamenti concianti contro microrganismi fungini. **Efficacity of seed medication against fungus microorganisms.**

15937 Foschi, S.   IT 061800/77/1017
Effetti di trattamenti chimici sulla fisiologia delle sementi. **Action of chemical treatments on the physiology of seeds.**

Sperm (B 6520)

See also 10668, 11061, 11258

15938 Colas, G.   FR 011501/69/7515
Congélation du sperme du bélier. **Deep freezing of ram semen.**

15939 Colas, G.; Brice, G.   FR 011501/77/7514
Conservation du sperme de bélier sous forme liquide. **Storage**

of liquid ram semen.

Other propagation materials (B 6590)

See also 2697, 4560, 4565, 4566, 4567, 4570, 4574, 4613, 5893, 10563, 10598, 15875, 16076, 16077, 16079, 16080, 16130

15940 Carls, J.; Delhey, R.   DE 105201/77/0006
Der Einfluss der Lagerungstemperatur auf den Nachbauwert von Pflanzkartoffeln. **The influence of storage temperature on the quality of seed potatoes.**

15941 Carow, B.   DE 138270/77/0012
Untersuchungen zur Lagerung von Gloriosa–Knollen. **Studies on storage of tubers of Gloriosa.**

15942 Hesen, J.C.   NL 010105/61/8329 N
De invloed van voorkiemmethoden op de opbrengst van aardappelen. **The influence of pre–sprouting methods on the yield of potato cultivars.** Publications.

15943 Kaltofen, R.S.   NL 010109/67/0648
De invloed van de bewaaromstandigheden voor broedeieren op de embryonale ontwikkeling en de broedresultaten. **The influence of storage circumstances of hatching eggs on embryonic development and hatching results.** Publications.

15944 Spithost, L.S.   NL 010206/73/5597
Bewaring van plantgoed van kasgewassen. **Storage of transplants of glasshouse crops.**

Fibre materials and wood products (B 6700)

See also 15826, 15901, 16026

15945 Roosen, P.; Leclercq, A.   BE 081000/72/0005 R
Etude des propriétés de conservation des panneaux à base de bois. **Study of conservation properties of wood based boards.**

15946 Roosen, P.; Leclercq, A.   BE 081000/72/0007 R
Efficacité fongicide des produits de protection du bois. **Fungicide efficiency of wood protection products.** Publications.

15947 Roffael, E.   DE 114450/74/0008
Einfluss des Ligningehalts von Beschichtungspapieren auf die Wetterbeständigkeit von phenol– harzgetränkten Papieren auf Holzwerkstoffen. **Influence of lignin content of laminating papers on the weather resistance of phenolformaldehyde impregnated papers overlays on wood–based panels.**

15948 Roffael, E.   DE 114450/74/0010
Untersuchung zur Verminderung der Formaldehydbelästigung durch Spanplatten. **Investigations on the reduction of formaldehyde emission from particle boards.**

15949 May, H.–A.   DE 114450/74/0013
Veränderung der Gebrauchseigenschaften von langzeitig gelagertem Kiefern–Sturmholz in künstlich beregneten Nasspoltern. **Change in the properties of wind–blown, longtime stored pine wood in overhead sprayed piling sites.**

15950 Blaschke, H.   DE 160061/75/0001
Äthylenbildung in Fichtenstreu. **Ethylene formation in litter of Picea abies.**

15951 Aufsess, H.von   DE 160333/74/0004
Licht– und rasterelektronenmikroskopische Untersuchungen über die Abbauerscheinungen verschiedener holzzerstörender Pilze im Holz sowie der anatomischen Merkmale ihrer Fruchtkörper und Myzelien. **Light and scanning electron microscopic in– vestigations on the decomposition of wood by several wood destroying fungi and on the anatomical features of their sporophores and mycelia.**

15952 Schneider, A.   DE 160334/78/0001 N
Untersuchungen über den Einfluss der Trocknungsbedingungen auf die Gleichmässigkeit der Schnittholztrocknung. **Investigations on the influence of the drying conditions on the uniformity of lumber drying.**

15953 Schneider, A.; Engelhardt, F.; Wagner, L.   DE 160334/78/0002 N
Vergleichende Untersuchungen über die Freilufttrocknung und die Solartrocknung von Schnittholz. **Comparative investigations on the air drying and solar drying of lumber.**

15954 Liese, W.; Peek, R.–D.   DE 202040/72/5010
Erhaltung der Holzqualität durch Verhütung von Transport– und Lagerschäden. **Conservation of wood quality through prevention of damages during transport and storage.**

15955 Gottwald, H.; Richter, J.; Seehann, G.   DE 202040/77/0002
Untersuchungen zur Morphologie und Schutzwirkung von Kernstoffen im Holz. **Investigations on morphology and protective effect of heartwood.**

15956 Schmidt, O.; Seehann, G.; Bauch, J.   DE 202040/77/0004
Ursachen und Auswirkung von Pilzbefall an Bäumen und Nutzhölzern. **Causes and effects of fungus attack on trees and timber.**

15957 Liese, W.; Parameswaran, N.; Peek, R.D.; Willeitner, H.   DE 202040/77/0005 R
Verbesserung von Eindringung und Wirksamkeit von Schutzmitteln in Hölzern. **Improvement of infiltration and effectiveness of preservatives in wood.**

15958 Willeitner, H.; Gottwald, H.   DE 202040/77/0006
Mitarbeit an der nationalen und internationalen Normung. **Studies on national and international standardization and testing of timber preservatives.**

15959 Schmidt, O.; Doppelreiter, H.; Seehann, G.   DE 202040/77/0007
Wirkung von Holzschutzmitteln auf Mikroorganismen und Insekten. **Effects of timber preservatives on microorganisms and insects.**

15960 Willeitner, H.; Peek, R.D.   DE 202040/77/0008 R
Untersuchungen zur Förderung umweltfreundlicher Holzschutzmassnahmen. **Improvement of wood preservation treatments favourable to the environment.**

15961 Doppelreiter, H.; Seehann, G.   DE 202040/77/0010 R
Untersuchungen an fremdländischen Holzschädlingen hinsichtlich ihrer Akklimationsfähigkeit. **Investigations of the environmental adaptability of wood destroying insects of foreign origin.**

15962 Doppelreiter, H.　　　　DE 202040/77/0011 R
Nichtchemischer Schutz des Holzes durch biologische und technische Massnahmen. **Non–chemical wood protection by means of biological and technical measures.**

15963 Petrowitz, H.–J.　　　　DE 217010/78/0002 N
Abgabe von Holzschutzwirkstoffen aus chemisch geschützten Bauhölzern. **Release of active substances of wood preservatives from chemically treated structural timber.**

15964 Kühne, H.; Kny, U.　　　　DE 217010/78/0003 N
Wirkung von Schutzmitteln für Holz und Holzwerkstoffe und Einflüsse der Alterung von Holz auf Termiten. **Efficacy of preservatives for wood and wood–based materials and influence of aging of wood on termites.**

15965 Gressel, P.; Mohl, H.–R.; Schneider; Vehlow
　　　　　　　　　　　　　　DE 913000/73/0003 N
Untersuchungen über die Durchfeuchtungsgeschwindigkeit und die Oberflächenfeuchteverteilung bei Holzwerkstoffen mit Hilfe von Radioisotopen. **Radio isotopic analyses of humidification speed and surface humidity distribution in timber material.**

15966 Pedersen, T.T.; Kofoed, S.S.; Persson, K.;
Christiansen, S.A.　　　　DK 030144/78/0002 N
Transport og lagring af snittet halm. **Use of straw for heating purposes.**

15967 Moroney, S.; Cummins, D.; Davis, B.
　　　　　　　　　　　　　IE 070200/69/7408 R
Preservation of spruce and its use in transmission lines. Publications.

15968 Moroney, S.; Cahill, D.　　　　IE 070200/78/9118 N
Preservation of sawn native timber.

Food and table luxuries in general (B 6800)

See also 2702, 8325, 8351, 15703, 16471, 16695

15969 Coppens, R.; Flambert; Deltour　　BE 010015/70/0001
Calcul des barèmes de traitements thermiques et des chaleurs de stérilisation en conserverie. Optimalisation des traitements thermiques au moyen de modèle mathématiques. **Calculation of thermic processes and sterilizing values in canned food – Optimalization of thermic process using mathematical models.** Publications.

15970 Deroanne, C.; Flambert, F.; Thonart, P.
　　　　　　　　　　　　　BE 010015/78/0004
Développement technologique pour les industries agroalimentaires. **Technological development for food industries.**

15971 Van Hoof, J.; Vansteenkiste, J.　BE 051200/77/0004 R
Belang van de wateractiviteit in de voedingsmiddelenindustrie. **The role of wateractivity in processing and storage of food.**

15972 Pfeilsticker, K.; Inkmann, A.　　　DE 111600/77/0002
Acrylnitril als Vorratsschutzmittel – Restmengen und Metabolisierung in Lebensmitteln. **Propenenitrile as protector of stored foods – residues and metabolites.** Publications.

15973 Stein, W.　　　　　　DE 129200/73/0001
Dipteren als Vorratsschädlinge und Vektoren von Mikroorganismen. **Diptera as stored–product pests and vectors of micro– organisms.**

15974 Stein, W.　　　　　　DE 129200/74/0005
Wanderung und Ausbreitung bei synanthropen Fliegen. **Migration and distribution of synanthropic flies.**

15975 Hadlok, R.　　　　　　DE 129700/72/0009
Schimmelpilze und Hefen, psychrotrophes und psychrophiles Wachstumsverhalten, Fermentaktivität unter besonderer Berücksichtigung der Kühllagerung von Fleischprodukten. **Growth of psychrotrophic and psychrophilic moulds and yeasts and the activity of their enzymes especially in cold–stored food products.**

15976 Loncin, M.; Schneeberger, R.　　DE 145150/72/0004
Untersuchung zur thermischen Abtötung von Mikroorganismen bei Temperaturen über 120 Grad C. **Studies of thermal death rates of micro–organisms at temperatures higher than 120 degrees C.**

15977 Loncin, M.; Schornick, G.　　　DE 145150/73/0002
Darstellung nichtschäumender, sporentötender quartärer Ammoniumverbindungen. **Synthesis of non–foaming, spore–killing quaternary ammonium compounds.**

15978 Loncin, M.; Schneeberger, R.　　DE 145150/73/0003
Bestimmung des Einflusses von Zucker und Salz auf die Diffusionskinetik organischer Substanzen. **Determination of the influence of sugar and salt on the diffusion kinetics of organic substances.**

15979 Loncin, M.; Fox, M.　　　　DE 145150/78/0003 N
Untersuchungen zur Ermittlung der optimalen Parameter bei der kombinierten Haltbarmachung von Nahrungsmitteln. **Investigations to determine the optimum parameters for the preservation of food using a combination of processes.**

15980 Niebergall, H.; Kutzki, R.; Hartmann, M.; Keinhorst, A.; Gioumatzidou, P.　　　DE 176151/78/0001 N
Grundlegende Untersuchungen über die Wechselwirkung zwischen Inhaltsstoffen von Verpackungsmaterialien und Lebensmitteln mittels neu entwickelter Methoden. **Basic investigations on the interaction between packaging materials and foodstuffs by new developed methods.**

15981 Dernedde, W.　　　　　DE 201070/78/0002 N
Nutzung der Sonnenenergie für die technische Trocknung landwirtschaftlicher Produkte. **Utilization of solar energy for drying of agricultural products.**

15982 Teuber, M.　　　　　　DE 207030/77/0007
Erhaltung und Verbesserung der Qualität von Lebensmitteln und ihrer Lagerfähigkeit. **Preservation and improvement of quality of food and of their shelf–life.**

15983 Wolf, W.　　　　　　DE 211020/77/0009
Das Sorptionsverhalten von Lebensmitteln im Bereich niedriger Wasseraktivitäten. **Sorption of food in the range of low water activities.**

15984 Adam, R.　　　　　　DE 211020/78/0003 N
Konservierung von Lebensmitteln durch Kombination von Benzoesäure– und thermischer Behandlung. **Food preservation by combined use of benzoic acid and thermal treatments.**

15985 Paulus, K.; Wolf, W.; Zohm, H.   DE 211020/78/0011 N
Anwendung flexibler Verpackungsmaterialien für die
Herstellung sterilisierter Lebensmittel. **Possible use of flexible
package materials for heat sterilization of foods.**

15986 Paulus, K.   DE 211020/78/0012 N
Abkühlen von Speisen im Hinblick auf die Festlegung von
Grenzwerten. **Cooling of meals and assessment of limiting
values.**

15987 Grünewald, T.; Rumpf, G.   DE 211040/70/5014
Technologie der Bestrahlung von Lebensmitteln. **Technical
experiments with irradiation of food.**

15988 Diehl, J.F.   DE 211050/77/0002
Bildung Vitamin–E–zerstörender Substanzen in erhitzten oder
bestrahlten Lebensmitteln. **Formation of vitamin E–destroying
substances in heated or irradiated foods.**

15989 Münzner, R.   DE 211050/77/0004
Mikrobiologische Aspekte des Einsatzes der Bestrahlung
anstelle der Verwendung chemischer Mittel. **Microbiological
aspects of using irradiation instead of chemical agents.**

15990 Rassmann, W.   DE 215030/74/5002
Versuche zur Bekämpfung der Speichermotte Ephistia elutella
durch Störung des photoperiodisch gesteuerten
Diapauseverhaltens. **Studies on control of the warehouse moth
Ephestia elutella interrupting the photoperiodically regulated
behaviour of diapause.**

15991 Reichmuth, C.   DE 215030/75/0002
Untersuchungen über die Wirkung von Sexuallockstoffen –
Pheromonen – in Grosslägern und Lebensmittelbetrieben zur
Bekämpfung von Mottenpopulationen. **Studies on the
attraction of pheromones in warehouses and food factories for
control of moth populations.**

15992 Wohlgemuth, R.   DE 215030/78/0001 N
Untersuchungen über die Befallssituation importierter
Vorratsgüter. **Survey on the infestation of imported
commodities by stored food insects.**

15993 Wohlgemuth, R.; Schmidt, H.–U.
   DE 215030/78/0002 N
Untersuchungen über die Widerstandsfähigkeit von
Verpackungsmaterialien gegen Vorratsschädlinge. **Tests on
resistance of packing materials to stored food insects.**

15994 Wohlgemuth, R.   DE 215030/78/0004 N
Vergleichende Untersuchungen über die Wirksamkeit von
Insektiziden im tropischen Vorratsschutz. **Comparative tests on
the efficiency of different insecticides in the preservation of
stored food in the tropics.**

15995 Rassmann, W.   DE 215030/78/0005 N
Untersuchungen über die Wirkung gasförmiger
Bekämpfungsmittel auf Vorratsmilben und ihre
Dormanzstadien. **Tests on the efficiency of fumigants against
stored food mites and their stages of dormancy.**

15996 Reichmuth, C.; Stratil, H.   DE 215030/78/0007 N
Einfluss von Kühllagertemperaturen auf die Entwicklung von
Eiern der Dörrobstmotte 'Plodia interpunctella'. **Effect of cold
temperatures in warehouses on the development of eggs of
'Plodia interpunctella' Hbn..**

15997 Grosch, W.; Weber, F.; Fischer, K.–H.
   DE 502502/73/0002
Enzymatischer Abbau von Carotinoiden in Lebensmitteln
pflanzlicher Herkunft. **The enzymatic degradation of
carotenoids in plant foodstuff.**

15998 Robinson, L.; Radtke, R.; Becker, K.
   DE 911000/77/0002
Zusammenhang zwischen Sauerstoffverbrauch und
Qualitätsveränderungen von Lebensmitteln. **Relations between
oxygen consumption and quality changes of foods.**

15999 Cerny, G.   DE 911000/77/0010
Entkeimung saurer Produkte: Abhängigkeit der thermischen
Abtötung von Mikroorganismen vom pH–Wert wässriger
Lösungen. **Dependence of thermic inactivation of
microorganisms on the pH–value of water solutions.**

16000 Cerny, G.; Schricker, G.; Robinson, L.
   DE 911000/77/0012
Entkeimen von Packmitteln mit Wasserstoffperoxid und
UV–Strahlen und mögliche Auswirkungen auf das
Heissiegelverhalten der Packmittel und die sensorische
Beeinflussung des Füllgutes. **Sterilization of packaging
materials by means of hydrogen peroxide and UV–rays and the
influence upon the heat sealability of the packaging materials
and the organoleptic behaviour of the packaged food.**
Publications.

16001 Robinson, L.   DE 911000/78/0004 N
Wechselwirkung Lebensmittel – Packstoffe 'Migration,
Eignung von Packstoffen, Lebensmittelgesetz'. **Interaction
between food and packing materials - migration, suitability of
packing materials, food law –.**

16002 Fleurat Lessard, F.; Le Torc'h, J.M.
   FR 010707/72/5213
Les acariens des denrées stockées. Ecologie et surveillance.
Mites of stored products. Ecology and keeping.

16003 Fleurat Lessard, F.; Turtaut, P.; Cangardel, H.; Le
Torc'h, J.M.   FR 010707/75/5225
Action des champs électromagnétiques de haute fréquence sur
les insectes des denrées alimentaires. **Effects of electromagnetic
fields on stored product insect.**

16004 Anderson   GB 030903/00/0108 R
**Monitoring efficiency of pirimiphos methyl against mites in
storage structures (especially a store).**

16005 Muttrie   GB 030903/00/0302 R
**Detection and monitoring of acaricide–resistant strains of
storage mites in Scotland.**

16006 Snowden   GB 030903/00/0304 R
**Monitoring to determine effective methyl bromide distribution
during fumigation of containers.**

16007 Hosie   GB 030903/00/0308 R
**Development of mite infestation in stored cereals and animal
feeding stuffs in Western Scotland.**

16008 Bell   GB 030903/69/0314 R
**Behaviour and ecology of Ephest Elutella in food storage and
handling premises in Scotland.**

16009 Collins GB 040104/79/0004 N
Studies on potential food spoilage yeasts.

16010 Burgess, K.J. IE 060400/76/1259 R
Study of functional properties of proteins with a view to predicting their behaviour in manufactured foods. Publications.

16011 Guerzoni, M.E. IT 040241/77/0204 R
Problemi relativi alla conservazione degli alimenti a basso e medio contenuto in acqua. **Problems relating to the preservation of foods with a low or averange water content.**

16012 Domenichini, G.; Sdraiati, D.; Frilli, F.; Cravedi, P.
IT 040402/76/0001
Mezzi e metodi per la protezione dei prodotti agricoli conservati. **Pest control of food-stuffs.** Publications.

16013 Peri, C. IT 040617/73/0274
Essiccamento e conservazione di prodotti alimentari disidratati. **Drying and preservation of dehydrated food products.** Publications.

16014 Cantoni, C.; Renon, P.; Bianchi, M.A.; D'Aubert, S.; Beretta, G.; Cattaneo, P. IT 040633/79/0002 N
Nitriti, nitrati e nitrosammine. **Nitrites, nitrates and nitrosammine.**

16015 Casolari, A.; Gola, S. IT 070500/78/0006 N
Fattori ambientali che influiscono sullo sviluppo e la sopravvivenza del Clostridium botulinum in prodotti conservati. **Effect of environmental factors on the growth and survival of Cl. botulinum in preserved foods.**

16016 Casolari, A.; Castelvetri, F. IT 070500/79/0003 N
Influenza della temperatura sulla probabilità di sviluppo dei microorganismi. **Effect of temperature on the probability of growth of micro-organisms.**

16017 Langerak, D.Is. NL 010110/64/7949
Toepassing van bestraling voor verbetering van de voedselhygiëne. **Applied aspects of food irradiation to improve food hygiene.** Publications.

16018 Stegeman, H. NL 010110/71/7947
Complementaire effecten van straling en andere voedselconserveringstechnieken op microorganismen in landbouwprodukten. **Complementary effects of irradiation and other food preservation techniques on microorganisms in agricultural products.** Publications.

16019 Heins, H.G. NL 010110/78/8978 N
Het geven van training aan bursalen uit ontwikkelingslanden in de technologie van het bestralingsprocédé en de afzet van het bestraalde produkt m.i.v. ontwikkeling van onderzoekmethoden voor kwaliteitscontrole van het bestraalde produkt. **International Facility for Food Irradiation Technology (Training of fellows from developing countries in food irradiation processes and handling of irradiated products, including development of research methodology for quality control of irradiated products).**

16020 Nieuwenhuizen, G.H. van NL 010118/73/4212
Temparatuurverdeling in een verkoopmeubel voor diepgevroren produkten. **Temperature distribution in a display case for frozen food.** Publications.

16021 Gorin, N. NL 010118/74/5278
Activiteit van uien tegen microben en mogelijke toepassingen hiervan in de levensmiddelenindustrie. **Anti–microbial activity of onions and possible application in food industry.**

16022 Beek, G. van NL 010118/78/7848
Energieverbruik van gekoelde ruimten. **Energy consumption of cold stores.**

16023 Berg, C. van den; Weldring, J.A.G.; Wolters, I.
NL 020031/68/5136
Waterdampsorptie–eigenschappen van levensmiddelen. **Watersorption characteristics of foods.** Publications.

16024 Kampelmacher, E.H. NL 020031/71/5119
Bederfpreventie van levensmiddelen. **Prevention of foods against spoilage.** Publications.

16025 Kampelmacher, E.H.; Schothorst, M. van
NL 020031/74/6371
Invloed van temperatuur, voedingsbodem en resuscitatie op de groei van salmonella. **Influence of temperature, medium and resuscitation on the growth of salmonella.**

16026 Beukema, K.J. NL 020031/75/6379
Warmte ontwikkeling in stapels biologische materialen. **Heat generation in stored living materials.**

16027 Liou, J.K. NL 020031/78/8893 N
De theorie van niet lineaire diffusie toegepast op het drogen van levensmiddelen. **Non lineair diffusion theory applied to drying of food.**

16028 Korthals Altes, F.W.; Pelgröm, J.A.
NL 040012/75/6592
Aangepaste apparatuur voor het drogen van produkten van de tropische land– en tuinbouw. **Intermediate technology for drying of products from tropical agriculture and horticulture.**

16029 Korthals Altes, F.W.; Pelgröm, J.A.
NL 040012/76/7278
Kunstmatig drogen van produkten van de tropische land– en tuinbouw. **Artificial drying of products of tropical agriculture and horticulture.**

16030 Warschauer, K.A. NL 050210/52/7685
Bewerken, verpakken en bewaren van voedingsmiddelen. **Storage, processing and packing of food products.** Publications.

16031 Hillenius, C. NL 050230/52/7685
Bewerken, verpakken en bewaren van voedingsmiddelen. **Storage, processing and packing of food products.** Publications.

Mill and bakery products (B 6810)

16032 Ahrens, E.; Samaras, F. DE 129080/77/0002
Mikroflora, Verderbnisanfälligkeit und Lagerungsverhalten des Getreides in Abhängigkeit von Anbaubedingungen. **Microflora, susceptibility to spoilage, and behavior of stored grain in relation to cultivation conditions.**

16033 Müller, H.–M.; Thaler, M. DE 144625/78/0001 N
Belüftungstrocknung von Körnermais und Weizen. **Ventilation**

drying of grain maize and wheat. Publications.

grain moth under natural conditions.

16034 Müller, H.–M.; Thaler, M.   DE 144625/78/0002 N
Konservierung von Körnerfrüchten in Bezug auf eine mögliche
Bildung von Mykotoxinen. **Preservation of cereals in relation to
possible mycotoxin formation.** Publications.

16035 Mühlbauer, W.; Kuppinger, H.   DE 144705/73/0005
Trocknung und Kühlung von Körnerfrüchten. **Drying and
cooling of grain cereals.**

16036 Bischoff, T.; Albrecht, D.   DE 144710/73/0002
Ermittlung technischer Koeffizienten der
konkurrierendege–Ermittlung technischer Koeffizienten der
konkurrierenden Verfahren in der Konservierung und
Verwertung von Körner– früchten sowie deren ökonomische
Einordnung hinsichtlich Verwertung und Aufbereitung.
**Determination of technical coefficients of competitive methods
in preserving and utilization of cereals and their economical
classification as to use and dressing.**

16037 Nierle, W.; Fretzdorff, B.; Wolff, J. DE 209010/77/0006
Biochemische Veränderungen bei der Lagerung von Getreide
und Mehl. **Biochemical changes in stored cereals and flours.**

16038 El–Baya, A.W.; Gerstenkorn, P. DE 209020/77/0012 R
Versuche zur Ermittlung von Lagerschwund bei der Lagerung
von Getreide. **Experiments for determination of shrinkage of
stored cereals.**

16039 Gerstenkorn, P.   DE 209020/77/0014
Qualitätsüberwachung der Getreidelager der Bundesanstalt
für Landwirtschaftliche Marktordnung. **Quality control of
cereal stores by the Federal Institute for Agricultural Market
Organization.**

16040 Spicher, G.   DE 209030/77/0001
Verhalten der Mikroflora des Getreides während dessen
Lagerung und Verarbeitung. **Action of microflora during
storage and processing of cereals.**

16041 Wohlgemuth, R.   DE 215030/72/4002
Versuche zum Schutz von Getreide auf Schüttbodenläger
gegen Mottenbefall durch DDVP–abgebende Strips.
**Experiments on the control of moths in grain stores with
dichlorvos.**

16042 Wohlgemuth, R.; Singh, K.   DE 215030/78/0003 N
Untersuchungen über unterschiedliche Befallsmöglichkeiten
von Reis durch Vorratsschädlinge. **Tests on infestation of
different types of rice by stored food insects.**

16043 Strehler, A.   DE 502600/77/0001
Lagerung und Aufbereitung von Körnerfrüchten. **Storing and
processing of grains.**

16044 Busnel, R.G.; Andrieu, A.J.   FR 010208/75/3206
Détection acoustique industrielle des insectes des grains en
silos. **Industrial acoustic detection of insect infestation in large
containers.**

16045 Stockel, J.   FR 010707/75/5221
Etude de l'influence du facteur trophique sur la rencontre des
sexes chez Sitotroga Cerealella en conditions naturelles.
Influence of trophic relations on sex meeting of Angoumois

16046 Stockel, J.   FR 010707/75/5222
Etudes sur l'utilisation et le mode d'action des phéromones
Recherches sur la confusion sexuelle chez Sitotroga Cerealella
et Ostrinia Nubilalis. **Studies on possibilities of use and effects
of insect synthetic pheromones Research on mating disruption
on Sitotroga Cerealella and Ostrinia nubilalis.**

16047 Cangardel, H.; Fleurat Lessard, F.   FR 010707/75/5223
Effets des médiateurs chimiques sur le comportement d'un
Lépidoptère des denrées Plodia Interpunctella. **Effects of sex
attractants on sexual behavior of a stored product moth Plodia
Interpunctella.**

16048 Cangardel, H.; Turtaut, P.   FR 010707/75/5224
Dynamique des populations d'insectes dans une masse de blé.
A study of stored wheat ecosystems.

16049 Fleurat Lessard, F.; Turtaut, P.   FR 010707/75/5226
Désinsectisation des denrées par des traitements physiques.
Action de la chaleur sur les insectes des produits céréaliers.
**Physical means of control of stored products pests Heat
treatment of cereal products.**

16050 Muttrie; Snowden   GB 030903/00/0303 R
**Efficiency of carbontetrachloride fumigation of grain in deep
silos and investigation of failures.**

16051 Lupton; Edwards   GB 030903/00/0307 R
**Development of mite infestation in stored cereals in Eastern
Scotland.**

16052 Cole; Muttrie   GB 030903/74/0315 R
**Ephestia khuniella: factors affecting successful development in a
Glasgow grain silo.**

16053 Jeffrey   GB 030903/75/0306 R
Taxonomy of stored products mites.

16054 Shearer   GB 051101/79/0012 N
Long term storage of flour.

16055 Shearer   GB 051101/79/0018 N
Prolonged storage of flour versus bread quality.

16056 Cunney, M.B.   IE 060500/70/0861 R
Investigations into grain storage and ventilation techniques.
Publications.

16057 Kavanagh, J.A.; O'Sullivan, E.   IE 120106/78/9172 N
**Investigations on the deterioration of stored barley/grain caused
by fungi.**

16058 Baldi, G.; Fossati, G.; Fantone, G.C.; Mazzini, F.;
Bonandin, E.; Grimaldi, A.   IT 011400/79/0010 N
Conservazione del riso: variazioni in contenuto proteico,
frazioni proteiche, composizione amminoacidica. **Storage of
rice: changes on proteins, protein fractions, amino acid
composition.** Publications.

16059 Sparenberg, H.   NL 010105/67/5472 R
Drogen en bewaren van granen, zaden en peulvruchten.
Drying and storage of grains, seeds and pulses. Publications.

16060 Sparenberg, H.   NL 010105/78/8359 R

Drogen, bewaren en behandelen van granen, zaden en peulvruchten in ontwikkelingslanden. **Drying, storage and handling of grains, seeds and pulses in developing countries.**

16061 Belderok, B.   NL 050302/78/7963
Invloed van verborgen en zichtbaar schot op de chemische samenstelling en eigenschappen van tarwe. **Effects of hidden and visible sprouting of wheat on its chemical and technological properties.**

Oils, fats and related products (B 6820)

See also 15794, 16572

16062 Seher, A.; Arens, M.   DE 213010/77/0009
Verbesserung der Lagerfähigkeit von Ölen und Fetten durch Zusatz bisher nicht benutzter natürlicher Antioxydantien. **Improvement of shelf–life of oils and fats by addition of natural antioxidants not used so far.**

16063 Seher, A.; Weiss, U.   DE 213010/77/0011
Beständigkeit von Ätherlipiden gegenüber Enzymen. **Stability of ether lipids to enzymes.**

16064 Cucurachi, A.; Mascolo, A.; Solinas, M.; Di Giovacchino, L.   IT 022100/72/0012
I polifenoli delle olive e dell'olio di oliva. **The polyfenols of olives and olive oil.**

16065 Catalano, M.   IT 040107/73/0916
Ricerche sull'autossidazione delle sostanze grasse. **Research on the autoxidation of fats and oils.** Publications.

16066 Rastovski, A.   NL 010105/76/8324 R
Onderzoek naar mogelijkheden voor kortstondige bewaring van suikerbieten. **Research into the possibilities of short storage of sugarbeets.** Publications.

16067 Loef, H.W.; Cozijnsen, J.L.   NL 020031/74/5122
Chemische en fysische veranderingen van vetten in voedingsmiddelen en van eetbare vetten en oliën gedurende bewaring en verwerking. **Chemical and fysical changes of fats in food and of edible fats and oil during processing and storage.** Publications.

16068 Jorritsma, J.   NL 060003/75/7719
Beperking van vorstschade en ademhalingsverliezen tijdens de opslag van suikerbieten. **Minimizing frost damage and respiration losses during storage of sugar beet.** Publications.

Sugar and starch products (B 6830)

See also 3205, 15828, 16085, 16111, 16614

16069 Müller, K.; Lopez, R.   DE 132062/75/0004
Physiologisch bedingte stoffliche Veränderungen in Kartoffelknollen verschiedener Sorten in der Endphase der Lagerung bis zum Konsum. **Physiologically induced changes of components in potato tubers of different varieties during the final phase of storage up to consumption.**

16070 Gerstenkorn, P.; Bolling, H.; El–Baya, A.W.; Zwingelberg, H.   DE 209020/71/5001
Veränderung der Inhaltsstoffe und der Verarbeitungsqualität bei der Lagerung und Trocknung von Mais. **Changes in maize composition and processing quality during heating and storage.**

16071 Putz, B.; Bergthaller, W.   DE 209040/77/0010
Die Veränderung von Inhaltsstoffen, der Schäl– und Veredlungseignung von Kartoffeln während der Langzeitlagerung. **Changes in constituents, peeling and processing suitability of potatoes during long–run storage.**

16072 Wedler, A.   DE 211010/75/0007
Der Einfluss von Licht auf den Solaningehalt von Speisekartoffeln in Abhängigkeit von der Verpackung und die Qualitätserhaltung im Einzelhandel. **Influence of light on the solanine content in food potatoes related to packing material and maintenance of quality in retail trade.**

16073 Langerfeld, E.   DE 215120/78/0002 N
Untersuchungen über Ursachen, Verbreitung und Bekämpfung von Lagerfäulen und Auflaufschäden bei Kartoffeln. **Investigations on causes, distribution and control of storage rots and emerging diseases of potatoes.**

16074 Dodd, V.A.   IE 120301/76/9053 N
Factors affecting sucrose losses during the storage of sugar beets. Publications.

16075 Montedoro, G.F.   IT 041011/72/0516
Indagine sui costituenti fenolici presenti nelle acque di vegetazione e negli oli di oliva, esame analitico in relazione alla stabilità dell'ossidazione e alla genuinità dell'olio. **Survey of phenolic elements present in plants waters and in olive oils; analysis with respect to the stability to oxidation and to the genuineness of the oil.** Publications.

16076 Rastovski, A.   NL 010105/67/0259
De invloed van bewaaromstandigheden op de kwaliteit van de aardappelen. **The influence of storage conditions on the quality of potatoes.** Publications.

16077 Rastovski, A.   NL 010105/67/3740 R
Kiemremming van aardappelen gedurende de bewaring m.b.v. chemische middelen en residu–onderzoek in de knollen en de daaruit vervaardigde produkten. **Sprout inhibition of potatoes during storage using chemicals and residue research on potatoes and potato products.**

16078 Es, A. van   NL 010105/67/8318
Onderzoek naar het verband tussen het koolhydraatmetabolisme en de temperatuur tijdens de bewaring in relatie tot van nature in de knol voorkomende remstoffen. **Investigations into the relationship between the carbohydrate metabolism and the storage temperatures in potato tubers and the possible role of endogenous sprout inhibitors.** Publications.

16079 Hesen, J.C.   NL 010105/67/8320
De geschiktheid van aardappelen voor bewaring, bewerking en verwerking. **The suitability of potatoes for storage, handling and processing.** Publications.

16080 Hesen, J.C.   NL 010105/67/8330
Bestrijding bewaarziekten bij aardappelen. **Control of potato storage diseases.** Publications.

16081 Rastovski, A.   NL 010105/73/5471
Ontwikkeling van eenvoudige bewaarsystemen voor veenkoloniale aardappelen. **Development of simple storage systems for starch potatoes.** Publications.

16082 Es, A. van   NL 010105/73/8327 R
Beinvloeding van de blauwgevoeligheid van aardappelen door teelt, veredeling en bewaring. **Influencing the blackspot susceptibility of potatoes by growing conditions, breeding and storage conditions.** Publications.

16083 Rastovski, A.   NL 010105/75/8325 R
Bewaring van aardappelen onder tropische en sub–tropische omstandigheden. **Storage of potatoes under tropical and sub–tropical conditions.** Publications.

16084 Keijbets, M.J.H.   NL 010105/76/8332 R
De invloed van methoden van vacuümverpakken op de kwaliteit van aardappelprodukten. **The influence of methods of vacuum packing on the quality of potato products.**

Fruit and vegetable products (B 6840)

See also 3837, 4068, 4127, 4131, 4152, 4617, 4627, 5728, 7085, 7289, 7321, 9630, 15823, 15824, 15867, 16059, 16060, 16064, 16661

16085 Van Lancker, J.   BE 030020/76/0001
Invloed van de temperatuur op de weerstand tegen beschadiging bij aardappelen en appelen. **Bruising of apples and potatoes in connection with temperature.**

16086 Huyghebaert, H.; Dimitropoulos
   BE 030025/72/0003 R
Degradatiereakties in diepvriesprodukten (groenten). **Degradation reactions in deepfrozen foods (vegetables).**

16087 Maton, A.; Priem, R.   BE 070300/69/0013 R
Studie van de invloed van de voorbehandeling van groenten op het verloop van het droogteproces en op de kwaliteit van het gedroogde produkt. **Research on the influence on the preparation operations of vegetables on their quality and on the course of their drying process.** Publications.

16088 Maton, A.; Priem, R.   BE 070300/73/0012 R
Studie van het drogen, lyophilizeren en diepvriezen van groenten. **Research on drying, lyophilization and deepfreezing of vegetables.** Publications.

16089 Linden, R.   BE 080200/55/0025 R
Surgélation de fruits et de légumes. **Deep–freezing of fruit and vegetables.** Publications.

16090 Linden, R.   BE 080200/60/0023 R
Réfrigération de fruits et de légumes. **Chilling of fruit and vegetables.** Publications.

16091 Linden, R.   BE 080200/76/0028 R
Lyophilisation de fruits et de légumes. **Freeze–drying of fruit and vegetables.**

16092 Vanderwaeren, R.; Herregods, M.; Goffings, X.
   BE 140000/76/0029 R
Studie van de optimale bewaaromstandigheden van fruit, groenten en siergewassen. **Study of the optimum storage conditions of fruit, vegetables and ornamentals.** Publications.

16093 Bielig, H.J.; Askar, A.   DE 105811/75/0001
Untersuchungen zur Bleiaufnahme verschiedener Füllgüter in Dosen. **Investigations on lead uptake of canned vegetable foodstuffs.**

16094 Bielig, H.J.; Schwaiger, M.   DE 105813/75/0001
Die Beeinflussung des Eignungswertes von Trockengemüse durch Vorbehandlung, Trocknung und Lagerung. **The aptitude value of dried vegetables as affected by pretreatment, drying and storage.**

16095 Bielig, H.J.; Rhee, C.   DE 105813/77/0002
Erhaltung der Qualitätseigenschaften von Trockengemüse durch gezielte Lagerungsbedingungen. **Quality preservation of dried vegetables by specified storage conditions.**

16096 Henze, J.   DE 111301/77/0002
Lagertechnik für Obst und Gemüse, einschliesslich CA–Lagerung. Nacherntephysiologie, Fruchtatmung. **Technical equipments in fruits and vegetables, incl. CA storage. Post–harvest physiology. Respiration of fruits.**

16097 Henze, J.; Bachmann, U.   DE 111301/77/0004
Folgen einer extremen Belastung der Atmung während der CA–Lagerung bei Äpfeln. **Consequences of an excessive inhibition of respiration during the CA–storage of apples.**

16098 Henze, J.; Ohse, K.   DE 111301/77/0006
Nachreifung von Birnen. **After–ripening of pears.**

16099 Ahrens, E.; Dizer, H.   DE 129080/77/0003
Die Bildung von Ameisensäure durch Pilze in Obst und Obstsäften. **Formation of formic acid by fungi in fruits and juices.**

16100 Ahrens, E.; El–Saidy, S.   DE 129080/78/0001 N
Der Einfluss von Transport– und Lagerungsbedingungen auf die epiphytische Mikroflora, die dissimilatorische Nitratreduktion und den Gehalt an Vitamin A und C bei Frischsalat und Spinat. **The influence of conditions of transport and of storage on the epiphytic microflora, the dissimilate nitrate reduction, and the content of vitamins A and C in salad and spinach.**

16101 Knösel, D.; Schickedanz, F.   DE 135052/74/0001
Enzymatische Zersetzung gelagerter pflanzlicher Produkte durch Mikroorganismen. **Enzymatic decomposition of stored vegetal products by micro–organisms.**

16102 Neubeller, J.   DE 144445/77/0019
Beziehung zwischen Lagerungsverhalten und der Zusammensetzung der Fruchtschale. **Relations between storage behavior and composition of the fruit skin.** Publications.

16103 Fritz, D.; Weichmann, J.   DE 161260/73/0005
Lagerfähigkeit verschiedener Sorten von Chinakohl. **The storage stability of different varieties of Chinese cabbage.**

16104 Fritz, D.; Weichmann, J.   DE 161260/75/0005
Qualitätserhaltung von Meerrettich bei CA–Lagerung. **Quality preservation of horse–radish at CA storage.**

16105 Fritz, D.; Weichmann, J.; Bomme, U.
   DE 161260/77/0008
Lagerverhalten verschiedener Weisskohlsorten. **Shelf–life of different cultivars of white cabbage.**

16106 Weichmann, J.; Turber, U.   DE 161260/78/0002 N
Einfluss der relativen Luftfeuchtigkeit auf Lagerfähigkeit und Qualitätserhaltung von Gemüse, zunächst bearbeitet mit

Wurzelgemüsen. **Influence of relative humidity on storability and preservation of quality of root vegetables.**

16107 Fritz, D.; Weichmann, J.   DE 161260/78/0005 N
Veränderungen der SEQ von Gemüse nach unterschiedlicher Lagerung. **Changes of sensoric and nutritional quality of vegetables after different methods of storing.**

16108 Bohling, H.; Hansen, H.   DE 211010/71/5003
Der Einfluss flüchtiger Stoffwechselprodukte von Früchten auf Reifung und Alterung. **The influence of organic volatile metabolites of fruit on the ripening process during storage time.**

16109 Bohling, H.   DE 211010/72/5003
Untersuchungen über Veränderungen an Aromastoffen von Früchten während der Lagerung. **Investigations into the alterations of flavour compounds of fruits during storage.**

16110 Bohling, H.; Hansen, H.   DE 211010/73/5001
Atmungsmessungen an verschiedenen Obst– und Gemüsearten und –sorten unter verschiedenen Lagerungsbedingungen. **Respiratory measurements in different species of fruit and vegetables under different storing conditions.**

16111 Hansen, H.; Bohling, H.   DE 211010/77/0005
Lagerbedingungen für Obst, Gemüse und Kartoffeln unter Anwendung kontrollierter Atmosphären. **Storing conditions for fruit, vegetables and potatoes using controlled atmospheres.**

16112 Hansen, H.; Bohling, H.; Overbeck, G.; Hentschel, H.
DE 211010/77/0006
Einfluss von Pflanzenschutzmassnahmen bei verschiedenen Gemüsearten und Sorten auf das Lagerungsverhalten. **Influence of plant protective measures on storing behaviour of different kinds of vegetables.**

16113 Wolf, W.; Paulus, K.; Wedler, A.   DE 211020/77/0002
Vergleichende Untersuchungen über die Veränderungen von Bohnen bei Trocknen, Gefrieren und Hitzesterilisieren unter Berücksichtigung unterschiedlicher Herstellungs– und Lagerungsbedingungen. **Comparative investigations on alterations in beans due to drying, freezing and heat sterilization in consideration of different conditions of production and storage.**

16114 Wolf, W.; Adam, R.   DE 211020/78/0005 N
Schwefelung getrockneter Karotten, Bohnen und Kartoffeln. **Sulfitation of dried carrots, beans and potatoes.**

16115 Müller, H.   DE 211030/77/0004
Untersuchungen über das Lagerverhalten von Äpfeln nach Tauchbehandlung mit Ethoxyquin mit Hilfe der C–14–markierten Verbindung. **Studies on storing behaviour of apples after dipping treatment with ethoxyquin using C–14–labelled compound.**

16116 Wucherpfennig, K.; Özmen, T.   DE 506104/78/0002 N
Die Veränderungen des Pektingehaltes bei der Lagerung und Kelterung von Obst. **Changes in pectin content during storage and pressing of fruit.**

16117 Tiemann, K.–H.; Blank, H.–G.   DE 507308/77/0001
Untersuchungen des Einflusses von Ca–Salzlösungen auf die Lagerfähigkeit von Apfelfrüchten durch Spritzen der Bäume bzw. Tauchen der Früchte nach der Ernte. **Studies on the influences of Ca–salt solutions on shelf–life of apples by spraying of trees and dipping of the fruits after harvest.**

16118 Ferry, P.   FR 010605/70/2220
Confisage de l'olive verte de table. **Preservation of green olives in saline solution.**

16119 Cangardel, H.; Turtaut, P.; Fleurat Lessard, F.; Le Torc'h, J.M.   FR 010707/73/5216
Etude écologique des insectes ravageurs du pruneau d'Agen. **Ecological study of several pests of stored prunes.**

16120 Le Torc'h, J.M.; Turtaut, P.   FR 010707/77/5228
Désinsectisation des denrées par des traitements physiques Action du froid et des atmosphères contrôlées sur les insectes du pruneau stocké. **Physical means of control of stored product pests Effect of cold treatment associated with controlled atmosphers on dried prunes insects.**

16121 Latrasse, A.   FR 011009/70/2200
Auto–oxydation des huiles essentielles de cassis. **Auto–oxidation of essential oils in black–currants.** Publications.

16122 Gormley, T.R.; MacCanna, C.   IE 060300/71/0078 R
A study of the efficiency of new and existing methods of keeping fresh and processed mushrooms white.

16123 Jeffares, M.   IE 060300/73/0773 R
Cooling of soft fruit. Effects of pre–cooling on storage life and subsequent shelf life of strawberries, rasberries and gooseberries. Publications.

16124 Cowan, C.A.; Sherrington, J.   IE 060600/75/1207 R
A comparison of French and Irish produced golden delicious apples at retail level. Publications.

16125 McKenna, B.   IE 120301/77/9061 N
Effect of drying methods on properties of selected fruit and vegetables (apples, carrots).

16126 Crivelli, G.; Senesi, E.   IT 021900/75/0005
Idoneità' varietale alla surgelazione di broccoli, cavolfiori, peperoni, melanzane, fagiolini, zucchini. **Researches on suitability of cauliflower, snap bean, squash, pepper, eggplant, broccoli to quick freezing.** Publications.

16127 Gorini, F.L.; Eccher Zerbini, P.; Sozzi, A.
IT 021900/75/0008
Caratteristiche qualitative delle mele "golden delicious" in funzione dell'ambiente di produzione e dell'epoca di raccolta. **Quality features of "Golden Delicious" apples depending on crop environment and picking date.** Publications.

16128 Gorini, F.L.; Eccher Zerbini, P.; Sozzi, A.
IT 021900/75/0012
Refrigerazione in polietilene di ortaggi e relativa conservabilita'. **Storage and keeping quality of vegetables packed in plastic films.** Publications.

16129 Gorini, F.L.   IT 021900/75/0013
Conservabilita' di nuovi ibridi di pomodori. **Storage susceptibility of new hybrids of tomatoes.** Publications.

16130 Gorini, F.L.; Eccher Zerbini, P.   IT 021900/75/0014
Influenza dei portinnesti nella conservabilita' delle mele.

Influence of root–stock on apple storage.

16131 Gorini, F.L.; Sozzi, A.   IT 021900/76/0002 N
Prevenzione della butteratura amara. **Prevention of bitter pit..**

16132 Gorini, F.L.; Eccher Zerbini, P.; Sozzi, A.
IT 021900/76/0003 N
Conservazione in A.C. delle pere.. **A.C. Storage of pears.**

16133 Gorini, F.L.; Eccher Zerbini, P.; Sozzi, A.
IT 021900/76/0004 N
Trattamento preconservazione con CO_2 alle pomacee..
Pre–Storage treatment with CO_2 to apple and pear fruit..

16134 Crivelli, G.; Maltini, E.   IT 021900/77/0002
Ricerche sull'essiccazione di alcuni ortofrutticoli e sulla loro
utilizzazione a livello intermedio di umidità. **Fruit and
vegetables drying as intermediate moisture food.**

16135 Gorini, F.L.; Sozzi, A.; Eccher Zerbini, P.
IT 021900/77/0003
Idrorefrigerazione di frutti ed ortaggi. **Fruit and vegetables
hydrocooling. Publications.**

16136 Gorini, F.L.; Testoni, A.; Sozzi, A.   IT 021900/77/0004
Tecniche di maturazione accelerata dei loti. **Persimmon fast
ripening.**

16137 Gorini, F.; Sozzi, A.; Testoni, A.   IT 021900/79/0001 N
Nuovi metodi di prevenzione del riscaldo delle mele. **New
methods for the prevention of scald in apples.**

16138 Gorini, F.; Testoni, A.; Sozzi, A.   IT 021900/79/0002 N
Indagine sul comportamento barico delle celle in atmosfera
controllata per la conservazione della frutta. **Research on baric
changes in controlled atmosphere storage rooms.**

16139 Gorini, F.; Sozzi, A.; Testoni, A.   IT 021900/79/0004 N
Trattamenti per la prevenzione dell'avvizzimento su mele.
Treatments for shrivelling prevention on apples.

16140 Crivelli, G.; Senesi, E.   IT 021900/79/0012 N
Influenza dei pretrattamenti alla congelazione di ortaggi.
Influence of pretreatments on freezing of vegetables.

16141 Maltini, E.; Torreggiani, D.   IT 021900/79/0013 N
Valutazione del comportamento termodinamico di ortaggi e
frutta durante il congelamento e modificazione del pH.
**Thermodynamical behaviour and changes of pH during
freezing of fruits and vegetables.**

16142 Crivelli, G.; Senesi, E.   IT 021900/79/0014 N
Congelamento in R12 di ortaggi preconfezionati. **Freezing with
freon 12 of prepackaged vegetables.**

16143 Brighigna, A.; Cucurachi, A.   IT 022100/72/0002
Sistemi e tecniche per la preparazione delle olive nere da
mensa. **Systems and techniques for black olives preserving.**

16144 Cucurachi, A.; Di Giovacchino, L.; Mascolo, A.;
Solinas, M.   IT 022100/73/0004
La conservazione dell'olio durante lo stoccaggio in massa.
Preservation of olive oil during mass storage.

16145 Brighigna, A.; Cucurachi, A.; De Angelis, M.
IT 022100/76/0003 N

Conservazione delle olive nere da tavola,essicate e
confezionate in piccoli contenitori. **Conservation of black table
olives,dried,boxed in small containers..**

16146 Pratella, G.C.; Tonini, G.   IT 040216/66/0003
Lotta postraccolta antimarciume su pere e mele: ricerca di
antiparassitari attivi contro Penicillium expansum, Botrytis
cinerea, e Gloeosporium album. **Apple and pear rot control
after picking: a research of products effective in Penicillium
expansum, Botrytis cinerea, and Gloeosporium album control.**
Publications.

16147 Pratella, G.C.; Bertolini, P.   IT 040216/77/0001 N
Conservazione delle pesche in Atmosfera Controllata per
trasformazione industriale.. **C.A. Storage of peaches for
industrial processing.**

16148 Pratella, G.C.; Bertolini, P.   IT 040216/77/0002 N
Conservazione in frigorifero a bassa umidità relativa di cipolle
stagionate e non stagionate. **Cold storage of cured and uncured
onions, with low relative humidity..**

16149 Pratella, G.C.; Bertolini, P.   IT 040216/77/0003 N
Trattamento con acqua a diverse temperature di castagne,
prima della conservazione.. **Water treatment of chestnuts at
different temperatures, before storage..**

16150 Pratella, G.C.; Bertolini, P.   IT 040216/77/0004 N
Influenza di Ca,Mg,Mn, Zn,Cu sulla comparsa delle
alterazioni fisiologiche durante la conservazione frigorifera di
arance e limoni. **Cn,Ca,Mg,Mn,Zn, effects on the appearance
of physiological diseases during the cold storage of oranges and
lemons.**

16151 Pratella, G.C.; Biondi, G.; Brigati, S.
IT 040216/78/0003
La conservazione dei kaki. **The storage of persimmons.**

16152 Pratella, G.C.; Menniti, A.M.   IT 040216/78/0004
Studio sulla fitotossicità dei gas d'ammoniaca sugli
ortofrutticoli conservati e sua prevenzione. **Toxic effects of
ammoniacal gas on stored fruits and vegetables and their
prevention.**

16153 Pratella, G.C.; Bertolini, P.   IT 040216/78/0005
Deumidificazione delle cipolle in cumuli e conservazione
ventilata. **Onion curing in bulks and ventilated storage.**

16154 Pratella, G.C.; Bertolini, P.   IT 040216/78/0006
Conservazione delle patate in cumuli ventilati. **Potato storage
in ventilated stacks.**

16155 Pratella, G.C.; Bertolini, P.   IT 040216/78/0007
Prevenzione del riscaldo molle delle mele con calcio e
fitormoni. **Preventing soft scald of apples with calcium and
growth regulators.**

16156 Budini, R.   IT 040244/77/0771
Ricerca chimico–biologica su conservazione prodotti
ortofrutticoli, indici di maturazione e alterazioni a basse
temperature. **Chemical and biological research on horticultural
produce conservation, grades of maturation and alterations due
to low temperatures.**

16157 Poma Treccani, C.   IT 040605/74/0001
Influenza della GA_3 sullo spostamento degli ioni nel frutto per

D 4420 – Storage and conservation

lo studio della butteratura amara delle mele. **Effect of GA₃ on ion movement in the fruit: study of bitter pit of apples.**

16158 Mattarolo, F. IT 064000/77/0770
Ricerca tecnico–ingegneristica sulla conservazione e trasporto ortofrutticoli a mezzo containers. **Technical engineering research on the preservation and transport of fruits and vegetables in containers.**

16159 Casolari, A.; Vicini, E.; Gola, S. IT 070500/78/0004
Effetto della velocità di congelamento e scongelamento nella sopravvivenza del Clostridium botulinum in ambiente definito e negli ortaggi. **Effect of freezing and thawing rate upon Cl. botulinum survival in defined media and in vegetables.**

16160 Hesen, J.C. NL 010105/78/8319 R
Onderzoek naar mogelijkheden van campagneverlenging in de groente– en fruitverwerkende industrie. **Research into the possibilities of campaign extension in the vegetable and fruit processing industry.** Publications.

16161 Rastovski, A. NL 010105/78/8366 R
Onderzoek naar methoden van kiemremming bij uien tijdens bewaring. **Research into sprout inhibiting methods for onions during storage.**

16162 Bergers, W.W.A. NL 010110/75/7950
Studies over de veranderingen in fenolische verbindingen in bestraalde groenten en fruit tijdens bewaring – het belang voor de consumptie–geschiktheid. **Studies on changes in phenolic compounds in irradiated fruit and vegetables during storage – its importance for wholesomeness.**

16163 Duvekot, W.S. NL 010118/73/4189
Verband tussen de chemische samenstelling van het blad, de plukdatum en de houdbaarheid van appels en peren. **Physiological condition of apples and pears in relation to storage time.** Publications.

16164 Schouten, S.P. NL 010118/73/4192
Gebruikswaarde van groenten als vers produkt (bewaarkwaliteit en houdbaarheid van nieuwe rassen). **Utilisation value of fresh vegetables. (Storage quality and keepability of new varieties).** Publications.

16165 Schouten, S.P. NL 010118/73/4193
Gebruikswaarde van fruit als vers produkt (bewaarkwaliteit en houdbaarheid van nieuwe rassen). **Utilisation value of fresh fruit. (storage quality and keepability of new varieties).** Publications.

16166 Staden, O.L. NL 010118/73/4194
Bestrijding van stip in appelen. **Control of bitterpit in apples.** Publications.

16167 Nieuwenhuizen, G.H. van NL 010118/73/4209 R
Klimaatbeheersing in opslagruimten en transportmiddelen voor tuinbouwprodukten. **Control of product temperature during storage and transport of horticultural products.** Publications.

16168 Rudolphij, J.W. NL 010118/73/4223
Fysische eigenschappen van tuinbouwprodukten bij bewaarprocessen. **Physical properties of horticultural produce during storage processes.**

16169 Duvekot, W.S. NL 010118/73/4235
Bewaring van Golden Delicious bij verschillende condities. **Storage of Golden Delicious in different conditions.**

16170 Rudolphij, J.W. NL 010118/74/5280 R
Relatie kwaliteitsverloop –bewaarklimaat bij de bewaring van tuinbouwprodukten. **Quality change of horticultural products during storage in relation to storage conditions.** Publications.

16171 Schouten, S.P. NL 010118/74/5282
De bewaring van groente. **Vegetable storage.** Publications.

16172 Staden, O.L. NL 010118/75/6000
Bestrijding van scald op appels. **Control of superficial scald on apples.** Publications.

16173 Steinbuch, E. NL 010118/75/6005 R
Invloed van conserveringsmethoden op de kwaliteit van groenteprodukten. **Effect of preservation methods on the quality of vegetables.** Publications.

16174 Schijvens, E. NL 010118/76/6653
Onderzoek naar de mogelijkheden ter verkrijging van een betere kwaliteit appelmoes. **Possibilities of obtaining a better quality apple sauce.**

16175 Gorin, N. NL 010118/76/6655
Chemische karakterisatie van uien. **Chemical characterization of onions.** Publications.

16176 Steinbuch, E. NL 010118/77/7264
De invloed van grondstof, oogst– en conserveringsmethode op de kwaliteit van tot zoetzuur geconserveerde groenten. **The effect of raw material, harvesting and preservation method on the quality of sweet–sour processed vegetables.**

16177 Schouten, S.P. NL 010118/77/7269
Houdbaarheid van de tomaat. **The tenability of tomatoes.**

16178 Kruistum, G. van NL 010207/77/8405
Verbetering van de bewaaromstandigheden van witlofwortels voor de late trek. **Improvement of conservation conditions of chicory roots for late forcing.**

16179 Snoek, N.J. NL 010207/78/8409
Bewaring van spruitkool aan de stam. **Storage of Brussels sprouts on the stem.**

Meat, meat products and fish products in general (B 6850)

See also 15868

16180 Stein, W.; Münzel, M. DE 129200/78/0001 N
Vorkommen und Entwicklung von Fliegen 'Dipt., Muscidae, Calliphoridae' an Lebensmitteln tierischer Herkunft. **Visit and development of flies 'Dipt., Muscidae, Calliphoridae' on food products of animal origin.**

Meat and meat products (B 6851)

See also 12084, 15787, 15861, 15888, 16695, 16705, 16706

16181 Coppens, R.; Duchêne, M.; Deroanne, C. BE 010015/70/0003
Etude de la conservation des viandes et produits dérivés par le

froid, notamment, la conservation en congélation des viandes hachées. **Study of cold preservation of meat and meat products, especially the freezing preservation of ground metat.** Publications.

16182 Sinell, H.–J.; Beyer, K. DE 104301/78/0001 N
Mikroflora von vorverpacktem Frischfleisch in Grossgebinden und Portionspackungen bei unterschiedlichen Lagerbedingungen. **Microflora of prepacked fresh meat in bulk and individual packs under varying conditions of storage.**

16183 Reuter, G.; Sasse, D.; Riemer, R.
DE 104302/78/0003 N
Untersuchungen zur Überlebensfähigkeit von Sarkosporidien im Schweinefleisch bei verschiedenen Gefriertemperaturen. **Investigations on the survival of Sarcocystis in pork tissues at different freezing temperatures.**

16184 Reuter, G.; Kerschner, K. DE 104302/78/0005 N
Das Vorkommen von Salmonellen auf Organen von Schlachttieren nach der Gewinnung und nach der Kühlung und dem Transport. **The incidence of salmonellae on organs of fat stock after slaughtering and after chilling and transport.**

16185 Hadlok, R.; Christen, U.; Binzel, R.–M.
DE 129700/75/0003
Wildfleischhygiene: Der mikrobielle Status und die Beschaffenheit von Hasenfleisch – Lepus europaeus – nach dem Erlegen und während der Lagerung des Wildes. **Game hygiene: the microbial status and quality of hare meat – Lepus europaeus – after shooting and during the storage of the game.**

16186 Lorenz, G.; Drews, M.; Einhoff, K.
DE 207070/78/0007 N
Wirtschaftlichkeitsberechnung verschiedener Formen der Vorratshaltung von Fleisch in öffentlicher Hand. **Economing of alternative methods of meat–storage in competence of public market–intervention.**

16187 Schön, L.; Ristic, M. DE 210010/77/0003
Lagerfähigkeit von Geflügelteilen in Abhängigkeit vom Zeitpunkt ihrer Gewinnung. **Shelf–life of parts of poultry depending on the date of their separation.**

16188 Tändler, K. DE 210020/75/0012
Eignung und Lagerstabilität von Bratengerichten und HackfleischSchnellbratgerichten aus Gefrierfleisch. **Suitability and stability for storage of roast dishes and minced–meat quick–roast dishes of frozen meat.**

16189 Tändler, K. DE 210020/75/0013
Entwicklung hitze– und lagerstabiler Sossen, Würzungen und Beilagen für Fleischgerichte. **Preparation of sauces, seasonings and dressings for meat dishes with stability of heating and shelf–life.**

16190 Wirth, F. DE 210020/75/0014
Pökeln von grossen Fleischteilen. Verminderung der Nitritund Nitratverarbeitung. **Preservation of great parts of meat in pickle. Reduction of using nitrite and nitrate.**

16191 Wirth, F. DE 210020/75/0015
Fleisch–Sosse–Gerichte in Grossbehältnissen als Vollkonserve. **Meat–and–sauce dishes in great containers as complete tins.**

16192 Tändler, K. DE 210020/78/0002 N

Verbesserung der Bevorratung von Rindfleisch der Staatsreserve. **Improvement of storage of government stored beef.**

16193 Krispien, K. DE 210030/74/5011
Messung und Beeinflussung der Wasseraktivität 'aw–Wert' von Oberflächen und damit Verbesserung der Haltbarkeit von Fleisch und Fleischerzeugnissen. **Measuring of and chances of taking influence on the activity of surface waters 'aw–value' and thus improvement of stability in meats and meat products.**

16194 Leistner, L.; Eckardt, C. DE 210030/78/0002 N
Natriumpropionat zur Behandlung der Oberflächen von Rohwürsten und Rohschinken zur Hemmung von unerwünschtem Schimmelpilzwachstum. **Use of potassium propionate to inhibit undesirable mold growth on fermented sausage and raw ham.**

16195 Leistner, L.; Hechelmann, H. DE 210030/78/0006 N
Alternativen zum Nitrit–Zusatz bei Pökelfleischerzeugnissen. **Alternatives to the nitrite addition to cured meats.**

16196 Leistner, L.; Hechelmann, H. DE 210030/78/0007 N
Verbesserung der Haltbarkeit von Schlachttierkörpern durch Beeinflussung des aw–Wertes und pH–Wertes der Oberfläche. **Improved shelf life of carcass meat due to aw and pH depression of the surface.**

16197 Partmann, W. DE 211010/71/5004
Erarbeitung und Vergleich der Muster ninhydrinpositiver Substanzen im Fleisch von warmblütigen Tieren und Fischen unter verschiedenen Lagerungsbedingungen. **Investigation and comparison of the patterns of ninhydrinreactive substances in meats of warmblooded animals and of fish stored under various conditions.**

16198 Partmann, W. DE 211010/71/5005
Verlängerung der Haltbarkeit von Frischfleisch und Fisch in kontrollierten Atmosphären bei Kühl– und Gefrierlagerung. **Prolongation of shelflife of fresh meat and fish in controlled atmospheres at cold and frozen storage.**

16199 Partmann, W. DE 211010/78/0004 N
Nachweis einer erfolgten Bestrahlung von verschiedenen Fleischarten. **Detection of irradiation applied to various meats.**

16200 Paulus, K.; Fricker, A.; Zohm, H.
DE 211020/78/0013 N
Zeit–Temperatur–Verhalten von Heidschnuckenfleisch während der Gefrierlagerung. **Time–temperature–tolerance of meat of Heidschnucken 'North German moorland sheep' during frozen storage.**

16201 Petersen, V.E.; Christensen, K.; Jensen, O.
DK 010203/77/8002 N
Lagringstidens indflydelse på smagen af kyllinger. **The influence of storing time of deep frozen broiler carcasses on the taste of grilled broilers.**

16202 Labadie, J. FR 010809/77/9528
Recherches d'antagonismes microbiens pour limiter la multiplication des micro–organismes pathogénes ou putréfiants des viandes. **Research of bacterial inhibitors to limit the growth of putrifying and pathogenic bacteria in meat.**

16203 Harper GB 040403/79/0017 N

Enzymology and biochemistry of novel pathways of microbial catabolism by bacteria involved in meat spoilage.

16204 Bergonzini, E.; Matassino, D.; Quadri, G.; Pilla, A.M.
IT 020700/77/0006 N
Stagionatura prosciutti. **Hams seasoning..**

16205 Crivelli, G.; Torreggiani, D.   IT 021900/79/0011 N
Comportamento del muscolo bovino al congelamento e al ricongelamento. **Behaviour of beef freezing and refreezing.**

16206 Cantoni, C.; Dragoni, I.; D'Aubert, S.; Cattaneo, P.; Bianchi, M.   IT 040633/76/0003
Studi sulla conservibilità della carne di cavallo. **Horse meat conservation.**

16207 Giuseppe Caserio; Gennari, M.   IT 040633/77/0001
Ricerca per l'utilizzazione di starters negli insaccati da stagionare per stabilire la loro efficacia come concorrenti vitali nei confronti di salmonelle e stafilococchi. **Research on the use of starters in dry sausage seasoning to determine their effectiveness as vital "Competitors" of salmonella and staphylococcus.**

16208 Cantoni, C.   IT 040633/77/0540 R
Studie sulla conservazione della carne equina. **Studies on the preservation of horse–flesh.**

16209 Cantoni, C.; Soncini, G.; Bianchi, M.A.; D'Aubert, S.; Beretta, G.; Perlasca, M.   IT 040633/79/0001 N
Studi sulla conservazione del prosciutto crudo. **Studies on dry ham conservability.**

16210 Muscarella, A.; Galofaro, V.; Macri, B.
IT 041703/77/0001
Isoenzimi della LDH negli estratti di muscolo fresco di bovini e dopo conservazione a –20 gradi C. **Isoenzymes of lactic dehydrogenase in fresh beef muscle extracts and after storage at –20 centigrades.** Publications.

16211 Baldini, P.; Palmia, F.   IT 070500/78/0001
Influenza delle caratteristiche chimiche e chimico–fisiche e della popolazione microbica iniziale nella stagionatura dei salami di tipo campagnolo. **Influence of chemical and physico–chemical characteristics and initial bacterial population on the ripening of country–style salami.**

16212 Baldini, P.; Palmia, F.   IT 070500/79/0001 N
Impiego di ridotte quantità di nitrito nella preparazione di salami stagionati italiani. Studio di nuove tecniche di produzione. **Use of reduced amounts of nitrite in the production of Italian dry salami. Study of new production techniques.**

16213 Baldini, P.; Parolari, G.   IT 070500/79/0002 N
Indagine sulla presenza di ammine secondarie nella carne e nei prodotti di carne. **Research on the occurrence of secondary amines in meat and meat products.**

16214 Gerrits, A.R.   NL 010109/69/2657
Bestudering van de grootte van ijskristallen in het spierweefsel van bevroren slachtkuikens. **Ice–crystals in the tissue of deep–frozen poultry.**

16215 Veerkamp, C.H.; Hofmans, G.J.P.   NL 010109/74/5962
Een alternatieve methode voor het koelen van geslacht pluimvee. **Alternative procedure for cooling eviscerated poultry**

carcasses. Publications.

Fish and marine food products (B 6852)

See also 16197, 16730

16216 Hovart, P.; Vyncke, W.   BE 070800/59/0006 R
Behandelingsprocessen en diepvriezen van vis en visserijprodukten. **Handling processes and deep–freezing of fish and fishery products.** Publications.

16217 Hovart, P.; Declerck, D.   BE 070800/60/0007
Technologisch onderzoek ter bewaring van visserijprodukten. **Technological research on the storage of fishery products.** Publications.

16218 Hovart, P.; Devriendt, H.   BE 070800/66/0009 R
Studie van de voorverpakking van vis en visserijprodukten. **Research on the pre–packaging of fishery products.** Publications.

16219 Karnop, G.   DE 208040/77/0005
Klassifizierung verderbsaktiver Bakterien an Hand biotopspezifischer Stoffwechseleigenschaften. **Classification of spoiling bacteria by specific biotopical metabolic properties.**

16220 Karnop, G.; Antonacopoulos, N.
DE 208040/78/0002 N
Haltbarkeit von Räucherfisch. **Shelf life of smoked fishery products.**

16221 Wit, J.C. de   NL 020031/77/7603
Betekenis van de pathogene en halofiele bederfflora bij het ontdooien van bevroren vis, schaal– en weekdieren.
Importance of the pathogenic and halophilic spoilage flora when thawing frozen fish and seafoods.

16222 Spreekens, K.J.A.   NL 050303/78/2971 N
De identificatie van bederf verwekkende micro–organismen en hun invloed op het bederfpatroon van verse vis. **Identification of spoilage micro–organisms and their influence on the spoilage pattern of fresh fish.**

16223 Houwing, H.   NL 050303/78/2974 N
Invloed van koeling, opslag en koolzuurhoudend zeewater, ontbloeding en overige voorbehandelingen op de kwaliteit van zowel het verse als het gevroren produkt. **The influence of cooling, storage and aerated seawater, bleeding and other pre–treatments on the quality of fresh and frozen fish products.**

16224 Pel, L. van   NL 050303/78/2980 N
Studie van de technologische en technische mogelijkheden van besparing van energiegebruik in koel– en vrieshuizen. **Study of the technological and technical possibilities of energy saving in cold stores and freezing stores for fish and fish products.**

Dairy products, eggs, egg products, ice cream in general (B 6860)

See also 16180

16225 Holt   GB 030203/00/0019 R
Factors affecting the stability of casein micelles.

16226 Anderson   GB 030903/00/0312 R
Survey of domestic and storage mites in premises storing cheese

in Western Scotland.

16227 Weldring, J.A.G. NL 020031/78/8527
Ultrafiltratie van melkwei–eiwit oplossingen. **Ultra–filtration of milk whey protein solutions.**

Milk products (B 6861)

See also 3367, 15695, 15787, 15850, 15924, 15927, 16840, 16849, 16866, 16888, 19325, 19336, 19384, 19439

16228 De Vilder, J.; Naudts, M. BE 070900/77/0038
De invloed van het bewaren op de fysische en chemische eigenschappen van melkpoeder. **The influence of storage on the physical and chemical properties of milk powder.**

16229 Mottar, J.; Naudts, M.; Waes, G.
BE 070900/77/0040 R
Sensorische eigenschappen van houdbare konsumptiemelk. **Sensoric properties of long–life types of milk.**

16230 Waes, G. BE 070900/79/0042 N
Bakteriologie van gepasteuriseerde melk met het oog op de hygiëne en de houdbaarheid. **Bacteriology of pasteurized milk in view of the hygiene and keeping quality.**

16231 Renner, E.; Müller, U. DE 129252/78/0002 N
Chemische und sensorische Qualitätskriterien der Buttermilch und deren Veränderungen während der Lagerung. **Chemical and sensoric quality criteria of buttermilk and their changes during storage.**

16232 Brauss, F.W.; Barth, H. DE 142101/70/0001
Bakteriologische Untersuchung von Milch, Speiseeis und Kindernahrung zur Erarbeitung von Keimzahl–Standards. **Bacteriological examination of milk, ice–cream, and infant food in order to obtain standard values for bacterial counts.**

16233 Guthy, K. DE 161340/77/0002
Lagerungseinflüsse auf die Stabilität von UHT–Milch. **Storage influences on UHT–milk stability.**

16234 Kiermeier, F.; Lechner, E. DE 502553/77/0002
Veränderung von UHT–Milch bei der Lagerung. **Changes of UHT–milk during storage.** Publications.

16235 Kirchmeier, O. DE 502553/77/0005
Denaturierung von Milchproteinen in Abhängigkeit von verschiedenen Erhitzungs– und Trocknungsverfahren. **Denaturation of milk protein in dependence on different heating and drying methods.** Publications.

16236 Jensen, G.K. DK 010300/77/0041
Produktions– og lagringsforholdenes indflydelse på varmebehandlingkontrollen af mælkepulverprodukter ved fosfataseprøven og Storch's prøve. **The influence of production and storage conditions on the heat treatment control of milk powder products as shown by the phosphatase and Storch's tests.**

16237 Jensen, G.K. DK 010300/77/0042
Opbevarings– og distributionsbetingelsernes betydning for konsummælksprodukternes holdbarhed. **The importance of the storaging and distribution conditions for the keeping properties of consumer milk products.**

16238 Birkkjær, H.E.; Werner, H. DK 010300/78/0028 N
Undersøgelse af omsætningen af nitrat i ost. **Investigations of the nitrate transformation in cheese.**

16239 Samuelsson, E.G. DK 030192/73/0001
Undersøgelser over mængden frit og bundet vand i forskellige proteinstoffer i første række mælkens proteiner og med henblik på en dybere forståelse af forskellige mejeriprodukters kvalitet og holdbarhed. **Investigations of the amount of free and combined water in different proteins, chiefly milk proteins, with reference to a deeper understanding of the quality and perishability of different dairy products.**

16240 McGann, T.C.A.; Donnelly, W.J.G.
IE 060400/75/1128 R
Structure and stability of casein micelles in milk and dairy products; with special reference to calcium and phosphate salts. Publications.

16241 McCarthy, D.D. IE 060400/75/2042 R
A study of the effect of nitrogen inputs, stocking rate and dairy merit on milk production. Publications.

16242 Emaldi, G.C.; Francani, R.; Toppino, P.M.; Nani, R.
IT 022200/76/0001 N
Tempo di maturazione del formaggio grana.. **Grana cheese ripening time..**

16243 Matteuzzi, D. IT 040210/73/0259
Studio fisiologico e biochimico dei batteri sporigeni anaerobi agenti di alterazioni dei prodotti caseari–gonfiore. **Physiological and biochemical study of anaerobic sporiferous bacteria, altering agents of industrial milk products–swelling.** Publications.

16244 Rossi, J.; Costamagna, L. IT 041023/72/0001 N
Aspetto chimico e microbiologico di materiali diversi ed applicazione di particolari aspetti tecnologici.. **Chemical and microbiologica features of various materials and application of special technological aspects..**

16245 Milani, R. IT 041802/74/0589
Ricerche di radiobiologia in piophila Casei L. **Radiobiologic research on Piophila casei L.**

16246 Milani, R. IT 041802/78/1090 N
Ricerche di radiobiologia in Piophila casei L. **Radiolobiological research on Piophila casei L.**

16247 Schipper, C.J. NL 010213/68/3380
Praktijkonderzoek naar de kwaliteit van diepgekoelde boerderijmelk en de geschiktheid van deze melk voor bewerking tot zuivelprodukten. **Field research about the quality of farm bulk milk and its suitability for processing into dairy products.** Publications.

16248 Kleter, G. NL 020031/75/6380
De invloed van ongedissocieerde zuren, voornamelijk melkzuur, op de groei van micro–organismen, met name Clostridium tyrobutyricum. **The influence of undissociated acids, particularly lactic acid, on the growth of micro organisms, particularly Clostridium tyrobutyricum.**

16249 Payens, T.A.J. NL 060002/68/4042
Gelering van gesteriliseerde, geëvaporeerde melk. **Age thickening of sterilized, evaporated milk.** Publications.

16250 Stadhouders, J.　　　　　NL 060002/70/4065
Het gebrek "bitter" in kaas. **The defect bitter in cheese.**
Publications.

16251 Stadhouders, J.　　　　　NL 060002/73/4066
De bestrijding van boterzuurgisting in Goudse kaas. **Control of
butyric acid fermentation in Gouda cheese.** Publications.

16252 Bouman, S.　　　　　NL 060002/74/5299
Condities in kaaspakhuizen. **Cheese storage conditions.**

16253 Elgersma, R.H.C.　　　　NL 060002/75/6604
Rose verkleuring van kaas. **Pink discoloration of the cheese
coating.**

16254 Exterkate, F.A.　　　　NL 060002/76/6616
Antibiotische werking van melkzuurstreptococcen ten opzichte
van pathogene micro–organismen. **Antibiotic action of lactic
acid bacteria on pathogenic micro–organisms.**

16255 Ubbels, J.　　　　　NL 060002/76/7243
Methoden om het energieverbruik bij het koelen van melk op
de boerderij te verminderen. **Methods of reducing the energy
consumption in the cooling of milk on farms.** Publications.

16256 Driessen, F.M.　　　　NL 060002/76/7251
Vetsplitsing in magere kwark tijden bewaren. **Lipolysis in
low–fat "quarg" during storage.**

16257 Neeter, R.　　　　　NL 060002/77/7924
Factoren die het voorkomen van N–nitrosaminen in kaas
beinvloeden. **Factors affecting the presence of N–nitrosamines
in cheese.** Publications.

16258 Payens, T.A.J.　　　　NL 060002/78/7919
Fysisch onderzoek betreffende de synerese van wrongel.
Physical research into the syneresis of curd.

16259 Stadhouders, J.　　　　NL 060002/78/7922
Ogenvorming in kaas. **Eye formation in cheese.**

16260 Berg, G. van den　　　　NL 060002/78/7923
Het weren van gist– en schimmelgroei op de kaaskorst.
Prevention of yeast and mould growth on the cheese rind.

Eggs and egg products (B 6862)

See also 19404

Other dairy products (B 6869)

See also 16232

Other foods (B 6870)

See also 16189, 16190, 16345

16261 Tändler, K.　　　　　DE 210020/75/0011
Hitze–, Kälte– und Lagerstabilität von Natur– und
Extraktgewürzen und sonstigen Würzstoffen. **Stability of
heating, freezing and storage of natural and extracted spices
and other seasoning substances.**

Alcoholic liquors, coffee, tea, tobacco and other table luxuries (B 6890)

See also 4392, 15825, 19439, 19461

16262 Wucherpfennig, K.; Wiegand, M.　　DE 506104/77/0003
Veränderungen der Most– und Weineiweissstoffe durch
verschiedene Kellerbehandlungsmittel. **Changes in proteins of
must and wine by divers cellarage agents.**

16263 Jelley, R.M.; Jeffares, M.; Kenny, T.A.
　　　　　　　　　　　　IE 060300/74/0128 N
Studies on wine production from gooseberries and other fruits.
Publications.

Other man–made resources (B 6900)

See also 2702, 15695, 15703, 15834, 15981

Waste products in general (B 7000)

See also 16093, 16323

Effluent, sewage (B 7100)

16264 Groneman, A.F.　　　　NL 010110/74/8979 N
Het ontsmetten van afvalwater, zuiveringsslib en
landbouwafval d.m.v. bestraling en de hierbij optredende
fysische en chemische veranderingen. **Disinfection by
irradiation and physical and chemical changes in waste waters,
sludge and agricultural wastes.** Publications.

Superfluous dung and urine (B 7200)

See also 14200, 15709, 15831, 15846, 16264

Refuse, garbage, industrial wastes (B 7300)

See also 15787, 16264

Other waste products (B 7900)

See also 15926

D 4430 – Processing

See also 4117, 7279, 14799, 15274, 15776, 18141

16265 Verachtert, H.; Van Oevelen, D.; Spaepen, M.
　　　　　　　　　　　　BE 040503/76/0006 R
Studie van de mengpopulaties actief in de fermentatie van
sommige levensmiddelen, speciaal de spontane wort
vergisting. **Study of mixed microbial populations involved in
food fermentative processes, especially spontaneous wort
fermentation.**

16266 Verachtert, H.; Peeters, C.　　BE 040503/77/0007 R
Studie van de warmte produktie in microbiële
afbraakprocessen. **Microbial heat production and its possible
utilization.**

16267 Knigge, W.; Broese, V.　　　DE 132780/75/0001
Einfluss der Stammkrümmung der Europäischen Lärche auf
die Holzeigenschaften des unteren Schaftteils. **The influence of
the curve of the stem of European larch on the wood properties
of the lower part of the trunk.**

16268 Orth, H.W.　　　　　DE 201070/75/0008

Untersuchung des Schneidvorgangs bei Trommel–Exakthäckslern unter besonderer Berücksichtigung der Gutzuführung. **Research on cutting problems with rotating chopping machines with special regard to the feeding of material.**

16269 Sonnenberg, H.   DE 201070/78/0001 N
Ermittlung und Verbesserung der verfahrenstechnischen Voraussetzungen für die Niedertemperaturtrocknung von Futterpflanzen. **Investigation and improvement of the technological conditions for low temperature drying of fodder plants.**

16270 Coretti, K.   DE 210030/75/0003
Dekontamination des mit Botulinum–Sporen verunreinigten Oberflächenwassers bei der Trinkwasseraufbereitung in Notständen. **Decontamination of surface water polluted with Clostridium botulinum spores during preparation of drinking water at times of emergency.**

16271 Mukherjee, K.D.; Ilsemann, K.; Mangold, H.K.
                    DE 213020/75/0010
Verwendung pflanzlicher Fettrohstoffe zur Herstellung von eiweissreichen Produkten. **Use of oleaginous plant raw materials for the production of products rich in protein.**

16272 Schmidt, B.; Leist, N.   DE 501014/78/0001 N
Untersuchungen zur Qualität von Hybridsaatmais – Abhängigkeit der Saatmaisqualität von der Kornform sowie der mechanischen Belastung bei der Aufbereitung. **Investigations about the quality of hybrid maize seeds – correlation between the quality of maize seeds and the shape of the kernels and the mechanical stress in the course of processing.**

16273 Poulsen, E.; Christensen, P.E.   DK 010102/69/3107
Undersøgelser af konsistens, aroma, farve og forarbejdningsmetoder, samt sortsegnethed af frugt og grønsager til industriel udnyttelse. **Investigations of consistency, aroma, colour and manufacturing methods, together with variety suitability, in fruit and vegetables for industrial use.**

16274 Jørgensen, G.   DK 010204/77/0001
Udvikling af risikofri konserveringsmetoder til fremstilling af fiskeensilage. **Development of risk–free preserving methods for use in fish silage preparation.**

16275 Knudsen, A.   DK 010300/77/0071
Støjdæmpende foranstaltninger i mejerianlæg. **Noise reduction measures in dairy plant equipment.**

16276 Holm, F.   DK 010800/73/0003
Industriel metode til separering af komponenterne fra byg og hvede. **Industrial method for separating components from barley and wheat.**

16277 Pedersen, T.T.   DK 030144/76/0002
Sønderdeling af græs før udpresning af saft. **Plant cell breakdown in grass prior to juice extraction.**

16278 Bech–Andersen, J.   DK 030500/77/8166
Identifikation af Mastesvamp A og B. **Identification of pole fungus A and B.**

16279 Turner; Loader   GB 010801/00/0007 R
Additives to improve performance of herbicides.

16280 Wilkinson; Hartley   GB 011202/79/0046 R
Chemical and biological methods to increase the digestibility of low quality forages and by products.

16281 Carruthers; Pirie   GB 012003/00/0029 R
Mechanical fractionation of forage crops and by–product leaves.

16282 Crozier   GB 050301/49/0018 R
Studies on existing methods of formulation analysis prior to collaborative work.

16283 Lovett   GB 050301/77/0022 R
Studies on new methods of formulation analysis prior to collaborative work.

16284 Gormley, T.r.   IE 060300/00/1439 N
Mushroom canning – processing factors. Publications.

16285 MacCanna, C.   IE 060300/69/0066 R
Improvement of casing media with particular reference to the 'spanned casing' technique for mushrooms. Publications.

16286 O'Keeffe, A.   IE 060400/76/1305 R
Improving the procedures for commercial production of casein and co–precipitate. Publications.

16287 Zambonelli, C.   IT 040210/74/0646
Studio e selezione di lieviti ad azione stabilizzante sul colore dei vini bianchi. **Study and selection of white wine colour stabilizing yeasts.**

16288 Bonadonna, T.; Succi, G.   IT 050100/76/0002
La conservazione prolungata del materiale spermatico per congelamento in comparazione con l'impiego di diversi mestrui diluitori. **Long conservation of frozen semen as compared with the use of different extenders.** Publications.

Feeding stuffs and drinking water for animals in general (B 6300)

See also 12037, 12056, 15472, 15888, 16406, 16457, 16815, 16892, 17100

16289 Hutt, W.; Oelschläger, W.; Sautter, D.
                    DE 144701/75/0001 N
Nährwertbeeeinflussung und Fremdstoffablagerung bei direktbeheizten Trocknern für Körnerfrüchte und Trocknungsverfahren. **Influence of burner emissions on nutritive value and toxious depositions with directly heated grain drying plants in dependence on fuel, contruction of the burner and construction of the drying plant.**

16290 Sonne–Frederiksen, P.; Jacobsen, E.E.; Thiesen, J.; Holm, F.; Rexen, B.   DK 010800/73/0001
Udvikling og afprøvning af hurtige kemiske og biologiske analysemetoder til belysning af foderblandingers foderværdi. **Development and testing of rapid chemical and biological analytical methods for the evaluation of quality in feedstuffs.**

16291 Faassen, H.G. van   NL 010103/74/5594
Laboratoriumonderzoek gericht op een optimale winning van microbiële biomassa uit mest. **Laboratory research directed towards maximum production of microbial biomass from**

manure. Publications.

16292 Leutscher, H.J.　　　　　NL 010105/74/8363
Technologisch onderzoek aan groenvoeder– en
veevoederprodukten t.b.v. opnameproeven. **Technological
research on green fodder and cattle feed products on behalf of
feeding and take–in trials. Publications.**

16293 Waart, J. de　　　　　NL 050301/75/6482
Het met microbieel eiwit verrijken van cellulosehoudend
materiaal, in het bijzonder rijstkafjes, door middel van
schimmels of bacteriën. **Microbial protein enrichment of
cellulosic waste material by means of moulds and bacteria.**

Concentrates (B 6310)

See also 11663, 11711, 12815, 16043, 16274, 16323, 16488,
16538, 16540, 16853, 16955, 16958, 16960, 16961, 16963, 16964,
17089, 17098, 19269

16294 Claus, H.G.; Kohlheb, R.　　　　　DE 132540/77/0001
Vorentwässerung von Halmfutter, Konzentration und
Gewinnung der Nährstoffe aus dem Saft. **Initial dehydration of
cereal crops for fodder, concentration and production of
nutrients from the juice.**

16295 Strauch, D.; Riedinger, O.　　　　　DE 144610/78/0007 N
Untersuchungen über die aus hygienischen Gründen
erforderliche Hitzeanwendung bei der Herstellung von
Tiermehlen unter besonderer Berücksichtigung neuer
technischer Verfahren. **Investigations on the necessary
temperatures because of hygienic conditions for production of
carcass meals in rendering plants.**

16296 Huss, W.; Deubelius, I.; Thormählen, M.; Keitel, K.
　　　　　DE 144625/73/0004
Auswirkungen thermischer Behandlung auf Quantität und
Qualität der Nährstoffe von Körnerfrüchten. **Effect of heat
treatment on quantity and quality of cereal nutrients.**

16297 Petersen, U.; Daenicke, R.　　　　　DE 201050/78/0008 N
Bewertung von Futterzusatzstoffen für Rinder und Schweine.
Valuation of feed additives for cattle and pigs.

16298 Pirkelmann, H.; Stangel, H.　　　　　DE 502602/71/0001 R
Einsatz von Flachsilofräsen Technologie der Herstellung von
Gärfutter– KraftfutterMischungen Vorlage von
komplettisierten Futtermischungen. Futter– technische
Grundlagen für standartisierte Futtermischungen 1971. **Use of
flat–silo cutters. Technology of preparing mixtures of silage and
concentrate feed. Feeding of completed feed mixtures. Feeding
conditions of standardized feed mixtures.**

16299 Jensen, G.K.　　　　　DK 010300/76/0043
Vallekoncentrater – fremstillingsteknologi og egenskaber. **The
manufacturing technology and properties of whey concentrates.**

16300 Jensen, G.K.　　　　　DK 010300/76/0044
Standardisering af mælkepulverprodukters sammensætning.
**The standardization of the composition of milk powder
products.**

16301 Jensen, G.K.　　　　　DK 010300/76/0045
Rensning af tørreluft ved brug af vådvasker i forbindelse med
fremstilling af mælkepulver. **The use of moist washes in
association with the dry air cleaning incorporated in the
manufacture of milk powder.**

16302 Casu, B.　　　　　IT 012200/77/0735 R
Studio della struttura dei polisaccaridi parietali di lieviti con
particolare riguardo al genere Candida mediante metodi
chimici, enzimatici e spettrometrici. **Study on the structure of
the wall polysaccharides of yeasts, particularly the Candida
species relying on chemical, enzymatical and spectrometric
methods.**

16303 Maltini, E.; Torreggiani, D.　　　　　IT 021900/79/0015 N
Sistema di utilizzazione dei residui della lavorazione degli
agrumi per produrre mangime integrato in pellets. **Production
of pellets for animal feeding from citrus processing waste.**

16304 Aversano, B.; Tonini, A.; Abet, M.
　　　　　IT 022300/79/0002 N
Utilizzazione della pianta di tabacco per l'estrazione di
materiale proteico. **Proteic material extraction from tobacco
plant.**

16305 Lerici, C.　　　　　IT 040208/77/0752 R
Formulati proteici a contenuto intermedio di umidità,
preparazione, caratterizzazione e valutazione della stabilità.
**Protein formulae with a medium humidity tenure,preparation,
characterisation and evaluation of stability.**

16306 Viviani, R.　　　　　IT 040231/77/0314 R
Produzione di aminoacidi essenziali ad opera di batteri
anaerobi. **Essential aminoacids production by anaerobic
bacteria.**

16307 Mordenti, A.　　　　　IT 040236/77/0246 R
Ricerche sull'acidificazione delle diete per lo svezzamento
precoce dei suinetti. **Research on the acidification of diets used
for the precocious weaning of piglets.**

16308 Craveri, R.　　　　　IT 040611/77/0739 R
Relazione fra caratteristiche fisiologiche e genetiche di lieviti
per la produzione di biomasse proteiche, influenza del
substrato colturale fonte di energia e carbonio sulla
composizione chimica delle biomasse, preparazione campioni
di biomasse per le varie U. O. **Relation existing between the
physiological and the genetical characteristics of yeasts used for
the production of protein biomasses; influence of the cultural
media as a source of energy and carbon on the biomass chemical
composition; the preparation of biomass samples for various U.
O..**

16309 Ipata, P.L.　　　　　IT 041128/77/0747 R
Studi sulla estraibilità delle proteine di materiale fogliario in
relazione alle proprietà funzionali del materiale stesso. Analisi
dei nucleosidi e neucleotidi di materiale fogliario. **Study on the
eventual extraction of proteins from leaves based on their
functional properties. Analysis of the nucleosides and the
nucleotides contained in leaves.**

16310 Materassi, R.　　　　　IT 061300/78/1128 N
Elementi necessari alla definizione dei costi di produzione di
biomassa algale. Qualità chimico–microbiologiche delle
biomasse algali prodotte non sterilmente. Trattamenti per
migliorare la digeribilità delle biomasse algali. **Basic elements
necessary to fix production costs of algae biomasses. The
chemical and micro–biological qualities of algae biomasses
produced in a non sterile environment. Procedures to improve**

the digestibility of algae biomasses.

16311 Volonterio, G. IT 062600/78/1129 N
Studio della microstruttura di prodotti estrusi e testurizzati con proteine non convenzionali. **A study of the micro–structure of extrusion compounds interwoven with non conventional proteins.**

16312 Felicioli, R. IT 063900/77/0743 R
Caratterizzazione biochimica e biofisica delle frazioni ottenute dalla proteina bianca di estratti di erba medica. **Biochemical and biophysical characterisation of the fractions obtained from the white protein extracted from lucerne.**

16313 Wieringa, G.W. NL 010102/76/6734
De winning en benutting van eiwit en andere bestanddelen uit gras. **The production and utilization of protein and other compounds from grass.**

16314 Zuilichem, D.J. van; Stolp, W. NL 020031/70/5133
Extrusie van levensmiddelen en veevoederpellets, met hoge druk en temperatuur en lage temperatuur en hoge druk. **Food and feed extrusion by expansion and press–forming processes.** Publications.

16315 Slump, P. NL 050301/70/6476
Verbetering van de voedingswaarde van diermeel en verenmeel. **Improvement of the nutritional value of meatmeal and feathermeal.** Publications.

16316 Beumer, H. NL 050302/74/6601
Onderzoek meel conditionering voor het persen. **Conditioning of meal to improve its pelletability.** Publications.

16317 Beumer, H. NL 050302/79/8994 N
Energiebesparing bij het maalproces voor de mengvoederbereiding. **Energy saving during the milling process in the mixed–feed preparation.**

16318 Kim, J.C. NL 050302/79/9001 N
Verbetering van de geschiktheid van botervet voor de bereiding van korstdeeg. **Improvement of the suitability of butterfat for preparation of puff–paste.**

Roughage (B 6320)

See also 3084, 3391, 3621, 3657, 11701, 11929, 12222, 12236, 12279, 15907, 15927, 16297, 16313, 16433

16319 Wieneke, F.; Pfeffer, E.; Claus, H.G.
DE 132540/74/0003
Aufschluss und Brikettierung von Stroh für die Ernährung von Wiederkäuern. **Treatment of straw and production of briquettes for ruminant feeding.**

16320 Voigtländer, G.; Schmidt, M.; Kühbauch, W.
DE 161255/72/0001
Sortencharakteristik wichtiger Gräser nach Menge und Polymerisationsgrad von Fruktosanen unter Beachtung der enzymatischen Steuerung; Abbau der Fruktosane bei der Frischkonservierung. **Characterization of some grasses in regard to amount and degree of polymerization of fructosanes with observation of enzymatic regulating; degradation of fructosanes during silage fermentation.**

16321 Zadrazil, F.; Grabbe, K.; Theune, H.H.

DE 201020/75/0014
Mikrobielle Aufbereitung von Stroh zu Futterzwecken. **Microbial treatment of straw for feeding purposes.**

16322 Weise, F. DE 201030/77/0001
Populationsdynamik von Gärfutter unter besonderer Berücksichtigung der Lactobazillenarten und der Proteolyten. **Population dynamics of silage feed in special consideration of lactobacillus species and of proteolytes.**

16323 Theune, H.H. DE 201030/77/0018 R
Wirkungsweise und Einsatzgrenzen von Zusatzstoffen bei der Konservierung von Futtermitteln unter besonderer Beachtung der Rückstandsproblematik. **Mode of action and Limits of using additives in preservation of feeds with special regard to the problems of residues.**

16324 Paul, C.; Theune, H.H. DE 201030/78/0001 N
Streubreite der in vitro–Verdaulichkeit von verschiedenen Sortimenten in Abhängigkeit vom Standort; Grundlagen zur Sortenbeurteilung. **Variation of in vitro digestibility of different assortments in relation to location; valuation of varieties.**

16325 Theune, H.H. DE 201030/78/0003 N
Minderung des Proteinabbaues und Verbesserung der N–Verwertung bei Grundfutter durch Zusatzstoffe. **Minimizing of protein breakdown and improving of N–utilization by use of silage–additives.**

16326 Schöllhorn, J.; Szokolai, P. DE 501201/72/0002
Wirkung von Silierzusätzen auf Vergärung, Stabilität und Nährstoffbilanz bei Wiesengras– und Maissilage. **The effect of silage additives on fermentation process, stability and balance of nutriments in meadow grass– and maize–silage.**

16327 Beck, T. DE 502055/72/0006
Mikrobiologische Untersuchungen zum Problem der Nachgärung bei der Gärfutterbereitung. **Microbiological studies of the postfermentation phase in silage making.**

16328 Gross, F.; Beck, T. DE 502300/72/0005
Vergleichende Untersuchungen über die Wirkung von Silierhilfsmitteln. **Comparative investigations on ensiling agents.**

16329 Gross, F. DE 502302/78/0001 N
Silierung proteinreicher Maissorten. **Silage making of maize varieties rich in protein.**

16330 Gross, F.; Graf, F. DE 502302/78/0002 N
Untersuchungen zur energetischen Bewertung der Verluste bei der Silagegärung. **Research on the energetic evaluation of losses during silage fermentation.**

16331 Waagepetersen, J. DK 030104/77/0001
Anatomiske og kemiske undersøgelser af NH₃, NaOH og Na₂SO₃ behandlet halm. **Anatomical and chemical investigations of NH₃, NaOH and Na₂SO₃ treated straw.**

16332 Lila, M.; Picard, J.; Berthelem, M.; Lenoble, M.
FR 012223/76/0406
Digestibilité in vitro des graines de lupin et de féverole en fonction de la présence d'alcaloïdes ou de tanins. **In vitro digestibility of lupin, field bean grains as a function of the presence of alkaloides or tannins.**

16333 Connell GB 011704/76/0025 R
Improving the feeding value of roughages by chemical and physical treatents.

16334 Lawlor, M.J.; Maguire, M.F.; O'Shea, J.; Spillane, T.A.; Wheeler, B.M. IE 060100/74/1204 R
The ammoniation and processing of straw. Publications.

16335 Gleeson, P.A.; Murphy, J. IE 060400/74/2050 R
Improving silage quality. Publications.

16336 Galvano, G. IT 040303/77/0190 R
Ricerche sul miglioramento del valore nutritivo delle paglie e di altri sottoprodotti agricolo–industriali, mediante trattamento chimico. **Research on the improvement of the nutritional value of straw and other agricultural–industrial by–products by means of chemical treatment.**

16337 Leutscher, H.J. NL 010105/67/8362
Technische en milieu–aspecten van het kunstmatig drogen van groenvoeders. **Technical and environmental aspects of the green crop drying process.** Publications.

16338 Leutscher, H.J. NL 010105/71/8361 R
Ontwikkeling van structuurhoudende resp. hoogwaardige veevoeders uit ruwvoedercomponenten. **Development of structured resp. high–graded cattle feed from roughage components.**

16339 Leutscher, H.J. NL 010105/75/8364
Begeleiding van de groenvoederdroog–industrie. **Technical assistance to the green crop drying industry.**

16340 Bosma, A.H. NL 010106/77/7605
Materiaaleigenschappen van maïs en gras in relatie tot opslagsysteem en verwerkingsapparatuur. **Material properties of grass and maize silage in relation to storage systems and handling equipment.**

16341 Schukking, S. NL 010208/72/3866
Diverse aspecten van hakselen van ruwvoer. **Various aspects of chopping roughage.** Publications.

Other feeding stuffs (B 6390)

See also 16853, 16962, 17062

16342 Foxell GB 011705/00/0025 R
Methods for production of protein concentrates from expressed forage juice.

16343 Paton GB 060220/00/0003 R
Preservation and stimulation of fermentation in grass juice.

16344 Wilson, R.K.; Maguire, M.F. IE 060100/74/1001 R
Preservation and feeding value of protein rich and other animal byproducts. Publications.

16345 Zambonelli, C. IT 040240/77/1126 N
Recupero e utilizzazione del lievito di cantina. **Recuperation and use of cellar yeasts.**

16346 Gargani, G. IT 040513/78/1123 N
Caratterizzazione sierologica di lieviti di interesse industriale con impiego di antigeni cellulari e antigeni parietali –fraz. meccanica–. Studio di eventuali fenomeni allergici. Patogenicità sperimentale con particolare riguardo alle prove su linee cellulari animali in vitro. **Serological characterisation of industrial yeasts using cellular and wall antigens – mechanical fraction –. A study of eventual allergic reactions. Experimental pathogenicity especially in "in vitro" tests on animal cellular lines.**

16347 Caretta, G. IT 041803/77/0733 R
Caratterizzazione immunosierologica e patogenicità sperimentale nell'animale di lieviti di interesse industriale. **Industrial yeasts : immuno–serological characterisation, experimental pathogenicity in the animal.**

16348 Clementi, F. IT 063800/77/1167 N
A) Aspetti morfologici di lieviti usati come fonte proteica. b) Aspetti morfologici di animali trattati con diverse diete. **a) Morphological aspects of yeasts used as a protein source. b) Morphological aspects of animals fed on different diets.**

Organic fertilizers (B 6410)

See also 1012, 15709, 15929, 17061, 17065, 17078, 17088, 17093

16349 Strauch, D.; König, W. DE 144610/78/0006 N
Hygienische Untersuchungen bei der Entwicklung eines Trockengranulates aus Schwarztorf und Klärschlamm als handelsfähiges Bodenverbesserungs– und Düngemittel. **Hygienic investigations during development of a dried granulate from black peat and sewage sludge as commercial soil improver and fertilizer.**

16350 Grabbe, K. DE 201020/78/0006 N
Stoffumsatz bei der Fermentation von Flüssigmist. **Turnover of organic matter during fermentation of liquid manure.**

16351 Hege, U.; Diez, T. DE 502055/78/0003 N
Verbesserung der Düngewirkung wirtschaftseigener Dünger. **Improvement of the fertilizing effect of manure.**

16352 Hammer, K.; Walser, M. DE 502306/78/0001 N
Untersuchungen über die Anwendbarkeit der Flüssigmistbelüftung im Dungkeller und der Umspülung mit belüftetem Flüssigmist in Mastschweineställen unter Praxisbedingungen. **Investigations on the practicability of liquid manure aeration in a dung cellar and on flushing dung channels with aerated liquid manure in stables for fattening pigs.**

16353 Berthelsen, L.; Nielsen, H.; Pedersen, P.T.
DK 030144/78/0004 N
Udnyttelse af komposteringsvarme. **Heating by means of aerobic fermentation of manure.**

16354 Albonetti, S.G.; Massari, G. IT 041607/76/0003 N
Microbiological aspects of a municipal waste composting system. Publications.

16355 Massari, G.; Albonetti, S.G. IT 041607/77/0002 N
Production of a stabilized compost in the rome dano plant. Publications.

16356 Jodice, R.; Ferrara, R. IT 120100/79/0002 N
Trasformazione in fertilizzante organico delle cortecce di abete e di pino. **Fir and pine bark composting.**

Mineral fertilizers (B 6420)

D 4430 – Processing

See also 16581, 17053, 17084, 17092

Pouring, sprinkling, and irrigation water (B 6430)

See also 1449

16357 Wolkewitz, H.; Nitsche, H.　　DE 105250/78/0006 N
Gewinnung von Süsswasser für Beregnung aus Salzwasser
durch solare Destillation. **Production of freshwater for
irrigation from salt–water by solar distillation.**

Amendments (B 6440)

See also 16349, 17086

Fibre materials and wood products (B 6700)

See also 16267, 16319, 16452, 17089

16358 Mottet, A.; Fraipont, L.　　BE 010001/66/0003 R
Etude du problème des émanations d'aldéhyde formique des
panneaux de particules encollés au moyen de résines du type
"urée–formol". **Research on formaldehydes's emanations from
particleboards glued with urea–formaldehyde resins.**
Publications.

16359 Mottet, A.; Paquot, M.; Deroanne, C.; Flambert, C.;
Fraipoint, L.; Thonart, P.　　BE 010001/76/0005 R
Récupération de vieux papiers. **Recuperation of waste papers.**
Publications.

16360 Mottet, A.; Paquot, M.; Thonart, P.; Fraipont;
Deroanne, C.　　BE 010015/76/0005 R
Revalorisation de la cellulose récupérée. **Upgrading of waste
cellulosic materials.**

16361 Antoine, R.; Avella, T.　　BE 020301/69/0002 N
Etude de la stabilisation dimensionnelle des bois utilisés
comme couvre–sols. **Study of dimensional stabilization of
flooring woods. Publications.**

16362 Antoine, R.; Avella, T.; Roussel, A.; Giot–Wirgot, P.

　　BE 020301/70/0003 R
Etude du greffage de radicaux organiques polymérisables sur la
cellulose, les hemicelluloses et la lignine. **Study of the grafting
products between cellulose, hemicellulose, lignine and
polymerisable organic radicals. Publications.**

16363 Antoine, R.; Avella, T.　　BE 020301/71/0004
Mise au point de matériaux composites à base de fibre de bois.
Perfecting composite materials based on wood fibre.

16364 Antoine, R.; Giot–Wirgot, P.　　BE 020301/75/0009
Etude des phénomènes fondamentaux à base de l'élaboration
de matériaux composites nouveaux au départ de matériaux
ligneux et de résines polymétriques. **Study of fundamental
phenomens based of the elaboration of new composite materials
started from ligneous materials and polymeric resins.**

16365 Raes, G.; De Langhe, E.　　BE 030016/00/0001
Studie van de membraanstrukturen van de plantaardige vezels
gebruikt in de textielindustrie. **Study of membranestructures of
plantfibers used in textielindustry. Publications.**

16366 Bismarck, C.von　　DE 114450/74/0004

Untersuchungen zur Verbesserung des Brandverhaltens von
speziellen Holzwerkstoff–Verbundplatten für das Bauwesen.
**Research on improving the fire performance of special wood
material boards for building purposes.**

16367 Böttcher, P.; Neigenfind, W.　　DE 114450/74/0005
Einfluss verschiedenartiger Oberflächenprofilierungen auf die
Erhöhung der Wetterbeständigkeit. **Effect of different surface
profiles on the weather resistance of wooden boards.**

16368 Roffael, E.　　DE 114450/74/0009
Einfluss der Extraktstoffe auf die Verwertungsmöglichkeiten
der Rinde von Fichte und Kiefer. **Influence of extractives on the
utilization of pine and spruce barks.**

16369 Böttcher, P.; Neigenfind, W.　　DE 114450/74/0011
Verbesserung des Feuchteschutzes von Holzleimbindern.
Improvement of water–repellent wood glue binders.

16370 Pungs, L.; Rauch, W.; Lamberts, K.
　　DE 114450/74/0012
Untersuchung des Einflusses einer
HochfrequenzNacherwärmung auf die Eigenschaften von
Holz– spanplatten mit erhöhter Witterungsbeständigkeit.
**Investigation on the influence of high–frequency secondary
thermal treatment on the properties of particle boards with
high weather resistance.**

16371 May, H.–A.　　DE 114450/74/0014
Untersuchungen über die Eignung von lange lagerndem
Sturmholz der Kiefer für Spanplatten. **Investigations on the
suitability of long–time stored, wind–blown pine wood for
producing particle boards.**

16372 Salje, E.; Polster, J.　　DE 114502/77/0001
Geräuschentwicklung in Abhängigkeit von der
Werkstückeinspannung beim Fräsen und Sägen
plattenförmiger Holzwerkstücke. **Sound generation of work
support during shaping and sawing of workpiece plates.**

16373 Salje, E.; Bartsch, U.　　DE 114502/77/0002
Kantenbearbeitung plattenförmiger Werkstücke aus
Holzwerkstoffen mittels Besäumzerspaner und Fräser. **Edge
cutting of workpiece plate with hogging cutter and milling
cutter.**

16374 Grammel, R.; Behler, H.　　DE 126650/75/0004
Die Verwertung der Rinde als technologisches, ökonomisches
und organisatorisches Problem. **The utilization of bark as a
technological, economical and organizational problem.**

16375 Grammel, R.　　DE 126650/77/0008
Untersuchungen zur optimalen Stammholzlänge. **Analysis
about the optimal timber–length.**

16376 Grammel, R.; Amri, A.　　DE 126650/77/0009
Aufkommen und Verwertung von Biomassespänen. **Recovery
and use of green chips.**

16377 Sachsse, H.　　DE 132780/74/0003
Vergleichende Untersuchung technologisch wichtiger
Holzeigenschaften verschiedener Klone der Japanischen
Lärche. **Comparative studies on technologically important
wood properties of different clones of Larix leptolepis MILL..**

16378 Möhler, K.; Ehlbeck, J.; Budianto, T.

DE 145400/75/0001
Bestimmung der Lochleibungsfestigkeit und des Last–Eindrückungsverhaltens von Holzspanplatten zur Festlegung zulässiger Beanspruchungen mechanischer Holzverbindungsmittel. **Destination of the hole–bearing strength and the load–slip behaviour of particle board for fixing the allowable loads of mechanical fasteners.**

16379 Möhler, K.; Steck, G.   DE 145400/75/0002
Rissbildung bei Brettschichtträgern durch Feuchtigkeitseinflüsse. **The rise of splints in glued laminated beams caused by the influence of moisture.**

16380 Möhler, K.; Ehlbeck, J.; Ong, T.K.
DE 145400/75/0003
Untersuchungen zur Festlegung zulässiger Belastungen von Vollholz–Holzwerkstoff–Verbindungen. **Investigations for fixing the allowable loads of joints between timber and wood–based materials.** Publications.

16381 Möhler, K.; Hemmer, K.   DE 145400/75/0004
Zusammenwirken von Längs–, Quer– und Schubspannungen – Torsionsspannungen – bei Brettschicht– und Vollholzbauteilen. **Interaction of normal, transverse and shear stresses in glued laminated timber and full–scale timber.**

16382 Möhler, K.; Gressel, P.   DE 145400/78/0001 N
Erfassung, systematische Auswertung und Ergänzung bisheriger Untersuchungen über das rheologische Verhalten von Holz und Holzwerkstoffen – ein Beitrag zur Verbesserung des Formänderungsnachweises nach DIN 1052 – Holzbauwerke. **Collection, systematic evaluation and completion of performed investigations on the rheological behaviour of wood and woodbased materials – a contribution to the improvement of the deformation proof by DIN 1052.**

16383 Schuck, H.J.   DE 160061/75/0003
Untersuchungen über traumatische Harze. **Investigations on traumatic resins.**

16384 Schulz, H.; Hey; Gregoriou; Tröger, G.
DE 160331/75/0002
Untersuchung des Einflusses verschiedenen Deckschichtmaterials auf die Oberflächenqualität von Spanplatten. **Investigation of the influence of different surface layer materials on the surface quality of particle boards.**

16385 Schulz, H.; Tröger, F.   DE 160331/78/0001 N
Biomasse und ihre Verwertung für plattenförmige Holzwerkstoffe. **Biomass and its utilization for wood–based panels.**

16386 Fengel, D.; Lucyszyn, G.W.   DE 160332/72/0003
Strukturuntersuchungen an Cellulose. **Studies on the structure of cellulose.**

16387 Fengel, D.; Wegener, G.   DE 160332/75/0001
Untersuchungen an schonend isoliertem Lignin aus Fichtenholz. **Investigations of lignin carefully isolated from spruce wood.** Publications.

16388 Fengel, D.; Wegener, G.; Heizmann, A.; Przyklenk, M.   DE 160332/77/0001
Versuche zum schonenden hydrolytischen Abbau von Holz und Polysacchariden. **Studies on the careful hydrolytic degradation of wood and polysaccarides.** Publications.

16389 Schneider, A.; Engelhardt, F.   DE 160334/75/0001
Untersuchungen über das Sorptionsverhalten von Holz im Temperaturbereich von 100 bis 170 Grad C. **Studies on the sorption behaviour of wood at temperatures in the range of 100 to 170 degrees C.**

16390 Schneider, A.; Engelhardt, F.; Wagner, L.
DE 160334/77/0002
Untersuchungen über die Wärmeleitfähigkeit von Hölzern in Abhängigkeit von ihrer kennzeichnenden Porenstruktur. **Investigations on the thermal conductivity of different woods as a function of their characteristic pore structure.**

16391 Schneider, A.   DE 160334/77/0003
Untersuchungen über das Sorptionsverhalten von Rinden. **Studies on the sorption behaviour of wood barks.** Publications.

16392 Heimeshoff, B.; Kersken–Bradley, M.; Krzykacz, B.
DE 161582/75/0002
Zuverlässigkeitsmodelle für Brettschichtbauteile. **Reliability models for glued laminated boams.**

16393 Kolb, H.; Goth, H.   DE 170301/75/0002
Klärung der zweckmässigen Reparaturmöglichkeit an Brettschichtträgern. **Determination of the functional possibility of repairing glued laminated beams.**

16394 Kolb, H.; Gruber, R.   DE 170301/77/0002
Prüfung von keilgezinkten Bauteilen aus Brettschichtholz mit Zwischenstücken aus Buchenfurnierplatten. **Testing of wedge–dovetailed construction elements of piled dealwood with intermediate beech veneer boards.**

16395 Kolb, H.; Gruber, R.   DE 170301/78/0002 N
Maschinelle Holzsortierung mit Isotopen. **Mechanical classification of wood with isotopes.**

16396 Kolb, H.; Frech, P.   DE 170301/78/0003 N
Festigkeitsverhalten von Leimverbindungen zwischen Baufurnierplatten und Brettschichtholz. **Strength beaviour of connectiong glue between building veneer boards and stacked board wood.**

16397 Parameswaran, N.   DE 202040/75/0004
Biologische Untersuchungen zur Rindennutzung. **Biological studies on bark utilization.**

16398 Bauch, J.; Klein, P.; Richter, J.; Gottwald, H.
DE 202040/77/0003
Biologische Untersuchungen holzwirtschaftlich wichtiger Pflanzenfamilien. **Biological investigations on plant families of importance for lumber industry.**

16399 Schweers, W.; Augustin, H.   DE 202050/72/5003
Entwicklung eines schwefelfreien Holzaufschlussverfahrens. **Development of sulphur free pulping processes.**

16400 Schweers, W.; Faix, O.; Simatupang, M.H.
DE 202050/72/5008
Analytische Untersuchungen am Lignin. **Analytical investigations into lignin.**

16401 Simatupang, M.H.   DE 202050/72/5015
Verbesserung der Eigenschaften mineralverbundener Holzwerkstoffe. **Improvement of properties of mineral–bound wood materials.**

16402 Dietrichs, H.H.; Puls, J.   DE 202050/75/0004
Biochemische Holzverwertung. **Biochemical utilization of timber.**

16403 Dietrichs, H.H.; Sinner, M.; Simatupang, M.H.
    DE 202050/77/0001
Analyse von Kohlenhydraten in der Holzchemie. **Analysis of carbohydrates in wood chemistry.**

16404 Weissmann, G.   DE 202050/77/0003
Versuche zur technischen Verwendung von Rinde. **Trials on technical use of bark.**

16405 Weissmann, G.   DE 202050/77/0004
Untersuchung von Harzbalsamen aus Kiefern. **Testing of resin balms from pines.**

16406 Dietrichs, H.H.; Puls, J.   DE 202050/78/0001 N
Herstellung von Futtermitteln aus Restholz und anderen lignocellulosischen Materialien. **Production of feeds of residual wood and other lignocellulosic materials.**

16407 Dietrichs, H.H.; Sinner, M.   DE 202050/78/0002 N
Dampf–Druck–Aufschluss von Holz und anderen lignocellulosischen Rohstoffen zur Gewinnung von chemischen Wertstoffen. **Steam pressure treatment of wood and other lignocellulosic raw materials for production of chemically valuable substances.**

16408 Schweers, W.; Faix, O.; Lange, W.; Meier, D.;
Schwesinger, H.; Dietrichs, H.H.   DE 202050/78/0003 N
Aufschluss von Holz und anderen lignocellulosischen Materialien mit Wasser und organischen Lösungsmitteln zur Gewinnung chemischer Wertstoffe. **Treatment of wood and other lignocellulosic materials with water and organic solvents for production of chemically valuable substances.**

16409 Schweers, W.; Garves, K.   DE 202050/78/0004 N
Erschliessung neuer Verwertungsmöglichkeiten für Zellstoffe aus Rest– und Abfallhölzern und anderen lignocellulosischen Materialien. **Development of new methods of utilizing celluloses of residual and refuse wood and other lignocellulosic materials.**

16410 Patt, R.   DE 202050/78/0005 N
Verwendung von Industrierestholz zur Herstellung von Holzstoff auf mechanisch–thermischem Wege. **Utilization of industrial residual wood for mechanicthermal production of wood pulp.**

16411 Patt, R.   DE 202050/78/0006 N
Umweltfreundliche Bleiche von Sulfitzellstoffen. **Bleaching of sulphite celluloses without impact on the environment.**

16412 Schweers, W.; Büsing, J.; Dietrichs, H.H.
    DE 202050/78/0007 N
Studie: Chemisch–technische Grundlagen zur Nutzung von Holz und Holzabfallstoffen als Chemierohstoffe. **Study on chemico–technical conditions for utilizing wood and refuse wood as chemical raw materials.**

16413 Faix, O.; Schweers, W.   DE 202050/78/0008 N
Analytische Untersuchung mexikanischer Holzarten und ihre Verwertbarkeit zur Zellstofferzeugung. **Analytical investigation of Mexican timber species and their possible utilization for chemical pulping.**

16414 Christoph, N.   DE 202060/71/5003
Untersuchungen zur thermischen Zersetzung und dem Brandverhalten von Holz und Holzwerkstoffen. **Studies on thermic decomposition and burning behaviour of wood and wood materials.**

16415 Roth, W.von   DE 202060/71/5005
Dauerfestigkeitsuntersuchungen an hölzernen Rahmenecken. **Studies on permanent stability of wooden frame edges.**

16416 Noack, D.; Frühwald, A.   DE 202060/72/5001
Untersuchungen über die Umweltrelevanz der mechanischen Holzindustrie. **Relevance of mechanical timber industry to environment.**

16417 Noack, D.; Lempfer, K.   DE 202060/74/5004
Hygroskopisches Verhalten beschichteter Holzwerkstoffe. **Hygroscopic behaviour of coated timber material.**

16418 Noack, D.; Wiemann, D.   DE 202060/74/5005
Beitrag zum Biegeverhalten dünner Holzwerkstoffe. **Bending behaviour of thin timber material.**

16419 Christoph, N.; Brettel, G.   DE 202060/77/0001
Untersuchungen über die thermischen Eigenschaften von Holz und Holzwerkstoffen. **Investigations on thermal properties of wood and wood–based materials.**

16420 Geissen, A.   DE 202060/77/0002
Untersuchungen über die Sorptionseigenschaften des Holzes. **Investigations on sorption properties of wood.**

16421 Becker, H.F.; Wiemann, D.   DE 202060/77/0003
Untersuchungen über das viskoelastische Verhalten des Holzes und der Holzwerkstoffe. **Investigations on the visco–elastic behaviour of wood and wood–based materials.**

16422 Schwab, E.; Bröker, F.; Frühwald, A.
    DE 202060/77/0004
Untersuchung der physikalisch–technologischen Eigenschaften tropischer Holzarten. **Investigations on technological properties of tropical woods.**

16423 Frühwald, A.; Ayla, C.   DE 202060/77/0005
Untersuchungen über die Holzverleimung. **Investigations on gluing of wood.**

16424 Noack, D.; Schwab, E.; Bröker, F.
    DE 202060/77/0007
Holztechnologische Untersuchungen als Grundlage nationaler und internationaler Normung. **Wood–technological investigations as a basis of national and international standardization.**

16425 Frühwald, A.; Albin, R.   DE 202060/77/0008
Untersuchungen über verfahrenstechnische Einflüsse bei der Herstellung von Schnittholz und Holzwerkstoffen. **Studies on processing of lumber and wood–based panels.**

16426 Albin, R.   DE 202060/78/0001 N
Untersuchungen über den Fertigungsablauf in der mechanischen Holzindustrie. **Studies on the production process of mechanical timber industry.**

16427 Geissen, A.   DE 202060/78/0002 N
Untersuchungen über die elektrischen Eigenschaften von Holz

und Holzwerkstoffen. **Studies on the electrical properties of wood and wood–based materials.**

16428 Christoph, N.   DE 202060/78/0003 N
Untersuchungen über die thermischen Eigenschaften und das Brandverhalten von Holz und Holzwerkstoffen. **Studies on thermal properties and burning behaviour of wood and wood–based materials.**

16429 Noack, D.; Schwab, E.; Bröker, F.
     DE 202060/78/0004 N
Untersuchungen über das Quell– und Schwindverhalten von Holz und Holzwerkstoffen. **Studies on swelling and shrinking behaviour of wood and wood–based materials.**

16430 Burmester, A.; Wille, W.   DE 217010/78/0001 N
Umformung von Holz. **Recombination of wood.**

16431 Gressel, P.; Reiter, L.   DE 913000/73/0002 N
Beschichtung von Holzwerkstoffen – insbesondere Spanplatten – Anforderungen an die Trägerplatte, Prüfverfahren. **The coating of timber material – especially of chip boards – requirements for carrier boards, test methods.**

16432 Keller, P.; Nielsen, V.   DK 010400/77/0002 N
Tekniske funktionskrav og arbejdsmæssige konsekvenser ved håndtering af halm i storballe. **Technical requirements and working consequences of handling straw in big bales.**

16433 Rexen, F.P.; Israelsen, M.   DK 010800/78/0002 N
Forarbejdning af celluloseholdige affaldsstoffer til foder med henblik på anvendelse til såvel kvæg som enmavede husdyr. **Processing of cellulose–rich waste for feed for cattle and mono–gastric farm animals.**

16434 Janin, G.; Letzelter, B.   FR 010304/68/4208 N
Techniques de cuisson et de microcuisson papetière. **Pulping and micropulping techniques.**

16435 Janin, G.; Letzelter, B.   FR 010304/72/4206 N
Raffinage – microraffinage des pâtes à papier. **Beating and microbeating.**

16436 Specty, R.; Conesa, A.; Aussenac   FR 010906/76/9066
Production de fibres cellulosiques sous épandage "d'eau chaude" rejetée par les Centrales Nucléaires de Fessenheim. **Production of cellulose–rich fibers through waste warm water effluents of the Fessenheim electro–nuclear power–stations.**

16437 Scrinzi, G.   IT 021800/78/0001
Variazioni di massa, di valore e di rendimento, degli assortimenti segati di prima lavorazione in relazione al variare dell'età media dei soprassuoli boschivi a dominanza di Picea. **Volume, value and yield variations of sawed assortments of first processing in relation to spruce stand age.**

16438 Bragadin, C.; Bianchi, A.; Freddi, G.
     IT 070700/78/0001 R
Studio comparativo degli amminoacidi presenti nelle sete da Bombyx Mori e presenti nelle sete non da gelso. **Comparative study of the amino–acids in Bombyx Mori silks and in non mulberry silks.** Publications.

16439 Hofenk, G.   NL 010105/73/5473
Chemische en technologische aspecten bij de verwerking van stro. **Chemical and technological aspects of straw processing.**

Publications.

Food and table luxuries in general (B 6800)

See also 2828, 15971, 15976, 15978, 16014, 16016, 16027, 16030, 16031, 16265, 16271, 16314, 16479, 16695, 17096, 17100, 17179, 18841, 18883, 18892, 18922, 18938

16440 Wasmund, R.   DE 105750/71/0002
Bestimmung der mechanischen und thermischen Stoffwerte CO_2–haltiger Flüssigkeitsgemische bei verschiedenen Zustandsbedingungen und in Abhängigkeit von der Zusammensetzung. **Determination of mechanical and thermal values of fluid mixtures enriched with CO_2 in dependence on different state conditions and concentrations.** Publications.

16441 Wasmund, R.; Wallrabe, R.   DE 105750/73/0001
Bestimmung des Wärmeleitkoeffizienten CO_2–haltiger Flüssigkeiten bei unterschiedlichen Zusammensetzungen, Drücken und Temperaturen. **Determination of thermal conductivity of fluids containing CO_2 in dependence on concentration, pressure and temperature.**

16442 Wasmund, R.; Fitzner, U.   DE 105750/77/0001
Gelöste und ungelöste Probleme der Automatisierung von Fermentationsprozessen. **Cleared and uncleared problems in automatization of fermentation processes.** Publications.

16443 List, D.; Palmer, J.   DE 105811/72/0003
Flüssigchromatographische Auftrennung und Bestimmung der organischen Säuren in pflanzlichen Lebensmitteln. Anwendung für Qualitätskontrolle der Rohware, Żwischen– und Fertigprodukte. **Separation and determination of organic acids in plant foods by fast liquid chromatography. Application to quality control of raw materials, intermediate and end products.**

16444 Bielig, H.J.; Emschermann, B.   DE 105813/78/0001 N
Optimierung des Sterilisationsprozesses für Fertiggerichte durch Erfassung der Texturveränderung an Einzelkomponenten. **Determination of sterilization optimum for ready–to–serve foods by texture measurements in single food components.**

16445 Baltes, W.; Söchtig, I.   DE 105900/75/0003
Untersuchungen an den niedermolekularen Aromastoffen von Raucharomaessenzen. **Investigations of low molecular aroma compounds in liquid smoke essences.**

16446 Dellweg, H.; Bernhardt, U.; Held, W.; Reimann, J.; Schlanderer, G.   DE 105988/77/0001
C1–Stoffwechsel in Hefen. **C1–metabolism in yeasts.**

16447 Dellweg, H.; Reuss, M.; Bronn, W.K.; Debus, H.
     DE 105988/77/0002
Reaktionstechnische Grundlagen von Fermentationen. **Basic parameters of fermentation processes.**

16448 Dellweg, H.; Kjer, I.   DE 105988/77/0003
Cellulose–abbauende Enzyme in Mikroorganismen – Funktion, Bildungskinetik, Regulation. **Cellulose degrading enzymes in microorganisms – function, kinetics of fermentation, regulation –.**

16449 Windisch, S.; Rehberg, R.   DE 105990/71/0002 N
Lyophilisation schwer konservierbarer Keime. **Lyophilization**

D 4430 – Processing

of micro–organisms difficult to conserve. Publications.

16450 Windisch, S.; Stobbe, M. DE 105990/77/0001
Untersuchungen über das Problem der Vorzucht von Hefen für neue Technologien am Beispiel von Spezialhefen. **Investigations on the problem of the pre–culture of yeasts for new technologies exemplified by special baking yeasts.**

16451 Maier, H.G.; Schmidt, F. DE 114100/74/0002
Bindung flüchtiger Aromastoffe an Proteine. **Sorption of volatile aromatic compounds to proteins.**

16452 Bruchmann, E.–E.; Betsch, E. DE 144241/78/0001 N
Biokonversion von Cellulose und verwandten Materialien. **Bioconversion of cellulose and related materials.** Publications.

16453 Gierschner, K.; Dörreich, K.; Otterbach, G.
DE 144260/78/0002 N
Weitere Untersuchungen über die bei der Verarbeitung pflanzlicher Rohware zu flüssigen oder breiigen Lebensmitteln oder Halbwaren auftretenden Probleme unter besonderer Berücksichtigung des gezielten Einsatzes technischer Pektinenzympräparate, ihrer Begleitenzyme bzw. anderer Enzympräparationen. **Further investigations on the problems appearing by the processing of plant raw materials to liquid or viscous foodstuffs with regard to a controlled application of industrial pectic enzymes, their attending enzymes, resp. other enzyme preparations.** Publications.

16454 Loncin, M.; Treiber, A. DE 145150/72/0003
Untersuchung der Zerkleinerungsmechanismen bei der Homogenisation von o/w–Emulsionen. **Studies of the mechanisms of size reduction at the homogenization of o/w–emulsions.**

16455 Loncin, M.; Tonnius, F.G. DE 145150/78/0001 N
Aufschluss von Einzeller–Protein mittels Hochdruckhomogenisation. **Disruption of single–cell protein with a high–pressure–homogenizer.** Publications.

16456 Loncin, M.; Plett, E. DE 145150/78/0002 N
Sorptionsisothermen–Messung an Trockenpulverlebensmitteln. **Measuring of sorption isotherms in dry–powder foods.**

16457 Erbersdobler, H. DE 160600/72/0022
Protein– und Aminosäurenschädigung bei Hitzebehandlung von Nahrungs– und Futtermitteln. **Damage of proteins and amino acids in food– and feedstuff by heat treatment.**

16458 Radola, B.J.; Goerth, K. DE 161100/75/0014
Anwendung von Cellulasen und Hemicellulasen in der Biotechnologie und Lebensmitteltechnologie. **Use of cellulases and hemicellulases in biotechnology and food technology.**

16459 Kessler, H.G.; Nassauer, J. DE 161350/77/0003
Verweilzeitverhalten beim Durchströmen von Rohrleitungen. **Residence time distribution in pipeline systems.**

16460 Kessler, H.G.; Gernedel, C. DE 161350/78/0001 N
Strömungstechnische Untersuchungen über den spezifischen Filtratfluss bei der Ultrafiltration von Lebensmittelbestandteilen. **Hydrodynamic investigations on specific flux in ultrafiltration of foodstuffs components.**

16461 Kessler, H.G.; Kammerlehner, J.

DE 161350/78/0003 N
Farbmessung zur Beurteilung lebensmitteltechnologischer Vorgänge. **Measuring of colour as a criterion for processes in food technology.**

16462 Koller, W.–D. DE 211020/78/0001 N
Modifizierung von Geruchs– und Geschmacksstandardsubstanzen durch lebensmitteltechnologische Behandlung. **Modification of odor and taste reference substances during food processing.**

16463 Adam, S.; Daruschy, S. DE 211040/78/0007 N
Chemische Veränderungen von Lebensmittelstoffen im Verlauf verfahrenstechnischer Prozesse. **Chemical changes in food constituents during processing.**

16464 Hoffmann, N.; Schubert, H.; Spiess, W.; Ehlermann, D.; Grünewald, T.; Adam, S. DE 211040/78/0010 N
Übertragung und Anwendung moderner verfahrenstechnischer Methoden auf Lebensmittel. **Exploitation and application of modern methods in process engineering to foods.**

16465 Grossklaus, D.; Levetzow, R. DE 305030/75/0017
Hygienische Gefährdung durch Gemeinschaftsverpflegung. **Hygienic risks involved in catering services.**

16466 Gerigk, K. DE 305030/75/0019
Hygiene–Code für Säuglingsnahrung. **Hygiene–code for baby–food.**

16467 Becker, K.; Schrader, U. DE 911000/77/0005
Diffusion, Löslichkeit und Reaktionskinetik von Sauerstoff in flüssigen und gelartigen Lebensmitteln bzw. Lebensmittelmodellen. **Diffusion, solubility and kinetics of reaction of oxygen in liquid and gelatinous foods respectively model foods.**

16468 Eichner, K.; Ciner, M. DE 911000/77/0006
Leitsubstanzen zur Erkennung beginnender Qualitätsveränderungen thermisch belasteter wasserarmer Lebensmittel und ihre Beziehung zu sensorischen Veränderungen. **Early indication of quality losses in heat processed low moisture foods by chemical indicators in relation to sensoric changes.** Publications.

16469 Eichner, K. DE 911000/77/0007
Verlauf der nicht–enzymatischen Bräunungsreaktion – MaillardReaktion – in Modellsystemen und wasserarmen Lebensmitteln, abhängig von deren Zusammensetzung und den Reaktionsbedingungen. **The course of non–enzymic browning reaction – Maillard–reaction – in model systems and low moisture foods dependent on their composition and the reaction conditions.**

16470 Eichner, K.; Ciner, M. DE 911000/77/0008
Sensorische Auswirkung flüchtiger Produkte der Maillard–Reaktion. **Sensoric effects of volatile products formed by the Maillard reaction.**

16471 Bøgh–Sørensen, L. DK 030131/77/0005 N
Råvarens, forarbejdningsprocessernes og pakningens betydning for frysevarers holdbarhed. **The influence of product, processing and packaging on the storage life of frozen food.**

16472 Flink, J.M.   DK 030194/78/0002 N
Aromaretention i frysetørrede fødevarer. **Aroma retention in freeze dried food products.**

16473 Flink, J.M.; Poll, L.   DK 030194/78/0003 N
Naturligt farvestof fra planter til brug i fødevarer. **Natural red coloring agent from elderberry for use in foods.**

16474 Flink, J.M.   DK 030194/78/0004 N
Udvikling af en computerkontrolleret frysetørrer. **Development of a computer controlled freeze dryer.**

16475 Schaeffer, A.; Meyer, J.P.   FR 010902/72/2235
Désacidification biologique par l'intermédiaire des levures Schizosaccharomyces. **Biological de-acidification by schizosaccharomyces yeasts.** Publications.

16476 Multon, J.L.; Bryon, G.   FR 012203/70/2245
Rôle de l'eau dans la rupture des liaisons S.S. dans les protéines. **Role of water in breaking S.S. bonding in protein.**

16477 Pifferi, P.G.   IT 040217/78/1086 N
Stabilità di antociani nel trattamento di prodotti alimentari liquidi con enzimi immobilizzati, studio di soluzioni modello. **Stability of anthocyan in the processing of liquid foodstuffs using stabilized enzymes; study on standard solutions.**

16478 Fatichenti, F.   IT 041312/78/1051 N
L'effetto – flor – nei lieviti e suoi riflessi applicativi. **The – flor – effect in yeasts and its possible applications.**

16479 Bray, F.   IT 120600/77/0731
Impiego delle proteine da siero nella produzione di gelati, caramelle mou, spreads e prodotti da forno lievitati naturalmente. **The use of serum proteins in the production of ice-creams fudge, spreads and oven products raised naturally.**

16480 Roozen, J.P.   NL 020031/72/5125
Het geschikt maken van eiwitisolaten afkomstig van afvalprodukten voor de verrijking van levensmiddelen. **Adoption of protein isolates from waste products to enrich foodstuffs.** Publications.

16481 Pilnik, W.; Rombouts, F.M.; Voragen, A.G.J.
NL 020031/72/5126
Het bereiden van model substraten m.b.v. pektine t.b.v. de bestudering van structuur en eigenschappen van polysacchariden. **Preparation of pectin derivatives for study of structure and properties of polysaccharides.** Publications.

16482 Pilnik, W.; Voragen, A.G.J.; Hooydonk, M.W.; Krop, J.J.P.; Rombouts, F.M.   NL 020031/72/5127
Toepassing van pektolytische enzymen. **Application of pectolytic enzymes.** Publications.

16483 Pilnik, W.; Rombouts, F.M.; Deventer–Schriemer, W.H. van; Voragen, A.G.J.; Hooydonk, M.J.
NL 020031/72/5128
Analyse en karakterisering van pektine. **Pectin analysis and characterization.** Publications.

16484 Luyben, K.C.A.M.   NL 020031/77/7604
Regulariteiten tijdens interstationair stoftransport in systemen met variabele diffusiecoëfficient. **Regularities during nonstationary mass transfer in systems with variable diffusion coefficient.** Publications.

16485 Walstra, P.   NL 020031/77/8524
Invloed van kristallen in de oliefase op de stabiliteit van olie–in–water emulsies. **The influence of crystals in the oil phase on the stability of oil–in–water emulsions.**

16486 Haven, M.C. van der   NL 020031/77/8525
Invloed van de fysische structuur van levensmiddelen op de smaakgewaarwording. **Influence of physical properties and texture of foods on taste and flavour perception.**

16487 Folstar, P.   NL 020031/78/8897 N
Fenolische verbindingen: structuur, voorkomen en omzettingen. **Phenolic substances: their structure, presence and reactivity.**

16488 Ruiter, A.   NL 030008/78/8959 N
Bereiden en stabiliseren van concentraten van polyonverzadigde vetzuren, zulks ten behoeve van voedings– en voederexperimenten. Begeleiding van deze experimenten. **Preparing and stabilizing of concentrates from poly unsaturated fatty acids for feed and food experiments. Accompanying of these experiments.** Publications.

16489 Waart, J. de   NL 050301/73/5310
Ontwikkeling van methodieken ten behoeve van biotechnologische processen. **Development of apparatus for biotechnological processes.**

16490 Kooij, E.G.   NL 060002/78/7926
Toepassing van gehydroliseerde lactose in andere dan specifieke zuivelprodukten. **Applications of hydrolyzed lactose into non–specific dairy products.**

Mill and bakery products (B 6810)

See also 2995, 6365, 16036, 16040, 16043, 17733, 19001, 19017

16491 Schildbach, R.; Gerstenkorn, P.   DE 105201/74/0001
Einfluss von Sorte und Trocknung des Erntegutes auf die technologische Qualität von Körnermais. **The influence of variety and drying of harvested crops on the technological quality of grain–maize.**

16492 Meuser, F.; El–Gawad, S.; Köhler, F.; Rajani, C.
DE 105820/77/0001
Versuche zur Aufklärung des anomalen technologischen Verhaltens nichtbackfähiger Weizen. **Experiments to explain the anomalous technical behaviour of nonmachinable wheats.**

16493 Windisch, S.; Kowalski, S.   DE 105990/75/0001
Spezialhefen mit erweiterten Anwendungsmöglichkeiten für die Lockerung von unterschiedlichen zucker– und fettreichen Teigen. **Special yeasts for broader application as raising agents for doughs with different richness in sugar and fat.**

16494 Pfeilsticker, K.; Ghori, M.   DE 111600/75/0001
Die Rheologie von Weizenmehlteigen in Zusammenhang mit der backverbessernden Wirkung von L–Ascorbinsäure. **Rheology of wheat doughs in connection with the ameliorating effect of L–ascorbic acid in baking.**

16495 Pfeilsticker, K.; Roeung, S.   DE 111600/75/0002
Untersuchungen zur backverbessernden Wirkung von Ascorbinsäure in Weizenteigen. **Studies on the ameliorating effect of ascorbic acid in baking of wheat doughs.**

16496 Pfeilsticker, K.; Beyern, K.   DE 111600/77/0001
Rheologie von Weizenmehlteigen in Abhängigheit von
Mehlqualität und Zusatzstoffen. **Rheology of wheat doughs
with regard to dependence on wheat quality and additives.**

16497 Pfeilsticker, K.; Schreiner, C.   DE 111600/77/0004
Mehlinhaltsstoffe und ihre Bedeutung für den Backwert.
Ingredients of flour and their significance to baking qualities.

16498 Pieper, H.J.; Gerster, H.   DE 144242/78/0003 N
Über den Einfluss hydrothermischer Verfahren auf
Inhaltsstoffe von Getreidekörnern unter besonderer
Berücksichtigung der Stärke. **Effects of hydrothermal methods
on constituents of cereal grains with special regard to starch.**

16499 Heimann, W.; Timm, U.   DE 145100/74/0002
Studien über Lipoxygenasen in Cerealien. **Studies on
lipoxygenases in cereals.**

16500 Lehmann, G.   DE 167100/75/0010
Verbesserung der Backfähigkeit schwacher Weizenmehle
durch Zusatz von Backverbesserungsmitteln. **Improvement of
the baking quality of weak wheat meals by adding baking
conditioners.**

16501 Bunnies, H.; Einhoff, K.   DE 207070/78/0006 N
Ökonomische Folgen der Substitution von Triticum durum
durch Triticum aestivum bei der Teigwarenherstellung.
**Economic consequences of the substitution of Triticum durum
by Triticum aestivum at the production of farinacevus pastes.**

16502 Nierle, W.; Wolff, J.; Ocker, H.–D.; El–Baya, A.W.
          DE 209010/77/0001
Studium der Beziehungen zwischen qualitätstragenden
Inhaltsstoffen und Verarbeitungswert von Getreide. **Studies on
correlations between quality–determinant constituents and
processing value of cereals.**

16503 Nierle, W.; Bolling, H.   DE 209010/77/0002
Untersuchungen an Weizensorten hinsichtlich ihrer Eignung
zur Brotherstellung. **Studies on wheat varieties regarding
suitability for bread production.**

16504 Nierle, W.   DE 209010/77/0008
Zusammenhang zwischen Proteinmuster und
Verarbeitungsqualität von Brotweizen. **Correlations between
protein pattern and processing quality of bread wheat.**

16505 Fretzdorff, B.   DE 209010/78/0001 N
Cytolytische Enzyme im Roggen. **Cytolytic enzymes in rye.**

16506 Wolff, J.; Fretzdorff, B.; Nierle, W.; El–Baya, A.W.;
Gerstenkorn, P.   DE 209010/78/0003 N
Einfluss der Trocknungsparameter auf die Qualität von
Getreide für die menschliche Ernährung. **Relation between
drying conditions and quality of cereals for human
consumption.**

16507 Weipert, D.; Bruemmer, J.–M.   DE 209020/77/0002
Untersuchungen über Ursachen der Backfähigkeit von
Roggen. **Studies on causes of baking capacity of rye.**

16508 Bolling, H.; Gerstenkorn, P.   DE 209020/77/0003
Müllereitechnische Massnahmen zur Verarbeitung von
Sorghum und anderer Getreidearten aus Entwicklungsländern.
Milling technological measures for processing of sorghum and
other cereals from developing countries.

16509 Researcher not indicated   DE 209020/77/0005
Einfluss müllereitechnologischer Verfahren auf die Qualität
von Vermahlungsprodukten. **Quality of milling products as
affected by milling technological process.**

16510 Bolling, H.   DE 209020/77/0007
Untersuchungen über den Verarbeitungswert von Weizen in
Abhängigkeit von Ausmahlung und Sorte. **Studies on the
processing value of wheat depending on milling and variety.**

16511 Meyer, D.   DE 209020/77/0008
Untersuchungen über die Verarbeitungseigenschaften von
inländischen Hafersorten zur Feststellung ihrer Eignung für die
Ernährungsindustrie. **Studies on processing properties of
domestic oats for determination of suitability for food industry.**

16512 Meyer, D.   DE 209020/77/0009
Feststellung und Überprüfung des Gehaltes an Inhaltsstoffen
von Mühlennachprodukten. **Determination and checking of the
content of constituents in milling by–products.**

16513 El–Baya, A.W.   DE 209020/77/0011
Einfluss der hydrothermischen Behandlung auf die chemischen
und physikalischen Eigenschaften des Reises. **Influence of
hydrothermic treatment on chemical and physical properties of
rice.**

16514 Spicher, G.   DE 209030/74/5001
Physiologie und Biochemie der Sauerteigbakterien. **Physiology
and biochemistry of leaven bacteria.**

16515 Seiler, K.   DE 209030/75/0001
Die Bedeutung des Ofenklimas für die Qualität feiner
Backwaren sowie für verschiedene Brotsorten. **Influence of
oven climates on the quality pastries and bread varieties.**

16516 Menger, A.   DE 209030/75/0003
Erforschung von Einflüssen der Herstellungsbedingungen auf
die Eigenschaften von Teigwaren. **Studies on the influence of
the processing conditions on the quality of macaroni products.**
Publications.

16517 Menger, A.   DE 209030/77/0002
Untersuchungen über die Einsetzbarkeit von Inland– und
EG–Weizen anstelle von Drittlandweizen zur
Teigwarenherstellung. **Studies on the use of domestic and EC
wheat for paste products instead of wheat from developing
countries.**

16518 Menger, A.   DE 209030/77/0003
Substitution konventioneller Rohstoffe für die Herstellung von
Back– und Teigwaren. **Substitution of conventional materials
for preparation of baked goods and paste products.**

16519 Seibel, W.   DE 209030/77/0005
Entwicklung und Bewertung bedarfsgerechter Brotnahrung.
**Development and valuation of bread food meeting the
demand.**

16520 Seiler, K.   DE 209030/77/0007 R
Untersuchung der Extrusionseigenschaften verschiedener
Rohstoffe, insbesondere Mais. **Investigations on extrusion
properties of different raw materials, esp. maize.**

16521 Ludewig, H.G.   DE 209030/77/0008 R
Untersuchungen zur Optimierung der Herstellungstechnik bei feinen Backwaren. **Studies on optimization of production technique for pastries.**

16522 Ludewig, H.G.   DE 209030/77/0009
Erforschung der produktbezogenen Eignung/Wirkung von Rohstoffen und Backmitteln für feine Backwaren. **Research on product–relevant suitability/effect of raw materials and baking agents for pastries.**

16523 Menger, A.   DE 209030/77/0010
Erarbeitung von Qualitätskriterien für Teigwarenrohstoffe und Teigwaren unter besonderer Beachtung der Kocheigenschaften. **Development of qualitative criteria for paste raw materials and for paste products with special regard to cooking properties.**

16524 Seibel, W.; Ludewig, H.G.   DE 209030/77/0011
Entwicklung von Standardbackversuchen für feine Backwaren. **Development of standardized trials on baking of pastries.**

16525 Bruemmer, J.–M.   DE 209030/77/0016
Untersuchungen über die Einsatzmöglichkeit von Zutaten, Zusatzstoffen, auch in Form von Backmitteln bei der Brotherstellung. **Investigations on the use of additions, admixtures, also as baking agents for bread production.**

16526 Rabe, E.   DE 209030/77/0017
Isolierung und backtechnische Wirkung von Inhaltsstoffen der Getreideerzeugnisse. **Isolation and baking effect of constituents of grain products.**

16527 Seibel, W.; Bruemmer, J.–M.   DE 209030/77/0020
Entwicklung lang lagerfähiger Produkte auf Getreidebasis. **Development of cereal products with long shelf–life.**

16528 Bruemmer, J.–M.   DE 209030/78/0001 N
Untersuchungen an Erzeugnissen aus Roggen, Weizen und anderen Getreidearten hinsichtlich ihrer Eignung zur Brotherstellung. **Investigations on the bread–baking behaviour of products from rye, wheat and other cereals.**

16529 Seiler, K.   DE 209030/78/0002 N
Ermittlung optimaler Arbeitsparameter beim Extrudieren. **Determination of optimum processing parameter with extrusion cooking.**

16530 Bruemmer, J.–M.   DE 209030/78/0003 N
Entwicklung und Anwendung sensorischer Methoden bei der Beurteilung von Rohstoffen, Zwischen– und Endprodukten. **Development and use of sensoric methods for the valuation of raw materials, intermediate products and end products.**

16531 Belitz, H.–D.   DE 502502/72/0003
Über die proteolytische Aktivität von Weizen. **About the proteolytic activity in wheat.**

16532 Knezevic, G.   DE 911000/77/0003
Möglichkeiten und Grenzen der Aufnahme von Metallspuren durch das Gut bei der Herstellung von Süsswaren. **Possibilities and limits of the uptake of metal traces by goods during manufacturing of chocolate products and biscuits.**

16533 Drapron, R.; Nicolas, J.   FR 012203/70/2249
Caractérisation des produits volatiles formés par action de la lipoxygénase au cours de la panification. **Characterization of volatil products formed by the action of lipoxygenase during bread making.** Publications.

16534 Petit, L.; Lefebvre, J.   FR 012203/70/2253
Formation du gluten au cours du pétrissage. **Gluten formation during kneading.** Publications.

16535 Muttrie   GB 030903/76/0106 R
Survey of pesticide usage in breweries, distilleries and maltings.

16536 Dwyer, E.   IE 060300/71/0765 R
The effects of additives on bakery products. Publications.

16537 Cubadda, R.   IT 011300/77/0343 R
Studio di micrometodi chimici e biochimici per la valutazione della qualità tecnologica e nutrizionale del frumento duro. **A study of chemical and biochemical micro–methods of measuring the technological and nutritional value of durum hard wheat.**

16538 Goldberg, F.L.   IT 040603/77/0746
Composizione chimica delle biomasse. Frazione minerale. **Chemical composition of biomasses. Mineral components.**

16539 Resmini, P.; De Bernardi, G.   IT 040609/70/0001 R
Chimica e tecnologia degli sfarinati di grano e delle paste alimentari. **Cereal chemistry and technology.** Publications.

16540 Galoppini, C.   IT 041108/77/0745
Proteine da foglie. Ricerche di carattere tecnologico. **Leaf proteins. Technological research.**

16541 Meppelink, E.K.   NL 050302/56/5144
Verwerkingswaarde van tarwerassen. **Milling and baking quality of home–grown wheat varieties.** Publications.

16542 Belderok, B.   NL 050302/70/6239
Technologisch onderzoek ter ondersteuning van het kweken van tarwe met een betere verwerkingswaarde. **Technological investigations in support of growing wheat with improved milling and baking quality.** Publications.

16543 Lonkhuysen, H.J. van   NL 050302/72/5154
Interactie van emulgatoren met deegcomponenten. **Interactions between emulsifying agents and dough constituents.** Publications.

16544 Bloksma, A.H.   NL 050302/73/5155
Ontwikkeling van een in bakkerijen toe te passen regeling van de deegtemperatuur. **Developing a device for controlling dough temperature in bakeries.**

16545 Sluimer, P.   NL 050302/76/6600
Rijsonderbreking bij de broodbereiding. **Dough retarding in breadmaking.** Publications.

16546 Kim, J.C.   NL 050302/77/7238 R
Hittebehandeling van tarwebloem en roggebloem voor de bereiding van kapsel– resp. ontbijtkoek. **Heat treatment of wheatflour and ryeflour for preparation of bakeryproducts.**

16547 Kim, J.C.   NL 050302/78/7965
Onderzoek naar de factoren die het gewicht en de afmetingen van spuitkoekjes (bv. sprits) beinvloeden. **Study of factors affecting weight and measures of deposit cookies (e.g. spritz**

cookies).

16548 Sluimer, P.   NL 050302/78/7966
De invloed van verschillende grondstoffen en werkwijzen op
de broodkwaliteit. **The influence of various raw materials and
processes on bread quality.** Publications.

16549 Graveland, A.   NL 050302/79/8996 N
Functie van diverse tarwe–eiwitten bij de vorming van deeg–
en broodstructuur. **Function of some wheat–proteins during the
formation of the dough and bread structure.**

16550 Graveland, A.   NL 050302/79/8997 N
Invloed van oxydatieve meelverbetermiddelen op het verloop
van de SN/SS–uitwisselingsreacties in deeg. **The influence of
oxydative improvers on the SH/SS exchange reactions in dough.**

16551 Bloksma, A.H.   NL 050302/79/8999 N
Azodicarbonamide als meelverbetermiddel.
Azodicarbonamide as an improver for meal.

16552 Kim, J.C.   NL 050302/79/9000 N
Verbetering van de gewichtsbeheersing bij de
ontbijtkoekbereiding. **Inprovement of weight control at Dutch
honey cake preparation.**

16553 Sluimer, P.   NL 050302/79/9002 N
Het bereiden van voedingsmiddelen met als eiwitcomponent
caseinaat of soja–isolaat. **Preparation of food with caseinate or
soya–isolate as protein component.**

16554 Kerkhof, P.   NL 060002/79/8689 N
Proceskundige analyse van de melkpoederbereiding. **Analysis
of the milk powder manufacturing process.**

Oils, fats and related products (B 6820)

See also 16064, 16067, 16271, 16493, 16532

16555 Huyghebaert, H.   BE 030025/71/0006 R
Studie van de afbraakreakties in verhitte voedingsvetten.
Study of the degradation reactions in heated food fats.

16556 Biehl, B.; Passern, D.; Mohr, W.   DE 114050/77/0001
Abhängigkeit der Bildung und Entwicklung von Kakaoaroma
im Verlaufe der Schokoladenfertigung von subzellulären
Strukturen des Rohkakaos 1.Subzelluläre
Strukturumbildungen durch Fermentation 2.Struktureinfluss
auf die Schokoladenfertigung. **Dependence of the formation
and development of cocoa flavour on subcellular structures of
raw cocoa during chocolate manufacturing 1.Transformation of
subcellular structures by fermentation 2.Influence of structure
on chocolate manufacturing.** Publications.

16557 Homberg, E.   DE 213010/72/0006
Veränderung von Sterinen bei der technischen Bearbeitung
von Fetten und Ölen. **Chemical modifications of sterols during
refining processing of fats and oils.**

.16558 Ilsemann, K.; Mukherjee, K.D.   DE 213020/75/0002
Auswirkung technologischer Verfahren auf die Inhaltsstoffe
von Fetten – Hydrierung, Raffination, Umesterung,
Veresterung, Fraktionierung –. **Effects of technological
processes on the constituents of fats – hydrogenation, refining,
interesterification, esterification, fractionation –.**

16559 Weber, N.; Ilsemann, K.   DE 213020/75/0008
Neue Methoden zur Verringerung von Schadstoffen und
anderen Rückständen in Fetten. **New methods for the removal
of harmful components and other residues in fats.**

16560 Brunner, E.   DE 911000/77/0004
Abhängigkeit der Entstehung des Kakaoaromas beim Rösten
von Rohkakao von dessen struktureller Beschaffenheit.
**Dependence of the development of cocoa flavor during
roasting of raw cocoa beans on its structure.**

16561 Jart, Aa.   DK 030192/74/0009
Hærdning af spiseolier. **Hardening of edible oils.**

16562 Jart, Aa.   DK 030192/77/0010
Udvikling af faste margarineråstoffer uden positions– og
trans–isomere fedtsyrer. **Development of solid margarine crude
substances without position and trans–isomeric fatty acids.**

16563 Vangheesdaele, G.; Fournier, N.   FR 011009/70/2206
Dégradation de l'essence de moutarde. **Degradation of
mustard essential oil.** Publications.

16564 Cucurachi, A.; Pelagatti, O.; Mascolo, A.; Solinas, M.;
Di Giovacchino, L.   IT 022100/72/0013
Utilizzazione delle acque di vegetazione delle olive e loro
depurazione. **Utilization and purification of the vegetation
waters of olives.**

16565 Materassi, R.; Cucurachi, A.; Pelagatti, O.; Brighigna,
A.; Florenzano, G.   IT 022100/74/0002
Sulla idrolisi della oleuropeina nei lieviti. **Ability of yeasts to
hydrolize oleuropein.** Publications.

16566 Cucurachi, A.; Di Giovacchino, L.; Mascolo, A.;
Solinas, M.   IT 022100/76/0001
L'estrazione diretta dell'olio dalle olive mediante solvente.
Direct solvent extraction of oil from olives.

16567 Cucurachi, A.; Camera, L.; Angerosa, F.M.P.
IT 022100/76/0002
Gli alcoli alifatici e triterpenici presenti nell'insaponificabile
dell'oliodi oliva. **Aliphatic and triterpenic alcohols present in
the unsaponifiable of olive oil.**

16568 Cucurachi, Angelo.; Mascolo, Angelo.
IT 022100/77/0003 N
Utilità di impiego dell'impianto OMISUD (ex
–SIMA–BAGLIONI – MATEMA) nel sistema classico della
doppia lavorazione delle olive. **Advantages of installation
OMISUD (ex SIMA– BAGLIONI– MATEMA) use in classical
system of the duple grinding of olives.**

16569 Solinas, Mario.; Angerosa, Franca.; Mascolo,
Antonio.; Cucurachi, Angelo.; Di Giovacchino, Luciano.
IT 022100/77/0005 N
Caratteristiche di qualità dell'olio di oliva in funzione dei
sistemi di lavorazione. **Quality characteristics of olive oil as
consequence of processing systems.**

16570 Vlahov, G.; Brighigna, A.   IT 022100/78/0003
I componenti dello spazio di testa di salamoie di olive verdi.
The volotile components of head space of green olives brines.

16571 Vlaov, G.; Marsilio, V.; Brighigna, A.
IT 022100/79/0001 N

Studio quali–quantitativo dei glucidi della polpa di olive e della loro evoluzione nel corso della maturazione e del processo di preparazione secondo il sistema Sivigliano. **Qualitative and quantitative determination of olives sugars during ripening and preparation of olives by lactic fermentation according of the Sivigliano system.**

16572 Daghetta, A.   IT 040603/77/0159 R
Prodotti di neo–formazione in conseguenza di processi di frittura degli olii di semi. Studi delle modificazioni della frazione sterolica degli ali di oliva in relazione ai sistemi di conservazione delle olive e di ottenimento degli oli. **Newly formed substances due to frying in seed oils. Study of the alterations in the sterol fractions of olive oils in relation to the methods of conservation of olives an of oil making.**

16573 Montedoro, G.   IT 041011/74/0590
Trattamenti con additivi enzimatici con detannizzanti ed altri coadiuvanti tecnologici, alle paste di olive ed ai mosti oleosi nell'estrazione dell'olio per centrifugazione. **Treatment of olive pastes and oil musts with enzymatic additives, detanning agents and other technological adjuvants in the process of oil extraction by centrifugation.**

16574 Montedoro, G.F.   IT 041011/77/0245 R
Estrazione dell'olio da paste di olive snocciolate. **Oil extraction from stoned olive pulp.**

16575 Galoppini, C.   IT 041108/74/0557
Utilizzazione dei sottoprodotti dell'industria olearia. **Utilization of olive industry byproducts.**

16576 Vodret, A.; Denti, M.   IT 041309/75/0001
Accertamento delle caratteristiche merceologiche e tecnologiche delle cv.s di olive sarde suscettibili di una utilizzazione diretta. **Assurance of marketable goods and technology characteristic of the cv.s of the sardinian olive for a direct utilization.** Publications.

16577 Vodret, A.   IT 041309/77/0315 R
Evoluzione dei componenti della drupa dell'olivo nel corso della trasformazione della stessa per l'utilizzazione da mensa. **The evolution of olive drupe components during processing for table use.**

16578 Korthals Altes, F.W.   NL 040012/75/6593
Aangepaste apparatuur voor het winnen van olie uit oliehoudende zaden: ontwerp, constructie en bouw. **Intermediate technology for the extraction of oil from oilseeds.**

16579 Thio Goan Loo   NL 040012/77/7280
Bereiding op kleine schaal van kokosolie uit verse kokos en benutting van de bijproduten voor humane voeding. **Small scale extraction of oil from fresh coconuts and use of byproducts for human nutrition.**

16580 Ong, T.L.   NL 050301/71/5311
Onderzoek naar de correlatie tussen de kenmerken van ruwe soja–oliën en de kwaliteit/stabiliteit na raffinage. **Study on the correlation between the characteristics of crude soybean–oil and its quality/stability after complete refining.**

Sugar and starch products (B 6830)

See also 3276, 15796, 16070, 16071, 16079, 16493, 16501,

17050, 17087, 19064, 19067

16581 Schildbach, R.; Lurz, E.   DE 105201/72/0002
Einfluss von Anbaugebiet, Jahreswitterung, Sorte und N–Düngung der Zuckerrübe auf Ertragsleistung und das Verhalten im Prozess der technologischen Verarbeitung und die Zuckerausbeute. **Influence of region, climate, variety and N–application on the yield of sugar beet, its behavior during the technological process and the sugar yield.**

16582 Wasmund, R.   DE 105750/73/0002
Bestimmung der mechanischen Stoffwerte einphasiger ÄthanolSaccharose–Wasser–Gemische in Abhängigkeit von der Temperatur und der Zusammensetzung. **Determination of mechanical values of single phase alcohol–saccharose–glucose–mixtures in dependence on temperature and concentration.** Publications.

16583 Mauch, W.; Dziengel, A.   DE 105830/78/0002 N
Zur technischen Bedeutung thermophiler Bacillus–Stämme und ihrer Enzyme im Bereich der Zuckertechnologie. **Concerning the technical significance of thermophilic bacteria stems and their enzymes in the sphere of sugar technology.**

16584 Mauch, W.; Kaiser, G.   DE 105830/78/0003 N
Aufbereitung und Weiterverarbeitung saccharidhaltiger Abwässer der Lebensmitteltechnologie unter besonderer Berücksichtigung der Zuckerindustrie. **The preparation and further processing of saccharide containing waste water in food technology under special consideration of the sugar industry.**

16585 Baloh, A.; Wittwer, E.   DE 105830/78/0004 N
Untersuchungen über das thermodynamische Gleichgewicht des Zweistoffsystems Saccharose–Wasser. **Investigations on the thermodynamic equilibrium of the bynary system sucrose–water.**

16586 Baltes, W.; Lessig, U.   DE 105900/77/0001
Isolierung und Aufklärung von Maillardprodukten aus der Umsetzung von Glucose mit p–Chloranilin. **Isolation and structure of Maillard–procucts from reaction of glucose with p–chloroaniline.**

16587 Baloh, A.   DE 105950/75/0001
Kontinuierliche Kristallisation und Zentrifugation zur Gewinnung von Verbrauchszucker bei der Zuckerfabrikation. **Continuous crystallization and centrifuging for the production of consumption sugar during sugar fabrication.**

16588 Baloh, A.   DE 105950/75/0002
Reverse Osmose zur Reinigung von Extrakten aus der Rohr– und Rübenzuckerindustrie. **Reverse osmosis for purification of extracts from the cane and beet sugar industry.**

16589 Baloh, A.   DE 105951/74/0001
Verbesserung der Wärmewirtschaft in der Rohrzuckerindustrie. **Melioration of heat economy in the cane–sugar industry.**

16590 Mauch, W.; Dziengel, A.   DE 105952/72/0001 N
Biochemische Saccharidkonversion unter den Bedingungen der Zuckergewinnung aus Zuckerrohr und –rübe. **Biochemical conversion of saccharide under conditions of sugar production from cane and beet.**

16591 Mauch, W.; Azzam, A.M.   DE 105952/75/0001

Reinigungsverfahren zur Herstellung von Flüssig– und Kristallzucker aus Rohr– und Rübenrohzucker. **Purification methods for the production of liquid and crystal sugar from raw sugar of cane and beet.**

16592 Müller, K.; Scheele, U.　　　DE 132062/77/0003
Einfluss von Höhe und Zusammensetzung des Trockensubstanzgehaltes der Kartoffel sowie ihrer Veränderungen im Verlauf kontrollierter Lagerhaltung auf Ölaufnahme und Geschmacksqualität von Kartoffelchips. **Influence of height and composition of the dry matter content of the potato and changes during controlled storage on oil uptake and taste quality of potato crisps.**

16593 Drawert, F.; Kassam, K.　　　DE 161100/75/0010
Rückgewinnung von Proteinen und Aminosäuren aus Kartoffel–Fruchtwässern. **Recovery of proteins and amino acids from potato fruit juices.**

16594 Acker, L.; Brauner, G.　　　DE 164150/77/0001
Untersuchungen von Lipiden der Getreidestärken. **Investigations on lipids of cereal starches.**

16595 Nierle, W.; Fretzdorff, B.; Voss, P.; Bergthaller, W.
　　　DE 209010/78/0002 N
Thermischer Einfluss auf qualitätsbestimmende Kartoffelenzyme. **Thermal influence on some potato enzymes of importance to quality.**

16596 Gerstenkorn, P.; Bolling, H.; Zwingelberg, H.
　　　DE 209020/72/5001
Analytische und mahltechnische Untersuchungen an deutschen Maissorten. **Analytical and milling quality studies on German maize varieties.**

16597 Gschwend, W.　　　DE 209040/75/0002
Untersuchung der Möglichkeit einer wirtschaftlichen Pülpeverwertung in der Kartoffelstärkeindustrie. **Investigation of the possibility of economic pulp utilization in potato starch industry.**

16598 Voss, P.; Putz, B.　　　DE 209040/77/0001
Die Auswirkung der Rohstoffeigenschaften der Kartoffel auf die Qualität von Trockenkartoffelveredlungsprodukten in Abhängigkeit von der Verfahrenstechnik. **Properties of raw potatoes and their effects on dried–potato processed products in dependence on technology.**

16599 Fehn, K.–H.　　　DE 209040/77/0002
Untersuchungen über den Einfluss der Schnittgrösse und des Trocknungsverlaufes von Kartoffeln auf die Rehydratationseigenschaften und die Qualität des stückigen und vermahlenen Trockengutes. **Investigations on rehydratation and quality of potato pieces and ground dried potatoes as affected by cut size and drying process.**

16600 Kempf, W.　　　DE 209040/77/0004
Entwicklung neuer und Anpassung bestehender Verfahren auf dem Gebiet der Getreide– und Kartoffelstärken. **Development of new methods and adjustment of existing methods in starch production of cereals and potatoes.**

16601 Wilhelm, E.　　　DE 209040/77/0005
Neue Anwendungsmöglichkeiten für Stärke und Stärkeerzeugnisse in technischen Bereichen. **New applications of starch and starch products on technical sector.**

16602 Kempf, W.; Tegge, G.　　　DE 209040/77/0006
Substitution von Drittlandmais bei der Gewinnung und Verzuckerung von Maisstärke. **Substitution of maize from developing countries in production and saccharification of maize starch.**

16603 Tegge, G.　　　DE 209040/77/0007
Entwicklung neuartiger Verzuckerungsprodukte auf Stärkebasis. **Development of new saccharification products of starch.**

16604 Tegge, G.　　　DE 209040/77/0008
Neue Verzuckerungsverfahren auf der Basis von reiner Stärke, Getreide und Kartoffeln. **New saccharification methods of pure starch, cereals and potatoes.**

16605 Bergthaller, W.; Putz, B.　　　DE 209040/77/0009
Einfluss von Jahr, Standort, Sorte und Düngung auf die Qualität und Zusammensetzung von Kartoffeln im Hinblick auf die Veredlungseigenschaften. **Quality and composition of potatoes regarding processing properties in dependence on year, location, variety and fertilization.**

16606 Putz, B.　　　DE 209040/77/0011
Technische Möglichkeiten zur Verbesserung der Qualität von Chips und Pommes Frites. **Technical possibilities for improving the quality of chips and pommes frites.**

16607 Tegge, G.　　　DE 209040/77/0012
Enzymatische Direktverzuckerung von Getreide und Kartoffeln. **Enzymatic direct saccharification of cereals and potatoes.**

16608 Putz, B.; Bergthaller, W.; Voss, P.
　　　DE 209040/77/0013
Beurteilung der Veredlungseigenschaften neuer Kartoffelsorten im Rahmen der Wertprüfung des Bundessortenamtes. **Valuation of processing properties of new potato varieties in quality control by the Federal Office on Varieties.**

16609 Tegge, G.　　　DE 209040/78/0001 N
Gewinnung von Monosacchariden – Glucose und Fructose – durch Auftrennung von Iso–Sirupen und Saccharose. **Extraction of monosaccharides – glucose and fructose – by separation of isosyrups and saccharose.**

16610 Bergthaller, W.　　　DE 209040/78/0002 N
Möglichkeiten zur Herstellung vorgeschälter frischer Kartoffeln und deren Qualitätserhaltung. **Methods for production of prepeeled fresh potatoes and preservation of their quality.**

16611 Wilhelm, E.　　　DE 209040/78/0004 N
Erforschung der Möglichkeiten zur Herstellung keimarmer Maisstärken mit möglichst geringem Restgehalt an Schwefeldioxid. **Investigations on the possibilities of producing low–germ maize starches with the lowest possible residual content of sulphur dioxide.**

16612 Paulus, K.; Duden, R.; Rumpf, G.; Zohm, H.
　　　DE 211020/78/0014 N
Veränderung wichtiger Inhaltsstoffe von Kartoffeln bei thermischen Behandlungen in Abhängigkeit von der Geometrie des Gutes im Temperaturbereich zwischen 80 und 130 Grad C.. **Influence of thermal treatments – 80–130 degrees**

Celsius – on important constituents of potatoes as function of the geometry of the product.

16613 Benda, I. DE 502155/75/0002
Untersuchungen über den Einfluss von Fungiziden auf Hefen. **Investigations into the influence of fungicides on yeasts.**

16614 Flink, J.M.; Islam, M.N.; Johansen, H.B. DK 030194/78/0001 N
Udvikling af stabile kartoffelprodukter. **Development of shelf–stable potato products.**

16615 Gallant, D.; Guilbot, A. FR 012203/70/2246
Evolution de l'ultrastructure du grain d'amidon sous l'action de traitements physiques, chimiques ou biochimiques. **Ultra–structural evolution of starch grain under the action of physical,chemical and biochemical treatments.** Publications.

16616 Charbonnieres, R.; Duprat, F. FR 012203/70/2247
Taux de cristallinité de la fraction glucidique des grains d'amidon de céréales et de tubercules natifs et traités. **Crystallization rate of the glucidic fraction of starch obtained from cereals and other plants.** Publications.

16617 Robin, J.P.; Charbonnieres, R. FR 012203/70/2248
Modifications physicochimiques du grain d'amidon au cours du traitement hydrothermique. **Physicochemical modifications of the starch grain during hydrothermic treatment.** Publications.

16618 Davin, A.; Davin, S. FR 012203/70/2255
Inventaire des variétés présentant une aptitude à la transformation industrielle. **Inventory of potato varieties suitable for industrial processing.** Publications.

16619 Pratella, G.C.; Tonini, G. IT 040216/73/0001
Adattabilita' varietale delle patate, coltivate in Italia, alla trasformazione in: chips, semifritte surgelate, fiocchi, preimpaccate sterilizzate. **Italy grown potato varieties suitable to processing for: Chips, Frozen French Fryes, Potato Flakes, and Pre–packed and Sterilized Potatoes.** Publications.

16620 Keijbets, M.J.H. NL 010105/67/8321
Ontwikkeling en verbetering van methoden en apparatuur voor de verwerking van aardappelen tot bestaande aardappelprodukten voor menselijke consumptie. **Development and improvement of methods and equipment for processing potatoes into existing potato products for human consumption.** Publications.

16621 Keijbets, M.J.H. NL 010105/67/8322
Ontwikkeling van kant en klare (ovenklare) aardappelprodukten alsmede van apparatuur voor de fabrikage. **Development of ready–to–use potato products and of equipment for the processing of these products.** Publications.

16622 Keijbets, M.J.H. NL 010105/67/8333
Onderzoek naar de mogelijkheden tot vermindering van lucht– en waterverontreiniging en van geluidshinder bij aardappelverwerkende bedrijven. **Research into possibilities of reducing air and water pollution and noise problems in the potato processing industry.** Publications.

16623 Keijbets, M.J.H. NL 010105/70/8334
Valorisatie van afvallen uit de aardappelverwerkende industrie tot produkten voor menselijke consumptie. **Valorisation of wastes from the potato processing industry into products for**

human consumption.

16624 Keijbets, M.J.H. NL 010105/73/8331
Microbiologische en hygiënische aspecten van de aardappelverwerking. **Microbiological and hygienic aspects of potato processing.** Publications.

16625 Plieger, P. NL 050208/50/5093
De aardappel als grondstof voor de zetmeelfabricage (verwerking, screening en selectie van nieuwe rassen). **Research on the chemistry and biochemistry of potatoes as a raw material for the starch industry (processing, screening and selecting new varieties).** Publications.

16626 Bellegem, T.M. van NL 050208/50/5094
Afvalwaterproblemen in de aardappelzetmeelindustrie. **Effluent research on behalf of the potato starch industry.** Publications.

16627 Steeneken, P.A.M. NL 050208/50/5095
Fysisch–chemisch onderzoek van zetmeel en zijn afgeleiden. **Research on physical and chemical properties of starch and starch derivatives.** Publications.

16628 Hokse, H. NL 050208/50/5098
Enzym–onderzoek op het gebied van zetmeelprodukten. **Research on enzymatic modification and breakdown of starch products.** Publications.

16629 Bellegem, T.M. van NL 050208/50/5099
Microbiologische omzettingen van koolhydraten in de aardappelzetmeelindustrie. **The application of procedures and microbiological techniques in the starch industry.** Publications.

Fruit and vegetable products (B 6840)

See also 3707, 3747, 3925, 4225, 4263, 6073, 6074, 7045, 15796, 15867, 16064, 16303, 16593, 16983, 17027, 18444, 19101, 19108, 19109, 20369

16630 Stan, H.–J.; Scheutwinkel–Reich, M. DE 105900/78/0002 N
Enzymatische Fettoxydation in Gemüse und Obst. **Enzymatic lipid oxidation in vegetables and fruit.**

16631 Henze, J.; Eschenbruch, B.; Hartmann, H.D. DE 111301/77/0005
Verhinderung von Infektionen während der Verarbeitung von Weintrauben und Kernobst. **Prevention from infections during processing of grapes and fruits.**

16632 Niese, G.; Müller, H.P. DE 129080/77/0005
Mikrobiologische Untersuchungen an Abläufen der Zitronensäureproduktion. **Microbiological studies on the effluents from the citric acid production.**

16633 Pieper, H.J. DE 144242/78/0001 N
Reduzierung der Methanolbildung bei der Vergärung von Obst. **Reduction of methanol formation in fermentation of fruit.** Publications.

16634 Pieper, H.J. DE 144242/78/0005 N
Brennereitechnologische Untersuchungen mit verschiedenen Tafeläpfelsorten gleichen Standortes unter besonderer Berücksichtigung von Erntejahr, Erntetermin und Lagerbedingungen. **Distilling technological investigations on**

different varieties of dessert apples of the same location with special regard to the year and date of harvest and to storing conditions.

16635 Gierschner, K.; Baumann, G.   DE 144260/73/0001
Veränderungen von Geruchs– und Geschmacksstoffen bei der Verarbeitung von pflanzlichen Lebensmitteln. **Changes in smell and taste during vegetal foodstuff processing.**

16636 Gierschner, K.; Hartmann, B.   DE 144260/78/0001 N
Kontaminanten in Filderkohl und technologische Möglichkeiten zu deren Reduzierung. **Contaminants in "Filder"-cabbage and the possibilities to reduce their content by technological means.**

16637 Junge, H.; Pressler, I.   DE 206000/75/0013
Farbveränderungen in Erbsen verschiedener Genotypen während und nach der Gefriertrocknung. **Colour changes in peas of different genotypes during and after lyophilization.**

16638 Schmidt, K.   DE 502108/74/0001
Verfärbungserscheinungen bei der Verarbeitung von weissem Gemüsen: II. Isolierung und Charakterisierung des bei der Verarbeitung von Blumenkohl auftretenden rosa bis blauvioletten Farbstoffs. **Discoloration of white vegetables by industrial processing: II. Isolation and identification of the dyestuff responsible for the pink resp. bluish violet discoloration of cauliflower.**

16639 Wucherpfennig, K.; Hsueh–err, C.   DE 506104/77/0004
Mineralstoffgehalt von Früchten und ihr Übergang in den Fruchtsaft in Abhängigkeit vom angewandten Kelterverfahren. **Mineral content of fruits and transfer of minerals into fruit juice in dependence on procedure of pressing.**

16640 Wucherpfennig, K.; Konrad, O.   DE 506104/77/0005
Über den Gehalt von Früchten an Eiweissstoffen und Aminosäuren und ihr Übergang in den Fruchtsaft in Abhängigkeit vom angewandten Kelterverfahren. **Protein content and amino acids in fruits and their transfer into fruit juice depending on procedure of pressing.**

16641 Henriksen, Aa.   DK 010117/77/2310
Ændringer i vegetabilske produkters kemiske sammensætning gennem de seneste ti år, bl.a. som følge af nye dyrkningsmetoder. **Changes in the chemical composition of vegetable products during the last ten years due in part to new growing methods.**

16642 Poll, L.   DK 030194/76/0001
Råvarens indflydelse på æblemosts kvalitet. **Influence of the raw material on the quality of apple juice.**

16643 Flink, J.M.   DK 030194/77/0001 N
Osmosekoncentrering af frugt og grønsager. **Osmotic concentration of fruits and vegetables.**

16644 Poll, L.   DK 030194/79/0001 N
Temperaturens indflydelse på forarbejdede frugtprodukters smagskvalitet. **Influence of temperature on the organoleptic quality of processed fruit products.**

16645 Mesnier, Y.   FR 010701/73/0235
Adaptation des procédés de séchage aux caracteristiques variétales des pruniers. **Adaptation of drying proceedings for varietal caracteristics of plum–trees.**

16646 Brian, C.; Imbernon, M.   FR 010703/75/0243
Production de protéines à partir de substrats variés, par le mycelium de différents champignons. **Proteins production from different substratums through the mycelium of different mushrooms.**

16647 Maugenet, J.; Mourgues, J.   FR 011403/58/2217
Produits nouveaux dérivés de la prune d'Ente et de la Stanley. **New products from the plum varieties "d'Ente" and "Stanley".** Publications.

16648 Kelso   GB 041404/79/0013 N
Yield and quality of Bramley apple juice and juice concentrates.

16649 McKenna, B.M.; Francke, R.   IE 120301/75/7860
Freeze drying of apples. Publications.

16650 Scaramucci, S.   IT 021000/79/0027 N
Caratterizzazione delle pectine isolate da ortaggi e studi relativi alla loro degradazione enzimatica. **Characterization of isolated pectins from horticultural plants and studies on their enzymatic degradation.**

16651 Restaino, F.; Interlandi, G.   IT 021000/79/0028 N
Studio delle modificazioni biochimiche della composizione flavonoidica (acidi fenolici) e della relativa base ereditaria. **Study on biochemical modifications of phenolic acid compositions and their hereditary base.**

16652 Giordano, I.   IT 021100/79/0020 N
Confettatura del seme di pomodoro. **Tomato seed pelleting.**

16653 Crivelli, G.; Senesi, E.   IT 021900/76/0007 N
Ricerche di nuove tecniche di utilizzazione industriale delle mele.. **Researches on new utilization techniques for apples.**

16654 Crivelli, G.; Maltini, E.; Senesi, E.
IT 021900/79/0007 N
Sistemi per la produzione di succo di pesca graduato, aromatico, concentrato, congelato o in polvere. **Methods for the production of graduated, aromatic, concentrated, frozen or powdered peach juice.**

16655 Crivelli, G.; Maltini, E.; Senesi, E.
IT 021900/79/0008 N
Sistemi per la produzione di succo neutro di mele in sciroppo e in polvere con recupero degli aromi. **Methods for the extraction and concentration of neutral apple juice in syrup or powder form with aroma recovery.**

16656 Crivelli, G.; Torreggiani, D.   IT 021900/79/0009 N
Applicazione dell'ascorbico ossidasi nella lavorazione e preparazione dei succhi di frutta. **Utilization of ascorbic oxidase for juices preservation fruit.**

16657 Brighigna, A.; Cucurachi, A.   IT 022100/72/0004
Sistemi e tecniche per la preparazione di olive verdi in salamoia. **Systems and techniques in pickling of green olives.** Publications.

16658 Brighigna, A.; Cucurachi, A.   IT 022100/72/0007
Caratteristiche merceologiche e tecnologiche delle olive destinate alla trasformazione in olive da tavola. **Marketable**

and technological features of olives meant for table use. Publications.

16659 Vlahov, G.; Cucurachi, A.; Brighigna, A.
IT 022100/75/0002
Gli acidi fissi nelle polpe di olive verdi e loro variazioni per effetto dei trattamenti e della fermentazione lattica. **Non–volatile acids in table olives. Their evolution during ripening and working processes.** Publications.

16660 Del Re, A.; Molinari, G.P.; Fontana, P.; Lazzarini, C.; Natali, P.; Battini, G. IT 040406/79/0004 N
Effetti delle tecniche di trasformazione sui residui di antiparassitari nel pomodoro e suoi derivati. **Pathways of pesticide residues in tomato during food processing.**

16661 Casolari, A.; Campanini, M. IT 070500/78/0005 N
Stabilizzazione delle olive in salamoia. **Stabilization of brined olives.**

16662 Sparenberg, H. NL 010105/73/8357 R
Winning en verwerking van eiwitten uit veld– en tuinbonen en andere peulvruchten. **Production and processing of proteins from Vicia Faba beans and other Leguminoseae.** Publications.

16663 Sparenberg, H. NL 010105/73/8358 R
Schadelijke factoren in en de kwaliteit van eiwitten uit veld en tuinbonen en andere peulvruchten. **Toxic constituents in and quality of proteins from Vicia Faba beans and other Leguminoseae.**

16664 Keijbets, M.J.H. NL 010105/78/8365
Onderzoek naar mogelijkheden tot vermindering van waterverontreiniging bij groente– en fruitverwerkende bedrijven. **Research into the possibilities of reduced water pollution in the vegetable and fruit processing industry.**

16665 Steinbuch, E. NL 010118/73/4196
Conservenwaarde van groentenrassen voor verwerking. **Utilisation value of vegetable for processing.** Publications.

16666 Gersons, L. NL 010118/73/4197
Gebruikswaarde van fruitrassen voor conservering. **Utilisation value of fruit for processing.** Publications.

16667 Steinbuch, E. NL 010118/73/4204
Het vergistingsproces van zuurkool. **Controlling the fermentation process of sauerkraut.**

16668 Klop, W. NL 010118/73/4226
Enzymenactivering en –reactivering bij verwerken van tuinbouwprodukten. **Enzyme inactivation and re–activation during processing of horticultural produce.** Publications.

16669 Steinbuch, E.; Koek, P.C. NL 010118/73/4231
Ecologie van melkzuurbacteriën bij vergisting van zuurkool. **Ecology of lactic acid bacteria at the fermentation of sauerkraut.**

16670 Steinbuch, E.; Steinbuch, E. NL 010118/73/4780
De invloed van grondstof en verwerkingsmethode op de kwalitliteit en de slinkverliezen bij gesteriliseerde champignons. **The effect of raw material and processing method on the quality and skrinkage of canned mushrooms.** Publications.

16671 Steinbuch, E. NL 010118/73/7853
De invloed van voorbewerkingsmethoden voor groenten en fruit op de produktie en vervuiling van afvalwater. **Influence of various pretreatment methods of vegetables and fruit on production and pollution of waste water.**

16672 Steinbuch, E. NL 010118/74/5279
Bereiding van vruchtesappen. **Production of fruit juices.**

16673 Steinbuch, E. NL 010118/78/7851
Het separaat drogen van uitgeperste groenten en de daaruit verkregen sappen. **The separate dehydration of pressed vegetables and their juices.**

16674 Steinbuch, E. NL 010118/78/7852
Technische en economische vergelijking van verschillende voorbewerkingsmethoden voor groenten en fruit. **Technological and economic comparison of pretreatment methods for vegetables and fruits.**

16675 Rombouts, F.M.; Pilnik, W.; Voragen, A.G.J.; Hooydonk, M.J. NL 020031/73/5124
Fundamenteel onderzoek van pectolytische enzymen o.a. m.b.t. de verwerking van groente en fruit. **Basic studies on pectolytic enzymes a.o. in relation with processing of vegetables and fruits.** Publications.

16676 Pilnik, W. NL 020031/75/6802
Vergelijkend onderzoek naar het werkingsmechanisme van pectine–esterase uit planten en schimmels i.v.m. de toepassing bij de vruchtensappen–technologie. **Comparison of substrate specificity and action pattern of pectino–esterase from plants and fungi, specially for application in the fruit juices technology.** Publications.

16677 Voragen, A.G.J. NL 020031/76/6803
De inwerking van polysaccharide splitsende enzymen op celwanden van groenten– en fruitweefsels. **The action of polysaccharide degrading enzymes on cell walls of vegetables and fruit tissues.** Publications.

Meat, meat products and fish products in general (B 6850)

16678 Van Hoof, J.; Dezeure–Wallays, B.
BE 051200/76/0006 R
Postmortale microbiologische en biochemische processen en technologische aspecten bij de produktie en verwerking van varkens en gevogeltevlees. **Biochemical and microbiological changes in porcmeat and poultrymeat and the technological aspects in relation to production and processing of this meat.** Publications.

Meat and meat products (B 6851)

See also 10557, 12473, 12553, 12815, 15888, 16184, 16189, 16211, 16212, 16213, 16957, 16965, 17144

16679 Henderickx, H.; Vandekerckhove, P.; Demeyer, D.
BE 030026/77/0007
Studie van vleesverwerking en kwaliteit onmiddellijk na slachten. **Study of meat–processing and quality immediately after slaughter.** Publications.

16680 Reuter, G.; Stolle, A. DE 104302/78/0007 N
Die Salmonellen–Kontamination von Einrichtung und Geräten

beim Rinder–Schlachtprozess. **Contamination of equipment and implements with salmonellae during the slaughter–process of cattle.**

16681 Ehinger, F.   DE 144685/78/0004 N
Der Einfluss des Schlachtvorganges auf den Fremdwassergehalt von Broilern. **Influence of slaughtering process on foreign–water content in broilers.**

16682 Schön, L.; Schön, I.; Freudenreich, P.
                                        DE 210010/75/0010
Auswirkungen thermischer Prozesse auf die Qualität von zubereitetem Rindfleisch. **Effects of thermal procedures on quality of prepared beef.**

16683 Wirth, F.   DE 210020/75/0001
Redoxpotentiale bei Rohwurst. Beeinflussung durch Zusatzstoffe. **Redox potentials of raw sausage as influenced by additives.**

16684 Klettner, P.G.   DE 210020/75/0006
Veränderungen der physikalisch erfassbaren Parameter bei der Rohwurstreifung. **Changes in physical parameters of raw sausage during ripening.**

16685 Klettner, P.G.   DE 210020/75/0007
Heissräucherung mit dem Friktionsrauch. **Hot smoking with friction smoke.**

16686 Hammer, G.   DE 210020/75/0008
Neue Technologien in der Kochwurstherstellung – Kochkutter –. **New technologies in the production of cooked sausage – cooking cutter –.**

16687 Tändler, K.   DE 210020/75/0010
Schnellreifung von Rindfleisch unter klimatisierten Bedingungen. **Rapid ripening of beef under climatised conditions.**

16688 Rödel, W.   DE 210030/75/0005
Möglichkeiten und Grenzen der Herstellung von Fleischerzeugnissen als IM–Meats. **Chances and limits of producing meat products as IM meats.**

16689 Potthast, K.   DE 210040/75/0004
Einfluss der Räuchertechnologie auf die vollständige Zusammensetzung der Fraktion der polycyclischen aromatischen Kohlenwasserstoffe in geräucherten Fleischwaren, in Rauchkondensaten und in Abgasen von Räucheranlagen. **Influence of smoking technology on the total composition of polycyclic aromatic hydrocarbon fraction in smoked meat products, smoking condensates, and in exhausts of smoking equipment.**

16690 Hamm, R.; Fischer, C.   DE 210040/75/0005
Ermittlung der optimalen Bedingungen des Salzens und des Gefrierens sowie der Gefrierlagerung von schlachtwarm zerkleinertem Fleisch zur Erhaltung der hohen Verarbeitungsqualität. **Determination of optimum conditions of salting and freezing and cold storage of warm minced carcass for preservation of high processing quality.**

16691 Hecht, H.   DE 210040/75/0017
Untersuchung der Sekundärkontamination durch toxische Elemente bei der Verarbeitung und Verpackung von Fleisch und Fleischerzeugnissen. **Investigations of secondary**

contamination with toxic elements during processing and packaging of meat and meat products.

16692 Potthast, K.   DE 210040/77/0003
Einfluss der Räuchertechnologie auf die Zusammensetzung von Rauchkondensaten und geräucherten Fleischerzeugnissen an Phenolen. **Effects of smoking technology on phenols in smoke condensates and smoked meat products.**

16693 Hamm, R.; Fischer, C.   DE 210040/77/0005
Studium der für die Wasserbindung und Fettverteilung im Brühwurstbrät wichtigen kolloidchemischen und biochemischen Parameter. **Studies on the colloid chemical and biochemical parameters of importance to water binding and distribution of fat in Bologna type sausage mix.**

16694 Hamm, R.; Rogowski, B.   DE 210040/78/0004 N
Einfluss moderner Verfahren der Be– und Verarbeitung von Fleisch auf den Gehalt der Produkte an nährwertbestimmenden Bestandteilen. **Influence of modern procedures of handling and processing of meat on the nutrient content of products.**

16695 Levetzow, R.   DE 305030/75/0006
Ermittlung optimaler Temperaturen für die Behandlung und Lagerung von Fleisch und anderen Lebensmitteln. **Determination of optimal temperatures for treatment and storage of meat and other foods.**

16696 Wormuth, H.–J.; Schütt, I.; Levetzow, R.; Weise, E.; Fessel, J.   DE 305031/77/0001
Tierschutzgerechte elektrische Betäubung von Schlachtgeflügel und mögliche Auswirkungen auf Lebensmittelhygiene und –qualität. **Electrical stunning of slaughter poultry in accordance with the requirements of animal protection and possible effects on food–hygiene and –quality.**

16697 Wismer–Pedersen, J.; Møller, A.J.
                                        DK 030191/78/0001 N
Optimale metoder til varmebehandling af oksekød. **Effect of heat treatment on beef muscle tenderness.**

16698 Wismer–Pedersen, J.   DK 030191/78/9022
Bestemmelse af planteprotein (soyaprotein) i varmebehandlede kødprodukter for at kunne kontrollere anvendelsens omfang. **Determination of plant protein (soya protein) in heat–treated meat products in order to control the extent of usage.**

16699 Desmoulin, B.; Sellier; Dumont   FR 010206/73/2939
Production de viandes. Etude de la qualité de la viande en liaison avec la qualité des carcasses (races normales et hypermusclées). **Meat production. Relationship between meat and carcass qualities (normal and doublemuscled types).**

16700 Desmoulin, B.   FR 010206/75/2940
Conditions d'emploi de viandes mâles plus ou moins défectueuses dans les produits de transformation. **Directions for use of meat of entire males for processing according to the quality.**

16701 Errecart, M.; Mainsant, P.; De Fontguyon, G.; Hy, M.
                                        FR 012205/75/8550
La transformation et la distribution des viandes fraîches en France. **Processing industry and distribution in France.**

16702 Short GB 041404/79/0015 N
Processing and colour of red meat.

16703 Reid, S. IE 060100/00/1467 N
The evaluation of pre–rigor meat in cooked ham production.
Publications.

16704 Reid, S. IE 060100/00/1468 N
The use of protein additives in cooked ham production.
Publications.

16705 Reid, S. IE 060100/00/1550 N
Research into colour formation and stability in cooked cured meat products. Publications.

16706 Hood, D.E.; Sheridan, J.J.; Joseph, R.L.
IE 060100/76/1247 R
A comparison between hot–boned and conventionally dressed beef in vacuumpacks in terms of yield, shelf life and tenderness.
Publications.

16707 Matassino, D.; Bordi, A.; Cosentino, E.; Girolami, A.; Zullo, A.; Barone, C. IT 040722/72/0004 R
Miopoiesi in bovini, bufali, suini, ovini, caprini, conigli e tacchini. **Miopoiesis in cattle, pigs, sheep, goats, rabbits and turkeys.** Publications.

16708 Baldini, P.; Parolari, G. IT 070500/78/0002
Influenza delle caratteristiche chimico–fisiche (pH, potere di ritenzione dell'acqua, ecc.) della materia prima nella preparazione del prosciutto crudo stagionato di Parma. **Influence of physico–chemical characteristics of raw material in the manufacture of cured Parma ham.**

16709 Germs, A.C. NL 010109/72/3904
De chemische samenstelling van vlees van drooggeslacht pluimvee. **Chemical composition of dry slaughtered poultry meat.** Publications.

16710 Boer, H. de; Bergstrøm, P.L. ; nijeboer, H. ; merkus, G.S.M. NL 010112/73/5397
Bepaling verwerkingswaarde van slachtvarkens. **Determining the realization value of pig carcasses.** Publications.

16711 Houben, J.H. NL 030008/71/5736
Thermoresistentie van niet–sporevormers in vlees.
Heatresistance of non–sporeforming bacteria in meat.
Publications.

16712 Logtestijn, J.G. van NL 030008/76/7773 R
Hygiënische aspekten bij de bereiding van samengestelde vleesprodukten. **Hygienic aspects of preparing comminuted meat products.** Publications.

16713 Hartog, J.M.P. den NL 030008/78/8957 N
Technologische aspekten van het desinfekteren van geïmporteerde varkensdarmen. (S.V.D.–virus, darmen, varkensdarmen). **Technological aspects of the desinfections of imported pork casings (S.V.D. virus, casings, pork casings).**

16714 Krol, B. NL 030008/78/8958 N
Ontwikkeling van veilige producten voor tropische gebieden (rundvleesproduct, geitevleesproduct, tropen). **Development of safe products for tropical regions (beef product, goat product, tropics).**

16715 Olsman, W.J. NL 050301/71/6491
Het chemisch gedrag van nitriet in vleeswaren. **The chemical significance of nitrite in meat products.** Publications.

16716 Moerman, P.C. NL 050301/72/5319
Onderzoek receptuur ambachtelijke vleeswaren. **Study of recipes in behalf of a handbook for the butchery trade.**
Publications.

16717 Labots, H.; Bemelmans, J. M. H. NL 050301/74/5316
Het aromatiseren van fabrieksmatig bereide vleesprodukten.
Flavour studies on industrially prepared meat products.

Fish and marine food products (B 6852)

See also 16216, 16685, 19269

16718 Christians, O. DE 208040/77/0003
Fermentation von Fischeiweiss. **Fermentation of fish protein.**

16719 Reinacher, E. DE 208040/78/0001 N
Auftauverfahren von Frostfisch. **Methods of thawing frozen fish.**

16720 Antonacopoulos, N. DE 208040/78/0003 N
Produkte aus gefrostetem Filet und Fischfarce. **Products of frozen fish fillet and fish farce.**

16721 Schreiber, W. DE 208040/78/0004 N
Technologie und Verfahrenstechnik der Verarbeitung von antarktischem Krill – Euphausia Superba –. **Technology and technics of processing antarctic krill 'Euphausia superba'.**

16722 Mackie; Ritchie GB 051001/00/0006 R
Preparation of liquid protein food from fish using added enzymes.

16723 Hodgkiss; Cann GB 051003/00/0023 R
Development of methods for the enumeration and identification of organisms encountered in fishery products.

16724 Cann; Hodgkiss GB 051003/61/0024 R
Bacteriology of fish processing in relation to food hygiene organisms of public health significance.

16725 Cann; Hodgkiss GB 051003/68/0017 R
Investigation of the normal commercial and spoilage flora of fishery products.

16726 Wignall; Tatterson GB 051009/00/0006 R
Fish silage production.

16727 Wignall; Tatterson GB 051009/00/0012 R
Production of fish meal using liquefaction before drying.

16728 Wignell; Potter GB 051009/69/0004 R
Control and improvement of the traditional fish meal process.

16729 Gibson; Murray GB 051011/00/0003 R
Biochemical, molecular, biological and genetic studies on selected groups of bacteria.

16730 Polesello, A.; Pizzocaro, F. IT 021900/76/0005 N
Aspetti biochimici della tecnologia e conservazione delle sardine ed alici.. **Biochemical aspects of progcressing and**

storage of pilchards and anchovies..

16731 Crivelli, G.; Senesi, E.; Torreggiani, D.
IT 021900/79/0010 N
Ricerche sulla tecnologia di affumicamento delle anguille e delle sardine. **Researches on the smoking technology of eels and sardines.**

16732 Spreekens, K.J.A. van　　NL 050303/78/2976 N
Bevordering en onderzoek van de hygiëne in visverwerkende bedrijven en microbiologisch onderzoek van verwerkte produkten. **Promotion of and research on hygiene in fish processing plants and microbiological research on processed products.**

16733 Oosterhuis, J.J.　　NL 050303/78/2981 N
Onderzoek naar de mogelijkheden van verwerking van gevroren grondstof in fileerinrichtingen. **Study of the possibilities of processing frozen raw materials in fish fillet units.**

16734 Houwing, H.　　NL 050303/78/2982 N
Onderzoek naar het fileerrendement van verschillende sorteringen van schar in diverse biologische stadia. **Study of the fillet efficiency of some dab gradings in various biological stages.**

16735 Pel, L. van　　NL 050303/78/2983 N
Verbetering van procesbeheersing in visrokerijen. **Improvement of process control in fish smoking.**

16736 Weber, C.J.　　NL 050303/78/2984 N
Het gebruik van makreelachtigen in marinades. **Use of mackerels in marinades.**

16737 Houwing, H.　　NL 050303/78/2986 N
Produkt ontwikkeling op basis van niet volledig benutte vissoorten, bij vangst, ondermaatse vis en afvallen. **Product development based on not fully utilized fish species, under-sized fish and fish offal.**

16738 Spreekens, K.J.A. van　　NL 050303/78/2987 N
Eliminatie van salmonella gedurende het roken van makreel. **Elimination of salmonella during the smoking of mackerel.**

16739 Bon, H.　　NL 050303/78/2988 N
Zuivering en hergebruik van pekels en marinade voorbaden. **Purification and re-use of brine and used marinades.**

Dairy products, eggs, egg products, ice cream in general (B 6860)

16740 Lacrosse, R.　　BE 080500/78/0010
Séchage par atomisation de ferments pour yoghourt. **Spray-dried dairy starters for yoghurt.**

16741 Manson　　GB 030203/00/0014 R
The ion carrying capacity of beta-casein.

16742 Dalgleish　　GB 030203/00/0016 R
Factors affecting the rate of aggregation of the caseins.

16743 Dalgleish　　GB 030203/00/0017 R
The thermochemistry of the alpha-S-casein-Ca and alpha-S-kappa-casein-Co systems.

16744 Horne　　GB 030203/78/0026 R
The effects of chemical modification on the physical properties of caseins.

16745 Berg, G. van den　　NL 060002/77/7256
Praktisch onderzoek naar de factoren tijdens de bereiding en rijping welke van invloed zijn op het voorkomen van "groen" in de kaaskorst. **Investigations concerning the influence of manufacturing and ripening conditions on the development of "green" of cheese rind in practise.**

Milk products (B 6861)

See also 3621, 11084, 12056, 12114, 12222, 12236, 12279, 15927, 16236, 16244, 16311, 16318, 16490, 16965, 17046, 17289, 19363, 19439, 20363

16746 Delbeke, R.　　BE 070900/72/0004 R
De membraantechnieken bij de behandeling van water en afvalwater. **Membrane techniques in the treatment of water and waste water.**

16747 Martens, R.; De Vilder, J.　　BE 070900/73/0021 R
Technologische problemen bij de bereiding van melkpoeder : beheersing van het vochtgehalte. **Technological problems in milkpowder manufacture : maintenance of water content.** Publications.

16748 Naudts, M.; Martens, R.　　BE 070900/78/0036
Beheersing van het kaasrijpingsproces. **Control of the cheese ripening process.**

16749 Renner, E.; Renz, A.　　DE 129252/73/0002
Möglichkeiten der Eiweissanreicherung von fettreduzierter Trinkmilch, deren ernährungsphysiologische und sensorische Bewertung und Verbraucherbeurteilung. **Possibilities of protein enrichment in fat-reduced drinking milk, the nutritional and sensorial value and consumer's valuation.**

16750 Renner, E.; Pental, A.　　DE 129252/77/0003
Verwendung von ultrafiltrierten Molkeneiweisskonzentraten für die Eiweissanreicherung von Nahrungsmitteln. **Utilization of ultrafiltrated whey protein concentrates for the protein enrichment of foods.**

16751 Renner, E.; Töter, D.　　DE 129252/77/0005
Einfluss von Faktoren der Ultrahocherhitzung auf sensorische, chemische und ernährungsphysiologische Kriterien der H-Milch. **Influence of factors of UHT-treatment on sensoric, chemical and nutritional criteria of UHT-milk.**

16752 Kielwein, G.　　DE 129701/78/0003 N
Beziehungen zwischen hygienischer Rohmilchqualität und Milchtechnologie. **Correlations between hygienic quality of raw milk and technological value of milk.** Publications.

16753 Grove, H.-H.; Weidmann, B.　　DE 160731/77/0001
Untersuchungen psychrotropher Mikroorganismen auf proteolytische Aktivität und Pyruvatbildungsvermögen in Milch. **Proteolytic activity of psychrotrophs in milk and their ability of pyruvate production.**

16754 Grove, H.-H.; Stauss, H.　　DE 160731/77/0005
Beeinflussung der Pyruvatbildung psychrotropher Mikroorganismen in Milch. **Investigations in changing the ability of producing pyruvate in milk by psychrotrophic**

mikroorganisms.

16755 Kirchmeier, O.　　　　DE 161340/70/0002 N
Untersuchungen über den Aufbau der Caseinmicelle.
Investigations on the structure of casein micelle.

16756 Guthy, K.　　　　DE 161340/70/0003 N
Über Einflüsse auf die Grössenverteilung von Partikeln in
Milch nach Labzusatz. **Influence of addition of rennet on size
distribution of particles in milk.**

16757 Kiermeier, F.; Mashaley, R.　　　DE 161340/73/0003
Über den Einfluss einiger in der Milchwirtschaft üblichen
Prozesse – mit Ausnahme der Schmelzkäseherstellung – auf die
Stabilität von Aflatoxin M. **The effect of some industrial
milk–processing practices – with the exception of processed
cheese production – on the stability of aflatoxin M.**

16758 Kirchmeier, O.　　　　DE 161340/74/0001
Denaturierung von Milchproteinen in Abhängigkeit von
verschiedenen Erhitzungs– und Trocknungsverfahren.
**Denaturation of milk protein in dependence on different
heating and drying methods.**

16759 Kessler, H.G.; Helming, G.　　　DE 161350/77/0002
Technologisch bedingte Farbänderungen fruchthaltiger
Sauermilcherzeugnisse. **Changes in colour of special cultured
milk products.**

16760 Kessler, H.G.; Walenta, W.　　　DE 161350/77/0004
Physikalische Einflussgrössen bei der Produktion von
Camembert–Käsen. **Studies on physical influences during
camembert production.**

16761 Kessler, H.G.; Horak, P.　　　DE 161350/77/0005
Verfahrenstechnische Einflüsse bei der direkten und
indirekten Ultrahocherhitzung von Milch. **Process influences
on direct and indirect UHT–heating of milk.**

16762 Kessler, H.G.; Gernedel, C.　　　DE 161350/77/0006
Der Einsatz der Ultrafiltration in der Käsereitechnologie.
Ultrafiltration in cheese–making.

16763 Schlünsen, D.　　　　DE 201090/75/0011
Rationalisierung des Melkprozesses durch
verfahrensspezifische Verbesserung der Vor– und
Nachroutinen. **Rationalization of the milking process by
improving the milking routine.**

16764 Teuber, M.; Wasserfall, F.　　　DE 207030/77/0003
Qualitätsförderung und Verbesserung der Technologie bei
Produktion und Verarbeitung von Milch und Milchprodukten.
**Increase in quality and improvement of technology in
production and processing of milk and milk products.**

16765 Researcher not indicated　　　DE 207030/78/0001 N
Qualitätsförderung und Verbesserung der Technologie bei
Produktion und Verarbeitung von Milch und Milchprodukten.
**Improvement of quality and technology in production and
processing of milk and milk products by starter cultures.**

16766 Timmen, H.; Klostermeyer, H.　　DE 207040/77/0001 R
Modifizierung von Milchfett und Milchfettprodukten.
Modification of milk fat and milk fat products.

16767 Reimerdes, E.H.; Klostermeyer, H.

DE 207040/77/0005
Neue Gewinnungs– und Verwertungsmöglichkeiten für
Milcheiweiss. **New ways for production and utilization of milk
protein.**

16768 Klostermeyer, H.; Reimerdes, E.H.; Baer, E.von;
Juergens, R.　　　　DE 207040/78/0001 N
Lactasebehandlung von Milchprodukten, bevorzugt
Magermilch, zur Gewinnung lactosereduzierter Produkte,
bevorzugt Magermilchpulver. **Lactase–treatment of milk
products, especially of skim milk, for producing milk products
with reduced lactose content, especially skim milk powder.**

16769 Frede, E.; Knoop, E.; Precht, D.　　DE 207050/77/0001
Untersuchung der Mischkristallbildung beim Mischen von
Milchfettfraktionen mit unterschiedlichen Schmelzbereichen
zur Erzielung optimaler Konsistenzeigenschaften der Butter.
**Investigations on formation of mixed crystals in mixing of milk
fat fractions with different melting range for attaining optimum
consistency in butter.**

16770 Knoop, E.; Samhammer, E.; Buchheim, W.; Knoop,
A.–M.　　　　DE 207050/77/0005
Bestimmung viskoelastischer Eigenschaften von
Milchprodukten in Abhängigkeit von ihrer Vorbehandlung.
**Determination of visco–elastic characteristics of milk proteins
depending on pretreatment.**

16771 Precht, D.; Frede, E.; Knoop, E.　　DE 207050/77/0008
Änderung der Kristallformen und der Kristallmodifikationen
von Milchfetten während der Be– und Verarbeitungsprozesse
bei der Herstellung fetthaltiger Milchprodukte. **Changes in
forms and modifications of crystals in milk fats during
treatment and processing in preparation of fat–containing milk
products.**

16772 Knoop, E.; Frede, E.; Precht, D.　　DE 207050/77/0010
Untersuchungen zur Verbesserung der Butterstreichfähigkeit.
Investigations on improvement of spreadability of butter.

16773 Knoop, E.; Buchheim, W.; Samhammer, E.; Knoop,
A.–M.　　　　DE 207050/77/0014
Auswirkungen der Be– und Verarbeitung von Milch und
Milchinhaltsstoffen auf physikalische Aspekte der
Produktqualität. **Effects of treatment and processing of milk
and milk constituents on physical quality of product.**

16774 Reuter, H.: Prokopek, D.　　　DE 207060/72/4015 N
Prozessleitpläne für die Herstellung von Käse. **Processing
standards for cheese making.**

16775 Reuter, H.　　　　DE 207060/72/5019
Fliessverhalten von Milch und Milcherzeugnissen in
technischen Apparaten. **Rheology of milk and milk products in
machinery.**

16776 Reuter, H.; Ladwig, H.–P.　　　DE 207060/77/0001
Temperatur– und Verweilzeitverhalten von Milch in
Plattenwärmeaustauschern. **Temperature behaviour and
detention time behaviour of milk in plate warmth exchangers.**

16777 Reuter, H.　　　　DE 207060/77/0002
Rühr– und Mischvorgänge im Molkereibetrieb. **Stirring and
mixing process in dairy.**

16778 Reuter, H.　　　　DE 207060/77/0003

D 4430 – Processing

Veränderung von Rohmilch durch Strömungsvorgänge.
Changes in raw milk by processes of flow.

16779 Reuter, H.; Voss, E.   DE 207060/77/0004
Untersuchungen über die Beurteilung von verschiedenen stark
erhitzten Milchpulvern. **Studies on valuation of powdered milk
treated with differently strong heat.**

16780 Reuter, H.; Prokopek, D.   DE 207060/77/0005
Untersuchungen zu den funktionellen Eigenschaften von
Ultrafiltrations–Konzentraten und –Filtraten. **Studies on
functional properties of ultrafiltration concentrates and
filtrates.**

16781 Reuter, H.; Prokopek, D.; Klobes, H.
                                   DE 207060/77/0006
Untersuchungen zu Kennwerten von Ultrafiltrationsanlagen.
Studies on characters of ultrafiltration plants.

16782 Reuter, H.; Prokopek, D.   DE 207060/77/0007
Untersuchungen zur Herstellung von Käse mit Ultrafiltration.
Studies on preparation of cheese by ultrafiltration.

16783 Haisch, K.–H.; Wörner, K.   DE 502552/70/0001
Kostenwirtschaftliche Beurteilung von Reinigungs– und
Desinfektionsverfahren. **Methods of detergent sterilization in
sight of cost degression.**

16784 Kirchmeier, O.   DE 502553/70/0001
Chemisch und chemisch–physikalische Grundprozesse der
Käsereitechnik. **Chemical and chemo–physical basic processes
of cheesemaking technology.** Publications.

16785 Kiermeier, F.; Lechner, E.   DE 502553/72/0002
Einfluss der verschiedenen UHT–Erhitzungsverfahren auf die
Bestandteile der Milch. **Influence of different UHT–processing
methods on milk components.**

16786 Kiermeier, F.; Weiss, G.   DE 502553/72/0003
Verwendung von Labaustauschstoffen bei der
Käseherstellung. **Use of rennin substitutes in cheese–making.**

16787 Kirchmeier, O.   DE 502553/72/0004
Sekundäre Phase der Labgerinnung – Synärese, Gelstruktur –.
**Secondary phase of milk coagulation by rennin – syneresis, gel
structure –.**

16788 Kirchmeier, O.   DE 502553/75/0001
Zusammenhänge zwischen thermischer Behandlung der Milch
und molekularer Hysteresis des Milchproteinsystems.
**Relationship between thermal treatment of milk and molecular
hysteresis of the milk protein system.**

16789 Kirchmeier, O.   DE 502553/77/0001
Chemische und chemisch–physikalische Vorgänge bei der
Käsereifung. **Chemical and physico–chemical processes on
cheese ripening.**

16790 Birkkjær, H.E.   DK 010300/69/0201
Udvikling og tilpasning af automatik og teknisk udstyr til osteri
og lagre. **Development and adaptation of automatic and
technical equipment for creameries and stores.**

16791 Werner, H.   DK 010300/70/0502
Undersøgelse af membranfiltrering i teknisk målestok samt
funktionelle egenskaber hos membranfiltrerede produkter.

Investigation of membrane filtration on the technical scale, and
the functional qualities of membrane–filtered products.

16792 Møller–Madsen, Aa.   DK 010300/74/0601
Undersøgelser vedrørende nogle mælkesyrebakteriers
proteolytiske enzymer. **Investigation of the proteolytic enzymes
of some lactic acid bacteria.**

16793 Møller–Madsen, Aa.   DK 010300/74/0603
Undersøgelser vedrørende DNA–binding i slægten
Streptococcus. **Studies of DNA binding in Streptococcus sp.**

16794 Møller–Madsen, Aa.   DK 010300/74/0604
Undersøgelser vedrørende syregraden i mælkefedtet i
leverandørmælk. **Investigation of the acidity of milk fat in retail
milk.**

16795 Birkkjær, H.E.   DK 010300/75/0021
Saltning af ost. **The salting of cheese.**

16796 Jensen, G.K.   DK 010300/75/0042
Undersøgelse af produktionsteknologiske faktorers betydning
for fedtholdige mælkeprodukters emulgeringsstabilitet. **An
investigation of the importance of various factors within
production technology for the emulsifying stability of
fat–containing milk products.**

16797 Mortensen, B.K.   DK 010300/76/0011
Forsøg med fremstilling af syrnet smør udfra usyrnet fløde. **The
experimental manufacture of sour butter from unsour cream.**

16798 Birkkjær, H.E.   DK 010300/76/0021
Forsøg med fremstilling af Svenboost. **The experimental
manufacture of Svenbo cheese.**

16799 Birkkjær, H.E.   DK 010300/76/0022
Forsøg med fremstilling af hvidskimmelost. **The experimental
manufacture of white mould cheese.**

16800 Birkkjær, H.E.   DK 010300/76/0023
Forsøg med fremstilling af blåskimmelost. **The experimental
manufacture of blue mould cheese.**

16801 Jensen, G.K.   DK 010300/76/0042
Forsøg med fremstilling af langtidsholdbare flødeprodukter
ved UHT–behandling og aceptisk emballering. **The
experimental manufacture of long–life cream products using
UHT–treatment and aseptic packaging.**

16802 Mortensen, B.K.   DK 010300/77/0011
Forsøg med anvendelse af lave flødesyrningstemperaturer ved
smørfremstilling. **An experiment with the use of low
cream–souring temperatures in the manufacture of butter.**

16803 Birkkjær, H.E.   DK 010300/77/0022
Forsøg med fremstilling og affarvning af Feta–ost. **The
experimental manufacture and decolourization of Feta–cheese.**

16804 Birkkjær, H.E.   DK 010300/77/0024
Varierende salpetertilsætning til ostemælken. **The variation in
the amount of salpetre added to cheese producing milk.**

16805 Poulsen, P.R.   DK 010300/77/0031
Procesteknologiske undersøgelser i forbindelse med
fremstilling af ymer på basis af ultrafiltreret mælk. **Process
technology orientated investigations in connection with the**

manufacture of junket based on the ultrafiltration of milk.

16806 Poulsen, P.R.   DK 010300/77/0032
Undersøgelser over forskellige teknologiske foranstaltninger i
forbindelse med steril aftapning af UHT steriliseret mælk.
**Investigations into the different technological provisions
associated with sterile drawing off of UHT sterilised milk.**

16807 Birkkjær, H.E.   DK 010300/78/0022
Forsøg med fremstilling af Danbo–ost af mælk tilsat
mælkepulver. **The experimental manufacture of Danbo cheese
from condensed milk.**

16808 Birkkjær, H.E.   DK 010300/78/0023 R
Forsøg med fremstilling af ost af ultrafiltreret mælk. **The
experimental manufacture of cheese from ultrafiltrated milk.**

16809 Birkkjær, H.E.; Forsingdal, K.; Thomsen, D.; Larsen,
H.   DK 010300/78/0024 N
Forskellige ostesyrevækkeres egenskaber ved varierende
ostningsteknik. **Characteristics of different starters by varying
cheesemaking technique.**

16810 Birkkjær, H.E.; Thomsen, D.; Sigersted, E.;
Forsingdal, K.; Braun, H.   DK 010300/78/0026 N
Bakteriologiske og kemiske omsætninger i Danbo og Cheddar
fremstillet under ensartede vilkår af mælk med og uden
indhold af nitrat. **Bacteriological and chemical transformations
in Danbo and Cheddar–cheese manufactured under uniform
conditions from milk with or without any content of nitrate.**

16811 Birkkjær, H.E.; Braun, H.; Forsingdal, K.
                    DK 010300/78/0027 N
Lysozym og æggehvide til ost. **Lysozym and white of eggs in
cheesemaking.**

16812 Poulsen, P.R.   DK 010300/78/0031 N
Undersøgelse af de foreliggende teknologiske muligheder for
fremstilling af langtidsholdbar, forbrugervenlig piskefløde.
**Investigation of the present technological possibilities for the
manufacture of long keeping and consumer appealing
whipping cream.**

16813 Poulsen, P.R.   DK 010300/78/0032 N
Fremstillingsteknologiske muligheder for fremstilling af lagdelt
tofaset syrnet mælkeprodukt. **Technological possibilities for the
manufacture of a two fase cultured milk product.**

16814 Jensen, G.K.   DK 010300/78/0041 N
Forsøg med to–trinstørring, agglomerering ved fines
returnering til forstøverzonen, rewett–agglomerering samt
lecithinbehandling af mælkepulver. **Two stage drying and
agglomeration by returning fines to the atomizer zone, rewett
agglomeration and lecithintreatment of milk powder.**

16815 Jensen, G.K.   DK 010300/78/0042 N
Anvendelse af valle og UF–permeat som foder til kvæg og svin.
**Application of whey and UF–permeate for feeding cattle and
pigs.**

16816 Knudsen, A.; Andersson, N.   DK 010300/78/0071 N
Måling af luft i mælkestrømme. **Determination of air content in
flowing milk.**

16817 Petersen, E.O.   DK 010300/78/0081 N
Forbrugstal og overgangstal ved ostefremstilling. **Conversion
figures in cheesemaking.**

16818 Samuelsson, E.G.   DK 030192/70/0002
Temperaturbehandling af fløde og smørrets konsistens.
**Temperature treatment of cream and the consistency of the
butter.**

16819 Christiansen, P.S.   DK 030192/72/0003
Syrnede mælkeprodukters viskositet og stabilitet. **The viscosity
and stability of acidified milk products.**

16820 Christiansen, P.S.   DK 030192/72/0004
Forskellige faktorers indflydelse på fedtkuglemembranens
sammensætning og betydning for produktteknologien.
**Influence of different factors on the composition of the fat
globular membrane and importance for product technology.**

16821 Samuelsson, E.G.   DK 030192/77/0006
Mælkeproteinernes funktionelle egenskaber. **Functional
properties of the milk proteins.**

16822 Samuelsson, E.–G.   DK 030192/78/0001 N
Fraktionering af smør. **Fractionation of butteroil.**

16823 Samuelsson, E.G.; Quist, K.B.   DK 030192/78/0002 N
Mælkens osteteknologiske egenskaber. **The technological
properties of milk for cheese–making.**

16824 Samuelsson, E.–G.   DK 030192/79/0001 N
Fremstilling af ymer og camembert ved hjælp af ultrafiltrering.
**Ultra–filtration of milk and the processing of "ymer" and
camembert.**

16825 Edelsten, D.   DK 030193/76/0001
Fjernelse af lactose fra modermælk ved forgæring med sac.
fragilis. **Removal of lactose from human milk by fermentation
with Sac. fragilis.**

16826 Edelsten, D.   DK 030193/79/0002 N
Undersøgelse af lactaseenzymet "Lactozym" og dets
anvendelse i fremstillingen af forskellige lactosehydrolyserede
mejeriprodukter. **The application of "Lactozym" in production
of different dairy products.**

16827 Reiter   GB 011701/79/0029 N
Isolation and practical use of lactoperoxidase.

16828 Reid, S.   IE 060100/00/1466 N
The use of high ultimate ph meat in meat processing.
Publications.

16829 Cogan, T.   IE 060400/69/2015 R
Concentrated cultures of cheese starters. Publications.

16830 Connolly, J.F.   IE 060400/75/2011 N
**Measurement of biochemically important ingredients by
continuous flow techniques.** Publications.

16831 Phelan, J.A.; O'Keeffe, A.   IE 060400/75/2017 N
Factors influencing cheese yield. Publications.

16832 Phelan, J.A.; Keogh, M.K.; O'Keeffe, A.; Kelly, P.
                    IE 060400/75/2032 R
Pilot seasonal survey of milk for processing. Publications.

16833 Phelan, J.A.   IE 060400/76/2018 R

D 4430 – Processing

Salt distribution in cheddar cheese. Publications.

16834 O'Keeffe, A.; Burgess, K.J.   IE 060400/77/1304 R
Hydrolysis of milk protein. Publications.

16835 Kelly, P.   IE 060400/77/1342 R
A study of factors influencing the heat stability and viscosity of milk powders. Publications.

16836 Kelly, P.   IE 060400/77/1343 R
A study of energy use in the commercial production of milk powders. Publications.

16837 Kelly, P.   IE 060400/77/1344 R
A study of powder losses and recovery systems in spray driers. Publications.

16838 Palmer, J.   IE 060400/77/2070 R
Potassium level in dairy effluent as an index of milk losses.

16839 Burgess, K.J.   IE 060400/77/2071 R
Effects of milk pre–treatment on skimming efficiency.

16840 Keogh, M.K.   IE 060400/78/1406 N
Relative contribution of proteases and milk composition to heat stability and gelation in UHT milk. Publications.

16841 Fox, P.F.; O'Connor, T.; Shanahan, R.M.
    IE 110101/70/7602 R
Heat stability of milk. Publications.

16842 Synnott, E.C.; Thomas, D.   IE 110106/79/9219 N
Factors affecting dust explosions and layer ignition in milk powders in spray drying.

16843 Rampilli, M.; Francani, R.; Bettenzoli, P.G.
    IT 022200/78/0002
Indagine sul punto di congelamento nei latti individuali e di stalla. Freezing point of single cow and of bulk tank milk.

16844 Nani, R.; Pasca Raymondo, M.; Aliano, N.
    IT 022200/78/0003
Inattivazione delle perossidasi nel latte. Peroxidase inactivation in milk.

16845 Bossi, M.G.; Toppino, P.M.; Cabrini, A.
    IT 022200/78/0005
Sopravvivenza dei fermenti lattici in yogurt liofilizzato. Cells survival in lyophilized yogurt.

16846 Cabrini, A.; Bossi, M.G.; Francani, R.
    IT 022200/78/0006
Estratti enzimatici proteolitici da lieviti nella maturazione dei formaggi. Proteolytic enzymes from yeast in cheese ripening.

16847 Nani, R.; Pasca Raymondo, M.; Francani, R.
    IT 022200/78/0007
Latte trattato con B–galattossidasi nella utilizzazione casearia. B–galactosidase treated milk, in cheese making.

16848 Toppino, P.M.; Cabrini, A.; Caroppo, S.
    IT 022200/79/0001 N
Preparazione di yogurt pastorizzato e successivo reinoculo del prodotto con fermenti lattici. Stabilized yogurt with added lactic acid bacteria.

16849 Nani, R.; Rampilli, M.; Montana Lampo, S.; Francani, R.   IT 022200/79/0002 N
Razionalizzazione dell'impiego di additivi nella produzione dei formaggi. Choice, level of use and technological reasons for some cheesemaking additives.

16850 Rampilli, M.; Cabrini, A.; Francani,; Morgante, D.
    IT 022200/79/0004 N
Indagini e valutazioni sulla composizione degli enzimi commerciali coagulanti il latte. Identification and determination of different milk clotting enzymes.

16851 Bossi, G.; Nani, R.; Montana Lampo, S.; Caroppo, S.
    IT 022200/79/0005 N
Prevenzione del difetto di gonfiore tardivo dei formaggi. Prevention of late cheese blowing.

16852 Cabrini, A.; Bossi, G.; Papetti, G.
    IT 022200/79/0006 N
Evoluzione della microflora del formaggio grana nelle prime ore dalla fabbricazione. Microbiology of grana cheese during the first hours after making.

16853 Emaldi, G.C.; Toppino, P.M.; Caroppo, S.; Aliano, N.
    IT 022200/79/0007 N
Fermenti lattici e polvere di siero nell'alimentazione dei conigli. Lactic acid bacteria and whey powder for rabbits feeds.

16854 De Felice, F.   IT 040111/74/0544
Strutture e trasformazioni conformazionali delle proteine del latte. Cinetica e termodinamica della coagulazione enzimatica. Structure and transformation of milk protein conformation. Kinetics and thermodynamics of enzymatic coagulation.

16855 Strocchi, A.   IT 040208/73/0952
I lipidi polari del latte. Milk's polar lipids. Publications

16856 Losi, G.   IT 040210/73/1819
Varianti genetiche delle caseine e attitudine alla coagulazione presamica del latte. Genetic variations in caseins and aptitude to rennet coagulation of milk. Publications.

16857 Scerra, V.   IT 040303/79/0002 N
Ricerche sulla composizione acidica ed aminoacidica del latte di pecora. Research on milk sheep fat–acids and amino–acids content.

16858 Russo, C.   IT 040308/78/1104 N
Ricerche sul contenuto di protidi e lipidi del latte di pecora, bufala e capra di razze allevate nella Sicilia orientale per la tipicizzazione dei derivati. The typification of milk derivates: research on the protein and lipid content of milk from ewes, buffalo–cows and goats belonging to races bred in Eastern Sicily.

16859 Del Re, A.; Molinari, G.P.; Lazzarini, C.; Rossi, E.
    IT 040406/79/0003 N
Effetti delle tecnologie di trasformazione sui residui di antiparassitari nel latte. Pathways of pesticides in milk technology.

16860 Bottazzi, V.   IT 040409/73/1810
Variazioni metaboliche in fermenti lattici. Metabolic variations in milk enzymes. Publications.

16861 Corradini, C.   IT 040609/74/0538

Comportamento di latti caratterizzati da diverse varianti genetiche delle caseine all'azione di agenti coagulanti di diverso tipo. **Response of milks characterized by several genetic variations of caseins to the action of different coagulating agents.**

16862 Ottogalli, G.   IT 040611/73/1196
Ricerche sulle proprietà fisiologiche ed ecologiche dei microorganismi che interessano alcuni prodotti alimentari fermentati–colostro, yogurt, formaggi tipici ed impasti acidi da panificazione. **Research on physiological and ecological properties of micro–organisms of some fermented food products–colostrum, yogurt, typical cheeses and acid bread donghs.**

16863 Ottogalli, G.   IT 040611/77/0253 R
Ricerche sulle proprietà fisiologiche ed ecologiche dei microrganismi che interessano alcuni prodotti di trasformazione del latte. **Research on the physiological and ecological properties of micro–organisms involved in milk processing.**

16864 Peri, C.   IT 040617/74/0600
Studio delle applicazioni dei processi per membrana e delle tecnologie di essiccamento nell'industria lattiero–casearia. **Study on the applications of membrane processing and drying techniques in milk and cheese industry.**

16865 Peri, C.   IT 040617/77/0258 R
Studio delle applicazioni dell'ultrafiltrazione e dell'essicamento nell'industria lattiero–casearia. **A study of ultrafiltration and drying applied to the dairy industry.**

16866 Lucisano, M.   IT 040617/78/1070 N
Sviluppo di tecniche di essiccamento e di concentrazione per prodotti lattiero caseari. **The development of desiccation and concentration methods applied to dairy produce in cheese making.**

16867 Albonico, F.   IT 040711/73/0126
Ricerche sulla caseina micellare di bufala. **Research on mycoloid casein of the buffalo.**

16868 Mincione, B.   IT 040711/73/2149
Ricerche sulle sieroproteine del latte di bufala, isolamento e frazionamento delle B–lattoglobuline. **Fractioning of lactoglobins isolated from buffalo milk.**

16869 Mincione, B.   IT 040711/78/1080 N
Acidi grassi liquidi nei formaggi tipici campani ed attività proteolitica della chimosina e pepsina bovina sulla caseina intera di bufala e sue frazioni. **Liquid fatty acids in typical cheeses from the Campagna; proteolytical activity of bovine chymosin and pepsin on whole or fractioned buffalo casein.**

16870 Formisano, M.   IT 040713/73/0211
Ricerche microbiologiche sul latte di bufala e possibilità di ottenimento di nuovi prodotti lattiero–caseari. **Microbiological research on buffalo milk and possibilities of obtaining new industrial milk products.** Publications.

16871 Rossi, J.; Costamagna, L.   IT 041023/70/0001 N
Bevande lattiche.. **Milk Beverages.**

16872 Haznedari, S.   IT 041023/71/0001 N
Fermentazione maloalcolica applicata al processo di

rifermentazione e all'impiego di colture adattate a basse temperature. **Maloalcoholic fermentation applied to the process of refermentation and to the use of crops adapted to low temperatures.**

16873 Rossi, J.   IT 041023/74/0617
La fisiologia e il biochimismo dei microrganismi del Kefir in relazione alla produzione del granulo. **Physiology and biochemistry of Kefir microorganisms in relation to granule production.**

16874 Rossi, J.; Rossi, J.   IT 041023/77/0001
I microrganismi dei "lieviti di pasta acida" e le loro implicazioni nel processo di fermentazione panaria. **The sour–doughs microorganisms and their relation with bread and other leavening products making.** Publications.

16875 Haznedari, S.   IT 041023/77/0002
Relazione tra alcuni lieviti fermentanti, differenti da Saccharomyces ellipsoideus e la produzione di sherry. **Relation between some fermentating yeasts, different from Saccharomyces ellipsoideus, and the flor sherry production.** Publications.

16876 Rossi, J.   IT 041023/77/0287 R
Impiego delle proteine del siero per la produzione di formaggi secondari e di bevande lattiche a base di L. acisophilus e di L. bifidus. **Use of serum proteins for the second production of cheeses and the production of milk drinks based on L. acisophilus and L. bifidus.**

16877 Rossi, J.   IT 041023/78/1101 N
La B–galattosidasi in lieviti lattosio–negativi con particolare riferimento ad aspetti di induzione, di repressione e di destinazione microbica dello enzima. **B–galactosidasis in lactose–negative yeasts with special regard to certain aspects of induction, of repression and microbic destiny of the enzyme.**

16878 Rossi, J.; Clementi, F.   IT 041023/79/0001 N
Aspetti microbiologici e tecnologici della fermentazione malolattica. **The microbiological and technological aspects of malolactic fermentation.** Publications.

16879 Costamagna, L.   IT 041023/79/0002 N
Immobilizzazione su gel di agar di microrganismi proteolitici. **The agar gel immobilization of proteolytic microorganisms.** Publications.

16880 Rossi, J.; Rosi, J.   IT 041023/79/0003 N
Essiccamento termico dello yogurt e dei fermenti lattici. **Thermal drying of the yogourt and the lactic acid bacteria.** Publications.

16881 Farris, G. A.   IT 041312/77/0173 R
Latte caprino ed ovino in Sardegna, indagini microbiologiche finalizzate alla introduzione di migliori e nuove tecniche di trasformazione. **Goat's and ewe's milk in Sardinia: microbiological research for the introduction of new and improved processing on techniques.**

16882 Resmini, P.   IT 062600/70/0116
Studi sul biochimismo della maturazione di alcuni importanti formaggi italiani. **Biochemical studies on the ripening of some important Italian cheeses.** Publications.

16883 Carini, S.   IT 062600/73/0115

Impiego dei cagli microbici ed in pasta. **The application of microbial and paste rennet.** Publications.

16884 Resmini, P. IT 062600/73/0117
Modificazioni delle caratteristiche chimiche e chimico–fisiche del latte sottoposto a trattamenti tecnologici diversi (essicazione e ultrafiltrazione). **Chemical and chemico–physical modifications of some milk components as effect of different dairy technologies (drying and ultrafiltration).** Publications.

16885 Carini, S. IT 062600/74/0114
Utilizzo di starter selezionati,conservati per congelazione e degli enzimi nella maturazione dei formaggi. **The use of selected starters,preserved by freezing and the use of the enzymes for the ripening of Italian cheeses.**

16886 Albonico, F. IT 062600/77/0884
Influenza dei trattamenti termici sul contenuto di metilchetoni del latte. **Action of thermic treatments on milk methyl–ketonic bodies content.**

16887 Albonico, F. IT 062600/77/0886
Studio delle possibili interazioni fra calcio e caseina durante la coagulazione presamica del latte. **A study of the possible interactions of calcium and casein during the rennet induced coagulation of milk.**

16888 Albonico, F. IT 062600/77/0887
Biochimismo della maturazione dei formaggi. **The biochemistry of cheese maturation.**

16889 Albonico, F. IT 062600/77/0888
Impiego di sistemi enzimatici coadiuvanti la caseificazione. **Use of enzymatic systems to assist the processes of cheese making.**

16890 Albonico, F. IT 062600/77/0889
Ricerche microbiologiche sui prodotti lattiero–caseari. **Microbiological research on dairy products.**

16891 Albonico, F. IT 062600/77/0890
Fattori capaci di influenzare le caratteristiche casearie del latte. **Factors influencing the cheese making qualities of milk.**

16892 Fagnoni, P.; Alberini, B. IT 090301/75/0001
Influenza dell'alimentazione delle bovine sulle caratteristiche casearie del latte. **The influence of cattle–feeding the casein qualities of milk.** Publications.

16893 Walstra, P.; Geurts, T.J.; Jong, L. de
NL 020031/49/5139
Microstructuur van melk en zuivelprodukten. **Microstructure of milk and dairy products.** Publications.

16894 Walstra, P.; Stempher, H.; Oortwijn, H.
NL 020031/65/4490
Vorming, homogenisatie van olie–in–water emulsies, zoals melkprodukten. **Formation and homogenization of oil–in–water emulsions, such as milk products.** Publications.

16895 Geurts, T.J; Mulder, H. NL 020031/66/4491
Diffusie van zout en water in kaas tijdens het pekelen en de daarbij optredende fysisch–chemische veranderingen. **Diffusion of salt and water in cheese during brining and pertinent physico–chemical changes.** Publications.

16896 Noomen, A. NL 020031/71/4488

De rijping van melkeiwit–rijke produkten zoals kaas; in het bijzonder de eiwitafbraak in deze produkten door microbiële en nietmicrobiële proteolytische enzymen. **Ripening of milkprotein–rich products such as cheese with special reference to proteinbreakdown in these products caused by microbial and non–microbial proteolytic enzymes.** Publications.

16897 Oortwijn, H. NL 020031/73/5140
Onderzoek van het gebrek "bitter" in kaas met behulp van een aseptische kaasbereidingsmethode. **Investigation of the effect "bitter" in cheese under controlled bacteriological conditions.**

16898 Walstra, P. NL 020031/77/8526
Synerese van wrongel en pasgevormde kaas. **Syneresis of curd and cheese before brining.**

16899 Kleter, G. NL 020031/78/8529
De invloed van levende en/of gedesintegreerde bacteriecellen op de rijping van kaas, te bestuderen met aseptische kaasbereidingstechnieken. **The influence of living and disrupted bacterial cells on the ripening of cheese, made under aseptic conditions.**

16900 Kleter, G. NL 020031/78/8530
De hitteresistentie van micro–organismen en enzymen die van belang zijn voor melk en melkproducten. **Heat resistance of micro–organisms and enzymes that are important for milk and milk products.**

16901 Stadhouders, J. NL 060002/65/3993
Bereiding van bevroren geconcentreerde suspensies van zuursel bacteriën. **Manufacture of frozen starter concentrates.** Publications.

16902 Staal, H.J. NL 060002/65/4064
Continu kaasbereiding; draineer– en vormapparatuur. **Continoous cheesemaking; draining and moulding equipment.** Publications.

16903 Schmidt, D.G. NL 060002/68/4040 R
Hittestabiliteit van melk en van geconcentreerde melk. **Heat stability of milk and concentrated milk.** Publications.

16904 Koning, P.J. de NL 060002/68/4056
Karakterisering en identificering van verschillende soorten stremsel. **Characterization and identification of different rennets.** Publications.

16905 Payens, T.A.J. NL 060002/70/3985
Structuur en eigenschappen van caseïne micellen in melk. **Structure and properties of micellar casein in milk.** Publications.

16906 Driessen, F.M. NL 060002/71/4035
Continu–bereiding van yoghurt. **Continuous making of yoghurt.** Publications.

16907 Steenbergen, A.E. NL 060002/71/4047
De beheersing van het vochtgehalte van melkpoeder. **Automatic control of the drying process for milk powder.** Publications.

16908 Stadhouders, J. NL 060002/71/4053
Bereidingsmethoden voor zure boter die minder zure karnemelk opleveren. **Making soured butter with less sour buttermilk.** Publications.

16909 Visser, S.   NL 060002/72/3982
Werking van rennine op synthetische peptiden gelijkend op K–caseïne. **Primary reaction of rennin on synthetic substrates similar to parts of K–casein.** Publications.

16910 Boer, R. de   NL 060002/72/7911 R
Proces–technologisch onderzoek m.b.t. membraam–processen (ultrafiltratie en omgekeerde osmose). **Proces–technological research concerning membrane processes (ultra filtration and reverse osmosis).** Publications.

16911 Dijk, R. van   NL 060002/72/7915
Bereiding van melkspecialiteiten volgens klassieke methode. **Manufacturing of milk specialities.** Publications.

16912 Payens, T.A.J.   NL 060002/73/3981
De stabiliserende werking van K–caseïne. **The stabilising action of K–casein.** Publications.

16913 Boer, R. de   NL 060002/74/5292
Bestudering van de ionenwisseling en elektrodialyse technieken ten behoeve van toepassingsmogelijkheden bij de verwerking van zuivelprodukten. **Study of ion exchange and electrodialysis techniques for application in dairy industry.** Publications.

16914 Boer, R. de   NL 060002/74/6097
Bereiding en toepassing van coprecipitaten uit melk. **Manufacture and uses of coprecipitates from milk.** Publications.

16915 Jansen, L.A.   NL 060002/75/6091
Directe verhitting van drooglucht door aardgas bij de bereiding van melkpoeder. **Manufacture of milkpowder with direct heating of drying air by means of natural gas.** Publications.

16916 Boer, R. de   NL 060002/75/6094
Het gebruik van geultrafiltreerde melk voor de kaasbereiding. **Use of ultrafiltrated milk for cheese making.** Publications.

16917 Alderlieste, P.J.   NL 060002/76/6607
Het dynamisch gedrag van verstuivingsdrogers en indampers. **Dynamic behaviour of spray–drying plants and evaporators.**

16918 Stadhouders, J.   NL 060002/76/6617
Oorzaken van de faagresistentie van praktijkzuursels. **Mechanism of phage resistance of practice starters.**

16919 Jansen, L.A.   NL 060002/76/7244
Energiebesparing in de zuivel industrie door warmteterugwinning uit de uitlaatlucht van droogtorens. **Saving of energy in the dairy industry by recovery of heat from the outlet air of spray dryers.**

16920 Jansen, L.A.   NL 060002/76/7246
Energibesparing door eigen elektriciteitsopwekking in de zuivelindustrie. **Saving of energy by generation of electricity at dairy factories.**

16921 Payens, T.A.J.   NL 060002/77/7239
Winning en karakterisering van as2 – caseïne. **Separation and characterization of as2 – casein.** Publications.

16922 Driessen, F.M.   NL 060002/77/7247
Sedimentatie en bacteriegroei in zuivelwerktuigen. **Sedimentation and growth of bacteria in dairy equipment.**

16923 Driessen, F.M.   NL 060002/77/7250
Symbiose van yoghurtbacteriën in continu culturen. **Symbiosis of yoghurt bacteria in continuous cultures.**

16924 Mol, J.J.   NL 060002/77/7252
De bereiding van instant vollemelkpoeder. **Manufacture of instant whole milk powder.**

16925 Schaap, J.E.   NL 060002/77/7253
Achtergrondonderzoek m.b.t. beheersing van de consistentie van boter. **Background investigations on control of butter consistency.**

16926 Berg, G. van den   NL 060002/77/7254
Praktijkonderzoek m.b.t. beheersing van de consistentie van boter. **Investigations in practice on control of butter consistency.**

16927 Wit, J.N.   NL 060002/77/7257 R
Karakterisering en toepassing van wei–eiwitten. **Characterizations and application of whey proteins.** Publications.

16928 Payens, T.J.   NL 060002/77/7906
Bestudering van het denaturatiegedrag van wei–eiwitten. **Study of the denaturation behaviour of whey proteins.**

16929 Hiddink, J.   NL 060002/77/7913
Vervuiling van het membraan bij ultrafiltratie en omgekeerde osmose van wei en melk. **Pollution of the membrane during ultrafiltration and reverse osmosis of whey and milk.**

16930 Kerkhof, P.   NL 060002/77/7918
Fysisch–technologisch onderzoek betreffende het vormen en persen van wrongel. **Physical–technological research into the moulding and pressing of curd.**

16931 Payens, T.A.J.   NL 060002/78/7907
Colloid–chemisch onderzoek van geconcentreerde zetmeelsuspensies t.b.v. het gebruik als verdikkingsmiddel in melkprodukten. **Colloid chemical study of concentrated starch suspensions to be used as thickening agents for milkproducts.**

16932 Jong, L. de   NL 060002/78/7916
Bereiding van melkspecialiteiten door toepassing van membraanprocessen. **Manufacturing of milkspecialities by application of membrane processes.**

16933 Jong, L. de   NL 060002/78/7917
Bereiding van melkspecialiteiten; Rheologisch achtergrondonderzoek. **Manufacturing of milkspecialities; Rheological background research.**

16934 Boer, R. de   NL 060002/78/7925
Bereiding van gehydroliseerde lactose. **Manufacturing of hydrolyzed lactose.**

16935 Payens, T.A.J.   NL 060002/78/8678 N
Coagulatiekinetiek m.b.t. melk en zuivelprodukten. **Kinetics of coalugation related to milk and dairy products.**

16936 Exterkate, F.A.   NL 060002/79/8679 N
Lokalisatie en eigenschappen van membraangebonden peptidasen in melkzuurstreptococcen. **Localisation and properties of membrane–bound peptidases in lactic acid**

streptococci.

16937 Exterkate, F.A. NL 060002/79/8680 N
Regulatie van de groei van melkzuurstreptococcen. **Regulation of growth of lactic acid streptococci in milk.**

16938 Langeveld, L.P.M. NL 060002/79/8683 N
Verlaging van het kiemgetal in UF- en OO–apparatuur. **Decrease of bacterial contamination by cleaning.**

16939 Stadhouders, J. NL 060002/79/8684 N
Kiemdoding en handhaving van een goede bacteriële kwaliteit van bedrijfswater t.b.v. het hergebruik bij de bereiding van zuivelprodukten. **Destruction of germs and maintenance of a good bacterial' quality of industrial water for re–use purposes at the manufacturing of dairy products.**

16940 Lankveld, L. NL 060002/79/8685 N
Slagroom stabiliteit. **Stability of whipping cream.**

16941 Lankveld, L. NL 060002/79/8686 N
Toepassing van zoete karnemelk. **Apllication for sweet–cream buttermilk.**

16942 Snoeren, T.H.M. NL 060002/79/8688 N
Karakterisering van melkpoeder in relatie tot hun toepassingen. **Characterization of milk powders in relation to their uses.**

16943 Kerkhof, P. NL 060002/79/8690 N
Invloed van afwijkende procescondities op het gedrag van indampers en op produkteigenschappen van melkpoeder. **Effect of changes in the proces conditions on the behaviour of evaporators and on product properties of milk powder.**

16944 Jansen, L.A. NL 060002/79/8691 N
Nieuwe werkwijze voor concentreren en drogen van melk en melkprodukten. **New methods of concentration and dehydration of milk and milkproducts.**

16945 Jansen, L.A. NL 060002/79/8692 N
Toepassing van doekfilters bij de melkpoederbereiding. **Use of bag filters at the milkpowder manufacturing process.**

16946 Schaap, J.E. NL 060002/79/8693 N
Het emulgeren van melkvet en het toepassen van verkregen emulsies. **Emulsification of milk fat and application of the emulsions obtained.**

16947 Stadhouders, J. NL 060002/79/8694 N
Het versnellen van de kaasrijping door toepassing van proteolytische enzymen van zuurselbacteriën. **Acceleration of the cheese ripening process by means of proteolytic enzymes of starter bacteria.**

Eggs and egg products (B 6862)

See also 12597, 16811

16948 Cagnasso Ravazzoni, C. IT 040604/74/0521
Preparazione di fosfatidilcoline allo stato puro da lecitina d' uovo. **Preparation of pure phosphatidilcholines from egg lecithin.**

16949 Uijttenboogaart, Th.G. NL 010109/75/6075
Onderzoek naar de kwaliteit van met behulp van ultrafiltratie

geconcentreerde eiprodukten. **Quality aspects of egg products, concentrated by ultrafiltration.** Publications.

Other dairy products (B 6869)

See also 16555

16950 Badings, H.T. NL 060002/72/3992 R
Identificatie en vorming van geur- en smaakstoffen in wei en weiprodukten. **Identification and formation of aroma compounds in whey and whey products.** Publications.

16951 Nieuwenhof, F.F.J. NL 060002/74/5291
Vergisting van vloeibare zuivel afval- en nevenprodukten. **Fermentation of liquid dairy byproducts and wastes.**

Other foods (B 6870)

See also 5035, 16189, 16302, 16304, 16305, 16309, 16310, 16311, 16345, 16346, 17098

16952 Bielig, H.J.; Schumann, U.; Krischke, H.
DE 105812/72/0001 N
Die Wirkung von Gewürzextrakten auf Bakterien, Hefen und Schimmelpilze und ihre technologische Anwendung. **Influence of aromatic extracts on bacteria, yeasts and moulds and their technological application.**

16953 Siebert, G.; Plessing, A. DE 144190/77/0001
Kovalente Verknüpfung von Aminosäuren mit Proteinen zur Verbesserung von Nährwert und technologischen Eigenschaften. **Improvement of nutritive value and technological properties of protein by covalent addition of amino acids.**

16954 Carnovale, E. IT 011300/77/0734
Preparazione di un concentrato proteico da fave e lupini. **Preparation of a protein concentrate extracted from beans and lupins.**

16955 Quaglia, G.B. IT 011300/77/0762
Preparazione di un concentrato proteico da sangue da macellazione. **Preparation of a protein extract from the blood of slaughtered animals.**

16956 Crisetig, G. IT 040231/78/1047 N
Produzione di aminoacidi essenziali ad opera di batteri anaerobi. **The production of essential amino–acids by anaerobic bacteria.**

16957 Lercker, G. IT 040240/77/0750 R
Valutazione tecnologica ed economica della valorizzazione per l'alimentazione umana dei sottoprodotti della macellazione. **Technological and economical evaluation of the recuperation for human consumption of the waste products of slaughtering.**

16958 Bottazzi, V. IT 040409/77/0730
Caratterizzazione di lieviti impiegati per la produzione di biomasse con particolare riguardo ad alcune specie che utilizzano il lattosio e le N–paraffine. **Characterisation of yeasts used in biomass production with special regard to certain species grown on lactose and N–paraffins.**

16959 Pompei, C. IT 040617/77/0759
Ricerche sull'estrazione, purificazione e l'impiego di proteine da leguminose da granella per l'alimentazione umana, in

particolare da lupino e fagiolo. **Research on the extraction, purification and use of pulse proteins for human consumption with special regard to lupines and beans.**

16960 Peri, C.   IT 040617/78/1125 N
Studio dell'essiccamento e della struttura di preparati proteici da varie fonti vegetali. **A study on the drying up and the structure of protein compounds of vegetal origin.**

16961 Corrao, A.   IT 040910/77/0737 R
Estrazione, purificazione e caratterizzazione di proteine da vinaccioli. Ricerche sulla preparazione di concentrati e isolati proteici del cece – Cicer arietinum L.–. **The extraction, purification and characterisation of grape–pips proteins. Research on the preparation of protein extracts from chick peas – Cicer arietinum L.–.**

16962 Martini, A.   IT 041013/78/1124 N
Determinazione del grado di riassociazione DNA–DNA per via spettrofotometrica di lieviti di interesse industriale. **Spectro–photometrical determination of the degree of DNA–DNA re–association in industrial yeasts.**

16963 Rossi, J.   IT 041023/77/0763
Proteine da microrganismi. Eumiceti con particolare riguardo ai lieviti sviluppati su substrati amilacei. **Proteins extracted from micro–organisms. Eumycetes with special regard to yeasts cultured on starch media.**

16964 Lanzani, A.   IT 070200/77/0748
Studio della composizione biochimica, studio della tecnologia di estrazione e purificazione di proteine da oleaginosi, girasole e vinaccioli. **Studies on the biochemical composition, on the technology of extraction and purification of proteins from oleaginous plants, sunflowers and grape–pips.**

16965 Baldini, P.   IT 070500/78/1121 N
Studio delle proprietà funzionali delle proteine del siero di latte e del plasma del sangue animale, preparazione di alimenti carnei in pasta e in pezzi. **A study of the functional properties of milk serum proteins and of animal plasma proteins; the preparation of meat feeds in paste or crumbs.**

Alcoholic liquors, coffee, tea, tobacco and other table luxuries (B 6890)

See also 6156, 6223, 6225, 7413, 7435, 9884, 16262, 16631, 17087, 19109, 19439, 19451, 19461

16966 Wasmund, R.   DE 105750/78/0001 N
Mathematische und experimentelle Untersuchung von Erwärmungs– und Abkühlvorgängen beim Bier. **Mathematical and experimental inquiry of processes in warming and cooling the beer.** Publications.

16967 Bielig, H.J.; Barudi, W.   DE 105813/78/0002 N
Die Filtration von Getränken mit Hilfe von 2–Komponententiefenfiltern. **Beverage filtration by means of 2–component filters with penetrative effect.**

16968 Krauss, G.; Schulze, D.   DE 105984/70/0003
Mälzungsarbeit und Malzqualität. **Influence of the malting method on malt quality.**

16969 Runkel, U.–D.; Fiederer, E.   DE 105985/74/0002
Der Einfluss der Sauerstoffaufnahme während der einzelnen

Prozessschritte auf die Bierqualität. **Influence of oxygen absorption on beer quality in different phases of the brewing process.**

16970 Runkel, U.–D.; Niemsch, K.   DE 105985/74/0003
Der Einfluss technologischer Massnahmen bei der Haupt– und Nachgärung auf die Filtrierbarkeit des Bieres. **Beer filterability in dependence on technological conditions in primary and secondary fermentation process.**

16971 Pfeilsticker, K.; Nickenig, R.   DE 111600/78/0005 N
Ultraschallbehandlung von Weinmosten und Schwefligsäurebedarf. **Ultrasonic treatment of grape musts and the demand for sulfurous acid.**

16972 Pieper, H.J.; Röhrig, G.   DE 144242/78/0002 N
Zum Einfluss verschiedener Werkstoffe von Destillierapparaten auf die Aromazusammensetzung von Obstbranntweinen. **Effect of different materials of distilling apparatus on the flavour composition of fruit spirits.**

16973 Pieper, H.J.   DE 144242/78/0004 N
Technische Alkoholgewinnung aus Alwafarin. **Technical production of alcohol from alwafarin.**

16974 Mändl, B.; Heyse, K.–U.; Piendl, A.
                                  DE 161770/72/0004
Enzymuntersuchungen an Hefen. **Studies of enzymes in yeasts.**

16975 Mändl, B.; Wagner, D.; Piendl, A.   DE 161770/72/0009
Untersuchungen über Aminosäuren im Substrat und im Hefepool in Abhängigkeit von technologischen Massnahmen. **Studies on amino acids in substrate and yeast pool related to technological measures.**

16976 Mändl, B.; Koller, A.   DE 161770/73/0003 R
Brauereiabwässer. **Brewery sewage.**

16977 Mändl, B.; Geiger, E.; Piendl, A.   DE 161770/75/0001
Untersuchungen zur Alterungsbeständigkeit des Bieres. **Flavour stability of beer.** Publications.

16978 Wullinger, F.; Heyse, K.–U.   DE 161770/77/0003
Einfluss von Mineralstoffen und Spurenelementen auf das Verhalten von Brauereihefe. **Influence of mineral substances and trace elements on the behaviour of brewing yeast.**

16979 Piendl, A.; Wagner, D.   DE 161770/77/0004
Nukleinbasen und Nukleoside – ihre Rolle in der Brauereitechnologie. **Nucleobases and nucleotides – their role in brewing technology.**

16980 Narziss, L.; Kunz, A.   DE 161790/71/0001
Der Einfluss verschieden stark gelöster Malze auf die Qualität der Biere unter Berücksichtigung einer mehrmaligen Führung der Hefe. **The influence of malts of different modification on beer quality by repeated use of the same yeast.**

16981 Narziss, L.; Kattein, U.   DE 161790/78/0001 N
Über das Verhalten von Schwefelsubstanzen insbesondere Dimethylsulfid und seinen Vorläufern bei der Bierbereitung. **About sulfur containing substances, p.e. dimethyl sulfide and their precursors during beer production.**

16982 Lemperle, E.   DE 501105/77/0001
Untersuchungen zur Inversion von Saccharose in

Traubenmost. **Investigations on the inversion of sucrose in grape musts.**

16983 Wucherpfennig, K.; Keding, K.   DE 506104/74/0003
Die Veränderungen des Säuregehaltes von Traubensaft und Wein mit Hilfe der Elektrodialyse. **Electrodialytic changes in the acid content of grape juice and wine.**

16984 Wucherpfennig, K.; Millies, K.–D.   DE 506104/74/0006
Eiweissstabilisierung von Wein mit Hilfe der Ultrafiltration. **Protein stabilization in wine by means of ultrafiltration.**

16985 Wucherpfennig, K.; Zürn, F.   DE 506104/77/0002
Verbesserung der Weinqualität durch Konzentrieren und Entsäuerung von Most und Wein durch Umkehrosmose. **Improvement of quality of wine by concentration and deacidification of must and wine by reverse osmosis.** Publications.

16986 Wucherpfennig, K.; Millies, K.–D.   DE 506104/77/0006
Einfluss der Polyphenole auf die Bindung und Bildung von Acetaldehyd in Weinen. **Binding and formation of acetaldehyde in wine as affected by polyphenols.**

16987 Dittrich, H.H.; Wenzel, K.   DE 506105/78/0001 N
H2S–Bildung während der Weinbereitung. **H2S–production during wine–making.**

16988 Jakob, L.   DE 509152/77/0001
Verminderung des Acetaldehydgehaltes von Wein. **Diminution of acetaldehyde in wine.**

16989 Eichhorn, K.W.; Lorenz, D.H.   DE 509153/78/0003 N
Mögliche Ursachen von Gär– und Geschmacksbeeinflussungen von Wein. **Possible causes of influences on fermentation and taste in wine.**

16990 Poll, L.   DK 030194/78/0005 N
Gæringens indflydelse på kvaliteten af kirsebærvin. **Influence of degree of fermentation on the quality of cherry wine.**

16991 André, P.; Flanzy, C.   FR 010605/65/2223
Connaissances générales sur la vinification par macération carbonique et maîtrise de cette technique. **Wine–making by carbonic maceration.** Publications.

16992 Flanzy, C.; Chambroy, Y.   FR 010605/66/2224
Fermentation intracellulaire de baies de raisin en anaérobiose liquide et phénomène de diffusions associés. **Intracellular fermentation of grapes in liquid anaerobiosis and the associated diffusion phenomenon.** Publications.

16993 Bidan, P.; Puissant   FR 011009/70/2204
Evolution des différentes fractions azotées dans les vins mousseux durant la prise de mousse. **Evolution of differents nitrogen fractions in sparkling wine during fermentation.**

16994 Barre, P.; Combe   FR 011202/71/2229
Etude de la fermentation continue à plusieurs étages des moûts de raisin. **Studies on continous multi–stages fermentation of grape musts.**

16995 Jouret, C.; Moutonet, M.   FR 011402/68/2241
Etude des phénomènes chimiques et physico–chimiques durant la maturation des eaux.de.vies. **Study of chemical and physicochemical phenomena during brandy maturation.**

16996 Bernard, P.; Bourzeix, M.   FR 011403/70/2215
Chauffage de la vendange. **Heating of the grapes for red wine production.** Publications.

16997 Minafra, A.   IT 022000/75/0013
Preparazione di un vino rosso da pasto con uve della zona di Barletta. **Preparation of a red table–wine with grapes of the province of Barletta.**

16998 Castino, M.; Ubigli, M.   IT 022000/78/0001 N
Influenza della defecazione dei mosti sulla qualità dei vini bianchi. **Influence of musts settling on white wines quality.**

16999 Usseglio–Tomasset, L.; Castino, M.; Bosia, P.D.   IT 022000/78/0002 N
Esperienze di vinificazione con disacidificazione controllata per il miglioramento del vino Barbera. **Wine–making tests with controlled de–acidification to improve Barbera wine.**

17000 Castino, M.   IT 022000/78/0003 N
Esame delle diverse attività enzimatiche isolate per gel filtrazione dai preparati pectolitici commerciali: loro influenza sulla vinificazione in rosso. **Investigation about the enzymatic activities isolated through gel filtration from pectolytic preparations: their influence in red wine making.**

17001 Castino, M.; Ubigli, M.   IT 022000/78/0004 N
Influenza del pH sull'estrazione dei polifenoli e degli antociani nella vinificazione con macerazione. **Influence of pH on polyphenols and anthocianins extraction in wine–making on the skins.**

17002 Usseglio–Tomasset, L.; Di Stefano, R.   IT 022000/79/0001 N
Evoluzione del colore dei vini rossi. **Colour variations in red wines.**

17003 Usseglio–Tomasset, L.; Bosia, P.D.   IT 022000/79/0002 N
Disacidificazione chimica dei vini. **Chemical de–acidification of wines.**

17004 Usseglio–Tomasset, L.; Bosia, P.D.   IT 022000/79/0003 N
Confronto delle condizioni di sovrasaturazione in cremore dei mosti e dei vini. **Comparison between the circumstances of supersaturation with cream of tartar in musts and wines.**

17005 Castino, M.   IT 022000/79/0006 N
Prove d'impiego di chiarificanti a base di gel di silice. **Use trials of on silica–gel based clarifiers.**

17006 Lovino, R.   IT 022000/79/0007 N
Influenza dell'impiego di un prototipo di macchina vendemmiatrice sulla produzione di vini rossi pugliesi. **Consequence of the use of a prototype mechanical harvester on the production of red wines in Puglia.**

17007 Lovino, R.   IT 022000/79/0008 N
Prove di vinificazione per migliorare la qualità del vino Castel del Monte bianco. **Wine–making tests to improve the quality of Castel del Monte white wine.**

17008 Castino, M.; Ubigli, M.   IT 022000/79/0009 N
Impiego sperimentale di un vinificatore rotativo nella

fermentazione con macerazione. **Trials of a rotating fermenter in maceration wine–making.**

17009 Delfini, C.   IT 022000/79/0010 N
Prove di impiego del Saccharomyces uvarum per il miglioramento del Passito di Caluso. **Use tests of Saccharomyces uvarum to improve Passito di Caluso wine.**

17010 Gaia, P.   IT 022000/79/0011 N
Influenza dei lieviti sull'illimpidimento e sul colore del vino ottenuto. **Influence of yeasts on clearing and colour of resulting wine.**

17011 Delfini, C.; Ciolfi, G.   IT 022000/79/0012 N
Valutazione delle caratteristiche enologiche dei lieviti: potere alcoligeno e velocità di fermentazione. **Evaluation of oenological characteristic of yeasts: alcohol yield and fermentation rate.**

17012 Tarantola, C.; Gaia, P.   IT 022000/79/0013 N
Impiego della pimaricina per la stabilizzazione dei vini dolci. **Use of pimaricin to stabilize sweet wines.**

17013 Gigliotti, A.   IT 022000/79/0014 N
Prove di vinificazione con diverse proporzioni di uve Trebbiano Toscano e Malvasia del Chianti. **Wine–making trials with different ratios of Trebbiano toscano and Malvasia del Chianti grapes.**

17014 Gigliotti, A.   IT 022000/79/0015 N
Prove di vinificazione con macerazione nella zona del Chianti Classico mediante l'impiego di un vinificatore rotativo. **Maceration wine–making test with use of a rotating fermenter in the Chianti Classico zone.**

17015 Piracci, A.; Spera, G.   IT 022000/79/0016 N
Prove di vinificazione con diverse proporzioni di uve Trebbiano e Malvasia. **Wine–making trials blending different ratios of Trebbiano and Malvasia grapes.**

17016 Spera, G.; Piracci, A.   IT 022000/79/0017 N
Studio dell'evoluzione dell'acido malico nei vini bianchi presso due enopoli del Lazio. **Malic acid variations in white wines of Lazio region.**

17017 Liguori, O.; Tumminello, M.   IT 022300/79/0005 N
Ricerche sulla fermentazione extrastagionale ad alta e bassa temperatura e confronto con i nuovi sistemi di trattamento termico recentemente adottati per i tabacchi orientali. **Research on high and low temperature extra seasonal fermentation and comparison with new systems of thermic treatment used for oriental tobaccos.**

17018 Tumminello, M.; Netta, E.   IT 022300/79/0009 N
Nuova tecnica di cura in capanna di plastica con elettroventilatore su tabacco Burley. **New curing technique with plastic box and electric ventilator of Burley tobacco.**

17019 Liguori, O.; Tumminello, M.   IT 022300/79/0010 N
Prove di cura in bulk–curing con allestimento delle foglie in filze tradizionali, pettini metallici e a pianta intera. **Leaf, whole plant and bulk–curing of oriental tobacco in bulk–barns.**

17020 Liguori, O.; Tumminello, M.   IT 022300/79/0011 N
Ricerche sulla cura–fermentazione dei tabacchi orientali a mezzo di una apparecchiatura termo–ventilata munita di contenitore–silos. **Research on oriental tobaccos curing–fermentation with thermo–aired apparatus with silos–container.**

17021 Aversano, B.   IT 022300/79/0012 N
Residui di alcuni erbicidi più usati per il diserbo del tabacco (Difenamide, Pebulate, Benfluralin) nella pianta e nel terreno. **Residues of some herbicides commonly used for tobacco weeding (Diphenamide, Pebulate, Benfluralin) in plant and soil.**

17022 Pallotta, U.   IT 040208/73/0942
Ricerche sulle moderne tecniche di vinificazione, sulla selezione di starters per la fermentazione, sulla stabilità dei vini bianchi, sulle caratteristiche di composizione dei vini a D.O.C., sull'analisi degli effluenti dell'industria enologica e distillatoria. **Research on modern wine making techniques, on the selection of fermentation starters, on the stability of white wines, on composition characteristics of wines carrying appellations of origin, on the analysis of effluents from distilleries and wine making industry.**

17023 Pallotta, U.   IT 040208/77/0254 R
Ricerche sulle moderne tecniche di vinificazione, sulla selezione di starters per la fermentazione, sulla stabilità dei vini bianchi, sulle caratteristiche di composizione di vini DOC sull'analisi degli effluenti dell'industria enologica e distillatoria. **Research on the modern techniques of wine–making, on the selection of fermentation starters, on the stability of white wines, on the characteristics of DOC wines and on the analysis of supplies to distilleries and to the wine–making industry.**

17024 Zambonelli, C.   IT 040240/77/0317 R
Caratterizzazione e selezione di lieviti per vinificare in presenza e in assenza di anidride solforosa. **Characterisation and selection of yeasts used in wine–making with or without production of sulphur dioxide.**

17025 Colagrande, O.   IT 040407/78/1046 N
Trattamento dei vini bianchi con betonite. **Treatment of white wines with betonite.**

17026 Cantarelli, C.   IT 040617/73/0159
Ricerche sulla tecnologia di fermentazione delle bevande. **Research on the technology of fermentation of alcoholic beverages.** Publications.

17027 Cantarelli, C.   IT 040617/74/0522
Indagine sulla macerazione e sull'estrazione del succo dall'uva e da altri frutti a bacca. **Study on maceration and juice extraction from grapes and other berries.**

17028 Pallavicini, C.   IT 040802/73/0270
Estrazione, purificazione e caratterizzazione della tannasi e di alcune peptidasi e deidrogenasi delle uve. **Extraction, purification and characterization of tannase, of some peptidase and dehydrogenase of grapes.** Publications.

17029 Zamorani, A.   IT 040802/77/0318 R
Caratteristiche di azione e possibilità di impiego di enzimi immobilizzati in enologia. **Modes of action and possible uses of immobilised enzymes in oenology.**

17030 Fantozzi, P.   IT 041011/77/0172 R
Vinificazione in rosso in continuo. Esame della qualità del

prodotto in relazione al calore e alla sua stabilità. **Continuous red–wine making. Testing of the quality of the product in relation to heat and to its stability.**

17031 Martini, A.   IT 041013/78/1078 N
Completamento della revisione sistematica e tecnologica della collezione dei lieviti vinari. **Completion of the systematic and technological revision of the wine yeast collection.**

17032 Vodret, A.; Puti, R.   IT 041309/79/0001 N
Influenza dei polifenoli nell'invecchiamento del vino vernaccia in fase ossidativa. **Influence of polyphenolic substances in ageing of vernaccia wine in oxidative phase.** Publications.

17033 Fatichenti, F.   IT 041312/73/0201
Genetica e fisiologia di alcuni lievits vinari isolati in Sardegna con particolare riferimento ai ceppi filmogeni della vernaccia sarda. **Genetics and physiology of some wine yeasts isolated in Sardinia with specific reference to the filmy vines of the Sardinian "vernaccia".** Publications.

17034 Fatichenti, F.   IT 041312/77/0174 R
Selezione ed impiego di starters per la fermentazione e l'invecchiamento controllati in enologia. **Selection and use of starters for controlled fermentation and maturing in wine–making.**

17035 Fici, P.; Bonfanti, S.   IT 091902/76/0002
Vini Cloro di Noto, ricerca della tecnologia piu rispondente. **Trials on the improvement of the wine –making technology of "Cloro di Noto" wine.**

17036 Folstar, P.   NL 020031/76/6805
Samenstelling van was en olie in groene en gebrande koffie. **The composition of wax and oil in green and roasted coffee beans.** Publications.

17037 Klopper, W.   NL 050304/71/5334 R
De invloed van de eiwitoplossingsgraad van het mout op de bierkwaliteit. **The influence of the protein dissolvation degree of malt on the beer quality.** Publications.

17038 Klopper, W.   NL 050304/77/8992 N
Invloed van de kookintensiteit op de bierkwaliteit. **The influence of cooking intensity on beer quality.**

Other man–made resources (B 6900)

See also 415, 16289, 16384, 16396, 16451, 16589, 16836, 16915, 16920, 16939, 17078, 17079, 17081, 17179, 19692, 19736

17039 Wilssens, A.; De Mey, L.   BE 030012/78/0004 N
Produktie van aminozuren en enzymen door bepaalde sporenvormers. **Production of amino–acids and enzymes by sporeforming rods.**

17040 Dellweg, H.   DE 105988/78/0001 N
Modellversuche zur Methangärung. **Model experiments with methanogenic bacteria.**

17041 Schreiber, K.–F.; Genkinger, R.   DE 164401/77/0003
1.Untersuchungen zur Entwärmung des Erdreiches mittels Wärmepumpen 2.Untersuchungen zur Wärmerückgewinnung aus kommunalen Abwässern. **1.Investigations on cooling of soil by means of heat pumps. 2.Investigations on heat recovery from communal waste waters.**

17042 Baader, W.; Schuchardt, F.; Orth, H.W.
                                            DE 201070/75/0010
Freisetzung von Wärme bei der mikrobiellen Selbsterhitzung organischer Stoffe. **Heat production with microbic self–heating of organic matter.**

17043 Kofoed, S.S.; Matzen, R.   DK 030144/78/0003 N
Varme fra vindkraft. **Transformation of wind energy into heat.**

17044 Ponchet, J.; Bellenand–Mayeur, P.; Gras, R.; Maia, N. Mme   FR 010502/72/6003
Huiles essentielles de lavandin. **Composition of the essential oil of lavandin.**

17045 Bellenand–Mayeur, P.   FR 010502/76/6012
Purification des extraits végétaux. **Purification of plants extracts.**

17046 Rossi, J.; Costamagna, L.   IT 041023/70/0003 N
Produzione di biomassa da materiali diversi. **Biomass production obtained from various materials..**

Waste products in general (B 7000)

See also 16323, 16611

17047 De Boodt, M.; De Vleeschouwer, D.; Verdonck, O.
                                            BE 030013/77/0007
Komitee voor het onderzoek van de valorisatie van afvalstoffen in de landbouw OOVAL'. **Comittee for the research and valorization of agricultural waste products.**

17048 De Boodt, M.; Verdonck, O.; De Vleeschouwer, D.
                                            BE 030013/77/0008
Nationaal R.D. programma over de ekonomie van de afvalstoffen en de secundaire grondstoffen. **National program for the economy of waste products and secondary products.**

Effluent, sewage (B 7100)

See also 1449, 11374, 15534, 16584, 16622, 16626, 16632, 16664, 16671, 16739, 16838, 16976, 17086, 17092, 19732

17049 Wesche, J.   DE 105255/72/0007 N
Unschädlichmachung von organischen Pflanzengiften in Müll–Abwasserschlamm–Komposten. **Neutralization of organic plant poisons in refuse–sewage sludge composts.**

17050 Meuser, F.; Smolnik, H.–D.   DE 105820/77/0002
Optimierung von Verfahren zur Gewinnung und Verwertung von gelösten Stoffen aus Kartoffelfruchtwasser mit Hilfe der Membranfiltration. **Optimisation of the process of recovery and utilisation of soluble substances of potato fruit water by membrane filtration.**

17051 Kayser, R.   DE 114550/75/0001 N
Ermittlung der Konzentration organischer und anorganischer Inhaltsstoffe von Sickerwasser aus Mülldeponien und deren biochemischer Abbaubarkeit. **Determination of the concentration of organic and inorganic components in drainage water from garbage disposals and of their biochemical degradability.**

17052 Kowald, R.; Faltin, M.; Vogel, C.   DE 129450/75/0002
Die technische Weiterentwicklung im Kläranlagewesen. Eine

Tendenzstudie zur Ermittlung der daraus resultierenden veränderten Verwertungsmöglichkeiten des Abwasserklärschlammes. **Further technical development in sewage treatment plants. A study investigating the changing possibilities for sewage sludge utilization.**

17053 Cervenka, L.; Timmermann, F.　　DE 132065/75/0001
Phosphateliminierung aus Siedlungsabwässern unter dem Gesichtspunkt der Gewinnung von P–Düngemitteln. **Phosphate elimination from municipal waste waters for producing phosphate fertilizers. Publications.**

17054 Mayr, A.; Mahnel, H.; Brodorotti, V.
　　　　　　　　　DE 160760/75/0002
Strahlenresistenz von Mikroorganismen im Klärschlamm unter besonderer Berücksichtigung der Virusarten. **Resistance of microorganisms in sewage sludge to radiation with special reference to viruses.**

17055 Bischofsberger, W.; Hegemann, W.; Englmann, E.
　　　　　　　　　DE 161860/75/0006
Untersuchungen über den Einfluss der Bestrahlung mit Gammastrahlen auf die Schlammeigenschaften und das Schlammwasser. **Studies on the influence of gamma–irradiation on the behaviour of sewage sludge and supernatent liquor.**

17056 Bischofsberger, W.; Brodisch, K.; Hegemann, W.; Teuber, M.　　DE 161860/75/0009
Ermittlung von Kennwerten zur Beschreibung der Kapazität belebten Schlammes und biologisch abbaubarer Substrate. **Research for new parameters describing the capacity of activated sludge and degradable substrates.**

17057 Baader, W.; Schuchardt, F.; Sonnenberg, H.
　　　　　　　　　DE 201070/78/0004 N
Aufbereitung von feststoffreichen organischen Schlämmen über Kompostierung. **Treatment of organic sludges rich in solid matter by composting.**

17058 Süss, A.; Schurmann, G.; Hauser, M.
　　　　　　　　　DE 502050/72/0018
Hygienisierung und pflanzenbauliche Verwertung von Klärschlamm. **Hygienization of sewage sludge by radiation.**

17059 Researcher not indicated　　DE 502650/78/0021 N
Möglichkeiten der Reinigung von Fischabwässern in der Kreislaufhaltung – Wasserkreislaufanlage System Schunke –. **Possibilities of cleaning of fish sewage in circulatory system – water circulation plant of Schunke system –.**

17060 Juste, C.; Solda; Gomez, A.; Dureau, P. Mme; Lineres; Lasserre　　FR 010704/75/6086
Etude du pouvoir complexant des matériaux contenus dans les boues de stations d'épuration vis-à-vis des oligo–éléments et des éléments toxiques. **Complexing ability of sewage sludge for minor and toxic elements.**

17061 Lefevre, G.; Minne; Hiroux, G.; Desmet; Bordeaux
　　　　　　　　　FR 012222/72/6043
Récupération et valorisation agricole des boues d'épuration biologique d'effluents industriels ou urbains. **Use and agricultural valorisation of muds from epuration of industrial and urban waste water.**

17062 Bergonzini, E.; Fabbri, R.; Rosi, M.A.
　　　　　　　　　IT 020700/79/0014 N

Utilizzazione dei liquami di porcilaia. **Utilization of pig effluents.**

Superfluous dung and urine (B 7200)

See also 11617, 15534, 15709, 16291, 16350, 16352, 16353, 17057, 17092, 19692, 19736

17063 Wilssens, A.; Van Assche, P.　　BE 030012/72/0003 N
Microbiële studie van de methaangasproduktie uit landbouwafvalprodukten. **Microbial study of the methane production from agricultural wastes. Publications.**

17064 Strauch, D.　　　　　　DE 144610/75/0009
Untersuchungen über die Tenazität pathogener Mikroorganismen bei der Behandlung von Flüssigmist aus Massentierhaltungen mit aeroben Belüftungsverfahren und mit Elektronenbeschleunigern. **Tenacity of pathogenic microorganisms during treatment of slurry from densely stocked livestock managements with aerobic and electron accelerators.**

17065 Isensee, E.; Balssen, W.　　DE 148150/77/0003
Umweltfreundliche Dungaufbereitung im landwirtschaftlichen Betrieb mittels Feststoffseparierung. **Treatment and handling of liquid manure in practical farms by liquid/solid separation for environmental protection.**

17066 Borkott, H.　　　　　　DE 201020/75/0008
Populationssteuerung bei der Behandlung von Schwemmisten. **Regulation of populations during the treatment of liquid manure.**

17067 Baader, W.　　　　　　DE 201070/75/0004
Technische Verfahren der Stabilisierung fermentativ aufbereiteten Flüssigmistes durch Protozoen. **Technical processes for stabilizing of treated liquid manure by protozoa.**

17068 Thaer, R.　　　　　　DE 201070/75/0012
Einfluss von Temperatur und Sauerstoffversorgung auf den Abbau organischer Substanz bei der Behandlung von Flüssigmist. **Influence of oxygen supply and temperature on the degradation of organic matter with treatment of liquid manure.**

17069 Thaer, R.　　　　　　DE 201070/75/0013
Einfluss technischer Parameter von Belüftungssystemen auf den Sauerstoffeintrag und auf die Dispergierung bei der Belüftung von Flüssigmist. **Influence of aeration systems on oxygen absorption and on dispersion effect in liquid manure.**

17070 Salmon–Legagneur, E.; Zelter, S.; Roustan, J.L.
　　　　　　　　　FR 010206/75/2941
Etude des possibilités méthanogènes des déjections animales (fumier et lisier). **Methane production from animal manure. Publications.**

17071 O'Callagham　　　　　　GB 023504/78/0003 N
Thermophilic oxidation of pig slurry.

17072 Hobson; Summers　　　　GB 030605/00/0011 R
Anaerobic digestion of piggery and other agricultural wastes.

17073 Mills　　　　　　　　GB 060221/00/0001 R
Farm waste treatment by processes other than anaerobic digestion.

17074 Mills GB 060221/00/0002 R
Treatment of farm waste by anaerobic digestion.

17075 Evans; Hissett GB 060308/00/0004 R
Treatment and utilisation of animal excreta: laboratory studies.

17076 Ellam; Evans GB 060308/00/0005 R
Treatment and utilisation of animal excreta: field scale and land drainage studies.

17077 Evans; Baines GB 060308/00/0006 R
The activities of the microorganisms involved in the aerobic treatment of animal wastes.

17078 Brogan, J.C.; O'Shea, J.; Spillane, T.A.
IE 060100/77/1329 R
The treatment of human and animal waste and production of slow release fertiliser and methane gas. Publications.

17079 McGrath, D.; Tunney, H. IE 060200/75/1119
The generation of methane from animal wastes. Publications.

17080 Fagnoni, Paride; Fantuzzi, Ugo IT 090301/78/0001
Utilizzazione agronomica dei liquami degli allevamenti Zootecnici. **Agricultural utilization of cattle breeding sewage.** Publications.

17081 Zijlstra, J.A. NL 010106/78/8721 N
Onderzoek naar de gebruiksmogelijkheden van methaangas in de praktijk. **Research into the uses of methane gas in practice.**

Refuse, garbage, industrial wastes (B 7300)

See also 5962, 12815, 15472, 16303, 16336, 16349, 16354, 16355, 16406, 16409, 16410, 16412, 16436, 16815, 16957, 17023, 17041, 17046, 17049, 17051, 17160

17082 Küster, E.; Schmitten, I.in–der DE 129080/75/0005
Bildung von antibiotisch wirksamen Stoffen bei der Kompostierung von Siedlungsabfällen. **Formation of antibiotics in the course of composting of town refuses.**

17083 Küster, E.; Filip, Z. DE 129080/77/0009
Bestimmung der biologischen Aktivität zur Kennzeichnung des Stabilisierungsvorganges in einer Abfalldeponie. **Biological activities as indicator of the stabilizing process in a waste deposit.**

17084 Kowald, R.; Aboubakr, M. DE 129450/78/0004 N
Müllkompostierung in Ägypten. **Refuse composting in Egypt.**

17085 Strauch, D.; König, W. DE 144610/78/0005 N
Hygienische Untersuchungen bei der Kompostierung und Trocknung von entwässertem Klärschlamm. **Hygienic investigations during composting and drying of dewatered sewage sludge.**

17086 Juste, C.; Lubet; Solda; Dureau, P. Mme; Lasserre
FR 010704/65/6085
Etude de la valeur amendement organique de déchets riches en matière organique (écorces, vinasses, ordures ménagères, boues de stations d'épuration). **Utilization of organic wastes (bark, town refuse, sewage sludge – residuary liquor from distillery) in agriculture.**

17087 Catroux, G. FR 011002/69/6294

Eaux résiduaires des sucreries et distilleries de betteraves. **Waste waters of sugar refineries and beet distilleries.**

17088 Lefevre, G.; Minne; Lefebvre, R. FR 012222/72/6042
Récupération et valorisation agricole des effluents de féculerie et de conserverie. **Use and agricultural valorisation of waste water of starch and canning industries.**

17089 Conte, L.; Montanari, S.; Castiglione, A.
IT 020600/78/0002 R
Impiego dei sottoprodotti aziendali legnosi e deiezioni animali in alimentazione animale. **Use of company wooden by–products and animal dejections in feeding animals.** Publications.

17090 Galoppini, C.; Fiorentini, R.; Anelli, G.; Massignan, L.; Lepidi, A.A. IT 041108/74/0001
Biomasse dai sottoprodotti delle industrie agrarie. **Biomasses from by–products of agricultural industries.** Publications.

17091 Pellegrini, N. IT 041123/77/0574 R
Utilizzione dei sottoprodotti della macellazione. **Utilization of the by –products of slaugthering.**

17092 Waart, J. de NL 050301/74/6496
Benutting van organisch afval via methaangisting. **Methane fermentation of organic refuse.** Publications.

Combustion products (B 7400)

See also 16289, 16622

Other waste products (B 7900)

See also 12222, 12236, 12279, 12585, 16293, 16295, 16315, 16433, 16439, 16480, 16623, 16737, 16922, 16951, 16981

17093 Hildebrand, E.; Zöttl, H.W. DE 126050/78/0013 N
Rindenkompostierung und vergleichende humuschemische Untersuchungen an Rinden und Rindenkomposten. **Bark composting and comparative humus chemical investigations of barks and bark composts.** Publications.

17094 Bisping, W. DE 139450/75/0004
Entwicklung bakteriologischer Methoden zur Prüfung von Sterilisationsanlagen in Tierkörperbeseitigungsanlagen entsprechend den Vorschriften des Tierkörperbeseitigungsgesetzes. **Development of bacteriological methods for testing of sterilization equipment in carcass disposal plant according to regulations of the carcass disposal law.**

17095 Strauch, D.; Schaffert, R. DE 144610/75/0008
Hygienische Untersuchungen an dem amerikanischen Müllkompostierungsverfahren "Varro Conversion System" und dem deutschen Verfahren der Firma Fahr AG Gottmadingen. **Hygienic evaluation of the American composting system "Varro Conversion System" and of the German Fahr Ltd. system.**

17096 Drepper, K.; Drepper, G. DE 148300/78/0006 N
Aufbereitung von Schlachttierblut zur Lebensmittelherstellung. **Preparation of blood of slaughter animals for food production.**

17097 Löffler, H.; Patzak, W.; Schulz, H.
DE 160310/78/0003 N

Modelle der Verwertung forstlicher Biomasse und gewerblicher Holzabfälle zur Energiegewinnung. **Models of the utilization of the forest biomass and industrial wood residue for energy production.**

17098 Graff, O.   DE 201020/77/0009
Erzeugung tierischer Biomasse durch Vermehrung auf landwirtschaftlichen Reststoffen. **Production of animal biomass by propagation on agricultural residual matters.**

17099 Knudsen, A.   DK 010300/77/0072
Muligheder for varmegenvinding i mejerianlæg. **The possibilities for recovering heat from dairy plant equipment.**

17100 Jeffares, M.   IE 060300/00/1441 N
Utilisation of horticultural waste as human or animal food and also identification of losses (fruit and vegetable) between farm and consumer. Publications.

17101 Hofenk, G.   NL 010105/78/8360 R
Chemische en technologische aspecten bij de verwerking van (plantaardige landbouw)–afvallen. **Chemical and technological aspects of (agricultural vegetable) waste processing.**

D 4440 – Transport and handling

17102 Petersen, E.O.   DK 010300/75/0081
Formulering og testning af principper for rationalisering af mejeriernes distributionsopgaver. **The formulation and testing of principles for the rationalization of the dairy distribution business.**

17103 Boa   GB 011603/00/0012 R
The preparation of vegetables in the packing shed.

17104 Wilson, R.K.; Flynn, A.V.; Collins, D.P.
                    IE 060100/76/0293 N
Laboratory studies on ensilage. (A) effect of different levels of N on the chemical composition of grass and quality of silage when ensiled. (B)quality of silage made from 16 different common grasses. Publications.

17105 Phelan, J.A.   IE 060400/72/0618 R
Evaluation of rennet and rennet substitutes. Publications.

17106 Fox, P.F.; Rahilly, J.; Daly, C.; O'Dwyer, A.;
Maguire, J.   IE 110101/70/7604 R
Biochemistry of cheddar cheese ripening. Publications.

Ornamentals and ornamental products in general (B 3700)

See also 16167, 17133, 17136, 17137

Bulbs (B 3710)

See also 15870, 17107, 17108, 17109

Flowers and pot plants (B 3720)

17107 Boer, W.C.   NL 010118/73/7259
Distributieaspecten bij snijbloemen. **Handling aspects of cut–flowers.** Publications.

17108 Staden, O.L.   NL 010118/78/7854
Voorraadvoeding bij de snijbloem i.v.m. kwaliteitsbehoud gedurende de distributie. **Pulsing of cut flowers.** Publications.

17109 Koek, P.C.   NL 010118/78/7885
Verbetering van de houdbaarheid van snijbloemen door beperking van het aantal micro–organismen in het water waarin snijbloemen na het snijden worden geplaatst. **Improvement of the keeping quality of cut flowers by control of micro–organisms in water used during storage.**

Ornamental shrubs (B 3730)

17110 Staden, O.L.   NL 010118/78/7884
Kleinverpakking van boomkwekerijgewassen met het oog op kwaliteitsbehoud tijdens de distributie. **Retail packaging of nursery stock for better quality retention during distribution.**

Feeding stuffs and drinking water for animals in general (B 6300)

See also 17100

17111 Meinhold, K.; Walter, K.   DE 201100/78/0022 N
Genauigkeit und Futterkosten. **Precision and costs of feeds.**

Concentrates (B 6310)

See also 17120

Roughage (B 6320)

See also 15966, 17104

Organic fertilizers (B 6410)

17112 Keller, P.; Høy, J.J.; Nielsen, V.
                    DK 010400/74/0006 N
Arbejdsbehov ved håndtering af staldgødning. **Labour requirement associated with the handling of farmyard manure.**

Seed for sowing (B 6510)

See also 16060

Other propagation materials (B 6590)

See also 15698, 16079, 17125

17113 Rastovski, A.   NL 010105/67/0264 R
Elektronisch sorteren van aardappelen op kwaliteit en grootte. **Electronic grading of potatoes and quality and size.** Publications.

17114 Kaltofen, R.S.   NL 010109/79/8718 N
Stoombevochtiging in voorbroedmachineś. **Steam moistening in incubators (setters).**

Fibre materials and wood products (B 6700)

See also 15966, 15967

17115 Böttcher, P.   DE 114450/72/0002
Untersuchungen über Baumverletzungen durch Maschineneinsatz und die Auswirkungen auf Holzqualität und Festigkeit von Bäumen oder Baumteilen. **Investigations of tree damage caused by machine–usage and their effect on the wood quality and on the strength of the trees or tree parts.**

17116 Kolb, H.; Frech, P.   DE 170301/78/0001 N
Prüfung verschiedener Verfahren zur Bildung von
Baustellenstössen bei grossen Brettschichtbauteilen. **Testing of
different methods for formation of piles of great stacked boards
structures on building plots.**

Food and table luxuries in general (B 6800)

See also 15518, 16008, 16030, 16031, 17100

17117 Robinson, L.; Radtke, R.; Becker, K.
\   DE 911000/77/0001
Verbesserung der Haltbarkeit sauerstoffempfindlicher
Lebensmittel durch verpackungstechnische Massnahmen.
**Improvement of shelf–life of oxygen–sensitive foods by
packaging.** Publications.

17118 Muttrie   GB 030903/00/0107 R
**Monitoring efficiency of dichlorvos against insects in food
premises and transport.**

17119 Smith, L.P.; Quinn, G.   IE 120501/76/9161 N
Retail food distribution. Publications.

17120 Zuilichem, D.J. van; Stolp, W.   NL 020031/68/5131
Pneumatisch transport van granulaire en poedervormige
materialen in pijpleidingen. **Pneumatic conveying of solids in
ducts.** Publications.

17121 Wit, J.C. de   NL 020031/76/7602
Invloed van ui– en knoflookextracten op de groei van en
toxinevorming van Cl. botulinum. **Influence of onion– and
garlic extracts on the growth and toxin formation of Cl.
botulinum.** Publications.

Mill and bakery products (B 6810)

See also 16060

Oils, fats and related products (B 6820)

17122 Seher, A.; Arens, M.   DE 213010/78/0006 N
Ermittlung von Schwundsätzen. **Determination of losses by
detailing of fats and oils in small rations.**

Sugar and starch products (B 6830)

See also 16079, 16082

17123 Hechelmann, H.–G.   DE 935000/75/0001
Erarbeitung von physiologischen Kriterien zur Selektion von
Kartoffelgenotypen mit hoher Verträglichkeit für mechanische
Belastungen bei dem Aufbereitungsprozess vor der
Einlagerung. **Elaboration of physiological criteria of selection of
potato genotypes regarding high compatibility with mechanical
stresses during the handling process before storing.**

17124 Løschenkohl, B.; Allerup, S.   DK 030104/79/0005 N
Cytologiske forandringer som følge af beskadigelser af
kartofler. **Cytological changes resulting from mechanical
injuries to potato tubers.**

17125 Rastovski, A.   NL 010105/67/0263 R
Onderzoek omtrent kwaliteitsbehoud van aardappelen tijdens
behandeling en transport. **Research on quality conservation of
potatoes during handling and transport.** Publications.

Fruit and vegetable products (B 6840)

See also 3783, 15798, 16060, 16100, 16158, 16167

17126 Dressler, H.–G.; Carlsson, M.   DE 138362/74/0002
Probleme der physischen Distribution bei frischem Obst und
Gemüse. **Problems in the physical distribution of fresh fruit and
vegetables.**

17127 Arnoux, M.   FR 010615/76/9035
Triage–calibrage des fruits. **Improving fruit sorting and
grading processes.**

17128 Gorini, F.; Testoni, A.; Sozzi, A.; Eccher Zerbini, P.
   IT 021900/79/0005 N
Trattamento delle fragole per migliorare la resistenza al
trasporto. **Transport of strawberries in modified atmosphere
for reducing market losses.**

17129 Pratella, G.   IT 040216/77/0773 R
Ricerca tecnico–biologica, biochimica e tecnico–ingegneristica
su trasporti ortofrutticoli in containers. **Biochemical, applied
biological and engeneering research on horticultural transports
in containers.**

17130 Favati, F.   IT 121500/77/0772
Tecnica, organizzazione, economia dei trasporti intermodali a
mezzo containers riferiti ai prodotti ortofrutticoli ed altri
prodotti agricolo–alimentari deperibili. **Technique,
organization and economics of intermodal transport in
containers of horticultural produce and other perishable
agricultural foods.**

17131 Rudolphij, J.W.   NL 010118/73/4201
Sorteren van fruit en groente. **Sorting and grading of fruits and
vegetables.** Publications.

17132 Greidanus, P.   NL 010118/73/4207
Voor– en kleinverpakking van groenten en fruit. **Prepackaging
of fruit and vegetables.** Publications.

17133 Nieuwenhuizen, G.H. van   NL 010118/73/4211
Luchtstromingen in en rond verpakkingen voor
tuinbouwprodukten. **Airflow through and around packages for
horticultural products.**

17134 Greidanus, P.   NL 010118/73/4213
Invloed van de distributiemethode op het kwaliteitsverloop
van groente en fruit. **Distribution methods in relation to
keeping qualities of vegetables and fruits.**

17135 Nieuwenhuizen, G.H. van   NL 010118/73/4222
Tijd – temperatuurmeting tijdens transport van verse
tuinbouwprodukten. **Time– temperature measurement in
product during transport of fresh horticultural products.**

17136 Duvekot, W.S.   NL 010118/73/4236
Transport van tuinbouwprodukten in de praktijk. **Transport of
horticultural products in practice.** Publications.

17137 Rudolphij, J.W.; Krieke, H. v d   NL 010118/78/7850
Ontwikkeling en toepassing van methoden voor het vaststellen
van de mechanische sterkte van tuinbouwprodukten i.v.m. de
geschiktheid voor gemechaniseerde behandelingen.
Mechanical strength of horticultural products in relation to

methods of handling.

Meat, meat products and fish products in general (B 6850)

See also 16180

17138 Veerkamp, C.H.　　　　NL 010109/75/6071
Het ontwikkelen van een betere verdovingstechniek voor pluimvee. **Developments of stunning techniques for poultry slaughtering.** Publications.

Meat and meat products (B 6851)

See also 16184, 16694, 16701, 16712

17139 Schulze, W.; Hazem, A.S.; Pahlen, H.–D.von der
　　　　DE 139750/74/0029
Betäubung von kleinen Wiederkäuern für die Schlachtung. **Stunning of small ruminants for slaughter.**

17140 Mickwitz, G.von　　　　DE 139750/74/0032
Schlachttierbetäubung "Stunning of animals". **Stunning of animals for slaughter.**

17141 Bem, Z.; Lücke, F.–K.　　　　DE 210030/77/0004
Anwendung von Trockeneis 'CO2' zur Transportkühlung von Frischgeflügel. **Use of dry ice 'CO2' for cooling of fresh poultry during transport.**

17142 Putten, G. van　　　　NL 010112/70/1196
Het ontwikkelen van methodieken ter voorkoming van transportschade bij varkens. **Development of methods for prevention of transport damage of slaughter pigs.** Publications.

17143 Hoenderken, R.　　　　NL 010112/75/6116
De effectiviteit van elektrische bedwelmingsmethoden bij slachtvarkens, gemeten met behulp van electro–encephalografie. **The efficiency of electrical stunning methods in slaughter pigs, measured by electro–encephalography.** Publications.

17144 Hoenderken, R.　　　　NL 010112/75/7898
De verbetering van het elektrisch bedwelmen van slachtvarkens door automatisering van het bedwelmingsproces. **Improvement of electrical stunning of slaughter pigs by automation of the stunning process.**

Fish and marine food products (B 6852)

See also 11448, 15812

17145 Westbroek, L.　　　　NL 010702/73/7157
Verwateren van mossels aan boord van vaartuigen en walinstallaties; ontwikkeling en verbetering van kokkelverwater– en verwerkingsinstallaties; verbetering van de machinale verwerking van mossels. **Mussel cleansing on board a ship and installations at shore; development and improvement of the cockle cleansing and processing equipment; improvement of mussel processing.** Publications.

17146 Drinkwaard, A.C.　　　　NL 010702/74/7004
Onderzoek naar de behandelingswijze van schelpdieren in de fase tussen de produktie en het marktgebeuren ten behoeve van een gelijkmatige marktvoorziening, houdbaarheid en zuiverheid. **Research on the handling of molluscan shellfish**

between production and marketing.

17147 Bon, J.　　　　NL 050303/78/2968 N
Onderzoek ter verbetering van de hygiëne van de behandeling van garnalen aan boord. **Research on inprovement of hygiene during handling of shrimps aboard.**

Dairy products, eggs, egg products, ice cream in general (B 6860)

See also 16180, 17105

Milk products (B 6861)

See also 16237, 16752, 17106, 17841

17148 Kessler, H.G.; Helming, G.　　　　DE 161350/77/0001
Wärmeübertragungs– und Temperaturausgleichsvorgänge bei Becherpackungen und ihre technologische Bedeutung für Milchprodukte. **Heat transfer and temperature balances of milk packages and their technological importance for milk products.**

17149 Haisch, K.–H.; Einögg, G.　　　　DE 502552/73/0001
Minimierung der Transportkosten im Vertriebsbereich. **Lowest costs of transport in the distribution system.**

17150 Petersen, E.O.　　　　DK 010300/76/0083
Omkostninger ved ind– og mellemtransport af mælk i forhold til størrelse, lokalisering og specialisering af mejeridriftspladser. **The costs of milk transportation in comparison to the size, locality and specialised nature og the dairy industry districts.**

17151 Fleming, M.　　　　IE 060400/77/2003 R
Evaluation of bulk milk tanker metering, sampling and loading systems. Publications.

17152 Fleming, M.　　　　IE 060400/78/2088 N
Evaluation of modern technology developments in the area of milk assembly. Publications.

17153 Vries. T. de　　　　NL 010213/70/3384
Onderzoek naar het filtreren van boerderijmelk. **The filtering of farm milk.**

17154 Langeveld, L.　　　　NL 060002/78/7914
Invloed van de verpakking op de groeimogelijkheden van schimmels en gisten in zure zuivelprodukten. **Effect of packaging materials on the growth of moulds and yeasts in cultured dairy products.**

Eggs and egg products (B 6862)

17155 Fuhrken, E.　　　　DE 511250/78/0005 N
Eischalen–Stabilität. **Stability of egg shells.**

17156 Morlry; Jones　　　　GB 010702/00/0001 R
Egg shell breakage, causes and prevention.

Drinking water (B 6880)

17157 Brauss, F.W.; Barth, H.　　　　DE 142100/70/0001
Qualitätsanforderungen an Anstriche und Folien für TrinkwasserBehälter. **Quality standards required of paints and foils used for drinking water containers.**

Other man–made resources (B 6900)

17158 Mickwitz, G.von; Pohlchristoph, H.; Schultze, K.;
Müller, W. DE 139750/74/0033
Gutachten: Tierschutzgerechter Transport von Tieren: See–
und Lufttransporte. **Transports of animals by sea and air in
accordance with conditions of animal protection.**

Waste products in general (B 7000)

See also 15812, 17145, 17153

Effluent, sewage (B 7100)

See also 19706

Superfluous dung and urine (B 7200)

17159 Seiler, H. DE 502551/78/0003 N
Floraanalysen an Chemieabwasserbelebungsanlagen. **Analyses
of microbiol flora of industrial activated sludge.**

Refuse, garbage, industrial wastes (B 7300)

17160 Küster, E.; Niese, G. DE 129080/75/0004
Beseitigung und Verwertung von industriellen
Fermentationsrückständen. **Removal and re–cycling of wastes
from the fermentation industry.**

Other waste products (B 7900)

See also 17100, 17125

D 5100 – Work management

See also 3963, 3990, 4356, 5047, 12281, 16957

17161 Maton, A.; Lips, J.　　　　BE 070300/75/0043 R
Arbeidskundig onderzoek in de sierteelt (azalea's). **Work study in horticulture.** Publications.

17162 Bekaert, H.; Eeckhout, W.　　　BE 070700/71/0021 R
Tijd– en arbeids besparende voedertechnieken bij fokzeugen. **Time– and labour –sparing feeding technics for sows.** Publications.

17163 Dufey, V.; Prade, J.　　　　BE 080400/60/0009
Economie de la mécanisation agricole. **Economy of agricultural mechanization.** Publications.

17164 Altherr, E.　　　　DE 501509/72/0003 N
Ermittlung von Stammholz–Rindenprozenten für die einheimischen Baumarten als Hilfsmittel für Aufmessung und Verkauf in Rinde. **Determination of trunk wood and bark percentage in indigenous tree species for measurement and sale of bark.**

17165 Korsgaard, S.　　　　DK 030181/76/0010 N
En metode til planlægning af den tekniske drift af småskove inden for rammerne af en skovejerforening i Sverige og Danmark. **A routine for the planning of logging operations on private forest estates within a Forest Owners Association in Sweden and Denmark.**

17166 MacCanna, C.　　　　IE 060300/71/0060 R
Development of efficient low cost production systems for mushroom growing. Publications.

17167 MacCanna, C.; Maher, M.J.　　IE 060300/72/0059 R
Work study on glasshouse crops. Publications.

Business enterprises in general (B 8200)

17168 Grammel, R.; Krohn, B.　　　DE 126650/77/0003
Methoden und Verfahren zur messtechnischen Erfassung und Speicherung der Einflussgrösse bei Arbeitsstudien. **Methods and proceeding for metrologic registration and storing of influential fact in work studies.**

17169 Gasparetto, E.　　　　IT 040610/73/0217
Definizione tecnico–economica di moduli e cantieri di lavoro ottimali per diversi livelli di meccanizzazione. **Technical– economic definition of optimal models and yards for various levels of mechanization.** Publications.

17170 Zander, J.　　　　NL 020026/72/4981
Onderzoek gericht op belastingsbeoordeling en optimalisering van mens–taak–systemen. **Research on work load evaluation and optimizing man–task–systems.** Publications.

17171 Loon, H. van　　　　NL 020026/72/8649 N
Inspanningsfysiologie. **Work physiology (Physical working capacity and fitness).**

Farms in general (B 8210)

See also 15305, 17163, 18289

17172 Piérard, J.　　　　BE 010007/69/0005
Etude de l'organisation de l'agriculture moderne en Afrique Noire. **Organization study of modern agriculture in Dark Africa.** Publications.

17173 Herinckx–Pirlot, J.　　　BE 010007/72/0004
Etude de la planification de l'agriculture : mise au point de modèles prévisionnels pour l'agriculture. **Agricultural plan study : elaboration of forecasting models for agriculture.** Publications.

17174 Maton, A.; Lips, J.　　　　BE 070300/66/0039
Het ergonomisch onderzoek in de landbouw. **Ergonomical research in agriculture.** Publications.

17175 Reisch, E.; Schmid, H.　　　DE 144745/73/0007
Ermittlung der Substitutionsbeziehungen zwischen dem Einsatz von Arbeit und technischen Hilfsmitteln für Teilbereiche verschiedener Produktionsverfahren auf unterschiedlichem Mechani– sierungsniveau. **Substitutional interrelations between labour and technical equipment for divers partial production activities on different levels of mechanization.**

17176 Steinkampf, H.　　　　DE 201090/72/5003
Energiebedarf für Arbeitsverfahren in der Feldwirtschaft unter Berücksichtigung des Bearbeitungseffektes. **Energyneed for working process of the field work by considering the working effect.**

17177 Thome, F.J.　　　　DE 201090/77/0005
Beanspruchung des arbeitenden Menschen durch verschiedene Belastungskomponenten, die einzeln oder kombiniert in einem Arbeitsplatzsimulator erzeugt werden. **Strain on man at work by different components of stress generated separately or in combination in a working–place simulator.**

17178 Thome, F.J.; Biller, R.H.　　　DE 201090/77/0006
Beanspruchung des Schlepperfahrers durch vorgegebene Arbeitsbelastung in konstruktiv unterschiedlich ausgebildeten Schlepperkabinen. **Strain on tractor–driver by given stress of work in structurally differing tractor cabs.**

17179 Pinstrup–Andersen, P.　　　DK 030149/79/0002 N
Samspillet mellem det teknologiske udviklingsforløb i landbruget og fødevareproduktion, ressourceforbrug og miljø. **The interaction between technological change in agriculture and food production, resource use and environment.**

17180 Reboul, C.; Badis, M.F.; Desbrosses, B.; Al Hamchari, M.C.　　　　FR 011706/60/3344
L'économie du travail sur l'exploitation agricole. **The economics of labour on farms.**

17181 Nuccitelli, G.; Marsili, A.　　　IT 020600/79/0005 N
Ergonometria ed affidabilità come fattori determinanti la sicurezza degli operatori agricoli durante i principali cicli operativi dell'azienda. **Ergonometry and feasibility as determining factors for the operators safety during the company's work cycles.**

17182 Palmieri Pedrini, E.　　　IT 040204/72/0526
Stalle sociali e fenomeni indotti nella organizzazione aziendale. **Social stables and phenomena induced in the organization of enterprises.** Publications.

D 5100 – Work management

17183 Ghironi, G.   IT 040912/77/0145 R
Analisi dei tempi di lavoro, manuale e meccanico, nelle principali operazioni colturali e per colture in differenti situazioni.. **Time and motion study of manual and mechanical work in the main cultural operations and under different conditions..**

17184 Oving, R.K.   NL 010106/69/6428
Ontwikkeling van een model voor en programmering van de keuze van de bedrijfsuitrusting en de werkorganisatie op landbouwbedrijven. **Development of a calculation model for the choice of work organization and the choice of farm equipment.** Publications.

17185 Kroeze, G.H.   NL 010106/75/6427
Ontwikkeling van een model en programmering van een arbeidsbegroting voor landbouwbedrijven. **Development of a computerized labour planning system for agricultural enterprises.** Publications.

17186 Werken, G. van de   NL 010106/75/6434
Ontwikkeling van een rekenmodel voor en de berekening van taaktijden voor bijzonder veldwerk. **Development of a calculation model for task times for "particular" fieldwork.**

17187 Belt, A.H.M.   NL 010106/79/9028 N
Een verkennend onderzoek naar mentale belasting bij boer en tuinder. **A survey of mental workload in agriculture.**

17188 Vos, H.W.   NL 010106/79/9029 N
Optimalisering werkindeling op landbouwbedrijven. **Optimizing job scheduling on farms.**

17189 Vos, H.W.   NL 020026/79/9029 N
Optimalisering werkindeling op landbouwbedrijven. **Optimizing job scheduling on farms.**

Arable farms (B 8211)

17190 Colzani, G.; Marsili, A.; Nuccitelli, G.
IT 020600/77/0001 N
Ergonometria Misura del lavoro e dell'affaticamento umano richiesto dall'impiego di macchine motrici e operatrici agricole nei principali cicli operativi.. **On the work and human fatiguing limit demanding by the use of machines and operative machines in the principal operative cycles.**

17191 Edens, F.J.   NL 010106/78/8350
Arbeidskundige vergelijking van sorteermethoden bij pootaardappelen op het akkerbouwbedrijf. **Comparison on the basis of labour requirements grading methods of seed potatoes on arable farms.**

17192 Penninkhof, J.   NL 040007/65/8489
Onderzoek naar werkbaar en onwerkbaar weer bij veldwerkzaamheden. **Research on working hours according to weather for field operations.**

Animal and grassland farms (B 8212)

See also 15696, 17162, 17216

17193 Maton, A.; Daelemans, J.   BE 070300/69/0019 R
Studie van de arbeidsbehoeften en huisvesting in de varkenshouderij. **Study of the labourtime requirement and animal housing on pig farms.** Publications.

17194 Maton, A.; Daelemans, J.   BE 070300/73/0018 R
Studie van de Arbeidsbehoefte en de huisvesting in de melkveehouderij. **Study of the labour time requirement and animal housing in milkproduction farms.** Publications.

17195 Eichhorn, H.; Weghe, van–dem; Lorenz, J.; Pflug, R.
DE 129400/74/0003
Arbeitsorganisation in der Schweineproduktion. **Working management in pig production.**

17196 Bischoff, T.; Meuther, R.   DE 144710/74/0003
Beurteilung und Verbesserung von Verfahren der Futterentnahme und –vorlage aus Heustapeln. **Criticism and improvement of the techniques of removing and serving forage from hay stacks.**

17197 Zäh, H.; Auernhammer, H.   DE 161523/72/0001 R
Erarbeitung von Zeitfunktionen und Planzeitwerten für die Milchviehhaltung 1972. **Evaluation of time functions and planned time values for dairy cattle keeping.**

17198 Schön, H.; Auernhammer, H.   DE 161524/71/0001 R
Simulation der Melkarbeiten durch stochastische Modelle im Anbindestall, im Fischgrätenmelkstand und in Rundmelkständen 1971. **Simulation of milking process by stochastic in tying stall, in fish–bone–like milking parlour and in round milking parlours.**

17199 Meinhold, K.; Schlünsen, D.; Walter, K.
DE 201090/77/0007
Weiterentwicklung und Bewertung eines teilautomatisierten Milchviehhaltungsverfahrens für bäuerliche Betriebe. **Further development and valuation of a partially automated dairy stock keeping system for farms.**

17200 Thome, F.J.   DE 201090/77/0009
Arbeitsplatzuntersuchungen bei verschiedenen Verfahren der Milchviehhaltung. **Examinations of working place in different systems of dairy stock keeping.**

17201 Mainie, P.; Hentgen, A.   FR 010112/76/9104
Enquête sur les comportements des éleveurs en matière de production et d'utilisation des fourrages. **Survey concerning the behaviour of stock–breeders with respect to forage production and use.**

17202 Mathal, P.; Evrard, Ph.   FR 012212/78/8538
Spécialisation et division du travail dans l'élevage bovin. **Specialisation and work division in cattle breeding (dairy and beef meat production).**

17203 Mannion, J.; Callaghan, J.; O'Brien, W.
IE 120109/78/9244 N
A study of a relief milking service group in county cork.

17204 Magistretti, A.   IT 041517/76/0001 N
Cooperazione e zootecnia : una proposta per incrementare il patrimonio bovino. **Cooperation and livestoch farming : a proposal to increase livestoch numbers..**

17205 Gerritsen, J.G.C.   NL 010106/65/6440
Samenstelling van taaktijden voor de pluimveehouderij. **Developing task times for poultry keeping.** Publications.

17206 Giessen, P.F.   NL 010106/74/5161 R
Arbeidsstudie van het inkuilen van gras en maïs en de afvoer
c.q. distributie van kuilprodukten. **Work study of the
harvesting of grass and maize for ensiling and transport of the
silage.** Publications.

17207 Voermans, J.A.M.   NL 010106/75/6170
Sociale, arbeidskundige en organisatorische aspecten van grote
melkveebedrijven (ca. 500 melkkoeien). **Social aspects of
labour and work management on large dairy farms (ca. 500
dairy cows).**

17208 Portiek, J.H.   NL 010106/77/7590 R
Het opstellen van werkbaarheidsnormen voor werkzaamheden
in de weidebouw. **The estabilishing of workability standards for
grassland management.**

17209 Werken, G. van de   NL 010106/77/7591
Het ontwikkelen van een rekenmodel voor de arbeidsbehoefte
bij zomerstalvoeding. **Development of a calculation model for
task times of zero–grazing.**

17210 Halman, Z.J.   NL 010106/78/8378
Vaststelling van de arbeidsbehoefte van het algemene werk op
de melkveebedrijven. **Determination of the labour
requirements of the so–called indirect work on dairy farms.**

17211 Werken, G. van de   NL 010106/78/8379
Arbeidsbehoefte van de gezondheidszorg op
rundveehouderijbedrijven. **Labour demand of health care in
cattle farming.**

17212 Gerritsen, J.G.C.   NL 010106/78/8380
De arbeidsbehoefte op grupstalbedrijven bij toepassing van
nieuwe elementen van indeling en inrichting voor de
verzorging van melkvee. **Labour requirement for the
traditional cowhouse (gutter stable) when applying new
elements of lay–out and appointments for dairy farming.**

17213 Wisselink, G.J.   NL 010116/75/6170
Sociale, arbeidskundige en organisatorische aspecten van grote
melkveebedrijven (ca. 500 melkkoeien). **Social aspects of
labour and work management on large dairy farms (ca. 500
dairy cows).**

17214 Snijders, P.J.M.   NL 010208/71/8745 N
Arbeidsverbruik bij diverse werkmethoden op
rundveebedrijven. **Use of labour with different labour methods
on cattle farms.** Publications.

17215 Boonman, D.C.M.   NL 010208/75/6170
Sociale, arbeidskundige en organisatorische aspecten van grote
melkveebedrijven (ca. 500 melkkoeien). **Social aspects of
labour and work management on large dairy farms (ca. 500
dairy cows).**

Mixed farms (B 8213)

17216 Maton, A.; Daelemans, J.   BE 070300/72/0015 R
Studie van de arbeidsbehoefte en de kostprijs bij het oogsten
van ruwvoeders. **Study of the labour time requirement and the
costprice for the harvest of roughage.** Publications.

Horticultural holdings (B 8214)

See also 3144, 3151, 3882, 4350, 15268, 15376, 15482, 15485,
17161, 17166, 17596, 17623

17217 Maton, A.; Lips, J.   BE 070300/67/0032 R
Arbeidsboekhouding en arbeidsstudie in de witloofteelt.
**Labour– bookkeeping and work–study in Belgian endive
culture.** Publications.

17218 Adams, K.; Back, W.; Nord   DE 509155/78/0001 N
Ermittlung von Arbeitszeitfunktionen in der Kellerwirtschaft.
Determination of functions of working hours in cellarage.

17219 Vergniaud, P.   FR 010610/75/9077
Recherche sur les éléments de systèmes de culture: les
précédents à une culture de tomates de conserve; incidence et
développement en fonction de l'intensification du système.
**Economic optimization of the canning tomato cropping
systems: choice of the preceeding crop and its growing impact
according to the intensity level of the system.**

17220 Lookeren Campagne, P. van   NL 010106/72/5345
Organisatie en arbeidskundig onderzoek van teeltsystemen in
de champignonteelt. **Comparison of growing techniques in
mushroom growing.** Publications.

17221 Hendrix, A.T.M.   NL 010106/72/5377
Organisatie en arbeidskundig onderzoek in de paprikateelt.
Management and work study in the production of peppers.
Publications.

17222 Gerritsen, J.G.C.   NL 010106/73/5378
Organisatie en arbeidskundig onderzoek bij het pellen van
bloembollen. **Improvement of work methods and work
organization of bulb peeling.**

17223 Saedt, A.P.H.   NL 010106/73/5379
Organisatie en arbeidskundig onderzoek bij het uitzoeken van
afwijkende planten en bollen in de bloembollenteelt.
**Improvements of work methods and work organization for
removing defective plants and bulbs in bulb growing.**

17224 Achten, J.M.F.H.; Hendrix, A.T.M.
     NL 010106/75/6437
Het effect van een variabele oogstperiode en de
arbeidsorganisatie op de teeltplan keuze in de tuinbouw. **The
effect of a variable harvesting time and work organization on
the choice of the cropping plan in horticulture.**

17225 Lookeren Campagne, P. van   NL 010106/76/6701
Organisatorische en arbeidskundige aspecten bij de inzet van
machines en werktuigen bij de oogst van hard fruit.
**Organizational and workstudy aspects by the use of machines
for the harvest of top fruit.** Publications.

17226 Krijgsman, H.K.   NL 010106/76/6702 R
Arbeidskundig onderzoek bij de opkweekmethoden van
chrysantenstek. **Work study of the propagation of cuttings of
chrysanthemum.** Publications.

17227 Hendrix, A.T.M.   NL 010106/76/9030 N
Bedrijfskundige vergelijking van doorteeltsystemen bij
tomaten. **Comparison of growing systems in tomatoes from the
viewpoint of labour requirements and costs.**

17228 Werken, G. van de   NL 010106/77/7586
Het opnemen van gegevens van de vollegrondsgroenteteelt in
de IMAG–DATASERVICE voor het berekenen van

taaktijden. **Insertion of labour data of open ground vegetable crops into the IMAG–DATASERVICE for the calculation of task times.**

17229 Edens, F.J. NL 010106/77/7587
Onderzoek naar de capaciteit en kwaliteit van het werk van de nieuwe spruitkooloogstcombinaties. **Research into the capacity and quality of the work with the new harvesting systems of Brussels sprouts. Publications.**

17230 Hendrix, A.T.M. NL 010106/78/8351
Bedrijfskundig onderzoek in de aubergineteelt. **Work management research in the culture of egg plants.**

17231 Hendrix, A.T.M. NL 010106/78/8352
Bedrijfskundig onderzoek naar de transportsystemen in de glasgroenteteelt. **Farm management research into transport systems in greenhouses.**

17232 Bulsink, A.J. NL 010106/78/8353
Het vaststellen van taaktijden en de samenstelling van een taaktijdenboek voor de bloembollenteelt. **Determination of task times and the composition of a task time catalogue for bulb growing.**

17233 Schoneveld, J.A. NL 010106/78/8408 N
Toetsing van verschillende planningsmogelijkheden bij eenmalige oogst van spruitkool. **Testing of a planning scheme for single harvested Brussels sprouts.**

17234 Achten, J.M.F.H. NL 010106/79/9031 N
De ontwikkeling en beproeving van een plannings– en informatiesysteem in de rozenteelt (MISTU). **Development and testing of a planning and information system in the production of roses.**

17235 Schutte, W. NL 010203/66/1518
Arbeidskundig onderzoek in de boomkwekerij. **Workstudies in the nurseries. Publications.**

17236 Bulsink, A.J. NL 010205/73/5378
Organisatie en arbeidskundig onderzoek bij het pellen van bloembollen. **Improvement of work methods and work organization of bulb peeling.**

17237 Bulsink, A.J. NL 010205/73/5379
Organisatie en arbeidskundig onderzoek bij het uitzoeken van afwijkende planten en bollen in de bloembollenteelt. **Improvement of work methods and work organization of removing defective plants and bulbs in bulb growing.**

17238 Bulsink, A.J. NL 010205/77/7585 R
Verbetering van werkmethoden en arbeidsorganisatie bij de produktie van bolbloemen. **Work study in growing, harvesting and processing of lilies.**

17239 Bulsink, A.J. NL 010205/78/8353
Het vaststellen van taaktijden en de samenstelling van een taaktijdenboek voor de bloembollenteelt. **Determination of task times and the composition of a task time catalogue for growing bulbs. Publications.**

17240 Hendrix, A.T.M. NL 010206/72/5377
Organisatie en arbeidskundig onderzoek in de paprikateelt. **Management and work study in the production of peppers. Publications.**

17241 Hendrix, A.T.M. NL 010206/75/6437
Het effekt van een variabele oogstperiode en de arbeidsorganisatie op de teeltplankeuze in de tuinbouw. **The effect of a variable harvesting time and work organization on the choice of the cropping plan in horticulture.**

17242 Hendrix, A.T.M. NL 010206/76/6702 R
Arbeidskundig onderzoek bij de opkweekmethoden van chrysantenstek. **Work study of the propagation of cuttings of chrysanthemum. Publications.**

17243 Hendrix, A.T.M. NL 010206/76/9030 N
Bedrijfskundige vergelijking van doorteeltsystemen bij tomaten. **Comparison of growing systems in tomatoes from the viewpoint of labour requirements and costs.**

17244 Hendrix, A.T.M. NL 010206/78/8351
Bedrijfskundig onderzoek in de aubergineteelt. **Work management research in the culture of egg plants.**

17245 Hendrix, A.T.M. NL 010206/78/8352
Bedrijfskundig onderzoek naar de transportsystemen in de glasgroenteteelt. **Farm management research into transport systems in greenhouses.**

17246 Schoneveld, J.A. NL 010207/77/7586
Het opnemen van gegevens van de vollegrondsgroenteteelten in de IMAG–DATASERVICE voor het berekenen van taaktijden. **Insertion of labour data of open–ground vegetable crops into the IMAG–DATASERVICE for the calculation of task times.**

17247 Schoneveld, J.A. NL 010207/77/7587
Onderzoek naar de capaciteit en kwaliteit van het werk van de nieuwe spruitkooloogstcombinaties. **Research into the capacity and quality of the work with the new harvesting systems of Brussels sprouts. Publications.**

Forest enterprises (B 8215)

See also 16426, 17164, 17165

17248 Prodan, M.; Roeder, A. DE 126601/72/0001
Bestimmung von Arbeitsumfang und –zeitbedarf zur Herleitung objektiver Organisationskriterien für die Gliederung von Forstbetriebsbezirken und Forstämtern. **Determination of work volume and required working hours for deriving objective criteria in organizing forest districts and administration.**

17249 Grammel, R.; Becker, G. DE 126650/77/0005
Technik, Einsatzorganisation und Leistung von Fällmaschinen für Durchforstungsbestände. **Technic, employment organisation and performance of feller bunchers for thinning.**

17250 Brabänder, H.D. DE 132840/77/0003
Rationalisierungsmöglichkeiten der Betriebsorganisation. **Possibilities to rationalize the organization of forest enterprises.**

17251 Häberle, S.; Jacke, H. DE 132900/77/0002
Ernte stehendbearbeiteter Fichten. **Cropping of standing lopped spruces.**

17252 Häberle, S.; Abeney, E.A. DE 132900/78/0001 N

Zusammenhänge zwischen körperlicher Arbeitsleistung und Erholungszeit unter besonderer Berücksichtigung tropischer Umweltbedingungen. **Correlations between physical working performance and recreational intervals with special regard to tropical environmental conditions.**

17253 Guglhör, W.; Loibl　　　　DE 160310/78/0004 N
Automatisierung von Arbeitsstudien mittels netzunabhängiger Datenaufnahme-, Speicher- und Übertragungssysteme mit integrierter Zeitmessung. **Automated work studies without power supply line by a data recording, storage and transfer system with integrated time measurement.**

17254 Guglhör, W.; Thurn, S.　　　DE 160310/78/0005 N
Betriebsuntersuchungen über das Rücken mit dem Mobilseilkran URUS–Gigant. **Operating study on the mobile yarder URUS–Gigant.**

17255 Guglhör, W.; Kloos　　　　DE 160310/78/0006 N
Betriebsuntersuchung über ein Durchforstungsverfahren mit dem Prozessor GP 822. **Study on a thinning operation with a Kockums GP 822 processor.**

17256 Eisenhauer, G.　　　　DE 202030/75/0003
Organisation des überbetrieblichen Maschineneinsatzes. **Organization of co–operative logging machinery utilization.**

17257 Lünzmann, K.　　　　DE 202030/75/0006
Belastung des Maschninenführers in der Forst- und Holzwirtschaft durch Vibration. **The vibration of machines in forestry and timber processing and the stress on the operator.**

17258 Eisenhauer, G.; Müller–Darss, H.　DE 202030/77/0003
Belastung des Menschen durch die Mechanisierung in der Forstarbeit. **Stress on man by mechanization in forestry.**

17259 Dietz, P.; Tritschler, A.　　DE 501505/72/0017
Entwicklung von Rückeverfahren mit Ästen und Kronen 1972. **Development of practices of skidding lop and top.**

17260 Dietz, P.; Dummel, K.; Schelshorn, H.
　　　　　　　　　　　　DE 501505/77/0002
Aufarbeitung von Rohstangen und schwachen Rohschäften. **Logging of raw poles and slender raw stems.**

17261 Dietz, P.; Tritschler, A.　　DE 501505/77/0006
Untersuchungen über die Entwicklung von Arbeitsvolumen, Arbeitskapazität, Arbeitsproduktivität, Mechanisierungsgrad. Erarbeitung von Entscheidungshilfen. **Studies on working volume, capacity and productivity, degree of mechanization, and developemnt of decision help.**

17262 Dietz, P.; Rieger, G.　　　DE 501505/78/0001 N
Maschinelles Fällen. **Mechanical felling.**

17263 Schöpfer, W.　　　　DE 501507/77/0005
Rücketarif Klosterreichenbach. **Skidding rate Klosterreichenbach.**

17264 Heding, N.　　　　DK 030181/78/0004 N
Arbejdsvidenskabelige studier vedr. håndteringen af løvtræ. **Workstudies on hardwood logging.**

17265 Christensen, J.B.　　　DK 030181/79/0001 N
Cost–benefit teoriens anvendelsesmuligheder inden for skovbruget. **Application of cost–benefit theory on forestry.**

17266 Mouton, B.　　　　FR 010308/75/3327
Les problèmes de la main d'oeuvre dans les branches d'activité sylviculture et exploitation forestière. **Labour problems in forestry and wood industry.**

17267 Berg, J.V. van den　　　NL 010106/76/6700 R
Ontwikkelen van een systeem voor rekenservice voor het onderhoud in de groene sector. **Development of a system for calculation service in amenity horticulture.** Publications.

17268 Leek, N.A.; La Bastide, J.G.A.　NL 010601/68/1885
Het ontwikkelen van bedrijfseconomisch verantwoorde technieken voor de oogst, verwerking en transport van hout. **Working techniques, working time, costs and returns, with timber harvesting.** Publications.

17269 Leek, N.A.　　　　NL 010601/73/4457
Kosten en methoden van verzorging in bestaande landschappelijke beplantingen. **Costs and methods of tending in mixed hardwood plantations.** Publications.

17270 Leek, N.A.　　　　NL 010601/74/5033
Kosten van aanleg van landschappelijke beplantingen. **Costs of establishment of plantations for landscaping.** Publications.

17271 Leek, N.A.; Vries, J.P. de　　NL 010601/74/6010
Technische organisatie van de zaadoogst bij naaldbomen. **Technical organization of seed collection of pine forest trees.** Publications.

17272 Leek, N.A.　　　　NL 010601/78/7882
Methoden en kosten van herbebossing. **Methods and costs of reforestation.**

17273 Leek, N.A.　　　　NL 010601/79/8720 N
Standaardisatie van begrippen en ontwikkeling van meet- en registratiemethodieken voor het bepalen van tijdnormen en kostprijsberekeningen. **Standardization of concepts and development of measuring and registration methods to draw up time standards and cost price calculations in forestry and landscape planning.**

17274 Heij, W.　　　　NL 020010/75/6783
Optimalisering korten van langhout. **Optimal tree bucking.**

17275 Boxsem, W.　　　　NL 040007/77/8503
Onderzoek naar het optimale snoeitijdstip bij populieren. **Research on the optimal pruning time for poplars.**

17276 Sleurink, J.P.　　　　NL 040007/78/8490
Processtudie van het transport van plantmateriaal naar de plantobjecten in Flevoland. **Research on improvement of working methods for transport of planting material to** ↘| **plantation areas in Flevoland.**

Fisheries (B 8216)

17277 Hovart, P.; Van den Broucke, G.; Van Hee, J.
　　　　　　　　　　　　BE 070800/61/0004 R
Rationalisatie van de arbeid in het visserijbedrijf. **Labour rationalisation in the fishing industry.** Publications.

17278 Lee, T.; Kelly, T.　　　IE 180111/78/8761 R
Experimental pair demersal trawling off the west coast of Ireland.

D 5100 – Work management

17279 Lee, T.; Kelly, T.   IE 180111/78/8763 R
Pair demersal bobbin trawling and exploratory fishing off the north coast of Ireland.

17280 Verbaan, A.   NL 010702/68/7152
Onderzoek naar arbeidsbesparende en arbeidsverlichtende werkmethoden en machines op visserijvaartuigen (mechanisatie van het uitzetten en inhalen van vistuigen, ontwikkeling en beproeving vangstsorteerder, alternatieve losmethoden, arbeidskundige aspecten van de routing van de vangst tijdens de verwerking, ontwikkeling van een techno–economisch simulatiemodel). **Improvement of working conditions and mechanization onboard fishing vessels (mechanization gear handling operations, development and testing of a sorting machine, alternative unloading methods, ergonomic aspects of catchprocessing, development of a techno–economical simulation model).** Publications.

Other farms (B 8219)

17281 Maton, A.; Daelemans, J.   BE 070300/72/0020 R
Arbeidsbehoefte en huisvesting in de pluimveehouderij. **The labour time requirement and animal housing in poultry houses.** Publications.

Service and supply firms (B 8220)

See also 18906

17282 Vos, H.W.   NL 020026/74/6352
Organisatie onderdelenvoorziening landbouwwerktuigen. **Spare parts inventory organisations agricultural machinery.** Publications.

17283 Kant, N.F. van de   NL 040007/78/8566
Processtudie van het vervoer van grond en verhardingsmaterialen t.b.v. recreatie–objecten in verband met de behoefte aan transportmaterieel bij de Inrichtingswerken. **Study of the transport of ground and road metals for recreation objects in relation to the need to transportation material for land lay–out activities.**

Marketing and processing firms (B 8230)

See also 17179, 17218, 19183

17284 Rudolph, H.; Kesselschläger, J.   DE 105987/77/0006 N
Investitionen und Rationalisierungserfolg in der Brauerei. **Investments and rationalization success in breweries.**

17285 Loncin, M.; Thor, W.   DE 145150/75/0001
Untersuchung der Nachspülvorgänge an Modellstrecken. **Studies on rinsing by models.**

17286 Wullinger, F.   DE 161770/75/0003
Untersuchungen zur Kontrolle und Optimierung der Reinigungsund Desinfektionsmitteltechnik im Brauereibetrieb. **Studies on control and optimization of cleaning and disinfecting techniques in brewing practice.**

17287 Wippermann, H.-J.   DE 202030/77/0002
Optimale Gestaltung des Arbeitsablaufs in Betrieben der Holzindustrie, insbesondere der Schwachholzbearbeitung. **Optimum organization of the working process in enterprises of timber industry, esp. of weak timber processing.**

17288 Reuter, H.; Grasshoff, A.   DE 207060/75/0001
Verfahrenstechnische Untersuchung des Reinigungsvorganges in Molkereien. **Process engineering investigations into cleaning operations in dairies.**

17289 Haisch, K.-H.; Schebler, A.   DE 502552/78/0001 N
Wirtschaftliche Aspekte des technischen und technologischen Fortschritts beim Produktionsprozess in der Molkereiwirtschaft. **Economic aspects of the technical and technological progress in industrial dairying.**

Recreational enterprises (B 8240)

17290 Gerritsen, J.C.G.   NL 010106/78/8376 R
Bedrijfskundig onderzoek ten behoeve van een doelmatig onderhoud van natte natuurgebieden. **Organisational research on behalf of efficiency in conserving wet nature areas.**

17291 Lemmens, R.H.E.   NL 010600/78/8376
Bedrijfskundig onderzoek ten behoeve van een doelmatig onderhoud van natte natuurgebieden. **Organisational research on behalf of efficiency in conserving wet nature areas.**

D 5200 – Farm management

See also 12001, 15656, 15658, 15725, 17865, 18058

17292 Ledent, A.; Bergans, J.; Lange, B.   BE 010007/00/0003
Etude théorique de la fonction de production en agriculture. **Theorical study of agricultural production function.** Publications.

17293 Maton, A.; Lips, J.   BE 070300/76/0044
Invloed van mechanisatie, arbeidsorganisatie op de kostprijs van witloof. **The influence of mechanisation and workorganisation on the cost prices of belgian endive.** Publications.

17294 Wippermann, H.–J.   DE 202030/75/0002
Zentrale Holzaufarbeitungsplätze für Stark– und Schwachholz – ZAP –; insbesondere Organisation und Gestaltung von Rundholzplätzen für die Holzindustrie. **Central conversion sites for large and small–sized timber, in particular operations in log–yards of wood–processing industries.** Publications.

17295 Haisch, K.-H.; Gross, E.   DE 502552/70/0002
Bestimmungsfaktoren der optimalen Betriebsgrösse in der deutschen Molkereiwirtschaft. **Determinant factors of the optimum size in the German dairy industry.**

17296 Larsen, A.   DK 010500/76/0001
Undersøgelse af mulighederne for ændring af mælkeproduktionens sæsonmæssige variation. **Investigation of the possibilities of changing the seasonal variation in milk production.**

17297 Jensen, E.V.   DK 010703/75/0002
Produktionssystemer i svineholdet. **Production systems in pig herds.**

17298 Jensen, E.V.   DK 010703/77/0001
Investeringsplanlægning i malkekvægholdet. **Investment planning in the dairy herd.**

17299 Møller, S.   DK 011000/77/0003

Udvikling af regnemaskineprogrammer til omkostnings– og arbejdsanalyser af fodringsanlæg til kvægstalde. **Development of calculator programmes for cost and work analyses of feeding systems for cattle stalls.**

17300 Kofoed, S.S.   DK 030144/76/0006
Automatisk identifikation af kvæg. **Automatic identification of cattle.**

17301 Nielsen, A.H.   DK 030149/76/0008
En analyse af energiforbruget i den primære jordbrugssektor. **An analysis of energy consumption in the primary agricultural sector.**

17302 Bleasdale   GB 011804/00/0026
Economic appraisal of projects and cropping systems.

17303 Tease   GB 040601/77/0004
Dairy herd replacement rearing survey.

17304 McBurney   GB 040601/78/0005
Farm and farmer characteristics which affect farm performance.

17305 McBurney   GB 040601/78/0006
Provisions made by Northern Ireland farmers for succession.

17306 Volans   GB 060108/00/0002
Store sheep marketing.

17307 Lilwall   GB 060108/00/0003
Grain marketing strategies.

17308 Anderson   GB 060108/00/0004
An economic survey of the Scottish seed and ware potato crop.

17309 Anderson   GB 060108/00/0006
Mandatory work for DAFS.

17310 Lilwall   GB 060108/00/0008
Co–operative organisation in agriculture.

17311 Blyth   GB 060111/00/0001
Factors influencing the level of fixed costs in farming systems.

17312 Rehman   GB 060111/00/0002
Application of computer models in extension work.

17313 Rowbottom   GB 060111/00/0003
Management recording systems.

17314 Hume   GB 060111/00/0004
Farm Management Manual.

17315 Horsburgh; Balm   GB 060311/00/0007
Linear programming of glasshouse crops production.

17316 Aitken; Wilson   GB 060311/00/0008
Primary sources of beef cattle and sheep for fattening in Scotland.

17317 Hunt   GB 060311/00/0009
The causes and implications of changes in fatstock marketing methods,including live and deadweight sales.

17318 Smith; Tweddle   GB 060311/00/0010

Required economics work–mandatory.

17319 Smith; Tweddle   GB 060311/00/0011
Required economic work–development.

17320 Hunt; Groves   GB 060311/00/0012
Monitoring EEC information.

17321 Smith   GB 060311/00/0013
Investigational work in connection with the production of the Agricultural Management Manual.

17322 Horsburgh   GB 060311/00/0014
Investigational work in connection with the production of the Horticultural Management Manual.

17323 Mainland; Balm   GB 060311/00/0015
Econometrics and mathematical modelling.

17324 Godfrey; Aitken   GB 060311/00/0016
Farm capital investigations.

17325 Hunt; Groves   GB 060311/00/0017
Resource use and productivity in agriculture and horticulture.

17326 Godfrey; Gill   GB 060311/00/0018
Auchincruive farm accounts.

17327 McCreath; McClellnd   GB 060311/00/0019
Kirkton farm accounts.

17328 Smith; Leaver   GB 060311/00/0020
Crichton farm accounts.

17329 Flynn, A.V.; Heavey, J.F.   IE 060100/70/0581 N
Ballinalack farm project – evaluation of beef production systems. Publications.

Business enterprises in general (B 8200)

17330 Seuster, H.; Wien, D.van   DE 129360/74/0001
Organisationsstrukturen des Managements in kooperativen Landwirtschaftsunternehmungen. **Organizational management structures in farmers' co–operatives.**

17331 Schinke, E.   DE 129381/71/0004
Veränderungen der Betriebsorganisation unter dem Einfluss der Wirtschaftsreformen in Osteuropa. **Influence of economic reforms in East Europe on farm organization.**

17332 Larsen, A.; Walther–Jørgensen, A.
                                                 DK 010500/75/0001 R
Undersøgelse af fordele og ulemper ved alternative besiddelsesformer i landbruget. **Investigation of the advantages and disadvantages of alternative types of tenure in agriculture.**

17333 Carles, R.; Nanquette, B.   FR 011808/68/8539
Systèmes de production agricole et disparités de revenus. **Systems of agricultural production and income disparity.**

17334 Angeli, L.   IT 040509/77/0104 R
Sperimentazione dei metodi di pianificazione aziendale nella attività di assistenza tecnica agricola in Toscana. **Trials of farm management methods conducted in connection with the techical assistance to agriculture program in Tuscany.**

17335 Omodei–Zorini, L.   IT 040509/78/1081 N
Analisi delle tipologie di strutture agricole e delle categorie di
lavoratori agricoli in Toscana. **Analysis of the different types of
farm holdings and of the different categories of farm labourers
in Tuscany.**

17336 Bregoli, A.   IT 061000/74/0019
Analisi dei risultati globali di gestione per l'anno 1974.
Analysis of the management total results for the year 1974.

17337 Marcelis, W.J.   NL 020023/70/4386
Besturing van het onderhoud. **Management of maintenance.**
Publications.

17338 Marcelis, W.J.   NL 020023/70/8520
De ontwikkeling van een integrale bestuurstheorie.
Development of an Integral Management Theory.

17339 Kampfraath, A.A.   NL 020023/75/8517
Bestuurlijke en organisatorische aspekten van de strategische
planning. **Administrative and organizational aspects of strategic
planning.** Publications.

17340 Marcelis, W.J.   NL 020023/76/8518
De hantering van matrix–organisatie. **The application of
matrix–organization.**

17341 Koeman, M.F.   NL 020023/78/8516
Management–ontwikkeling in ontwikkelingsgebieden.
Management development in developing countries.

17342 Kampfraath, A.A.   NL 020023/78/8521
Longitudinaal onderzoek van veranderingsprocessen.
Longitudinal research in organizational change.

Farms in general (B 8210)

See also 2449, 15308, 15577, 15715, 15748, 17184, 17292,
17301, 17636, 17999, 18031, 18060, 18097, 18837, 19847

17343 Ledent, A.; Breuer, J.F.; Bergans, J.; Lange, B.
BE 010007/76/0007
Etude de la gestion des exploitations agricoles. **Study of farm
management.**

17344 Wautier, E.; Leclercq, J.; Degand, J.
BE 020200/79/0019 N
Modèle de simulation appliquée à la gestion des exploitations
agricoles. **Simulation models applicated on management of
farms.**

17345 Richter, L.   DE 105400/77/0002
Gebirgslandwirtschaft – Probleme zwischen
Wirtschaftswachstum und Landschaftsplanung. **Upland
farming – problems between economic growth and landscape
planning.**

17346 Henrichsmeyer, W.; Bauer, S.; Rothe, M.
DE 111651/77/0001
Agrarsektoranalyse auf betrieblicher Informationsbasis.
Agricultural sector analysis on farm information systems.
Publications.

17347 Lipinsky, E.E.; Pütz, H.–P.   DE 111652/75/0003
Die Funktion der genossenschaftlichen Einrichtungen als
Hilfsbetriebe für landwirtschaftliche Unternehmungen. **The**
**function of co–operative establishments as auxiliary firms of
farming enterprises.**

17348 Steffen, G.; Pauli, G.   DE 111701/77/0001
Entwicklung von Vollerwerbsbetrieben unter dem Einfluss von
Förderungsmassnahmen auf verschiedenen Standorten des
Landes Nordrhein–Westfalen. **Development of full–time
farming under the influence of subsidy programs in different
regions of Northrhine Westphalia.**

17349 Skomroch, W.; Majohr, M.   DE 111702/70/0002
Gliederungskriterien für landwirtschaftliches Einkommen der
Testbetriebe. Sicherheitswahrscheinlichkeit der Aussage 1968.
**Criteria for classification of the incomes of test forms.
Probability of reliability of statements.**

17350 Skomroch, W.; Janinhoff, A.   DE 111702/72/0001
Zur Abschätzung der Entwicklung von Einzelbetrieben 1972.
Valuation of individual–farm development.

17351 Manshard, W.   DE 126700/75/0001
Landwirtschaft in den Tropen. **Tropical agriculture.**

17352 Kuhlmann, F.   DE 129301/75/0002
Entwicklung und Test von
Management–Informations–Systemen für grössere
landwirtschaftliche Unternehmungen. **Development and test of
management information systems for large farms.**

17353 Kuhlmann, F.; Römert, W.   DE 129301/78/0003 N
Bestimmung landwirtschaftlicher Betriebsgrössen in der
agrarstrukturellen Vorplanung. **Determination of sizes of
agricultural firms in agrostructural forecasting.**

17354 Kuhlmann, F.; Wiesner, W.   DE 129301/78/0004 N
Kontrollsysteme für den Arbeitsaufwand als Bestandteil eines
Management–Informations–System – MIS – in grösseren
landwirtschaftlichen Betrieben. **Control systems for labour
expense as part of a management information system – MIS – of
bigger agricultural firms.**

17355 Kuhlmann, F.; Weiershäuser, L.   DE 129301/78/0005 N
Zur Ermittlung standardisierter Werte von variablen Kosten
mit Gemeinkostencharakter. **Determination of standardized
values of variable costs.**

17356 Kuhlmann, F.; Grenzebach, E.   DE 129301/78/0007 N
Betriebsplanung für ausgewählte Betriebstypen der
Gediz–Ebene. **Farm planning for selected farm types in the
Gediz plain.**

17357 Spitzer, H.; Schmidt, G.   DE 129302/75/0001
Beziehung zwischen regionaler und betriebsgrösseneigener
Spezialisierung der landwirtschaftlichen Erzeugung. **Relation
between regional and individual i.e. farm size related
specialization of agricultural production.**

17358 Zilahi–Szabo, M.G.; Wrede, R.   DE 129304/73/0003
Erarbeitung neuer Wege der Informationserschliessung und
–aufbereitung für den Planungsprozess landwirtschaftlicher
Unternehmen. **Development of new methods of information
analysis and informa– tion processing for farm planning
process.**

17359 Zilahi–Szabo, M.G.; Stolte, F.   DE 129304/73/0004
Theoretische und organisatorische Grundlagen eines

computerunterstützten Abweichungskontrollsystem –CAS– im Rechnungs– wesen landwirtschaftlicher Unternehmen. **Fundamental theoretical and organizational principles of a computer–supported check aberration system –CAS– of farm accounting.**

17360 Schinke, E.; Loncarevic, I.   DE 129381/70/0003
Kooperation zwischen landwirtschaftlichen Betrieben unterschiedlicher Organisations– und Eigentumsformen in Jugoslawien. **Co–operation of farms with different forms of organization and property in Yugoslavia.**

17361 Kuhnen, F.; Wagenhäuser, F.J.A.   DE 132250/75/0002
Zum Wandel in der Agrarstruktur der Türkei unter dem Einfluss der Wanderarbeit in Westeuropa. **The organization of peasant farms under the influence of Turkish guest–worker employment in Western Europe.**

17362 Köhne, M.; Dumstorf, H.   DE 132360/78/0001 N
Scheingewinnermittlung in landwirtschaftlichen Betrieben. **Determination of apparent profit of farms.**

17363 Weinschenck, G.; Lüer, G.   DE 144750/70/0012
Moderne Kriterien zur Beurteilung der Kreditwürdigkeit landwirtschaftlicher Betriebe. **Modern methods to evaluate credit rating of farms.**

17364 Weinschenck, G.; Kögl, H.   DE 144750/75/0006
Investitionsplanung bei Unsicherheit. **Investment planning under uncertainty.**

17365 Weinschenck, G.; Piening, K.   DE 144750/75/0007
Eine empirische Analyse unterschiedlicher Typen von Entwicklungspfaden in Buchführungsbetrieben Niedersachsens. **An empirical analysis of different growth of bookkeeping farms in Lower Saxony.**

17366 Riebe, K.; Sundermeier, H.H.   DE 148400/78/0001 N
Einzelbetriebliche Düngungskostenminimierung mit Hilfe Linearer Programmierung. **Cost–minimum of fertilizer use in single farms with linear programming.**

17367 Langbehn, C.; Heitzhausen, G.   DE 148401/74/0004
Analyse des Betriebsleiterverhaltens und der Entwicklung der einzelbetrieblichen Produktionsstruktur. **Analysis of farm manager's behaviour and the improvement of individual–farm production structures.**

17368 Hanf, C.H.; Wölcke, D.   DE 148405/78/0003 N
Bedeutung der expliziten Berücksichtigung von Unsicherheit in der landwirtschaftlichen Betriebsplanung. **Agricultural management planning under explicit consideration of risk.**

17369 Zapf, R.; Thoma, H.   DE 161400/77/0001
Betriebliches Wachstum unter besonderer Berücksichtigung steuerlicher Aspekte. **Growth of agricultural firms with special regard to the aspects of taxation.**

17370 Steinhauser, H.; Bach, P.   DE 161440/73/0001
Möglichkeiten der nebenberuflichen Bewirtschaftung von Grünlandbetrieben dargestellt am Beispiel der Region Berchtesgaden. **Possibilities of part–time farming in grassland areas, shown by the Berchtesgaden region.**

17371 Steinhauser, H.; Weber, T.   DE 161440/75/0001
Beitrag zur Quantifizierung der Höhe des Umlaufvermögens in landwirtschaftlichen Betrieben. **A contribution to quantify the level of the circulating fund of farms.**

17372 Steinhauser, H.; Kreul, W.   DE 161440/77/0002
Steuerliche Gewinnermittlung im landwirtschaftlichen Betrieb. **Farm profit recording in consideration of income tax.**

17373 Steinkampf, H.   DE 201090/77/0002
Aufstellung einer Energiebilanz für Produktionsverfahren in der Feldwirtschaft. **Balance of energy for production system in agriculture.**

17374 Meinhold, K.; Schmidt, B.   DE 201100/77/0005
Die Wirkung der Feldberegnung auf Produktionsprogramm und –richtung landwirtschaftlicher Betriebe. **Effect of field irrigation into programme and trend of production of farms.**

17375 Meinhold, K.; Schmidt, B.   DE 201100/77/0006
Ermittlung von Ertragsunterschieden zwischen nicht beregnenden und beregnenden Betrieben mittels Zeitreihenanalysen. **Determination of differences in crop yields of non–irrigating and irrigating farms by means of time series analyses.**

17376 Meinhold, K.; Kögl, H.   DE 201100/78/0013 N
Empirische Analyse des Entscheidungsverhaltens von Landwirten bei Unsicherheit. **Empirical analysis of farmers' decision behaviour under uncertainty.**

17377 Meinhold, K.; Schmidt, B.   DE 201100/78/0015 N
Prüfung ökonomischer Rückwirkungen neuer Erkenntnisse hinsichtlich der Steuerung des Beregnungseinsatzes. **Economic valuation of recent improvements in irrigation control.**

17378 Meinhold, K.; Kögl, H.; Hinrichs, P.
                    DE 201100/78/0019 N
Ökonomische Auswirkungen von Umweltauflagen in der Tierhaltung auf die Wachstumsfähigkeit landwirtschaftlicher Betriebe. **Inhibitory effects on farm growth by environmental restrictions of animal production.**

17379 Neander, E.; Klare, K.   DE 201120/72/5003 N
Analyse der Auswirkungen einzelbetrieblicher Förderungsmassmahmen auf die Entwicklung landwirtschaftlicher Betriebe in ausgewählten Regionen Niedersachsens. **Analysis of effects of measures for subvention of individual farms on the development of farms in selected regions of Lower Saxony.**

17380 Neander, E.; Peters, W.   DE 201120/75/0002
Untersuchungen zur gesamtwirtschaftlichen Effizienz einzelbetrieblicher Förderungsmassnahmen in der Landwirtschaft. **Investigations into the economic efficiency of programmes for the development of individual farms.**

17381 Neander, E.; Wilstacke, L.   DE 201120/78/0003 N
Weiterentwicklung des Agrarstrukturberichts. **Improvement of the biannual report on agicultural structure.**

17382 Schulz–Borck, H.; Tiede, S.   DE 201120/78/0005 N
Budgetuntersuchungen in landwirtschaftlichen Voll– und Nebenerwerbsbetrieben. **Survey of income formation and utilization on full–time and part–time farms.**

17383 Hülsen, R.   DE 914003/77/0003
Buchführungsauswertung bei Landwirten. **Accounting system**

D 5200 – Farm management

of farmers.

17384 Kraus, R.W.H.   DE 916000/78/0004 N
Die Entwicklung der bäuerlichen Landwirtschaft im Oberen
Medjerdatal/Tunesien. **The development of farming agriculture
in the Upper Medjerde Valley/Tunisia.**

17385 Larsen, A.; Pedersen, T.D.   DK 010500/16/0001 R
Årlige repræsentative regnskabsanalyser af danske
landbrugsbedrifters eksterne omsætning. **Annual
representative account analyses of external turnover in Danish
agricultural holdings.**

17386 Larsen, A.; Pedersen, T.D.   DK 010500/16/0002 R
Årlige repræsentative regnskabsanalyser af danske
landbrugsbedrifters interne omsætning. **Annual representative
account analyses of the internal turnover of Danish agricultural
holdings.**

17387 Larsen, A.; Walther–Jørgensen, A.; Melgård, P.;
Rasmussen, S.   DK 010500/66/0002 R
Analyser og årlige prognoser over udviklingen i landbrugets
økonomi. **Analysis and yearly forecasts for the development in
the economy of agriculture.**

17388 Larsen, A.; Walther–Jørgensen, A.
                                        DK 010500/69/0001 R
Undersøgelser med henblik på forbedring af sikkerheden i
repræsentative regnskabsanalyser. **Investigations with
reference to the improvement of accuracy in representative
account analyses.**

17389 Larsen, A.; Pedersen, T.D.   DK 010500/72/0001 R
Metoder til indsamling og bearbejdning af regnskabsdata til
EF's informationsnet. **Methods of collecting and processing
data from farm accounts for the EEC information network.**

17390 Jensen, E.V.   DK 010703/71/0001
Udvikling af regnskabssystem – S–72 – herunder systemer for
budgettering og budgetkontrol til brug for landbrugsbedrifter.
**Development of the S 72 accounting system, including systems
for budgetting and budget control for use on farms.**

17391 Grandclaude, L.; Richet, G.; Houdard, Y.; Teilhard de
Chardin, B.; Mennessier, P.   FR 010112/75/3033
Etude d'exploitations agricoles novatrices. **Study of the
evolution of farms adopting innovations.**

17392 Richet, G.; Mennessier, P.; Bruno, J.F.; Fretault, B.;
Teilhard de Chardin, B.; Houdard, Y.   FR 010112/75/9095
Suivi d'entreprises dynamiques, adéquation des techniques de
production, diffusion de l'innovation. **Follow–up of dynamic
farms, adjustment of production techniques, innovation
diffusion.**

17393 Mainie, P.   FR 010112/75/9102
Enquête sur l'évolution actuelle des exploitations du marais de
Rochefort. **Survey concerning the present evolution of farms
and farming in the Rochefort marshes area.**

17394 Mahe, L.; Montaigne, E.   FR 011302/77/8671
Un modèle économétrique des relations viandes, céréales,
protéines CEREDIANE. **An econometric model of the
livestock, Feed stuffs subsector.**

17395 Blanc, M.   FR 011408/77/8624

Typologies des exploitations et analyse des couches sociales
agricoles dans la France contemporaine. **Farms types and
analysis of agricultural social strata in France.**

17396 Capillon, A.   FR 011701/75/6171
Méthode d'étude du fonctionnement des exploitations
agricoles d'une petite région agricole. **Method of study of farm
fonctioning in a given agricultural area.**

17397 Attonaty, J.M.; Chatelin, M.H.; Hautcolas, J.C.;
Chartier, R.   FR 011808/74/8669
Modèles de simulation pour la gestion des entreprises
agricoles. **Simulation models for farm managment purpose.**

17398 Sourie, J.C.; Marsal, P.   FR 011808/75/3308
Le surplus de productivité dans les entreprises agricoles.
Productivity surplus on farms.

17399 Carles, R.   FR 011808/75/3310
Analyse des revenus et du fonctionnement d'entreprises
agricoles. **Analysis of farm Income and management.**

17400 Attonaty, J.M.; Chartier, R.; Flament, M.; Chatelin,
M.H.; Hautcolas, J.C.   FR 011808/75/3311
Modèles de simulation pour la gestion des entreprises.
Simulation models for farm management.

17401 Mergui, G.; Nefussi, J.; Fromentin, G.
                                        FR 012205/78/8665
Mise au point de typologie d'exploitations agricoles sur la base
de données techniques et humaines. **Farm characterization
with technical and human data.**

17402 Bergmann, D.   FR 012212/73/8506
Dynamique de la propriété et de l'exploitation dans les
Landes. **Land ownership and farms in the Landes department.
A dynamic analysis.**

17403 Postel–Vinay, G.   FR 012212/75/8504
Rapport de la propriété aux structures d'exploitation. Cas du
département de la Sarthe. **Relationship between property and
farm: Structure study for Sarthe department.**

17404 Ponchelet, D.   FR 012212/77/8509
Les salariés agricoles des grandes exploitations de
Seine–et–Marne depuis 1850. **Agricultural workers of large
farms in Seine et Marne since 1850.**

17405 Servolin, C.; Barcelo, R.; Nallet, H.; Wolfer, B.
                                        FR 012212/78/8523
Diffusion du progrès technique et développement des
exploitations. **Technical progress diffusion and farms
development in France.**

17406 Brookes; Hunter   GB 040601/79/0008 N
**A study of the nature of structural changes in Northern Ireland
farming.**

17407 Grant   GB 060226/79/0007 N
Monitoring developments on Forsinard estate Sutherland.

17408 Heavey, J.F.; Power, R.; Harkin, M.; Connolly, W.
                                        IE 060600/72/0573 N
Farm production efficiency. Publications.

17409 Cox, P.G.   IE 060600/72/1025 R

Irish governments farm modernisation scheme. Problems. Publications.

17410 Frawley, J.   IE 060600/73/0895 N
Personal, social and situational factors related to innovativenes and farm management performance. Publications.

17411 O'Farrell, F.; Cunney, M.B.   IE 060600/78/1405 N
Experimental passive solar farm dwelling. Publications.

17412 Lucey, D.I.F.; Cahillane, G.   IE 110105/79/9233 N
Impact of the farm modernisation scheme on income distribution within Irish farming.

17413 Callaghan, J.; Mannion, J.; Lohan, E.
                                IE 120109/78/9249 N
A study of the effects of the smallholders assistance on far m development.

17414 Pugliese, L.   IT 040108/77/0271 R
Costi di produzione dei principali prodotti agricoli pugliesi. Production costs of the main agricultural produce of Puglia.

17415 Piccinini, A.   IT 040224/74/0604
Studio dei metodi di analisi di gestione più idonei per l'assistenza tecnica nelle aziende agricole dell'Emilia occidentale. Study of suitable management analysis methods for technical assistance to farm enterprises of western Emilia.

17416 Pirani, A.   IT 040606/77/0262 R
Indagine sulle cooperative agricole della Lombardia. Research on agricultural cooperatives in Lombardy.

17417 De Angelis, L.   IT 040706/77/0321 R
Sperimentazione dei metodi di pianificazione aziendale nella attività di assistenza tecnica agricola in una zona della Italia meridionale. Trials of farm management planning methods in a zone of Southern Italy as part of the technical agricultural assistance program.

17418 De Benedictis, M.   IT 040732/74/0542
Analisi economica dei processi d'investimento nell'azienda agraria. Economic analysis of capital investment processes in the farm enterprise.

17419 Favaretti, G.; Boatto, V.   IT 040804/79/0001 N
Bilanci energetici aziende agricole. Farms energy consumption.

17420 Abbozzo, P.; Ciani, A.   IT 041009/75/0002
Le aziende part-time in Italia Centrale. The part–time farms of Central Italy.

17421 Iacoponi, L.   IT 041105/77/0206 R
Analisi delle metodologie di rilevazione e di elaborazione dei dati contabili delle aziende agrarie. Analysis of date entering and processing methods in farm book–keeping.

17422 Montanini, C.; Copelli, A.; Magistretti, A.
                                IT 041517/68/0001 N
Dinamica della patologia fondiaria e aziendale in Italia (1931–1967).. Dynamics of farm and farm management pathology in Italy (1931–1967)..

17423 Gallerani, V.   IT 061000/71/0024
Impiego e costo delle macchine in aziende agrarie. Machines

employment and cost in some farms. Publications.

17424 Cipriani, L.   IT 061000/74/0020
Analisi dei singoli processi produttivi per l'anno 1974. Analysis of the single enterprises for the year 1974.

17425 Sarti, D.   IT 061000/74/0021
Analisi dell'aspetto finanziario della gestione in aziende a diverso indirizzo produttivo. Analysis of the management financial position in farms of different type of farming.

17426 Alvisi, F.   IT 061000/74/0025
Organizzazione dei servizi di rilevazione contabile in agricoltura nei Paesi della Comunità Economica Europea e negli Stati Uniti d'America. Organization of the farm book–keeping services in the E.E.C. countries and in U.S.A. Publications.

17427 Lisa, L.   IT 063300/61/0068
Meccanizzazione collinare. Technical and economical aspects of mechanization in hill–side farms. Publications.

17428 Swierstra, D.   NL 010106/72/4737
Ontwikkelen van een (computer) systeem voor de bouwkostenbegroting en indexering van agrarische bedrijfsgebouwen (Agrarische Gebouwen Bouwkosten Informatie Systeem – AGBIS). Development of a computer system to determine building costs of farm building systems. Publications.

17429 Eriks, A.   NL 010116/50/2952
Ontwikkeling en toepassing van programmeringstechnieken voor bedrijfs–planning. Development and application of various programming techniques for farm planning.

17430 Eriks, A.   NL 010116/50/2953
Ontwikkeling en toepassing van bedrijfsvergelijkende analyse. Development and application of methods of farm – comparative analysis.

17431 Zachariasse, L.   NL 010116/50/2954 R
Opstelling en gebruik van verhoudingsgetallen ten behoeve van aggregatie en beoordeling van bedrijfsresultaten. Development and use of standards for statistical and analytical evaluation of farm results. Publications.

17432 Bos, C.   NL 010116/70/2961 R
Analyse van gegevens betreffende financiële positie, inkomensvorming en inkomensbesteding in de landbouw. Dataanalysis concerning the financial position, formation of income and income spending in farming. Publications.

17433 Zachariasse, L.   NL 010116/70/2964 R
Voorcalculaties van rentabiliteit en productiviteit van landbouw–bedrijven. Analysis and precalculations of profitability and productivity of farms. Publications.

17434 Veer, J. de   NL 010116/73/3935 R
Financiële positie beginnende ondernemers. Financial position of new farmers. Publications.

17435 Cleveringa, C.J.   NL 010116/77/7694
Bedrijfseconomische uitkomsten van landbouwbedrijven, die "biologische" teeltmethoden toepassen. Farmeconomical results of farms with "biological" agriculture. Publications.

D 5200 – Farm management

17436 Giessen, L.B. van der   NL 010116/78/8575 N
De ontwikkelingsmogelijkheden voor het middenbedrijf. **The possibilities to develop in middle farm.**

17437 Kostelijk, S.   NL 020001/78/8390
Investeringsplanning op land– en tuinbouwbedrijven. **Investment planning on agricultural and horticultural holdings.**

17438 Hoeve, H.   NL 040007/67/4326
Beheers– en uitgiftevraagstukken m.b.t. bijzondere bedrijfsvormen en exploitatievormen (afwijkende bedrijfsomstandigheden; eigenbeheer van graspercelen langs bos, wegen en watergangen; alternatieve landbouwmethoden). **Management problems related to special kinds of land use and exploitation (unusual farm circumstances; self–management of grass areas adjoining woods, roads and waterways; alternative agricultural methods).**

Arable farms (B 8211)

See also 2710, 2711, 17588

17439 Compère, R.; Antoine, A.; Boulet, B.
    BE 010003/76/0013 R
Contrôle et amélioration de l'exploitation de trois fermes expérimentales et démonstratives dans trois régions herbagères du Sud Hainaut. **Control and improvement of management of three experimental farms en three different pastoral regions in South–Hainaut.**

17440 Steffen, G.; Wüsten, H.   DE 111701/77/0002
Die ökonomische Gestaltung von Arbeitsabläufen im Getreidebau. **The economical formation of flow of process in corn–growing.**

17441 Reisch, E.; Hartmann, W.   DE 144745/78/0001 N
Ökonomische Beurteilung und organisatorische Einordnung neuer Verfahren der Bestell–, Dünge und Pflanzenschutztechnik in der Körnerfruchtproduktion. **Economic analysis and organizational implementation of new techniques in grain production with special reference to sowing, fertilization and plant protection.**

17442 Ruthenberg, H.; Lang, H.   DE 144755/73/0001
Die Ökonomik moderner Anbauformen des unbewässerten Reisbaues in Westafrika. **Economics of modernized rainfed rice cultivation methods in West Africa.**

17443 Langbehn, C.   DE 148401/74/0005
Ermittlung von Daten zur Feldwirtschaft in Grossbetrieben auf Ackerbaustandorten. **Investigations of characteristics of cropping in large farms on arable land.**

17444 Steinhauser, H.; Fenner, J.   DE 161440/77/0001
Energetische Betrachtungen zur Herstellung konkurrierender Süssungsmittel. **Survey into the production of competitive sweeteners under energetic aspects.**

17445 Keller, P.; Nielsen, V.   DK 010400/74/0007 N
Arbejdsbehov ved reduceret jordbearbejdning. **The influence of minimum tillage on labour requirement.**

17446 Sørensen, B.; Parsby, M.   DK 010500/78/0007 N
Driftsøkonomisk vurdering af fordele og ulemper ved dyrkning af vinterbyg. **Economic analysis and evaluation of growing winter–barley.**

17447 Grillenzoni, M.   IT 061000/74/0022
Produttività ed economie di scala in aziende a indirizzo cerealicolo. **Productivity and economies of scale in cereals farms.**

17448 Elderen, E. van   NL 010106/78/8349
Beoordeling van onderdelen van enkele bedrijfsplanningsmethoden. **Evaluation of parts of some farm planning methods.**

17449 Bos, C.   NL 010116/63/0189 R
Onderzoek naar de financiële positie van de landbouwbedrijven. **Micro economic research into the financial position of the farms participating in the A.E.R.I. book–keeping scheme.** Publications.

17450 Cleveringa, C.   NL 010116/70/2948
Overzicht van bedrijfsuitkomsten en voorlopig overzicht bedrijfsuit komsten op basis van steekproef van landbouwbedrijven. **Annual statistical survey of farming results based on sample of farm accounts.** Publications.

17451 Zachariasse, L.C.   NL 010116/71/3265 R
Bedrijfsonderzoek akkerbouw op basis van studiebedrijven. **Economic research of modern arable farming systems.** Publications.

17452 Zachariasse, L.C.   NL 010116/71/3698
Bedrijfseconomische aspecten van bijzondere akkerbouwvormen. **Investigation into the farm–economic aspects of new developments in arable farming.** Publications.

17453 Draisma, M.; Lalkens, R.H.   NL 010116/72/3699
Bedrijfseconomische consequenties voortvloeiende uit de nieuwe aardappelteelt regeléng. **Farm–economic impacts of regulations concerning potato growing.** Publications.

17454 Zachariasse, L.C.   NL 010116/76/7620
Perspectieven voor akkerbouw op lichte en droogte–gevoelige gronden. **Economic prospects of arable farming on sandy soils.**

17455 Zachariasse, L.C.   NL 010116/77/7621
Macro– en micro–economische aspecten van de aardappel (teelt). **Macro and micro economic aspects of potatoes.** Publications.

17456 Zachariasse, L.C.   NL 010116/77/7622
Boer en bedrijf; resultaat na tien jaar ontwikkeling. **Farmer and farm; result after ten years of development.**

17457 Zachariasse, L.C.   NL 010116/77/8573 N
Micro– en macro economische aspecten van de suikerbietenteelt. **Micro and macro economic aspects of sugarbeet.**

17458 Zachariasse, L.C.   NL 010116/79/9041 N
Analyse van 25 jaar ontwikkelingen op BIEB–bedrijven. **Analysis of developments on groups of farms in the new Lake IJssel polders.**

17459 Preuter, H.   NL 010207/71/3262 R
Economische evaluatie van het vruchtwisselingsonderzoek en bouwplanprogrammering. **Economic evaluation and programming of crop rotations.** Publications.

D 5200 – Farm management

17460 Zacheriasse, L.C.   NL 010207/71/3265 R
Bedrijfsonderzoek akkerbouw op basis van studiebedrijven. **Economic research of modern arable farming systems.** Publications.

17461 Ast, K.J. van; Lalkens, R.H.   NL 010207/71/3698
Bedrijfseconomische aspecten van bijzondere akkerbouwvormen. **Special arable farming systems.** Publications.

17462 Cevaal, P.K.   NL 010207/76/6624 N
Onderzoek naar de bedrijfseconomische toepasbaarheid van beregeningssystemen op akkerbouwbedrijven. **The economic possibilities of sprinkler irrigation systems for arable farms.**

17463 Preuter, H.   NL 010207/76/6626
Analyse, interpretatie en evaluatie van gegevens uit de structuurenquête akkerbouw en vollegrondsgroentebedrijven. **Analysis, interpretation and evaluation of the data from the inquiry into the structure of farms (arable and vegetables in the open).**

17464 Zachariasse, L.C.   NL 010207/76/7620
Perspectieven voor akkerbouw op lichte en droogte–gevoelige gronden. **Economic prospects of arable farming on sandy soils.**

17465 Zachariasse, L.C.   NL 010207/77/7621
Macro– en micro–economische aspecten van de aardappel (teelt). **Macro and micro economic aspects of potatoes.** Publications.

17466 Zachariasse, L.C.   NL 010207/77/7622
Boer en bedrijf; resultaat na tien jaar ontwikkeling. **Farmer and farm; result after ten years of development.**

17467 Zacheriasse, L.C.   NL 010207/77/8573 N
Micro– en macro economische aspecten van de suikerbietenteelt. **Micro– and macro economic aspects of sugar beet.**

17468 Cevaal, P.K.   NL 010207/78/8349
Beoordeling van onderdelen van enkele bedrijfsplanningsmethoden. **Evaluation of parts of some farm planning methods.**

17469 Zachariasse, L.C.   NL 010207/79/9041 N
Analyse van 25 jaar ontwikkelingen op BIEB–bedrijven. **Analysis of developments on groups of farms in the new Lake IJssel polders.**

17470 Cevaal, P.K.   NL 010207/79/9042 N
Toepassing en evaluatie van het systeem van bedrijfseconomische advisering met standaardmatrices voor akkerbouwbedrijven. **Introduction, application and evaluation of the system of farm managemert advising with master matrices for arable farms.**

17471 Niejenhuis, J.H. van   NL 020001/72/4242
Het afleiden van samenwerkingsverbanden tussen landbouwbedrijven. **Economic aspects of cooperation between arable farmers.**

17472 Haverkamp, H.C.M.   NL 020001/78/8391
De toepassingsmogelijkheden van een bedrijfsspel, gebaseerd op een Nederlands akkerbouwbedrijf, met behulp van het Reading University Business and Modelling Program. **The possibilities of an arable farm business game by means of Reading University Business and Modelling Program.**

17473 Sital, J.T.   NL 020027/67/4482
Economische aspecten van het bedrijfsgrootte vraagstuk in de rijst–cultuur in het Nickery–district in Suriname. **Economic of the farmsize–structure in the culture of rice in the Nickerie district in Surinam.** Publications.

Animal and grassland farms (B 8212)

See also 10480, 10717, 10728, 10870, 10878, 11055, 11569, 13144, 13282, 14366, 15416, 16783, 17207, 17208, 17213, 17215, 17295, 17296, 17329, 17439, 17449, 17450, 17873, 18408

17474 Weniger, J.H.; Schellenberg, R.; Plessow, C.   DE 105550/77/0002
Produktionstechnische und betriebswirtschaftliche Untersuchungen zur Milch– und Rindfleischproduktion in landwirtschaftlichen Betrieben in den karibischen Nordprovinzen Kolumbiens. **Investigations into economics and management of combined production of beef and milk in ranches situated in the northern provinces of Colombia.**

17475 Researcher not indicated   DE 111000/78/0001 N
Untersuchungen zur ökonomischen Bedeutung verschiedener Verfahren der Gesundheitskontrollen und Metaphylaxe in der Milchviehhaltung. **Studies on the economic importance of different methods of health control and metaphylaxis in dairy farming.**

17476 Schmitten, F.; Jüngst, H.; Finke, K.   DE 111500/78/0001 N
Einfluss von Getreidesubstituten auf die Wirtschaftlichkeit der Mastschweineproduktion. **Influence of cereal substitutes on the economy in fattening pig production.**

17477 Simon, D.; Giesen, H.; Harbeck, J.   DE 111502/77/0001
Organisationsformen in Schweinezucht und –produktion in NRW. **Organizing in breeding and production of pigs in NRW.**

17478 Momm, H.; Schweer, H.   DE 144680/77/0003
Stand und Entwicklung bäuerlicher Organisationen für die Hybridzüchtung beim Schwein. **Situation and development of farmers' organizations for hybrid breeding in swine.**

17479 Lanser, E.   DE 144690/71/0002
Prüfung und Entwicklung von Managementprogrammen für Produktionen mit weiblichen Rindern in unterschiedlichen Alters– und Laktationsstadien. **Management–programs for dairying and dairy–cattle rearing.**

17480 Reisch, E.; Röhner, M.   DE 144745/72/0006
Untersuchungen über die produktionstechnischen Verfahren der Viehwirtschaft für Vergleichsgebiete der Bundesrepublik Deutschland. **Economic investigations of live–stock production processes – esp. cattles – for comparable regions of the Federal Republic of Germany.**

17481 Langbehn, C.; Raue, F.   DE 148401/78/0002 N
Ein Beitrag zur Definition zeitgemässer Produktionssysteme der Bullenmast auf Ackerbaustandorten Norddeutschlands. **A contribution to definition of modern systems of bull fattening in arable regions in the north of the Federal Republic of Germany.**

D 5200 – Farm management

17482 Zapf, R.; Vogt, L.   DE 161400/73/0001
Modellrechnungen für die nebenberufliche
Landbewirtschaftung in Futterbauregionen. **Model calculations
for part–time farming in forage growing regions.**

17483 Meinhold, K.; Walter, K.   DE 201100/77/0002
Hinweise zur Entwicklung von technischen Fortschritten für
Milchviehhaltungsverfahren. **Tendencies in the development of
technical progress in dairy stock keeping systems.**

17484 Meinhold, K.; Walter, K.   DE 201100/77/0003
Weiterentwicklung und Bewertung eines teilautomatisierten
Milchviehhaltungsverfahrens für bäuerliche Betriebe. **Further
development and valuation of a partially automated dairy stock
keeping system for farms.**

17485 Meinhold, K.; Walter, K.   DE 201100/77/0004
Wettbewerbsfähigkeit der Sommerstallhaltung bei hoch
mechanisierten Milchviehhaltungsverfahren. **Competitive
ability of zero–grazing in high mechanical dairy stock keeping
system.**

17486 Meinhold, K.; Walter, K.   DE 201100/77/0010
Ökonomische Aspekte höherer Melk– und
Fütterungsfrequenzen. **Economic aspects of increased milking
and feeding frequencies.**

17487 Meinhold, K.; Hinrichs, P.; Heinrich, I.; Kögl, H.
     DE 201100/78/0001 N
Auswirkungen von Tierschutzauflagen auf die
Einkommenslage verschiedener Betriebsgruppen. **Effects of
restrictions resulting from animal protection on the income
situation in different farming enterprises.**

17488 Meinhold, K.; Heinrich, I.; Walter, K.; Boeckmann, U.

     DE 201100/78/0010 N
Entwicklung ökonomischer Informations– und
Kontrollsysteme für Betriebe mit ausgeprägter tierischer
Veredlung. **Development of economic information– and
–control systems for farms with intensive animal production.**

17489 Drews, M.   DE 207070/77/0002
Ziele, Verfassung und Organisation in Molkereiunternehmen.
Aims, conditions and organization of dairies.

17490 Brehm, K.–P.   DE 207070/77/0003
Planung in Molkereiunternehmungen. **Planning in dairies.**

17491 Jureit, S.   DE 207070/77/0005
Wirtschaftliche Auswirkung von Umweltschutzmassnahmen
auf Molkereibetriebskosten. **Economic effects of environment
protective measures on expenses of dairies.**

17492 Wenner, H.L.; Krinner, L.   DE 502603/73/0001
Analyse des Kapitalbedarfes bei Gebäuden der Rinderhaltung.
Analysis of building capital requirements in cattle keeping.

17493 Christensen, J.   DK 010500/78/0001 N
Udvikling af rådgivningsprogrammer med henblik på
investeringer og produktionsudvidelser i kvæagholdet.
**Development of an extension programme for investments and
expansion of production on cattle farms.**

17494 Christensen, Johs.; Parsby, M.; Rasmussen, Sv.
     DK 010500/78/0003 N

17495 Brun, A.; Osty, P.   FR 010112/74/3036
Driftsøkonomisk vurdering af biogas– og komposteringsanlæg i
kvæg– og svinebesætninger. **The economics of biogas and
composting systems on cattle and pig farms.**

Fonctionnement technico–socio–économique des exploitations
agricoles du "Causse.Méjan". **Technical social and economical
aspects of the management of the farms in the district "Causse
Méjan".**

17496 Jeannin, B.   FR 010112/75/9094
Modalités de l'intensification du pâturage dans les
exploitations d'élevage des secteurs à S.T.H. dominante.
**Means of intensifying grazing capacity on livestock farms of
predominalty grassy regions.**

17497 Lienard, G.   FR 010810/70/8534
Economie des troupeaux de vaches allaitantes. **Economic
factors and results of suckling herds.**

17498 Lienard, G.   FR 010810/75/8577
Possibilités d'évolution des élevages laitiers de montagne.
Economic aspects of dairy herds in mountains.

17499 Carrere, G.; Lienard, G.   FR 010810/76/8535
Systèmes de production en élevage bovin charolais. **Economic
choices of production with charolais cattle.**

17500 Lienard, G.; Geay, Y.; Malterre, C.; Beranger, G.;
Robelin, J.   FR 010810/77/8536
Choix économiques des types de production de viande bovine
en élevage Limousin. **Economic choices of production with
limousin cattle.**

17501 Lienard, G.; Beranger, C.; Micol, D.; Petit, M.;
Malterre, C.   FR 010810/77/8537
Intensification fourragère et production de viande. Essai
d'analyse économique. **Intensive forage production for beef
cattle. An economical analysis.**

17502 Boutonnet, J.P.; Bourliaud, J.; Chabert, J.P.
     FR 011205/77/8648
Economie ovine dans la perspective des relations privilégiées
de la CEE avec les pays méditerranéens. **Sheep economy in the
outlook preferential relationships between EEC and
mediterranean countries.**

17503 Aubert, D.; Debailleul, G.   FR 011302/77/8612
Groupements de producteurs et stratégies du capital dans le
secteur agroalimentaire : le cas de la production porcine.
**Producers groups and capitalism strategy in the agricultural
and food industry : the case of pig production.**

17504 Mouchet, C.; Barloy, J.   FR 011302/78/8520
Etude des systèmes fourragers dans l'Ouest. **Fodder system
analysis in the west.**

17505 Lassaut, B.; Persuy, P.   FR 012205/78/8527
Production et transformation laitière en Savoie : valorisation
des produits laitiers régionaux. **Milk production and processing
industry in Savoie : traditional milk products valorization.**

17506 Coulomb, P.; Nallet, H.; Bitoun, B.; Remy, J.;
Dupont, Y.; Alphandery, P.   FR 012212/77/8599
Les modèles technico–économiques de développement des
exploitations agricoles: l'exemple du lait et du jeune bovin.

D 5200 – Farm management

Technico economical models for farms development: exemple with milk and young bovin.

17507 Bourliaud, J.; Brossier, J.; Boussard, J.M.
FR 012212/77/8676
Programmation linéaire et planification de l'alimentation du troupeau. Application à la production laitière à Cuba. **Model of optimal feeding of Cuban livestoock.**

17508 Collins, D.P.
IE 060103/00/1484 N
Influence of grazing system in farm management. Publications.

17509 Bruno, R.
IT 040108/78/1038 N
Aspetti economici dell'allevamento ovino in Puglia. **Economic aspects of sheep breeding in Puglia.**

17510 Messori, F.
IT 040224/74/0588
Ricerca e definizione del modulo ottimale dell'impresa zootecnica tesa alla produzione del formaggio grana parmigiano–reggiano. **Research for and definition of the optimal cattle breeding unit for the production of reggiano parmesan cheese.**

17511 Mantovani, A.
IT 040229/77/0567 R
Valutazione dei danni socio–economici da malattie degli animali domestici. **Evaluation of the socio–economic prejudice caused by farm animal diseases.**

17512 Lechi, F.
IT 040606/77/0213 R
Analisi delle componenti principali dei ricavi e dei costi nelle aziende a prevalente produzione di latte in Lombardia. **Analysis of the principal components of proceeds and costs in dairy farms in Lombardy.**

17513 Polelli, M.
IT 040621/73/0283
Determinazione dell'ordinamento produttivo di massima convenienza e applicazioni concrete della programmazione lineare negli allevamenti bovini della cascina lombarda irrigua. **Determination of the most convenient production order and concrete application of linear programming in cattle enterprises of the irrigated Lombardian Cascina.** Publications.

17514 Polidori, F.
IT 040646/77/0577
Studio per la intensificazione della produzione nazionale di carne bovina e suina attraverso il controllo della produttività e della redditività degli allevamenti. **A study for the increment of the national production of beef and pork through the supervision of output and profitability in cattle farms.**

17515 Favaretti, G.; Frison, A.; Gratton, C.
IT 040804/75/0001 R
Costi produzione agricoltura veneta. **Production costs venetian agriculture.** Publications.

17516 Ferro, O.; Boatto, V.; Marchesini, C.; Merlo, M.; Gottardo, C.; Bittante, G.
IT 040804/79/0002 N
Ricerca di un modello di programmazione di medio lungo periodo per settore zootecnico. **Research programming model medium long run for beef production.**

17517 Iacoponi, L.
IT 041105/77/0322
Rilevazione di coefficienti tecnici ed economici in allevamenti bovini da carne, condotti allo stato brado in ambienti collinari toscani, al fine di individuare modelli aziendali ottimali per la valorizzazione di terre marginali. **Recording technical and economic factors in beef cow range farming on tuscan hills to select types of management best suited to turning marginal lands to account.**

17518 Tartari, E.
IT 041216/77/0588 R
Economia dell'alimentazione nella produzione della carne bovina con speciale riferimento all'impiego di sottoprodotti aziendali ed industriali con sperimentazione presso aziende viti–vinicole ed altre. **The economics of feeding in beef production particularly in relation to the use of agricultural and industrial bye–products; experiments carried out on vine–growing and wine–making estates and others.**

17519 Montanini, C.
IT 041517/71/0001 N
L'Azienda di erogazione lattiero–casearia: sua dimensione ottimale e tendenze.. **The dury farm: its optimal dimensions and tendecies.**

17520 Saedt, A.P.H.; Elderen, E. van; Halman, Z.J.; Philipsen, P.J.J.
NL 010106/72/3934
Weidemodel en bedrijfsplanning; dagelijks weerkerende beslissingen over de werkindeling bij het graslandgebruik. **Grasslandmodel and farmplanning; short term decisions for the use of grassland.**

17521 Zachariasse, L.C.
NL 010116/50/0202 R
Technisch – economische begeleiding van de bedrijfsontwikkeling in de varkenshouderij. **Techno – economic research concerning farm development in pig–breeding and pig fattening.** Publications.

17522 Wisselink, G.J.
NL 010116/50/2940
Onderzoek moderne bedrijfssystemen in de melkveehouderij op basis van studiebedrijven. **Analysis of modern farming systems in dairy farming.** Publications.

17523 Zachariasse, L.C.
NL 010116/50/2944 R
Kostprijs en rentabiliteit van consumptie–eieren en broedeieren. **Unitcost calculations and profitability research of consumption eggs and hatching eggs.** Publications.

17524 Zachariasse, L.
NL 010116/50/2945 R
Technisch – economische ontwikkeling van de bedrijfsontwikkeling in de pluimveehouderij. **Techno – economic research concerning farm development in poultry keeping.** Publications.

17525 Zachariasse, L.
NL 010116/50/2946
Kostprijs en rentabiliteit slachtpluimvee. **Unit cost calculations and profitability research of slaughter poultry.** Publications.

17526 Zachariasse, L.
NL 010116/50/2947 R
Ontwikkeling van kosten en opbrengsten voor de varkenshouderij. **Analysis and forward calculations of the profitability of weaners and pork.** Publications.

17527 Doeksen, J.
NL 010116/62/0389 R
Rentabiliteit van de rundveemesterij als nevenbedrijf of als hoofdbedrijf. **Investigation into the profitability of cattlefattening as sideline – or main enterprise.** Publications.

17528 Giessen, L.B. van der; Reitsma, A.
NL 010116/69/2942
De rentabiliteit van grasdrogen als voederwinningsmethode. **The profitability of grassdrying as a method of harvesting and conservation of roughage.** Publications.

17529 Giessen, L.B. van der
NL 010116/71/3369 R

D 5200 – Farm management

Systemen van begroting, controle en planning voor moderne melkveehouderijbedrijven. **Systems for management, control and planning of modern dairy farms.** Publications.

17530 Hoornweg, J.; Bogaerds, N.   NL 010116/73/5952
Kostprijs en rentabiliteit van bedrijven met kalkoenen. **Unit cost calculation and profitability research for turkey producing holdings.**

17531 Giessen, L.B. van der   NL 010116/74/6540 R
Consequenties van landschapsbeheer en natuurbehoud voor de ontwikkeling van weidebedrijven. **The consequences of protecting the landscape and the environment for the development of dairy–farms.** Publications.

17532 Giessen, L.B. van der   NL 010116/74/6543 R
Perspectieven van snijmais op melkveebedrijven. **The perspectives of ensiled cut maize on dairy farms.** Publications.

17533 Doeksen, J.   NL 010116/74/6545 R
Rentabiliteit van de schapenhouderij. **The economic results of sheep–breeding.** Publications.

17534 Zachariasse, L.   NL 010116/74/6557 R
Economische aspecten van gezondheid en produktiviteit van zeugen. **Economic aspects of health and productivity of sows.**

17535 Giessen, L.B. van der; Beumer, J.   NL 010116/75/6544
De perspectieven van een vierdaagse werkweek op melkveebedrijven. **The perspectives for a four–days working–week on dairy–farms.**

17536 Giessen, L.B. van der   NL 010116/76/7695 R
Analyse van de ontwikkeling van melkveebedrijven gedurende 6 jaren. **Analysis of the development of dairy farms during 6 years.**

17537 Vervoort, M.J.; Zachariasse, L.C.   NL 010116/76/7709
Gezondheid en produktiviteit leghennen. **Health and productivity of laying hens.**

17538 Giessen, L.B. van der   NL 010116/78/8574 N
De betekenis van inkomenstoelagen en contingenteringen voor de bedrijfsvoering en de bedrijfsuitkomsten van melkveebedrijven. **The significance of income supports and quota systems for management and farm results of dairy farms.**

17539 Giessen, L.B. van der   NL 010208/50/0205 R
Samenstelling en ontwikkeling van de Nederlandse rundveestapel. **Composition and development of the national cowherd; prognosis of production and consumption of milk and meat.** Publications.

17540 Wisselink, G.J.   NL 010208/50/2940
Onderzoek moderne bedrijfssystemen in de melkveehouderij op basis van studiebedrijven. **Analysis of modern farming systems in dairy farming.** Publications.

17541 Doeksen, J.   NL 010208/62/0389 R
Rentabiliteit van de rundveemesterij als nevenbedrijf of als hoofdbedrijf. **Investigation into the profitability of cattlefattening as sideline – or main enterprise.** Publications.

17542 Giessen, L.B. van der   NL 010208/71/3369 R
Systemen van begroting, controle en planning voor moderne melkveehouderijbedrijven. **Systems for management, control and planning of modern dairy farms.** Publications.

17543 Reitsma, A.   NL 010208/72/3933
Bedrijfseconomische aspecten van het wintermelken in het Zuidelijke Zandgebied. **Farm economic aspects of winter milking in the South Sandy soil region.**

17544 Wieling, H.; Rompelberg, L.E.M.   NL 010208/72/3934
Weidemodel en bedrijfsplanning; dagelijks weerkerende beslissingen over de werkindeling bij het graslandgebruik. **Grassland model and farmplanning; short term decisions for the use of grassland.** Publications.

17545 Giessen, L.B. van der   NL 010208/74/6543 R
Perspectieven van snijmais op melkveebedrijven. **The perspectives of ensiled cut maize on dairy farms.** Publications.

17546 Doeksen, J.   NL 010208/74/6545 R
Rentabiliteit van de schapenhouderij. **The economic results of sheep–breeding.** Publications.

17547 Straten, H. van der   NL 010208/75/6171
Het met behulp van lineaire programmering nagaan van de invloed van bepaalde technische ingrepen op het bedrijfsresultaat van rundveehouderijbedrijven. **The influence of several changes in technical equipment a.s.o. on the farm income of dairy farms by using linear programming.** Publications.

17548 Straten, H. van der   NL 010208/75/6172
Mogelijkheden van rundveehouderij in gebieden met beperkende bepalingen van grondgebruik en technische voorzieningen. **Possibilities for cattle husbandry in for agriculture limited regime.** Publications.

17549 Raterink, R.   NL 010208/75/6173
Het onderzoek naar praktisch bruikbare bedrijfsinformatie en beheerssystemen voor rundveehouderijbedrijven. **Research on farm information and management systems for dairy farms.** Publications.

17550 Doornbos, J.   NL 010208/75/6175
Het rentabiliteitsvraagstuk van diverse opslag– en voersystemen voor gras en snijmaïs afzonderlijk of in combinatie. **The profitability of several storage and feeding systems.**

17551 Wieling, H.   NL 010208/75/8731 N
Berekening van de invloed van milieubeschermende maatregelen op de graslandexploitatie en voedervoorziening. **Calculation of the influence of restrictions on land use and technical equipment on grassland management and feed supply.** Publications.

17552 Kekem, A.J.T. van   NL 010208/76/6584 R
Model onderzoek naar het effekt van verschillende fokrichtingen op de rentabiliteit van het melkveebedrijf. **Model research into the effect of different breeding aims on the profitability of the dairy farm.**

17553 Straten, H. van der   NL 010208/76/6942
Bedrijfseconomische mogelijkheden van centrale jongvee–opfok. **The economic possibilities of central young stock rearing.**

17554 Straten, H. van der   NL 010208/77/8726 N

Onderzoek naar optimale bedrijfsopzetten voor de vleesproduktie. **Research into optimal farming plans for beef and mutton productions.** Publications.

17555 Kekem, A.J.T. van   NL 010208/78/8725 N
Economische gevolgend van verschillende graslandexploitaties in bedrijfsverband. **Economical consequences of different grassland management in farming systems.**

17556 Kekem, A.J.T. van   NL 010208/78/8728 N
Invloed van voersystemen op melkbedrijven op het bedrijfsresultaat. **Influence on farming results of feeding systems on dairy farms.** Publications.

17557 Giesen, G.W.J.   NL 020001/77/8389
Oorzaken van verschillen in bedrijfsuitkomsten op melkveehouderij graslandbedrijven. **Causes of differences in the economic results of dairy farms.** Publications.

17558 Giesen, G.J.W.   NL 020001/78/8820 N
De betrouwbaarheid van factor–analyseresultaten in het bedrijfsvergelijkend onderzoek. **The reliability of factor analysis results in the interfirm comparison research.**

17559 Renkema, J.A.   NL 030009/77/7751 R
Bepaling ekonomische betekenis van ziekten en ziektebestrijding bij landbouwhuisdieren. **Assessing the economic significance of animal diseases and health.** Publications.

Mixed farms (B 8213)

See also 17449, 17450

17560 Speidel, G.; Kathol, G.   DE 126450/72/0001
Die Bedeutung des Waldanteils in gemischten land– und forstwirtschaftlichen Betrieben. – Integrationsmöglichkeiten des forstlichen Betriebsteils in einem Zusammenschluss. **The importance of the farm woodland for combined forestry and agricultural enterprises.– Possibilities of integrating forestry enterprises into co–operatives.**

17561 Cordonnier, P.; Guinet, A.   FR 011808/70/8647
Modèles d'analyse d'entreprises de polyculture–élevage dans les différents pays de la communauté européenne. **Analysis models for mixed farms in EEC.**

17562 Zachariasse, L.C.   NL 010116/75/6256 R
Economische perspectieven van bedrijven met gemengd grondgebruik. **Economics of mixed farms with arable and grassland exploitation.** Publications.

17563 Zachariasse, L.C.   NL 010207/75/6256 R
Economische perspectieven van bedrijven met gemengd grond–gebruik. **Economics of mixed farms with arable and grassland exploitation.** Publications.

Horticultural holdings (B 8214)

See also 1500, 4063, 4235, 17217, 17230, 17231, 17244, 17245, 17293, 17301, 17459, 17830

17564 Richter, L.   DE 105400/70/0003
Ökonomie des Gemüsebaues. **Economic aspects of vegetable farming.**

17565 Stoffert, G.; Rohlfing, H.–R.   DE 138360/71/0001
Schaffung von Kalkulationsunterlagen für Betriebswirtschaft im Erwerbsgartenbau. **Ascertainment of calculation data on management in horticulture.**

17566 Storck, H.; Fey–Kimmig, R.   DE 138360/77/0001
Entwicklung eines Modells zur kurzfristigen Vorschätzung der Ertragslage von Gartenbaubetrieben. **Development of a model for short–term pre–estimate of crop yields in horticultural enterprises.**

17567 Storck, H.; Berndt, M.   DE 138360/78/0001 N
Entwicklung und Erprobung eines Leitfadens für langfristige Betriebsentwicklungsplanung von Gartenbaubetrieben. **Development and test of a manual for long–range planning in horticultural firms.**

17568 Storck, H.; Hinken, J.   DE 138361/74/0001
Zielsetzungs– und Entscheidungsverhalten gartenbaulicher Unternehmer und deren Einfluss auf die Betriebsergebnisse. **Goal setting and decision behaviour of horticultural entrepreneurs and their influence on the management results.**

17569 Jochimsen, H.   DE 138361/77/0001
Untersuchung über wirtschaftliche Entwicklung und Planrealisation von im einzelbetrieblichen Förderungsprogramm geförderten niedersächsischen Gartenbaubetrieben. **Investigation on economic development and plan–realization of Lower Saxonian horticultural farms under the farm investment aid program.**

17570 Schnekenburger, F.   DE 501103/77/0001
Untersuchungen über den Bewirtschaftungsaufwand in Rebflächen am Steilhang unter besonderer Berücksichtigung von Gross– und Kleinterrassen und Seilzuglagen. **Research on the input of steep vineyards in big and small terraces and in parcels working with motor winch.**

17571 Kalinke, H.; Stumm, G.   DE 506114/77/0002
Einfluss der Vermarktungsformen – Freier Fassweinverkauf, Verkauf im Rahmen von Erzeugergemeinschaften und Winzergenossenschaftsanschluss – auf die Einkommenssituation der Weinbaubetriebe in den landwirtschaftlichen Entwicklungsgebieten in Rheinland–Pfalz. **Influence of marketing systems – free sale of wine by the barrel, sale by community organizations for cropping and wine growers' co–operatives – on the income situation of viticultural enterprises in agricultural developing areas in Rheinland–Pfalz.**

17572 Kalinke, H.; Sommer, W.   DE 506114/77/0004
Vergleichende Untersuchung buchführender und nicht buchführender Weinbaubetriebe unter besonderer Berücksichtigung der Vermarktungsformen und des Umlaufvermögens. **Comparative examination of accounting and non–accounting viticultural enterprises in special consideration of marketing systems and working capital.**

17573 Kalinke, H.; Bergweiler, P.H.   DE 506114/77/0005
Strukturanalyse der Weinkellereien in Rheinland–Pfalz. **Structural analysis of wine cellarages in Rheinland–Pfalz.**

17574 Kalinke, H.   DE 506114/77/0006
Analyse der Arbeitswirtschaft und der Bewirtschaftungskosten bei Querterrassierung am Hang im Vergleich zum Steillagenweinbau in Fallinie. **Analysis of labour input and**

D 5200 – Farm management

management costs in cross terracing on slope in comparison with steep–slope viticulture in line of slope.

17575 Kalinke, H.; Stumm, G.　　　DE 506114/78/0001 N
Analyse der Einkommen flaschenweinvermarktender Weinbaubetriebe in Rheinland/Pfalz. **Analysis of the incomes of bottled–wine marketing viniculturists in Rheinland–Pfalz.**

17576 Zörcher, H.　　　DE 509155/77/0002
Untersuchungen über die Einsatzmöglichkeiten der elektronischen Datenverarbeitung zur weitergehenden Betriebsabrechnung in Betrieben mit Weinbau. **Use of electronic data processing for continuing accounting in viticultural farms.**

17577 Andersen, F.; Nielsen, A.H.　　　DK 030149/79/0001 N
Økonomiske optimeringsprocedurer for frugtavls– og gartnerivirksomheder. **Economic optimization procedures in horticultural firms.**

17578 Lauret, F.; Montigaud, J.C.　　　FR 011205/60/8528
Fruits et légumes frais et transformés : problèmes économiques. **Fruit and vegetables economics.**

17579 Laurent, F.; Montigaud, J.C.; Delord, B.
　　　FR 011205/68/3358
Economie des fruits et légumes : production, transformation, distribution, consommation. **Fruits and vegetables economics : production, processing, marketing, consumption.**

17580 Boulet, D.; Laporte, J.P.　　　FR 011205/77/8610
Processus de soumission de l'agriculture au mode de production dominant. Le cas de la sphère d'activité des vins de table. **Submission process of agriculture to the dominant mode of production : the case of wine–table industry.**

17581 Jullian, P.　　　FR 011808/78/8533
L'économie de la production dans les exploitations maraichères. **Farm management and production analysis in horticulture.**

17582 Arnaud, C.; Berger, A.　　　FR 012212/75/8546
Evolution à long terme du secteur des vins fins. **Evolution of sector of quality wines.**

17583 Leusie, M.　　　FR 012400/77/8532
L'économie légumière dans les pays de la Loire. **Vegetables economics for the pays de la Loire.**

17584 Mariggio, A.　　　IT 040102/78/1074 N
Aspetti economici dell'impresa viticola in Puglia. **The economic aspects of wine producing concerns in Puglia.**

17585 Milano, G.　　　IT 040108/73/0262
Economia della vite in Puglia mediante l'analisi contabile aziendale. **The wine economy in Apulia through the analysis of enterprise accounts.** Publications.

17586 Velicogna, E.　　　IT 040204/77/0718 R
Meccanizzazione della raccolta della barbabietola da zucchero, costo e competitività produzioni. **Mechanization of sugar beet harvesting, cost and competitive value of production.**

17587 Bellucci, V.　　　IT 040508/74/0512
Economia dei boschi di castagno in Italia. **The economy of chestnut woods in Italy.**

17588 Galigani, P.F.　　　IT 040512/74/0554
Influenza della forma e dimensione dell'unità di coltura sulla produttività di alcuni cantieri di lavoro foraggicoltura e viticoltura. **Influence of shape and size of unit area on the productivity of some forage and grapevine producing stations.**

17589 Ferro, O.　　　IT 040806/74/0552
Analisi dei costi e ricavi in aziende agricole vitali del Veneto e del Friuli Venezia Giulia. **Analysis of costs and returns in viable farm enterprises of Veneto and Friuli Venezia Giulia.**

17590 Rossi, A.C.　　　IT 041007/77/0711 R
Meccanizzazione della raccolta delle olive, costi di produzione e competitività coltura. **Mechanization of olive harvesting, cost and competitive value of production.**

17591 Rossi, A.C.　　　IT 041007/77/0712 R
Meccanizzazione della raccolta del tabacco, costi e competitività produzioni. **Mechanization of tobacco harvesting, cost and competitive value of production.**

17592 Alvisi, F.　　　IT 061000/77/0722
Costi e competitività colturale per pomodoro, fagiolino e pisello. **Costs and cultural competitive qualities of tomatoes french beans and peas.**

17593 Huijs, J.P.G.　　　NL 010106/63/6461
Economische aspecten van een doelmatig energie gebruik bij klimatisering van kassen. **Economic aspects of energy use of climatization in glasshouses.** Publications.

17594 Huijs, J.P.G.　　　NL 010106/75/6460
Economische orientatie en evaluatie van nieuwe ontwikkelingen op tuinbouwtechnisch gebied. **Economic information and evaluation of recent developments in horticultural engineering.** Publications.

17595 Achten, J.M.F.H.　　　NL 010106/76/6705
De ontwikkeling en de beproeving van een planning en informatie systeem in de tuinbouw. **The development and testing of a planning and information system in horticulture.** Publications.

17596 Krijgsman, H.K.　　　NL 010106/77/7584
Onderzoek van management– en arbeidssystemen op potplantenbedrijven. **Management and work system research on pot–plant nurseries.** Publications.

17597 Noort, L. van　　　NL 010116/50/0402
Jaarlijks onderzoek naar de bedrijfsuitkomsten van tuinbouwbedrijven in verschillende produktiegebieden. **Annual research into the financial results of horticultural holdings in various production centres.** Publications.

17598 Haan, W.G. de　　　NL 010116/69/2703 R
Onderzoek tulpen–opbrengsten via factoranalyse. **Research into the yields of tulip–bulbs by means of factor–analysis.**

17599 Haan, W.G. de　　　NL 010116/69/2706
Programmering bedrijfstypen bloembollenteelt. **Linear programming for bulb–growing farms.** Publications.

17600 Spoor, P.A.　　　NL 010116/71/3684 R
Economische aspecten van de teelt van stookkomkommers. **Economic aspects of cucumber growing.**

17601 Spoor, P.A.; Goedegebure, J.; Vornooy, J.C.M.
NL 010116/72/3930
Bedrijfsvergelijkend onderzoek ter verklaring van de verschillen in bedrijfsresultaten van fruitteeltbedrijven. **Farm comparative research into the differences of financial farmingresults of fruitholdings.**

17602 Haan, W.G. de
NL 010116/74/5939 R
Bedrijfseconomische aspecten van de teelt van leliebollen en het trekken van leliebloemen. **Farm economic aspects of the cultivation of lilie bulbs and the forcing of lilie flowers.** Publications.

17603 Spoor, P.A.
NL 010116/74/6553 R
Economische positie van de augurkenteelt onder glas. **Economic aspects of gherkin growing under glass.**

17604 Haan, W.G. de
NL 010116/74/6891 R
Bedrijfseconomische aspecten van nieuwe teeltmethoden van freesia. **Farm economic aspects of new cultural methods with freesia.** Publications.

17605 Haan, W.G. de
NL 010116/75/6893 R
Bedrijfsvergelijkend onderzoek naar de oorzaken van verschillen in fysieke en geldelijke opbrengsten bij kasrozen. **Analysis of differences in physical yields and financial returns in growing glasshouses–roses.** Publications.

17606 Haan, W.G. de
NL 010116/75/6894 R
Analyse van de oorzaken van verschillen in bedrijfsuitkomsten van bloembollenbedrijven. **Investigation in difference in profitability of bulbgrowingholdings.**

17607 Spoor, P.A.
NL 010116/75/6896 R
Analyse van de verschillen in opbrengstniveau en bedrijfsresultaat van fruitbedrijven in verschillende produktiecentra. **Analysis of difference between yield capacity and farm result of fruitholding at different locations.**

17608 Spoor, P.A.
NL 010116/75/6899 R
Relatie van de plantdichtheid, kg–opbrengst en vruchtgrootte van Golden Delicious. **Analysis of relations between planting density, physical yields and fruitsize of Golden Delicious apple.** Publications.

17609 Verhaegh, A.P.; Spoor, P.A.
NL 010116/76/7703
Bedrijfseconomische aspecten van grote glasbedrijven. **Economic aspects of big glasshouse holdings.**

17610 Boers, A.
NL 010116/76/7705
Financiële positie nieuw gevestigde glastuinders. **The development of the financial position of young producers on holdings in glasshouse production.**

17611 Spoor, P.A.
NL 010116/77/7734 R
Economische evaluatie van de mogelijkheden tot een rationelere toepassing van energie voor verwarmingsdoeleinden in de glastuinbouw. **Economic evaluation of the possibilities for more efficient use of energy, used for heating in the glasshouse industry.**

17612 Spoor, P.A.
NL 010116/77/7735
Raming van de bedrijfsuitkomsten van de tuinbouw. **Estimation of financial results in horticulture.** Publications.

17613 Haan, W.G. de
NL 010116/78/8577 N
Economische aspecten van het gebruik van roltafels in de potplantenteelt. **Economic aspects of using rolling tables in producing potplants.**

17614 Koppert, G.
NL 010116/78/8578 N
Betekenis van inflatieneutrale winstberekening voor de tuinbouw. **The consequence of an inflation neutral profit calculation for horticultural holdings.**

17615 Spoor, P.A.
NL 010116/78/8583 N
Bedrijfseconomische aspecten van het opkweken van vruchtbomen. **Business–economic aspects of fruit tree nursing on fruit holdings.**

17616 Spoor, P.A.
NL 010116/78/8584 N
Economisch structurele aspecten van de opengrondsgroenteteelt. **Economic and structural aspects of outdoor vegetable growing.**

17617 Spoor, P.A.
NL 010116/78/8585 N
Enkele bedrijfseconomische aspecten van de watervoorziening in de fruitteelt. **Some micro–economic aspects of watering in fruit growing.**

17618 Boers, A.
NL 010116/78/8587 N
Expansie en de ontwikkeling van de financiële positie van glastuinbouwbedrijven. **Expansion of glasshouse holdings in horticulture in relation to development of financial position.**

17619 Haan, W.G. de
NL 010116/78/8902 N
Optimale teeltcombinatie bij potplanten. **Optimising cropping schemes in potplant production.**

17620 Spoor, P.A.
NL 010116/79/8905 N
Bedrijfs economische– en marktkundige aspekten van een biologisch–dynamisch opengrondsgroenteteeltbedrijf te Drempt. **Farm– economical and market aspects on a farm with biological–dynamical outdoor vegetable growing.**

17621 Spoor, P.A.
NL 010116/79/8908 N
Bedrijfseconomische aspecten van het voorsorteren van fruit. **Business–economic aspects of pre–grading of fruit.**

17622 Rijssel, E. van
NL 010201/75/6893
Bedrijfsvergelijkend onderzoek naar de oorzaken van verschillen in fysieke en geldelijke opbrengsten bij kasrozen. **Analysis of differences in physical yields and financial returns in growing glasshouses–roses.**

17623 Goorts, A.C.J.
NL 010201/77/7584
Onderzoek van management– en arbeidssystemen op potplantenbedrijven. **Management and work system research on pot–plant nurseries.** Publications.

17624 Vroomen, C.O.N. de
NL 010205/69/2703
Onderzoek tulpe–opbrengsten via factoranalyse. **Research into the yields of tulip–bulbs by means of factor–analysis.**

17625 Vroomen, C.O.N. de
NL 010205/74/5939
Bedrijfseconomische aspecten van de teelt van leliebollen en het trekken van leliebloemen. **Farm economic aspects of the cultivation of lily bulbs and the forcing of lily flowers.** Publications.

17626 Visser, A.J. de
NL 010206/72/4677 N

Bedrijfseconomische analyse van nieuwe ontwikkelingen in onderzoek en praktijk bij de teelt van kasgewassen. **Economic analysis of new developments in research and industry in glasshouse growing.**

17627 Visser, A.J. de   NL 010206/74/6553 R
Economische positie van de augurkenteelt onder glas. **Economic aspects of gherkin growing under glass.**

17628 Visser, A.J. de   NL 010206/74/6891
Bedrijfseconomische aspecten van nieuwe teeltmethoden van freesia. **Farm economic aspects of new cultural methods with freesia.** Publications.

17629 Hendrix, A.T.M.   NL 010206/76/6705
De ontwikkeling en beproeving van een planning– en informatiesysteem in de tuinbouw. **The development and testing of a planning and information system in horticulture.**

17630 Cevaal, P.K.   NL 010207/79/9043 N
Het opstellen van standaardmatrices t.b.v. de bedrijfseconomische advisering voor kleinere bedrijven met overwegend groenteteelt. **The development of master matrices for the farm management advising of smaller farms with considerable field production of vegetables.**

17631 Goedegebure, J.   NL 010212/75/6896
Analyse van de verschillen in opbrengstniveau en bedrijfsresultaat van fruitbedrijven in verschillende produktiecentra. **Analysis of difference between yield capacity and farm result of fruitholding at different locations.**

17632 Spoor, P.A.   NL 010212/78/8583 N
Bedrijfseconomische aspecten van het opkweken van vruchtbomen. **Business–economic aspects of fruit tree nursing on fruit holdings.**

17633 Spoor, P.A.   NL 010212/78/8585 N
Enkele bedrijfseconomische aspecten van de watervoorziening in de fruitteelt. **Some micro–economic aspects of watering in fruit growing.**

17634 Spoor, P.A.   NL 010212/79/8907 N
Bedrijfseconomische aspecten van kwaliteitsverschillen in plantmateriaal van appelen. **Business–economic aspects of differences in quality of maiden apple trees.**

17635 Spoor, P.A.   NL 010212/79/8908 N
Bedrijfseconomische aspecten van het voorsorteren van fruit. **Business–economic aspects of pre–grading of fruit.**

Forest enterprises (B 8215)

See also 2439, 2608, 8865, 15789, 17261, 17262, 17268, 17270, 17272, 17273, 17275

17636 Brabänder, H.D.; Kato, F.   DE 132840/75/0002
Der Beitrag des Waldes zum Betriebseinkommen in aus Land– und Forstwirtschaft gemischten Betrieben aufgrund der Verhältnisse in Westfalen–Lippe. **The contribution of the forest to the income of mixed managements of agriculture and forestry – represented by the situation in Westphalia–Lippe.**

17637 Brabänder, H.D.; Keuffel, W.; Brass, E.
DE 132840/75/0003
Analyse der Ertrags– und Aufwandsstruktur in staatlichen und privaten Forstbetrieben. **Analysis of the structure of yield and expenditure in State and private forest managements.** Publications.

17638 Speidel, G.; Keuffel, W.   DE 132840/75/0004
Analyse der Aufwand–Ertragsstrukturen von Betriebszieltypen und Intensitätsprobleme im Forstbetrieb. **Analysis of the structures of expenditure and yield of management target types; problems of intensity in forest managements.**

17639 Brabänder, H.D.; Keuffel, W.   DE 132840/75/0005
Untersuchung über betriebliche Möglichkeiten zur Senkung der Lohnnebenkosten bei den Betriebsarbeiten. **Study on the possibility of forest managements of lowering the labour ancosts.**

17640 Kato, F.   DE 132840/75/0007
Fortentwicklung der forstlichen Investitions– und der Waldwertrechnung. **Further development of forest investment account and of forest valuation.** Publications.

17641 Brabänder, H.D.   DE 132840/77/0002
Betriebsvergleich und Betriebsanalyse zur Verbesserung der Ertragslage im Privatwald. **Cost analysis as an instrument for the economical improvement in private forests.**

17642 Brabänder, H.D.; Koester, U.   DE 132840/78/0001 N
Nutzen–Kosten–Analyse der forstwirtschaftlichen Zusammenschlüsse. **Cost–benefit analysis on forestry cooperatives.**

17643 Franz, F.; Seltzer, E.   DE 160210/77/0006 N
Entwicklung eines fortentwickelten Verfahrens für die Forsteinrichtung–Inventur auf der Basis von Stichproben. **The development of an advanced method for forest management inventory based on sampling methods.**

17644 Kroth, W.; Bartelheimer, P.   DE 160302/77/0002
Entwicklung eines computergestützten Planungsmodells für die Forstwirtschaft. **Construction of a computer–assisted planning model for forestry.**

17645 Kroth, W.; Sinner, H.–U.   DE 160302/77/0003
Betriebswirtschaftliche Auswertung von Schälschäden durch Rotwild im Bayerischen Forstamt Kempten. **Economic assessment of bark damage by red deer in the Bavarian forest district of Kempten.**

17646 Kroth, W.; Sinner, H.–U.; Gleissner, G.
DE 160302/77/0004
Erhebungen zur Organisation der Forstverwaltung an verschiedenen bayerischen Forstämtern. **Inquiry of the organization structure in several Bavarian forest districts.**

17647 Kroth, W.; Hoyer, R.; Röhle, H.
DE 160302/78/0001 N
Die Belastung der Forstbetriebe aus der Schutz– und Erholungsfunktion des Waldes, ihre Erfassung, Bewertung und rechtliche Beurteilung. **The registration, valuation, and legal judgement of the burden of forest enterprises originating from the forests protective and recreational functions.**

17648 Kroth, W.   DE 160302/78/0002 N
Verbesserung der methodischen Grundlagen des BML–Testbetriebsnetzes Forstwirtschaft. **Improvement of the**

metholodical bases for the test–network of forest enterprises – BML –.

17649 Löffler, H.; Guglhör, W.   DE 160310/75/0004
Möglichkeiten und Grenzen der Simulation als Methode zur Analyse, Leistungsvorhersage und zum Verfahrensvergleich in der Schwachholzernte. **Simulation as a tool to analyse and forecast the performance and to compare different methods in thinning operations.**

17650 Löffler, H.; Thieme, F.; Kaierle   DE 160310/77/0002
Untersuchungen über Leistung und Kosten von mobilen Seilbringungssystemen. **Productivity and costs of yarding with cable systems.**

17651 Löffler, H.; Thieme, F.   DE 160310/78/0001 N
Untersuchungen über Planung von Erschliessungsmassnahmen im Kleinprivatwald und deren Bewertung mit systemanalytischen Methoden. **Investigations on accessibility planning in small–forest ownerships and evaluation by methods of systems–analysis.**

17652 Löffler, H.; Proebst, D.   DE 160310/78/0002 N
Geländeklassifikation, Vorratsinventur und Erschliessungsplanung in einem Privatwaldkomplex des bayerischen Hochgebirges. **Terrain classification, inventory of stands and accessibility planning in a private ownership in a mountainous region of Upper Bavaria.**

17653 Eisenhauer, G.   DE 202030/77/0001
Rationelle Nutzung des Naturwaldes. **Economical utilization of natural forests.**

17654 Volk, H.; Spahl, H.   DE 501504/78/0005 N
Erarbeitung von Bewirtschaftungsgrundsätzen für den Erholungswald, Stufen I und II der Waldfunktionenkartierung. **Development of management principles for the recreational forest, stages I and II of the forest functions mapping.**

17655 Dietz, P.; Dummel, K.; Pfeil, C.   DE 501505/77/0001
Erweiterter Sortentarif Prämienlohn. **Extended assortment piece rate. Premium wage.**

17656 Dietz, P.   DE 501505/77/0009
Forsttechnische Geländeklassifikation, Entwicklung eines praktikablen Verfahrens im Anhalt an die Vielzahl bereits vorliegender Vorschläge. **Terrain–classification, development of a practicable system according to already existing proposals.**

17657 Dietz, P.   DE 501505/77/0010
Optimale Walderschliessung – Versuch, konkrete Aussagen zum Problem der optimalen Erschliessung zu erarbeiten. **Optimizing forest road networks – Trying to find general rules for practical use.**

17658 Dietz, P.; Meng, W.; Stoll, H.F.   .DE 501505/78/0002 N
Aufnahme und Auswertung von Rückeschäden in Probeflächen zur Bestimmung des Ausmasses und der Auswirkung der Schäden in Abhängigkeit von Sortenlängen, Rückeverfahren und Zeitpunkt des Rückens. **Survey and evaluation of hauling damages in sampling areas for determination of extent and effects of damages depending on varietal lengths, hauling procedure and time of hauling.**

17659 Siebenbürger   DE 501506/77/0002 R

Untersuchungen über die Wirtschaftsführung im Kleinprivatwald – unter 10 ha –. **Investigations on growth promotion in spruce plantations using herbicides and fertilizers.**

17660 Hodapp, W.   DE 501506/77/0003
Untersuchung über die Entwicklung der Einheitswerte im Staatsforstbetrieb Baden–Württembergs sowie der Hebesätze der Gemeinden für die Grundsteuer A. **Studies on development of unit values in state forestry enterprise of Baden–Württemberg and of communal collection rates for land tax A.**

17661 Hodapp, W.; Graf   DE 501506/78/0002 N
Erstellung einer Indexreihe für Einkaufspreise forstwirtschaftlich genutzter Wirtschaftsgüter. **Setup of index series for cost prices of economic goods utilized in forestry.**

17662 Schöpfer, W.; Niemann, U.   DE 501507/75/0003
Optimierung der Schnittholzausbeute. **Optimizing the yield of sawn timber.**

17663 Schöpfer, W.; Hradetzky, J.; Niemann, U.; Nieuwoudt, F.   DE 501507/77/0001
Erweiterter Sortentarif und Zuschlagssystem. **Extended assortment piece rate and extras.**

17664 Schöpfer, W.   DE 501507/78/0001 N
Vorarbeiten für den Entwurf neuer Hilfstabellen für die Forsteinrichtung. **Preliminary work for the outline of new auxiliary tables for forest management.**

17665 Henne, A.   DE 506401/77/0002 N
Alternativenbewertung in der forstlichen Planung. **Evaluation of alternatives in forest planning. Publications.**

17666 Henne, A.; Heuser, V.   DE 506404/77/0007
Landschaftspflege in der mittelfristigen forstlichen Betriebsplanung – Forsteinrichtung –. **Landscape management in forest management planning.**

17667 Buttoud, G.   FR 010308/73/3322
Economie de la fertilisation du pin maritime adulte dans les Landes de Gascogne. **Economics of fertilization of mature "Pinus pinaster" in the Landes of Gascogne.**

17668 Guillon, P.   FR 010308/74/3321
Economie de la première éclaircie des peuplements résineux artificiels. **Economics of first thinning in artificial conifer stands.**

17669 Normandin, D.   FR 010308/75/3329
Economie des transports forestiers. **Economics of wood transport in forest areas.**

17670 Bonin, M.   FR 010308/75/3330
Etude méthodologique de la rentabilité des reboisements. **Study of the profitability of plantations.**

17671 Elyakime, B.   FR 010308/75/8540
Les exploitations forestières : entreprises de plus de 4000 m3(r) en 1975 en France. **French logging enterprises of more than 4000 m3 (r) in 1975.**

17672 Brun, A.; Poupardin, D.   FR 012303/77/8541
Propriété foncière et gestion de l'espace en Sologne. **Forest

D 5200 – Farm management

and estate management in Sologne.

17673 Gajo, P. IT 040508/78/1055 N
Indagine economica sulla realtà e sulle prospettive dei
castagneti italiani. **An economic study of the present condition
of and the outlooks for italian chestnut woods.**

17674 Marinelli, A. IT 040508/78/1075 N
L'economia del bosco ceduo, realtà e prospettive. **The
economics of coppices, the present situation and future
outlooks.**

17675 Hippoliti, G. IT 040527/77/0205
Ricerca tecnico economica su sistemi e mezzi di lavoro per i
primi diradamenti in boschi di montagna. **Technical and
economic research on systems and equipment in the initial
thinning out of mountain woods.**

17676 Veldhuyzen, C.J. NL 010116/67/1294 R
Onderzoek bedrijfsuitkomsten bosbouw. **Investigation into the
financial returns from forestry.** Publications.

17677 Boven, B. van NL 010116/72/8911 N
Begroting van houtopstanden en kosten/batenanalyse.
Calculation for different tree–stands and cost/benefit analyses.

17678 Boven, B. van NL 010116/72/8912 N
Financiële resultaten van populierenbeplantingen. **Financial
results of poplar growing.**

17679 Boven, B. van NL 010116/76/8916 N
Literatuur onderzoek bedrijfsverslaggeving in de bosbouw in
de verschillende West–Europese landen. **Investigation on
accounting results in Western European countries.**

17680 Boven, B. van NL 010116/77/8913 N
Het analyseren van de financiële resultaten van bosbedrijven.
Analysis of financial results on foresty–estates.

17681 Veldhuyzen, C.J. NL 010116/78/7880
Onderzoek van de bosbouwkundige planning en het
beoordelen van het beheer van bosbedrijven.
Forestry–planning and judging forestry–farm management.

17682 Holterman, H.J.W. NL 010116/78/8914 N
Vooronderzoek met betrekking tot de economische aspekten
van het kweken en de aanwending van bosplantsoen.
**Pre–research on the economic aspects of the growing and the
use of planting material.**

17683 Veldhuyzen, C.J. NL 010601/67/1294 R
Onderzoek bedrijfsuitkomsten bosbouw. **Investigation into the
financial results of forestry.** Publications.

17684 Goor, C.P. van NL 010601/78/7880
Onderzoek van de bosbouwkundige planning en het
beoordelen van het beheer van bosbedrijven.
Forestry–planning and judging forestry–farm management.

17685 Slangen, L.H.G. NL 020004/76/7558
Economische aspecten van de bosbouw. **Economic aspects of
forestry.** Publications.

17686 Boxsem, W. NL 040007/75/8488
Onderzoek naar het ontsluitingspatroon van bossen in de
IJsselmeerpolders. **Research on forest communication networks**

in the IJsselmeerpolders.

17687 Boxsem, W. NL 040007/76/8491
Onderzoek naar de mogelijkheden tot verlaging van de
inboetkosten van beplantingen in de IJsselmeerpolders.
**Research on the possibilities for decreasing the replanting costs
of plantations in the IJsselmeerpolders.**

17688 Boxsem, W. NL 040007/76/8504
Onderzoek naar de optimale bedrijfsomloop voor populier.
Research on the optimal circulation time for poplar.
Publications.

Fisheries (B 8216)

See also 11412, 17280

17689 L'Hostis, D. FR 012400/77/8587
Conditions du maintien et du développement de la pêche
maritime en Bretagne Sud. **How to keep and develop fisheries
industry in south Britain.**

17690 Smit, W. NL 010116/62/0128 N
Bedrijfsresultaten van de voornaamste takken van de
Nederlandse visserij. ("Visserij in cijfers"). **Costs and earnings
of the main branches of the Dutch fishing industry.**
Publications.

17691 Rijneveld, R. NL 010116/67/1292
Onderzoek naar de financiële positie van de kleine zeevisserij.
The financial position of the Dutch fishing industry.
Publications.

17692 Smit, W. NL 010116/69/2855 R
Jaarlijks onderzoek naar de bedrijfsresultaten van de kleine
zeevisserij en de garnalenvisserij. **Annual research into costs
and earnings of the Dutch near fisheries and shrimp fisheries.**
Publications.

17693 Smit, W. NL 010116/69/5943 R
Jaarlijks onderzoek naar de bedrijfsresultaten in de grote
zeevisserij. **Annual research into costs and earnings of the
Dutch middle water fisheries.** Publications.

17694 Rijneveld, R. NL 010116/70/3362 R
Structuuronderzoek zeevisserij. **Structural econometrics
research of the seafisheries.** Publications.

17695 Rijneveld, R. NL 010116/73/5944 R
Technisch–economisch onderzoek in de zeevisserij.
Techno–economic research in the sea–fisheries.

17696 Smit, W. NL 010116/73/5945 R
Bedrijfsuitkomstenstatistiek Zeeuwse Mossel bedrijven. **Costs
and earning statistics of the Zeeland musselculture.**
Publications.

17697 Rijneveld, R. NL 010116/74/6554 R
Struktuuronderzoek garnalenvisserij. **Structural research of
the shrimp fisheries.** Publications.

17698 Rijneveld, R. NL 010116/78/8909 N
Structuuronderzoek grote zeevisserij. **Research into the
structure of the middle water fisheries.**

Service and supply firms (B 8220)

See also 15284, 17347, 17423

17699 Weinschenck, G.; Ambros, J.　DE 144750/73/0001
Optimaler Maschinenbestand und optimale
Maschinenverteilung bei überbetrieblicher
Maschinenverwendung. **The optimum stock and allocation of
farm machinery in machinery co–operatives.**

17700 Hanf, C.H.; Röhner, M.; Uhlemann, P.
　　　　　　　　　　　　DE 148405/78/0001 N
System der Datenerfassung und –verarbeitung in
Maschinenringen. **Developing of a data collection and
processing system for machinery cooperatives.**

17701 Rothenburger, W.; Götz, W.　DE 161460/73/0001
Kostenrechnung in Landschaftsarchitekturbüros. **Cost
accounting in landscape architect bureaus.**

17702 Kalinke, H.; Stumm, G.　DE 506114/77/0003
Der Selektionsaufwand in der Klonenzüchtung. **Selection input
in clone breeding.**

17703 Oving, R.K.　　　　　　NL 010106/77/7583
De toepassing van rekenhulpmiddelen bij het bedrijfsbeleid op
agrarische loonbedrijven. **Application of calculation
programmes in the management of contract workers in
agriculture.**

17704 Lely, J. v.d.　　　　　NL 010116/76/8581 N
Onderzoek naar de factoren die bepalend zijn voor een
doelmatige en economisch gezonde exploitatie van het
loonwerkbedrijf. **An inquiry into the costs and returns of
contractors.**

17705 Visser, G.R.　　　　　NL 020023/71/8515
Inrichting en funktioneren van de besturing in non–profit
organisaties. **Management of non–profit organizations.**

17706 Vrij, J.M.　　　　　　NL 020023/77/8519
De besturing van landbouwcoöperaties. **Management of
agricultural cooperatives in the Netherlands.**

Marketing and processing firms (B 8230)

See also 17149, 17294, 17295, 17394, 17503, 17505, 17506,
17580, 17582, 17706

17707 Richter, L.; Kesselschläger, J.　DE 105410/78/0002 N
Die Rentabilität der deutschen Brauereien in Abhängigkeit
von ihren Investitionen. **The profitability of German breweries
relative to their investments.**

17708 Researcher not indicated　　DE 126000/77/0002 R
Vergleichende Untersuchungen über forstliche
Kooperationsformen in Schweden und Deutschland
1977–1978. **Comparative investigations on forms of cooperation
in forestry in Sweden and Germany.**

17709 Lauenstein, H.; Hoppe, R.　DE 132360/75/0002
Schätzung von Produktionskoeffizienten eines
MehrproduktUnternehmens unter besonderer
Berücksichtigung von Parameteränderungen im Zeitablauf.
**Estimation of the production function of a multi–product firm
with emphasis on time varying parameters.**

17710 Jochimsen, H.　　　　　DE 138361/77/0002
Betriebsvergleich in der Gemüse– und
Obstkonservenindustrie. **Inter–firm–comparison in the
canned–vegetable and fruit industry.**

17711 Weinschenck, G.; Uhlemann, P.; Aldinger, F.
　　　　　　　　　　　　DE 144750/77/0003
Untersuchungen zur Kostenstruktur und Kostenfunktion von
Schlachthöfen. **Studies on cost–structure and cost–functions of
slaughter–houses.**

17712 Schad, F.; Krebs, G.　　DE 144900/73/0001
Rechtsnatur und Haftung für Genossenschaften und andere
agrarwirtschaftliche Zusammenschlüsse im
Gründungsstadium. **Legal character and liability of farmers'
co–operatives during the founding phase.**

17713 Krüger, R.; Schmitt, A.　DE 161480/77/0001
EDV–Kosten in Brauereien. **Costs of EDP in German
breweries.**

17714 Krüger, R.; Wochner, J.　DE 161480/78/0001 N
Die Profit Center–Konzeption als Führungsinstrument in
Brauereien. **Brewery management by profit centers.**

17715 Behme, G.; Panholzer, J.　DE 207070/72/5005
Molkerei–Unternehmensvergleich. **Interplant comparisons of
dairies.**

17716 Drews, M.; Müller, B.; Besse, H.　DE 207070/78/0003 N
Kurzfristige Produktionsprogrammplanung in Molkereien mit
Hilfe der linearen Programmierung. **Determination of the
short–term optimum production program of a dairy plant by
means of linear programming.**

17717 Drews, M.　　　　　　DE 207070/78/0004 N
Markt oder Intervention – eine Entscheidungsfrage aus
molkereibetriebwirtschaftlicher Sicht. **Dairy production for
market public intervention – a decision problem in view of dairy
management.**

17718 Drews, M.　　　　　　DE 207070/78/0005 N
Kooperation zwischen Molkereien als Alternative zur Fusion
unter besonderer Berücksichtigung des Problems der
Verrechnungspreisbildung. **Cooperation between
dairy–enterprises as an alternative of fusion with special regard
to the problems of internal pricefixing.**

17719 Schnekenburger, F.　　DE 501103/74/0002
Untersuchungen über die Wirtschaftlichkeit von Investitionen
in der Weinwirtschaft. **Investigations on the profitability of
investments in viticulture.**

17720 Haisch, K.–H.; Stöckl, J.　DE 502552/73/0001
Zur Bestimmung optimaler Erfassungs–, Produktions– und
Vertriebskosten in Molkereien. **Determination of optimal costs
for milk–shipping, –production and distribution in dairy plants.**

17721 Broussolle, C.; Fouet, J.P.　FR 011302/77/8670
Localisation et choix des investissements dans l'industrie
laitière. **Choice of localization and type of investments in milk
industry.**

17722 Mazenc, L.　　　　　　FR 011408/77/8559

Minimisation des coûts de transport dans les industries agroalimentaires. **Transport cost minimization in Agri–food industries.**

17723 Mergui, G.; Nefussi, M.   FR 012205/78/8666
Echantillon permanent des entreprises des industries alimentaires. **Constant sample of food industry firms.**

17724 Evrard, P.   FR 012212/78/8544
Les industries de la phytotechnie. **Phytotechnics industries.**

17725 Zitt, M.   FR 012400/76/8558
Recherche et energie dans les i.a.a.: industrie du lait –industrie de la conserve. **Research and energy in food industries : study for milk and preserved food industries.**

17726 Zitt, M.; Saudan, M.   FR 012400/77/8561
Genèse des grandes innovations dans les industries agro–alimentaires de 1945 à 1977. **Study of the main innovations in food industry from 1945 to 1977.**

17727 O'Connor, J.C.   IE 070400/79/9227 N
Survey of heat preserved food industries in Ireland.

Recreational enterprises (B 8240)

17728 Leek, N.A.   NL 010601/77/8674 N
Onderzoek naar de aanleg– en onderhoudskosten van recreatieve beplantingen. **Costs of establishment and treatment of recreation forests.**

Other business enterprises (B 8290)

See also 17402, 17403

17729 Kirsch, O.C.   DE 916000/78/0002 N
Förderung der Zentralgenossenschaft Nebhana/Tunesien. **Promotion of the central cooperative union in Nebhana/Tunisia.**

17730 Minderhoud, M.   NL 020019/77/8636 N
Sociaalwetenschappelijke en bedrijfskundige aspecten bij de wachttijden in de poliklinieken van drie ziekenhuizen in Amersfoort en Soest. **Study of the social and managerial aspects of the out–patient care.**

D 5300 – Marketing

See also 17122, 17455, 17465, 17519, 17539, 17564, 17600, 17620, 17900, 17978, 17990, 18000, 18032, 18141, 18155

17731 Ledent, A.; Bergans, J.   BE 010007/50/0002 R
Etude des marchés des produits agricoles et horticoles. **Marketstudy on agricultural and horticultural products.** Publications.

17732 Bublot, G.; Thonon, A.   BE 020200/76/0014 R
Etude des marges de commercialisation des produits agricoles; aspects macro– et microéconomiques; analyses globales et sectorielles. **Study of the agricultural products commercialization margins; Macro– and microeconomic aspects; aggregate and sectorial analysis.** Publications.

17733 Casier, J.; Goffings, G.; De Paepe, G.; Willems, H.
          BE 040501/70/0002
Pilotstudie betreffende de industriële pentosanproduktie, de produktiekostprijs berekening, de pentosan toepassingen en de marktprospectie. **Pilotresearch of the industrial pentosanproduction the production cost calculation, the pentosan applications and the marktprospection.** Publications.

17734 Boddez, G.; Vandepitte, W.; Ernens, M.; De Wever, L.   BE 040601/74/0005 R
Prognoses 1985 van de vraag naar en het aanbod van landbouwprodukten in de negen lidstaten en in de E.E.G. als geheel genomen. **Projections 1985 of the demand for and the supply of agricultural products in the nine member states and in the European Economic Community as a whole.** Publications.

17735 Nicolaus, L.   BE 120000/70/0004
Formation et évolution des prix des fleurs coupées en Belgique. **Price fixation and evolution of cut flowers in Belgium.** Publications.

17736 Ackerman, L.   BE 120000/72/0005
Enquête permanente auprès des consommateurs en vue de promouvoir la commercialisation des produits agricoles. **Permanent consumption panel in order to promote the marketing of agricultural products.** Publications.

17737 Muermans, L.   BE 120000/73/0007 R
Structuuranalyse van de groenten– en fruitsector in België. **Structure analysis of the fruit and vegetable sector in Belgium.** Publications.

17738 Cosse, V.   BE 120000/73/0008 R
La commercialisation des bovins et de la viande bovine en Belgique. **The commercialisation of cattle and beef in Belgium.**

17739 Vertessen, J.; Van Heghe, G.; Ackerman, L.; Muermans, L.; Nicolaus, L.; Nutelet, R.
          BE 120000/75/0019 R
Recherches sur la consommation et la distribution des produits agricoles. **Research concerning consumption and distribution of agricultural products.**

17740 Callier, C.   BE 120000/79/0029 N
Analyses van de houdingen en de gedragingen van de konsumenten t.a.v. vlees en vleesprodukten. **Analysis of consumer's attitudes and behaviour with respect to meat products.**

17741 Mante, W.; Raschke, M.   DE 105350/75/0001
Zur Chancengleichheit der Entwicklungsländer auf Agrarmärkten der Industrieländer dargestellt am Beispiel von Obst und Gemüse in der Bundesrepublik Deutschland. **On the equality of chances of developing countries in the agricultural markets of industrial nations, with special reference to fruit and vegetables in the Federal Republic of Germany.**

17742 Mante, W.   DE 105350/75/0003
Der deutsche Markt für Obst und Gemüse aus Entwicklungsländern. **The German market for fruit and vegetables from developing countries.**

17743 Richter, L.; May, T.   DE 105410/78/0001 N
Zur Bedeutung des Marketing in der Brauwirtschaft unter besonderer Berücksichtigung der Marktsegmentierung. **The significance of marketing in the brewing trade with special regard to market segmentation.**

17744 Richter, L.; Pellengahr, R.   DE 105410/78/0003 N

Kooperation und Wettbewerbsfähigkeit der mittelständischen Brauindustrie in der Bundesrepublik Deutschland. **Co–operation and competitive ability of the medium–sized brewing industry in the Federal Republic of Germany.**

17745 Hottes, K.   DE 108152/77/0001
Wochenmärkte im Ruhrgebiet. **Weekly markets in the Ruhr District.**

17746 Henrichsmeyer, W.; Bauersachs, F.; Bauer, S.
                                        DE 111651/72/0003
Konkurrenzvergleich landwirtschaftlicher Standorte. **Interregional competition of agricultural production.**

17747 Wolffram, R.–E.; Zelada, L.   DE 111655/74/0002
Analyse der Vermarktungsstruktur bei Obst in Chile. **Analysis of fruit marketing structure in Chile.**

17748 Wolffram, R.–E.; Weihofen, J.   DE 111655/78/0001 N
Nutzen–Kosten–Analyse der Weinmarktordnung in der um Griechenland, Spanien und Portugal erweiterten Europäischen Gemeinschaft. **Cost–benefit–analysis of wine market regulation of the EC enlarged by Greece, Spain and Portugal.**

17749 Wolffram, R.–E.; Born–Siebicke, G.
                                        DE 111655/78/0002 N
Möglichkeiten der Marktforschung für kommunale Versorgungsunternehmen, – dargestellt am Beispiel der Wasserversorgung. **Possibilities of market research in communal utility enterprises, exemplified by water supply.**

17750 Wolffram, R.–E.; Möhlmann, L.   DE 111655/78/0003 N
Kosten–Nutzen–Analyse markt– und preispolitischer Massnahmen auf den Weltmärkten für pflanzliche Öle und Fette hinsichtlich ihrer Auswirkungen in ausgewählten Entwicklungsländern. **Cost–benefit–analysis of marketing and price political measures on world markets for plant oils and fats regarding their effects in selected developing countries.**

17751 Wolffram, R.–E.; Bückers, E.   DE 111655/78/0004 N
Untersuchung zur Funktionsfähigkeit von Marktstabilisierungsfonds unter Berücksichtigung der Erfahrungen auf dem Eiersektor – Nutzen–Kosten–Überlegungen –. **Analysis of running of market stabilization fonds with regard to experiences on egg market – cost–benefit–considerations –.**

17752 Wolffram, R.–E.; Niepenberg, K.A.
                                        DE 111655/78/0005 N
Die Wettbewerbssituation bei Milch und Milchprodukten in Nordrhein–Westfalen und Möglichkeiten zur Verbesserung der Marktstellung der nordrhein–westfälischen Molkereiunternehmen. **The competitive situation of milk and milk products in Northrhine–Westphalia and possibilities of improving the marketing conditions of dairies in Northrhine–Westphalia.**

17753 Wolffram, R.–E.; Möckelmann, T.
                                        DE 111655/78/0006 N
Beurteilung der zukünftigen Absatzchancen für Inlandsgetreide in der Bundesrepublik Deutschland. **Estimation of marketing prospects for domestic cereals in the Federal Republic of Germany.**

17754 Wolffram, R.–E.   DE 111655/78/0007 N
Wettbewerbsunterschiede der Weine der Unteren–Mosel.

Differences in competition of wines of the Lower Moselle region.

17755 Wolffram, R.–E.; Fiedler, K.   DE 111655/78/0008 N
Die Entwicklungstendenzen des Absatzes von Fleisch über Fleischmärkte in der Bundesrepublik Deutschland. **Marketing trends of meat via meat markets in the Federal Republic of Germany.**

17756 Researcher not indicated   DE 129000/77/0001
Bilanzierungsmethoden der EG–Milchstatistik und Möglichkeiten ihrer Verbesserung. **Methods of balancing milk statistics of the EC and possibilities of improvement.**

17757 Researcher not indicated   DE 129000/77/0002
Untersuchung von Niveau und Entwicklung des Nahrungsverbrauchs in den Mitgliedsländern der EG einschliesslich voraussichtlicher Beitrittsländer mittels Mehrländervergleich. **Studies on level and trend of food consumption in member countries of the EC including potential member countries using comparisons of several countries.**

17758 Renner, E.; Kess, U.   DE 129252/77/0001
Verbrauchermeinung und Verbraucherverhalten zur H–Milch. **Consumer opinion and behaviour with respect to UHT–milk.**

17759 Warmbier, W.   DE 129301/78/0002 N
Qualitative Untersuchung zu Marketingsystemen bei der Direktvermarktung von Wein. **Qualitative analysis of marketing systems for direct sale of wine.**

17760 Kuhlmann, F.; Warmbier, W.   DE 129301/78/0008 N
Zur Planung von Marketing–Informations–Aktion–Systemen für den Direktabsatz von Trinkmilch. **Planning of marketing information action systems for direct sale of milk.**

17761 Wöhlken, E.; Meyer, H.   DE 129320/74/0001
Querschnittsanalyse der Nahrungsmittelnachfrage. **Cross–section analysis of the demand for food.**

17762 Wöhlken, E.; Saleh, O.   DE 129320/75/0001
Absatz von ägyptischem Reis im Binnenmarkt, am Weltmarkt und in der EG. **Egyptian rice economy and the world rice market.**

17763 Besch, M.; Koch, S.   DE 129320/75/0002
Marktsegmentierung beim Absatz von Lebensmitteln. **Market segmentation in food marketing.**

17764 Wöhlken, E.; Bohr, K.–P.; Kalinke, H.
                                        DE 129320/77/0001
Wirtschaftliche Kooperation im Weinhandel in wettbewerbspolitischer Sicht. **Cooperation in the distribution of wine and competition.**

17765 Wöhlken, E.; Bergs, C.   DE 129320/77/0002
Aussagekraft und Berechnung internationaler Kaufkraftparitäten für den Agrarbereich. **International comparison of agricultural product and factor prices.**

17766 Besch, M.; Lenz, M.   DE 129320/77/0003
Entwicklung und experimentelle Tests von zielgruppenorientierten Strategien zur Beeinflussung des Ernährungs– verhaltens bei Convenience–Produkten. **Development and empirical test of strategies concerning selected groups of consumers to influence nutrition– behaviour**

with convenience–products.

17767 Wöhlken, E.; Kissel, G.; Besch, M. DE 129320/77/0004
Probleme der physischen Distribution beim Absatz von
Agrarprodukten – Theoretische Ansätze und empirische
Untersuchungen auf ausgewählten Märkten. **Problems of
physical distribution in agricultural marketing. – Theoretical
approach and practical research on selected markets.**

17768 Wöhlken, E.; Priebe, P.; Uhle, H.–J.
DE 129320/78/0005 N
Export von Milcherzeugnissen aus der Bundesrepublik
Deutschland. **Exports of dairy products from Germany – FR –.**

17769 Kowald, R.; Vogel, C. DE 129450/78/0003 N
Untersuchungen über Absatzmöglichkeiten für Müllkompost
in 5 ausgewählten Gemeinden des Main–Kinzig–Kreises.
**Investigations on possibilities of marketing refuse compost in
five selected communities of the Main–Kinzig district.**

17770 Kuhnen, F.; Mai, D. DE 132250/71/0007
Organisation und Effizienz der landwirtschaftlichen
Beschaffungsmärkte am Beispiel westpakistanischer Dörfer.
**Organization and efficiency of agricultural factor markets in
the case of West–Pakistan villages.**

17771 Grosskopf, W. DE 132361/72/0009
Die Effizienz der Vermarktung landwirtschaftlicher Produkte.
The efficiency of agricultural marketing.

17772 Heidhues, T.; Aeikens, H. DE 132364/77/0001
Die Entwicklung des Milchangebotes in den Mitgliedsländern
der EG in Abhängigkeit von autonomen Ertragssteigerungen
sowie betrieblichen Auf– und Abstockungsprozessen.
**Development of milk supply in the EC–member countries in
dependency on autonomous increase of yield per low and
increasing and decreasing herd sires.**

17773 Heidhues, T.; Schäffer, R. DE 132364/77/0002
Entwicklung von Kriterien zur Bestimmung einer optimalen
Vorratspolitik auf den Weltgetreidemärkten. Analyse des
Einflusses staatlicher Vorratshaltung auf die Preisbildung bei
Rohstoffen und Anwendung der Ergebnisse auf die
Weltgetreidemärkte. **Elaborating of criteria for determining
the optimum of storing policy on world grain markets. Analysis
of the influence of public storing on pricing of raw materials and
application of the results to the world grain markets.**

17774 Grosskopf, W.; Alter, R. DE 132364/77/0004
Der angemessene Verbraucherpreis als Zielvariable der
EGAgrarpolitik – der Einfluss des Nahrungsmittelpreisniveaus
auf Einkommensdistribution und Faktorallokation. **The
appropriate consumer price as a targetvariable of the
EG–agricultural policy the influence of the foodprice on income
distribution and factor allocation.**

17775 Grosskopf, W.; Rüther, W. DE 132364/77/0005
Bestimmungsfaktoren der Preis– und Mengenschwankungen
auf Rindermärkten der EG. **Factors determining changes in
prices and quantities of cattle in the EC.**

17776 Reinhardt, W. DE 132364/78/0001 N
Strukturplanung in der Ernährungsindustrie. **Stuctural
planning in the food industry.** Publications.

17777 Leserer, M.; Polifka, U. DE 132366/77/0001

Anwendungsmöglichkeiten kontrolltheoretischer Methoden
auf agrarökonomische Probleme – dargestellt am Beispiel des
Rindfleischmarktes der Bundesrepublik Deutschland.
**Applications of optimal–control–methods to agricultural
economics with special reference to the beef markets of the
Federal Republic of Germany.**

17778 Knigge, W.; Denninger, W. DE 132780/77/0006
Stand und Aussichten der Holzverwendung im unbearbeiteten
bzw. wenig bearbeiteten Zustand. **Status and trends of the
utilization of roundwood in different industrial trades.**

17779 Storck, H.; Timm, G. DE 138360/77/0002
Marktanalyse für Schnittblumen und Topfpflanzen als
Grundlage für die Entwicklung absatzpolitischer
Konzeptionen für den deutschen Zierpflanzenbau. **Market
analysis for cut flowers and pot plants as a basis for the
development of marketing conceptions for the German
floriculture.**

17780 Momm, H.; Dietzsch–Doertenbach, M.
DE 144680/78/0001 N
Marktorientierte Organisationen für Rinderzüchtung in den
USA. **Market–orientated organizations for cattle breeding in
the USA.**

17781 Lorenzl, G.; Heinrich, F. DE 144855/77/0001
Möglichkeiten der Leistungsbeurteilung von
Vermarktungssystemen unter den Bedingungen
wirtschaftlicher Entwicklung. Das Beispiel der Vermarktung
von Obst und Gemüse in Kenia. **Evaluating the performance of
agricultural marketing systems in developing countries. The
example of marketing fruit and vegetables in Kenya.**
Publications.

17782 Böckenhoff, E.; Burchard, E. DE 144855/77/0002
Die Entwicklung des Lebensmittelumsatzes der
Grossverbraucher und ihre Auswirkungen auf die
Landwirtschaft. **The trend of food use by large–scale consumers
and effects on agriculture.**

17783 Henze, A.; Mühlbauer, F. DE 144855/77/0003
Einzel– und gesamtwirtschaftliche Effizienz der Förderung
nach dem Marktstrukturgesetz unter Wettbewerbsaspekten.
**Privat and public efficiency of support according to the Market
Structure Act as evaluated under aspects of competition.**

17784 Böckenhoff, E.; Mohr, C. DE 144855/78/0001 N
Möglichkeiten zur Verbesserung der Markttransparenz auf
Agrarmärkten für Schlachtvieh und Ferkel. **Possibilities to
improve the market transparancy on markets for slaughter
animals and piglets.** Publications.

17785 Röhm, H.; Egeler, W. DE 144860/73/0001
Organisation und Entwicklung der genossenschaftlichen
Schlachtviehvermarktung in Württemberg. **Organization and
development of co–operative slaughter livestock marketing in
Württemberg.**

17786 Riebe, K.; Wendt, R. DE 148401/75/0002
Optimale Verkaufsentscheidungen in der Schweinemast.
Optimal sales decisions in pig fattening.

17787 Stamer, H.; Schubert, W. DE 148452/72/0006 R
Entwicklung der Verbraucherpreise für landwirtschaftliche
Erzeugnisse in den einzelnen Bundesländern sowie Gründe der

auftretenden Differenzen 1972. **Development of consumer prices for agricultural produce in the single Federal States and causes of occuring differences.**

17788 Researcher not indicated   DE 148453/77/0001
Untersuchung der Absatzmöglichkeiten für traditionelle und neuartige Milcherzeugnisse. **Analysis of marketing chances for traditional and new milk products.**

17789 Hülsemeyer, F.; Graser, S.   DE 161421/73/0002
Das Angebotsverhalten der bayerischen Schlachtschweineerzeuger – ein Beitrag zur positiven Angebotsanalyse. **The supply behaviour of pigs–for–slaughter producers in Bavaria – a constitution to positive supply analysis.**

17790 Krüger, R.; Fischer, H.   DE 161480/74/0001
Brauereiverkäufe – Eine empirische Analyse zur Unternehmensbewertung. **Selling of breweries – an empirical analysis in the valuation of a firm.**

17791 Krüger, R.; Meier, H.   DE 161480/75/0002
Absatzplanung in Brauereien. **Marketing planning in breweries.**

17792 Krüger, R.; Spielmann, H.   DE 161480/78/0002 N
Verkaufsorganisation und Marketingstrategie von Brauereien. **Sales organization and marketing strategy of breweries.**

17793 Wendt, H.; Basler, A.   DE 201110/77/0004
Entwicklungstendenzen der Welternährungswirtschaft und des Welthandels mit Agrarprodukten. **Trends of world food economy and worldwide marketing with agricultural products.**

17794 Bremen, L.von   DE 201110/77/0006
Analyse der Betriebsmittelmärkte – Dünger, Futtermittel, Pflanzenschutzmittel, Brenn– und Schmierstoffe, Maschinen, Dienstleistungen –. **Analysis of working means markets – fertilizers, feedstuffs, plant protectives, fuels, lubricants, machines, services –.**

17795 Schmidt, E.   DE 201110/77/0007
Analyse des Zuckermarktes in der Bundesrepublik Deutschland und der EG unter Berücksichtigung der Versorgungslage in der Welt. **Analysis of the sugar market in the Federal Republic of Germany and in the EC with special regard to world supply situation.**

17796 Kersten, L.   DE 201110/77/0008
Analyse der Märkte für Eier und Geflügel in der Bundesrepublik Deutschland und der EG. **Analysis of marketing of eggs and poultry in the Federal Republic of Germany and in the EC.**

17797 Ramm, G.   DE 201110/77/0009
Analyse des Milchmarktes in der Bundesrepublik Deutschland und der EG. **Analysis of the milk market in the Federal Republic of Germany and in the EC.**

17798 Probst, F.–W.   DE 201110/77/0010
Analyse der Märkte für Rind– und Schweinefleisch in der Bundesrepublik Deutschland und der EG. **Analysis of markets for beef and pork in the Federal Republic of Germany and in the EC.**

17799 Uhlmann, F.   DE 201110/77/0011
Analyse der Märkte für Getreide und Kartoffeln in der Bundesrepublik Deutschland und der EG. **Analysis of markets for cereals and potatoes in the Federal Republic and in the EC.**

17800 Frassine, W.   DE 201110/77/0012
Veränderungen der Absatzstrukturen und des Verbraucherverhaltens auf ausgewählten Nahrungsmittelmärkten. **Changes in market structures and reaction of consumers to selected food markets.**

17801 Buchholz, H.E.   DE 201110/77/0013
Bestimmungsgründe und Analyse der Agrarpreise. **Determinants and analysis of agricultural prices.**

17802 Buchholz, H.E.   DE 201110/77/0014
Ernährungswirtschaftliche Versorgungsbilanzen der EG. **Food economic balances of supply in the EC.**

17803 Bremen, L.von   DE 201110/77/0016
Faktoreinsatz im Agrarsektor. **Factorial use on the agricultural sector.**

17804 Manegold, D.   DE 201110/78/0001 N
Bestimmungsgründe des innergemeinschaftlichen Warenverkehrs. **Determinants of internal exchange of goods in the EC.**

17805 Neander, E.; Fasterding, F.   DE 201120/74/5001 N
Untersuchungen zur Beurteilung alternativer Möglichkeiten der Versorgung eines Ballungsraumes mit Schlachtvieh und Fleisch, dargestellt am Raum Braunschweig. **Critical examination of alternative possibilities of supplying an agglomeration with slaughter livestock and meat, exemplified by the Brunswick area.**

17806 Neander, E.; Höhm, H.–P.   DE 201120/75/0005
Analyse der Distribution von Fleisch und Fleischwaren auf der Endverbraucherstufe in der Bundesrepublik Deutschland. **Analysis of the present structure and future development of market channels for livestock and meat in the Federal Republic of Germany.**

17807 Becker, M.   DE 202010/77/0008
Markt und Absatz als Forschungsgegenstände in der Forst– und Holzwirtschaft. **Market and sale as objects of research in forestry and lumber industry.**

17808 Ollmann, H.   DE 202010/77/0009
Der Holzverbrauch der Bundesrepublik Deutschland 1980 bis 1985. Holzmarktanalysen – Holzverbrauchsanalysen – Holzverbrauchsprognose. **Timber consumption in the Federal Republic of Germany 1980–1985. Analyses of timber market – timber consumption analyses – prognosis of timber consumption.**

17809 Wiebecke, C.; Wendorff, G.B.von; Maydell, H.–J.von
     DE 202010/77/0010
Forst– und holzwirtschaftsgeographische Analysen aussereuropäischer Länder im Hinblick auf ihre Bedeutung für die Weltholzversorgung. **Geographical analyses of forestry and lumber industry in non–European countries with special regard to their importance for world timber supply.**

17810 Roth, W.von   DE 202060/77/0006
Förderung der Holzverwendung im Bauwesen. **Promotion of wood utilization in building construction.**

17811 Gravert, H.O.   DE 207010/77/0007
Angebotsregulierung am Milchmarkt. **Organization of supply on the milk market.**

17812 Drews, M.   DE 207070/77/0001
Probleme der Marktverfassung. **Problems of market order.**

17813 Wietbrauk, H.   DE 207070/77/0004
Marktforschung der betriebswirtschaftlichen Kalkulation zu neuen Produkten und Absatzwegen. **Market research on farm economic calculation for new products and marketing circuits.**

17814 Longuet, D.   DE 207070/77/0007
Verpackungssysteme bei Konsummilch in der Bundesrepublik Deutschland. **Packing system for market milk in the Federal Republic of Germany.**

17815 Wietbrauk, H.   DE 207070/78/0001 N
Einzelhandelsdistribution von Desserts. **Consumption and retail trade – distribution of desserts containing milk.**

17816 Drews, M.; Krell, E.   DE 207070/78/0010 N
Marketing–Konzeption einer zweiten, staatlich verbilligten Buttersorte. **Marketing–conception of a second butterbrand, subsidized by EEC.**

17817 Schön, L.; Bach, H.   DE 210010/75/0007
Erarbeitung des wissenschaftlich–technischen Know–how zur Verbesserung der Vermarktung von Fleisch. **Elaboration of scientifico–technical Know–how for ameliorating the marketing of meat.**

17818 Schön, L.   DE 210010/75/0009
Markttransparenz bei Fleisch. **Transparence of meat–markets.**

17819 Schön, L.   DE 210010/77/0004
Volkswirtschaftliche Bedeutung der Schlachtnebenprodukte. **Economic importance of slaughter by–products.**

17820 Schön, L.   DE 210010/77/0005
Versorgungsbilanzen für Fleisch. **Balance of meat supply.**

17821 Linke, H.   DE 210030/75/0009
Sytematisierung von Fleisch und Fleischerzeugnissen. **Systematization of meats and meat products.**

17822 Larsen, A.; Pedersen, T.D.   DK 010500/16/0003 R
Registrering af priser på produktionsmidler og produkter i dansk landbrug. **Recording of prices for production items and products in Danish agriculture.**

17823 Guillon, P.   FR 010308/73/3320
La filière bois française. **French wood marketing channels.**

17824 Buttoud, C.   FR 010308/74/3323
La ressource française en peuplier et ses perspectives d'évolution. **French poplar resources and its evolution.** Publications.

17825 Rochot, A.; Normandin, D.; Bonin, M.
    FR 010308/74/3325
Evaluation des disponibilités en bois à moyen terme (1985). **Wood supply forecasts for the year 1985.**

17826 Normandin, D.   FR 010308/78/8526
La formation des prix de revient de la matière première bois (essences résineuses) rendue parcs usines de fabrication des pâtes à papiers et cartons. **Determinants of pulpwood mil prices (sifwood).**

17827 Rochot, A.; Xieng, S.   FR 010308/78/8606
Le commerce extérieur français des bois et produits dérivés :structure, évolution, conséquences économiques et sociales. **Wood and wood products foreign trade in France ; structure, evolution, economical and social consequences.**

17828 Soufflet   FR 011012/75/3304
Analyse des flux de bovins et viande bovine. Systèmes d'approvisionnement des zones de consommation. **Analysis of marketing channels for cattle and beef. Supply system for consumption areas.**

17829 Soufflet, J.F.   FR 011012/78/8553
Pratique de l'exportation des bovins et de la viande bovine. Rôle des petites et moyennes entreprises. **Cattle and beef meat exports ; part of small and medium firms.**

17830 Boulet, D.; Laporte, J.P.   FR 011205/65/3359
Etude du système de production – transformation – distribution du vin de France. **Study of the production and marketing system of wine in France.**

17831 Boutonnet, J.P.   FR 011205/72/8604
Opérateurs du marché de la viande ovine en France. **Sheep–meat marketing in France.**

17832 Boutonnet, J.P.   FR 011205/73/3367
Structure de la filière ovine en France. **The structure of french mutton market.**

17833 Boulet, D.; Laporte, J.P.   FR 011205/74/3361
Etude de l'évolution de la concurrence et de la concentration dans l'industrie des boissons en France. **Study of the evolution of competition and concentration in French wine industry.**

17834 Boulet, D.; Laporte, J.P.; Lifran, R.
    FR 011205/75/8659
Environnement international du marché du vin et de la viticulture languedocienne. **International environnement of the wine market and Languedoc wine industry.**

17835 Montigaud, J.C.; Lauret, F.; Labonne, M.
    FR 011205/76/8603
Structures et organisation des marchés des produits agricoles et alimentaires. **Market structure and organization for farm and food products.**

17836 Broussolle, C.   FR 011302/72/3347
Ajustement de l'offre à la demande et structures de production. **Supply/demand adjustment and production structures.**

17837 Mahe, L.   FR 011302/73/3354
Analyse économétrique des fluctuations de prix agricoles. **Econometric Analysis of Agricultural Prices Fluctuations.**

17838 Dubos, J.; Ferrand, J.J.; Roux, M.   FR 011408/60/3319
Le marché vinicole – offre et demande. **Wine market – supply and demand.**

17839 Mazenc, L.   FR 011408/73/3318

Le marché de la viande bovine. **The French beef market.**

17840 Dronne, Y.; Harel, M.; Bourdon, J.P.; Marloie, M.
FR 012205/74/8661
Les marchés internationaux des matières de l'alimentation animale. **International markets of raw materials in animal feeds.**

17841 Lassaut, B.; Gorse, P.
FR 012205/77/8548
La distribution physique du lait pasteurisé en région parisienne: analyse des problèmes et examen des solutions possibles. **Physical distribution of pasteurized milk in the parisian area: an analysis of its problems and an investigation on its settlement.**

17842 Hy, M.; Errecart, M.; Gallezot, J.
FR 012205/77/8551
Les gains et les transfers de productivité dans le secteur de gros des viandes bovines. **The surplus accounting method, applied to beef wholesale market.**

17843 Hy, M.; Gallezot, J.
FR 012205/77/8555
Les gains et les transfers de productivité au sein de la filière porc. **The surplus accounting method, applied to pork branch.**

17844 Errecart, M.; Mainsant, P.; Frat, Y.
FR 012205/78/8549
Le commerce de viande et le déséquilibre avant–arrière en viande bovine. **The trade of meat and the lack of balance between fore and back quarter of beef.**

17845 Persuy, P.
FR 012205/78/8564
Contribution à l'analyse des capitaux investis dans le secteur de la distribution alimentaire en France. **Contribution to the analysis of capital invested in the french food distribution's sector.**

17846 Bertrand, J.P.; Chabert, J.P.; Lebas, L.; Marloie, M.
FR 012212/73/8662
Marché mondial des "Oléo–protéagineux" et développement agricole. **The world market of oilseeds and products and agricultural development.**

17847 Viau, C.; Altmann, C.
FR 012212/77/8605
Disparités des prix des céréales à la production. **Cereals price disparities in France.**

17848 Cook
GB 040601/00/0001 R
A supply–response model for Northern Ireland potatoes.

17849 Couston
GB 060104/00/0001 R
Exploring structures for co–operative honey marketing.

17850 Lilwall
GB 060108/78/0009 N
Commodity markets.

17851 Volans
GB 060108/78/0010 N
Situation and outlook information on commodities and farm inputs.

17852 MacCanna, C.
IE 060300/69/0064 N
Investigation of mushroom markets. Publications.

17853 Riordan, E.B.; Joseph, R.L.; Hood, D.E.
IE 060300/73/0888 R
Marketing of grilling beef with assured characteristics. Publications.

17854 Murphy, R.F.
IE 060300/76/1311
Methods of supporting dried peas. Publications.

17855 Riordan, E.B.; Joseph, R.L.; Harrington, D.
IE 060600/72/0563 R
Study of the market suitability of Irish young bull beef. Publications.

17856 Riordan, E.B.
IE 060600/73/1115 R
Trade in vacuum packaged beef. Publications.

17857 Riordan, E.B.
IE 060600/74/1027 R
Pre–packed and over the counter beef – shoppers perceptions and objective assesment. Publications.

17858 Riordan, E.B.
IE 060600/78/1349 R
The evolution of retailing and its implications for the distribution of Irish food products. Publications.

17859 Riordan, E.B.
IE 060600/78/1350 R
Projection of beef demand and supply within the E.E.C. Publications.

17860 Cuddy, M.; Quilligan, A.
IE 130201/78/8000
To investigate the factors influencing the composition of agricultural production in the west of Ireland 1956–1976.

17861 Castellani, C.; Del Favero, R.; Tabacchi, G.
IT 021800/78/0006
Costruzione di tariffe di cubatura per alcune specie forestali italiane. **Construction of volume tables for some Italian forestal species.**

17862 Crivelli, G.; Senesi, E.
IT 021900/77/0001
Indagini sulla valorizzazione del pesce azzurro delle acque costiere. **Utilization of sardines and anchovies from Adriatic coasts.**

17863 Rosato, E.
IT 040118/78/1100 N
Il prezzo di indifferenza della carne e del latte in allevamenti bovini dell'Italia meridionale continentale. **The production costs equivalent price of meat and milk in bovine cattle farms in continental Southern Italy.**

17864 Brugnoli, A.
IT 040224/78/1036 N
Impiego dei modelli econometrici per lo studio del mercato dei prodotti zootecnici. **The use of quantitative economic models in market research on animal produce.**

17865 Zucchi, G.
IT 040224/78/1107 N
Analisi economica della struttura produttiva e di mercato del settore del formaggio grana Parmigiano–Reggiano. Ricerca delle possibilità di adattamento per una migliore efficienza di impresa. **Economic analysis of the production set–up and marketing of Parmigiano–Reggiano cheese. Research on the possibilities of improving management efficiency.**

17866 Di Fazio, S.
IT 040306/77/0167 R
Ricerche sul mercato fondiario in alcune aree della Sicilia orientale. **Research into the property market in some areas of eastern Sicily.**

17867 Sturiale, C.
IT 040306/78/1113 R
Ricerche sulle strutture distributive e sui costi di commercializzazione delle produzioni agrumarie in Sicilia. **Research on the distribution system and the trading costs of**

D 5300 – Marketing

citrus production in Sicily.

17868 Perone–Pacifico, C. IT 040732/77/0259 R
La bilancia estera nel settore ortofrutticolo. **The foreign trade
balance of the fruit and vegetable industry.**

17869 Pagella, M. IT 041205/74/0593
La dinamica dei prezzi dei prodotti agricoli e dei prezzi dei
mezzi di produzione impiegati in agricoltura, in rapporto
all'evoluzione del settore agricolo. **Price dynamics of
agricultural products and of agricultural inputs in relation with
development trends in the agricultural sector.**

17870 Copelli, A. IT 041517/76/0002 N
Aspetti economici del mercato delle fragole e relative
tendenze. **Economics aspects of the strawberry market and its
trends.**

17871 Copelli, A.; Magistretti, A. IT 041517/77/0001 N
Il mercato del pollame in Italia: situazione e prospettive. **The
poultry market in Italy: situation and prospects.** Publications.

17872 Brioschi, F. IT 064200/78/1127 N
Ricerca di mercato sugli impianti attuali e potenziali delle
proteine non convenzionali. **Market research on existing and
potential plants for the production of non conventional proteins.**

17873 Giessen, L.B. van der NL 010116/50/0205 R
Samenstelling en ontwikkeling van de Nederlandse
rundveestapel. **Composition and development of the national
cow herd; prognosis of production and consumption of milk and
meat.** Publications.

17874 Timmer, W. NL 010116/67/1295 R
Onderzoek naar het verbruik van inlands rondhout in
verschillende verbruikssectoren. **Investigation into the use of
inland spar by the various groups of users.** Publications.

17875 Kleijn, E.H.J.M. NL 010116/71/3689 N
Onderzoek naar de prijsvorming, het aanbod van en de vraag
naar spruiten. **Market research (middle long run turn) for
Brussels sprouts in the Netherlands (a simultaneous model
approach).** Publications.

17876 Meÿaard, D.; Kleyn, E.H.J.M. de NL 010116/73/5942
Analyse van de prijsvorming van irisbloemen. **Iris flowers,
market positions and prospects (a market research).**

17877 Graaff, G.C. de NL 010116/74/6537
De commercialisatie van ingevoerde verse groente en fruit in
de E.G. met betrekking tot de berekening van de
invoerprijzen. **An investigation into the marketing of imported
fresh fruit and vegetables with reference to the calculation of the
entry prices.**

17878 Rijneveld, R. NL 010116/75/8579 N
Marktonderzoek visserijprodukten. **Market research on fishery
products.** Publications.

17879 Kleyn, E.H.J.M. de NL 010116/76/7704 R
Aggregatie marktonderzoek tuinbouwprodukten. **Econometric
market research in different branches – An approximation with
the help of aggregation.** Publications.

17880 Kleyn, E.H.J.M. de NL 010116/76/7707 R

Marktonderzoek sla. **Econometric market research for lettuce.**

17881 Graaff, G.C. de NL 010116/77/8571 N
De mogelijke invloed van marktkanalen en contracten op de
betaalde en ontvangen prijzen in de varkensmesterij. **The
influence of market channels and contract production on the
financial results in pig fattening.**

17882 Holterman, H.J.W. NL 010116/78/8915 N
Vooronderzoek naar de mogelijkheden van een
houtmarktstatistiek. **Pre–research on the possibilities of
statistics of the wood–market.**

17883 Kortekaas, B.M.M. NL 010116/79/8903 N
Economische aspecten van kwaliteit van tuinbouwprodukten.
Economic aspects of quality of horticultural products.

17884 Kleijn, E.H.J.M. de NL 010116/79/8904 N
Effecten van de import van snijbloemen op de prijsvorming
van het Nederlandse produkt. **Price influence from imported
cutflowers on home grown cutflowers.**

17885 Boer, W.C. NL 010118/74/5277
De economie bij de distributie van groenten en fruit.
Economics of distribution of fruit and vegetables. Publications.

17886 Timmer, W. NL 010601/67/1295 R
Onderzoek naar het verbruik van inlands rondhout in
verschillende verbruikssectoren. **The consumption of home
grown roundwood in various trade sectors.** Publications.

17887 Dijk, G. van NL 020004/78/8506
Vertikale prijsvorming van vee en vlees in West Europa.
**Vertical price formation of meat and livestock in Western
Europe.**

17888 Meulenberg, M.T.G. NL 020032/72/4802
Prijs als marketingvariabele bij landbouwprodukten en
voedingsmiddelen. **Price as marketing instrument for
agricultural and food products.** Publications.

17889 Tilburg, A. van NL 020032/75/6806
Onderzoek naar mogelijkheden voor de bezorgende
melkdetailhandel. **Posibilities for the home delivery
milk–retailing–trade.**

17890 Tilburg, A. van NL 020032/75/6807
Koopgedrag van gezinnen t.a.v. snijbloemen en potplanten.
Family buying behaviour of cutflowers and potplants.
Publications.

17891 Wierenga, B. NL 020032/76/7364
Beslissingsmodellen van consumenten. **Consumer decision
models.** Publications.

17892 Bouman, F.J.A. NL 020050/76/8539
Ontwikkeling van rijstcoöperaties in Midden–Java.
Development of rice co–operatives in Central Java, Indonesia.

17893 Bouman, F.J.A. NL 020050/77/8540
De afzet van groenten en fruit via coöperaties in West–Java.
Marketing of vegetables and fruits in West–Java.

D 5400 – Economic policy

See also 1552, 2400, 10419, 17265, 17381, 17402, 17403, 17406,

17439, 17579, 17732, 18213, 18222, 18232, 18239, 18254, 18259, 18274, 18275, 18304, 18316, 18340, 18474

17894 Ledent, A.; Herinckx–Pirlot, J.   BE 010007/55/0001
Etude de l'intégration de l'agriculture dans la Communauté Economique Européenne. **Agriculture integration within the European Economic Community.** Publications.

17895 Bublot, G.; Defraigne, J.P.; Gérard, E.; Hallet, A.M.; Mertens, P.   BE 020200/79/0020 N
Promotion de l'emploi et des revenus dans l'agriculture wallonne. **Promotion of employment and income by wallonish agriculture.** Publications.

17896 Niclaus, L.; D'Haese, L.   BE 120000/77/0022 R
De Belgische potplantenteelt. **Belgian potplant production.** Publications.

17897 Verbeke, N.   BE 120000/77/0023 R
Ekonomie van de Belgische Zeevisserij. **Economics of the Belgian seafishing.**

17898 Stuyck, D.   BE 120000/79/0030 N
Analyse van de invloed van het landbouwinvesteringsfonds op de ontwikkeling van de bedrijfsstruktuur. **Analysis of the influence of investment aid on the development of farm structure.**

17899 Devisch, N.   BE 120000/79/0031 N
Analyse van de problematiek van het grondkapitaal. **Analysis of the problems of land use.**

17900 Lorenzl, G.; Dürr, G.   DE 105350/77/0003
Zur Ökonomie der Kartoffelproduktion und –vermarktung in Kenia. **Economics of potato production and marketing in Kenya.** Publications.

17901 Yarahmadi, F.S.; Lorenzl, G.   DE 105350/77/0004
Zur Ökonomie der Kartoffelproduktion im Iran. **Economics of potato production in Iran.**

17902 Agrawal, R.C.   DE 105350/77/0005
Produktivitätsberechnung in der Landwirtschaft im Hinblick auf die Verwendung von Düngemitteln. **Estimation of productivity in agriculture with special reference to the use of fertilizers.**

17903 Blanckenburg, P.von; Joseph, C.   DE 105351/78/0001 N
Die Funktion öffentlicher Bevorratung beim Ausgleich von Ernteschwankungen in Entwicklungsländern. **Stocks for compensating harvest fluctuations in developing countries – the role of public stock policy –.**

17904 Blanckenburg, P.von; Moog, F.J.   DE 105352/75/0005
Untersuchungen zur Ökonomie der Agrarberatung in Entwicklungsländern. **Economics of agricultural extension in developing countries.**

17905 Andreae, B.; Baumgarten, K.   DE 105400/71/0001 R
Stufen der Arbeitswirtschaft im Zuge der volkswirtschaftlichen Entwicklung. **Steps of agricultural labour economic in economic growth.**

17906 Andreae, B.; Hoffmann, H.   DE 105400/73/0002
Wandlungen in der Verfahrenstechnik bei der Aufbereitung von Ölfrüchten im Wirtschaftswachstum. **Changes in the**

technical procedure of dressing oil–seeds in the course of economic increase.

17907 Andreae, B.; Maass, C.   DE 105400/77/0001
Die Rolle der landwirtschaftlichen Grossbetriebe im Wirtschaftswachstum. **The part of large farms in economic growth.**

17908 Richter, L.; Maier, M.   DE 105400/77/0004
Mittlere Datentechnik in Brauereien. Eine Untersuchung zum Informationswesen und Entscheidungsprozess auf der Grundlage automatisierter Datenverarbeitung in mittleren und kleineren Unternehmungen der deutschen Brauwirtschaft. **Medium data systems engineering in breweries. An analysis of information system and decision process on the basis of automated data processing in medium and small enterprises of German brewery industry.**

17909 Andreae, B.   DE 105400/77/0005
Betriebsformen der Weltlandwirtschaft. **Types of farming in the world.** Publications.

17910 Andreae, B.   DE 105400/78/0001 N
Agrarregionen unter Standortstress Produktionsverfahren der Bodennutzung in Marginalzonen des Weltagrarraumes. **Agricultural regions under locational stress conditions Production methods of land use in stress belts in world agriculture.**

17911 Merkel, K.   DE 105520/72/0001
Gesamtrechnungen über die sektorale Mengenproduktion der Landwirtschaft in der DDR. **Aggregation of the agricultural output in the German Democratic Republic.**

17912 Rudolph, H.; Kesselschläger, J.   DE 105987/70/0006
Investitionen und Rationalisierungserfolg in der Brauerei 1970. **Investments and results of rationalization in brewing industry.**

17913 Rudolph, H.; Zscheile, D.   DE 105987/77/0003 N
Bestimmingsgründe für die Konzentration in der deutschen Brauindustrie seit der Währungsreform. **Determinants for the concentration of brewing industry since the monetary reform.**

17914 Henrichsmeyer, W.; Bauersachs, F.; Bauer, S.   DE 111651/77/0002
Längerfristige Einkommensentwicklung in der Landwirtschaft der BRD für den Gesamtsektor, Agrarregionen und Betriebsgruppen. **Long–run projection of income in the agricultural sector of the FRG – sector, regions and farm groups –.**

17915 Henrichsmeyer, W.; Zöller, H.   DE 111651/77/0003
Landwirtschaftliche Vorranggebiete – agrar– und regionalpolitische Bedeutung. Ein Beitrag zur Theorie der landwirtschaftlichen Vorranggebiete. **Areas of agricultural priority – agrarian and regional political importance. A contribution to the theory of areas of agricultural priority.**

17916 Henrichsmeyer, W.; Wolf, W.   DE 111651/78/0001 N
Analyse der kurzfristigen Einkommensentwicklung der europäischen Landwirtschaft. **Analysis of short–term trend of incomes in European agriculture.**

17917 Henrichsmeyer, W.; Niebuhr, J.   DE 111651/78/0002 N
Auswirkungen von Mengensteuerungen im Agrarbereich.

Effects of quantity rates in agriculture.

17918 Henrichsmeyer, W.; Hermann, J.; Schlöder, F.-R.
DE 111651/78/0003 N
Quantitative Analyse der Einkommensverteilung im Agrarsektor im Hinblick auf die Konzeption eines Systems direkter Einkommensübertragungen. **Quantitative analysis of income distribution in agricultural sector regarding the concept of a system of direct income redistribution.**

17919 Lipinsky, E.E.; Petuelli, W. DE 111652/73/0001
Beziehungen zwischen Agrarverfassung und Entwicklung der Landwirtschaft in Tunesien. **The interrelations between agricultural systems and farming development in Tunesia.**

17920 Lipinsky, E.E.; Haupt, W. DE 111652/73/0002
Agrarverfassungen in Lateinamerika. **Agricultural systems in Latin America.**

17921 Junghans, K.H.; Bender, R. DE 111653/78/0001 N
Das Image der Dritten Welt und der deutschen Entwicklungshilfepolitik in der Bundesrepublik Deutschland. **The image of the Third World and of the German foreign aid policy in the Federal Republic of Germany.**

17922 Skomroch, W.; Beek, A.van-der DE 111702/73/0001
Einkommensmöglichkeiten landwirtschaftlicher Betriebe unter Berücksichtigung der Ungewissheit über die Entwicklung der Daten. **Possibilities of farm income with regard to the uncertain data development.**

17923 Popp, H. DE 120200/77/0001 N
Wirtschafts- und sozialgeographische Probleme der Bewässerungslandwirtschaft Marokkos. **Economic and social geographical problems of the irrigated lands in Morrocco.** Publications.

17924 Müller-Hohenstein, K. DE 120200/77/0003
Landnutzung und Bodenerosion im Rif – Marokko –. **Land use practice and soil erosion in the Rif – Morocco –.**

17925 Israng, A. DE 120250/78/0001 N
Der Weinbau im württembergischen Unterland. Eine spezielle Betrachtung der Grosslage Kirchenweinberg in bezug auf Kooperation der Weingärtner und ihrer Absatzmöglichkeiten. **Viticulture in the lowland of Wuerttemberg. A special study of Kirchenweinberg area with regard to co-operation of vinedressers and their marketing chances.**

17926 Brigelius, G. DE 120250/78/0002 N
Die Regnitzniederung im Stadtgebiet von Erlangen und ihre heutige Nutzung. **Lowland by the Regnitz river in Erlangen area and its present utilization.**

17927 Weigt, E.; Steffen, E. DE 120250/78/0005 N
Der Hopfenanbau in der Bundesrepublik Deutschland unter besonderer Berücksichtigung der Hallertau. **Hops growing in the Federal Republic of Germany, especially in the Hallertau region.**

17928 Matznetter, J. DE 123205/78/0001 N
Die verschiedenen Betriebsgrössen und -formen im Kakaoanbau am Beispiel der Guinea-Insel S.Tome, in Ghana, an der Elfenbeinküste und in Brasilien. **The different sizes of management area in the production process of cocoa plantations – with examples from Sao Tome Island, Ghana and Ivory Coast**

and Brasil –. Publications.

17929 Tangermann, S.; Kiessling, H.-J.
DE 123280/78/0001 N
Analyse agrarpolitischer Entscheidungen. **Analysis of decision-making in agricultural policy.**

17930 Haen, H.de; Frohberg, K.; Debois, J.-M.; Braun, J.von; Tangermann, S. DE 123280/78/0002 N
Der Beitrag der EG zur Verbesserung der Welternährungslage. **The contribution of the European Community to the improvement of the world food situation.**

17931 Priebe, H.; Hammann, H.; Ort, W. DE 123300/77/0001
Zum Problemkreis der Koordinierung von Regionalpolitik und Agrarstrukturpolitik. **On problems of coordination between regional policy and agricultural structure policy.** Publications.

17932 Priebe, H.; Ort, W.; Meyer, H.von
DE 123300/78/0001 N
Räumliche Auswirkungen der Agrarpolitik. **Spatial effects of agrarian politics.**

17933 Speidel, G.; Oesten, G. DE 126450/74/0002
Untersuchungen zum Problem der Nachwuchsrekrutierung der Landesforstverwaltungen. **On the problems of recruiting in national forestry administration.**

17934 Stadelbauer, J. DE 126700/77/0002 N
Horizontale Kooperation und vertikale Integration in der sowjetischen Agrarwirtschaft. **Horizontal cooperation and vertical integration in soviet agriculture.**

17935 Kuhlmann, F.; Jamaran, I. DE 129301/78/0001 N
Ökonomische Analyse der indonesischen Kokosnussindustrie und Möglichkeiten zur Verbesserung ihrer Wirtschaftlichkeit. **Economic analysis of Indonesian coconut-industry and possibilities of improving its profitableness.**

17936 Spitzer, H.; Müller, G. DE 129302/78/0001 N
Auswirkungen von Nutzungsbeschränkungen auf die landwirtschaftliche Produktion. **Effects of restricted land-use on agricultural production.**

17937 Zilahi-Szabo, M.G.; Müller, W. DE 129304/71/0001 N
Betriebswirtschaftliche Bilanz aus methodischer und entscheidungstheoretischer Sicht. **Methodical and decision-theoretical aspects of economic balance.**

17938 Wöhlken, E.; Filip, J. DE 129320/78/0001 N
Untersuchung von Niveau und Entwicklung des Nahrungsverbrauchs in den Mitgliedsländern der EG einschliesslich voraussichtlicher Beitrittsländer mittels Mehrländervergleich. **Multicountry comparison of level and trend of food demand in the member countries of the EC including the prospective joining countries.**

17939 Wöhlken, E.; Büdinger, A. DE 129320/78/0002 N
Der Weltmarkt für Schlachtvieh und Fleisch unter dem Einfluss wachsenden Wohlstands und nationaler Agrarpolitik. **The influence of increasing incomes and national agricultural policies on the world market for slaughter livestock and meat.**

17940 Wöhlken, E.; Meyer, H. DE 129320/78/0003 N
Auswertung der Einkommens- und Verbrauchsstichprobe 1973 im Hinblick auf die Nachfrage nach Lebensmitteln.

Analysis of food demand based on random sample of income and consumption survey 1973.

17941 Wöhlken, E.; Horn, G.; Besch, M.
DE 129320/78/0004 N
Rückwirkungen verminderten Wirtschaftswachstums auf die Landwirtschaft. **Influence of diminishing economic growth on agriculture.**

17942 Harsche, E.; Bähr, H.–G.   DE 129340/74/0006
Implikationen der landwirtschaftlichen Unternehmensstrukturen für die Agrarrechts–Ordnung – Regionale Differenzierung in der Bundesrepublik Deutschland. **Implications of farm structures in agricultural law – regional differentiation in the FRG –.**

17943 Harsche, E.; Müller, U.   DE 129340/74/0011
Das Eigentum an Bauboden im Meinungsfeld ländlicher und urbaner Wohnbevölkerung. **Building estate in the view of rural and urban residential population.**

17944 Harsche, E.; Razafimahefa, G.A.   DE 129340/74/0012
Wirtschaftssoziologische Implikationen der Genossenschaftsarbeit in den Hauts Plateaux von Madagaskar. **Economic and social implications of agricultural co–operatives in the high plateaus in Madagascar.**

17945 Bodenstedt, A.A.; Britsch, W.   DE 129340/77/0001
Interdependencen zwischen den unterschiedlichen Aspekten des Bedürfnisbegriffs in der Ernährungspolitik. **Different aspects of primary needs and their interdependencies in nutrition policy.**

17946 Harsche, E.; Stitz, V.; Goytom, W.M.
DE 129341/77/0001
Die Entwicklung der Agrarstruktur der äthiopischen Zentralprovinz Shoa unter dem wirtschaftlichen und sozialkulturellen Einfluss der Reichshauptstadt Addis–Abeba. **The development of the agrarian structure of the Ethiopian central province Shoa under the economic and sociocultural influence of the capital Addis–Abeba.**

17947 Seuster, H.; Post, A.   DE 129360/75/0002
Ökonomische Auswirkungen der Verwendung von Personenhandelsgesellschaften in der Landwirtschaft, dargestellt am Beispiel von zwei Kooperationen im Produktionsbereich. **The economic influence of "Personenhandelsgesellschaften" on agricultural cooperations.**

17948 Bohnet, A.; Schinke, E.   DE 129380/78/0001 N
Entwicklungstendenzen und Strukturwandel des Agraraussenhandels der RGW–Länder. **Developing trends and structural change of agricultural foreign trade of COMECON countries.**

17949 Wädekin, K.–E.   DE 129381/77/0001
Sozialistische Agrarpolitik in Osteuropa, Bd. 2: Entwicklung und Probleme 1960–1976. **Socialist agrarian policies in Eastern Europe and the Soviet Union, vol. 2: Development and problems 1960–1976.** Publications.

17950 Wädekin, K.–E.   DE 129381/77/0002
Sowjetische Agrarpolitik unter Breschnew. **Soviet agrarian policies under Brezhnev.**

17951 Schinke, E.; Hunacek, Z.   DE 129381/77/0003
Die Kooperation im Agrarrecht der CSSR, DDR und UdSSR. **Cooperation in the agricultural law of Czechoslovakia, GDR and Soviet Union.** Publications.

17952 Schinke, E.; Hunacek, Z.   DE 129381/77/0004
Das landwirtschaftliche Bodenrecht in der Tschechoslowakei. **Law of agricultural land in Czechoslovakia.** Publications.

17953 Schinke, E.; Crönlein, J.   DE 129381/77/0005
Die Förderung der überbetrieblichen Zusammenarbeit in der Landwirtschaft durch die öffentliche Hand. **Supporting cooperation in agriculture by public institutions.**

17954 Wädekin, K.–E.; Wagner, E.   DE 129381/77/0006
Die Entwicklung der Agrarstruktur in Rumänien. **Development of agrarian structure in Roumania.**

17955 Schinke, E.; Krebs, C.   DE 129381/77/0007
Die Industrialisierung der Landwirtschaft in der DDR. **Industrialisation of agriculture in the GDR.**

17956 Kuhnen, F.; Berger, M.   DE 132250/71/0008
Motivationen und Bedingungen bei Nachfrage und Vergabe landwirtschaftlicher Kredite. **Motivations for, and conditions of demand and supply of agricultural loans.**

17957 Mai, D.; Bergmann, T.; Kahnt, G.; Mehner, H.; Martius, H.; Kuhnen, F.   DE 132250/77/0001
Mechanisierung der Landwirtschaft und sozialökonomische Entwicklung im Vorderen und Mittleren Orient. Empirische Analyse makroökonomischer, mikroökonomischer, ökologischer, technologischer, sozialer und agrarstruktureller Auswirkungen und entwicklungspolitische Beurteilung von Konsequenzen einzel– und überbetrieblicher Mechanisierungsprozesse. **Agricultural mechanization und socio–economic development in Near and Middle East. Empirical analysis of macro– and microeconomic, ecological, technological and social agrarian structural consequences and their development political valuation in mechanization of individual farms and co–operation.**

17958 Kuhnen, F.; Marquez–Tavero, M.S.
DE 132250/77/0003
Agrarentwicklung und Agrarplanung im östlichen Bolivien. **Agricultural development and planning in Eastern Bolivia.**

17959 Jentzsch, E.G.   DE 132250/77/0005
Ernährungswirtschaftliche und ernährungspolitische Bedeutung der Selbstversorgung mit Nahrungsmitteln in Entwicklungsländern. **The impact of self–sufficiency on food economics and politics in developing countries.** Publications.

17960 Bhatti, M.H.   DE 132250/78/0001 N
Determinanten der Angebotsfunktion der Arbeit im ländlichen Raum Pakistans. **Determinants of labour supply function in rural Pakistan.**

17961 Klennert, K.   DE 132250/78/0002 N
Ausserbetriebliche Erwerbstätigkeiten landwirtschaftlicher Kleinbewirtschafterhaushalte in Entwicklungsländern. Eine empirische Studie im Punjab Pakistans. **Changing external occupational patterns in small agricultural households in developing countries. An empirical study in the Punjab of Pakistan.**

17962 Manig, W.   DE 132250/78/0003 N

D 5400 – Economic policy

Besteuerung des Agrarsektors und rurale Entwicklung in Entwicklungsländern. **Agricultural taxation and rural development in developing countries.** Publications.

17963 Grosskopf, W.; Strangmann, U.   DE 132360/78/0002 N
Struktur und wirtschaftliche Bedeutung von Exportpräferenzen für Agrarprodukte aus entwicklungspolitischer Sicht – diskutiert am Beispiel der EG–Lieferabkommen für Zucker. **Development political aspects of structure and economic importance of export preferences for agricultural produce – discussed on the example of EC supply contract for sugar.**

17964 Köhne, M.; Nis, L.   DE 132361/78/0001 N
Untersuchung der Gründe der Betriebsaufgabe unter besonderer Berücksichtigung der Auswirkungen eines verminderten gesamtwirtschaftlichen Wachstums. **Analysis of reasons for farm abandonment with special regard to effect of reduced overall economic growth.** Publications.

17965 Schmitt, G.; Seegers, T.   DE 132363/75/0001
Theoretische und empirische Wirkungsanalyse von durch nationale agrarpolitische Massnahmen hervorgerufenen Wettbewerbsverzerrungen. **Theoretical and empirical analysis of the distortions of competition caused by national agricultural policy measures.**

17966 Koester, U.; Schmitz, P.M.   DE 132363/77/0001
Möglichkeiten der Anwendung von Regelmechanismen im agrarpolitischen Entscheidungsprozess. **Chances of using decision–rules in agricultural policy – the example of price– and market–policy.**

17967 Schmitt, G.; Seebohm, E.   DE 132363/77/0003
Ökonomische Analyse und Bewertung der vom Beihilfe–Katalog der EG–Kommission aufgeführten agrarpolitischen Massnahmen. **Economic analysis and evaluation of farm policy instruments presented by the Commission of the European Economic Community in its catalogue of subsidies.**

17968 Schmitt, G.; Grolig, H.–H.   DE 132363/78/0001 N
Empirische Analyse des Investitionsverhaltens der Landwirtschaft in der Bundesrepublik Deutschland und dessen Bestimmungsgründe unter besonderer Berücksichtigung der staatlichen Investitionsförderung im Rahmen der Agrarpolitik. **Empirical analysis of investment behaviour in agriculture in the Federal Republic of Germany and determinant factors with special regard to investment subvention by state within agricultural policy.**

17969 Heidhues, T.; Beusmann, V.   DE 132364/77/0003
Die Auswirkungen der Agrarpreispolitik auf den landwirtschaftlichen Strukturwandel. **The influence of agricultural price policy on structural change of the agricultural sector.**

17970 Götz, V.; Obermann, S.   DE 132450/77/0001
Lebensmittelrecht in Frankreich. **Food law in France.**

17971 Götz, V.; Münster, K.P.   DE 132450/77/0002
Die Anwendung des Bundesimmissionsschutzgesetzes auf die Landwirtschaft. **Application of the Federal Immission Control Act on the agricultural sector.**

17972 Zundel, R.; Lessmann, D.   DE 132870/72/0004

Untersuchungen über die derzeitige Struktur des Waldes der Realverbände in Niedersachsen und ihrer Mitglieder sowie der zukünftigen Entwicklungsmöglichkeiten 1972. **Studies of the present–day structure of forests in joint ownership by Realverbände in Lower Saxony and members as well as studies of developing prospects.**

17973 Lessmann, D.   DE 132870/78/0002 N
Auswirkungen der Gebietsreform auf die Waldverteilung in politischen Gemeinden in Niedersachsen. **Effects of regional reform on the distribution of forests in political communities in Lower Saxony.**

17974 Storck, H.; Huss, H.M.   DE 138360/73/0004
Prognosen zur konjunkturellen Entwicklung im Gartenbau. **Short–term and medium–term forecasts for cyclical development in horticulture.**

17975 Bögemann, B.; Fey–Kimmig, R.; Hinken, J.; Möller, C.   DE 138361/78/0001 N
Deutsche Gartenbaubetriebe im Jahre 1998. **German horicultural firms in 1998.**

17976 Urff, W.von; Kropp, E.W.   DE 142200/72/0002
Einfluss der Industrialisierung auf die Erwerbsstruktur und Umfang der Kapitalbildung landwirtschaftlicher Haushalte im Dhanbad District – Bihar, Indien –. **Occupational structure and capital formation of agricultural households under the impact of regional industrialization.**

17977 Urff, W.von; Ahrens, H.; Zingel, W.–P.   DE 142200/78/0001 N
Möglichkeiten und Implikationen einer Entwicklungsstrategie zur Verminderung der Abhängigkeit von Kapitalimporten: Ein Planungsmodell für Pakistan's Politik der 'self–reliance'. **Possibilities and implications of a development strategy aimed at reducing the dependence on capital imports: a planning model for Pakistan's policy of 'self–reliance'.**

17978 Ewald, U.   DE 142300/73/0001
Salzgewinnung und Salzhandel in der Wirtschaftsstruktur mexikanischer Dörfer. **Salt production and salt trade as an economical factor in Mexican villages.** Publications.

17979 Momm, H.   DE 144680/74/0001
Wettbewerb und staatliche Förderung in der Tierzüchtung. **Competition and state promotion in animal breeding.**

17980 Reisch, E.; Röhner, M.   DE 144745/75/0001
Entwicklung der Produktionsstruktur und Produktionstechnik in der Rindviehhaltung für ausgewählte Regionen der Bundesrepublik Deutschland. **Patterns and techniques of milk and beef production and their development in selected regions of the Federal Republic of Germany.**

17981 Reisch, E.; Pfeiffer, J.   DE 144745/75/0002
Gruppenlandwirtschaft in Frankreich. **Cooperative farming in France.**

17982 Reisch, E.; Langendorf, D.   DE 144745/78/0002 N
Struktur und Entwicklung des Anbaus wichtiger Ackerfrüchte in den Staaten der EG unter besonderer Berücksichtigung der regionalen Produktions– und Wettbewerbsverhältnisse. **Structure and changes of production of important field crops in the European Community with special regard to the economic situation in the most important regions.**

17983 Weinschenck, G.; Küpper, B. DE 144750/74/0002
Wandlungen der Produktionsstruktur als Folge einer
Verknappung der Nahrungsmittelversorgung. **Changes in the
production structure owing to shortage of food supply.**

17984 Weinschenck, G.; Segger, V.; Weindlmaier, H.
DE 144750/77/0001
Die bisherige und zukünftige Entwicklung der Agrarstruktur
und des Faktoreinsatzes in der Landwirtschaft der EG. **The
past and future development of structural change and resource
use in the agriculture of the EC.** Publications.

17985 Ruthenberg, H.; Schreiber, J. DE 144755/77/0001
Die Ökonomik der Rinderhaltung auf Kunstweiden in
Westafrika. **The economics of beef production on artificial
pastures in West Africa.**

17986 Ruthenberg, H.; Rüdenauer, M. DE 144755/77/0003
Ökonomik der Rindfleischproduktion in der Feuchtsavanne
Togos. **Economics of beef production in the humid savannas of
Togo.**

17987 Ruthenberg, H.; Sere, C.; Ruthenberg, H.; Sere, C.
DE 144755/77/0004
Entwicklungsmöglichkeiten milchviehhaltender Betriebe in
den subtropischen und gemässigten Klimazonen Südamerikas.
**Dairy development in the subtropic and temperate zones of
South America.**

17988 Zeddies, J. DE 144755/77/0005
Nutzen züchterischer Fortschritte in der Rindviehhaltung im
strukturellen Wandel der Produktions- und
Absatzbedingungen. **Use of breeding progress in cattle
husbandry in structural change of production and marketing
conditions.** Publications.

17989 Böckenhoff, E.; Maag, G. DE 144855/75/0001
Die Ermittlung der Gesamtproduktion an Schlachtvieh und
Fleisch auf der Grundlage der Meldungen über die
Schlachtungen in den grösseren Schlachtbetrieben. **Calculation
of the total commercial production of slaughter livestock and
meat on the basis of notifications about the slaughterings in
larger slaughter enterprises.**

17990 Böckenhoff, E.; Guth, D. DE 144855/75/0002
Das Auftreten eines Rinderzyklus in den EG–Ländern und
seine Ursachen sowie Massnahmen einer wirksamen
Begegnung mit dem Ziel der Herstellung eines besseren
Marktgleichgewichts. **The existence of a cattle cycle in the EEC,
its reasons, and effective measures to improve the market
balance.**

17991 Böckenhoff, E.; Ruetz, F. DE 144855/75/0003
Möglichkeiten der Verbesserung der kurz- und mittelfristigen
Vorhersage der Produktion an Schlachtrindern und -kälbern.
**Improving the short and middle run forecast of beef and veal
production.**

17992 Argast, J. DE 144860/71/0001 R
Der Strukturwandel der Weinbaubetriebe und seine
Auswirkung auf Funktionen und Organisationsstruktur der
Winzergenossenschaften im südbadischen Raum 1971.
**Structural changes in viticultural farms and effect on functions
and organizational structure of vintagers co–operatives.**

17993 Röhm, H.; Stark, J. DE 144860/75/0001
Wirtschaftliche Entwicklung und Gewerbeansiedlung in
strukturschwachen ländlichen Gebieten Baden–Württembergs
– Arbeitstitel –. **Economical development and industry
settlement in structurally deficient rural areas of
Baden–Wuerttemberg.**

17994 Röhm, H.; Doll, M.J. DE 144860/75/0002 N
Die Auswirkungen der Bevölkerungs– und
Wirtschaftsentwicklung in Ländlichen Problemgebieten auf die
Ländlichen Warengenossenschaften. **Effects of development of
population and economy in rural problematic areas on rural
trade co–operatives.**

17995 Röhm, H.; Bakonyi, E.; Gaese, H. DE 144860/77/0001
Wandel der Agrarstruktur in ausgewählten strukturschwachen
Räumen Baden–Württembergs. **Changes in agrarian structure
in selected low–structure regions of Baden–Wuerttemberg.**

17996 Röhm, H.; Wenzel, F. DE 144860/77/0002
Entwicklungsprobleme der Weinproduktion und der
Weinvermarktung im Bereich Südliche Weinstrasse. **Problems
of development of wine production and wine marketing in the
region "Südliche Weinstrasse".**

17997 Röhm, H.; Bakonyi, E.; Doll, M.J.
DE 144861/78/0001 N
Der Förderauftrag der Bankgenossenschaften im Urteil der
Mitglieder und des Managements. **The co–operative promotion
of bank co–operatives in view of the members and the
management.**

17998 Bergmann, T.; Thomae, H. DE 144865/75/0003
Einkommensstruktur und Einkommensverteilung in
landwirtschaftlichen Produktionsgenossenschaften – LPG –
sozialistischer Länder am Beispiel Ungarn und Polen.
**Composition and distribution of income in co–operative farms
of the two socialist countries Hungary and Poland.**

17999 Kreeb, K.; Arnold, H.; Bergmann, T.
DE 144865/75/0004
Die langfristige Entwicklung des Produktionsmitteleinsatzes
und der Agrarerzeugung in der Bundesrepublik Deutschland –
ökologische Begrenzungen und agrarpolitische Probleme. **The
long–term development of inputs and agricultural production in
the GFR – ecological limitations and problems in farm policies.**

18000 Schad, F.; Kohler, R. DE 144900/70/0004 N
Steuerrechtliche Sonderregelungen für die Landwirtschaft im
Bereich der Umsatzsteuer. **Special privileges in fiscal law for
sales tax in agriculture.**

18001 Schad, F.; Laiblin, W.–D. DE 144900/72/0003 R
Die Organisation der Agrarverwaltung in der Bundesrepublik
Deutschland unter besonderer Berücksichtigung
BadenWürttembergs 1972. **The organization of agrarian
administration in the Federal Republic of Germany, especially
in Baden–Wuerttemberg.**

18002 Schad, F.; Maier, K. DE 144900/73/0003
Das staatliche Aufsichtsrecht gegenüber den
Siedlungsunternehmen. **State control law over settlement
projects.**

18003 Kreuzer, K.; Engelhard, W. DE 144900/75/0001 N
Die Entwicklung des Landpachtrechts in England seit 1945.

Rechtsvergleichende Untersuchungen der neueren Entwicklung des englischen und deutschen Landpachtrechts insbesondere im Hinblick auf die anstehende Reform des Landpachtrechts in der Bundesrepublik Deutschland. **The development of land lease law in England since 1945. Comparative legal study of the recent developments of English and German land lease law, especially with regard to the pending reform of the land lease law in the Federal Republic of Germany.**

18004 Planck, U.; Mohamed, H.   DE 144965/77/0001
Auswirkungen der syrischen Agrarreform. **Effects of the Syrian land reform.**

18005 Planck, U.; Philipp, H.–J.   DE 144965/77/0002
Geschichte und Entwicklung der Oase al–Hasa, Saudi–Arabien. **History and development of the oasis of al–Hasa, Saudi Arabia. Publications.**

18006 Langbehn, C.; Jochimsen, H.   DE 148401/74/0002
Quantitative Untersuchungen zur Entwicklungsfähigkeit landwirtschaftlicher Betriebe in Schleswig–Holstein. **Quantitative investigations of possibilities of future farm growth in Sleswick–Holstein.**

18007 Langbehn, C.; Diddens, W.   DE 148401/78/0001 N
Prognose zum Strukturwandel der Landwirtschaft in Schleswig–Holstein. **Forecasting structural change of agriculture in Schleswig–Holstein.**

18008 Hanf, C.H.; Voigt, H.   DE 148405/78/0002 N
Buffer–stock Politiken – Rohstoffwirtschaft –. **Buffer–stock politics.**

18009 Hanf, C.H.; El–Kazaz, N.   DE 148405/78/0004 N
Die Möglichkeiten der landwirtschaftlichen Produktionsausdehnung Ägyptens durch optimale regionale Produktions– struktur. **Possibilities of agricultural production expansion in Egypt with optimal regional structure of production.**

18010 Scheper, W.; Wulf, R.   DE 148451/75/0001
Ländliche Entwicklungsmodelle – Entwicklungsländer –. **Models of rural development – developing countries –.**

18011 Researcher not indicated   DE 148601/73/0001
Wirkungsanalyse sektoraler, strukturpolitischer Massnahmen und Nachfrageentwicklung in der Ernährungsindustrie. **Effect analysis of sectoral structure–political decisions and demand increase in food industry.**

18012 Löffler, H.; Timinger, J.   DE 160310/75/0001
Kosten–Nutzen–Untersuchung über den forstlichen Wirtschaftswegebau. **Cost–benefit–analysis of opening up forests.**

18013 Boettcher, E.; Romberg, A.   DE 164301/78/0001 N
Standortbedingungen im Agribusiness – Untersucht am Beispiel der Landwirtschaft in hochentwickelten Volkswirtschaften. **Conditions of location in agribusiness – The case of agriculture in developed economies.**

18014 Thoss, R.   DE 164350/75/0001
Die Konsistenz der Agrar– Energie– und Verkehrspolitik mit der regionalen Wirtschaftspolitik. **Consistency between agricultural policy, energy policy, transport policy and economic policy.**

18015 Researcher not indicated   DE 164351/77/0001
Landwirtschaftliche Vorranggebiete – Planungskonzept sowie agrar– und regionalpolitische Bedeutung. **Areas of agricultural priority – planning conception and importance to agricultural and regional policy.**

18016 Meckelein, W.   DE 170250/77/0001
Desertifikation in extremariden Gebieten – besonders der Oasen –. **Desertification in extremely arid environments – notably in oases –. Publications.**

18017 Borcherdt, C.   DE 170255/77/0002
Die neuere Entwicklung der Agrarreform in Venezuela. **Recent trend of agrarian reform in Venezuela.**

18018 Borcherdt, C.; Schneider, H.   DE 170255/77/0003
Neue Schwerpunkte der landwirtschaftlichen Entwicklung in den venezolanischen Llanos sowie im Orinoco–Delta. **New centers of farming development in Venezuelan llanos and in the delta of Orinoco river.**

18019 Neander, E.   DE 201020/78/0007 N
Beurteilung der Ausgleichszulage unter Berücksichtigung agrar–, raumordnungs– und umweltpolitischer Zielsetzungen. **Valuation of additional compensation with special regard to objectives of agrarian policy, area planning policy and environmental policy.**

18020 Meinhold, K.; Schrader, H.; Haxsen, G.
          DE 201100/77/0007
Entwicklung eines methodischen Konzeptes zur Beurteilung von Förderungsmassnahmen im Rahmen der Gemeinschaftsaufgabe. **Development of a methodical conception for valuation of promoting measures in the EC.**

18021 Meinhold, K.; Hinrichs, P.; Schrader, H.; Tries, B.
          DE 201100/77/0012 R
Projektion der sektoralen und betriebsgruppenspezifischen Entwicklung des Faktoreinsatzes und der Einkünfte in der deutschen Landwirtschaft. **Projection of factor allocation and income trends for the German agricultural sector as a whole and for special subdivisions.**

18022 Meinhold, K.; Hollmann, P.; Tries, B.
          DE 201100/78/0002 N
Analyse der Struktur des Energieverbrauchs im Agrarsektor der Bundesrepublik Deutschland. **Analysis of the structure of energy consumption in the agricultural sector of the Federal Republic of Germany.**

18023 Meinhold, K.; Heinrich, I.; Kögl, H.
          DE 201100/78/0007 N
Die Veränderung der Wettbewerbsrelationen zwischen den Produktionszweigen durch Tierschutzauflagen. **Changes in the competitive relations between agricultural production activities due to restrictions resulting from animal protection.**

18024 Meinhold, K.; Kleinhanss, W.   DE 201100/78/0011 N
Wirtschaftliche Auswirkungen von Energiepreiserhöhungen auf die Landwirtschaft. **Economic effects of increasing fuel prices on agriculture.**

18025 Meinhold, K.; Hollmann, P.; Kleinhanss, W.; Tries, B.
          DE 201100/78/0012 N

Produktivitätsfortschritte im Agrarsektor unter dem Aspekt des Energieeinsatzes. **The progress of agricultural productivity as related to the input of energy.**

18026 Meinhold, K.; Schmidt, B.   DE 201100/78/0014 N
Prüfung der ökonomischen Tragfähigkeit verminderter Einsatzmengen mineralischer Düngemittel unter Berücksichtigung neuer Erkenntnisse über Wertgrenzproduktivitäten von Düngemitteln. **Examination of the economic tolerances of reduced fertilizer inputs taking into account recent results of the marginal productivity of fertilizers.**

18027 Meinhold, K.; Schrader, H.   DE 201100/78/0016 N
Anpassungserfordernisse in landwirtschaftlichen Betriebsgruppen bei wechselnden gesamtwirtschaftlichen Rahmenbedingungen und Alternativen der Agrarpreispolitik. **Requirements for farm adjustment under changing economic conditions and alternative price policy in agriculture.**

18028 Meinhold, K.; Schrader, H.   DE 201100/78/0017 N
Betriebsgrösse und privatwirtschaftliche Kosten der Agrarproduktion im interregionalen und internationalen Vergleich. **Farm size and private economic costs of agricultural production under different regional and national comparative conditions.**

18029 Meinhold, K.; Bühner, T.   DE 201100/78/0018 N
Ökonomische Beurteilung von Förderungsmassnahmen für pflanzliche Eiweissfuttermittel aus einzelbetrieblicher Sicht. **Micro-economic evaluation of governmental operations to support the production of vegetal protein feedstuffs.**

18030 Meinhold, K.; Schrader, H.; Haxsen, G.; Bühner, T.
DE 201100/78/0020 N
Zur Ermittlung der Kosten der Agrarpolitik. **How to determine the costs of agricultural policy.**

18031 Meinhold, K.; Hinrichs, P.   DE 201100/78/0021 N
Entwicklung eines Ansatzes zur Ermittlung der optimalen Nutzungsdauer von Investitionsgütern bei unsicherer Leistungserwartung und technischem Fortschritt. **An approach to optimal use of investment goods taking into account uncertainty of performance and technical progress.**

18032 Lasch, R.; Sommer, V.   DE 201110/77/0005 R
Betriebs- und marktwirtschaftliche Untersuchungen im Berich der Fischwirtschaft. **Managing and marketing studies in the field of fishery.**

18033 Manegold, D.   DE 201110/77/0015
Integrationswirkungen agrarpolitischer Massnahmen in der EG. **Integrating effects of agricultural-political measures in the EC.**

18034 Manegold, D.   DE 201110/77/0017
Auswirkungen konjunktur- und währungspolitischer Massnahmen auf dem Agrarsektor. **Consequences of stimulation of economic policy and monetary policy on the agricultural sector.**

18035 Neander, E.; Doll, H.   DE 201120/77/0001
Analyse und Projektion der regionalen Entwicklung der Anzahl sowie der Grössen- und Produktionsstruktur der hauptteil- und nebenberuflich bewirtschafteten landwirtschaftlichen Betriebe in der Bundesrepublik

Deutschland. **Analysis and projection of regional development of quality and size and production structures of full–time and part–time farms in the Federal Republic of Germany.**

18036 Neander, E.; Doll, H.   DE 201120/77/0003
Analyse und Projektion der räumlichen Verteilung und Grössenstruktur der Schweinehaltung in der Bundesrepublik Deutschland. **Analysis and projection of spatial distribution and size structure of pig keeping farms in the Federal Republic of Germany.**

18037 Neander, E.; Dirksmeyer, W.   DE 201120/77/0004 R
Die einzelbetriebliche Entwicklung von Fläche, Kuhhaltung und sozialökonomischen Betriebstyp in Nordrhein–Westfalen zwischen 1969 und 1973. **The development of area, dairy cattle husbandry and socioeconomic type of single farms in Northrhine–Westphalia from 1969 to 1973.**

18038 Neander, E.; Dirksmeyer, W.; Doll, H.
DE 201120/78/0001 N
Entwicklung von Faktorausstattung, Produktionsrichtung und –kapazität und sozialökonomischem Betriebstyp von landwirtschaftlichen Betrieben in Nordrhein–Westfalen 1969/70, 1973 und 1977. **Development of factor endowment, ressource allocation, production capacity and socio–economic type of farms in Northrhine–Westphalia 1969/70, 1973 and 1977.**

18039 Neander, E.; Höhm, H.–P.   DE 201120/78/0002 N
Entwicklung von Angebot und Nachfrage auf den Arbeitsmärkten im ländlichen Raum der Bundesrepublik Deutschland. **Development of supply and demand for labor in the rural areas of the Federal Republic of Germany.**

18040 Maydell, H.–J.von   DE 202010/70/5010
Massnahmen zur Förderung forst- und holzwirtschaftlicher Investitionen in Entwicklungsländern. **Effective policies for stimulating forest and forest industry investment in developing countries.**

18041 Drews, M.   DE 207070/78/0002 N
Bedeutung aktueller Massnahmen zur Herstellung des Gleichgewichts am Milchmarkt. **Balance of supply and demand on the milk–market; EEC–measures for steering the balance of milk–market.**

18042 Müller, B.; Drews, M.; Einhoff, K.
DE 207070/78/0008 N
Betriebswirtschaftliche Konsequenzen hinsichtlich der Wettbewerbssituation der deutschen Obst- und Gemüseverarbeitungsindustrie bei einem EG–Beitritt der Länder Griechenland, Spanien und Portugal. **Economic consequences of the accession of Greece, Spain and Portugal to EEC for the position of German fruit and vegetable manufacturing industry.**

18043 Hodapp, W.   DE 501506/75/0003 N
Grundzüge der Besteuerung der Forstwirte und der forstwirtschaftlichen Zusammenschlüsse – Steuerhandbuch Forstwirtschaft –. **Fundamentals of tax on foresters and on forestry integrations – Tax Handbook Forestry –.**

18044 Weber, H.   DE 501506/77/0001 N
Vergleichende Untersuchungen über die Gemeinkostenanteile – insbesondere die Sozialausgaben und die sonstigen Lohnnebenkosten – in Wirtschaftsbetrieben. **Comparative**

D 5400 – Economic policy

studies on general expenses – especially social expenditure and other wage extras – of forestry enterprises.

18045 Schmütz, W.; Oettler, G.; Schnell, F.W.
DE 501700/74/0001
Methodische Probleme der Vermehrungsflächenstatistik der Getreide- und Kartoffelsorten in der Bundesrepublik Deutschland. **Methodical problems of surveying the annual increase areas of cereal crop and potatoe cultivars in the Federal Republic of Germany.**

18046 Weimann
DE 506402/70/0001
Grundsätze und Methoden der Waldwertschätzung. **Principles and methods of forest evaluation.**

18047 Roos, H.–J.; Bade, R.; Holla, M.
DE 914004/77/0001
Untersuchung der gesamtwirtschaftlichen Entwicklungsmöglichkeiten in landwirtschaftlichen Problemgebieten. **Investigation on developmental chances of total economy in rural problem areas.**

18048 Roos, H.–J.
DE 914004/77/0002
Herkunft von Aufstockungsflächen in entwicklungsfähigen Betrieben. **Provenience of expansion in developmentable farms.**

18049 Merkel, K.; Hohmann, K.; Schmitt, H.; Schneider, H.
DE 916500/77/0001
Die industriemässig betriebene tierische Agrarproduktion in der DDR – Organisationsformen, Produktionsverfahren und ökonomische Effizienz – mit vergleichenden Betrachtungen zur tierischen Produktion in der Bundesrepublik Deutschland. **The industrial animal production in the GDR – forms of organization, process of manufacture and economic efficiency – with comparative considerations on animal production in the Federal Republic of Germany.**

18050 Bohnet, A.
DE 916600/77/0002
Die Beteiligung der COMECON Länder am Welthandel. **Participation of COMECON member countries in world trade.**

18051 Bohnet, A.
DE 916600/77/0003
Die Umverteilung des Volkseinkommens in der Sowjetunion zwischen den Wirtschaftszweigen. **Redistribution of national income in the Soviet Union among the economic industries.**

18052 Leibfritz, W.; Parsche, R.; Spanakakis, G.; Oppenländer, K.H.
DE 917003/77/0002
Die Einkommensbesteuerung der Landwirtschaft in den EG–Partnerländern. **Agricultural income–tax in EC member countries.**

18053 Larsen, A.
DK 010500/77/0001
Udvikling af model til analyse af konsekvenserne ved prisændringer for landbrugsprodukter. **Development of model for analysing the consequences of price changes for agricultural products.**

18054 Kyed, K.
DK 030149/74/0007
Analyse af de vigtigste faktorer, som påvirker prisniveau og prisudvikling for landbrugsejendomme. **Analysis of the most important factors influencing price level and price development for agricultural holdings.**

18055 Kristensen, E.
DK 030149/76/0006

Landbrugsøkonomiens udvikling. **Development of the agricultural economy.**

18056 Pinstrup–Andersen, P.
DK 030149/77/0001 N
Analyse af sammenhængen mellem international og national landbrugsforskning, ny landbrugsteknologi og accelereret økonomisk udvikling i U–landene. **An analysis of the relationships among international and national agricultural research, new agricultural technology and accelerated economic development in developing countries.**

18057 Scheibelein, E.R.
DK 030149/77/0003 N
Landbrugets finansiering. **Financing of the agricultural sector.**

18058 Thomsen, C.
DK 030149/78/0002 N
En analyse af produktionssystemer inden for husdyrbruget i Vesteuropa. **Animal production systems in Western Europe.**

18059 Pinstrup–Andersen, P.
DK 030149/79/0003 N
Metoder til beregning af de ernæringsmæssige konsekvenser af landbrugsprojekter og landbrugspolitiske indgreb i U–landene. **Methods for estimating the nutritional consequences of agricultural projects and policies in developing countries.**

18060 Stryg, P.E.
DK 030149/79/0004 N
Anvendelse af programmeringsmetoder i landbrugets drifts– og investeringsplanlægning. **Programming methods in agricultural management and investment planning.**

18061 Stryg, P.E.
DK 030149/79/0005 N
Landbrugssektorens betydning for regionaløkonomien. **The importance of the agricultural sector with regard to regional economics.**

18062 Wulff, H.
DK 030149/79/0006 N
Offentlig regulering af jordbrugserhvervene. **Government regulation of agriculture.**

18063 Albertsen, T.H.
DK 030149/79/0007 N
Landbrugslovgivningens administration. **The administration of agricultural law in Denmark.**

18064 Helles, F.
DK 030181/73/0001
Analyse af hedeskovbrugets regionaløkonomiske betydning. **Analysis of the regional economic importance of heath forestry.**

18065 Ranfelt, L.W.
DK 030181/79/0002 N
Skovbrugets rolle i den regionale udvikling. **Forestry and regional development.**

18066 Nicolas, Ph.
FR 010000/65/8608
Rôle du mouvement coopératif dans l'économie et la politique agro–alimentaires.Organisation et développement des entreprises et des appareils coopératifs.Intercoopération intersectorielle internationale. **Role of the co–operative movement in agri–business and agricultural policy. Organisation and development of co–operative firms and networks. Intercooperative relations : interbranch and international.**

18067 De Ravignan, F.
FR 010000/77/8590
Voies possibles du développement économique et social dans les Monts du Forez (Loire). **Possibility of economic and social development in Forez hills.**

18068 Deffontaines, J.P.; De Casabianca, F.; Raichon, C.; De Verneuil, H.; Moisan, H.   FR 010112/74/3037
Stratégies possibles du développement de l'agriculture dans deux régions de la montagne Corse. **Possible strategies for the development of agricultural activities in two mountainous districts of Corsica.** Publications.

18069 Osty, P.L.; Petit, F.E.; Brun, A.; Chassany, J.P.
FR 010112/74/9099
Evolutions économique et écologique de zones à faible productivité le "Causse Méjean". **Economic and ecological evolutions of low–productivity rural areas; case study of the"Causse Méjean" plateau.**

18070 Deffontaines, J.P.; de Verneuil, B.H.; Raichon, C.; de Casabianca, F.   FR 010112/74/9101
Stratégies possibles de développement de l'agriculture dans deux régions de la montagne corse. **Possible strategies for the agricultural development of two regions of Corsica.**

18071 Mouton, B.; Favier, M.A.   FR 010308/74/3326
Les transferts de propriété des surfaces boisées. Le cas du canton de Badonviller –54. **Private forest ownership changes in a small area.**

18072 Buttoud, G.; Rochot, A.; Favier, M.A.
FR 010308/75/3324
L'exonération trentenaire des boisements et les finances communales. **Tax exempted woodlots and to local finances.** Publications.

18073 Mouton, B.; Elyakime, B.; Bonin, M.; Favier, A.; Buttoud, G.; Normandin, D.   FR 010308/77/8649
Le rôle de la petite propriété forestière en zone rurale dans la CEE. **The role of the small woodland property in rural areasin EEC.**

18074 Rochot, A.   FR 010308/78/8667
Les corrélations entre l'activité économique nationale, l'activité des branches exploitation forestiére et scierie et les rentrées de la taxe unique forestiére. **Correlations between the level of the national economy, the logging and sawing activities and the receipts of the single forestry tax.**

18075 Larrere, G. (Economie); de Montard, F.X. (Agro)
FR 010802/74/6106
Etude des systèmes agraires des dômes. **Study of Agricultural Systems in Dome mountains.**

18076 Decourt, M.; Larrère, G.; de Montard, F.
FR 010802/76/6107
Etude des systèmes agraires et de la forêt en margeride. **Study of Agricultural Systems and Forest management in Margeride hills.**

18077 Lienard, G.; Wolfer, G.; Larrere, G.; Bazin, G.
FR 010810/75/8576
Evolution de l'agriculture d'une région de demi–montagne : le Plateau Sud des Dômes. **Evolution of the agriculture of a mountain's area : the Dômes highlands.**

18078 Barthelemy, D.   FR 011012/74/3305
Modes de propriété du sol et formes de processus de travail. **Relationship between land tenure and labour division.**

18079 Thiebaut, L.   FR 011012/75/3302

L'industrie en milieu rural et ses liens avec l'espace régional (aux niveaux: de la force de travail, du foncier, du capital, politique). Son influence sur les structures agricoles. **Industry in rural environment and its relationships with the regional area (with special concern on labor, land and capital). Influence on agricultural structures.**

18080 Viallow, J.B.   FR 011012/75/3307
La croissance agricole en France et en Bourgogne, de 1850 à nos jours. **Agricultural growth in France and Burgundy, from 1850 to 1970.**

18081 Cavailhes, J.; Gogue, A.M.; Thiebaut, L.; Perrier–Cornet, Ph.; Loyat, J.   FR 011012/76/8620
Question agraire et développement du capitalisme : l'influence de l'évolution de l'emploi rural non agricole. **Agrarian question and capitalism development : evolution of nonagriculture employement.**

18082 Cavailhes, J.; Perrier–Cornet, Ph.; Loyat, J.; Thiebaut, L.; Gogue, A.M.   FR 011012/76/8622
Question agraire et développement du capitalisme. Evolution des formes de production en Beaujolais viticole. **Agrarian question and capitalism development : regional study in Beaujolais.**

18083 Cavailhes, J.; Perrier–Cornet, Ph.; Loyat, J.; Thiebaut, J.L.; Gogue, A.M.   FR 011012/77/8619
Question agraire et développement du capitalisme : Evolution de l'agriculture depuis le XIXe siècle, exemple de la France, de l'Allemagne, et de la Grande–Bretagne. **Agrarian question and capitalism development. Evolution of agriculture from XIXe century. Exemple of France, German and Grand Britain.**

18084 Nicolas, Ph.   FR 011205/70/3357
La coopérative agricole dans l'économie et la politique agro–alimentaire. **Farm cooperatives and the economy and policy of the food industry.**

18085 Lifran, R.; Delord, B.; Lacombe, Ph.; Monney, R.
FR 011205/72/3364
Structures agraires et développement économique. **Land structures and economic development.**

18086 Brun, A.; Chassany, J.P.; Osty, P.   FR 011205/74/3362
Etude des aspects économiques des études pluridisciplinaires sur les régions à basse productivité agricole. **Economical aspects of multidisciplinary studies regions with low agricultural productivity.**

18087 Pouliquen, A.   FR 011205/74/8653
Analyse comparée des transformations agro–alimentaires dans les pays socialistes. Les échanges agro–alimentaires intra COMECON et Est–Ouest. **Transformations of the agrifood sectors in the socialist countries; intra COMECON and EAST–WEST agrifood exchanges.**

18088 Mazoyer, M.; Sylvander, B.; Nicolas, Ph.; Reboul, C.
FR 011205/75/3360
Analyse comparative des économies et des politiques agro–alimentaires dans les pays nord–européens (notamment scandinaves). **Comparative analysis of the economy and policy of the food industry in North Europen country (scandinavia).**

18089 Pouliquen, A.; Proust, J.F.   FR 011205/75/3363
Transformation des relations entre l'agriculture et son

environnement économique. **Transformations of the relationships between agriculture and its economic environment.**

18090 Labonne, M.; Degert, G.; Cibenel, C.
FR 011205/75/3366
Prospectives alimentaires et agricoles pour la zone méditerranéenne. **Future prospects for food and agriculture in the mediterranean area.**

18091 Labonne, M. FR 011205/75/8675
Macrogestion des écosystémes. **For eco systems long term agricultural policies.**

18092 Casas, J. FR 011205/76/8654
Developpement agricole et rural dans les pays sous–développés socialistes. **Agricultural and rural development in socialist less developped countries.**

18093 Flament, J.C.; Labouesse, F.; Langlet, A.; Molenat; Chassany, J.P. FR 011205/77/8570
Etude socio–économique des complémentarités entre zones à potentiels différents : le cas du Larzac. **Sociological and economic study of complementatities between areas affering different possibilities : the case of Larzac.**

18094 Rainelli, P.; Bonnieux, F.; Miclet, G.
FR 011302/73/3355
Indicateurs socio–économiques liés à la qualité de l'eau. **Socio–economic factors in relation with water quality.**

18095 Brangeon, J.L.; Jegouzo, G. FR 011302/74/3346
La pauvreté en agriculture. **Farm poverty.**

18096 Leon, Y. FR 011302/74/3353
Le partage du revenu des ménages agricoles entre la consommation et l'épargne. **Division between consumption and saving of the farm family income.**

18097 Bompard, J.P.; Leon, Y.; Aubert, D.; Postel–Vinay, G. FR 011302/76/8596
Politique économique de l'Etat et endettement de l'agriculture. **State economic policy and increasing of debt for farms.**

18098 Rainelli, P.; Bonnieux, F.; Fouet, J.P.
FR 011302/77/8585
Les disparités économiques régionales dans l'agriculture nationale et européenne. **Regional economic disparities in agriculture in France and EEC.**

18099 Dauce, P.; Leon, Y. FR 011302/77/8588
Les transformations de l'agriculture en Bretagne depuis la fin du 19ème siecle. **Evolution of Britany agriculture from end of 19th century.**

18100 Broussolle, C. FR 011302/77/8672
Structures de production et inflation dans l'agriculture et les industries alimentaires. **Structural aspects of inflation in agriculture and food industry.**

18101 Boussard, J.M.; Leflambé, H.; Makagon, S.
FR 011706/70/3338
Rédaction d'un générateur de matrices de programmes linéaires appliqués à l'agriculture. **Preparation of a matrix generator for agricultural linear programming models.**

18102 Bergmann, D. FR 011706/72/3333
Politique agricole des pays développés – France en particulier– Un essai de synthèse. **Agricultural policy in developed countries – with particular reference to France – atentative synthesis.** Publications.

18103 Boussard, J.M.; Foulhouse, I.; Over, A.M.; Leflambé, H. FR 011706/72/3345
Construction d'un modèle économétrique de l'agriculture française. **Building of an econometric model of French agriculture.** Publications.

18104 Bergmann, D. FR 011706/73/3335
Agriculture et sylviculture dans les Landes de Gascogne. Concurrence ou complémentarité?. **Farming or forestry in the Landes de Gascogne area. Competition or complementarity?.** Publications.

18105 Boussard, J.M.; David, C. FR 011706/74/3332
Rédaction d'un programme universel de manipulation de données in put/out put agricole. **Multi purpose agricultural data system.**

18106 Bergmann, D. FR 011706/74/3334
Politique des structures et perspectives en matière de structures agricoles. Europe du Nord–Ouest, France en particulier. **Structural policy and projections of agricultural structure. North–Western Europe, particularly France.** Publications.

18107 Reboul, C.; Al Hamchari, M.C. FR 011706/74/3343
Accumulation du capital et différenciation des systèmes de culture et d'élevage. **Capital accumulation and diversification of crop and livestock patterns.**

18108 Bazin, G. FR 011706/78/8598
Analyse des premiers résultats de l'application en France de la politique des plans de développement. **First results analysis of the application in France of the development plans policy.**

18109 Cordonnier, P.; Grandclaude, L.; Guinet, A.
FR 011808/73/3313
Systèmes de production de polyculture–élevage de la Communauté Européenne. **Mixed farming production systems in the E. E. C.**

18110 Jullian, P.; Cordonnier, P. FR 011808/75/3309
Modèles d'orientation de la production et de la transformation des produits agricoles dans la région de Voivodine (Yougoslavie). **Orientation models for production and processing of agricultural products in the Voivodine area (Yougoslavia).**

18111 Marsal, P.; Sourie, J.C.; Gorse, P. FR 011808/75/3312
Problèmes économiques posés par la récupération des pailles. **Economic problems of straw recuperation.**

18112 Sourie, J.C.; Troizier, M.; Jayet, A.
FR 011808/75/8525
Etude socio–économique des perspectives de production et de consommation des énergies renouvelables issues de la biomasse agricole. **Socio–economical study for outlook of production and consumption in renouable energy from agricultural biomass.**

18113 Mainie, P.; Damour, L. FR 012201/75/3035

Enquête sur l'évolution actuelle des exploitants du Marais de Rochefort. **Survey of the actual evolution of the farms in the Marsh district near Rochefort.**

18114 Mergui, G.; Fromentin, G.; Nefussi, J. FR 012205/74/8563
Construction d'un tableau entrées–sorties du complexe agro–alimentaire. **Building of an Input Output Table for the French–Agriculture.**

18115 Bergmann, D. FR 012212/72/8593
Politique agricole: essai de synthèse provisoire. **Agricultural policy: a provisional synthesis.**

18116 Reboul, C. FR 012212/72/8655
Economie de la production agricole sénégalaise. **Economics of Senegalese agricultural production.**

18117 Deverre, C.; Ponchelet, D. FR 012212/75/8505
L'évolution de la grande propriété foncière en Brie. **Large landed property evolution in "Brie".**

18118 Gervais, M.; Nallet, H.; Roger, C. FR 012212/75/8594
Crédits budgétaires à l'agriculture de 1945 à 1978. **Budgetary credit to french agriculture from 1945 to 1978.**

18119 Hairy, D.; Perraud, D. FR 012212/75/8611
Problèmes d'organisation de l'économie laitière. **Milk economy policy.**

18120 Chabert, J.P.; Bertrand, J.P. FR 012212/75/8663
Relations Est–Ouest et agriculture. **East–West relations and agriculture.**

18121 Cranney, C.; Rio, P. FR 012212/76/8552
Rôle de l'Etat dans la constitution d'une industrie de la viande bovine en France. **The role of the state in the creation of a beef industry in France.**

18122 Saunier, P.; Schaller, B. FR 012212/76/8554
Les voies de l'industrialisation de l'agro–alimentation : Etude de l'aviculture française de 1955 à 1975. **The french poultry industry 1955–1975.**

18123 Lebas, L. FR 012212/76/8650
Politique agricole, politique des échanges et évolution des structures agricoles en Espagne. **Spain food and exchange policy and agricultural structure evolution.**

18124 De Crisenoy, C. FR 012212/77/8503
Les conflits fonciers dans la Manche 1960–1978. **Land conflict in the "Manche" department 1960–1978.**

18125 De Crisenoy, Ch. FR 012212/77/8507
Application du statut du fermage et du métayage. **Application of farming and share–cropping rules.**

18126 Foulhouze, I.; Boussard, J.M. FR 012212/77/8521
Etude de la productivité de l'agriculture française. **French agricultural sector productivity.**

18127 Ossard, H. FR 012212/77/8621
Question agraire et développement du capitalisme : Etude pour la région parisienne. **Agrarian question and capitalism development : Study for the Yvelines department.**

18128 Evrard, P.; Debailleul, G. FR 012212/77/8652
Le secteur agro–alimentaire au Quebec. **Agro–industry in Quebec.**

18129 Boussard, J.M. FR 012212/77/8677
Théorie et pratique de l'analyse avantage/coût en matière de projets de developpement agricole. **Theory and practice of benefit cost analysis in agricultural projects.**

18130 Berlan, J.P. FR 012212/78/8545
Contrôle génétique et production agricole. **Genetic control of agricultural production.**

18131 Viau, C.; Hassan, D. FR 012212/78/8597
Politique agricole commune et problèmes monétaires. **Agricultural policy of E.E.C. and monetary problems.**

18132 Bergmann, D. FR 012212/78/8651
Prospective de l'agriculture espagnole. **The future of spanish agriculture.**

18133 Berlan, J.P. FR 012212/78/8660
Division internationale du travail et le complexe américain du soja. **International division of labor, and the rise of the US soyabean complex.**

18134 Brun, A.; Osty, P.L.; Chassany, J.P.; Petit, F.E. FR 012303/74/8571
Evolutions économiques et écologiques de zones à faible productivité : Le Causse Mejean. **Economical and ecological evolution in low productivity areas : the Causse Mejean.**

18135 Poupardin, D. FR 012303/74/8573
Evolution des systèmes agraires du Briançonnais. **Dynamics of agrarian systems in the Briançonnais.**

18136 Nougarede, O.; Decourt, N.; Larrere FR 012303/77/8574
Réorganisation de l'espace et transformation des systèmes agraires par le mode de production capitaliste, en Margeride. **The space reorganization and the transformation of agrarian systems by capitalism in Margeride.**

18137 Mollard, A.; Le pape, Y.; Bel, F.; Fleury, A. FR 012600/74/8674
Choix des techniques et planification de l'environnement, le cas de l'agriculture française. **Choice of techniques and environment planning : French agriculture as an example.**

18138 Fleury, A. FR 012600/77/8522
Essai sur le concept de productivité en agriculture. **Study about agricultural productivity.**

18139 Bye, P.; Pernet, F.; Fleury FR 012600/77/8543
Stratégies de mécanisation agricole et développement de l'industrie du machinisme agricole. **Strategies of Agricultural Mechanization and industrial agricultural machinery development.**

18140 Mollard, A.; Bye, P. FR 012600/77/8609
L'internationalisation des conditions de production et d'échange : la division internationale du travail dans le secteur agro–alimentaire. **Internationalisation of production and exchange conditions : international division of labor in the food sector.**

D 5400 – Economic policy

18141 Hutchinson GB 040601/78/0007 N
Value added by processing and marketing Northern Ireland pig and poultry produce.

18142 O'Brien, D. IE 050100/75/9243 N
Economic inferences of crop management.

18143 O'Brien, D. IE 050100/75/9253 N
Economic inferences of tree crop management.

18144 Lee, J.; Harte, F.J.; Walsh, J.P. IE 060200/78/1378 R
Agricultural development study of mrdo region. (Counties Laois, Offaly, Westmeath, Roscommon, Longford). Publications.

18145 Cox, P.G. IE 060600/72/1005 R
Irish governments scheme of encouragement to leave farming. Publications.

18146 Lucey, D.I.F. IE 110105/74/7784 N
EEC effect on input–supply and product–processing for agriculture in an all–Ireland context.

18147 Lucey, D.I.F.; Cahill, C.; Hunt, P.; Cahillane, G.
IE 110105/74/7785 N
EEC effect on production, trade and consumption of farm products in all–Ireland.

18148 Lucey, D.I.F. IE 110105/77/7788 N
Developments in the economic theory of co–operation. Publications.

18149 O'Connor, R.; Whelan, B.J.; Crutchfield, J.; Mellon, K. IE 150000/78/8315 R
Development of the Irish sea fishing industry and its regional implications.

18150 Nardone, A. IT 012400/77/0579
Le strutture demografiche e la produzione della carne. **Demographic structures and meat production.**

18151 Grittani, G. IT 040102/77/0202 R
Possibilità di sviluppo della zootecnica montana pugliese. **Development of the possibilities of livestock breeding in the Puglia mountains.**

18152 Tartaglia, A. IT 040102/77/0305 R
I lavori agricoli dipendenti in Puglia. **Hired agricultural labour in Puglia.**

18153 Patuelli, V. IT 040204/73/1199
Agricoltura e sistema economico generale. **Agriculture and the overall economic system.** Publications.

18154 Biancardi, V. IT 040204/74/0516
Ricerca svolta a verificare la diversità delle soluzioni tecniche in agricoltura e a valutarne il grado di razionalità. **Research for assessing the range of technical solutions applied in agriculture and evaluation of their degree of rationality.**

18155 Maugeri, G. IT 040306/77/0236 R
Ricerche sull'economia della produzione e del mercato delle coltivazioni orticole in ambiente protetto in Sicilia. **Research on the economics of producing and marketing horticultural produce grown in a sheltered environment in Sicily.**

18156 Galizzi, G. IT 040410/74/0555
Formazione di capitale e produttività nell'agricoltura lombarda. **Capital formation and productivity in the agricultural sector in Lombardia.**

18157 Casati, D. IT 040606/73/0167
Programma coordinato triennale di ricerche per la definizione tecnico–economica di moduli e cantieri di lavoro ottimali per diversi livelli di meccanizzazione. **3–year coordinated research programme in view of a technical–economic definition of optimal models and work yards for various levels of mechanization.**

18158 Marenco, G. IT 040706/74/0585
Determinazione dei redditi lordi dell'agricoltura italiana. **Estimating of gross incomes in Italian agriculture.**

18159 Favaretti, G. IT 040804/77/0176 R
Ricerche sulla struttura dei costi di produzione di alcuni prodotti agricoli. **Research on the components of production costs of some agricultural products.**

18160 Ferro, O. IT 040804/78/1052 N
Strumenti di analisi quali–quantitativa nelle politiche attuate a livello regionale in Europa. **Analytical qualitative and quantitative tools applied to regional policies in Europe.**

18161 Agostini, D. IT 040806/78/1022 N
Ricerca sulla metodologia di pianificazione e gestione del territorio rurale in Italia, Inghilterra e Svezia. **Research on planning and management methodology applied to rural territories in Italy, England and Sweden.**

18162 Schifani, C. IT 040912/77/0296 R
L'agricoltura del Mezzogiorno di fronte ai problemi posti dall'integrazione dei Paesi mediterranei nella CEE. **Agriculture in southern Italy and the problems arising in Mediterranean countries from EEC membership.**

18163 Montanini, C.; Benassi, A.; Magistretti, A.; Copelli, A.
IT 041517/78/0001 N
Condizioni economico–produttive del settore agricolo nella provincia di Parma e adattamento alla direttive CEE 160/72. **Economic–productive conditions of the agricultural sector in the province of Parma and their adjustment to the EEC 160/72 directive.** Publications.

18164 Montanini, C.; Benassi, A.; Magistretti, A.; Copelli, A.
IT 041517/79/0001 N
Grado di autoapprovvigionamento agricolo–alimentare in Emilia–Romagna. **Degree of agricultural and food products self–supply in Emilia–Romagna.**

18165 Scarpa, G.; Trevisan, G. IT 041901/76/0001 N
Proprietà e imprese nella campagna veneta agli inizi del secolo scorso. **Landed property and farms in the venetian country–side at the beginning of the last century.**

18166 Giacomini, C. IT 041901/79/0001 N
Il credito come strumento di politica agraria nei Paesi della CEE. **Credit as an instrument of agricultural policy in the Common Market.**

18167 Vries, R.L. de NL 010106/71/3489
Prognose van de ontwikkeling en het gebruik van werktuigen in de Nederlandse landbouw. **Prognosis of the development and**

the use of implements in Dutch agriculture.

18168 Post, J.H.   NL 010116/66/0092 R
Macro–economische input/output analyse van de Nederlandse landbouw als geheel en de sectoren daarvan. **Macro–economic input/output analysis of Dutch agriculture, in total and in sectors.**

18169 Post, J.H.   NL 010116/69/2709 R
Economisch jaaroverzicht van de Nederlandse landbouw. **Annual economic review of Dutch agriculture.** Publications.

18170 Douw, L.   NL 010116/72/3921 R
Ontwikkelingstendenties bij het aantal bedrijven en bij het bedrijfstype in de bollenteelt in West–Friesland. **Development tendencies in number and farm types of holdings for flower bulb growing in West–Friesland.**

18171 Post, J.H.; Ploeg, B. van de; Haan, W.G. de
    NL 010116/72/3922
Ontwikkelingstendenties bij het aantal bedrijven en bij het bedrijfstype in de bollenteelt in de Zuidhollandse bollenstreek. **Development tendencies in the number and farm types of holdings for flowerbulb growing in Zuid–Holland.** Publications.

18172 Graaff, G.C. de; Vlieger, J.J. de   NL 010116/73/5932
Vertikale integratie in de varkenshouderij. **Vertical integration in the pig industry.** Publications.

18173 Rijneveld, R.   NL 010116/73/5946
Oriënterend onderzoek naar de visserij in West–Europa. **Research on Western Europe's fisheries.** Publications.

18174 Douw, L.   NL 010116/74/6533 R
Agrarisch structurele en bedrijfsstructurele aspekten van de intensieve veehouderij. **Aspects of intensive cattle–breeding. (Structural aspects).** Publications.

18175 Meijaard, D.   NL 010116/74/6547 R
Analyse van de structurele ontwikkelingen in de tuinbouw. **Analysis of the structural economic developments in Dutch horticulture.** Publications.

18176 Meijaard, D.   NL 010116/74/6548 R
Sectoraal onderzoek in de tuinbouw. **The economic significance of the Dutch horticultural sector.**

18177 Overgaauw, J.G.A.; Aukema, S.   NL 010116/74/6558
Het landbouwkrediet in Nederland. **Agricultural credit in the Netherlands.**

18178 Bos, C.   NL 010116/75/6566
Analyse inkomensverdeling in de landbouw (akkerbouw en veehouderij). **Analysis of the distribution of incomes in agriculture.**

18179 Bauwens, A.L.G.M.   NL 010116/75/6881 R
Inventariserend onderzoek naar tuinbouw in de open grond op akkerbouwbedrijven. **Horticulture in the open on arable farms (a statistical research).**

18180 Douw, L.   NL 010116/75/6884 R
Structuurvisie van de land– en tuinbouw in het noorden van ons land. **Outlook upon the structure of agricultural and horticulture in the northern part of the Netherlands till 1984.**

18181 Bauwens, A.L.G.M.   NL 010116/75/6887 R
Sociaal–economische beschrijving van de land– en tuinbouw in Rijsbergen en Zundert. **Socio economic description of agriculture in the Rijsbergen and Zundert region in the Netherlands.**

18182 Kortekaas, B.M.M.; Haan, W.G. de
    NL 010116/75/6890
Structuuronderzoek bloembollenbedrijfstak. **Structural aspects of dutch bulbgrowing industry.**

18183 Haan, W.G. de; Stein, A.   NL 010116/75/6895
Structuuronderzoek opengrondbloementeelt. **Structural aspects of growing outdoor flower crops.**

18184 Post, J.H.   NL 010116/75/8586 N
Ontwikkelingen in de bedrijfsstructuur in Nederland. **Socio–economic research into the farm structure in the Netherlands.**

18185 Post, J.H.   NL 010116/76/7693 R
Analyse en evaluatie van doeleinden en instrumenten van het gemeenschappelijk landbouwbeleid. **The Common Agricultural Policy: an analysis and evaluation of objectives and instruments.** Publications.

18186 Douw, L.   NL 010116/76/7700 R
De aantalsontwikkeling en de aantalsmutaties bij de agrarische bedrijven. **Development of number and mutations in the number of farms.** Publications.

18187 Bos, C.   NL 010116/76/7710
Prognosemodel met betrekking tot financiering. **Forecast model concerning finance.**

18188 Graaff, G.C. de   NL 010116/76/7737
De verticale integratie in de pluimveehouderij. **Vertical integration in the poultry industry.**

18189 Bauwens, A.L.G.M.   NL 010116/77/8568 N
Problematiek en perspectieven van bedrijven in de middengroep. **Problems and perspectives of middle classed farms.**

18190 Bauwens, A.L.G.M.   NL 010116/77/8899 N
Ontwikkeling bij de bedrijfsstructuur. **Developments in farm structure.**

18191 Meester, G.   NL 010116/77/8917 N
Een economisch model van de Nederlandse landbouw (algemeen en coördinatie). **An economic model of Dutch agriculture (general and coördination).**

18192 Meester, G.   NL 010116/78/8918 N
Een economisch model van de Nederlandse landbouw (vraaganalyse). **An economic model of Dutch agriculture (demand analysis).**

18193 Meester, G.   NL 010116/78/8919 N
Een economisch model van de Nederlandse landbouw (aanbodanalyse). **An economic model of Dutch agriculture (supply analysis).**

18194 Meester, G.   NL 010116/78/8920 N
Een economisch model van de Nederlandse landbouw (Intermediaire landbouwproducten en veevoer model). **An**

D 5400 – Economic policy

economic model of Dutch agriculture (Intermediate agricultural products; feed model).

18195 Meester, G.   NL 010116/78/8921 N
Een economisch model van de Nederlandse landbouw (grondmarkt). **An economic model of Dutch agriculture (the agricultural land market).**

18196 Meester, G.   NL 010116/78/8922 N
Een economisch model van de Nederlandse landbouw (celovergangen). **An economic model of Dutch agriculture (movements of farmers between types and sizes of farmes).**

18197 Dijkstra, H.   NL 020001/75/3656
De concurrentiepositie van de Nederlandse melkveehouderij in vergelijking met de melkveehouderij in andere gebieden binnen de EEG. **The economic strength of Dutch dairy farming compared with dairy farming systems in other regions of the Common Market.** Publications.

18198 Oskam, A.J.   NL 020004/71/4244
Instrument–modellen voor de Nederlandse landbouwpolitiek. **Instrument –models for the Dutch agriculture policy.** Publications.

18199 Noort, P.C. van den   NL 020004/73/4847
De betekenis van de veehouderij voor de Nederlandse graanhandel. **Grainsupply and livestockfarming in the Netherlands.**

18200 Oskam, A.J.   NL 020004/75/6772
Kwantitatieve analyse van de inkomensverdeling van agrarische zelfstandigen in Nederland en de uitwerking van het overheidsbeleid. **Quantitative analysis of income distribution of Dutch farmers and the influence of government policy.** Publications.

18201 Oskam, A.J.   NL 020004/77/7559
Mogelijkheden van beleidsalternatieven voor een E.G.–zuivelbeleid. **Possible alternatives for E.G.–dairy policy.** Publications.

18202 Slangen, L.H.G.   NL 020004/77/7560
Financieel–economische gevolgen van landbouw onder beperkende omstandigheden. **Financial–economical consequences of agricultural production under environmental restrictions.** Publications.

18203 Dijk, G. van   NL 020004/78/8505
De argrarische waarde en prijsvorming van landbouwgrond. **Agricultural value and price formation of agricultural land.**

18204 Riezebos, E.P.   NL 020027/75/4680
Enige economische aspecten van landhervorming. **Some economic aspects of land reform.**

18205 Luning, H.A.   NL 020027/77/7365
Methoden van regionaal onderzoek ten behoeve van plattelandsontwikkeling. **The process of regional planning.** Publications.

18206 Bouman, F.J.A.   NL 020050/73/6815
Traditionele vormen van coöperatie. **Traditional savings and credit societies in the Third World.** Publications.

18207 Hoeve, H.   NL 040007/78/8487

Onderzoek naar de economische gevolgen van een gewijzigd uitgiftebeleid inzake bedrijfsgrootte van nieuwe landbouwbedrijven in de IJsselmeerpolders. **Economic consequences of a changed policy concerning farm size of new farms in the IJsselmeerpolders.**

D 6100 – Social policy

See also 17384, 17395, 18081, 18082, 18083, 18093, 18099, 18112, 18149

18208 Sachs, R.   DE 105350/72/0003
Soziologische Aspekte landwirtschaftlicher Entwicklungsprojekte. **Sociological aspects of agricultural development projects.**

18209 Lipinsky, E.E.; Otte, E.   DE 111652/75/0002
Verfügungsbeschränkungen der landwirtschaftlichen Vererbungsgesetze und agrarstrukturpolitische Reformvorstellungen. **Restrictions of farmers' right of disposal by laws of succession and political conceptions of structural reform in agriculture.**

18210 Junghans, K.H.; Weber, J.   DE 111653/75/0001
60 Jahre Chotanagpur Kath. Kredit–Genossenschaft. Eine Studie über die Rolle der ländlichen Genossenschaften im regionalen Entwicklungsprozess in überbevölkerten Agrargebieten Süd–Asiens. **60 years Chotanagpur Cath. Credit Association. – A study of the role of rural co–operatives in the process of regional development and social cultural development in densely populated rural areas of South Asia.**

18211 Niesslein, E.; Brucker, A.P.   DE 126500/75/0008
Die rechtliche Verfügbarkeit und Zuordnung der Sozialfunktionen des Waldes. **Statutory availability and assignment of social functions to the forest.**

18212 Kuhnen, F.; Wittmann, H.   DE 132250/75/0003
Innovations– und Migrationsverhalten türkischer Gastarbeiter ländlicher Herkunft nach ihrer Rückkehr. **Innovation in agriculture and outmigration to regional central places by returning guest–workers who originate from farms in Turkey.**

18213 Scholz, F.; Asche, H.; Janzen, J.   DE 132512/75/0001
Moderner Wandel im beduinischen/bäuerlichen Lebensraum der kleinen Golf-Staaten – Abu Dhabi, Kuwait, Oman –. **Modern change in the Bedouin/rural areas of the Gulf States Abu Dhabi, Kuwait, Oman.**

18214 Urff, W.von   DE 142200/75/0005
Die Bedeutung von Nahrungsmittellieferungen unter PL–480 für die Entwicklungsländer, dargestellt unter besonderer Berücksichtigung des indischen Agrarsektors. **The importance of food aid under PL–480 for developing countries with special regard to India's agriculture.**

18215 Urff, W.von; Matzdorf, M.   DE 142200/75/0006
Der Beitrag "angepasster" Technologien zur Überwindung der Unterentwicklung im Rahmen des Self–Reliance–Konzeptes. **The contribution of "adapted" technologies towards overcoming underdevelopment within the framework of the self–reliance approach.**

18216 Volk, H.   DE 501504/78/0004 N
Auswertung der Besucherbefragung anlässlich des landwirtschaftlichen Hauptfestes in Stuttgart – 24.9.–2.10.1977 –. **Evaluation of inquiry of visitors on the occasion of the main agricultural festivity in Stuttgart – 24.9.–2.10.1977 –.**

18217 Decourt, N.   FR 010301/73/4079
Forêts et paysages – attitude du public vis-à-vis des paysages forestiers. **Forêts and landscape.**

18218 Kalaora, B.   FR 010301/74/4078
Etude sociologique de la fréquentation des forêts suburbaines. **The frequentation of suburban forests; sociological study.**

18219 Laurent, C.   FR 011012/78/8586
Décentralisation industrielle et peuplement rural. **Industrial décentralization and rural population.**

18220 Barthez, A.   FR 011012/78/8637
Etude sociologique des rapports familiaux comme rapports de domination en agriculture. **Sociological analysis of relationships between family members in farms.**

18221 Petit, M.   FR 011012/78/8657
Les pratiques agraires traditionnelles dans les collines préhimalayennes du Népal. **Traditional farm practices in the pre–himalayan hills of Nepal.**

18222 Labouesse, F.   FR 011205/75/3365
Relations entre structures sociales, technologies et évolution technique, spécialement dans les zones marginales. **Relationships between social structures technologies and technical evolution specially in marginal areas.**

18223 Lacombe, P.; Lifran, R.   FR 011205/75/8625
Contribution à l'étude des couches sociales dans l'agriculture française. **Social strata in french agriculture.**

18224 Boisseau, P.   FR 011205/75/8633
Essai théorique sur l'innovation et ses "structures d'accueil" en agriculture. **Théorical essay on innovation and its degree of acceptance in agriculture.**

18225 Miclet, G.   FR 011205/78/8642
Opinions et comportements à l'égard de l'environnement. **Opinions and behaviours concerning natural environment.**

18226 Jegouzo, G.   FR 011302/70/8636
Les jeunes et l'agriculture. **Youth and agriculture.**

18227 Brangeon, J.L.; Jegouzo, G.   FR 011302/72/8638
Pauvreté et inégalités sociales en agriculture. **Poverty and social discrepancies in agriculture.**

18228 Henry, J.B.   FR 011302/76/8629
La question agraire dans la société bretonne. **The agrarian question in Britanny.**

18229 Painvin, R.M.; Berlan, M.; Lebas, L.; Altmann, C.   FR 011302/77/8510
Etude comparative interrégionale des conditions de vie et de travail des femmes dans les exploitations agricoles. **Living and labor conditions of women in farms.**

18230 Houee, P.   FR 011302/78/8589
Les mutations des espaces ruraux bretons de 1954 à 1975. **Rural space evolution in Britanny from 1954 to 1975.**

18231 Blanc, M.   FR 011408/77/8623
Question agraire et développement du capitalisme : différenciation des couches sociales agricoles et accumulation du capital dans le Lauragais–Tarnais. **Agrarian question and capitalism development : differentiation of agricultural social**

D 6100 - Social policy

stata and capital accumulation in Lauragais–Tarnais.

18232 Deverre, C.   FR 012212/72/8656
Les communautés paysannes au service du capitalisme agraire
en Améreque Latine. **Peasant community for agrarian
capitalism in latin America.**

18233 Grignon, C.; Grignon, Ch.; Soliman, M.L.
                                 FR 012212/74/8643
Sociologie des pratiques alimentaires. **Food pratises sociology.**

18234 Saunier, P.   FR 012212/75/8644
Les déterminants économiques et sociaux de la consommation
alimentaire. **Economic and social restraints, in food consuption.**

18235 Nallet, H.; Barres, D.; Colson, F.   FR 012212/76/8617
La jeunesse agricole catholique (JAC). Son rôle dans
l'évolution de l'agriculture et du mouvement paysan. **The
catholic Agricultural Youth Movement. Its part in the
development of french agriculture and of the peasant
movements.**

18236 Commins, P.; Cox, P.G.; Curry, J.
                                 IE 060600/76/1351 R
Alternative social and economic policies/on rural areas.
Publications.

18237 Barberis, C.   IT 012700/78/1028 N
Nuove ricerche sull'agricoltura a mezzo tempo. **New research
on part time agriculture.**

18238 Panero, V.   IT 040529/78/1083 N
Rapporti degli aglomerati principali con il territorio agricolo
forestale della Maremma toscana nel periodo del loro
maggiore sviluppo. **Correlation of the main populated areas at
the time of their maximum development with the rural and
forest areas of the Tuscan Maremma region.**

D 6110 - Agricultural sociology and wellfare

See also 2135, 2500, 2748, 15672, 17404, 17729, 17923, 17924,
17934, 17957, 18005, 18044, 18065, 18078, 18079, 18095, 18150,
18450, 19688, 19772

18239 Bublot, G.; Sneessens, J.F.   BE 020200/78/0016 R
Progrès techniques et problèmes agricoles; analyse des
exigences d'adaptation et du coût social entrainés par
l'adoption des progrès techniques en agriculture. **Technical
progress and agricultural problems; Analysis of the adaptation
needs and the social cost due to the adoption of technical
progress in agriculture.** Publications.

18240 Keymeulen, H.   BE 120000/77/0021 R
Onderzoek naar indikatoren van de relatieveinkomenspositie
van de landbouwers. **Research on indicators to the farmer's
income position.**

18241 Fekri–Erschad, M.; Blanckenburg, P.von
                                 DE 105350/77/0002
Einfluss der Urbanisierung auf die ländliche Bevölkerung im
Iran. **Impact of urbanization on the rural population in Iran.**

18242 Weckwerth, H.   DE 105650/71/0005 R
Die Teilnahme der Berliner Bevölkerung an der
Freiraumerholung in ausgewählten Nahbereichen der

Gross–Stadt Berlin nach sozialen und räumlichen Kriterien
1971. **The participation of the inhabitants of Berlin in recreation
in selected open areas in the near surroundings of Berlin by
social and spatial criteria.**

18243 Researcher not indicated   DE 105650/77/0007
Berufsfeldanalysen für Absolventen des Studiums der
Landespflege an Universitäten und Fachhochschulen. **Analyses
for the professional field of students of landscape management
at universities and special colleges.**

18244 Hottes, K.; Becker, F.; Meyer, U.
                                 DE 108202/78/0001 N
Bestand und Entwicklung von zentralen Funktionen nach
verkehrlicher Innovation in der A.R. Jemen. **Status and
development of central functions after traffic innovation in the
A.R. of Jemen.** Publications.

18245 Boeker, P.; Diekmann, J.; Wechsel, R.; Neetix, H.;
Weltzien, H.C.; Radermacher, H.   DE 111353/78/0001 N
Die wechselseitige Beeinflussung von Wirtschaft, Kultur und
Gesellschaft im modernen Bahrain. – Eine systematische
Fallstudie über Eintwicklungsprobleme innerhalb arabisch –
islamischer Länder und ihre Kooperationsmöglichkeiten. **The
alternating influence of economy, culture and society in the
modern state of Bahrain. – A systematical study on development
problems in arabic–islamic countries and their possibilities of
cooperation.**

18246 Junghans, K.H.; Reufels, H.   DE 111653/75/0002
25 Jahre Stahlwerk Rourkela. – Eine Studie über die
Wechselbeziehung von regionaler Industrialisierung und
sozio–kulturellem Wandel in überbevölkerten Agrargebieten
Süd–Asiens. **25 years Rourkela Steel Plant. – A study on the
interrelationship between regional industrialization and
socio–cultural change in densely populated rural areas of South
Asia.**

18247 Liu, N.; Junghans, K.H.   DE 111653/77/0001
Die Bedeutung sozialökonomischer Faktoren für die regionale
Entwicklung der taiwanesischen Landwirtschaft. **The role of
socio–economic factors for regional development of Taiwan
agriculture.**

18248 Junghans, K.H.; Mtetwa, J.   DE 111653/77/0003
Die Rolle des Rindes im sozialökonomischen
Entwicklungsprozess traditionaler südafrikanischer
Gesellschaften. **The role of cattle in the process of
socio–economic development of South–African rural societies.**

18249 Junghans, K.H.; Benad, A.   DE 111653/77/0004
Der Einfluss natürlicher, ökonomischer und sozialer
Standortfaktoren auf das Innovationsverhalten der Bauern auf
Sumatra. **Interrelationship of natural environment, economic
and social factors and farmers' innovationness in Sumatra.**

18250 Junghans, K.H.; Scholz, U.   DE 111653/77/0005
Die natürlichen, ökonomischen und sozialen
Bestimmungsgründe der landwirtschaftlichen
Betriebsorganisation Indonesiens. **Natural, economic and
social factors effecting the organizational form of agriculture in
Indonesia.**

18251 Junghans, K.H.; Gura, S.   DE 111653/77/0006
Die ökonomische Rolle der Frau im ländlichen
Entwicklungsprozess Indonesiens – das Beispiel Minangkabau

The economic role of woman in the rural development process of Indonesia, test case Minangkabau.

18252 Steffen, G.; Küst, R. DE 111701/75/0001
Formen der Nebenerwerbslandwirtschaft und ihre Bedeutung für die Wirtschafts– und Sozialstruktur. **Forms of part–time farming and their importance for economical and social structure.**

18253 Hütteroth, W.–D.; Abdulfattah, K.
DE 120200/77/0005 N
Siedlungs– und Agrarstruktur von Asir, Saudiarabien. **Structures of settlement and agriculture in Asir, Saudi Arabia.**

18254 Meyer, G. DE 120200/78/0001 N
Wirtschafts– und sozialgeographische Probleme syrischer Neulandgebiete – Euphrat– und Ghab–Projekt –. **Economic and socio–geographical problems of the new lands in Syria – Euphrate and Ghab project –.**

18255 Niesslein, E.; Köppe, D. DE 126500/75/0002
Die Gehöferschaften in Rheinland–Pfalz, eine forstpolitische, forstgeschichtliche und forstrechtliche Untersuchung. **Medieval forest communities "Gehöferschaften" in Rhineland–Palatinate, a study in forest policy, forest history and forest law.**

18256 Becker, G. DE 126650/77/0001
Teilzeitarbeit in der Forstwirtschaft – betriebliche, soziale, beschäftigungspolitische Aspekte. **Part–time jobs in forestry – economic, social aspects and aspects of employment.**

18257 Nickel, H.J.; Herbert, J. DE 126700/77/0001
Rekrutierung von Arbeitskräften und Schuldknechtschaft in mexikanischen Haciendas der Kolonialzeit. **Worker recruitment and debt peonage in Mexican haciendas of the colonial period.** Publications.

18258 Kuhlmann, F.; Müller, H. DE 129301/77/0001
Elemente des Marketings für Akademiker, dargestellt am Beispiel des Diplom Agrar Ingenieurs. **Elements of the marketing of academicians, shown by the example of diplomaed agricultural engineer.** Publications.

18259 Spitzer, H.; Uffmann, J. DE 129302/75/0002 R
Das landwirtschaftliche Produktionspotential in seinem Einfluss auf das Bevölkerungspotential – dargestellt an ländlichen Gemeinden in Hessen. **Influence of agricultural production potential on population potential, exemplified by rural communities in Hesse.**

18260 Harsche, E. DE 129340/72/0003
Das "Gada"–System der "Oromo"–Völker West– und SüdÄthiopiens als soziales Interaktionssystem halbnomadischer Rinderhirten–Hackbauern. **The 'Gada'–System of the 'Oromo'–tribes of Western and Southern Ethiopia as a system of social interactions of half nomadic cattlebreeder–hoecultivators.**

18261 Harsche, E.; Jung, H. DE 129340/74/0007
Der Einfluss der Farbwerke Hoechst auf den Wandel der Berufsund Siedlungsstruktur, der Siedlungsformen und des Wohnverhaltens in den nördlichen Untermain–Regionen – Versuch einer sozial–kri– tischen Analyse –. **The influences of Farbwerke Hoechst as to the changes in occupation and settlement structures, settlement types and housing behaviour in the northern Lower Main region – a socio–critical analytical approach –.**

18262 Harsche, E.; Kölb, V. DE 129340/74/0008
Landwirtschaftliche Erbsitten im Kraftfeld industriegesellschaftlichen Strukturwandels. **Agricultural inheritance traditions in the field of changes in industrial society structures.**

18263 Harsche, E.; Manker, L. DE 129340/74/0010
Motivationsstruktur und sozialer Strukturwandel im Handelsvertretergewerbe der Fachgruppe Nahrungs– und Genussmittel. **Motivation structure and social structural changes in the trade of mercantile agent in the foodstuff and luxuries line.**

18264 Wädekin, K.–E. DE 129381/70/0002
Die landwirtschaftliche Bevölkerung der Sowjetunion 1965. **Rural populations in the Soviet Union.**

18265 Kuhnen, F.; Choi, H.–J. DE 132250/75/0004
Rückwirkungen der Land–Stadt–Migration auf den ländlichen Raum in Süd–Korea. **Feedback of rural–urban migration in rural areas in South–Korea.**

18266 Kuhnen, F.; Adviye, A. DE 132250/77/0006
Gastarbeiter und ländliche Entwicklung in ihren Heimatländern am Beispiel der Türkei. **Migrant workers and rural development in their countries of origin, exemplified by Turkey.** Publications.

18267 Schmitt, G.; Hagedorn, K. DE 132363/75/0002
Die Finanzierung alternativer Modelle agrarsozialer Sicherung in der Bundesrepublik Deutschland. **The financing of alternative systems for the social security of the agricultural sector of the Federal Republic of Germany.**

18268 Schmitt, G.; Eggers, K.J. DE 132363/77/0002
Agrarsoziale Sicherung im internationalen Vergleich der Bundesrepublik Deutschland, Frankreichs und Italiens. **An international comparison of the agricultural schemes of social security in the Federal Republic of Germany, in France and Italy.**

18269 Haen, H.de; Braun, J.von DE 132367/75/0001
Sektorale und regionale Projektion der Zahl landwirtschaftlicher Arbeitskräfte. **Sectoral and regional projection of the agricultural labour force.**

18270 Haen, H.de; Bauer, J. DE 132367/75/0002
Simulation des regionalen Strukturwandels mit einem dynamischen Systemmodell. **Simulation of regional structural change by means of a dynamic systems model.**

18271 Jürgensen, C.; Fipke, P. DE 138365/78/0001 N
Berufsfeldanalyse für Agrarfachkräfte, Struktur und Dynamik des Arbeitsmarktes der Absolventen des Gartenbaustudiums an Universitäten und Fachhochschulen. **Analysis of the professional field of specialists in agriculture, structure and dynamics of labour market for students of horticulture at universities and special colleges.**

18272 Buchwald, K.; Scharpf, H. DE 138600/72/0001 N
Regionale Analyse des Fremdenverkehrs auf Landwirtschaftlichen Betrieben. **Regional analysis of tourist traffic on farms.**

18273 Fuhs, F.W.   DE 142200/72/0003
Ländliche Entwicklungs– und Beschäftigungsprobleme in
Thailand. **Rural development and employment problems in
Thailand.**

18274 Urff, W.von; Zingel, W.–P.   DE 142200/75/0004 R
Das Problem regionaler Entwicklungsunterschiede in
Entwicklungsländern. Eine theoretische und empirische
Analyse dargestellt am Beispiel Pakistans unter Verwendung
der Hauptkomponentenanalyse. **The problem of different
regional development levels in developing countries. A
theoretical analysis and case study of Pakistan by means of the
principal components method.**

18275 Fuhs, F.W.; Klempin, A.   DE 142200/75/0008 R
Beitrag der staatlich gelenkten Landbesiedlung zur
landwirtschaftlichen Entwicklung. Eine umfassende Fallstudie
der Landbesiedlung und des Thai–Deutschen
landwirtschaftlichen Entwicklungsprojektes Saraburi.
**Contribution of state–directed land settlement to agricultural
development. A comprehensive case study of the land
settlement and Thai–German agricultural development project
Saraburi.**

18276 Blosser–Reisen, L.; Stiefel, M.–L.
             DE 144795/77/0001
Zur Bewältigung von Hilfs– und Pflegebedürftigkeit älterer
Menschen im privaten Haushalt. **On mastering indigence and
need of nursing of older people in private households – senior
citizens –.**

18277 Becker, H.–J.   DE 144860/70/0002 R
Regionale Unterschiede im agrarstrukturellen
Entwicklungsstatus und ihre Ursachen 1970–1978. **Regional
differences in the status of development of agrarian structure
and their causes.**

18278 Röhm, H.; Bakonyi, E.; Doll, M.J.; Stark, J.;
Dobberkau, E.   DE 144860/74/0003 R
Sozialökonomische Mobilität in ländlichen Räumen.
Socio–economic mobility in rural areas. Publications.

18279 Röhm, H.; Dobberkau, E.   DE 144860/77/0003
Die Abwanderung der Bevölkerung aus ländlichen
Problemgebieten, dargestellt am Beispiel strukturschwacher
Regionen Baden–Württembergs. **The exodus of population
from rural problem areas, exemplified by low–structure regions
in Baden–Wuerttemberg.**

18280 Bergmann, T.; Paulini, T.   DE 144865/75/0001
Agrarreform und agrarische Bewegungen dargestellt am
Beispiel des indischen Bundesstaates Kerala. **Agrarian reform
and agrarian movements in Kerala/India.**

18281 Schultz–Klinken, K.R.   DE 144885/74/0001
Nomenklatur und Systematisierung prähistorischer und
historischer Haken und Pflüge auf primär funktioneller sowie
konstruktiver Grundlage im Rahmen der historischen
Entwicklung und der regionalen Verbreitung. **Nomenclature
and systematization of prehistoric and historical hooks and
ploughs on a primarily functional and constructional basis in
the scope of historical development and regional distribution.**

18282 Winkel, H.   DE 144885/78/0001 N
Die Mechanisierung der Landwirtschaft im ausgehenden 19.
Jahrhundert. **Farm mechanization at the end of the nineteenth**
century.

18283 Herrmann, K.   DE 144885/78/0002 N
Die deutsche Weinwirtschaft während des II. Weltkriegs. **The
German wine industry in the years 1939–1945.**

18284 Albrecht, H.; Hoffmann, V.   DE 144960/72/0002
Motivation und Managerverhalten –dargestellt am Beispiel
württembergischer Kreditgenossenschaften. **Motivation and
managerial behavior –demonstrated by the example of
credit–cooperatives in Württemberg–.**

18285 Planck, U.; Pfeifer, H.–J.   DE 144965/78/0001 N
Sozialökonomische Probleme bei der Überführung des
tradierten Oasenlandbaus in eine moderne
Bewässerungswirtschaft. **Socio–economic problems in the
transfer of traditional oasis agriculture into modern irrigation
systems.**

18286 Hesse, K.–F.; Röper, C.   DE 148451/77/0003
Sozialökonomische Lebenshaltungsvergleiche ausgewählter
privater Haushalte und Haushaltsphasen. **Socio–economic
comparisons of standards of living of selected private
households and household cycles.**

18287 Köstler, J.N.; Feldner, R.   DE 160150/70/0003 R
Waldgesellschaften und Waldgeschichte der Ammergauer
Berge 1966. **Forest associations and forest history of the
mountains of Ammergau.**

18288 Ziche, J.   DE 161423/73/0001
Positive und negative Stimuli im Dorfleben Zentralafrikas
Studien in Dörfern Zambias und Malawis. **Positive and
negative stimuli to village–life in Central Africa. Research on
Zambian and Malawian villages.**

18289 Jahns, G.   DE 201060/78/0008 N
Bewerten der an Arbeitsplätzen in der Landwirtschaft
auftretenden Belastungen hinsichtlich ihrer Auswirkungen auf
den Menschen. **Valuation of effects on man by environmental
and work load at agricultural working places.**

18290 Kretschmann, R.; Pieper, I.   DE 914000/78/0001 N
Leben in kleinen ländlichen Orten – Untersuchung zu
Komponenten der Attraktivität aus der Sicht von Bewohnern
–. **Living conditions in small villages – analysis of components of
attractiveness in view of the inhabitants –.**

18291 Riemann, F.; Bendixen, E.O.; Lienau, E.
             DE 914000/78/0002 N
Betreuung von kranken und pflegebedürftigen Menschen auf
dem Lande – Möglichkeiten zur Stärkung der Selbst– und
Nachbarschaftshilfe. **Services to rural patients and persons in
need of care – possibilities of intensifying of self–help and help of
neighbours.**

18292 Riemann, F.; Bendixen, E.O.   DE 914000/78/0003 N
Die Bedeutung flankierender Hilfen für die Existenzsicherung
landwirtschaftlicher Familien. **Significance of flanking help for
the security of living conditions of farmers families.**

18293 Holla, M.   DE 914001/78/0001 N
Hemmfaktoren für die Industrieansiedlung in ausgewählten
Schwerpunktorten. **Inhibitory factors for localization of
industries in selected centers.**

18294 Holla, M.   DE 914001/78/0002 N
Auswirkungen des Krankenhausfinanzierungsgesetzes auf die Struktur des Krankenhauswesens und die Versorgung der Bevölkerung im ländlichen Raum. **Effects of the hospital financing law on structure of hospital and medical services to rural population.**

18295 Hülsen, R.   DE 914003/78/0001 N
Die Situation der Ehefrauen in der Nebenerwerbslandwirtschaft. **Situation of farmers' wives in part–time agriculture.**

18296 Roos, H.–J.; Bade, R.   DE 914004/78/0001 N
Der Einfluss von Strukturveränderung und Funktionswandel in kleinen ländlichen Ortschaften auf den Zustand der Bausubstanz und deren mögliche Nutzung. **Influence of structural functional changes in small villages on the state of building substance and its possible utilization.** Publications.

18297 Riemann, F.; Pieper, I.   DE 914005/78/0001 N
Gemeinschaftsleben in unseren Dörfern – Beispiele von Vereinsaktivitäten und des öffentlichen Engagements von Frauen. **Social life in our villages – examples of club activities and public engagement of women.** Publications.

18298 Kirsch, O.C.   DE 916000/78/0001 N
Die Rolle von Selbsthilfegruppen in ländlichen Entwicklungsprojekten. **The role of self–help groups in rural development projects.**

18299 Brun, A.; Deffontaines, J.P.   FR 010112/75/3038
Pays, paysans, paysages dans les Vosges du Sud. Dynamique sociale et transformation de l'espace. **Country, peasants, landscape in the south of the Vosges. Social evolution and landscape transformation.**

18300 Buttoud, G.   FR 010308/77/8618
Les propriétaires forestiers privés en France : anatomie d'un groupe de pression. **Private forest owners in France, anatomy of a lobby.**

18301 Larrere, G.; Nougarede, O.; Lienard, G.   FR 010810/77/8575
La société paysanne et la maîtrise sociale de l'espace rural en Margeride. **Peasant communities in Margeride highlands and social allocation of rural area.**

18302 Barthez, A.   FR 011012/74/3306
Sociologie des conflits en agriculture. **Sociology of conflicts in Agriculture.**

18303 Brun, A.; Brossier, J.; Deffontaines, J.P.; Bonnemaire, J.; Osty, P.; Teissier, J.H.   FR 011012/75/3300
Pays, paysans, paysages dans les Vosges du Sud. Dynamique sociale et transformation de l'espace. Eléments pour une stratégie du développement. **Farmers and landscapes in south "Vosges". Social dynamics and changes in the country side. Elements for a development strategy.**

18304 Brossier, J.; Marshall, E.   FR 011012/75/3301
Décision des agriculteurs – Décisions individuelles et décisions collectives. Relations avec le développement rural et régional. **Farmers decision – Individual and collective decisions – Relation with rural and regional development.**

18305 Blanc, M.   FR 011012/75/3303
Les classes sociales à la campagne. **Social classes in the country.**

18306 Brossier, J.   FR 011012/75/8591
Conditions de régulation du développement socio–économique régional. Le cas du pays Choletais. **Control condition of socio–economical regional development.**

18307 Barthez, A.   FR 011012/75/8640
L'évolution du remembrement comme facteur de transformation du travail en agriculture. **Re–allocation of land as a change factor of work in agriculture.**

18308 Barthelemy, D.   FR 011012/76/8502
Propriété foncière et rapports de production agricole. **Landownership and agricultural production relationships.**

18309 Monney, R.   FR 011205/76/8582
Equipement et services collectifs en milieu rural : l'exemple de l'Hérault. **Equipment and social services in rural areas : the exemple of Herault.**

18310 Chassany, J.P.; Labouesse, F.   FR 011205/77/8580
Etude des modes de subsistance et d'utilisation de l'espace dans les populations du Hoggar. **Study of types of subsistance and space utilization for the Hoggar population.**

18311 Lifran, R.   FR 011205/77/8626
Les couches sociales dans la viticulture languedocienne. **Classes of society in Languedoc.**

18312 Lacombe, P.; Lifran, R.   FR 011205/77/8627
Couches sociales : mobilité et renouvellement de la population agricole languedocienne. **Social strata : mobility and renovation of the rural population in "Languedoc".**

18313 Lacombe, P.; Cortot, J.; Boisseau, B.; Chassany, J.P.   FR 011205/77/8641
Le changement social en Languedoc–Roussillon. **Social change in Languedoc–Roussillon.**

18314 Boisseau, P.   FR 011205/78/8572
Emploi et formation en zone dévitalisée, étude sur les montagnes du Languedoc–Roussillon. **Employment and education in poor areas : the mountains of Languedoc Roussillon.**

18315 Lacombe, P.; Labouesse, F.; Chassany, J.P.; Miclet, G.; Cortot, J.   FR 011205/78/8628
Les transformations dans l'utilisation et la gestion de l'espace rural et leurs répercussions sur les sociétés et les différents groupes sociaux locaux. **Changes concerning the utilization and the control of rural space and their consequences on the societies and different social groups.**

18316 Henry, J.B.   FR 011302/70/3349
Evolution économique et transformation des rapports sociaux: le problème laitier breton. **Economic evolution and transformation of social relationships: the dairy problem in Brittany.**

18317 Jegouzo, G.   FR 011302/70/3350
Les jeunes et l'agriculture. **Young people and the farm career.**

18318 Jegouzo, G.; Brangeon, J.L.   FR 011302/70/3351
Les paysans et l'école. **Farmers and school.**

18319 Dauce, P.   FR 011302/74/3348
Le retard de la préscolarisation dans les campagnes. **The lag of nursery–schooling in Rural areas.**

18320 Lambert, Y.   FR 011302/75/3352
Société rurale et religion. **Rural society and religion.**

18321 Lambert, Y.; Bremaud, M.A.   FR 011302/75/8635
Religion et changement social et culturel en milieu rural. **Religion and socio–cultural change in rural world.**

18322 Brangeon, J.L.; Jegouzo, G.; Poupa, J.C.
    FR 011302/77/8639
Les conditions de travail en agriculture: relations entre travail agricole et santé. **Working conditions in agriculture: relation between agriculture work and health.**

18323 Grignon, C.   FR 011706/68/3337
Les stratégies éducatives des familles paysannes. **Educative strategies in families.**

18324 Grignon, C.   FR 011706/70/3339
Les fonctions sociales de l'enseignement agricole. **Social missions of agricultural teaching.**

18325 Champagne, P.; Chamboredon, J.C.
    FR 011706/74/3341
Les déterminants sociaux de l'opposition ville/campagne. **The social determinants of the opposition city/country.**

18326 Champagne, P.   FR 011706/75/3340
Les relations entre générations en milieu paysan. **Relationships between generations in rural environment.**

18327 Reboul, C.; Butault, J.P.; Leon, Y.
    FR 011706/75/3342
Les dépenses de consommation des agriculteurs. **Farmers' consumption expenses.**

18328 Roux, B.   FR 011706/75/3356
Développement agricole et changement social. **Agricultural development and social transformation.**

18329 Reboul, C.; Leon, Y.; Champagne, P.
    FR 012212/76/8514
Consommation, revenu des agriculteurs et reproduction des conditions de production. **Farmer's consumption expenses.**

18330 Roger, C.; Gervais, M.   FR 012212/76/8595
Revenus des agriculteurs et dépenses de l'Etat en faveur de l'agriculture. **Agricultural income and state expense for agriculture.**

18331 Deverre, C.   FR 012212/77/8513 N
L'organisation des migrations tournantes de travailleurs agricoles saisonniers en France, USA et Mexique.
Organisation of turning migrations for agricultural seasonal workers in France, USA and Mexique.

18332 Tarassuk, M.   FR 012212/77/8568
Le retour à la terre efficacement encouragé peut–il faire revivre une région en déclin. **Coming back to farming is it a good way for a revival of declining region.**

18333 Reboul, C.; Al Hamchari, M.C.   FR 012212/77/8607
Les coopératives d'utilisation du matériel en commun –

C.U.M.A. **Cooperative for common use of machinery.**

18334 Ponchelet, D.   FR 012212/77/8616
L'Internationale paysanne de Moscou et ses rapports avec les PC européens. **Moscow Internationale for peasant and relation ship with européen communist parties.**

18335 Grignon, C.; Grignon, Ch.; Soliman, M.L.
    FR 012212/77/8634
L'église et la formation de l'élite paysanne. **Church and peasan elite formation.**

18336 Bergmann, D.   FR 012212/78/8508
Régimes fonciers et modes de tenure en France. **Land ownership and land tenure in France.**

18337 Berlan, J.P.; Berlan, M.   FR 012212/78/8673
Théorie du marché du travail et conditions de travail en agriculture intensive. **Theory of the labor market and work conditions in intensive agriculture.**

18338 Brun, A.; Lacombe, P.; Laurent, C.
    FR 012303/65/8516
Agricultures à temps partiel. **Part–time farming.**

18339 Kalaora, B.; Pelosse   FR 012303/75/8583
Le tourisme en forêt de Fontainebleau. **Tourism and leisure in Fontainebleau forest.**

18340 Brun, A.; Poupardin, D.; Decourt, N.; Kalaora, B.; Larrere, G.; Nougarede, O.   FR 012303/78/8578
Etude comparée de travaux socio–écologiques dans des régions françaises à faible productivité. **Comparison between some recent socio–ecological research works related to low agricultural productivity french areas.**

18341 Collombel, B.; Meunier, A.   FR 012502/78/8614
Les rapports agriculture–industrie : la formation et la localisation du revenu des agriculteurs dans la région Nord–Pas–de–Calais. **The relations between agriculture and food industry : formation and localisation of farmers income. A case study : the area of Nord – Pas de Calais.**

18342 Pernet, F.; Lepape, Y.   FR 012600/77/8567
Signification du retour à la terre de citadins. **The meaning of coming back to land for town people.**

18343 Frawley, J.   IE 060600/72/1132 R
Indicators of the level of living on family farms in Ireland. Publications.

18344 Callaghan, J.; Mannion, J.; Breathnach, C.
    IE 120109/78/9246 N
A study of three schemes for agricultural and social develop ment in county donegal.

18345 Callaghan, J.; Mannion, J.; O'Sullivan, M.
    IE 120109/78/9250 N
A study of the operation of the farm retirement scheme in co unty galway.

18346 Mullany, M.; Smith, L.P.   IE 120501/79/9162 N
Member and employee relations in agricultural cooperatives.

18347 Cuddy, M.; Curtin, C.   IE 130201/79/9220 N
Peasant agriculture 1891 in the west of Ireland – degree of

commercialisation in agriculture.

18348 Tartaglia, A. IT 040102/74/0640
I lavoratori agricoli dipendenti in Puglia. **Hired agricultural labour in Puglia.**

18349 Galizzi, G. IT 040410/77/0188 R
Analisi della domanda di beni e servizi incorporati negli alimenti nei Paesi della Comunità Economica Europea. **Analysis of the request for goods and services incorporated in food–stuffs available in EEC countries.**

18350 Sorbi, U. IT 040526/77/0301 R
Riforma tributaria e catasto; la scienza estimativa nel quadro della moderna dinamica economica e sociale, lineamenti e tendenze. **Tax reform and land registers; the science of appraising in relation to modern economic and social development main lines and trends.**

18351 Gottardo, C.; Boatto, V. IT 040804/75/0006
Comportamento dell'impresa agricola familiare verso il risparmio e l'indebitamento. **Behaviour of family farm with respect to savings and debts.** Publications.

18352 Veer, J. de NL 010116/70/3365 R
Onderzoek naar de samenstelling van de groep verpachters. **Investigation into the composition of the group landlords.**

18353 Bauwens, A.L.G.M.; Biemans, J.M.
NL 010116/73/5935
Ontwikkelingstendenties bij de opvolgingssituatie in Noord–Brabant. **Developments of succession in the North Brabant region in the Netherlands.** Publications.

18354 Bauwens, A.L.G.M. NL 010116/73/5936 R
Onderzoek naar de omvang, samenstelling en aantalsontwikkeling van de agrarische beroepsbevolking. **Investigation into the size, composition and number of the agrarian working population.**

18355 Bauwens, A.L.G.M. NL 010116/75/6879
Agrarische structurele aspekten van de problematiek van de oudere boer en tuinder zonder opvolger. **The problematic of the older farmer without successor.**

18356 Wigboldus, J.S. NL 020001/76/6770
Sociale en economische geschiedenis van ruraal Zuidzuidwest–Ceylon omstr. 1700. **Social and economic history of rural Southsouthwest–Ceylon ca.1700.**

18357 Woude, A.M. van der NL 020002/73/4247
De geschiedenis van sociale veranderingen ten plattelande in Nederland in de 19e eeuw. **History of social changes in the rural areas of the Netherlands in the 19th century.**

18358 Schuurman, A. NL 020002/74/6312
De materiële cultuur op het Nederlandse platteland van de 16e tot de 19e eeuw. **Rural history of the material development in the Netherlands from the 16th till the 19th century.**

18359 Woude, A.M. van der NL 020002/77/7323
Van plattelandsgemeenschappen tot industriestad; de demografische en sociale geschiedenis van Eindhoven, 1810–1940. **Eindhoven 1810–1940; its demographic and social developments.**

18360 Wigboldus, J.S. NL 020002/77/8435
Plattelandsgeschiedenis van de Minahasa 1600–1900. **Rural history of Minahasa 1600–1900.** Publications.

18361 Bos, R.W.J.M. NL 020002/78/8436
Factorprijzen, technologie en marktstructuur: Nederland 1850–1940. **Factor prices, technology and market structure: the Netherlands 1850–1940.** Publications.

18362 Samson, M.R.S.Ch. NL 020002/78/8821 N
Grensmigratie tussen Nederland en Duitsland, 1900–1940(demografische en sociale veranderingen). **Border migration between the Netherlands and Germany, 1900–1940 (demographic and social changes).**

18363 Wigboldus, J.S. NL 020002/78/8822 N
Algemene tendenties en regionale verscheidenheid in de agrarische geschiedenis van koloniaal Indonesië. **General trends and regional variety in the agrarian history of colonial Indonesia.**

18364 Roessingh, H.K. NL 020002/78/8823 N
Landbouwsystemen in Nederland, 1500–1815. **Agricultural systems in the Netherlands, 1500–1815.**

18365 Woude, A.M. van der. NL 020002/78/8824 N
De bevolkingsgeschiedenis van Nederland 1500–1800. **Dutch demographic development 1500–1800.**

18366 Wigboldus, J.S. NL 020002/78/8825 N
Ontwikkeling van de voedselteelt en exportlandbouw in pre– en vroegkoloniaal Indonesië. **Development of food cropping and export agriculture in ancient and early colonial Indonesia.**

18367 Lier, R.A.J. van; Dusseldorp, D.B.W.M. van
NL 020003/73/6308
Agrarische ontwikkeling en daarbij betrokken instituties in Kameroen. **Rural sociology and involved institutions of Cameroon.** Publications.

18368 Lette, R.J. NL 020003/75/4251
Verandering in samenwerkingsvormen in relatie tot incorporatie en schaarsere produktiemiddelen. **Incorporation and social change.**

18369 Kalshoven, G. NL 020003/75/4514
Structuur en functie van dienstverlenende instellingen bij de rurale ontwikkeling in Maleisië. **Rural institutions: communication patterns and their organizational framework (Malaya).**

18370 Rive Box, L. de la NL 020003/77/8648 N
Cassaveteelt in Zuid–Amerika: teeltsociologische aspecten van cassave, afzet en verbruik. **Manioc and man in South America; towards a cropsociological approach on cassava production, distribution and consumption in selected South American countries.**

18371 Ouden, J.H.B. den NL 020003/77/8826 N
De maatschappelijke consequenties van het incorporatieproces in een Bamiléké regio, Cameroun. **Social, economic and political effects of the process of incorporation in a Bamiléké region, Cameroun.**

18372 Lier, R.A.J. van NL 020003/78/8827 N
Sociaal economische veranderingen als gevolg van technische

vernieuwingen in de rijstverbouw in Colombia. **Consequences of the introduction of new rice technology in Colombia.**

18373 Lier, R.A.J. van   NL 020003/78/8828 N
Boerenparticipatie en agrarische hervorming in Algerije. **Participation of peasants and agrarian reform in Algeria.**

18374 Dusseldorp, D.W.B.M. van   NL 020003/78/8829 N
Evaluatie van ontwikkelingsprojecten. **Evaluation of development projects.**

18375 Dusseldorp, D.W.B.M. van   NL 020003/78/8830 N
Participatie en geplande ontwikkeling, planning op het locale niveau. **Participation and planned development, local level planning.**

18376 Lak0, C.   NL 020019/77/8637 N
Ongezond gedrag van groepen mensen in relatie tot gezondheidsvoorlichting en –opvoeding. **Unhealthy behaviour of groups of people in relation to health education.**

18377 Jansen, M.J.   NL 020048/66/4811
Constructie van een internationaal gestandaardiseerde Persoonlijkheidsdifferentiaal. **Construction of an internationally standardized Personality Differential.** Publications.

18378 Jansen, M.J.   NL 020048/68/4810
Interactie buitenlanders/nederlanders; typerende voorvallen voor gebruik bij het onderwijs in de cultuurvergelijkende psychologie. **Interaction foreign nationals/dutch nationals; critical incidents for use in courses of crosscultural psychology.**

18379 Soomer, K. de   NL 020048/77/8538
Onderzoek naar psychosociale facetten van verdelende rechtvaardigheid, in het bijzonder met het oog op helpgedrag. **Psychosocial aspects of distributive justice with respect to helping behaviour.**

18380 Jansen, M.J.   NL 020048/78/8805 N
Relatie mens/natuur, cultuurvergelijkend. **Relationship human being/nature, crossculturally.**

18381 Hofstee, E.W.   NL 020051/46/4264
Bevolkings ontwikkeling in Nederland in de 19e en 20e eeuw. **Demographic development of the Dutch population in the 19th and 20th century.** Publications.

18382 Hofstee, E.W.   NL 020051/69/4263
Verschuiving in de verhouding bouwland–grasland in de provincie Groningen als sociaal–cultureel veranderingsproces. **Changes and rates between arable land – grassland in the province Groningen as a social cultural process of change.**

18383 Benvenuti, B.   NL 020051/72/4260
De aard van institutionele determinanten van de rationaliteit in het economisch handelen in de landbouw. **The nature of institutional determinants of the rationality in the economic behaviour in farming.** Publications.

18384 Huys, H.W.J.M.   NL 020051/75/6819
Differentiële geografische mobiliteit in Nederland. **Differential geographical mobility in the Netherlands.**

18385 Hoog, C. de   NL 020051/76/6820
Partnerselectie in Nederland. **Mate–selection in the**

Netherlands.

18386 Koning, N.B.J.   NL 020051/76/6821
Verzelfstandiging van zuivelcoöperaties. **Development of independence of dairy co–operatives.**

18387 Olde Daalhuis, A.G.   NL 020051/78/8541
Oorzaken van drempelvrees bij potentiële kliënten van huwelijksbureau's. **Entrance fear with potential clients of matrimonial agencies.**

18388 Wolffensperger, I.   NL 020051/78/8542 R
Samenwonen onder jongeren: een nieuwe verschijningsvorm van de man/vrouw relatie. **Living together among younger people: a new manifestation of the relationship between men and women.**

18389 Weeda, C.J.   NL 020051/78/8809 N
Motieven voor echtscheiding. **Motives for divorce.**

18390 Edema, J.M.P.   NL 020062/76/8655 N
Sociologie van de voeding; een begrippenapparaat voor de bestudering van voedselproblemen. **Sociology of nutrition; a conceptual framework for the study of food problems.** Publications.

18391 Hartog, A.P. den   NL 020062/77/8657 N
Sociaal wetenschappelijke facetten van de voeding in ontwikkelingslanden (Derde Wereld). **Sociological aspects of nutrition in third world communities.** Publications.

18392 Hartog, A.P. den   NL 020062/78/8660 N
Voedingsmiddelen en consumenten (de invloed van de sociale structuur en maatschappelijke ontwikkelingen op de effectieve voedselkeuze). **Foods and consumers (the influence of the social structure and societal change on food choice).** Publications.

18393 Pennartz, P.J.J.   NL 020067/74/6366
Het sociaal–ecologisch gedrag van bewoners in hun woning. **The social–ecological behaviour of people in their home environment.** Publications.

D 6120 – Didactics of extension and advisory services

See also 17405, 18425, 19522, 20326

18394 Devisch, N.; Hellemans, R.   BE 120000/78/0025 R
Evaluation prévisionnelle de la situation économique des exploitations agricoles et horticoles professionnelles. **Forecast of the economic results obtained on professional agricultural and horticultural holdings.**

18395 Bodenstedt, A.A.; Leuchtmann, E.   DE 129340/74/0015
Innovationen und Beratungserfolge bei traditionellen Bauern in Malawi. **Innovations and extension effects on traditional farmers in Malawi.**

18396 Albrecht, H.; Hillger, R.   DE 144960/71/0002
Analyse der praktizierten Verfahrensweisen in der sozialökonomischen Beratung auf die ihnen zugrundeliegenden theoretischen Ansätze. **Analysis of approaches in socio–economic extension work.**

18397 Albrecht, H.; Denzinger, P.   DE 144960/72/0001

Probleme der Organisation landwirtschaftlicher Offizialberatungsdienste in Württemberg und Bayern. **Organizational problems of agricultural official advisory services in Württemberg and Bavaria.**

18398 Albrecht, H.; Sülzer, R.   DE 144960/78/0001 N
Beratungsmodelle für ländliche Entwicklung. **Concepts of advisory work – extension – for integrated rural development.**

18399 Albrecht, H.; Sülzer, R.   DE 144960/78/0002 N
Verfahren der Situationsanalyse in einem Beratungsprojekt im Jemen al-Bawn. **Proceedings of situation analysis within an extension project for Yemen Arab Republik – Al-Bawn –.**

18400 Albrecht, H.; Lu, C.–C.   DE 144960/78/0003 N
Organisation und Arbeitsweise der landwirtschaftlichen Beratung in Taiwan. **Organization and work of Taiwanese agricultural extension.**

18401 Albrecht, H.; Radwan, A.   DE 144960/78/0004 N
Kommunikationsprozesse und Problemlösung bei ägyptischen Landwirten. **Communication process and problem solving of Egyptian farmers.**

18402 Albrecht, H.; Schmitt–Duchardt, J.
                                         DE 144960/78/0005 N
Informationsverhalten von Landwirten. **Informations behaviour of farmers.**

18403 Hülsen, R.   DE 914003/77/0002
Aus– und Fortbildung sozialökonomischer Berater. **Training and extension of socio–economic advisers.**

18404 Kirsch, O.C.; Kretzschmar, R.; Lippitz, K.; Schmidt, P.   DE 916000/78/0003 N
Landwirtschaftliche Versuchs– und Demonstrationsstation Hodna, Algerien. **Agricultural experimentation and demonstration station in Hodna, Algerien.**

18405 Brossier, J.   FR 011012/77/8511
Analyse économique et gestion des exploitations. Documents de synthèse à l'usage des enseignants, conseillers et agriculteurs. **Synthetic documents about the economic analysis and management of farms for teachers, farmers'advisers and farmers.**

18406 Boisseau, P.   FR 011205/75/8592
Action expérimentale de développement de Chaumont–Porcien (Ardennes). **Extension service activity in Chaumont–Porcien (Ardennes).**

18407 Grignon, C.; Grignon, Ch.; Soliman, M.L.
                                         FR 012212/72/8630
L'enseignement agricole. **Agricultural Education.**

18408 Colson, F.; Porin, F.   FR 012400/78/8613
La diffusion du progres technique en production porcine. Le role des groupements de producteurs dans l'elaboration et la diffusion de modeles techniques dominants. **Speading of advanced technologies in pig production. Action of producers for emergence and speading of prevarling technical models.**

18409 Runcie   GB 060117/00/0001 R
Investigation into the methodology of agricultural advisory effort.

18410 Frawley, J.   IE 060600/77/1356 R
Evaluation of the dissemination of recommended farm practices and technology emanating from research control (Ballintubber). Publications.

18411 Mannion, J.; Callaghan, J.; Murphy, T.
                                         IE 120109/78/9251 N
The role of the senior instructor in the irish agricultural advisory service.

18412 Ban, A.W. van den   NL 020063/70/4858
Het schrijven van een leerboek over voorlichtingskunde. **Writing a textbook on extension education.**

18413 Ban, A.W. van den   NL 020063/76/7351
Literatuuronderzoek naar voorlichting aan achtergebleven groepen. **Survey of the literature on extension education with poor people.**

18414 Woerkum, C. van   NL 020063/76/7352
Relatie onderzoek en beleid bij voorlichting via de massamedia de betekenis van aangepaste methodologie. **Relationships between research and policy in education via the mass media; the significance of adapted methodology.** Publications.

18415 Blokker, K.J.   NL 020063/76/7353
De toepassing van gespreksvaardigheid en gesprekstherapie door de diëtist bij de begeleiding van obese kliënten. **The utilization of personal communication skills and behaviour therapy by the dietician in the guidance of obese clients.** Publications.

18416 Zuurbier, P.J.P.   NL 020063/77/8456 R
Onderzoek naar het functioneren van het management van de voorlichtingsdienst van het ministerie van landbouw en visserij. **The functioning of the management of the Dutch agricultural extension service.**

D 6130 – Didactics of education and training

See also 18314, 18407, 20373

18417 Blanckenburg, P.von; Nagel, U.–J. DE 105350/74/0001
Die landwirtschaftlichen Universitäten Indiens als Träger der Landwirtschaftsberatung. **The role of Indian Agricultural Universities in agricultural extension.**

18418 Zilahi–Szabo, M.G.; Müller, W.   DE 129303/73/0001
Fachliche Erwachsenenbildung für das Förderungsprogramm der mehrbetrieblichen Maschinenverwendung in Hessen 1972. **Adult education within the programme of stimulating machine utilization in Hessen 1972–75.**

18419 Zilahi–Szabo, M.G.; Dienstbach, I. DE 129304/72/0001
Methodik – Didaktik des agrarwissenschaftlichen Studiums – insbesondere der Wirtschafts– und Sozialwissenschaften des Landbaus 1972. **Methodology – didactics of studies of agricultural science – especially of economics and sociology of agriculture.**

18420 Ziche, J.; Knappick, D.   DE 161423/74/0001
Lehrzielkontrolle in der Erwachsenenbildung am Beispiel des Staatsinstituts für die Aus– und Fortbildung landwirtschaftlicher Berater München. **Control of teaching objectives in adult education exemplified by the Institute for Teaching Agricultural Extension Workers in Munich State.**

18421 Moisan, H.   FR 010112/76/9105
Enquête : "la Qualification Professionnelle en Agriculture"
(E.Q.P.A.). **Survey on the professional skills and proficiency**
required in the agricultural professions.

18422 Brossier, J.   FR 011012/76/8512
Recherche–Action sur la formation économique des
agriculteurs. **Research–action on the economic education of**
farmers Economic decisions of farmers.

18423 Brossier, J.; Deffontaines, J.P.; Petit, M.
                                         FR 011012/78/8615
Relations entre les organisations professionnelles agricoles et
les agriculteurs dans les deux départements : Marne et Vosges.
Relations between professional agricultural organisations and
farmers in two departments : Marne, Vosges.

18424 Jegouzo, G.; Brangeon, J.L.; Dauce, P.
                                         FR 011302/70/8632
Les paysans et l'école. **School and peasantry.**

18425 Grignon, C.; Grignon, Ch.; Soliman, M.L.
                                         FR 012212/72/8631
Les paysans et l'école. **Peasant and school.**

18426 Stevenson   GB 041402/00/0002 R
Factors related to college recruitment.

18427 Stevenson; Hull   GB 041402/78/0003 R
The prediction of achievement on NCA–type courses.

18428 Black   GB 060311/00/0021 R
Careers of diploma students.

18429 Callaghan, J.; Mannion, J.; Harty, J.J.
                                         IE 120109/78/9245 N
A study of the operation of the farm apprenticeship and trai nee
farmer schemes.

18430 Callaghan, J.; Mannion, J.; Keating, J.
                                         IE 120109/78/9247 N
The sources and channels of information used by the members
of the agricultural advisory service.

18431 Mannion, J.; Callaghan, J.; Treacy, T.
                                         IE 120109/78/9248 N
A study of the farm demonstration as an advisory method in a
griculture.

D 7100 – Domestic science

18432 Bielig, H.J.; List, D.; Feier, U.; Förster, U.

DE 105813/74/0001

Ernährung in Einrichtungen der klinischen Versorgung. **Nutrition in clinical systems of supply.**

18433 Bielig, H.J.; Schulz–Gursch, W.H.

DE 105813/77/0001

Erstellung eines Planungsmodells für die apparative und maschinelle Einrichtung von Convenient–Küchen. **Development of a planning model for equipment and machinery in convenient–kitchen.**

18434 Schätzke, M.; Seifert, B.   DE 111851/73/0006

Entwicklung der Arbeitsweise und der technischen Einrichtungen des privaten Haushalts in den letzten 40 Jahren. **Development of working principle and technical equipment of private households of the late 40 years.**

18435 Schätzke, M.   DE 111851/75/0002

Untersuchungen über Möglichkeiten der energie– und zeitsparenden Speisenzubereitung im Backofen. **Studies on the possibilities of energy–saving and cost–saving food preparation in the baking–oven.**

18436 Schätzke, M.; Ritterbach, U.   DE 111851/78/0001 N

Erarbeiten von Grundlagen zur Optimierung und Rationalisierung der thermischen Zubereitung von Lebensmitteln auf der Basis einer Kombination von Elektrobackofen und Kochplatten. **Development of conditions for optimization and rationalization of thermic preparation of foods on the basis of combined electric baking oven and boiling plates.**

18437 Isensee, E.; Greis, B.   DE 129400/73/0001

Mahlzeitzubereitung aus Rohware oder aus vorgefertigten Produkten. **Preparation of meals with uncooked food or finished products.**

18438 Blosser–Reisen, L.; Christian–Meyer, C.

DE 144795/72/0001

Ausserlandwirtschaftlicher Zuerwerb durch Teilzeitarbeit der Frau. Eine Analyse der Berufsbildungswege, deren Kosten und der zu erwartenden Einkommen unter besonderer Berücksichtigung von Haushaltssituation, Bildungsvoraussetzungen und Standortgegebenheiten. **Income by alternatives of part–time employment of farm women.**

18439 Blosser–Reisen, L.; Weindlmaier, G.

DE 144795/74/0001

Zum Einsatz von Konsumentenkredit im privaten Haushalt. **The use of consumer credit in private households.**

18440 Blosser–Reisen, L.; Wohlleber, C.

DE 144795/78/0001 N

Rahmenkonzeption zur Gestaltung des Informations– und Beratungsangebots für die Haushaltsführung. **Framework for the shaping of information and advisory services with respect to home management.**

18441 Hesse, K.–F.   DE 148454/75/0001

Sozialökonomische Lebenshaltungsvergleiche ausgewählter privater Haushalte und Haushaltsphasen. **Socio–economic comparisons of standards of living of selected private**
households and household cycles.

18442 Schulz–Borck, H.   DE 201120/78/0004 N

Zeitbudgetuntersuchungen in privaten Haushalten. **Investigations on time and labour input in private households.**

18443 Schulz–Borck, H.; Grimmer, B.   DE 201120/78/0006 N

Untersuchung der Auswirkung verschiedener Standorte auf die Versorgung der Haushalte. **Analysis of the effect of different locations on the supply of private households.**

18444 Duden, R.; Paulus, K.   DE 211020/78/0007 N

Blanchieren pflanzlicher Produkte bei Temperaturen zwischen 50 und 90 Grad C. **Blanching of vegetables at temperatures between 50 and 90 degrees Celsius.**

18445 Werner, R.; Piekarski, J.; Opletal, L.

DE 211100/77/0003

Rückwirkungen der Ausser–Haus–Verpflegung auf das Ernährungsbudget ausgewählter Haushalte. **Effects of outdoor board on nutritional budget of selected households.**

18446 Piekarski, J.   DE 211100/77/0004

Technische Einrichtungen für die Schulverpflegung mit sterilisierten und gekühlten Speisen. **Technical equipment for school catering with sterilized and cooled food.**

18447 Werner, R.   DE 211100/77/0005

Kosten der Schulverpflegung bei Verwendung gekühlter und sterilisierter Speisen. **Costs of school catering using cooled and sterilized food.**

18448 Stübler, E.; Estele, E.   DE 211100/77/0010

Arbeitswirtschaftliche Grundlagen zur Organisation der Schulverpflegung mit gekühlten und sterilisierten Speisen. **Labour programming conditions for organization of school catering with cooled and sterilized food.**

18449 Stübler, E.   DE 211100/77/0011

Erstellung eines Planzeitkataloges für den Verpflegungsbereich. **Establishment of planning time catalogue for catering.**

18450 Backus, H.C.S.   NL 020030/73/4841

De deelname van de vrouw aan activiteiten buitenshuis in relatie tot structuur en functioneren van huishouding en gezin. **Differential social participation of woman and the affect on or relation to the structure of their household and family.**

18451 Hogenboom–Kesler, B.E.Th.A.   NL 020030/76/7612

Evaluatie onderzoek van het experimentele woningbouwproject "Centraal wonen Hilversume Meent". Veranderingen in de woon en verzorgingssituatie bij de overgang van een autonome naar meer collectieve leefwijze. **Evaluation of an experimental project "Centraal wonen Hilversume Meent" Changes in the living– and Houshold situation in moving from an autonomous to a more collective way of life.** Publications.

18452 Logman, W.J.   NL 020030/76/8800 N

Energieverbruik en energiebesparing in gezins huishoudingen. **Use and conservation of energy in family households.**

18453 Presvelou, C.   NL 020030/77/8394 R

Ontwikkelingen met betrekking tot de theorievorming en toepassing van de huishoudkunde. **Development in theories and** application of home economics. Publications.

18454 Wit, J.C. de   NL 020031/76/7601
Kruisbesmetting door Salmonella (paratyphus) in de keuken,
veroorzaakt door diepvrieskuikens. **Cross–contamination by
Salmonella (paratyphus) in the kitchen, caused by frozen
broilers.** Publications.

18455 Backus, H.C.S.   NL 020067/76/7612
Evaluatie onderzoek van het experimentele
woningbouwproject "Centraal wonen Hilversume Meent".
Veranderingen in de woon en verzorgingssituatie bij de
overgang van een autonome naar meer collectieve leefwijze.
**Evaluation of an experimental project "Centraal wonen
Hilversumse Meent" Changes in the living– and houshold
situation in moving from an autonomous to a more collective
way of life.** Publications.

D 7200 – Human nutrition and food research

See also 3797, 3973, 11545, 16009, 16678, 19561, 19562, 19563,
19564, 19565, 19762, 20202

18456 Thonart, P.; Paquot, M.; Deroanne, C.
     BE 010015/72/0006
Etudes des applications des microorganismes (spécialement de
mutants) et des enzymes dans les industries agro–alimentaires.
**New developments in the use of microorganisms (especially
mutants) and enzymes (free and immobilized) to improve
technological properties.** Publications.

18457 Coppens, R.; Thonart, P.; Paquot, M.; Deroanne, C.
     BE 010015/74/0007 R
Immobilisation d'enzymes utilisés en industries
agro–alimentaires. **Immobilization of enzymes used in food
industries.** Publications.

18458 Huyghebaert, H.   BE 030025/76/0012 R
Fundamentele studie van de reologische eigenschappen van
modelsystemen en levensmiddelen. **Basic study of the
rheological properties of model systems and foods.**

18459 De Moor, H.; Van Heddeghem, A.; De Doncker, P.
     BE 030025/76/0013 R
Studie van contaminanten in melk, zuivelprodukten,
babyvoeding en moedermelk. **Study of the contaminants in
milk, dairy products, infant food and human milk.**

18460 Casier, J.; Willems, H.; De Paepe, G.; Goffings, G.;
Brummer, J.   BE 040501/68/0007
Invloed van de endosperm–celwand pentosanen van tarwe en
rogge op de deegeigenschappen de bakwaarde en de
vershoudbaarheid bij graangewassen, bloem en zetmeelrijk
materiaal. **Influence of endosperm cellwall pentosan of wheat
and rye on the baking value, dough properties and staling
prevention in cereal floor and other starch material.**
Publications.

18461 Casier, J.; Willems, H.; Van Herterijck, H.; Goffings,
G.; De Paepe, G.   BE 040501/72/0005
Onderzoek naar de chemische, fysiko chemische en
technologische grondslagen van de endospermcelwand
pentosanen van tarwe en rogge als bakfactor. **Research on the
basic relationship between the chemical structure of the
physico–chemical and the technological propertus of the
endospermcellwall pentosanfraction of wheat and rye as**

backing factor.

18462 Casier, J.; Van Herterijck, H.   BE 040501/72/0006
Onderzoek van het pentosanasestelsel van tarwe en rogge als
invloedsfaktor op de bakwaarde. **Study of the pentosaneses in
the rye and wheat kernel and their influence on the
bakingsprocessus.**

18463 Casier, J.   BE 040501/75/0008
Verbakken van sorghum en millet door toevoeging van
roggepentosanen als broodvormende factor. **Breadmaking of
sorgum and millet using rye pentosan as addition.**

18464 Fiévez; Vacoboinie   BE 060005/79/0002 N
Etude des anabolisants chez la bête bovine – Cinétique et
résidus dans les viandes. **Study of anabolic agents for cattle –
Kinetic and residues in meat.**

18465 Maton, A.; Priem, R.   BE 070300/73/0014 R
De bepaling van de sorptie–isothermen van
landbouwprodukten. **The determination of the
sorption–isothermes of agricultural products.**

18466 Hovart, P.; Vyncke, W.   BE 070800/63/0005 R
Studie van de kwaliteit van vis en visserijprodukten. **Quality
research on fish and fishery products.** Publications.

18467 De Vilder, J.; Martens, R.   BE 070900/73/0002
De fysische en chemische eigenschappen van melkpoeder. **The
physical and chemical properties of milk powders.** Publications.

18468 Waes, G.   BE 070900/76/0024
Zuursels voor zuivelprodukten. **Starters for dairy products.**
Publications.

18469 Delbeke, R.; Naudts, M.   BE 070900/77/0041 R
Hydrolyse van de laktose. **Hydrolysis of lactose.**

18470 Jamotte, P.; Laloux, J.   BE 080500/75/0007 R
Mécanisation et automation de la détermination du nombre
total de bactéries dans le lait cru. **Mecanisation and
automatisation of the determination of total bacteria in row
milk.** Publications.

18471 Jamotte, P.; Guyot, A.   BE 080500/76/0005 R
Obtention de beurre frigo tarinable par malaxage de fractions
butyriques sous réfrigération. **Obtaining cold spreading of
butter by using liquid and solid butterparts.**

18472 Jamotte, P.; Lacrosse, R.; Beirens, P.; Guyot, A.
     BE 080700/79/0011 N
Procédés nouveaux de fabrication de beurre acide et de
babeurre doux à partir de crème douce. **New process for
manufacturing cultured butter and sweet buttermilk from sweet
cream.**

18473 Bronchart, R.; De Barsy, T.   BE 140000/76/0042 R
Examen histologique et morphologique des produits agricoles.
Histological and morphological examination of plant products.
Publications.

18474 Strecker, O.; Römerscheidt, M.-H.
     DE 111650/71/0001
Der Lebenszyklus von Erzeugnissen der Ernährungsindustrie.
The product–life–cycle of brands in the food industry.

18475 Roll, R. DE 305010/75/0011
Teratologische und chemogenetische Untersuchungen mit Aflatoxinen und Patulin. **Teratological and chemogenetic studies of aflatoxins and patulin.**

18476 Rottka, H. DE 305010/75/0016
Ernährung in Einrichtungen der klinischen Versorgung – SFB Krankenhausbau –. **Nutrition in institutions of clinical care.**

18477 Jakobsen, M. DK 030137/77/0002
Alternative konserverende principper ved industriel fremstilling af sure frugt– og grøntprodukter. **Alternative preservation principles in the industrial manufacture of sour fruit and vegetable products.**

18478 Boulet, D.; Laporte, J.P. FR 011205/74/8645
Structure et évolution de la consommation des boissons. **Structure and dynamics of drinks consumption.**

18479 Land; Hobson–frohock GB 010203/00/0019
Define substances in rapeseed meal associated with crab–like or fishy taints in eggs.

18480 Curtis; Fenwick GB 010203/00/0021
Analyse glucosinolates (and degradation products) of cruciferous vegetables and relate to food safety and flavour.

18481 Chan; Levett GB 010203/00/0028
Investigation of reactions of products from oxidative deterioration of unsaturated fatty acids.

18482 Coxon; Price GB 010203/00/0033
Steroid glycoalkaloids of Solanaceae.

18483 Rhodes; Harkett GB 010203/00/0050
The physiology of potato tuber dormancy and sprout growth and their control during storage.

18484 Selvendran GB 010203/00/0054
Identification and quantification of cell walls during growth and senescence of edible plants.

18485 Curtis; Coxon GB 010203/76/0043
Mycotoxins: new analytical methods; presence in moulded plant material for processing; decontamination proce.

18486 Fenwick; Curtis GB 010203/76/0044
Investigate reaction products of sulphur dioxide in food and food model systems.

18487 Rhodes; Bacon GB 010203/76/0056
Explain secondary changes in chill injured tomatoes to extend storage.

18488 Selvendran GB 010203/76/0057
Define and determine xylans and glycoproteins in the structural components of food plants.

18489 Selvendran; King GB 010203/76/0058
Define and determine polysaccharides in the structural components of food plants.

18490 Selvendran GB 010203/77/0046
Composition and properties of cell wall polymers in foods:dietary fibre of apple,cabbage,carrot,potato,cereals(with Dnu).

18491 Southgate, P. GB 010203/77/0047
Isolation and analysis of different forms of folates in foods and the effect of processing thereon (with Dnu).

18492 Waites GB 010204/00/0003
Physiology of bacterial spores, especially germination of clostridial spores.

18493 Buhagiar GB 010204/00/0008
Isolation and properties of yeasts found on vegetables, fruits and edible birds.

18494 Lund GB 010204/00/0012
Bacterial spoilage of potatoes.

18495 Lund GB 010204/00/0013
Physiology of vegetable spoilage bacteria.

18496 Payne GB 010204/00/0021
Effects of heat on non–sporing bacteria.

18497 Geeson GB 010204/75/0027
Storage disorders of winter white cabbage.

18498 Dennis GB 010204/75/0028
Physiology of soft fruit spoilage fungi.

18499 Dennis GB 010204/75/0029
Fungal spoilage of tomatoes during cool storage and subsequent shelf life in relation to quality.

18500 Dennis; Lund GB 010204/76/0031
Define bacteria, yeasts and moulds of chopped vegetable preparations; clarify role in spoilage.

18501 Peel; Lund GB 010204/77/0032
Define alkali–tolerant microorganisms of potato waste and their biochemical activities.

18502 Geeson GB 010204/77/0033
Physiology of botrytis cinerea in relation to survival in vegetable and fruit stores.

18503 Barnes GB 010205/00/0009
Microbiology of poultry in relation to carcase quality and shelf life.

18504 Robinson; Browne GB 010205/00/0013
Optimum conditions for maintaining quality in storage of vegetables.

18505 Robinson; Browne GB 010205/00/0014
Optimum conditions for maintaining quality in storage of soft fruit.

18506 Jones GB 010205/76/0042
Define method for detection of 'incubator rejects' in liquid whole egg after normal commercial processing.

18507 Jones; Mead GB 010205/77/0007
Process requirements for poultry carcases, especially turkeys and ducks; effects on all aspects of quality.

18508 Jones; Monsey GB 010205/77/0045
Develop a test to confirm attainment of heat requirements for

egg white pasteurisation.

18509 Hughes; Grant   GB 010205/78/0031
Study physical physiological and anatomical properties of
potato tubers and external damage due to handling.

18510 Land; Hobson–frohock   GB 010206/00/0031
Factors which affect the flavour of substances which occur in
systems in foods.

18511 Southgate   GB 010206/79/0040 N
Characterisation and measurement of dietary fibre in mixed
diets.

18512 Bruce   GB 010505/00/0001
Environmental radioactivity : assay of Sr90, Cs137 and I131 in
milk.

18513 Patterson   GB 010601/75/0010 R
Define factors affecting utilisation of boars for production of
fresh and processed meat.

18514 Lister   GB 010601/76/0061 N
Study physiological basis of industrial practice pre–slaughter to
improve meat quality.

18515 Harries   GB 010602/00/0040
Define parameters of beef and lamb carcasses for predicting
retail value.

18516 Williams   GB 010602/00/0050
Develop rapid non–destructive and partial dissection methods of
post–slaughter carcass evaluation.

18517 Williams   GB 010602/00/0070
Compare dissection methods and interpretation thereof for
determining carcass composition.

18518 Miles   GB 010602/00/0080
Assess physical methods for non–destructive carcass evaluation
on the live animal.

18519 Taylor   GB 010602/77/0100
Application of meat research:define parameters for processing
animals into consumer acceptable packaged meat.

18520 Dainty   GB 010603/00/0060
Identify compounds changing with microbial growth during
chill storage of fresh, vacuum–packed and cured meats.

18521 Bailey   GB 010604/00/0020
Provide data on heat and water transfer in meat handling to
improve chilling, freezing and thawing practices.

18522 Miles   GB 010604/00/0030
Provide data on physical properties of meat relating to heat
transfer and to measurement of quality and composition.

18523 Bailey   GB 010604/00/0050
Survey commercial handling of meat; provide data on
temperature, air speed, pH. water transfer etc.

18524 Roberts   GB 010605/00/0040
Define factors affecting toxin production by clostridium
botulinum in pasteurised cured meat.

18525 Dransfeld   GB 010606/00/0040
Develop instrumental methods for measuring the texture of
meat.

18526 Patterson   GB 010606/00/0140
Identify and quantify off–flavours, taints and hazardous
substances in meat and meat products.

18527 Rhodes   GB 010606/00/0150
Study production and process factors and interactions affecting
meat eating quality using taste panels and instruments.

18528 Bailey   GB 010606/75/0060 R
Define muscle collagen, variation between muscles and changes
therein in relation to meat texture.

18529 Mottram   GB 010606/77/0160 R
Defining and measuring the flavours of cooked meats to
improve them and identify precursors.

18530 Bendall   GB 010606/78/0070 N
Define chemical and physical changes during rigor: ATP–ASE
activation by CA++, relate to cold–shortening in meat.

18531 Mottram   GB 010606/78/0170
Define effects of cooking conditions on the eating quality of
meat.

18532 Shannon   GB 010707/00/0037
The composition of eggs.

18533 Sharples; Stow   GB 011004/00/0001
Optimum conditions for storage of apple varieties.

18534 Knee   GB 011004/00/0003
Fruit physiology in relation to storage.

18535 Perring; Knee   GB 011004/00/0004
Fruit composition in relation to storage.

18536 Johnson; Topping   GB 011004/00/0006
Prestorage factors affecting transport and storage of soft fruit.

18537 Sharples; Chappell   GB 011004/75/0009
Advice and trouble shooting in connection with the storage of
apples and pears.

18538 Nichols; Hammond   GB 011102/00/0031
Post–harvest physiology of mushrooms.

18539 Maw; Davies   GB 011103/00/0004
Flavour constituents of tomato fruit and other edible glasshouse
crops.

18540 Timberlake; Bridle   GB 011502/00/0001
Isolate and identify phenolic components in flavour of apples,
apple juices and cider.

18541 Williams; Tucknott, A.A.   GB 011502/00/0002 R
Isolate and identify aroma components of fruit and fruit
products to produce factors for flavour improvement.

18542 Tucknott; Williams A.A.   GB 011502/00/0003
Isolate and identify causes of mousy taint and study sulphur
based taints in foods and beverages.

18543 Bridle; Timberlake GB 011502/00/0004
Isolate identify and study reactions of sulphite–resistant plant anthocyanins for non–toxic food colours.

18544 Burroughs GB 011502/00/0005
Effect of pomological factors and processing on composition of unfermented and fermented fruit juices.

18545 Williams GB 011502/00/0006 R
Influence of phenolics, organic acids and aroma compounds on flavour of cider.

18546 Carr; Davenport GB 011502/00/0007
Source and nature of yeasts and acid tolerant bacteria of fruit juice products.

18547 Burroughs; Goverd GB 011502/00/0008
Nutrition of yeasts in fruit juice fermentation. Soluble nitrogen compounds and B group vitamins in cider.

18548 Carr; Goverd GB 011502/00/0009
Effect of nutrition on malo–lactic fermentation of fruit juices.

18549 Whiting; Coggins GB 011502/00/0010
Biochemical pathways in the metabolism of organic acid by yeasts in fruit juice fermentation.

18550 Carr; Burroughs GB 011502/00/0011
Effect of environmental factors and inhibitors on microbial growth.

18551 Beech GB 011502/00/0012
Effect of fermentation system, strain of yeast and storage on flavour in fruit juice products.

18552 Cousins; McKinnon GB 011701/00/0001
Methods of cleaning and disinfecting milking equipment.

18553 Cousins; McKinnon GB 011701/00/0002
Sources of bacteria in cow milk.

18554 Davies GB 011701/00/0006
Factors in milk controlling the germination of bacterial spores.

18555 Sharpe; Law GB 011701/00/0007
Role of bacteria in the production of Cheddar cheese flavour.

18556 Garvie; Law GB 011701/00/0013
Physiology, classification and identification of lactic acid bacteria.

18557 Garvie GB 011701/00/0014
National collection of dairy organisms.

18558 Law; Cliffe GB 011701/00/0017
Psychrotrophic bacteria in milk.

18559 Cousins; McKinnon GB 011701/00/0019
Assessment of hygienic quality of raw milk.

18560 Reiter; Cousins GB 011701/00/0022
Conservation of milk by methods other than heating.

18561 Davies GB 011701/75/0023
Bacteriological aspects of yoghurt manufacture.

18562 Davies; Gasson GB 011701/75/0024
Selection or genetic modification of lactic acid bacteria for improved strains for manufacture of dairy products.

18563 Anderson; Cheeseman GB 011703/00/0008
Effect of heating and cooling milk on fat globule membrane composition.

18564 Anderson; Cheeseman GB 011703/00/0009
Fat globule membrane, structure, composition, function and enzyme action in relation to off flavours.

18565 Lyster; Green GB 011703/00/0012
Structure of aggregation and colloidal stability of the casein micelle.

18566 Green; Marshall GB 011703/00/0013
Factors in milk affecting the formation, properties and syneresis of curd.

18567 Lyster GB 011703/00/0014
Heat–induced denaturation of whey protein and effect of factors during milk production.

18568 Andrews; Cheeseman GB 011703/00/0015
Heat–induced interaction between milk caseins and carbohydrates.

18569 Andrews GB 011703/00/0016
Effect of heat–stable enzymes on milk during processing and storage.

18570 Lyster; Hillier GB 011703/00/0017
Composition and properties of milk and whey powders. Solubility, and the effect of processing on this.

18571 Anderson; Andrews GB 011703/77/0022
The influence of mastitis on milk composition and on manufacture and storage of dairy products.

18572 Storry; Millard GB 011703/78/0023
Effect of composition on processing properties and quality of products. Relationship of diet to constituents.

18573 Brumby GB 011703/78/0024
Influence of milk constituents on the oxidation of milk fat.

18574 Andrews; Sukan GB 011703/79/0027 N
Application of protein hydrolysis and the plastein reaction to the utilization of milk proteins.

18575 Perkin GB 011705/00/0017
Methods of UHT sterilisation with special reference to the quality of the product.

18576 Burton GB 011705/00/0021
Factors affecting deposit formation from heated milk on surfaces.

18577 Chapman; McIntyre GB 011705/75/0026
Cheese quality in relation to bacteriological, chemical and physical properties of milk.

18578 Chapman; McIntyre GB 011705/75/0027
Cheese–making technology.

18579 Skudder; Lane   GB 011705/75/0031
Evaluation of thermal and membrane methods of milk concentration and of the resultant products.

18580 Researcher not indicated   GB 011705/76/0032
Evaluation of methods for utilising whey constituents.

18581 Pavey   GB 011705/76/0034
Effect of container properties on product quality during storage (particularly heat–treated milk).

18582 Perkin   GB 011705/76/0035
Container sterilization in aseptic filling processes.

18583 Thompson   GB 011708/00/0014
Determination of fat soluble vitamins in food. Effect of diet on level of fat soluble vitamins in milk.

18584 Ford; Salter   GB 011708/00/0015
Nutritional significance of vitamin–binding proteins in milk.

18585 Ford; Thompson   GB 011708/00/0017
Effect of heat treatment, processing and storage on nutritive value of milk.

18586 Kilshaw; Coates   GB 011708/77/0020
The aetiology of allergies to foods or their digestion products in animals and man.

18587 Manning   GB 011709/00/0001
Analysis of flavour of dairy products (cheese).

18588 Prentice; Glover   GB 011709/00/0002
Physical properties of dairy products.

18589 Phipps   GB 011709/00/0006
Homogenization of milk and cream.

18590 Prentice   GB 011709/00/0007
Structure of dairy products.

18591 Glover; Stothart   GB 011709/00/0008
Concentration of milk by reverse osmosis and ultra–filtration.

18592 Andrews   GB 011712/00/0011
Isolation and characterisation of folate–binding proteins.

18593 Tucker   GB 011804/00/0014
Factors affecting onion storage life, especially dormancy, variety and temperature. Develop storage systems.

18594 Taylor; Dudley   GB 011807/00/0012
Bacterial deterioration of vegetables in store and tissues in culture.

18595 Hodge   GB 011908/78/0006 R
Rapid identification of potential malting quality in barley.

18596 Lapwood   GB 012009/00/0034
Disease of potatoes during storage.

18597 Green   GB 012201/00/0011
Structure and occurrence of hop constituents.

18598 Green   GB 012201/00/0027
Chemical factors relating to deterioration of hops during storage.

18599 Muir; Sweetsur   GB 030201/00/0015
Factors affecting the dispersibility of "instant" dried milks.

18600 Muir   GB 030201/00/0017
Influence of somatic cell count of raw milk on quality of pasteurized milk and dried whole milk (with WSAC).

18601 Taylor   GB 030201/00/0018
Use of water–agar test to determine hygienic quality of milk products.

18602 White   GB 030201/00/0023
Analytical methods for milk and milk products done at request of BSI, ISO, IDF and AOAC.

18603 Banks; Ferrie   GB 030201/00/0029
Effect of ratio of C18 to C16 fatty acids in the feed on the quality of butter fat and butter.

18604 Muir; Abbot   GB 030201/75/0034
Studies on spray–dried milk products.

18605 Muir; Griffiths   GB 030201/77/0035
Whey utilisation – isolation and properties of a heat–stable B–galactosidase.

18606 Muir; Banks   GB 030201/77/0036
Cheese yield in relation to milk composition.

18607 Dalgleish; Holt   GB 030203/00/0009
Studies of the size distribution of particles in skim milk.

18608 Holt   GB 030203/00/0018
Development of methods for characterizing casein micelles.

18609 Davies   GB 030203/00/0020
Development of rapid methods for the analysis of mixtures of caseins.

18610 Mason   GB 030203/00/0021
The preparation of specialized nutritional products from casein.

18611 Manson; Annan   GB 030203/77/0024
The chemistry of proteins in heated milk.

18612 Mason   GB 030701/00/0040
Post–harvest handling of soft fruit.

18613 Allison   GB 030804/78/0010
Develop and automate small scale tests for malting distilling, brewing and milling quality.

18614 Davidson   GB 030805/78/0004
Screen breeding material for cooking and processing quality. Develop and use improved screening techniques.

18615 Gilmour   GB 040101/00/0005
Microbial studies on the ripening of Cheddar cheese.

18616 Gilmour   GB 040101/00/0007 R
The identification and control of spore–forming bacteria in milk and dairy products.

18617 Gilmour　　　　　　　GB 040101/76/0008
The influence of lipolytic and proteolytic bacteria on the suitability of milk for processing.

18618 Patterson; Gibbs　　　　GB 040102/00/0002
Typing of isolates of staphylococcus aureus.

18619 Patterson; Gibbs　　　　GB 040102/00/0003
Bacteriology of packaged meat.

18620 Gibbs　　　　　　　　GB 040102/00/0005
Development and application of the fluorescent antibody technique.

18621 Gibbs; Patterson　　　　GB 040102/00/0006
The biochemical activities of bacteria leading to spoilage of meat.

18622 Damoglou　　　　　　GB 040103/00/0009
Identification of volatiles produced by lactic acid bacteria.

18623 Damoglou　　　　　　GB 040103/76/0007
Enzymes from fish slime bacteria.

18624 Damoglou　　　　　　GB 040103/78/0010
The microbiology of vacuum–packaged fish.

18625 Pearce　　　　　　　GB 040403/00/0014
Lipid characteristics in intensively reared lambs in relation to flavour.

18626 Johnston; McCracken　　GB 040404/00/0001
Factors affecting the quality of bacon backfat.

18627 Johnston　　　　　　GB 040404/77/0006
The influence of cooking technique on dietary fibre levels of boiled potatoes.

18628 Foster　　　　　　　GB 041305/73/0004
The identification of eggs with shells of poor quality.

18629 McLain　　　　　　　GB 041403/75/0002
Water conveyancing methods for chipped potatoes or similar food substances.

18630 Legge　　　　　　　GB 041403/76/0003
Egg packaging.

18631 Wotton　　　　　　　GB 041404/00/0002
The effect of the deep–freezing of vacuum–packed primal beef cuts on meat quality.

18632 Drysdale　　　　　　GB 041404/00/0003
Lye–peeling of Bramley apples.

18633 O'Hara; Weatherup　　　GB 041404/00/0004
The technology of yoghurt production.

18634 McGill　　　　　　　GB 041404/00/0006
An investigation of the production of non–fermented breads.

18635 Lang　　　　　　　　GB 041404/00/0010
An evaluation of the effectiveness of systems of cleansing milk processing plant using ambient temperatures.

18636 Wright　　　　　　　GB 041404/75/0009
The production of flavoured butter with improved keeping quality.

18637 Trimble　　　　　　　GB 041404/78/0011
Textural quality of foodstuffs.

18638 Researcher not indicated　GB 050164/00/0007
Milk products: manufacture and storage.

18639 Jones　　　　　　　　GB 050301/65/0020
Taint from pesticides.

18640 Frerichs; Wijeratne　　　GB 050509/00/0024
Assessment of EEC test for screening antimicrobial substances in animal tissues.

18641 Smith　　　　　　　　GB 050601/00/0003
Migration of plastic constituents into food.

18642 Smith　　　　　　　　GB 050601/78/0004
Determination of starch.

18643 Smith　　　　　　　　GB 050601/78/0005
Survey of commercial analytical instruments and aids.

18644 Smith　　　　　　　　GB 050601/78/0006
EEC analytical methods.

18645 Walters; Saxby　　　　GB 050602/00/0001
Determine amines in foodstuffs and their ni–nitrosation under conditions found in the human stomach.

18646 Saxby　　　　　　　　GB 050603/00/0003
Stability of food additives during food processing and storage.

18647 Saxby　　　　　　　　GB 050603/78/0004
Re–examination of the analytical method for fentin in cocoa beans.

18648 Seager　　　　　　　GB 050604/00/0002
Investigate factors which control the process of sugar panning.

18649 Jewell　　　　　　　GB 050605/00/0001
Determine analytical parameters for assessment of fruit content as a test of authenticity of citrus juices.

18650 Jewell　　　　　　　GB 050605/00/0003
Suitability of soft and stone fruit cultivars for jam manufacture.

18651 Jewell　　　　　　　GB 050605/00/0004
Taint in jams from horticultural chemicals.

18652 Jewell　　　　　　　GB 050605/00/0005
Stability of colours in fruit products.

18653 Jewell　　　　　　　GB 050605/00/0006
Verification of authenticity of lemon juice.

18654 Ranken　　　　　　　GB 050605/78/0007
Properties of plant cells.

18655 Weir; Marrs　　　　　GB 050606/00/0003
Mechanism of gelation in combination with other gelling agents.

18656 Weir   GB 050606/78/0004
The gel and thickening properties of mixed food hydrocolloids.

18657 Slight   GB 050607/00/0001
Develop methods for measurement or control of factors influencing the mechanical handling of foodstuffs.

18658 Slight   GB 050607/00/0002
Develop physical methods for in–line measurement of fat content of food products during manufacture.

18659 Slight   GB 050607/00/0003
Develop methods for in–line measurement of temperature of foods during processing.

18660 Slight   GB 050607/00/0004
Establish a method for controlling the moisture content of products during manufacture.

18661 Slight   GB 050607/00/0005
Instrumental methods for in–line process control of temperature humidity and mass flow rates.

18662 Slight   GB 050607/00/0006
Microprocessors.

18663 Elson; Slight   GB 050607/78/0007
Extrusion cooking technology.

18664 Jarvis; Wood   GB 050608/00/0003
Develop instrumentation for separation of microorganisms from food and their rapid estimation.

18665 Jarvis   GB 050608/00/0004
Evaluation of disinfectants and detergents for use in the meat processing industry.

18666 Jarvis   GB 050608/00/0006
Potentiation of antimicrobial activity by polyphosphates.

18667 Jarvis   GB 050608/78/0007
Statistical implications of microbiological counting methods.

18668 Jewell   GB 050609/00/0002
Determine the fine structure of foodstuffs and food systems to solve processing problems.

18669 Jarvis   GB 050609/00/0003
Detection of organisms of family Enterobacteriaceae.

18670 Jewell   GB 050609/00/0004
The microscope as an analytical tool.

18671 Meara   GB 050610/00/0005
The role of unsaponifiable matter in flavour stability of edible oils.

18672 Meara   GB 050610/00/0006
The study of natural antioxidants.

18673 Elson; Dodson   GB 050611/00/0005
Physical properties of foods important in handling and processing.

18674 Elson   GB 050611/00/0006
Technological implications of different materials etc at product/machinery and product/product interface.

18675 Elson   GB 050611/00/0007
Seek practical means of treating food trade wastes which may contain fat protein and carbohydrates.

18676 Elson   GB 050611/00/0008
Application of the heat pipe in the food industry.

18677 Elson   GB 050611/00/0009
Heat transfer to food materials in plant and equipment.

18678 Elson   GB 050611/78/0011
Thermal economy in drying processes.

18679 Jewell   GB 050619/00/0003
Microbiology of pickles.

18680 Jewell   GB 050619/00/0004
Develop methods for measuring and controlling the consistency of jams.

18681 Ranken   GB 050619/00/0006
Factors affecting the water and fat binding properties of meat and fish products during processing.

18682 Seager; Jewell   GB 050619/00/0008
Develop techniques for the study of graining of sucrose in confectionery products.

18683 Meara; Smith   GB 050619/00/0009
Collaborative studies on standardisation testing and development of analytical methods for foods.

18684 Jewell; Meara   GB 050619/00/0012
Study structure of chocolate as influenced by fat composition and temper.

18685 Jarvis; Saxby   GB 050619/00/0014
Mycotoxins in foods.

18686 Walters; Weir   GB 050619/00/0016
The use of chemiluminescence to study spoilage reactions in food.

18687 Jarvis; Jewell   GB 050619/00/0017
Interactions of preservation systems in foods.

18688 Elson; Weir   GB 050619/00/0018
Studies using pulsed NMR.

18689 Ranken; Walters   GB 050619/00/0019
Chemistry of cured meat pigments.

18690 Jarvis; Saxby   GB 050619/00/0021
Isolation and determination of B vitamins in foods.

18691 Rankin; Jarvis   GB 050619/77/0015
Shelf life of meat products in relation to water activity and composition.

18692 Researcher not indicated   GB 050701/00/0002
Origin of lesions in testicular tissue and loss of fertility induced chemically by substances in food.

18693 Researcher not indicated   GB 050701/00/0003

Tissue culture and host–mediated assay systems as short–term tests for carcinogenicity.

18694 Researcher not indicated GB 050701/00/0004
Mechanism of hepatic nodule formation in response to the food colour Ponceau MX.

18695 Researcher not indicated GB 050701/00/0006
Toxicological significance of caecal enlargement, its biochemistry and role in nutritional deficiency.

18696 Researcher not indicated GB 050701/00/0008
Transformation of heavy metals to organometal derivatives by gut bacteria and its effect on absorption.

18697 Researcher not indicated GB 050701/00/0009
Penetration of particulate and macromolecular food additives through gastrointestinal tissues.

18698 Researcher not indicated GB 050701/00/0010
Indirect assessment by urinary d–glucaric acid of hepatic microsomal enzyme activity as an index of toxicity.

18699 Researcher not indicated GB 050701/00/0012
Inhibition of in–vivo metabolic activation of carcinogens.

18700 Researcher not indicated GB 050701/00/0013
Hormonal effects and resulting carcinogenicity of food and animal feed additives.

18701 Researcher not indicated GB 050702/00/0001
Programme to evaluate the safety of food additives, packaging materials, cosmetics and toilet preparations.

18702 Arthey; Esseen GB 050801/00/0001
Taint tests to assess the effects of new agricultural chemicals on flavour of processed fruit and vegetable products.

18703 Arthey; Esseen GB 050801/00/0002
Schedules for product quality appraisal in respect of new processing and packaging methods.

18704 Arthey; Oswin GB 050801/00/0003
Processing trials to assess suitability for canning and freezing of soft fruit varieties grown elsewhere.

18705 Arthey; Bennett GB 050801/00/0004
Processing trials to assess suitability of varieties of vegetables grown at other centres.

18706 Arthey; Bedford GB 050801/00/0005
Field trials of calabrese varieties Quick freezing and quality appraisal of products.

18707 Arthey; Bedford GB 050801/00/0006
Field trials of new varieties of french beans; canning and quick freezing and quality appraisal.

18708 Arthey; Bedford GB 050801/00/0008
Field trials of new varieties of peas; canning, freezing, bottling tests and quality appraisal.

18709 Arthey; Bedford GB 050801/00/0009
Field trials of new varieties of potato; canning tests and quality appraisal of products.

18710 Arthey; Bedford GB 050801/00/0010
Field trials of brussel sprouts for quick–freezing and quality appraisal.

18711 Arthey; Bedford GB 050801/00/0011
Field trials on sweet corn varieties for suitability for canning or freezing and quality appraisal.

18712 Arthey; Esseen GB 050801/00/0012
Examination of taints and off flavours in navy beans (with FRI).

18713 Arthey GB 050801/00/0013
Quick frozen quality specifications.

18714 Arthey; Bennet GB 050801/00/0014
Maturity in vegetable crops for processing.

18715 Arthey GB 050801/00/0015
Carrots for canning.

18716 Henshall GB 050802/00/0001
Factors affecting corrosivity of can contents.

18717 Henshall; Jewell GB 050802/00/0002
Electrochemical processes of tinplate can bodies fitted with tin–free steel ends.

18718 Henshall; Smith GB 050802/00/0004
Metal pick–up changes in organoleptic quality during long–term storage of canned products.

18719 Henshall; Jewell GB 050802/00/0005
Comprehensive survey of prevailing lead content of canned foods.

18720 Blundstone GB 050803/00/0001
Stabilisation of natural colours in legumes on processing.

18721 Brown; Thorpe GB 050803/00/0004
HTST processing/aseptic filling of particulate foods: enzyme inactivation in regeneration in vegetables/meat.

18722 Adams; Hall GB 050803/00/0005
Blanching of vegetables;factors affecting quality and shelf–life in canned and frozen vegetables.

18723 Thorpe; Atherton GB 050804/00/0001
Process evaluation for canned fruits and vegetables.

18724 Atherton GB 050804/00/0002
Standardize tenderometers and prepare and process standardization peas as a service to members.

18725 Thorpe; Brown GB 050804/00/0005
Effect of pH on heat resistance and recovery after heating of spores of Bacillus and Clostridium species.

18726 Thorpe; Atherton GB 050804/00/0006
Quality control procedures for safe production of foods in heat sterilizable flexible pouches.

18727 Brown; Thorpe GB 050804/00/0007
HTST processing/aseptic filling of particular foods: thermal death rate studies of sporing bacteria.

18728 Brown; Thorpe   GB 050804/00/0008
Cannery bacteriological quality control procedures.

18729 Thorpe; Brown   GB 050804/00/0009
Process determination using spores in spheres.

18730 Thorpe; Evans   GB 050804/00/0010
Sterilizable flexible packaging – processing, packaging and safety aspects.

18731 Thorpe; Atherton   GB 050804/00/0011
Guidelines for safe processing of canned foods in continous cookers.

18732 Holdsworth; Samnang   GB 050805/00/0002
HTST processing/aseptic filling of particulate foods: thermal processing/chemical engineering requirements.

18733 Holdsworth; Samnang   GB 050805/00/0003
Heat transfer studies in relation to processing equipment.

18734 Hall; Ball   GB 050806/00/0002
To develop and apply recommended methodology for the microbiological examination of frozen foods for E. coli.

18735 Hall; Henshall   GB 050809/00/0001
Effect of frozen storage on nutrients in frozen meat, fish and vegetable products.

18736 Thorpe; Arthey   GB 050809/00/0003
Determine technical and safety requirements for glasspacking of fruits and vegetables.

18737 Blundstone   GB 050809/00/0004
Toxicity of processed potato berries (joint with Bibra).

18738 Gough; McDermott   GB 050901/00/0001
Amylolytic activity, gelation of starch and structural quality in baked goods made from soft wheats.

18739 Fisher   GB 050901/00/0003
Nutritional and prophylactic properties of bran including lignin composition and rat feeding trials.

18740 Fisher; Berry   GB 050901/00/0004
Toxicological studies on flour treatment agents.

18741 Hodge; Robb   GB 050902/00/0001
Effects of process variables and ingredient properties on production of cake and pastry in continuous mixers.

18742 Stevens; Pritchard   GB 050902/00/0002
Identify and quantify the major parameters of ingredients and processes for short–sweet biscuit making.

18743 Chamberlain   GB 050902/00/0003
Develop modified processes to enable increased use of home–grown wheat in breadmaking.

18744 Ewart; Parkinson   GB 050903/00/0001
Correlation with baking characteristics of natural variations in structure and composition of wheat proteins.

18745 Thewlis   GB 050903/00/0002
Determine action of improving agents (bromate/metabisulphite) on the wheat flour in baked goods.

18746 Lawson; Cornford   GB 050903/00/0003
Measurement and control techniques for biscuit cake and breadmaking processes.

18747 Redman   GB 050903/00/0005
Tests for the identification of wheat varieties and the baking quality of wheat.

18748 Researcher not indicated   GB 050903/00/0006
Factors affecting bread staling.

18749 Stewart; Dodds   GB 050904/00/0001
Determine milling and baking qualities of new home grown wheats as a routine evaluation service.

18750 Stevens; Hinton   GB 050904/00/0003
Improvements in the milling process and in the treatment of by–products.

18751 Ferguson   GB 050904/00/0004
Effect of environmental factors on wheat quality.

18752 Dodds   GB 050904/00/0005
Wheat testing for the Intervention Board.

18753 Seiler   GB 050905/00/0001
Microbiological examination of flour milled from home grown cereals and of bakery products.

18754 Cranford   GB 050905/00/0002
Develop analytical techniques for emulsifying agents improvers and pesticide residues in wheat or flour.

18755 Hart   GB 050905/00/0003
Provision of analytical service to the other departments of the Research Association.

18756 Wardhough; Nagrecha   GB 050909/00/0001
Standardize chemical and microbiological methods of test for ingredients and bakery products.

18757 Hume; Mackie   GB 051001/00/0010
New fish protein products with desirable functional properties.

18758 Mackie; Thomson   GB 051001/00/0015
Spun fish proteins.

18759 Keay; Hardy   GB 051002/00/0032
Innovation of consumer fish products particularly from underutilised resources.

18760 Hardy; Murray   GB 051002/67/0034
Identification and origin of the odour and flavour components of fresh and deteriorating fish and shellfish.

18761 Cann; Hodgkiss   GB 051003/00/0021
Development of sterile and pasteurised fishery products.

18762 Love; Whittle   GB 051004/00/0007
Extend the useful range of cell fragility measurements for indicating cold storage deterioration in fish.

18763 Love; Whittle   GB 051004/00/0009
Investigations of problems associated with laminated fish block production.

18764 Love; Hume   GB 051004/00/0010
Study of farmed turbot, sole and salmonids in relation to their suitability for processing.

18765 Jason; Kent   GB 051005/00/0016
Moisture measurement in fish meal.

18766 Graham; Mcdonald   GB 051006/00/0015
Freezing at sea of herring and mackerel.

18767 Graham; Roger   GB 051006/00/0029
Effect of design and operation on weight loss in cold storage of fish.

18768 Storey; Davis   GB 051007/00/0020
Quality changes due mainly to dehydration in fish stored under non–ideal conditions.

18769 Storey; Davies   GB 051007/00/0021
Changes in fluorescence of fish and fish products during cold storage.

18770 Storey; Owen   GB 051007/00/0023
Survey of humidity in cold stores (fish).

18771 Storey; Owen   GB 051007/00/0024
Sublimination of water from frozen fish.

18772 Storey; Davies   GB 051007/00/0025
Digesting enzymes in fish.

18773 Storey; Moini   GB 051007/00/0028
Chemical changes in frozen stored smoked fish.

18774 Storey; Bannerman   GB 051007/66/0004
Parameters of the smoking process improvements to commercial smoke curing practice.

18775 Storey; Davis   GB 051007/66/0008
Improve extend panel procedures score systems develop non–sensory methods of assessing fish quality.

18776 Wignall; Storey   GB 051009/00/0013
Survey of the frozen fish distribution network.

18777 Early; Aitken   GB 051010/00/0007
Investigation of shellfish handling, processing and storage, in particular squids, crab and cockles.

18778 Early; Aitken   GB 051010/00/0008
Innovation of shellfish consumer products particularly from underutilised resources (squid,crab,whelk,winkle).

18779 Aitken; Cheyne   GB 051010/00/0010
Development of quality control procedures, sensory and non–sensory, for industrial or official use.

18780 Campbell; Aitken   GB 051010/00/0011
Methods of analysis of fish products relating to food standards eg glaze,added water ,batter, polyphosphate.

18781 Campbell; Aitken   GB 051010/69/0002
The use of polyphosphates and some other additives in the treatment of wet and frozen fish.

18782 Aitken; Cheyne   GB 051010/73/0009
Development of sensory methods for assessing the quality of fish and fish products.

18783 Gibson; Murray   GB 051011/00/0002
Studies of fish spoilage using historical, biochemical and bacteriological techniques.

18784 Mcweeny   GB 051101/79/0002 N
Packaging: substances in food arising from the use of plastic packaging.

18785 Singer   GB 051101/79/0023 N
Oil and fat wastes in industry.

18786 Singer   GB 051101/79/0024 N
Sugar/confectionery/preserves waste in industry.

18787 Singer   GB 051101/79/0025 N
Hospital food waste cost–benefits in industry.

18788 Anderson   GB 060102/00/0031
Factors affecting the quality of eating eggs.

18789 Prescott   GB 060102/00/0035
Carcass and meat quality evaluation.

18790 Broadbent   GB 060208/78/0017
The prediction of yield of saleable meat from all–concentrate fed Friesian bulls.

18791 Robinson   GB 060220/00/0002
Review of microbiological spoilage in eggs and egg products.

18792 Crawford; Galloway   GB 060303/00/0001
The quality of milk and milk products.

18793 O'Donnell   GB 060303/00/0002
Production,characterisation and utilisation of extracellular enzymes produced by psychrotrophic organisms.

18794 Crawford   GB 060303/00/0003
Quality of whole milk powders.

18795 Crawford; Galloway   GB 060303/00/0005
Cheese production methods.

18796 Galloway   GB 060303/00/0006
New or modified cheese varieties.

18797 Crawford; O'Donnell   GB 060303/00/0007
The examination of coagulants for cheese making.

18798 Smith   GB 060303/00/0008
Hydrolysis procedures in manufacturing methods aimed at utilising milk by–products for human nutrition.

18799 Bruce; Johnston   GB 060308/00/0001
The value of microbiological tests for milk quality and their use for the assessment of production methods.

18800 D'Ambrosio, M.; Persano, L.; Intoppa, F.
     IT 020400/75/0005
Ricerche su mieli mono ed eteroflora. **Researches on mono and eterofloral honeys.** Publications.

18801 Catalano, M. IT 040107/74/0530
Ricerche sulle sostanze grasse alimentari. **Research on edible oils and fats.**

18802 Zamorani, A. IT 040308/73/2164
Studio sui prodotti degli agrumi, etc.. **Study on citrus products, etc..**

18803 Rossi, J. IT 041023/74/0618
Alcuni aspetti del biochimismo di L. Bulgaricus in rapporto alla fisiologia dei lieviiti. **Some aspects of the biochemistry of L. Bulgaricus in relation to the physiology of yeasts.**

18804 Carini, S. IT 062600/68/0113
La microflora casearia e le sue principali attività enzimatiche (potere riducente, acidificante, caseinolitico, lipolitico). **The enzymatic activities of dairy microflora (reducing, acidifying, caseinolytic, lipolytic power). Publications.**

18805 Capitani, C. IT 120700/77/0732
Ricerca di mercato su nuove fonti proteiche e nuove formulazioni alimentari. **Market research on new protein sources and new nutritional formulae.**

18806 Labots, H. NL 050301/61/5314
Normalisatie van methoden voor het microbiologisch onderzoek van vlees en vleeswaren. **Standardization of methods for the microbiological analysis of meat and meat products.**

18807 Olsman, W.J. NL 050301/72/6487
Ontwikkeling van een methode voor de kwantitatieve bepaling van spiervleeseiwit in gepasteuriseerde vleeswaren. **Development of a method for quantitative determination of meat proteins in pasteurized meat products. Publications.**

18808 Pfundt, L.A.J. NL 050302/78/7962 R
Onderzoek naar de bederfelijkheid van banketprodukten onder verschillende omstandigheden n.a.v. het concept kokswarenbesluit. **Study of the liability of confectionary products to microbial deterioration.**

D 7210 – Food composition

See also 2954, 3202, 5192, 8371, 10541

18809 Nys, L.; Biston, R. BE 080900/63/0006
Valeur culinaire et industrielle de la pomme de terre. **Organoleptic testing and processing value of potato varieties.**

18810 Baltes, W.; Piloty, M. DE 105900/75/0002
Umsetzung von Aminosäuren mit Alpha–Dicarbonylverbindungen unter den Bedingungen des Strecker–Abbaues. **Reaction of amino acids with alpha–diketones under conditions of Strecker degradation.**

18811 Baltes, W.; Otto, R. DE 105900/75/0011
Zwischenprodukte der Maillard–Reaktion bei Reaktion von Glucose mit p–Chloranilin. **Intermediate products of the Maillard reaction in the reaction of glucose with p–chloroaniline.**

18812 Lang, K. DE 129700/75/0013 N
Substantielle Beschaffenheit und hygienische Qualität von handelsüblichen Seefischen und Seefischteilen. **Chemical and hygienic quality of commercial sea–fish.**

18813 Fleckenstein, J.; Grabbe, K. DE 201020/78/0004 N
Untersuchungen zum Schwermetallgehalt von Wildpilzen. **Investigations on the content of heavy metals in higher fungi.**

18814 Frahm, H. DE 207030/75/0003
Probleme der Schulverpflegung. **Problems of school catering.**

18815 Linke, H. DE 210030/78/0010 N
Systematisierung von Geflügelfleischteilen und roher Stückware. **Definition for poultry meat and raw hams.**

18816 Weinmann, W. DE 215080/77/0001 R
Analysenmethode zur Bestimmung von Alpha–Napthylessigsäure auf und in Äpfeln, Birnen, Pfirsichen, Pflaumen, Weinbeeren. **Analytical methods for determination of alpha–naphtylacetic acid on and in apples, pears, peaches, plums and grapes.**

18817 Weinmann, W. DE 215080/77/0002 R
Analysenmethode zur Bestimmung von Indolyl–3–Buttersäure, Indolyl–3–Propion– und Indolyl–3–Essigsäure auf und in Äpfeln, Birnen, Gurken, Johannisbeeren, Kirschen und Möhren. **Analytical methods for determination of indole–3–butyric acid, indole–3–propionic acid and indole–3–acetic acid on and in apples, pears, cucumbers, currants, cherries and carrots.**

18818 Enkelmann, R. DE 501104/74/0001
Untersuchungen über den Bleigehalt auf Trauben, im Most und Wein. **Investigations on the lead concentration in grapes, must and wine.**

18819 Schmid, G.; Weigelt, H. DE 502050/72/0006 R
Einfluss landwirtschaftlicher Düngungs– und Bewirtschaftungsmassnahmen auf die Gesundheit des Trinkwassers 1972. **Influence of agricultural measures of fertilization and cultivation on the soundness of drinking water.**

18820 Senser, F. DE 502500/78/0001 N
Vorkommen von Aflatoxin in Haselnüssen. **Occurrence of aflatoxin in hazel nuts.**

18821 Jørgensen, M.B.; Hansen, H. DK 010115/73/4505
Vækst– og kvalitetsundersøgelser i frilandsgrønsager til bestemmelse af udbytte og ernæringsmæssig værdi. **Growth and quality investigations in outdoor vegetables for the determination of yield and nutritive value.**

18822 Ambrosen, T. DK 010203/76/0003
Æggets kemiske sammensætning (kolesterol– og tørstofindhold) i to stærkt specialiserede linier af Hvid Italiener racen. **The chemical composition of the egg (cholesterol and drymatter) in two strongly specialized lines of the White Italian race.**

18823 Møller–Madsen, A. DK 010300/75/0061

Bakteriologiske undersøgelser i forbindelse med staldtypeforsøg. **Bacteriological investigations in connection with stall type experiments.**

18824 Larsen, P.O.   DK 030106/75/0019
Massespektroskopi med henblik på identifikation og strukturbestemmelse af naturstoffer, lægemiddelmetabolitter og pesticider. **Mass spectroscopy with reference to the identification and structural determination of naturally occurring substances, medicinal metabolites and pesticides.**

18825 Skovgaard, N.; Hald, B.; Bjergskov, T.; Olsen, C.B.
                    DK 030137/77/0003 N
Undersøgelser af betingelserne for dannelse af histamin og andre toksiske aminer i fisk og fiskeprodukter. **Formation of histamine and other toxic amines in fish and fish products.**

18826 Heidemann, F.   DK 030191/77/0006 N
Karakterisering af smagsstoffer i saltede kødprodukter. **Flavour components of cured pork products.**

18827 Macdougll   GB 010606/00/0030 R
Assessing eating quality of meat from rabbit, deer and other lesser used species.

18828 Rhodes   GB 010606/79/0210 N
Study the interaction of production and acceptability of beef in E E C countries.

18829 Spillane, P.A.; Dwyer, E.   IE 060300/75/1205 R
Quality standards for milling wheat. Publications.

18830 O'Keeffe, M.; Eades, J.F.K.   IE 060500/77/1333 R
Pesticide residues in crops. Publications.

18831 Connolly, J.F.; Headon, D.R.; McCarthy, M.
                    IE 130102/78/9160 N
Identification of biochemical constituents in bovine milk and dairy products which are responsible for off flavours.

18832 Florenzano, G.   IT 061300/77/0968
Produzione fotosintetica di biomasse batteriche ed algali. **Photo–synthetic production of bacteric and algal biomasses.**

Food and table luxuries in general (B 6800)

See also 313, 5183, 9006, 11541, 11542, 15984, 16443, 16462, 16463, 18814, 19074, 19518, 19669

18833 Vanbelle, M.; Vervack, W.; Foulon, M.
                    BE 020601/74/0007
La composition en acides aminés des aliments consommés par l'homme. **The aminoacid composition of human food.** Publications.

18834 Lambert, J.; Forceille, M.J.   BE 020602/78/0012
Etude et contrôle de la qualité des productions agricoles de base et de produits alimentaires qui en dérivent. **Study and quality control of basic agricultural productions and of the food products that derive from them.**

18835 Huyghebaert, H.   BE 030025/73/0004 R
Studie van de niet enzymatische bruinkleuring in levensmiddelen. **Study on the non enzymatic browning in foods.**

18836 Monseur, X.; Jennen, A.   BE 100000/73/0024 R
Onderzoek naar de kwantitatieve en kwalitatieve bepaling van organisch kwik–en loodverbindingen in natuurprodukten. **Research concerning the qualitative and quantitative determination of organomercury and organo lead compounds in natural products.** Publications.

18837 Hildebrandt, G.; Berner, H.–J.; Sinell, H.–J.; Siems, H.; Weiss, H.   DE 104301/73/0002
Einsatz moderner statistischer Verfahren bei der amtlichen Lebensmittelüberwachung sowie der innerbetrieblichen Kontrolle. **Use of modern statistical methods in official food control and in intra–farm control.** Publications.

18838 Sinell, H.–J.; Mentz, I.   DE 104301/74/0001
Identifizierung und quantitative Bestimmung von Proteinen unterschiedlicher Herkunft in Lebensmitteln unter besonderer Berücksichtigung sogenannter Fremdeiweisse. **Identification and quantitative determination of food proteins of different origin with special reference to so–called 'foreign proteins'.** Publications.

18839 Sinell, H.–J.; Kusch, D.   DE 104301/77/0001
Häufigkeit und Übertragungsmöglichkeit plasmiddeterminierter Antibiotikaresistenz bei Staphylokokken aus Lebensmitteln. **Frequency and possibility of transferability of plasmid mediated antibiotic resistance in staphylococci isolated from food.** Publications.

18840 Bielig, H.J.; Kolb, H.   DE 105812/78/0001 N
Hygienisch–technologische Aspekte bei der Ausser–Haus–Verpflegung. **Hygienic–technological aspects of institutional feeding.**

18841 Meuser, F.; Klingler, R.   DE 105820/75/0002
Versuche zur Charakterisierung mechanisch modifizierter Stärke im Hinblick auf Anwendungsmöglichkeiten in der Lebensmittelindustrie. **Characterization of mechanically modified starches with regard to their uses in food industry.**

18842 Tressl, R.; Apetz, M.   DE 105983/72/0001
Synthese mikrobieller Zwischenprodukte unter Verwendung unkonventioneller Rohstoffe. **Synthesis of microbiological intermediate products by unconventional substrata.**

18843 Pfeilsticker, K.; Engel, C.   DE 111600/75/0003
Die Bedeutung der Oberflächenspannung für den Geschmackseindruck von bitteren Stoffen. **Significance of surface tension to the taste impression of bitter substances.**

18844 Pfeilsticker, K.; Wagner, C.   DE 111600/78/0003 N
Die Metabolisierung von Blausäure in begasten Lebensmitteln. **The metabolising of hydrocyanic acid in fumigated food.**

18845 Maier, H.G.; Abidin, I.   DE 114100/78/0001 N
Bestimmung von Estern aus organischen Säuren und Zuckern in Lebensmitteln. **Determination of esters from organic acids and sugars in foods.**

18846 Renner, E.; Renz, A.   DE 129252/77/0002
Untersuchungen über die sensorische und ernährungsphysiologische Qualität von Flüssigfertignahrungen in der Säuglingsernährung. **Investigations on the sensoric and nutritional quality of fluid ready–foods for the nutrition of infants.**

18847 Bitsch, I.   DE 129900/72/0016
Untersuchungen zur Beeinflussung chemisch–analytischer und biologischer Thiaminbestimmungsmethoden durch Lebensmittelinhaltsstoffe. **Studies on the influence of food constituents on chemo–analytical and biological methods for determination of thiamine.**

18848 Stelte, W.; Cremer, H.–D.   DE 129900/72/0018
Untersuchungen über die Kontamination von Nahrungsmitteln mit Spurenelementen. **Investigations on contamination of food with trace elements.**

18849 Heimann, W.; Folkers, G.   DE 145100/78/0001 N
Fett–Antioxydantien und Synergisten – Reaktionsmechanismus. **Fat–antioxidants and synergistic compounds – reaction mechanism.**

18850 Weisser, H.   DE 145150/70/0003
Bestimmung von Stoffwerten von Lebensmitteln. **Determination of physical properties of food.**

18851 Weisser, H.; Hahn, G.   DE 145150/73/0001
Digitale Dichtemessungen an Lebensmitteln. **Digital measurement of the density of foods.**

18852 Weisser, H.; Hahn, G.   DE 145150/77/0001
Kernresonanzspektroskopische Untersuchungen an Lebensmitteln. **Nuclear magnetic resonance studies on foodstuffs.**

18853 Erbersdobler, H.; Beck, H.; Gropp, J.; Fischer, M.; Giesecke, D.; König, K.   DE 160600/75/0009
Ernährungsphysiologische Charakterisierung biosynthetischer Nahrungs– und Futtermittel. **Nutritional value, utilization and analytical characteristics of single cell proteins in feeds.**

18854 Erbersdobler, H.; Holstein, B.   DE 160600/78/0001 N
Vorkommen und Bedeutung von Lysinoalanin in Nahrungsund Futtermitteln. **Presence and importance of lysinoalanine in foods and feeds.**

18855 Thier, H.–P.; Glück, U.   DE 164150/77/0002
Analytik der als Dickungsmittel verwendeten Polysaccharide in Lebensmitteln. **Analysis of polysaccharides used as thickening agents in foods.**

18856 Acker, L.; Littmann, S.   DE 164150/78/0002 N
Anwendung der Kapillargaschromatographie auf spezielle lebensmittelanalytische Probleme. **The application of capillary gas chromatography to special problems in food analysis.**

18857 Bösenberg, H.   DE 164201/71/0001 N
Nachweis und Wirkung von Mykotoxinen. **Identification and effect of mycotoxins.**

18858 Lehmann, G.; Linkersdörfer, J.   DE 167100/75/0012
Über die Entstehung von Hydroxymaltol in Lebensmitteln beim Erhitzen. **On the formation of hydroxymaltol in foods during heating.**

18859 Brieskorn, C.H.; Betz, R.   DE 176150/74/0001
Ungesättigte Steroide in Lebensmitteln und ihr Nachweis mit Brom–Essigsäure. **Unsaturated steroids in foodstuffs and their identification by use of bromoacetic acid.**

18860 Niebergall, H.; Kutzki, R.   DE 176150/75/0004
Modelluntersuchungen zur Migration von Folieninhaltsstoffen in Lebensmittel und Simulantien unter Einsatz der Hochdruckflüssigkeitschromatographie. **Basic research on the migration of additives from plastics into foodstuffs and simulants using the high pressure liquid chromatography.**

18861 Teuber, M.   DE 207030/77/0002
Ernährungsphysiologische und toxikologische Beurteilung von diätetischen und kalorienreduzierten Lebensmitteln. **Nutritional and toxicological valuation of dietetic and low–calorie food.**

18862 Wasserfall, F.; Engel, G.   DE 207030/77/0004
Durch Mikroorganismen hervorgerufene unerwünschte Veränderung der Lebensmittel. **Undesirable changes in food by micro–organisms.**

18863 Milczewski, K.E.von   DE 207030/77/0005
Einfluss von Verarbeitung und Zubereitung auf die ernährungsphysiologische Wertigkeit von Lebensmitteln. **Nutritional value of food as affected by processing and preparation.**

18864 Wasserfall, F.   DE 207030/77/0006
Festlegung von Qualitätskriterien und –normen für einzelne Lebensmittel und Entwicklung sowie Verbesserung von Methoden zu deren Bestimmung. **Standardization of qualitative criteria and norms for foods and development as well as improvement of methods for their determination.**

18865 Researcher not indicated   DE 207030/78/0002 N
Festlegung von Qualitätskriterien und –normen für einzelne Lebensmittel und Entwicklung, sowie Verbesserung von Methoden zu deren Bestimmung. **Determination of qualitative criteria and standards of single foods and development as well as improvement of methods for determination.**

18866 Researcher not indicated   DE 207030/78/0003 N
Durch Mikroorganismen hervorgerufene unerwünschte Veränderung der Lebensmittel. **Undesired changes in foods caused by microorganisms.**

18867 Stiebing, A.   DE 210020/78/0005 N
Entwicklungs– und Erprobungsarbeiten für die Verpflegung der Bundeswehr. **Developing and testing of the army food supply.**

18868 Lötzsch, R.   DE 210030/77/0001
Mykotoxin–Bildung in Lebensmitteln, in Abhängigkeit von der Wasseraktivität des Substrates. **Formation of mycotoxins in foods depending on water activity of the substrate.**

18869 Leistner, L.; Hofmann, G.   DE 210030/78/0001 N
Untersuchungen zur Verbesserung des Nachweises neurotoxischer Mykotoxine. **Improvement of detection methods for neurotoxic mycotoxins.**

18870 Leistner, L.; Hofmann, G.   DE 210030/78/0003 N
Vorkommen und Bedeutung toxinogener Fusarien bei Lebensund Futtermitteln der Bundesrepublik Deutschland. **Occurrence and significance of toxinogenic fusaria for foods and feeds of the Federal Republic of Germany.**

18871 Hofmann, K.   DE 210040/78/0001 N
Einsatz der Gel–Elektrophorese von Proteinen in der

Lebensmittelüberwachung zur Lösung schwieriger analytischer Probleme. **The use of gel electrophoresis of protein for solving difficult analytical problems in the food control.**

18872 Frank, H.K.; Siegfried, R.　DE 211010/77/0007
Vorkommen und Bildungsbedingungen sowie Bestimmung von Patulin und Aflatoxinen in Lebensmitteln pflanzlicher Herkunft. **Occurrence and conditions of formation as well as determination of patulin and aflatoxins in vegetal foods.**

18873 Paulus, K.　DE 211020/77/0005
Beeinflussung der Schwellenwerte der Grundgeschmacksrichtungen durch Temperatur und Viskosität des Versuchsmaterials. **Threshold values of basic tastes as affected by temperature and viscosity of test material.**

18874 Zohm, H.　DE 211020/78/0004 N
Eisen- und Zinnbestimmungen in Dosenkonserven. **Determination of tin and iron in canned foods.**

18875 Paulus, K.　DE 211020/78/0010 N
Verbesserung und Standardisierung sensorischer Untersuchungsmethoden. **Improvement and standardization of sensory evaluation methods.**

18876 Fischer, E.　DE 211030/70/5001
Reaktionen von Hexamethylentetramin mit Inhaltsstoffen von Lebensmitteln. **Reactions of hexamethylentetramine with food constituents.**

18877 Schelenz, R.　DE 211030/70/5004
Entwicklung der Neutronenaktivierungsanalyse zur Multielementbestimmung in Lebensmitteln. **Application of the neutron activation analysis to the determination of multi-elements in foodstuffs.**

18878 Kalus, W.　DE 211030/71/5004
Reaktionen von Schwefeldioxid mit Inhaltsstoffen von Lebensmitteln. **Reactions of sulphur dioxide with components of foodstuffs.**

18879 Schelenz, R.; Boppel, B.　DE 211030/77/0001
Feststellung der Gehalte an Arsen, Blei, Cadmium, Quecksilber in Lebensmitteln pflanzlicher Herkunft, in küchenfertigem oder verzehrsfähigem Zustand. **Determination of content of As, Pb, Hg, Cd in vegetal food ready–to–serve or ready–to–eat.**

18880 Frindik, O.　DE 211030/77/0006
Untersuchungen zur Überwachung von Lebensmitteln auf eine radioaktive Kontamination durch Plutonium und andere Alpha–Radionuklide. **Studies for control of food for radioactive contamination with plutonium and other alpha–radionuclides.**

18881 Fischer, E.; Müller, H.　DE 211030/77/0007
Untersuchungen zur Überwachung von Lebensmitteln auf eine radioaktive Kontamination durch Tritium und Kohlenstoff–14. **Studies for control of food for radioactive contamination with tritium and C–14.**

18882 Schelenz, R.; Boppel, B.　DE 211030/77/0012
Bestimmung der Mineralstoffzusammensetzung von Gesamtmahlzeiten. **Determination of mineral composition of complete meals.**

18883 Schelenz, R.　DE 211030/78/0001 N

Ermittlung von Gehaltsveränderungen an Mineralstoffen, essentiellen und toxischen Spurenelementen in Lebensmitteln bei der Verarbeitung der Rohware zum verzehrsfertigen Produkt. **Determination of variations of the content of mineral substances, essential and toxic elements in foods during the processing of the raw material to the ready–to–eat product.**

18884 Boppel, B.　DE 211030/78/0003 N
Bestimmung von Blei und Cadmium in ausgewählten Lebensmitteln. **Determination of Pb and Cd in selected foods.**

18885 Adam, S.　DE 211040/77/0003
Gaschromatographische Untersuchung von kohlenhydrathaltigen Lebensmitteln. **Gas chromatographic analysis of carbohydrate–containing foods.**

18886 Grünewald, T.; Bognar, A.; Boppel, B.; Schelenz, R.　DE 211040/77/0007
Bestimmung von Spurenelementen in Lebensmitteln. **Determination of trace elements in foods.**

18887 Grünewald, T.; Spiess, W.; Rudolf, M.; Trömel, I.; Bauer, B.　DE 211040/78/0001 N
Charakterisierung von Lebensmitteln durch objektive Messung der Festigkeit, des Verformungsverhaltens und der Farbe. **Characterisation of foods by objective measurement of consistence, deformation behaviour and colour.**

18888 Ehlermann, D.; Bauer, B.; Kretzschmar, K.H.　DE 211040/78/0002 N
Charakterisierung von Lebensmitteln durch elektrische Messmethoden. **Characterisation of foods using electrical methods.**

18889 Frank, A.; Bauer, B.　DE 211040/78/0003 N
Anwendung radiometrischer Verfahren zur Ermittlung physikalischer und chemischer Eigenschaften von Lebensmitteln. **Application of radiometric techniques for the determination of physical and chemical properties of foods.**

18890 Hoffmann, N.　DE 211040/78/0004 N
Charakterisierung disperser Lebensmittel durch objektive Messmethoden. **Characterisation of disperse foods using objective methods.**

18891 Schubert, H.; Bauer, B.; Dorth, H.　DE 211040/78/0005 N
Beurteilung von Instantprodukten und Agglomeraten mit physikalischen Messmethoden. **Characterisation of instant products and agglomerates using physical methods of measurement.**

18892 Spiess, W.　DE 211040/78/0006 N
Sorption von Wasser durch Lebensmittel. **Sorption of water by foods.**

18893 Spiess, W.; Lengerer, J.; Bauer, B.; Höbel, B.　DE 211040/78/0008 N
Untersuchungen der Gefrierkette und Erarbeitung von Daten zur Beurteilung des Zeit–Temperatur–Verhaltens tiefgefrorener Lebensmittel. **Investigations on the "cold chain" and compilation of data for the assessment of time–temperature properties of deep–frozen foods.**

18894 Schubert, H.; Dorth, H.　DE 211040/78/0009 N
Untersuchung von Zeit/Temperatur–Indikatoren zur Kontrolle

tiefgefrorener Lebensmittel. **Investigations on time–temperature–indicators for the quality control of deep–frozen foods.**

18895 Delincee, H.; Adam, S.; Jakubick, V.

DE 211050/75/0001

Analytische Untersuchungen als Grundlage zur gesundheitlichen Beurteilung und zur Identifizierung bestrahlter Lebensmittel. **Analytical studies as basis for evaluating the wholesomeness and for identification of irradiated foods.**

18896 Delincee, H. DE 211050/77/0001

Entwicklung biochemischer Methoden zur Erkennung subklinischer Wirkungen von toxischen Spurenelementen. **Development of biochemical methods for diagnosis of subclinical effects of toxic trace elements.**

18897 Münzner, R. DE 211050/77/0003

Prüfung von Lebensmitteln auf mutagene Wirkungen mit Hilfe verbesserter in vitro Tests. **Examination of foods for mutagenic effects by means of improved in vitro tests.**

18898 Renner, H. DE 211050/77/0006

Toxikologische Prüfung bestrahlter Lebensmittel. **Toxicological examination of irradiated foods.**

18899 Diehl, J.F. DE 211050/78/0001 N

Untersuchungen über die den Vitamin E–Bedarf des Säugetierorganismus beeinflussenden Faktoren. **Factors influencing the vitamin E–requirement of the mammalian organism.**

18900 Diehl, J.F.; Jakubick, V. DE 211050/78/0002 N

Umwandlung und Speicherung von Zusatzstoffen im Säugetierorganismus. **Metabolism and storage of food additives in the mammalian organism.**

18901 Zacharias, R. DE 211100/77/0007

Sensorische Qualität von sterilisierten und gekühlten Speisen für die Schulverpflegung. **Sensory quality of sterilized and cooled food for school catering.**

18902 Zacharias, R. DE 211100/77/0008

Entwicklung von spezifischen Bewertungsschemas für die Beurteilung des Genusswerts von Speisen. **Development of specific schemata for valuation of quality of food.**

18903 Bognar, A. DE 211100/77/0009

Bestimmung von Thiamin, Riboflavin, Niacin, Pyridoxin, Folsäure und Pantothensäure mit Hilfe der Hockdruckflüssigkeitschromatographie – HPLC –. **Determination of thiamine, riboflavin, niacin, pyridoxine, folic acid and pantothenic acid using high pressure liquid chromatography.**

18904 Bognar, A. DE 211100/77/0012

Nährwert von sterilisierten und gekühlten Speisen für die Schulverpflegung. **Nutritive value of sterilized and cooled food for school catering.**

18905 Werner, R. DE 211100/78/0001 N

Ermittlung der altersgemässen Portionsgrössen in der Schulverpflegung. **Determination of a portion measure according to age in school feeding programs.**

18906 Stübler, E. DE 211100/78/0002 N

Arbeitswirtschaftliche Grundlagen zur Organisation der Schulverpflegung beim System "Mischküche". **Work load and personal management in combined systems of school feeding programs. Aspects of food quality and working methods.**

18907 Wessels, H. DE 213010/78/0008 N

Bestimmung der Erucasäure neben anderen Isomeren der Docosensäure. **Determination of erucic acid in the presence of other docosenoic acid isomers.**

18908 Weber, N.; Mangold, H.K.; Stumpf, P.K.

DE 213020/75/0005

Lipide in unkonventionellen Rohstoffen für die Ernährung. **Lipids in unconventional raw materials for foods.**

18909 Mangold, H.K.; Yanishlieva, N. DE 213020/75/0021

Vorkommen und ernährungsphysiologische Bedeutung von Ätherlipiden beim Menschen und in Nahrungsmitteln. **Occurrence and nutritional significance of ether lipids in man and foodstuffs.**

18910 Rottka, H. DE 305010/75/0013

Verzehrserhebung. **Food intake studies.**

18911 Zausch, G.T. DE 305011/75/0001 N

Ermittlung von einheitlichen Riechstoffen als Standard Bezugssubstanzen für sensorische Eindrücke. **Determination of uniform aromatic substances as standard reference substances for sensory impressions.**

18912 Becker, F.; Zausch, G.T. DE 305011/78/0001 N

Festlegung von einheitlichen Begriffen als Beschreibung für sensorische Eindrücke. **Agreement on uniform terms as description for sensory impressions. Publications.**

18913 Zausch, G.T. DE 305012/77/0001

Normung sensorischer Prüfungen. **Standardization of sensory assessment. Publications.**

18914 Zausch, G.T. DE 305012/77/0002

Erarbeitung von Normen für sensorische Prüfverfahren und die hierfür erforderlichen Hilfsmittel. **Development of standards for methods of sensory assessment and of technical aids required for this purpose. Publications.**

18915 Grossklaus, D.; Levetzow, R. DE 305030/75/0014

Weiterentwicklung von Untersuchungsverfahren für die amtliche Lebensmittelüberwachung. **Further development of methods of analysis for official food inspection purposes.**

18916 Levetzow, R. DE 305030/75/0018

Tiefkühlkost – Wiederbelebung. **Deep–frozen meals – resuscitation.**

18917 Hamann, R.; Marx, M. DE 305033/77/0001

Die Bedeutung hygienischer Parameter zur Beurteilung von Säuglingsnahrungsmitteln. **The significance of hygienic criteria for the examination of baby–food.**

18918 Belitz, H.–D.; Treleano, R.; Jugel, H.; Chen, W.; Wieser, H. DE 502500/78/0002 N

Beziehung zwischen der chemischen Struktur von Verbindungen und ihrem Geschmack. **Correlations between the chemical structure of compounds and their taste.**

D 7210 – Food composition

18919 Eichner, K.; Robinson, L.   DE 911000/77/0009
Ursache der Qualitätsveränderungen von Fertiggerichten.
Factors causing quality changes of ready–to–serve meals.
Publications.

18920 Hollaender, J.   DE 911000/77/0011
Metallaufnahme durch Füllgüter. **Metal uptake by canned food.**

18921 Piringer, O.   DE 911000/78/0002 N
Erarbeitung spurenanalytischer Methoden mit dem Ziel der
Erfassung von Lebensmittelinhaltsstoffen und
Lebensmittelkontaminanten. **Development of trace analytical
methods for the purpose of analysis of food constituents and
contaminants.**

18922 Bories, G.; Durand, E.   FR 011412/75/9503 N
Mise au point du dosage des hydrocarbures aromatiques
polycycliques cancérogènes dans les milieux biologiques.
Enquête sur la contamination des denrées alimentaires et sur
l'effet de certains traitements technologiques. **Determination of
carcinogenic polycyclic aromatic hydrocarbons in biological
samples. Survey of food contamination: incidence of food
processing.**

18923 Jemmali, M.; Paysan, Melle   FR 012203/70/2256
Etude sur les caractéristiques des aflatoxines. **Study on
aflatoxine characteristics.** Publications.

18924 Meunier, A.; Collombel, B.   FR 012502/78/8565
La taxation internalisante des déchets solides: premiers
éléments pour la détermination de l'assiette de la taxation dans
le cas des déchets solides agroalimentaires. **First analysis to
settle basis of taxation for solid waste from food industry.**

18925 Povey   GB 022003/78/0003 N
Ultrasonic apparatus to measure the physical properties of food.

18926 Flint   GB 022005/79/0002 N
Histology of individual manufactured food products.

18927 Nursten   GB 023904/79/0002 N
Sensory properties of important flavour components.

18928 Buss george   GB 051101/79/0009 N
Fatty acids and sterols in total diet and individual food items.

18929 Hubbard.   GB 051101/79/0019 N
**Home preservation techniques versus microbiological and
organoleptic quality.**

18930 Hunter, A.T.   IE 070400/79/9228 N
**Application of microprocessor control to the sterilisation of
food.**

18931 Cremin, F.M.; Flynn, A.; Fox. P.F.; Flynn, P.
    IE 110101/78/9189 N
Nutrient losses during domestic and industrial cooking.

18932 Morrissey, P.A.; Cross, P.   IE 110101/79/9184 N
**Quantitative analysis of vitamin A and vitamin D by high speed
liquid chromatography.**

18933 Fox, P.F.; Daly, C.; Stepaniack, L.
    IE 110101/79/9187 N

**Isolation and characterisation of proteinases of psychotrophic
bacteria.**

18934 Collins, J.K.; Cullinane, D.   IE 110102/79/9230 N
Isolation of enteroviruses from water and foods.

18935 McCarthy, D.   IE 110106/78/9147 N
Measurement of thermal conductivity of foodstuffs.

18936 Kevany, J.P.; Stuart, M.; Kelly, A.; Harrington, D.
    IE 140401/76/9115 N
**The design of a nutritional surveillance system based on
currently available sectoral information.**

18937 Polesello, A.; Pizzocaro, F.; Forni, E.
    IT 021900/78/0001
Ricerche sulla utilizzazione dei coloranti di estrazione
naturale. **Natural colorants for additives in food.**

18938 Giangiacomo, R.; Polesello, A.   IT 021900/79/0006 N
Applicazione della spettrofotometria di riflettanza e di
assorbimento ad alta densità ottica per lo studio delle
caratteristiche qualitative degli alimenti. **Non destructive
quality evaluation in foods by reflectance and absorption
spectrophotometry.**

18939 Catalano, M.   IT 040107/77/0136 R
Ricerche sulle sostanze grasse alimentari. **Research on
nutritional fats.**

18940 Capella, P.   IT 040208/73/0915
Problema di stabilità dei lipidi alimentari. **Stability problem in
edible lipids.** Publications.

18941 Capella, P.   IT 040208/77/0129 R
Problemi di stabilità e struttura dei lipidi alimentari. **Problems
of stability and structure in food lipids.**

18942 Matteuzzi, D.   IT 040210/77/0235 R
Batteri sporigeni anaerobi agenti di alterazioni di prodotti
alimentari. **Anaerobic sporigenic bacteria responsible for the
degradation of food–stuffs.**

18943 Domenichini, G.; Cravedi, P.; Bielli, E.; Gasco, F.
    IT 040402/79/0002 N
Diffusione di microrganismi patogeni negli alimenti ad opera di
Insetti. **Pathogenic microorganisms diffused in foodstuffs by
Insects.** Publications.

18944 Domenichini, G.; Cravedi, P.; Platè, M.; Sdraiati, D.
    IT 040402/79/0003 N
Ricerche sull'inquinamento degli alimenti causato dagli Insetti
infestanti. **Alterations in foodstuffs caused by Insects.**

18945 Volonterio, G.   IT 040609/74/0645
Ricerche sul contenuto di 14C e 3H nei prodotti alimentari.
Research on 14C and 3H content of food products.

18946 Dragoni, I.; Comi, G.   IT 040633/79/0003 N
Muffe negli alimenti. **Moulds in foods.**

18947 Marino, G.   IT 040746/78/1076 N
Analisi di trigliceridi in alimenti di origine animale mediante
gas–cromatografia con OTC. **Analysis of triglycerides found in
food–stuffs of animal origin by gas–chromatography with OTC.**

18948 Foschi, S.   IT 061800/77/1018
Impiego di tecniche estrattive per la rilevazione dei fitofarmaci e dei loro eventuali prodotti di trasformazione. **The use of extractive methods for the detection of herbicides and their eventual metabolites.**

18949 Kooij, J.G. van   NL 010110/71/7948 R
Consumptiegeschiktheid van bestraald voedsel gemeten op basis van chemische omzettingen. **Chemical changes in irradiated food as a basis for adequate wholesomeness testing.** Publications.

18950 Tuinstra, L.G.M.T.; Ruig, W.G. de
                                       NL 010211/03/0019
Onderzoek naar het vóórkomen van verontreinigingen in en naar de samenstelling en eigenschappen van melk, melkprodukten, zuivelprodukten, oliën, vetten, vethoudende produkten, eiprodukten, vis, visprodukten, vlees, vleesprodukten, groenten, fruit en verwante voedings– en voedermiddelen. **Investigation into the occurrence of contaminants in and the composition and characteristics of milk, milk products, oils, fats, fat products, egg products, fish, fish products, meat, meat products, vegetables, fruit and related foods and fodders.** Publications.

18951 Swan Djien, Ko.; Kampelmacher, E.H.
                                       NL 020031/72/5113
Mogelijkheid van mycotoxine–vorming in gefermenteerde levensmiddelen. **Possibilities of mycotoxin formation in fermented foods.** Publications.

18952 Roozen, J.P.   NL 020031/74/6372
Analyse van aminozuren en eiwitten in levensmiddelen. **Analysis of amino acids and proteins in foodstuffs.** Publications.

18953 Folstar, P.   NL 020031/76/6800 R
Samenstelling en stabiliteit van rode kleurstoffen in bieten i.v.m. toepassingsmogelijkheden als levensmiddelen kleurstoffen. **Composition and stability of red pigments in beets for possible utilization as food couloring agents.**

18954 Wit, J.C. de   NL 020031/78/8528
De persoonlijke hygiëne van de werknemers in de levensmiddelenindustrie. **The hygiene of personnel engaged in food industry.**

18955 Kampelmacher, E.H.   NL 020031/78/8894 N
De invloed van wateractiviteit en temperatuur op de productie van enkele mycotoxinen. **The affect of water activity and temperature on the production of some mycotoxins.**

18956 Katan, M.B.   NL 020062/74/6332
Bepaling van het cholesterolgehalte, vetgehalte, vetzuursamenstelling, aminozuursamenstelling e.d. in voedingsmiddelen, alsmede de invloed van verhitting, bewaring, fermentatie e.d. h erop. **Determination of cholesterol and fat content, fatty and amino acid composition in food, as influenced by heating, storage, fermentation.** Publications.

18957 Schothorst, M. van   NL 040011/67/7438
Onderzoek standaardisatie van gebruikte methodieken op het gebied van microbiologisch levensmiddelen onderzoek. **Investigation on standardization of used methods concerning microbiological food research.**

18958 Northolt, M. D.   NL 040011/73/7444
Onderzoek beschimmelde levensmiddelen. **Investigation on mycotoxic foods.** Publications.

18959 Northolt, M.D.   NL 040011/73/7445
Oriënterend onderzoek naar het toxinevormend vermogen van Cladosporium Herbarum. **Preliminary investigation on the toxin–forming potency of Cladosporium Herbarum.**

18960 Kroes, R.   NL 040011/73/7508
Het gebruik van levercelculturen voor de bepaling van hepato–toxiciteit en carcinogeniteit van aflatoxine M_1. **The use of liver cell cultures for the determination of the hepatotoxicity and carcinogenicity of aflatoxin M_1.** Publications.

18961 Greve, P.A.   NL 040011/73/7519
Harmonisatie van analysemethoden voor pesticide–residuen in EEG–verband. **Harmonization of analytical methods for pesticide residues in the framework of the European Community.**

18962 Northolt, M.D.   NL 040011/74/7446
Onderzoek naar het voorkomen van toxinogene schimmels in levensmiddelen. **Investigation on the prevalence of toxinogenic fungi in foodproducts.** Publications.

18963 Schuller, P.L.   NL 040011/74/7465
Onderzoek naar het gehalte aan zware metalen in levensmiddelen. **Investigation on the levels of heavy metals in food.**

18964 Schothorst, M. van; Schuller, P.L.   NL 040011/76/7450
Onderzoek naar de invloed van Aw en temperatuur op de produktie van mycotoxinen. **Investigation on the influence of Aw and temperature on the production of mycotoxins.**

18965 Schothorst, M. van   NL 040011/76/7451
Ontwikkeling van detectiemethoden voor Staphylococcen–Enterotoxinen in levensmiddelen. **Development of detection methods for Staphylococci–Enterotoxins in food products.**

18966 Schothorst, M. van   NL 040011/76/7452
Ontwikkeling van nieuwe detectiemethoden voor Clostridium Botulinum toxinen in levensmiddelen en onderzoek naar het voorkomen van C. Botulinum in diverse substraten. **Development of new detection methods in Clostridium Botulinum toxins in food products and investigation on the prevalence of C. Botulinum in various substrates.**

18967 Olthof, P.D.A.   NL 050301/67/6471
Ontwikkeling van methoden voor de bepaling van residuen van pesticiden in voedingsmiddelen. **The development of methods for analyzing pesticide residues in food.**

18968 Maarse, H.   NL 050301/70/6504
Onderzoek inzake her ontstaan of veranderen van geur– en smaakstoffen in voedingsmiddelen tijdens hun ontwikkeling (groei, rijping, enz.), industriele verwerking, opslag en transport. **Study of the origin and changes in flavour of food products during their development (growth, ripening, a.o.), industrial processing, transport and storage.** Publications.

18969 Dokkum, W. van   NL 050301/73/6465
Onderzoek naar de fysiologische en organoleptische

eigenschappen van nieuwe eiwitten. **Physiological and organoleptic properties of textured vegetable protein.**

18970 Willems, M.I. NL 050301/73/6756
Onderzoek van pancreasveranderingen bij ratten geïnduceerd door tin in de voeding. **Study of pancreaschanges induced by tin (experiments with rats).** Publications.

18971 Bemelmans, J.M.H. NL 050301/74/5306
Onderzoek van geur- en smaakafwijkingen ("off–flavours") van voedingsmiddelen. **Research on off–flavours in food.** Publications.

18972 Luyken, R.; Dokkum, W. van NL 050301/75/6464
Invloed van vetgehalte en vetzuur samenstelling van de Nederlandse voeding op calcium en ijzer behoefte. **Influence of fat content and fatty acid composition of Dutch nutrition on calcium and iron requirements.**

18973 Wijngaarden, A. van NL 050301/75/6467
Ontwikkelen van analysemethodes voor voedingsmiddelen met inbegrip van een nadruk op snelle methodes en automatisering. **Developments of methods for the analysis of foodstuff, esp. rapid and automated methods.**

18974 Groot, A.P. de NL 050301/75/6757
Onderzoek naar het metabolisme van lysino–alanine bij kleine proefdieren en de mens. **Study on the metabolism of lysino–alanine in laboratory animals and man.** Publications.

18975 Vos, R.H. de NL 050301/76/6749
Kwantitatief onderzoek naar de aanwezigheid van additieven en chemische contaminanten in totale dagvoedingen. **Quantitative study on additives and chemical contaminants in total diets.**

18976 Harrewijn, G.A. NL 050301/76/6751
Microbiologische aspecten van keukenbedrijven van grote instellingen. **Microbiological aspects of institutional food service.**

18977 Fielliettaz Goedhart, R.L. de NL 050301/76/6752
Invloed van bereiding en distributie op de organoleptische kwaliteit van warme maaltijden. **Influence of preparation and distribution on the organoleptic quality of hot meals.**

18978 Ferow, V.J. NL 050301/76/6755
Oraal en inhalatoir toxiciteitsonderzoek van vinylchloride monomeer bij ratten. **Studies on the oral and inhalation toxicity of vinlychloride monomer in rats.**

Mill and bakery products (B 6810)

See also 6337, 16055, 16506, 16537, 16539, 18829, 19099, 19664

18979 Pfeilsticker, K.; Maklad, M. DE 111600/73/0001
Einfluss der Herbizide und Fungizide auf die Qualität von Weizen. **Influence of herbicides and fungicides on the quality of wheat.**

18980 Pfeilsticker, K.; Tillmanns, U. DE 111600/78/0001 N
Untersuchungen über Pentosane und Pentosanasen in Weizenmehl und Teigen. **Investigations of pentosanes and pentosanases in wheat flour and doughs.**

18981 Pfeilsticker, K.; Kolloch, M. DE 111600/78/0002 N
Zur Struktur der backwertbeeinflussenden Pentosane in Weizenmehl. **On the structure of baking quality influencing pentosanes in wheat flour.**

18982 Pfeilsticker, K. DE 111600/78/0006 N
Restmengen an Chlorcholinchlorid in diätetischen Lebensmitteln auf Getreidebasis und in Gemüse. **Residues of chlorocholinechloride in dietetic grainfoods and in vegetables.**

18983 Pfeilsticker, K.; Marx, F.; Liermann, A. DE 111600/78/0007 N
Restmengen von Chlorcholinchlorid in Getreide. **Residues of chlorocholinechloride in cereals.** Publications.

18984 Niemann, E.–G.; Christoffers, D. DE 138180/73/0002 N
Fluorometrische lysinbestimmung in Getreidemehlen. **Fluorometric determination of lysine content in grainmeal samples.**

18985 Fritz, D.; Weichmann, J. DE 161260/73/0004
Einfluss verschiedener CA–Lagerbedingungen auf die Haltbarkeit von Chinakohl. **The influence of different CA–storing conditions on the stability of Chinese cabbage.**

18986 Fretzdorff, B.; Ocker, H.–D. DE 209010/77/0004
Cancerogene, polycyclische Kohlenwasserstoffe in Getreide und Getreideprodukten. **Carcinogenic polycyclical hydrocarbons in cereals and cereal products.**

18987 Ocker, H.–D. DE 209010/77/0005
Dekontamination von Schadstoffen bei Getreide. **Decontamination of noxious substances in cereals.**

18988 Wolff, J. DE 209010/77/0007
Charakterisierung qualitätsrelevanter Kohlenhydratkomponenten in Getreide durch chromatographische Verfahren. **Characterization of quality–relevant carbohydrate components in cereals by chromatography.**

18989 Ocker, H.–D. DE 209010/77/0009
Laufende Untersuchungen der deutschen Getreideernten auf Schadstoffe – Schwermetalle, Pflanzenschutzmittelrückstände u.a. –. **Continuous analyses of German cereal crops for noxious substances – heavy metals, residues of protectives a.o. –.**

18990 Ocker, H.–D.; Fretzdorff, B. DE 209010/77/0010
Quantitative Erfassung von Schadstoffen in Rohstoffen, Halbund Endprodukten auf der Basis von Getreide und Kartoffeln. **Quantitative determination of noxious substances in raw materials, semi– and final products of cereals and potatoes.**

18991 Ocker, H.–D.; Nierle, W. DE 209010/77/0011
Standardisierung von Untersuchungsmethoden auf nationaler und internationaler Ebene. **Standardization of test methods on national and international level.**

18992 Ocker, H.–D. DE 209010/77/0012
Pflanzenschutzmittelrückstände in Getreide und Getreideprodukten. **Residues of protectives in cereals and cereal products.**

18993 Wolff, J. DE 209010/77/0013
Toxische Schwermetalle in Getreide und Kartoffeln. **Toxic heavy metals in cereals and potatoes.**

D 7210 – Food composition

18994 Ocker, H.–D.   DE 209010/77/0014
Feststellung des Schadstoffgehaltes von Roggen und Weizen
im Rahmen der besonderen Ernteermittlung. **Determination of
the content of noxious substances in rye and wheat in special
crop analysis.**

18995 Bolling, H.; Meyer, D.   DE 209020/77/0004
Feststellung des Eignungswertes von neuen Weizensorten im
Rahmen der Wertprüfung des Bundessortenamtes.
**Determination of qualitative value of new wheat varieties in
quality control by the Federal Office on Varieties.**

18996 Bolling, H.; Gerstenkorn, P.; Weipert, D.
                    DE 209020/77/0006
Feststellung der Beschaffenheit der inländischen
Brotgetreideernte. **Determination of qualtiy of domestic bread
cereal crop.**

18997 Gerstenkorn, P.; El–Baya, A.W.; Weipert, D.
                    DE 209020/77/0010
Entwicklung, Verbesserung und Standardisierung von
Methoden zur Analyse von Getreide und Getreideprodukten.
**Development, improvement and standardization of methods
for analysis of cereals and cereal products.**

18998 Weipert, D.   DE 209020/77/0017
Feststellung des Eignungswertes neuer Roggensorten im
Rahmen der Wertprüfung des Bundessortenamtes, Hannover.
**Determination of qualitative value of new rye varieties in
quality control by the Federal Office on Varieties.**

18999 Spicher, G.   DE 209030/74/5002
Faktoren der Schimmelinfektion von Brot und Backwaren.
Conditions of mould infection in bread and pastries.

19000 Seiler, K.   DE 209030/77/0004
Qualitätsbeurteilung von Speisen auf Getreidebasis im
Rahmen des gemeinsamen Forschungsvorhabens
"Gemeinschaftsverpflegung" – Schulen –. **Qualitative valuation
of food of cereals in the joint research project "catering"–
schools –.**

19001 Menger, A.   DE 209030/77/0006
Analytik von feinen Backwaren, Extruderproduktion und
Teigwaren auch für bestimmte Ernährungserfordernisse.
**Analytics of pastries, extruder products, and paste products for
certain nutritive requirements.**

19002 Rabe, E.   DE 209030/77/0013
Analytik organischer Säuren. **Analytics of organic acids.**

19003 Rabe, E.   DE 209030/77/0015
Entwicklung, Verbesserung und Anwendung von Methoden
der chemischen Analytik. **Development, improvement and
application of methods for chemical analytics.**

19004 Spicher, G.   DE 209030/77/0018
Die Ursachen des Auftretens von Mykotoxinen in Getreide,
Backwaren und Teigwaren. **Causes of occurrence of mycotoxins
on cereals, baked goods and paste products.**

19005 Spicher, G.   DE 209030/77/0019
Die Mikroflora des Getreides und der Getreideprodukte.
Microflora of cereals and cereal products.

19006 Bruemmer, J.–M.   DE 209030/77/0021
Beurteilung von Getreideerzeugnissen, auch zur Einteilung in
Qualitätsklassen. **Quality classes of cereal products.**

19007 Harmuth–Hoene, A.E.   DE 211050/78/0004 N
Ernährungsphysiologische Prüfung von Brotsorten mit
erhöhtem Rohfasergehalt. **Nutritional evaluation of bread
types containing elevated levels of indigestible fibre.**

19008 Hoeser, K.; Wolf, E.   DE 502058/73/0012
Untersuchungen zur Mahlfähigkeit, zur Teig– und
Backqualität des Weizens. **Studies on grinding suitability,
pasting and baking quality of wheat.**

19009 Grosch, W.; Weber, F.   DE 502500/77/0004
Verfahren zur Bestimmung von reduziertem und oxidiertem
Glutathion in Weizenmehlen. **Methods for the assessment of
reduced and oxidised glutathione in wheat flours.**

19010 Britsch, W.D.; Meuser, F.   DE 916000/78/0005 N
Verwendung von Mischmehl für die menschliche Ernährung.
Use of composite flour for human nutrition.

19011 Feillet, P.; Brillot, P.   FR 011202/72/2262
Etablissement d'un barème d'appréciation de la qualité
commerciale des blés durs, et produits dérivés. **Establishment
of commercial grades of quality for hardwheat and cereal
products.**

19012 Multon, J.L.; Guilbot, A.   FR 012203/70/2250
Dosage de l'eau dans les produits et appréciations de leur
affinité pour l'eau. **Water determination in cereal products and
estimation of water affinity.** Publications.

19013 Tollier, M.T.; Guilbot, A.   FR 012203/70/2252
Appréciation de la pureté technologique des semoules.
Estimation of the technological purity of semolina.

19014 Dwyer, E.   IE 060300/74/1079 R
Microbiology of flour and milling by–products. Publications.

19015 Greve, P.A.   NL 040011/76/7523
Fumiganten, fungiciden en bromide in graan. **Fumigants,
fungicides and bromide in grain.** Publications.

19016 Bloksma, A.H.   NL 050302/74/6241
Standaardisatie van onderzoekmethoden voor granen en
graanprodukten. **Standardization of methods of investigation
for cereals and cereal foods.**

19017 Belderok, B.   NL 050302/75/6238
Invloed van alternatieve methoden bij de teelt en de
verwerking van tarwe op de kwaliteit van de produkten. **Effect
of alternative methods of growing and processing of wheat on
the quality of wheat products.**

19018 Lonkhuysen, H.J. van   NL 050302/76/6598
Rassenidentificatie van granen in handelspartijen door
electroforese. **Identification of cereal varieties in commercial
lots by means of electrophoresis.** Publications.

19019 Bloksma, A.H.   NL 050302/78/9003 N
Orienterend onderzoek over de bereiding van een ijkstof voor
de farinograaf van Brabender t.b.v. de beoordeling van de
tarwebloemkwaliteit. **Orientation about the preparation of a
gauging–substance which could be used in the "farinograaf of**

Brabender" for the assessment of the wheat flour quality.

19020 Lonkhuysen, H.J. van   NL 050302/79/8995 N
Ontwikkeling van een snelle asbepaling bij bloem.
Development of a quick method for determinating the ash content in flour.

19021 Graveland, A.   NL 050302/79/8998 N
Onderzoek naar de coeliakie–veroorzakende component uit granen. **Research on the component in cereals which is responsible for the coeliac disease.**

19022 Bloksma, A.H.   NL 050302/79/9004 N
De relaxatietijd van deeg als maat voor de deegontwikkeling en de bakkwaliteit. **The relaxation time of dough as a standard for dough development and baking quality.**

Oils, fats and related products (B 6820)

See also 16064, 16576, 16579, 18908, 19358, 19668

19023 Renard; Severin, M.; Wathelet, J.   BE 010006/71/0002
Recherches sur la composition des lipides isolés de champignons et de graines de légumineuses. **Researches on the composition of fats from mushrooms and legumeseeds.** Publications.

19024 Coppens, R.; Renard, M.; Deroanne, C.; Severin, M.

                BE 010006/72/0001 R
Etude de la cristallisation fractionnée de l'huile de palme. **Study of fractional cristalization of palm oil.** Publications.

19025 Renner, E.; Yoon, Y.C.   DE 129252/78/0003 N
Untersuchungen über isomere Formen von ungesättigten Fettsäuren in Nahrungsfetten und –ölen. **Investigation on isomeric forms of unsaturated fatty acids in edible fats and oils.**

19026 Weisser, H.; Hahn, G.   DE 145150/72/0001
Bestimmung des Fest–Flüssig–Verhältnisses teilkristallisierter Fette. **Determination of the solid/liquid ratio in partially crystalline fats.**

19027 Lehmann, G.; Linkersdörfer, J.   DE 167100/73/0007
Bestimmung des Puringehaltes zur Errechnung des Kakaoanteils in Schokolade. **Determination of purine content for calculating the cocoa ratio in chocolate.**

19028 Jork, H.; Hansen, R.   DE 167102/73/0009
Aufklärung der ätherischen Ölzusammensetzung bei Estragon. **Clarification of etheric oil composition in tarragon.**

19029 Jork, H.; Juell, M.S.   DE 167102/73/0010
Isolierung und Strukturaufklärung von Sesquiterpenalkoholen in Artemisia vulgare L.. **Isolation and structural determination of sesquiterpen alcohols in Artemisia vulgare L..**

19030 Jork, H.; Zenz, V.   DE 167102/73/0011
Phytochemische Untersuchungen an ätherischen Ölen von Artemisia abrotanum. **Phytochemical studies on etheric oils of Artemisia abrotanum.**

19031 Jork, H.; Scherf, U.   DE 167102/77/0005
Vergleich der ätherischen Öle bei schwarzem, weissem und grünem Pfeffer. **Comparison of etheric oils in black, white and green pepper.**

19032 Schön, I.   DE 210050/78/0002 N
Fettsäuremuster in originären Fettgeweben und Muskeln verschiedener Lokalisation an Schlachttierkörpern von Schweinen. **Fatty acid spectrum in original fatty tissue and muscles in different localizations on carcasses of pigs.**

19033 Schön, I.   DE 210050/78/0003 N
Kennwerte in tierischen Fettgeweben. **Analytical values in fatty tissue of animals.**

19034 Seher, A.; Gundlach, U.   DE 213010/77/0002
Nachweis und Bestimmung von Isomeren der langkettigen Monoensäuren. **Identification and determination of isomers of long–chain monoen acids.**

19035 Seher, A.; Arens, M.   DE 213010/77/0003
Bestimmung polymerer Fettsäuren in Speisefetten. **Determination of polymeric fatty acids in edible fats.**

19036 Seher, A.   DE 213010/77/0005
Methode zur Erkennung raffinierter Kadaverfette in Speisefetten. **Method for identification of refined carcass fats in edible fats.**

19037 Schiller, H.; Seher, A.; Gundlach, U.
                DE 213010/77/0008
Identifizierung von Minorfettsäuren in Pflanzenölen. **Identification of minor fatty acids in vegetable oils.**

19038 Seher, A.; Weiss, U.   DE 213010/77/0010
Eigenschaften von Äther–Lipiden. **Properties of ether lipids.**

19039 Arens, M.   DE 213010/77/0012
Bestimmung der Veränderungsprodukte von Fetten, die beim Fritieren entstehen. **Determination of products of changed fats resulting from fritting.**

19040 Seher, A.; Arens, M.; Weiss, U.   DE 213010/77/0013
Zusammensetzung von Speiseölen und –fetten als Grundlage für internationale Qualitätsnormen. **Composition of cooking oils and fats as basis of international quality standards.**

19041 Seher, A.; Ivanov, S.A.   DE 213010/77/0014
Natürliche Antioxydantien in Fetten und Ölen. **Natural antioxidants in fats and oils.**

19042 Homberg, E.   DE 213010/78/0004 N
Trennung und Identifizierung von Oxidationsprodukten von Sterinen. **Separation and identification of oxidation products of sterols.**

19043 Seher, A.; Arens, M.   DE 213010/78/0005 N
Bestimmung geringer Gehalte von trans–Fettsäuren in Fetten und Ölen. **Determination of small amounts of trans–fatty acids in oils and fats.**

19044 Seher, A.; Arens, M.   DE 213010/78/0007 N
Nationale Vereinheitlichung von Untersuchungsmethoden. **Standardization of analytical methods for fats and fatty foods in Germany.**

19045 Wessels, H.   DE 213010/78/0009 N
Untersuchung von erhitzten Fetten. **Analysis of heated fats.**

19046 Wessels, H.; Paksoy, S.   DE 213010/78/0010 N
Entwicklung von Kriterien zur Differenzierung von Palmöl

und Palmöl–Fraktionen. **Identity characteristics of palmoil and palmoil fractions.**

19047 Mukherjee, K.D.; Reichwald, I.; Ilsemann, K.
DE 213020/75/0003
Ernährungsphysiologische Eigenschaften hydrierter sowie umgeesterter Fette. **Nutritional properties of hydrogenated and interesterified fats.**

19048 Mangold, H.K. DE 213020/75/0004
Herstellung und ernährungsphysiologische Eigenschaften "nicht fettender" Fette. **Preparation and nutritional properties of "non–fattening" fats.**

19049 Reichwald, I.; Ilsemann, K.; Mukherjee, K.D.
DE 213020/75/0020
Erarbeitung von Methoden zur Bestimmung der ernährungsphysiologischen Wertigkeit von Fetten und anderen Lipiden. **Development of methods for the determination of nutritional value of fats and other lipids.**

19050 Grosch, W.; Tsoukalas, B.; Schieberle, P.
DE 502500/78/0003 N
Oxidativer Fettverderb: Untersuchungen von Modellsystemen. **Oxidative fat deterioration: studies on model systems.**

19051 Cucurachi, A.; Di Giovacchino, L.; Solinas, M.; Angerosa, F.M.P. IT 022100/77/0006 N
Il contenuto in Tocoferoli dell'olio di oliva in dipendenza della varietà di olive, del grado di maturazione, dei sistemi di lavorazione, e della conservazione del prodotto.. **Tocopherol content of olive oil as a function of olive varieties, ripening step, processing systems and product storage.**

19052 Cucurachi, A.; Solinas, M.; Angerosa, F.M.P.
IT 022100/78/0001
Caratteristiche quali–quantitative dei difetti dell'olio di oliva mediante analisi gas–cromatografica dello spazio di testa. **Quali–quantitative standardization of olive oil faults by gas–chromatographic analysis of the head space.**

19053 Brighigna, A.; Marsilio, V.; Solinas, M.; De Angelis, M.; Vlahov, G. IT 022100/78/0004
I costituenti pectici delle olive da tavola in rapporto alla consistenza e alla composizione chimica del frutto. **Pectic substances of the table olives with reference to the texture parameters and the chemical composition of fruits.**

19054 Galoppini, C. IT 041108/74/0558
Costituzione lipidica degli oli alimentari. **Lipid composition of edible oils.**

19055 Fedeli, E. IT 070200/77/0740
Studio qualitativo dei lipidi presenti nelle biomasse. **A qualitative study of lipids present in biomasses.**

19056 Germs, A.C. NL 010109/75/6069
Het teruglopen van het eigeelgehalte in slasaus en mayonaise. **Decrease in egg yolk percentage in salad dressing and mayonnaise.**

19057 Greve, P.A. NL 040011/73/7520
Ontwikkeling en verbetering van analyse methoden voor bestrijdingsmiddelen residu's in vetten. **Development and improvement of analytical methods for pesticides residues in fats.**

19058 Vos, H.J. NL 050301/63/6753
Chemische en fysische onderzoekmethoden m.b.t. samenstelling en eigenschappen van oliën en vetten, inclusief normalisatie van analysevoorschriften. **Development of chemical and physical methods for determination of composition and properties of oils and fats including standardization of methods.** Publications.

19059 Hoek, W. van der NL 050301/73/5312
Onderzoek betreffende de structuur en kwaliteit van margarine en halvarine. **Investigations into the structure and quality of margarine.**

19060 Vinkenborg, C. NL 050301/73/6494
Onderzoek naar het verband tussen samenstelling en eigenschappen enerzijds en kwaliteit, houdbaarheid alsmede toepasbaarheid anderzijds van oliën, vetten en vetbevattende produkten. **Investigations on the composition and properties of fats, oils and fat–containing products, interallia aimed at improving their quality and keepability.**

19061 Veen, J. van de NL 050301/73/6495
Onderzoek naar de schadelijkheid van vetten en oliën gebruikt voor frituren. **Investigations on the harmfullness of fats and oils used for frying.**

Sugar and starch products (B 6830)

See also 9451, 16077, 16594, 16612, 16624, 18809, 18990, 18993, 19084, 19423

19062 Müller, K. DE 132062/77/0001
Vergleichende Untersuchungen über die Zusammensetzung des Eiweisses in der Kartoffel und über Beziehungen zwischen freien und gebundenen Aminosäuren – Lysin, Methionin –; Erarbeitung einer Methode zur schnellen Eiweiss– und Lysinbestimmung in Kartoffeln. **Comparative studies on the composition of protein in potato, on relations between free and bound amino acids – lysine, methionine –; working out of a method for quick determination of protein and lysine in potatoes.**

19063 Bergner, K.–G.; Sabir, D.M. DE 170050/75/0004
Nähere Identifizierung der Honigproteine. **Qualified identification of honey proteins.** Publications.

19064 Fehn, K.–H. DE 209040/78/0003 N
Verbesserte Nutzung des Eiweissgehaltes von Kartoffeln und Kartoffelprodukten. **Improved utilization of protein content in potatoes and potato products.**

19065 Paulus, K.; Rumpf, I. DE 211020/77/0004
Erarbeitung von Texturprofilen für Kartoffeln und Fleisch. **Development of texture profiles for potatoes and meat.**

19066 Louveaux, J.; Tassencourt, L. Mme FR 010114/76/5148
Classification des miels à partir de caractères physico–chimiques et microscopiques. **Honey classification according to physico–chemical and microscopic features.**

19067 Tassencourt, L.; Louveaux, J. FR 010214/76/8266
Analyse pollinique de miel (2). **Pollen analysis of honey.**

19068 Guennelon, R. FR 010601/73/6263

Contamination éventuelle des miels de la région de Fessenheim (H.R.). **Possible contamination of honeys in the fessenheim area.**

19069 Piazza, M.G.; Persano, L.; Accorti, M.
IT 020400/79/0004 N
Analisi fisico–chimiche, organolettiche e melissopalinologiche per la tipicizzazione dei mieli italiani. **Essential composition, quality factors and melissopalynological analysis to characterize the italian honeys.**

19070 Keijbets, M.J.H.
NL 010105/67/8323
Sensorische kwaliteitsaspecten en voedingswaarde van aardappelprodukten. **Sensoric quality aspects and nutritional value of potato products.** Publications.

19071 Bellegem, T.M. van; Plieger, P.
NL 050208/50/5097
Het opsporen van verontreinigingen, residuen van hulpstoffen en micro–organismen in zetmeel en andere produkten uit aardappelen. **Detection of contamination of starch and products derived from potatoes.** Publications.

Fruit and vegetable products (B 6840)

See also 8770, 9667, 16064, 16100, 16663, 18818, 18982, 19434

19072 Schamp, N.; Willaert, G.; Dirinck, P.
BE 030005/71/0002 R
Aroma – analyse van voedingsmiddelen zowel wat betreft fruit en groenten als zuivel– en vleesprodukten. **Aroma analyses of foods on fruits, vegetables, dairy– and meatproducts.** Publications.

19073 Henriet, J.; Galoux, M.
BE 080700/72/0004 R
Enquête sur la présence de résidus de pesticides dans les fruits et légumes destinés à l'exportation. **Study on pesticide residues in exported fruits and vegetables.** Publications.

19074 Istas, J.; Neirinckx, G.; Van Hoeyweghen, P.
BE 100000/78/0035 R
Cd–en Pb– gehalten in groenten, fruit en enkele andere voedingsstoffen. **Cd –and Pb content in vegetables, fruit and some other foods.**

19075 Bielig, H.J.
DE 105811/78/0001 N
Selengehalt in frischen und verarbeiteten pflanzlichen Lebensmitteln deutscher Herkunft. **Selenium in fresh and processed vegetable food stuffs of German origin.** Publications.

19076 Bielig, H.J.; Barudi, W.
DE 105814/77/0001
Schwermetallgehalt in oberirdisch wachsenden Gemüsen und Obstarten. **Heavy metal content in vegetables and fruits.**

19077 Ahrens, E.; Aping, R.
DE 129080/78/0002 N
Vorkommen von Patulin in Kernobst und Kernobstprodukten unter Berücksichtigung von Sorte, Herkunft und Lagerung. **Occurrence of Patulin in stone–fruit and stone–fruit products with regard to variety, provenance and storage.**

19078 Herrmann, K.; Hanefeld, M.; Teuber, H.; Vösgen, W.; Galensa, R.; Reichert, A.
DE 138750/74/0001
Die im Gemüse natürlich vorkommenden phenolischen Inhaltsstoffe und deren Bedeutung. **Natural phenolics in vegetables and their importance.**

19079 Herrmann, K.; Henning, W.; Schäfers, F.–I.
DE 138750/78/0001 N
Phenolsäuren und Flavonoide des Obstes. **Phenolic acids and flavonoids of fruit.**

19080 Schreier, P.; Scopel, A.; Mick, W.; Winkler, F.; Kuchenbauer, F.; Drawert, F.
DE 161100/75/0016
Pflanzliche Aromastoffe, deren Biogenese und Veränderungen. **Vegetable aromatic substances – biogenesis and modifications.** Publications.

19081 Jork, H.; Wingertzahn, U.
DE 167102/77/0004
Bestimmung von Amygdalin und Prunasin in bitteren Mandeln mit Hilfe der DC–Photometrie. **Determination of amygdalin and prunasin in bitter almonds by means of DC photometry.**

19082 Brieskorn, C.H.; Besgen, D.
DE 176150/77/0001
Der chemische Aufbau der Mandelschale. **The chemical structure of the cuticle of almond.**

19083 Schwerdtfeger, E.
DE 211010/75/0009
Charakterisierung des Frischegrades von Obst und Gemüse durch objektiv messbare Grössen – Inhaltsstoffe –. **Characterization of freshness of fruit and vegetables by objective measurable values – plant constituents –.**

19084 Wedler, A.; Overbeck, G.; Schwerdtfeger, E.
DE 211010/77/0003
Sortenabhängiges Vorkommen von natürlichen, unerwünschten Inhaltsstoffen in Gemüse – Nitrat – und Kartoffeln – Alkaloide –. **Occurrence of natural undesirable constituents in vegetables – nitrate – and in potatoes – alkaloids – depending on variety.**

19085 Frank, H.K.; Hentschel, H.
DE 211010/78/0008 N
Mykotoxine bei pflanzlichen Ernteprodukten. **Mycotoxins in foodstuffs of plant origin.**

19086 Paulus, K.
DE 211020/77/0003
Erarbeitung eines speziellen Bewertungsschemas für die sensorische Prüfung von Möhren und Bohnen. **Development of a special valuation scheme for sensory check of carrots and beans.**

19087 Koller, W.–D.; Paulus, K.; Wolf, W.
DE 211020/77/0007
Veränderungen des Aromas bzw. einzelner Aromakomponenten von Gemüse durch thermische Verarbeitungsverfahren. **Changes in aroma resp. single aromatic components of vegetables by thermic treatment.**

19088 Adam, R.
DE 211020/78/0002 N
Abbau von Patulin in Apfelprodukten durch schweflige Säure. **Breakdown of patulin in apple products by sulphurous acid.**

19089 Duden, R.
DE 211020/78/0006 N
Nachweis und Charakterisierung lipidabbauender Enzyme in Blatt–Gemüsepflanzen. **Detection and characterization of lipid degrading enzymes in leaf vegetables.**

19090 Duden, R.; Paulus, K.; Rumpf, G.
DE 211020/78/0009 N
Korrelation zwischen Nähr– bzw. Genusswert und Handelsklassen pflanzlicher Produkte. **Correlation between trade standards and nutritive and sensorial quality of vegetables.**

D 7210 – Food composition

19091 Grosch, W.; Kim, I.–S.   DE 502500/78/0004 N
Lipoxygenase in Obst und Gemüse. **Lipoxygenase in fruits and vegetables.**

19092 Grosch, W.; Moll, C.; Biermann, U.
                   DE 502500/78/0005 N
Untersuchungen über das Vorkommen, die Bildung und den Geschmack von Trihydroxyfettsäuren. **Studies on occurrence, formation and taste of trihydroxyfatty acids.**

19093 Belitz, H.–D.; Konecny, S.; Weder, J.K.P.
                   DE 502500/78/0006 N
Bestimmung von Trypsin–Inhibitoren in Sojaerzeugnissen: Methodenvergleich. **Determination of trypsin inhibitors in soya products: comparison of methods.**

19094 Wucherpfennig, K.; Bretthauer, G.
                   DE 506104/77/0007
Feststellung der Schwankungsbreite analytischer Kennzahlen von Fruchtsäften. **Determination of fluctuations in analytical characters of fruit juices.**

19095 Souty, M.   FR 010605/71/2221
Etudes sur les pêches de table et les abricots. Critère de qualité. **Study on table peaches and apricots. Quality criteria.** Publications.

19096 Moutonet, M.; Puech, J.L.   FR 011402/70/2239
Arôme du pruneau d'Agen. **Prune aroma.** Publications.

19097 Gormley, T.R.   IE 060300/71/0087 R
Tomato quality – tomatoes from cultivar nutrition and storage trials and from commercial markets are tested for quality.

19098 Jeffares, M.; Gormley, T.R.; Eades, J.F.K.
                   IE 060300/74/0984 R
Use of gas liquid chromatography for gas analysis in glasshouses, soils, growing athmospheres, fruit stores and in individual fruits, and also for pesticide, sugar and other compositional analyses. Publications.

19099 Gormley, T.R.   IE 060300/75/1141 N
Dietary fibre content of Irish grown fruit and vegetables and of Irish made brown bread. Publications.

19100 Gormley, T.R.; Jeffares, M.   IE 060300/77/1299 N
Nutritive value of Irish grown fruit and vegetables in relation to vitamins, mineral elements, nitrates etc, as measured after harvesting, storage, processing, and at retail outlets. Publications.

19101 Marchesini, A.; Garofalo, F.   IT 020200/79/0001 N
Valutazione biochimica della qualità dei prodotti agrari. **Biochemical investigations on the quality of the fruits and vegetables.**

19102 Badino, M.; Allavena, A.   IT 021000/79/0025 N
Studio dei fattori antinutrizionali presenti nel seme di fagiolo (Ph. vulgaris). **Study on antinutritional factors in bean seeds (Ph.vulgaris).**

19103 Gorini, F.L.; Eccher Zerbini, P.; Sozzi, A.
                   IT 021900/75/0009
Ricerche sulle caratteristiche qualitative della frutta con metodi oggettivi. **Objective methods for quality evaluation of fruit.** Publications.

19104 Polesello, A.; Pizzocaro, F.; Forni, E.
                   IT 021900/78/0002
Ricerche sulla composizione degli aromi nei succhi di frutta. **Aroma recovery and composition from fruit juices.**

19105 Balloni, W.; Florenzano, G.; Brighigna, A.; Pelagatti, O.; Cucurachi, A.   IT 022100/72/0003
La microbiologia delle olive da mensa. **Mycrobiology of table olives.** Publications.

19106 Maccarrone, A.; Lupo Cataldi, M.C.
                   IT 040308/78/0002
Gli zuccheri contenuti nei succhi di agrumi. **Sugars content in the citrus juices.**

19107 Maccarrone, A.   IT 040308/78/0004
Contenuto di Vitamina C nei succhi di agrumi prodotti in Sicilia. **Vitamin C content in the citrus juices produced in Sicily.**

19108 Maccarrone, A.; Nicolosi Asmundo, C.
                   IT 040308/79/0001 N
Caratteristiche dei succhi ottenuti da diverse varietà di uva. **Characteristics of juice obtained from grape different varieties.**

19109 Del Re, A.   IT 040406/77/0489 R
Determinazione residui di antibotritici nelle uve, nei mosti e nei vini. **Identification of anti–botrytis residues in grapes, musts and wines.**

19110 Barbina, M.; Spessotto, C.   IT 090701/76/0003
Determinazione con metodi chimici e biologici dei residui di anticrittogamici in campioni di frutta e di vini della Regione Friuli Venezia Giulia. **Determination with chemical and biological methods of anticriptogamic residuals in samples of fruits and wines of the Friuli Venezia Giulia district.** Publications.

19111 Meer, M.A. van der   NL 010118/73/4175
Objectivering van kwaliteitscriteria bij diepvries groenten en fruit. **Objective measuring of subjective quality criteria for quick frozen fruits and vegetables.**

19112 Gersons, L.   NL 010118/73/4176
Kwaliteitseisen groente– en vruchtenprodukten. **Quality requirements for processed horticultural products.** Publications.

19113 Gersons, L.   NL 010118/73/4177
Kwaliteitsnormen in EEG–verband van verwerkte tuinbouwprodukten. **Quality Standard for horticultural produce in the Common Market.**

19114 Gersons, L.   NL 010118/73/4178
Kwaliteitsnormen voor groente– en vruchtenprodukten t.b.v. de Codex Alimentarius. **Quality standards for the Codex Alimentarius.** Publications.

19115 Meer, M.A. van der   NL 010118/73/4179
Objectieve sensorische kwaliteitscriteria bij de appel. **Objectivation of sensoric quality criteria for apple.**

19116 Meer, M.A. van der   NL 010118/73/4180 R
Consumptiekwaliteit van vroege appel en peer. **Consumer quality of early apples and pears.**

19117 Steinbuch, E. NL 010118/73/4181
Invloed van temperatuurschommelingen op de kwaliteit van diepgevroren groenten. **Quality of quick frozen vegetables in relation to fluctuating temperatures during distribution.**

19118 Gersons, L. NL 010118/73/4182
Analyses van groente en fruit en verwerkte produkten t.b.v. de Nederlandse Voedingsmiddelentabel. **Quality standards for processed horticultural products.**

19119 Schijvens, E. NL 010118/75/6004 R
Lekgewicht van groente– en vruchtenconserven. **Drained weight of canned fruits and vegetables.**

19120 Gersons, L. NL 010118/76/6651
Omzettingen van nitraat in wortelen ma de oogst. **Nitrate conversions in carrots after harvesting.** Publications.

19121 Gersons, L. NL 010118/77/7263
Vruchtgehaltebepaling in jams. **Determination of fruit content in jams.**

19122 Tamminga, S.K.; Beumer, R.R.; Kampelmacher, E.H.

NL 020031/71/5116
Mikrobiologische methoden om na te gaan of aardbeien en andere voedingsmiddelen bestraald zijn. **Microbiological methods to determine whether strawberries and other foods have been irradiated.** Publications.

19123 Pilnik, W. NL 020031/76/6801
Tingehalte in vruchtensappen. **Tin content in fruit juices.**

19124 Hoeven, J.C.M. van de NL 020055/78/8546 R
De mutagene eigenschappen van groente extracten. **Possible mutagenic properties of vegetable extracts.**

19125 Vaessen, H.A.M.G. NL 040011/71/7460
Onderzoek naar een analysemethode voor de gehaltebepaling van thiabendazol (TBZ = 2 – (4'–thiazolyl) benzimidazol) residuen op citrusvruchten. **Investigation on an analytical for the determination of the levels of thiabendazole (TBZ = 2 –(4'–thiazol) benzimidazole) residues on citrus fruits.**

19126 Schuller, P.L. NL 040011/72/7462
Ontwikkeling van een methode van onderzoek voor de bepaling van patuline in vruchtensappen. **Development of a detection method for determination of patulin in fruit–juices.** Publications.

19127 Greve, P.A. NL 040011/73/7518
Ontwikkeling en verbetering van analysemethoden voor bestrijdingsmiddelen residu's in groenten en fruit. **Development and improvement of analytical methods for residues of pesticides in fruit and vegetables.** Publications.

19128 Schothorst, M. van; Schuller, P.L. NL 040011/76/7449
Onderzoek naar de vorming van Patuline in appels; mede in relatie tot bewaartemperatuur, bewaartijd en appelsoort. **Investigation on the formation of Patulin in apples in relation to storage temperature, storage time and apple species.**

19129 Schothorst, M. van NL 040011/76/7454
Residuen van strptomycine op peren. **Residues of streptomycin on pears.**

19130 Brouwer, A.E. NL 050301/74/6474
Analytisch–chemisch onderzoek betreffende de persistentie van bestrijdingsmiddelen in tuinbouwprodukten. **Analytical research on the persistance of pesticide residues in horticultural products.** Publications.

Meat, meat products and fish products in general (B 6850)

19131 Charlier, J.; Deroanne, C.; Duchêne, M.
BE 140000/78/0070 N
Etude de conservation et distribution de plats à base de viande porcine. **Study of conservation and distribution of pork dish.**

19132 Kreuzer, W.; Hollwich, W. DE 160732/71/0001
Untersuchungen auf Rückstände an toxischen Metallen und organischen Umweltchemikalien von Lebensmitteln tierischer Herkunft, insbesondere in Schlachttieren, Geflügel, Wild und Fleischprodukten sowie Milch, Eiern und Fischen. **Studies on residues of toxic metals and organic environmental chemicals in food of animal origin, esp. in slaughter animals, poultry, game and meat products as well as in milk, eggs and fish.**

19133 Siewert, E. DE 305032/77/0001
Arzneimittelrückstände in Lebensmitteln tierischer Herkunft. **Drug residues in foods of animal origin.**

19134 Bories, G.; Durand, E. FR 011412/78/9504
Mise au point d'une méthodologie d'étude de la disponibilité des résidus présents dans les denrées animales, lors de la consommation par une seconde espèce (situation du consommateur humain). **Fate of residues present in animal products after feeding by a another specie (human consumer situation).**

19135 Polesello, A.; Pizzocaro, F. IT 021900/75/0019
Metodi di analisi non distruttiva dei pigmenti mioglobinici delle carni fresche e congelate. **Non destructive methods of analysis for myoglobine in fresh and frozen meat.**

19136 Polesello, A.; Pizzocaro, F. IT 021900/75/0020
Indici di autolisi nelle carni congelate. **Autolysis indexes for frozen meat.**

19137 Luten, J. NL 050303/78/2975 N
Ontwikkeling en verbetering van methoden voor chemisch onderzoek ter beoordeling van de kwaliteit van visserijprodukten. **Development and improvement of chemical methods for quality assessment of fish products.**

Meat and meat products (B 6851)

See also 2614, 10537, 10538, 10539, 10759, 10937, 10942, 10976, 11214, 11253, 11354, 12816, 13046, 13299, 13300, 13875, 14368, 14666, 15467, 15861, 16202, 16694, 16707, 16710, 16712, 18826, 18827, 18828, 19036, 19065, 19072, 19186, 19383, 19389, 19667, 20262

19138 Martin, J.; Verbeke, R.; Van De Voorde, G.
BE 030026/60/0005
Beoordeling en meting van karkaskwaliteit en van vleeskwaliteit van slachtrunderen en slachtvarkens. **Appraisal and grading of carcasses and meat of beefcattle and pigs.** Publications.

19139 Van Hoof, J.; Dezeure–Wallays, B.

BE 051200/75/0002 R

Onderzoek naar biochemische en microbiologische veranderingen in het vlees van geslacht gevogelte. **Study of some biochemical and microbiological changes in poultry meat post–mortem.** Publications.

19140 Casteels, M.; Bekaert, H. **BE 070700/76/0035**
De objectieve bepaling van de karkaskwaliteit van slachtvarkens. **Study of an objectif grading system for pig carcasses.** Publications.

19141 Hildebrandt, G.; Königsmann, R.; Sinell, H.–J.; Thein, G.; Weiss, H. **DE 104301/73/0001**
Zur Methodik der histometrischen Komponentenbestimmung in Fleischerzeugnissen unter Berücksichtigung der Bild–Computer–Analyse. **Method of histometric determination of components in meat products considering the image computer analysis.**

19142 Sinell, H.J.; Siems, H.; Hildebrandt, G.; Arndt, G. **DE 104301/73/0006 R**
Methodenvergleich von Anreicherungen zum Nachweis von Salmonellen aus Lebensmitteln tierischer Herkunft sowie deren quantitative Bestimmung mit Hilfe der MPN–Technik. **Comparative studies on enrichment methods for identification of salmonellae in foods of animal origin and quantitative analysis by means of 'MPN' technique.** Publications.

19143 Reuter, G.; Strasser, L.; Sasse, D. **DE 104302/77/0003**
Schnellmethoden zum Nachweis der Hygienequalität von Fleisch und Fleischerzeugnissen sowie der in Betracht kommenden Einrichtungs– und Bedarfsgegenstände. **Rapid methods for proving the hygiene quality of meat and meat products and of equipments concerned.**

19144 Reuter, G.; Riemer, R. **DE 104302/78/0001 N**
Untersuchungen zur Durchführbarkeit einer Fleischuntersuchung bei im Inland erlegten Wildtieren. **Investigations on the practicability of meat inspection of game killed in Germany.**

19145 Reuter, G.; Sibomana, G. **DE 104302/78/0002 N**
Vergleichende Untersuchungen über die Brauchbarkeit von Verfahren zur Oberflächenkeimzahlbestimmung bei Schlachttierkörpern. **Comparative investigations on methods for determination of surface flora of carcasses.**

19146 Reuter, G.; Seelig, I. **DE 104302/78/0004 N**
Ökologische Erhebungen über das Vorkommen von Salmonellen auf der Oberfläche geschlachteter Rinder. **Ecological investigations on the occurrence of salmonellae at the surface of slaughtered cattle.**

19147 Reuter, G.; Stolle, A. **DE 104302/78/0006 N**
Vergleich der Methoden für die amtliche bakteriologische Fleischuntersuchung in mitteleuropäischen Ländern. **Comparison of methods for official bacteriological examination of carcass meat in Central European countries.**

19148 Retzlaff, N.; Severins, H. **DE 104302/78/0008 N**
Untersuchungen über die Tri– und TetrajodthyroninWerte im Blutserum von Schlachtschweinen. **Investigations on tri– and tetrajodthyronin levels in blood serum of slaughtered pigs.**

19149 Reuter, G.; Wachelau, G. **DE 104302/78/0009 N**
Prüfung von radioimmunologischen Methoden zur Erfassung Thyreostatika–gefütterter Mastrinder. **Proving radioimmunological methods for identification of cattle fed with thyreostatica.**

19150 Retzlaff, N.; Hiepe, W. **DE 104302/78/0010 N**
Untersuchungen über die Beziehungen zwischen histologischen und histometrischen Merkmalen der Schilddrüsen von Schlachtschweinen und dem Thyroxingehalt im Blutserum dieser Tiere. **Investigations on the relation between histological and histometrical criterions of thyroid glands of slaughtered pigs and the content of thyroxin in blood serum of these animals.**

19151 Stan, H.–J.; Hohls, F.W. **DE 105900/78/0001 N**
Untersuchungen über das Vorkommen von Anabolika–Rückständen in Fleisch. **Field investigation on the occurrence of residues of anabolic substances in meat.** Publications.

19152 Stan, H.–J.; Ingerowski, G. **DE 105900/78/0003 N**
Nachweis von Östrogen–Rückständen in Fleisch mit Hilfe des Östrogenrezeptors aus Rinderuterus. **Detection of residues of estrogenic substances in meat by means of the estrogenic receptor protein from bovine uterus.** Publications.

19153 Greuel, E.; Röss, H. **DE 111404/78/0001 N**
Untersuchungen zur serologischen Differenzierung von Fleisch afrikanischer Wildarten. **Investigations on serological differentiation of meat of different African game species.**

19154 Greuel, E.; Gehrigk, U. **DE 111404/78/0002 N**
Hygienekontrolle von importiertem Rotwild. **Control of hygienic condition of imported deer meat.**

19155 Greuel, E.; Kockelke, B. **DE 111404/78/0003 N**
Hygienekontrolle von importiertem Schwarzwild. **Control of hygienic condition of imported wild boars meat.**

19156 Pfeilsticker, K.; Schmidt, W.D. **DE 111600/74/0002**
Korrelationen zwischen Inhaltsbestandteilen von Würsten. **Correlations between constituents of sausages.**

19157 Hadlok, R.; Hellwig, I.; Stegen, D.; Rheinhaben, K.von **DE 129700/74/0001**
Mikroorganismen in der Fleischhygiene: Gattung Enterokokken; Micrococcus; Hefen. **Microorganisms in meat hygiene: genus of enterococcus; micrococcus; yeasts.**

19158 Thiel, W.; Knothe, D,; Wenzel, S. **DE 139560/78/0001 N**
Untersuchungen über die chemische Zusammensetzung von Brühund Rohwurstprodukten aus dem Handel unter besonderer Berücksichtigung des Nicht–Protein–Stickstoffgehaltes. **Investigations on the chemical structure of commercial scalded and raw sausage products with special regard to non–protein–nitrogen content.**

19159 Hinrichsen, J.K. **DE 144675/77/0006**
Untersuchungen über den Oestron–, Oestradiol– und Progesterongehalt des Fleisches von vorgenutzten Färsen zu verschiedenen Schlachtzeitpunkten. **Studies on estrone, estradiol, and progesterone content in meat of one–calf heifers slaughtered at various stages of pregnancy.**

19160 Kotter, L.; Herrmann, C. **DE 160734/72/0001**
Direkte Bestimmung des Anteils an bindegewebsfreiem

Fleischeiweiss in Fleischerzeugnissen. **Direct determination of meat protein, free from connective tissue, in meat products.**

19161 Geiger, G.　　　　　DE 160735/72/0002
Nachweis und Interpretation von HAA in Seren und Sekreten von Tieren, die für die Lebensmittelgewinnung vorgesehen sind. **Detection and interpretation of the occurrence of HAA in serum and secretion of animals destined for food.**

19162 Geiger, G.; Handlos, B.　　　　DE 160735/73/0001
Nachweis von Hepatitis assoziiertem Antigen in Seren von hepatopathischen Schlachtrindern. **Detection of hepatitis–associated antigen –HAA– in serum of hepatopathic cattle–for–slaughter.**

19163 Kreuzer, W.; Wissmath, P.　　　DE 160736/72/0003
Untersuchungen über die Ursachen der Schwermetallkontamination von Nutz– und Schlachttieren sowie davon stammender Lebensmittel. **Studies of the causes of contamination with heavy metals in productive livestock and foodstuff of animal origin.**

19164 Thier, H.–P.; Petz, M.　　　DE 164150/78/0003 N
Analytik von Rückständen des Coccidiostatikums Amprolium in Fleisch und Eiern. **Analysis of anticoccidial amprolium residues in meat and eggs.**

19165 Schön, L.; Scheper, J.　　　DE 210010/75/0005
Entwicklung von Methoden zur Früherkennung der Beschaffenheit von Schweinefleisch. **Development of methods for early estimation of the status of pork.**

19166 Schön, L.; Sack, E.　　　　DE 210010/75/0013
Erfassung des Muskelfleischanteils an Schlachttierkörpern von Schweinen mit dem dänischen KSA–Gerät. **Determination of the muscular meat portion of swine carcass by means of the Danish KSA implement.**

19167 Schön, L.; Kühne, D.　　　DE 210010/75/0015
Cholesteringehalt in Geweben von Schlachttieren. **Cholesterol content in carcass tissues.**

19168 Schön, L.; Augustini, C.; Fischer, K.
　　　　　　　　　　　　　DE 210010/78/0002 N
Beziehungen zwischen belastenden Umweltbedingungen, individueller Reaktion und Fleischbeschaffenheit beim Schwein. **Relations between environmental stress conditions individual reaction and meat quality of pigs.**

19169 Schön, L.; Kühne, D.　　　DE 210010/78/0003 N
Mineralstoffgehalt im Fleisch von Schlachttieren und in Eiern in Abhängigkeit von Lokalisation und Produktionsbedingungen. **The amount of minerals in carcasses and eggs dependent on the localization and productive conditions.**

19170 Schön, L.　　　　　　DE 210010/78/0005 N
Elektronische Klassifizierung von Schweinehälften. **Objective grading of pigs by electronic equipment.**

19171 Stiebing, A.　　　　　DE 210020/78/0001 N
Farbverbesserung bei Blutwurst. **Colour improvement in blood sausages.**

19172 Hammer, G.　　　　　DE 210020/78/0003 N
Fettsäuren in Leberwurst. Beeinflussung durch

Rohstoffauswahl und technologische Massnahmen. **Fatty acids in liver–sausage. Influences exerted by raw–material selection and technology.**

19173 Hammer, G.　　　　　DE 210020/78/0004 N
Verarbeitungseignung von gefriergelagerten Rohstoffen zur Herstellung qualitativ hochwertiger Leberwurst. **Suitibility of frozen stored raw materials for the production of liver–sausage of high quality.**

19174 Rödel, W.　　　　　　DE 210030/71/5008
Optimierung der Bestimmung der Wasseraktivität 'aw–Wert' von Fleisch und Fleischerzeugnissen. **Optimum determination of water activity 'aw–value' in meats and meat products.**

19175 Schmidt, U.　　　　　DE 210030/72/5001
Rückstände in Schlachttierkörpern von Kälbern und Schweinen nach nutritiver Verabreichung schwer resorbierbarer Antibiotika. **Residues in carcasses of calves and swine after nutritive application of antibiotics difficult to resorb.**

19176 Hechelmann, H.　　　　DE 210030/74/5003
Vorkommen und Bedeutung von Yersinia enterocolitica bei Fleisch, einschliesslich Geflügel. **Incidence and role of Yersinia enterocolitica in meat including poultry meat.**

19177 Woltersdorf, W.　　　　DE 210030/74/5012
Untersuchung zum Fremdwassergehalt von Schlachtgeflügel. **Analysis of foreign water content in market poultry.**

19178 Hechelmann, H.　　　　DE 210030/77/0002
Realisierbarkeit des Nitratverbotes für Rohpökelwaren im Stück. **Realization of prohibition of using nitrate in cured raw meats all of a piece.**

19179 Lücke, F.–K.　　　　　DE 210030/77/0003
Mikrobiologische Stabilität von Fleischkonserven, bei vermindertem Nitritzusatz. **Microbiological stability of canned meat products by reduced nitrite addition.**

19180 Rödel, W.　　　　　　DE 210030/77/0006
Überleben von Finnen in Pökelfleischerzeugnissen in Abhängigkeit von der Wasseraktivität. **Survival of cysticeri in cured meat products depending on water activity.**

19181 Leistner, L.; Hofmann, G.　　　DE 210030/78/0004 N
Carry–over von Mykotoxinen, die keine Aflatoxine sind. **Carry–over of mycotoxins other than aflatoxins.**

19182 Leistner, L.; Marasas, W.F.O.　　DE 210030/78/0005 N
Mikrobiologische Standards für rohes Fleisch unter Berücksichtigung von Wildfleisch. **Microbiological standards for raw meat and venison.**

19183 Leistner, L.; Schmidt, U.　　　DE 210030/78/0008 N
Optimierung der Reinigungsverfahren für fleischverarbeitende Betriebe. **Improvement of cleansing procedures in meat processing plants.**

19184 Linke, H.　　　　　　DE 210030/78/0012 N
Morphologische Studien an geformten Fleischerzeugnissen. **Morphological studies on reconstituted meat products.**

19185 Linke, H.　　　　　　DE 210030/78/0013 N
Qualitätsbeurteilung der nicht zu den Leberwürsten zählenden

Kochstreichwürste. **Criteria of spreadable cooked sausages which are not liver sausages.**

19186 Woltersdorf, W.   DE 210030/78/0014 N
Schnellbestimmung von Fremdwasser in Schlachtgeflügel.
Rapid method for determining the extraneous water content of poultry.

19187 Woltersdorf, W.   DE 210030/78/0015 N
Morphologische Studien über die Feinstruktur von Brühwurst.
Morphological studies of sausage emulsions with electron microscopy.

19188 Hecht, H.   DE 210040/75/0002 N
Untersuchungen zur Erfassung des "carry–over" Effektes für
Arsen, Quecksilber, Selen, Brom, Zinn, Kupfer, Zink und
andere toxische Elemente bei Schlachttieren. **Studies on the
carry–over effects at slaughter animals with regard to arsenic,
mercury, selenium, bromine, tin, copper, zinc and other toxic
elements.**

19189 Mirna, A.; Coretti, K.   DE 210040/77/0004
Untersuchungen über Ersatzstoffe für Nitrit und Nitrat bei
Fleischerzeugnissen; Bildung von Nitrosaminen. **Investigations
on substitutes for nitrite and nitrate in meat products;
formation of nitrosamines.**

19190 Arneth, W.   DE 210040/78/0002 N
Verbesserung der Bestimmung von Milcheiweiss in
Fleischwaren. **Improvement of the assay of dairy proteins in
meat products.**

19191 Schön, I.   DE 210050/75/0002
Exogene und endogene Einflussfaktoren auf die
ernährungsphysiologische Wertigkeit von tierischem Gewebe.
**Exogenous and endogenous influence on nutritional value of
animal tissue.**

19192 Mirna, A.   DE 210060/78/0001 N
Kontamination von Fleischerzeugnissen durch Radionuklide
bei Verwendung von Separatorenfleisch. **Contamination of
meat products with radionuclides using mechanically deboned
meat.**

19193 Seher, A.   DE 213010/77/0006
Nachweis der Raffination von Rindertalg. **Determination of
refining of suet.**

19194 Englert, H.K.; Kluge–Wilm, R.   DE 501325/75/0001
Konzeption eines Arbeitsprogrammes für den serologischen
Fremdeiweissnachweis in Fleischwaren. **Conception of a
working programme for the serological proof of foreign protein
in meat products.**

19195 Shan   GB 010603/79/0130 N
Classify bacteria from meat and meat products.

19196 Mackey   GB 010603/79/0140 N
**Investigate bacterial damage by heat, cold, drying, radiation,
preservation and its repair.**

19197 Dransfield   GB 010606/00/0090 R
Relating muscle components and pre and post slaughter
treatments to meat texture.

19198 Etherington   GB 010606/75/0110 N

Define role of enzymes and structural changes involved in
conditioning of meat.

19199 Cheah   GB 010606/79/0180 N
**Relate biochemical and biophysical changes in meat to stress
susceptibility in animals to improve quality.**

19200 Jeacocke   GB 010606/79/0190 N
Study changes in mechanical properties of muscle fibres during
rigor and after ageing and cooking.

19201 Trinick   GB 010606/79/0200 N
Define mechanism and factors affecting interaction of
contractile proteins in relation to meat texture.

19202 Trimble   GB 041404/78/0012 N
Textural quality of beef.

19203 Sheridan, J.J.   IE 060100/77/1276 R
The bacteriology of the skirt and neck in beef sides.
Publications.

19204 O'Keeffe, M.; Eades, J.F.K.   IE 060500/77/1331 R
**Pesticide and other chemical residues in animal tissues and
animal products.** Publications.

19205 Hunter, A.T.; Langan, J.W.; Kierstan, M.
          IE 070400/77/9123 N
**Determination of meat protein in food products containing meat
and non–meat proteins.**

19206 Daly, C.; Buckley, J.; Horgan, V.   IE 110102/79/9231 N
Study of greening defect of cured meats, especially cooked ham.

19207 Tully, F.R.   IE 110203/78/9128 N
**Measurement of purine nucleotide concentrations in meats fro
m different meat animals at all stages of meat production, a nd
assessment of their role as indicators of meat quality.**

19208 Romita, A.; Gigli, S.; Borghese, A.   IT 020700/76/0002
Confronto tra le caratteristiche chimico–fisiche e alimentari
delle carni di vitelli bufalini e bovini. **Comparison between
chemical, physical and food characteristics of meat from calves
and buffalo calves.**

19209 Zezza, L.   IT 040111/77/0592 R
Studio delle caratteristiche fisico–chimico–bromatologiche
delle carcasse agnelline. **Study of the physical, chemical and
nutritional characteristics of lamb carcasses.**

19210 Giordani, G.; Martinelli, M.; Minoccheri, F.; Grazia,
S.; Negrini, F.   IT 040212/76/0003
Ricerche sulla produttività zootecnica e la qualità delle carni in
differenti razze di piccioni. **Research on the productivity and
the meat quality of different pigeon breeds.** Publications.

19211 Geri, G.C.   IT 040520/77/0556 R
Caratteristiche chimiche, fisiche ed istologiche della carne
suina e fattori che le influenzano nei riflessi della loro
accettazione da parte del consumatore. **Chemical, physical and
histological characteristics of pork and the factors affecting
them having regard to their acceptableness by the consumer.**

19212 Corsico, G.   IT 040639/77/0738
Caratteristiche igienico–sanitarie di carni di pollo disossate
meccanicamente. **Characteristics, from the point of view of**

health and hygiene, of chicken meat boned mechanically.

19213 Balestrieri, C.　　　　IT 040745/74/0508
Studi sul valore nutritivo di nuove fonti proteiche, indagini biochimiche su frazioni proteiche da muscolo scheletrico di animali scarsamente utilizzati ai fini alimentari: bufalo, coniglio, etc. **Studies on the nutritive value of new protein sources, biochemical studies on protein fractions from skeletal muscles of animals only occasionally used for human consumption: buffalo, rabbit, etc.**

19214 Accardi, F.　　　　IT 040907/73/0907
Ricerca delle relazioni tra composizione chimica di tagli campione, della carcassa e dell'intero corpo negli ovini. **Research on the relationships between chemical composition of sample cuts, carcass and whole body in sheep.**

19215 Accardi, F.　　　　IT 040907/78/1020 N
Ricerca sulle connessioni tra composizione chimica di tagli campioni delle carcasse e dell'intero corpo di ovini di razza" Barbaresca siciliana, derivati"berrichon"e"comisane", per gli studi sulla calorimetria indiret. **A study on indirect calorimetry : research on the connections between the chemical composition of the whole body of "Barbaresca siciliana" sheep of "berrichon" and "comisane" offsprings and sample cuts of their carcasses.**

19216 Gerrits, A.R.; Bolder, N.M.　　　　NL 010109/74/6074
Het bepalen van de hoeveelheid been in "meat" van pluimvee. **Determination of the bone content of "mechanically" deboned poultry.** Publications.

19217 Steverink, A.T.G.; Gerrits, A.R.; Frijters, J.E.R.; Kan, C.A.; Mulder, R.W.A.W.; Zegwaard, A.
　　　　NL 010109/76/7865
Smaakbeïnvloeding van pluimveevlees en eieren door houtkrullen. **The influence of woodshavings on flavour and taint of poultry and eggs.** Publications.

19218 Boer, H. de; Bergström, P.L.; Boer, Tj. de; Nijeboer, H.　　　　NL 010112/76/6145
Europese (EAAP) classificatienormen, samenstelling en uitsnijrendement van runderkarkassen. **European (EAAP) classification standards, composition and yield of cattle carcasses.** Publications.

19219 Boer, H. de　　　　NL 010112/78/7896
Ontwikkeling van uniforme methodes voor de classificatie van varkenskarkassen in de E.G. **Development of uniform methods for the classification of pig carcasses in the E.C.** Publications.

19220 Tamminga, S.K.　　　　NL 020031/77/8522
Ontwikkeling van voedselvergiftende bacteriën in vers vlees, in het bijzonder bij lagere temparaturen. **Development of food poisoning bacteria in fresh meat, especially at low temperatures.**

19221 Kampelmacher, E.H.　　　　NL 020031/78/8895 N
Voorkomen en betekenis voor de volksgezondheid van Staphylococcus aureus in een slachtlijn voor varkens. **Occurence and health significance of Staphylococcus aureus in a pig slaughter line.**

19222 Tamminga, S.K.　　　　NL 020031/78/8896 N
De bacteriologische kwaliteit van hamburgers en de invloed van het verhittingsproces daarop. **The bacteriological quality of hamburgers and the influence of the heating procedure on it.**

19223 Dijkman, K.E.; Koopmans, M.T.A.G.F.
　　　　NL 030008/73/5744
Gisten, schimmels en andere psychrotrofe mikro–organismen in gehakt. **Yeasts, moulds and other psychrotrophic micro–organisms in minced meat.**

19224 Mossel, D.A.A.; Eelderink, I.　　NL 030008/74/5742 R
Mikrobiële ecologie van verkleind rauw vlees, in het bijzonder met betrekking tot Enterobacteriaceae (mikrobiële ekologie, gehakt, Enterobacteriaceae). **Microbial ecology of comminuted fresh meats with special reference to Enterobacteriaceae (microbial ecology, minced meat, Enterobacteriaceae).**

19225 Krol, B.　　　　NL 030008/77/8955 N
Kwaliteit van verhitte samengestelde vleeswaren, waarin varkens–separatorvlees is verwerkt. (kwaliteit, vleesproducten, separatorvlees, vert–oxidatie). **Quality of cooked comminuted meat products containing mechanically deboned pork, lipid oxidation. (quality, meat products, mechanically deboned pork, lipid oxidation).** Publications.

19226 Krol, B.　　　　NL 030008/77/8956 N
Kwaliteit van linolzuurrijk varkensvlees en hiervan bereidde producten. (kwaliteit, varkensvlees, meervoudig onverzadigde vetzuren, vet–oxidatie). **Quality of high linoeic pork and pork products (quality, pork, polyunsaturated fatty acids, lipid oxidation).** Publications.

19227 Schothorst, M. van; Schuller, P.L.; Rauws, A.G.
　　　　NL 040011/64/7529
Ontwikkeling en verbetering van de urinesneltest en identificatiemethoden voor het aantonen van antibiotica bij slachtvee. **Development and improvement of the rapid–urine–test and identification method for detection of antibiotics in slaughter animals.** Publications.

19228 Schothorst, M. van　　　　NL 040011/69/7440
Onderzoek naar het voorkomen van Salmonella in gehakt en andere vleesprodukten. **Investigation to prevalence of Salmonella on minced and other meatproducts.** Publications.

19229 Greve, P.A.　　　　NL 040011/69/7511
Onderzoek naar residuen van vleesvreemde stoffen in vlees en vleeswaren van rund en varken. **Investigation on residues of chemicals in meat and meat products from cattle and pigs.** Publications.

19230 Northolt, M.D.　　　　NL 040011/70/7442
Microbiologisch onderzoek in vlees en vleeswaren naar mycotoxinen. **Microbiological investigation in meat and meat–products on mycotoxins.** Publications.

19231 Schuller, P.L.　　　　NL 040011/70/7471
Onderzoek naar het gehalte aan kwik, lood, cadmium en zink in varkens en rundernieren en in kippelevers en naar het gehalte aan koper, cobalt en kwik in schapelevers. **Investigation on the levels of mercury, lead, cadmium and zinc in porcine and bovine kidneys and in chicken livers and on the quantity of copper, cobalt and mercury in sheep bovine livers.** Publications.

19232 Schuller, P.L.　　　　NL 040011/70/7472
Onderzoek naar het gehalte aan arseen in varkens– en rundernieren en in kippelevers. **Investigation on the quantity of**

arsenic in porcine and bovine kidneys and in chicken livers. Publications.

19233 Kroes, R. NL 040011/71/7498
Ontwikkeling van diagnostische methoden voor detectie van anabole stoffen bij mestkalveren. **Development of diagnostic methods for detection of anabolic agents in fattening calves.** Publications.

19234 Kroes, R. NL 040011/71/7500
Onderzoek naar de toediening van oestrogenen aan mestkalveren. **Examination on the administration of oestrogens to fattening calves.** Publications.

19235 Ruitenberg, E.J. NL 040011/71/7506
Ontwikkeling van methoden voor bepaling van verboden weefsels in vleeswaren. **Development of methods for determination of forbidden tissues in meat products.**

19236 Schothorst, M. van; Schuller, P.L.; Rauws, A.G. NL 040011/73/7441
Ontwikkeling van detectiemethoden voor residuen van diergeneesmiddelen met een anti-biotische activiteit. **Development of detectionmethods of residues of animal drugs with an antibiotic activity.** Publications.

19237 Schothorst, M. van NL 040011/73/7443
Methodiekontwikkeling voor detectie van antibiotica-residuen t.b.v. de controle van geimporteerd vlees. **Development of a method for detection of antibiotic-residues for control of import-meat.**

19238 Stephany, R.W. NL 040011/73/7461
Kwalitatieve bepaling van diethylstilboestrol (DES) in diepgevroren runderlevers met behulp van dunnelaag chromatografie. **Qualitative determination of diethylstilboestrol (DES) in frozen cattle livers by means of the thin layer chromatography method.**

19239 Schuller, P.L. NL 040011/73/7463
De ontwikkeling van referentie preparaten door isolatie en zuivering van hormoonglucuroniden uit konijnen-urine t.b.v. onderzoek op het voorkomen van hormoonpreparaten bij slachtdieren. **Development of reference preparations by isolation and purification of hormone glucuronides from rabbit urine for detection of hormone preparations in slaughter animals.**

19240 Schuller, P.L.; Freudenthal, J. NL 040011/73/7464
Ontwikkeling van een methode van onderzoek voor de kwalitatieve en kwantitatieve bepaling van vluchtige N-nitrosaminen in vleeswaar, m.b.v. de combinatie gas chromatografie-massaspectrometrie. **Development of a detection method for the qualitative and quantitative determination of volatile N-nitrosamines in meat products by means of a combination gas chromatography mass spectrometry.** Publications.

19241 Kroes, R. NL 040011/73/7499
Detectiemogelijkheden en werkingsmechanisme van zowel oestrogene als andere anabool werkende stoffen in vlees en organen van slachtdieren (incl. import-vlees en veevoeder). **Detection methods and mode of action of both oestrogenic and other anabolic agents in meat and organs of slaughter animals (including import meat and animal feeds).** Publications.

19242 Logten, M.J. van NL 040011/73/7514
Stapeling van persistente bestrijdingsmiddelen in varkensvlees. **Accumulation of persisting pesticides in pig meat.** Publications.

19243 Kroes, R. NL 040011/74/7507
Onderzoek van mycotoxinen afkomstig van veevoeders en voedingsmiddelen van dierlijke oorsprong naar toxiciteit en mogelijke carcinogeniteit op levercellen in vitro. **Investigation of mycotoxins from animal feeds and feed products of animal origin on the toxicity and possible carcinogenity on liver cells in vitro.** Publications.

19244 Logten, M.J. van NL 040011/74/7521
Chronisch toxiciteitsonderzoek van geautoclaveerd en bestraald vlees bij ratten. **Chronic toxicity examination of autoclaved and irradiated meat in rats.**

19245 Schuller, P.L. NL 040011/75/6489
Bepaling van N-nitrosamines in vleeswaren. **Determination of N-nitrosamines in meat products.** Publications.

19246 Schothorst, M. van NL 040011/75/7447
Onderzoek naar de houdbaarheid van leverworst. **Investigation on the stability of liver-sausage.**

19247 Schuller, P.L.; Esch, G.J. van NL 040011/75/7467
De kwantitatieve bepaling van vijf verschillende vluchtige N-nitrosaminen in bestraalde hammonsters. **The quantitative determination of 5 different volatile N-nitrosamines in irridiated ham samples.**

19248 Schothorst, M. van; Schuller, P.L. NL 040011/76/7455
Onderzoek naar de vorming van mycotoxinen in vleeswaren. **Investigation on the formation of mycotoxins in meat products.**

19249 Schuller, P.L. NL 040011/76/7466
De invloed van opslagduur en opslagtemperatuur op terugwinning van sporen methylthiouracil (MTU) toegevoegd aan rundvlees en runderurine. **The effect of storage time and storage temperature on detection of spores of methylthiouracil (MTU) administered to cattle muscle and cattle urine.**

19250 Schuller, P.L. NL 040011/76/7470
Het stanaardiseren en ontwikkelen van methoden van onderzoek voor de chemische detectie van coccidiostatica residuen in pluimvee. **The standardization and development of detection methods for the chemical detection of coccidiostatica residues in chickens.**

19251 Schuller, P.L. NL 040011/76/7473
Dunnelaagchromatografisch onderzoek naar de aanwezigheid van methylthiouracil (MTU) in 30 monsters runderschildklier afkomstig uit Limburg, Noord-Brabant en België. **Thin layer chromatography investigation on the presence of methylthiouracil (MTU) in 30 samples of bovine thyroid from Limburg, North Brabant and Belgium.**

19252 Schuller, P.L. NL 040011/76/7479
Onderzoek naar het gehalte aan tin in nieren en levers van runderen en varkens en kippelevers. **Examination of the level of tin in kidneys and livers of cattle and pigs and in chicken livers.** Publications.

19253 Schuller, P.L. NL 040011/76/7483
Ontwikkeling van een methode van onderzoek voor de

bepaling van seleen in diervoeders en in organen van slachtdieren. **Development of a detection method for selene in animal feeds and in organs from slaughter animals.**

19254 Schuller, P.L. NL 040011/76/7484
De introductie van de Thermal Energy Analyzer (TEA) als specifieke detector voor het N–nitrosamine onderzoek in materiaal van dierlijke oorsprong. **Introduction of the Thermal Energy Analyzer (TEA) als specific detector of the N–nitrosamin investigation in material from animal origin.**

19255 Schuller, P.L. NL 040011/77/7482
Onderzoek naar het voorkomen van aflatoxine in dierlijke organen. **Investigation on the prevalence of aflatoxin in animal organs.**

19256 Moerman, P.C. NL 050301/67/1209
Het opheffen van bezwaren verbonden aan de produktie van gemeste beertjes. **Elimination of the difficulties connected with the production of meat from male pigs.** Publications.

19257 Moerman, P.C. NL 050301/72/6490
Onderzoek naar de spreiding in de samenstelling van door ambachtelijke bedrijven vervaardigde vleeswaren. **Quality evaluation of meat products prepared by the butchery trade.** Publications.

19258 Labots, H. NL 050301/74/5315
Invloed van de samenstelling van vleesprodukten op de thermoresistentie van Bacillus sporen. **Influence of the composition of meat products on the thermoresistance of Bacillus spores.** Publications.

19259 Olsman, W.J. NL 050301/75/6485
Methoden voor de bepaling van de maximale kerntemperatuur bij gepasteuriseerde hammen en schouders. **Method of determination of maximum centre temperature in pasteurized hams and shoulders.**

19260 Groenen, P.J. NL 050301/75/6489
Bepaling van N–nitrosamines in vleeswaren. **Determination of N–nitrosamines in meat products.** Publications.

19261 Moerman, P.C. NL 050301/76/6754
Macro– en micronutrienten in vlees en vleeswaren. **Macro– and micro–nutrients in meat and meat products.** Publications.

Fish and marine food products (B 6852)

See also 2148, 2284, 10417, 11418, 16720, 18825

19262 Hovart, P.; Deschacht, W.; Declerck, D.
BE 070800/60/0008 R
Onderzoek naar de kwaliteit van de afgewerkte visprodukten. **Research to the quality of the processed fishery products.** Publications.

19263 Antonacopoulos, N.; Reinacher, E.
DE 208040/70/4001
Standardisierung der Untersuchungsverfahren. **Standardization of test methods.**

19264 Antonacopoulos, N.; Reinacher, E.
DE 208040/70/4007 R
Untersuchungen über die Qualitätseigenschaften von Frischund Gefrierfisch sowie von Fischkonserven 1962. **Studies on qualitative properties of fresh meat and of frozen meat as well as of tinned fish.**

19265 Feldt, W.; Siebert, W.; Lauer, R. DE 208050/70/5001
Die radioaktive Kontamination von Wasser und Fisch. **Radioactive contamination of water and fish.**

19266 Harms, U. DE 208050/72/4005
Bestimmung des Gehaltes, der Anreicherung und der Verteilung von Spurenelementen – Schwermetallen – in Frisch– und Seewasserfischen. **Determination of concentration, accumulation and distribution of trace elements – heavy metals – in fresh and seawater fish.**

19267 Ehlermann, D. DE 211040/77/0005
Nachweis einer erfolgten Bestrahlung von Fisch. **Proof of irradiation of fish.**

19268 Mangold, H.K.; Kaiser, H.; Hudalla, B.
DE 213020/75/0017
Lipide im Fleisch von Fischen. **Lipids in the meat of fish.**

19269 Reusse, U.; Geister, R.; Hafke, A.
DE 505100/77/0001 N
Untersuchung zur Salmonellenabtötung in Fischmehl durch Propionsäure. **Investigation on killing Salmonella in fishmeal by propionic acid.**

19270 Collins, J.K.; Buckley, J.; Daly, C.; Horgan, V.;
Morrissey, P. IE 110102/79/9232 N
The development of fish marinades, a feasability study.

19271 Kerkhoff, M.A.T. NL 010702/59/7121
Onderzoek naar de invloed van waterverontreiniging op de gehalten aan organohalogeenverbindingen, minerale olie, geur en smaakstoffen in vis en schaal– en schelpdieren. **Investigation into the influence of water pollution on the content of organohalogene compounds, mineral oil, tainting and smelling compounds in fish and shellfish.** Publications.

19272 Kerkhoff, M.A.T. NL 010702/72/7128
Onderzoek naar de invloed van waterverontreiniging op de sanitaire kwaliteit van levende schaal– en schelpdieren. **Investigation into the influence of water pollution on the sanitary quality of living shellfish.** Publications.

19273 Kerkhoff, M.A.T. NL 010702/72/7129
Onderzoek naar de aanwezigheid van fytoplanktontoxinen in schelpdieren in verband met het voorkomen van giftige fytoplanktonsoorten. **Investigation into the presence of phytoplanktontoxins in shellfich in relation to the occurrence of toxic phytoplankton species.** Publications.

19274 Broek, M.J.M. van den NL 030008/77/7775 R
Vibrio parahaemolyticus. **Vibrio parahaemolyticus (seafoods, vibriosis).**

19275 Luten, J. NL 050303/78/2967 N
Onderzoek naar de invloed van vetzuren uit vis op de samenstelling en eigenschappen van het bloed van consumenten. **Research on the influence of fatty acids from fish on human blood composition and properties.**

19276 Luten, J. NL 050303/78/2969 N
Verbetering van methoden ter bepaling van spoorelementen in visserijprodukten en onderzoek naar het vóórkomen van deze

elementen. **Improvement of methods for assessment of trace elements in fish products and research on the occurrence of these elements.**

19277 Luten, J.   NL 050303/78/2970 N
Analyses van amines en amine–oxyden in vis in het kader van een onderzoek naar de mogelijkheid tot vorming van N–nitrosamines in levensmiddelen. **Analysis of amines and amine–oxydes in fish within the framework of an investigation into the possibilities of the formation of N–nitrosamines in food.**

19278 Oosterhuis, J.J.   NL 050303/78/2972 N
Sensorische beoordeling van visserijprodukten, mede in relatie tot de uitkomsten van objectieve analysemethoden, zoals de instrumentele meting van de textuur. **Sensorial assessment of fish products, also in relation to the results of objective methods of analysis such as the instrumental measurement of texture.**

19279 Doesburg, J.J.   NL 050303/78/2977 N
Onderzoek ten behoeve van de opstelling van normen voor visserijprodukten en desbetreffende "Codes of Practice" binnen het raam van de Codex Alimentarius. **Study of the suitability, or adaption of draft standards for fishery products and "Codes of Practice" within the framework of the Codex Alimentarius.**

19280 Houwing, H.   NL 050303/78/2978 N
Onderzoek voor aanpassing van het Visbesluit (Warenwet), uitvoeringsbesluiten van de Landbouwkwaliteitswet, inrichtingseisen voor visverwerkende bedrijven en overige maatregelen van kwaliteitsbeheer. **Study of possibilities for adapting the Fish Regulation (Netherlands Merchandise Act), execution resolutions of the Dutch Agricultural Quality Act, requirements and standards for fish processing plants and other regulations for quality management.**

19281 Luten, J.   NL 050303/78/2979 N
De vorming van bederfprodukten, in het bijzonder biogene aminen tijdens het bederf van vis. **Formation of spoilage products, especially biogenic amines, during the spoilage of fish.**

Dairy products, eggs, egg products, ice cream in general (B 6860)

See also 19132, 19133, 19134

19282 Werner, H.; Larsen, J.   DK 010300/78/0051 N
Mejeriprodukternes indhold af næringsstoffer. **The content of nutrients in dairy products.**

19283 Cheeseman; Barnett   GB 011705/00/0008 R
Measurement of milk quantity.

19284 McLarty   GB 060113/00/0001 R
Microbiology of milk.

19285 Cantoni, Carlo; Caserio, Giuseppe; D'Aubert, Simona; Dragoni, Ivan   IT 040633/76/0002
Azione degli u.v. sulla flora batterica del latte. **U.v. effect on the normal flora of milk.**

Milk products (B 6861)

See also 10741, 11084, 12103, 14152, 16231, 16257, 16765, 16845, 16869, 16886, 16890, 16891, 18831, 19161, 19163, 19190,

19217, 19243, 19439, 19555, 19661

19286 De Moor, H.   BE 030025/76/0011 R
Bereiding en eigenschappen van slagroom. **Manufacture and properties of whipped cream.**

19287 Bossuyt, R.; Naudts, M.; Waes, G.   BE 070900/70/0010
De bepaling van de bakteriologische kwaliteit van diepgekoelde melk. **Determination of the bacteriological quality of refrigerated milk.** Publications.

19288 Bossuyt, R.   BE 070900/70/0033
De waardebepaling van de melk. **Determination of the value of milk.**

19289 Van Renterghem, R.; Devlaminck, L.
                    BE 070900/75/0025 R
Zware metalen in melk en zuivelprodukten. **Heavy metals in milk and dairy products.**

19290 Van Renterghem, R.; Devlaminck, L.
                    BE 070900/75/0026 R
De kontaminatie van melk enzuivelprodukten door pesticiden. **Pesticides contamination of milk and dairy products.** Publications.

19291 Van Renterghem, R.; Devlaminck, L.
                    BE 070900/77/0034
Gepolychloreerde biphenylverbindingen in melk en zuivelprodukten. **Polychlorinated biphenyls in milk and dairy products.** Publications.

19292 De Vilder, J.   BE 070900/79/0044 N
Het opsporen van weipoeder in melkpoeder. **The detection of whey powder in milk powder.**

19293 Delbeke, R.; NAudts, M.   BE 070900/79/0045 N
Na – en zoutarme drinkmelk. **The manufacturing of modified milk drinks. Na and salt deficient milk.**

19294 Mottar, J.; Naudts, M.   BE 070900/79/0046 N
Gemodificeerde melkdrank (cichorei). **Chicory flavoured milk.**

19295 Van Reusel, R.   BE 080500/77/0009 R
Problèmes de calibration de l'appareil Milk–Scan pour la détermination de la matière grasse, des protéines et du lactose. **Calibration problems of the milko–scan apparatus in fat, protein and lactose determinations.**

19296 Renner, E.; Schöny, A.   DE 129252/77/0004
Untersuchungen zur Standardisierung einer Eiweissbestimmungsmethode für Milch. **Investigations on the standardization of a method for the protein determination in milk.**

19297 Renner, E.; Öztek, L.   DE 129252/78/0001 N
Aromasubstanzen in türkischen Käsesorten. **Aromatic compounds in Turkish cheese varieties.**

19298 Kielwein, G.; Melling, H.   DE 129701/75/0002
Die Übersäuerung von Sauermilcherzeugnissen. **Hyperacidity of fermented milk products.**

19299 Kielwein, G.   DE 129701/75/0004
Untersuchungen zum Vorkommen, zur Differenzierung und

zur milchhygienischen Bedeutung von Enterokokken. **Investigations into occurrence, differentiation and importance of Enterococci in milk.**

19300 Kielwein, G.   DE 129701/75/0007
Untersuchungen zum enzymatischen Abbau der Milchproteine durch Bakterien. **Proteolysis of milk protein by bacteria.** Publications.

19301 Kruse, E.; Wiesner, H.–U.   DE 139650/78/0003 N
Einfluss von Bacillus cereus auf die Haltbarkeit kontaminationsfrei abgefüllter kurzzeiterhitzter Milch. **Influence of Bacillus cereus on stability of contamination–free bottled short–time heated milk.** Publications.

19302 Terplan, G.; Bierl, J.; Grove, H.–H.
          DE 160731/75/0017
Technologische Bedeutung des Pyruvates in der Rohmilch. **Technological significance of pyruvate in raw milk.**

19303 Grove, H.–H.; Hartel, G.   DE 160731/77/0007
Bedeutung des Pyruvatgehalts der Bestandsmilch als Indikator für die Produktionshygiene des Milcherzeugerbetriebes. **The pyruvate content of bulk milk as an indicator for the production hygiene in dairy farms.**

19304 Guthy, K.   DE 161340/75/0002
Untersuchungen zur Gerinnung von Milch und Milch–Produkten. **Investigations on coagulation of milk and milk products.**

19305 Kiermeier, F.; Miller, M.   DE 161340/77/0001
Aflatoxine in Milch und Milchprodukten. **Aflatoxins in milk and milk products.**

19306 Kessler, H.G.; Horak, P.   DE 161350/78/0002 N
Ermittlung des Abtöteverhaltens 'Q10–Werte' ausgewählter Mikroorganismen aus der Rohmilchflora. **Determination of the inactivation–characteristics of selected microorganisms in raw milk.**

19307 Bergner, K.–G.; Matthiessen, E.; Hermann, A.
          DE 170050/78/0001 N
Einwirkung von Luftsauerstoff auf Milch. **Effect of air oxygen of milk.**

19308 Kaufmann, W.; Hagemeister, H.   DE 207010/77/0008
Butterqualität. **Quality of butter.**

19309 Gravert, H.O.; Pabst, K.   DE 207010/77/0009 N
Milcheiweiss. **Milk protein.**

19310 Heeschen, W.; Suhren, G.; Tolle, A.
          DE 207020/72/5009 N
Zur Eignung des Pyruvatgehaltes dis Analogparameter der bakteriologischen Beschaffenheit der Milch unter Praxisbedingungen. **Pyruvate pool as an analogous parameter of bacteriological quality of milk under practical conditions.**

19311 Suhren, G.; Heeschen, W.; Tolle, A.
          DE 207020/74/0007
Beziehung zwischen Pyruvatgehalt und Verderbnisrisiko von Milch. **Correlation between pyruvate content and spoilage risk of milk.**

19312 Blüthgen, A.; Heeschen, W.; Tolle, A.

19313 Blüthgen, A.; Heeschen, W.   DE 207020/74/0008
Tierexperimentelle Untersuchungen zum Verhalten von PCB's und HCB in der Nahrungskette PflanzeMilchtier–Milch–Mensch. **Experiments with laboratory animals to study the behaviour of PCBs and HCB in the food chain plant–dairy animals–milk–man.**

19313 Blüthgen, A.; Heeschen, W.   DE 207020/74/0011
Biozide und Umweltchemikalien in Säuglingsnahrungsmitteln – Humanmilch – und in Gewebeproben von Säuglingen und Kleinkindern. **Biocides and environmental chemicals in baby food –esp. human milk– and in tissue samples of babies and infants.**

19314 Heeschen, W.   DE 207020/77/0001
Einrichtung eines Referenz– und Zentrallabors für Standardisierungszwecke: Entwicklung eines Leukozytenstandards zur Zählung somatischer Zellen in der Milch. **Establishment of a reference central laboratory for standardization: development of a leucocyte standard for counting somatic cells in milk.**

19315 Heeschen, W.; Suhren, G.; Tolle, A.
          DE 207020/77/0004
Untersuchungen zur hygienischen Wertigkeit ultrahocherhitzter und sterilisierter Milch unter besonderer Berücksichtigung des zur Herstellung verwandten Rohstoffes. **Investigations on hygienic value of UHT–sterilized milk with special regard to raw material used for preparation.**

19316 Heeschen, W.; Blüthgen, A.; Tolle, A.
          DE 207020/77/0005
Untersuchung zum mikrobiologischen Um– und Abbau chlorierter Kohlenwasserstoffe – insbesondere HCH–Isomere –. **Investigations on microbiological transformation and breakdown of chlorinated hydrocarbons – esp. HCH–isomers –.**

19317 Heeschen, W.; Blüthgen, A.; Tolle, A.
          DE 207020/77/0007
Nachweis, Vorkommen und lebensmittelhygienische Bedeutung chlorierter Insektizide in Milch und Milchprodukten. **Proof, occurrence and food hygienic importance of chlorinated insecticides in milk and milk products.**

19318 Hahn, G.; Tolle, A.   DE 207020/77/0008
Untersuchung zur gesundheitlichen und lebensmittelhygienischen Bedeutung von Pseudomonas aeruginosa in Milch. **Investigations on sanitarian and food hygienic importance of Pseudomonas aeruginosa in milk.**

19319 Heeschen, W.   DE 207020/78/0001 N
Untersuchungen zur hygienischen Beschaffenheit von Roh– und Trinkmilch – bakteriologische Beschaffenheit, somatische Zellen, Problempestizide. **Investigations of the hygienic quality of raw milk and milk for consumption –bacteriological status, somatic cells, problematic pesticides–.**

19320 Tolle, A.; Hahn, G.; Suhren, G.
          DE 207020/78/0002 N
Untersuchungen zur quantitativen und qualitativen hygienisch–bakteriologischen Beschaffenheit von Milchprodukten 'Produkt–Hygiene–Monitor'. **Investigations on the quantitative and qualitative hygienic–bacteriological quality of milk products – product–hygiene–monitor –.**

19321 Heeschen, W.; Nijhuis, H. DE 207020/78/0003 N
Situationsanalyse und Bewertung der Nitrat–Nitrit–Gehalte in Rohmilch, Trinkmilch und Frischkäse unter besonderer Berücksichtigung belastender Einflüsse wie Wasserversorgung und Fütterung. **Analysis of situation and evaluation of nitrate–nitrite–contents in raw milk, milk for consumption and fresh cheese with special regard to certain influences as water supply and feeding.**

19322 Heeschen, W.; Blüthgen, A. DE 207020/78/0005 N
Vorkommen und Bewertung von Aflatoxin M in der Trinkmilch in der Bundesrepublik Deutschland. **Presence and valuation of aflatoxin M in milk for consumption in the Federal Republic of Germany.**

19323 Thomasow, J.; Klostermeyer, H. DE 207040/77/0002
Entwicklung von Methoden zur Bestimmung von Qualitätskriterien bei Milch und Milchprodukten. **Development of methods for determination of qualitative criteria in milk and milk products.**

19324 Thomasow, J.; Klostermeyer, H. DE 207040/77/0003
Entwicklung von Kriterien zur Aufstellung von Qualitätsstandards bei Milch und Milchprodukten. **Development of criteria for establishment of qualitative standards in milk and milk products.**

19325 Timmen, H. DE 207040/77/0004
Qualität und Haltbarkeit von Milchfetterzeugnissen. **Quality and shelf–life of milk fat products.**

19326 Samhammer, E.; Buchheim, W. DE 207050/72/4004
Untersuchung physikalischer Eigenschaften getrockneter Milcherzeugnisse im Hinblick auf die Qualität. **Studies on physical properties of milk powder regarding quality.**

19327 Buchheim, W.; Knoop, A.–M.; Knoop, E. DE 207050/77/0003
Untersuchung physikalischer Eigenschaften von Milchproteinen. **Investigations on physical characteristics of milk proteins.**

19328 Knoop, A.–M.; Buchheim, W.; Knoop, E. DE 207050/77/0004
Untersuchungen physikalischer Eigenschaften von Käse und Käseerzeugnissen im Hinblick auf die Qualität. **Investigations on physical characteristics of cheese and cheese products regarding the quality.**

19329 Wiechen, A.; Heine, K. DE 207050/77/0006
Entwicklung und Anwendung von neutronenaktivierungsanalytischen Methoden für Untersuchungen über die Spurenelementverschiebung in Milch und Milchprodukten als Folge von Umwelteinflüssen. **Development and use of methods analyzing the activation of neutrons for investigations on shifting of trace elements in milk and milk products in consequence of environmental conditions affected.**

19330 Knoop, E.; Samhammer, E. DE 207050/77/0009
Erarbeitung von Normen für physikalische Stoffeigenschaften von Milchprodukten. **Development of standards for physical characteristics in milk products.**

19331 Knoop, E.; Buchheim, W.; Finger, H.; Samhammer, E.; Knoop, A.–M.; Precht, D. DE 207050/77/0011

Weiterentwicklung physikalischer Mess– und Untersuchungsmethoden für Milchprodukte und Milchinhaltsstoffe. **Further development of methods for measuring and analyzing milk products and milk constituents.**

19332 Busse, M.; Grillenberger, G.; Ellner, R.; El–Tobgui, H. DE 502551/77/0002
Forschungsvorhaben 'Emmentalerqualität'. **Research project of Swiss cheese quality.**

19333 Busse, M.; Wallner, U.; Kotzekidou, P.; Kleinmann, V.; Degle, I. DE 502551/78/0001 N
Weichkäsequalität. **Quality of soft cheese.**

19334 Schleifer, K.–H.; Seiler, H. DE 502551/78/0002 N
Taxonomie und Diagnostik der coryneformen Bakterien. Entwicklung und Anwendung eines diagnostischen Bestimmungsschlüssels. **Taxonomy and identification of coryneform bacteria. Development and application of a diagnostic identification code.**

19335 Kirchmeier, O. DE 502553/77/0004
Kennzeichnung der spezifischen Zustandsform von Schmelzkäsen. **Studies on the specific state of processed cheese.**

19336 Id, D.; Schaal, E. DE 508454/78/0001 N
Zur Mikrobiologie der ultrahocherhitzten Milch. **On microbiology of UHT milk.**

19337 Werner, H. DK 010300/73/0501
Undersøgelse af indhold af tungmetaller i mejeriprodukter. **Investigation of the content of heavy metals in dairy products.**

19338 Mortensen, B.K. DK 010300/76/0012
Smørfedtets sammensætning og egenskaber og indflydelse heraf på smørrets konsistens. **The composition and properties of butter fat and its influence on the consistency of butter.**

19339 Mortensen, B.K. DK 010300/76/0014
Undersøgelse af bakterievækst i forskellige smørtyper. **An investigation of bacterial growth in different types of butter.**

19340 Poulsen, P.R. DK 010300/76/0031
Undersøgelser over emulsionsstabiliteten i flødeprodukter. **Investigations into the emulsion stability of cream products.**

19341 Poulsen, P.R. DK 010300/76/0036
Frysepunktsbestemmelse i mælk. **Freezing point determination in milk.**

19342 Poulsen, P.R. DK 010300/76/0037
Undersøgelser over syrnede konsummælksprodukters strukturelle opbygning og konsistensegenskaber. **Investigations of the structural conformation and properties of acidified consumer milk products.**

19343 Poulsen, P.R. DK 010300/76/0038
Syringsforløbets indflydelse på yoghurtens konsistensegenskaber. **The effect of acidification on the consistency of yoghurt and its properties.**

19344 Werner, H. DK 010300/76/0051
Undersøgelse af indhold af nitrat og nitrit i mejeriprodukter. **An investigation of the nitrate and nitrite content of dairy products.**

19345 Mortensen, B.K. DK 010300/77/0012
Undersøgelse af smag og aroma i mildt syrnet smør. **An investigation of taste and aroma in mildly soured butter.**

19346 Mortensen, B.K. DK 010300/77/0013
Målemetoder til vurdering af smørrets konsistens. **Methods used to estimate the consistency of butter.**

19347 Birkkjær, H.E. DK 010300/77/0023
Fremstilling og indsamling af forskellige danske oste til bestemmelse af nitrat, nitrit og nitrosaminer. **The manufacture and collection of Danish cheeses to determine their nitrate, nitrite and nitrosamine content.**

19348 Jensen, G.K. DK 010300/77/0043
Undersøgelser til belysning af variationer i mælkeprodukters næringsindhold. **Investigations to illustrate the variations in the nutrient value of milk products.**

19349 Jensen, G.K. DK 010300/77/0044
Karakterisering af proteinfraktionerne i mælkepulverprodukter – kvalitativt og kvantitativt. **The qualitative and quantitative characterization of the protein fractions found in milk powder products.**

19350 Werner, H. DK 010300/77/0051
Undersøgelse vedr. dannelse og forekomst af nitrosaminer i ost. **An investigation of the formation and occurence of nitrosamines in cheese.**

19351 Werner, H. DK 010300/77/0052
Undersøgelse af mælkeproteiners sammensætning og egenskaber. **An investigation of the composition and characteristics of milk proteins.**

19352 Werner, H. DK 010300/77/0053
Undersøgelse af konsummælksprodukters mineralsammensætning. **An investigation into the mineral composition of consumer milk products.**

19353 Mortensen, B.K. DK 010300/78/0011
Undersøgelser af fodermidlers indflydelse på smørfedtets sammensætning og på smørrets kvalitet (Rapskager). **Investigations of the influence of feedstuffs on the fat composition and quality of butter.**

19354 Mortensen, B.K.; Danmark, H. DK 010300/78/0013 N
Smørrets holdbarhed i relation til pakningsstørrelsen. **Keeping quality of butter in relation to package size.**

19355 Masson, C.; Rousseaux, P.; Decaen, C. FR 011013/74/6566 N
Qualité des fromages de Comté en fonction des conditions de production et de traitement du lait. **Quality of Comte cheese in relation with the conditions of production and milk treatment.**

19356 Sylvander, B.; Persuy, P.; Lassaut, B.; Picard, S. FR 012205/76/8646 N
Consommation et qualités alimentaires : le cas de l'emmenthal. **Food consumption and quality : emmenthal cheese case.**

19357 Lyster; Wong GB 011703/79/0028 N
Measurement of functional properties of milk proteins.

19358 Johnston GB 040404/79/0009 N
Seasonal variations in butter composition of relevance to spreadability.

19359 Connolly, J.F. IE 060400/00/1454 N
Nutritional aspects of dairy products. Publications.

19360 Connolly, J.F. IE 060400/68/2007 R
Quantification and identification of off–flavour components in susceptible milks and resultant dairy products. Publications.

19361 O'Connor, F. IE 060400/71/2009 R
Evaluation of new methods for milk quality. Publications.

19362 Phelan, J.A.; O'Keeffe, A. IE 060400/71/2020 R
Rate of maturation of cheddar cheese. Publications.

19363 Phelan, J.A. IE 060400/75/1112 R
Low calorie cheese and spreads. Publications.

19364 Cogan, T.; O'Connor, F. IE 060400/76/1118 R
Determination of significance of heat stable psychmotrophic bacterial enzymes in milk and dairy products. Publications.

19365 Fox, P.F.; Finn, N.; Costello, M. IE 110101/79/9185 N
Modification of the functional properties of milk proteins through the plastein reaction.

19366 Fox, P.F.; Daly, C.; Godhino, M. IE 110101/79/9186 N
Factors influencing the ripening of blue cheese.

19367 Doonan, S.; Fox, P.F.; Greer, N. IE 110101/79/9188 N
Determination of the primary sequence of milk lipase.

19368 Daly, C.; O'Gara, F.; O'Brien, M.; Herlihy, M.; Fitzgerald, G.; Kiely, G. IE 110102/78/9144 N
Provision of an improved starter culture system for fermented milk products by biochemical and genetic studies of lactic streptococci and their bacteriophages. Publications.

19369 Synnott, E.C.; Mansfield, E. IE 110106/77/9145 N
Dielectric properties of butter and its variation with moisture and salt content, season, frequency and temperature.

19370 Doonan, S.; Fox, P.F.; Greer, S.M. IE 110203/79/9183 N
Studies on the structures and activities of lipases from mil k.

19371 McNulty, P.B.; Gibney, M. IE 120301/77/9059 N
Coagulation properties of milk and milk replacers. Publications.

19372 Donnelly, W.; Headon, D.; Barry, J.G. IE 130102/77/9159 N
The quantitative analysis of individual caseins. Publications.

19373 Toppino, P.M.; Pasca Raymondo, M.; Aliano, N. IT 022200/78/0001
Contenuto di colesterolo nel formaggio grana. **Cholosterol content in grana cheese.**

19374 Emaldi, G.C.; Pasca Raymondo, M.; Papetti, G. IT 022200/78/0008
Formaggi da grattugia con titolo di grasso superiore a quello normale. **Cheese for grating with high fat content.**

19375 Vitagliano, M. IT 040107/73/0955
Le caratteristiche di qualità dei formaggi a pasta filata. **Quality**

characteristics of semi–hard cheeses. Publications.

19376 Losi, G.   IT 040240/77/0218 R
Determinazione del contenuto in piombo nel formaggio
parmigiano reggiano prodotto in alcune zone del comprensorio
di produzione a alta concentrazione industriale. **Determination
of the lead contents in Parmesan cheese produced in certain
zones included in an area of high industrial concentration.**

19377 Losi, G.   IT 040240/77/1068 N
Determinazione del contenuto in piombo nel burro prodotto in
alcune zone ad alta concentrazione industriale. **Assessment of
the lead content of butter produced in certain heavily
industrialized areas.**

19378 Ruffini Castrovilli, C.M.   IT 040602/78/1103 N
Ricerche sperimentali sull'eventuale passaggio nel latte delle
prostaglandine iniettate a bovine per la sincronizzazione degli
estri. **Experimental research on the eventual presence in cow
milk of prostaglandines injected to the animals to secure the
synchronisation of their oestrum.**

19379 Cantoni, Carlo; Caserio, Giuseppe; D'Aubert, Simona;
Dragoni, Ivan   IT 040633/76/0001
Azione degli u.v. sui germi patogeni nel latte. **U.v. effect on the
pathogenic bacteria in milk.**

19380 Mincione, B.   IT 040711/77/0242 R
Ricerche sul latte di bufala, studi sulla struttura primaria e sulle
frazioni sedimentabile e solubile delle caseine. **Research on
buffalo–cow's milk, studies on the primary structure and on the
sedimentary and soluble fractions of caseins.**

19381 Rania, U.; Bordi, B.; Izzi, R.; Vecchione, G.
                                IT 051000/78/0003 N
Indagini sulle caratteristiche igienico–sanitarie del latte
prodotto nella provincia di Napoli. **Research on the hygienic
sanitary features of milk produced in the province of Naples.**

19382 Albonico, F.   IT 062600/77/0885
Composizione e fattori tossici di latti di diversa specie e di loro
derivanti. **Composition and toxic factors of different milks and
of their derivates.**

19383 Kommerij, R.   NL 010208/79/8775 N
Onderzoek naar residuen van genees– en bestrijdingsmiddelen
in melk en vlees. **Research into residua of medicines and
pesticides in milk and meat.**

19384 Schipper, C.J.; Dijkman, A.J.; Vries, Tj.de; Brouwer,
J.; Zandstra, T.   NL 010213/66/3376
Onderzoek naar methoden en normen voor het vaststellen en
het beoordelen van de kwaliteit van boerderijmelk. **Research
to methods and standards for determination and judging of
farmmilk quality.** Publications.

19385 Schothorst, M. van; Schuller, P.L.   NL 040011/76/7456
Onderzoek naar de vorming van mycotoxinen in kaas.
Investigation on the formation of mycotoxins in cheese.

19386 Schuller, P.L.   NL 040011/76/7476
De aanwezigheid van nitrosoverbindingen, waaronder
N–nitrosaminen in Nederlandse kaas. **The presence of
nitroso–compounds including N–nitrosamines in Dutch cheese.**

19387 Schuller, P.L.   NL 040011/76/7477

Het vóórkomen van aflatoxine M_1 in babyvoedingsmiddelen
bereid op basis van melkprodukten. **The prevalence of aflatoxin
M_1 in baby foods prepared from milk products.**

19388 Schuller, P.L.   NL 040011/76/7478
Het vóórkomen van aflatoxine M_1 in Nederlandse
consumptiekaas. **The prevalence of aflatoxin M_1 in dutch
consumption cheese.**

19389 Schuller, P.L.   NL 040011/76/7480
Het ontwikkelen van een methode van onderzoek voor het
bevestigen van de aanwezigheid van aflatoxine M_1 in melk,
melkprodukten en dierlijke weefsels op de dunnelaagplaat.
**The development of a detection method for the confirmation
of the presence of aflatoxin M_1 in milk, milk products and
animal tissues on the thin layer plate.**

19390 Schuller, P.L.   NL 040011/76/7487
Onderzoek naar de aanwezigheid van vluchtige
N–nitrosamines in Nederlandse exportkaas. **Investigation on
the prevalence of volatile N–nitrosamines in dutch export
cheese.**

19391 Schuller, P.L.   NL 040011/77/7485
Het ontwikkelen van een dunnelaagchromatografische
methode van onderzoek voor het bepalen van aflatoxine M_1 in
babyvoedingsmiddelen. **Development of a thin layer
chromatography method of investigation for determination of
aflatoxin M_1 in baby foods.**

19392 Duin, H. van   NL 060002/70/3991
Identificatie en vorming van geur en smaakstoffen in kaas en
kaas–poeder. **Identification and formation of aromatic
constituents in cheese and cheesepowder.** Publications.

19393 Badings, H.T.   NL 060002/71/3990
Identificatie van geur– en smaakstoffen in melk. **Identification
of aroma constituents of milk and milkpowder.** Publications.

19394 Veringa, H.A.   NL 060002/73/4024
Het aantonen van mycotoxinen in melk en zuivelprodukten.
Determination of mycotoxins in milk and dairy products.
Publications.

19395 Stadhouders, J.   NL 060002/74/5286
Het aantonen van antibiotica in melk. **Detection of antibiotics
in milk.** Publications.

19396 Driessen, F.M.   NL 060002/77/7249
Invloed van melkprotease en bacterieel protease op smaak en
consistentie van UHT produkten. **Influence of milk protease
and bacterial protease upon taste and consistency of UHT
products.** Publications.

19397 Nieuwenhof, F.F.J.   NL 060002/78/7921
Invloed van lactobacilli op de kwaliteit van kaas. **The influence
of lactobacilli on the quality of cheese.**

19398 Koops, J.   NL 060002/79/8677 N
Evaluatie van chemische analysetechnieken voor de
zuivelindustrie. **Evaluation of chemical methods of analysis for
the dairy industry.**

19399 Stadhouders, J.   NL 060002/79/8681 N
Evaluatie van microbiologische analysetechnieken voor
zuivelprodukten. **Evaluation of microbiological methods of**

analysis for the dairy industry.

19400 Langeveld, L.P.M. NL 060002/79/8687 N
Voorkomen van pathogene bacteriën in UHT–produkten.
Presence of pathogenic bacteria in UHT–Products.

19401 Berg, G. van den NL 060002/79/8695 N
De oorzaken van het optreden van ribessmaak bij kaas, anders
dan door verfbestanddelen. **The catty flavour defect in cheese;
other causes than paint constituents.**

Eggs and egg products (B 6862)

See also 11281, 12594, 13875, 18822, 19056, 19163, 19164,
19169

19402 Ehinger, F. DE 144685/78/0002 N
Schalenstabilität von Eiern. **Shell stability of eggs.**
Publications.

19403 Krieg, R. DE 201300/78/0006 N
Beeinflussung der inneren Eiqualität – unter Berücksichtigung
des Aminosäuren– und Fettsäuremusters – durch die
Fütterung. **Influence of the feed on inner egg quality – with
regard to the amino acid and fatty acid content.**

19404 Partmann, W.; Bomar, M.T.; Wedler, A.
DE 211010/78/0003 N
Untersuchungen zur Haltbarkeit von hartgekochten Eiern.
Investigations on the storage stability of hard–boiled eggs.

19405 Simons, P.C.M.; Beuving, G.; Teunis, G.P.; Japing,
H.M. NL 010109/72/7729
De kwaliteit van consumptieeieren. **Quality of consumption
eggs.** Publications.

Other dairy products (B 6869)

See also 19289

19406 Martens, R.; Naudts, M.; Paelinck, H.
BE 070900/75/0027 R
De bereiding van nieuwe kaassoorten. **The fabrication of new
types of cheese.**

Other foods (B 6870)

See also 7928

19407 Jork, H.; Untersteller, G. DE 167102/77/0001
Die Isolierung und quantitative Bestimmung von Piperin in
verschiedenen Pfeffer–Provenienzen. **Isolation and
quantitative determination of piperine in divers proveniences of
pepper.**

19408 Jork, H.; Merten, D. DE 167102/77/0002
Isolierung und quantitative Bestimmung von Flavonglykosiden
in Potentilla tormentilla–Rhizomen. **Isolation and quantitative
determination of flavonic glycosides in Potentilla tormentilla
rhizomes.**

19409 Teuber, M. DE 207030/77/0001
Ernährungsphysiologische Eigenschaften von
Einzeller–Proteinen. **Nutritional properties of single–cell
proteins.**

19410 Dronne, Y. FR 012205/75/8556
Les protéines nouvelles en alimentation humaine. **New
proteins in human foods.**

19411 Spadoni, M.A. IT 011300/77/0765
Valore nutrizionale di nuove preparazioni proteiche animali e
vegetali. **Nutritional value of new protein foods of animal and
vegetal origin.**

19412 Paglialunga, S. IT 012300/77/0756
Contributo allo studio tossicologico di nuove fonti proteiche.
**Contribution to the toxicological study of new sources of
proteins.**

19413 Scolastico, C. IT 040604/77/0764
Composizione chimica delle biomasse, acidi nucleici,
aminoacidi e proteine, vitamine. **The chemical composition of
biomasses, nucleic acids, aminoacids and proteins, vitamins.**

19414 Albonico, F. IT 040609/77/0729
Composizione e requisiti funzionali di proteine estratte da
favino vicia faba minor–. **Composition and functional
properties of proteins extracted from vicia faba minor.**

19415 Fidanza, F. IT 041027/77/0741
Valutazione della qualità nutrizionale di proteine da
leguminose, semi oleaginosi, foglie, pollame e formulati.
**Evaluation of the nutritional quality of pulse proteins and of
proteins extracted from oil–seeds, leaves, poultry and
formulations.**

19416 Ko Swan Djien. NL 020031/75/6799
Enige factoren die de toxine–vorming door Pseudomonas
cocovenenans in témpé bongkrèk beinvloeden. **Influence of
some factors on the production of toxins by P. cocovenenans in
témpé–bongkrèk.**

Drinking water (B 6880)

See also 18934

19417 Schweisfurth, R.; Bumb, F. DE 167150/77/0002
Crenothrix polyspora – ihre Massenvermehrung in
Trinkwasserversorgungsanlagen – ökologische, systematische
und morphologische Untersuchungen. **Crenothrix polyspora –
their propagation in drinking–waterwells – ecology, systematics
and morphology.**

19418 Researcher not indicated DE 502650/78/0010 N
Toxizität wassergefährdender Stoffe Ringtest zur Absicherung
der von ROBRA – Ruhrverband – entwickelten Methode.
**Toxicity of water endangering substances. Ring test for
ensuring the method developed by ROBRA – Ruhrverband –.**

19419 Hebert, J. FR 012503/73/6163
Modification de la teneur en azote nitrique des eaux potables
dans le périmètre de l'Agence de Bassin Artois–Picardie.
**Changes in the nitrate–N content of the drinking waters of the
area of the Artois–Picardie Basin Agency.**

Alcoholic liquors, coffee, tea, tobacco and other table luxuries (B 6890)

See also 4396, 7928, 17022, 17023, 18818, 19109, 19110

19420 Baltes, W.; Herrmann, G. DE 105900/78/0004 N

Isolierung und Zuordnung flüchtiger Kaffeeröststoffe. **Isolation and coordination of volatile roast–compounds of coffee.**

19421 Baltes, W.; Kemper, K.   DE 105900/78/0006 N
Versuche zur Isolierung und Konstitutionsaufklärung von braunen Kaffeeröststoffen. **Experiments for the isolation and the structural instruction of brown roast–compounds of coffee.**

19422 Pfeilsticker, K.; Leyendecker, A.
                    DE 111600/78/0004 N
Die Metabolisierung von Äthylenoxid in Kakaopulver. **The metabolising of ethyleneoxide in cocoa powder.** Publications.

19423 Maier, H.G.; Ollroge, I.   DE 114100/75/0003
Nachweis und Bestimmung von Zuckern in Kaffee–Extrakten. **Detection and determination of sugars in coffee extracts.**

19424 Bächmann, K.; Zielkowski, R.   DE 117050/74/0001
Charakterisierung von Weinen durch Patternanalyse der Spurenelemente. **Characterization of wines by pattern analysis of the trace elements.** Publications.

19425 Rapp, A.; Knipser, W.; Heimann, W.
                    DE 145100/78/0002 N
Biogenese von Aromastoffen in speziellen Rebsorten. **Biogenesis of flavorcompounds in special vine–species.**

19426 Mändl, B.; Müller, K.; Piendl, A.   DE 161770/75/0002
Vorkommen und physiologische Bedeutung der B–Vitamine in Bier. **Occurrence and physiological importance of B–vitamins in beer.**

19427 Piendl, A.; Bohmann, H.   DE 161770/77/0001
Geschmacksstabilität des Bieres. **Flavor stability of beer.**

19428 Piendl, A.; Westner, H.   DE 161770/77/0002
Hochdruck–Flüssigkeitschromatographie in der Brauereianalytik. **High pressure–liquid–chromatography in brewing analysis.**

19429 Narziss, L.; Graf, H.   DE 161790/77/0001
Carbonyle und Bierqualität – ein Beitrag zur Geschmacksstabilität des Bieres. **Carbonyles and beer quality – a contribution to flavor stability of beer.**

19430 Bergner, K.–G.; Petrich, H.   DE 170050/75/0002
Nachweis und Verhalten einiger Pesticide in Wein. **Identification and behaviour of some pesticides in wine.**

19431 Rapp, A.; Hastrich, H.   DE 204000/71/4033
Untersuchungen über die Aromastoffe des Mostes und des Weines. **Studies on quality–determinant components of must and wine.**

19432 Fischer, E.   DE 211030/77/0003
Untersuchungen über das Verhalten von Dithiocarbamaten in Tabak. **Studies on behaviour of dithiocarbamates in tobacco.**

19433 Wucherpfennig, K.; Kettern, W.   DE 506104/73/0003
Senkung des Gehaltes an gebundener schwefliger Säure von Weinen mit Hilfe der Elektrodialyse. **Reduction of sulphurous acid content in wine by electrodialysis.**

19434 Wucherpfennig, K.; Danvirutai, P.
                    DE 506104/78/0001 N

Übergang von siliciumhaltigen Verbindungen von Filterhilfsmitteln in Wein und Obstsaft. **Transfer of silicium–containing compounds of filtrating media into wine and fruit–juice.**

19435 Sponholz, W.R.   DE 506105/73/0002
Organische Säuren und Aldehyde in Mosten und Weinen. **Organic acid and aldehydes in musts and wines.**

19436 Sponholz, W.R.; Dittrich, H.H.   DE 506105/77/0002
Charakterisierung verdorbener Weine durch typische Metaboliten bestimmter Bakterien. **Characterisation of spoiled wines by typical metabolites of special bacteria.**

19437 Boeck, D.   DE 909000/78/0001 N
Bestimmung von Nucleosiden und Nucleobasen in Würze und Bier. **Determination of nucleosides and nucleobases in wort and beer.**

19438 Ziegleder, G.   DE 911000/78/0001 N
Analytische Erfassung der Kakao–Röstbegleitstoffe im Überröstbereich. **Analysis of substances related to roasted cocoa in overroasting phase.**

19439 Ziegleder, G.   DE 911000/78/0003 N
Bedeutung einzelner Milchbestandteile in Schokolademassen für Verarbeitungsvorgänge und Lagerverhalten. **Importance of single milk constituents in chocolate masses to processing and storage.**

19440 Sapis, J.C.   FR 010714/70/2227
Recherche et identification des substances combinant l'anhydride sulfureux dans les vins. **Research and identification of sulfurdioxide complexes in wines.** Publications.

19441 Jouret, C.; Puech, J.L.   FR 011402/69/2240
Substances participant à l'arôme des armaqnacs et des rhums. **Armagnac brandy and rum aroma compounds.** Publications.

19442 Garofolo, A.; Piracci, A.; Spera, G.   IT 022000/75/0016
Indagine analitica sui vini a D.O.C. dei Castelli Romani: Frascati, Marino e Velletri. **Analytical research on D.O.C. wines of Castelli Romani.**

19443 Usseglio–Tomasset, L.; Di Stefano, R.; Delfini, C.
                    IT 022000/77/0009
Studio sul vino Recioto della Valpolicella. **A research on the "Recioto della Valpolicella" wine.**

19444 Usseglio–Tomasset, L.; Barbero, L.
                    IT 022000/79/0004 N
Valutazione della limpidezza dei vini con misure nefelometriche. **Evaluation of wine clearness through nephelometric measurements.**

19445 Spera, G.; Piracci, A.   IT 022000/79/0018 N
I contenuti in prolina ed in microelementi dei vini del Lazio. **Analytical survey on proline and trace elements in the wines of Lazio.**

19446 De Filice, M.A.   IT 040107/78/1048 N
Ricerche sui metaboliti microbici tossici nei prodotti enologici. **Research on wine toxic metabolites originating from microrganisms.**

19447 Maccarone, A.; Nicolosi Asmundo, C.; Russo, C.

D 7210 – Food composition

IT 040308/78/0003
Il tenore di microelementi nei vini della Sicilia Orientale. **Microelements content in wines of eastern Sicily.**

19448 Del Re, A.   IT 040406/71/0001
Determinazione di 2 – imidazolidintione (Etilentiourea) nei vini. **Determination of 2 – imidazolidinetione (Ethylenethiourea) in wines.** Publications.

19449 Del Re, A.; Molinari, G.P.; Ansaldi, M.
                                        IT 040406/74/0001
Fenoli volatili nei vini. **Volatile Phenols in Wines.**

19450 Colagrande, O.   IT 040407/73/0179
Formazione nel mosto e nel vino di acido cianidrico e altri metaboliti di antiparassitari agricoli. **Formation in must and wines of cyanuric acid and other metabolites from agricultural pesticides.**

19451 Colagrande, O.   IT 040407/74/0536
Effetti degli antiparassitari sulla fermentazione dei mosti e sulle caratteristiche chimiche e organoelettiche dei vini. **Effects of pesticides on the fermentation of musts and on chemical and organoleptic characteristics of wines.**

19452 Stella, C.   IT 040511/74/0638
Studio selettivo della composizione di vini toscani a D.O.C. in relazione anche all'annata di produzione e prova di vinificazione con inoculo di startes per la degradazione dell'acido malico. **Selective study of the composition of tuscan wines with controlled appellation of origin also in relation with the year of production and wine making trial with inoculation of starters for the degradation of malic acid.**

19453 Sabatelli Gellini, M.P.   IT 040511/77/0292 R
Studio selettivo di componenti secondari di vini toscani a d.o.c. in relazione anche all'annata di produzione, per una loro razionale tipicizzazione e discriminazione. **A selective study of secondary compounds in d.o.c. Tuscan wines also in relation to the year of production and in view of a rational typication and selection.**

19454 Florenzano, G.   IT 040513/76/0001
Microbiologia del vino. **Wine microbiology.** Publications.

19455 Volonterio, Gaspare.; Resmini, Pierpaolo.
                                        IT 040609/72/0001
Problemi analitici concernenti il controllo di vini e di altri prodotti enologici. **Analytical problems on the control of wines and alcoholic products.** Publications.

19456 Cerutti, G.   IT 040609/74/0534
Ricerca di prodotti tossici e additivi non intenzionali nel vino. **Research for toxic substances and unintentional additives in wine.**

19457 Cerutti, G.   IT 040609/77/0144 R
Ricerca di prodotti tossici e additivi non intenzionali nel vino. **Research on unintentional toxic substances and additives in wine.**

19458 Bertuccioli, M.   IT 041011/78/1033 N
Possibile valutazione obiettiva delle caratteristiche aromatiche dei vini mediante correlazione tra analisi sensoriale e strumentale. **Possibility of an objective evaluation of the aromatic characteristics of wines by correlating sensorial and instrumental analysis.**

19459 Anelli, G.   IT 041108/73/0133
Le frazioni proteiche responsabili degli intorbidamenti dei vini. **Protein fractions responsible for turbidity of wines.**

19460 Madau, G.   IT 041309/77/0221 R
Caratterizzazione dei vini sardi doc, Monica di Sardegna e Vermentino di Gallura. **Characterization of doc Sardinian wines, Monica of Sardinia and Vermentino of Gallura.**

19461 Fici, P.   IT 091902/76/0001
Caratteristiche cromatiche dei vini da uva "Nero d'Avola" (o calabrese). **Chromatic characteristics of "Nero d'Avola" ("Calabrese") wine.**

19462 Klopper, W.J.; Tuning, B.   NL 050304/47/5331
Normalisatie en harmonisatie van analysemethoden voor de kwaliteitsbepaling van bier en mout. **Normalisation and harmonisation of methods of analysis for determination malt and beer quality.** Publications.

19463 Klopper, W.   NL 050304/78/8991 N
Onderzoek naar residuen van bestrijdingsmiddelen in mout en bier. **Research on residues of pesticides in malt and beer.**

D 7220 – Physiology of nutrition

See also 12387, 16488, 19102, 19359

19464 Hötzel, D.; Urban, G.; Pietrzik, K.
                                        DE 111550/78/0001 N
Vergleichende Untersuchungen biochemischer und hämatologischer Messgrössen zur Beurteilung des Versorgungszustandes an Folsäure. **Biochemical and haematological parameters for the estimation of folate status.** Publications.

19465 Hötzel, D.; Simon, I.; Leinert, J.
                                        DE 111550/78/0002 N
Untersuchung des Vitamin B6–Versorgungszustandes ausgewählter Bevölkerungsgruppen anhand unterschiedlicher Parameter. **Estimation of the vitamin B6–status of selected population groups by different parameters.** Publications.

19466 Hötzel, D.; Bitsch, R.; Becker, D.; Kling–Steines, B.; Leinert, J.; Urban, G.   DE 111550/78/0003 N
Erfassung des Ernährungszustandes an kritischen Nährstoffen bei Industriearbeitern. **Evaluation of the supply with critical nutrients of industrial workers.** Publications.

19467 Pietrzik, K.   DE 111550/78/0004 N
Ermittlung des Pantothensäurebedarfs. **Estimation of pantothenic acid requirement.** Publications.

19468 Bitsch, R.; Hansen, J.; Mönks, C.
                                        DE 111550/78/0005 N
Einfluss chronischer Alkoholbelastung auf den Thiamin– und Ribiflavinstoffwechsel der Ratte. **Thiamine and Riboflavin metabolism of the rat as affected by chronic alcohol administration.**

19469 Wirths, W.   DE 111570/73/0004
Langfristige Erhebung über die Nährstoffversorgung von Altenheiminsassen. **Long–run survey on nutrient supply of elderly people.**

19470 Wirths, W. DE 111570/74/0001
Energieumsatzbestimmungen bei unterschiedlichem
Körpergewicht und verschiedenen Tätigkeiten. **Energy
expenditure in different body weights and in different activities.**

19471 Wirths, W. DE 111570/78/0001 N
Patientenernährung im Krankenhaus in
ernährungsphysiologischer Sicht. **Patient nutrition in hospitals
in nutrient physiological view.**

19472 Wirths, W. DE 111570/78/0002 N
Berodiät V im Aspekt der empfehlenswerten Höhe der
Energie– und Nährstoffzufuhr. **Berodiet V in aspect of the
recommended intake of energy and nutrients.**

19473 Wirths, W. DE 111570/78/0003 N
Energieumsatz bei muskulärer Arbeit. **Energy expenditure in
different kinds of muscular work.**

19474 Rehner, G. DE 129900/72/0003
Untersuchungen über die intestinale Resorption von Thiamin,
Riboflavin und Pyridoxin. **Investigations on intestinal
resorption of thiamine, riboflavin, and pyridoxine.**

19475 Elmadfa, I.; Feldheim, W. DE 129900/72/0004
Tocopherol–Stoffwechsel. **Tocopherol metabolism.**

19476 Menden, E.; Elmadfa, I. DE 129900/73/0003
Die ernährungsphysiologischen Auswirkungen der
nichtenzymatischen Bräunungsreaktion – Maillard–Reaktion
–. **Nutritional effects of non–enzymatic browning reaction.**

19477 Elmadfa, I.; Menden, E. DE 129900/73/0004
Aufwertung von Proteinen durch Zusatz essentieller
Aminosäuren. **Revaluation of proteins by supplementary
essential amino acids.**

19478 Siebert, G.; Grupp, U. DE 144190/73/0003
Untersuchungen zum Stoffwechsel von Palatinit, einem süss
schmeckenden Disaccharidalkohol. **Studies on the metabolism
of palatinitol, a sweet–tasting disaccharide alcohol.**

19479 Severin, T.; Ledl, F.; Supp, W. DE 160581/70/0001
Untersuchungen zur Maillard–Reaktion Thermische
Umwandlung von Aminosäuren in Lebensmitteln Reaktion
von Tryptophan mit Zucker. **Studies on Maillard–reaction
Thermal decomposition of amino acids in food Reaction of
tryptophan with sugar.**

19480 Severin, T.; Ledl, F.; Popp–Ginsbach, H.
 DE 160581/72/0006
Untersuchungen zur Maillard–Reaktion Thermische
Zersetzung von Proteinen und Aminosäuren. **Studies on
Maillard–reaction Thermal decomposition of proteins and
amino acids.**

19481 Severin, T.; Rothmoser, J. DE 160581/74/0001
Reaktionen von Zuckern mit Aminosäuren und anderen
Aminen. **Reactions of sugars with amino acids and other
amines.**

19482 Winne, D. DE 173155/77/0001
Die Grenzschicht im Darm in vivo. **Intestinal unstirred layer.**
Publications.

19483 Schelenz, R. DE 211030/77/0002

Anwendung von Markierungssubstanzen zur Untersuchung
der Verweilzeit von kalorienreduzierten Lebensmitteln im
Magen–Darmtrakt. **Use of labelling substances for examination
of detention time of low–calorie food in gastro–intestinal tract.**

19484 Harmuth–Hoene, A.E.; Jakubik, V.; Schelenz, R.
 DE 211050/75/0003 R
Ernährungsphysiologische und toxikologische Beurteilung von
kalorienreduzierten Nahrungsmitteln mit erhöhtem Gehalt an
schwerverdaulichen Polysacchariden. **Nutritional and
toxicological valuation of foods with reduced calories and
increased content of indigestable polysaccharides.**

19485 Homberg, E. DE 213010/77/0004
Wirkung langkettiger Monoensäuren auf den
Cholesteringehalt im Blutserum und in Organen. **Influence of
long–chain monoen acids on cholesterol content in blood serum
and organs.**

19486 Homberg, E. DE 213010/77/0007
Wirkung einzelner Phytosterine auf den Cholesteringehalt in
Blutserum und Organen. **Effects of single phytosterols on
cholesterol content in blood serum and organs.**

19487 Seher, A.; Arens, M.; Homberg, E. DE 213010/77/0015
Ernährungsphysiologische Wirkung von Rapsölen mit
unterschiedlichem Gehalt an Erucasäure. **Nutritional effects of
rape oils with different erucic acid content.**

19488 Mangold, H.K.; Reichwald, I.; Kaiser, H.; Hudalla, B.

 DE 213020/75/0007
Erforschung der Stoffwechselwirkung langkettiger Fettsäuren
aus Pflanzen und Tieren. **Studies on the metabolism of
long–chain fatty acids from plants and animals.**

19489 Rozen, R. FR 010205/78/9569
H.L.A. dans les obésités humaines. **H L A in human obesity.**

19490 Raibaud, P.; Ducluzeau, R. FR 010216/75/9606
Ecologie microbienne : premieres etapes de la colonisation du
tube digestif chez le nouveau–ne humain holoxénique.
**Microbial ecology : The first steps of the gastrointestinal tract
colonization in the holoxenic newborn human baby.**

19491 Hautvast, J.g.A.J. NL 020062/68/8658 N
Invloed van verschillende voedingsbestanddelen op het
lipidenmetabolisme (proeven met konijnen en ratten).
**Influence of various food constituents on lipid metabolism
(experiments with rabbits and rats).** Publications.

19492 Katan, M.B. NL 020062/68/8659 N
Interventieonderzoek bij gezonde vrijwilligers naar het effect
van voedingsbestanddelen (vet, eiwit, vezel) op het
lipidenmetabolisme en andere risicoindicatoren). **Controlled
dietary trials with healthy volunteers on the effects of food
constituents (fats, proteins, fibre) on parameters of lipid
,etabolism and other risk indicators.** Publications.

19493 Nijkrake, H.G.M. NL 020062/74/6330 R
Regulering energiebalans; het ontwikkelen en toepassen van
methoden ter bepaling van de energiebalans en de
lichaamssamenstelling in situaties van over– en ondervoeding.
Regulation of human energy balance. Publications.

19494 Pikaar, N.A. NL 050301/48/5322

Onderzoek darmstoornissen bij kinderen. **Investigations into intestinal disturbances in children.** Publications.

19495 Waard, H. de   NL 060002/74/5287 R
De betekenis van de calcium/fosfaat verhouding in de voeding voor de calciumstofwisseling en voor de botdichtheid bij gezonde bejaarden. **Significance of the calcium–phosphate ratio in the diet for the calcium metabolism and the bone density in healthy aged people.**

19496 Schaafsma, G.   NL 060002/75/6615
De voedingsfysiologische interrelaties tussen calcium, fosfor en lactose. **Nutritional interrelations between calcium, phosphorus and lactose.** Publications.

19497 Waard, H. de   NL 060002/77/7909
De betekenis van de verhouding essentiële en niet–essentiële aminozuren voor de eiwitkwaliteit. **Significance of the ratio of essential to non–essential amino acids for the protein quality.**

19498 Waard, H. de   NL 060002/78/7908 R
De betekenis van de calcium/fosfaat verhouding in de voeding voor de calciumstofwisseling en voor de botdichtheid bij vrouwen in de meno pauze. **Significance of the calcium–phosphate ratio in the diet for the calcium metabolism and the bone density in woman during the meno pause.**

19499 Beresteyn, E.C.H. van   NL 060002/79/8682 N
De invloed van de voeding op de lipoproteïne samenstelling. **Effect of the diet on the composition of lipoproteins.**

D 7230 – Feeding

See also 11640, 18233, 18234, 18905, 19313

19500 Henderickx, H.   BE 030026/64/0004 R
Onderzoek en invoer van eiwitrijke produkten, inzonderheid van soja, in de voeding van de gebieden met eiwitondervoeding. **Research on and introduction of protein rich products, especially soy, to feed population in protein deficient areas.** Publications.

19501 Hötzel, D.; Becker, D.; Bitsch, R.; Kling–Steines, B.; Simon, I.; Pietrzik, K.   DE 111550/74/0002
Ermittlung des Versorgungszustandes ausgewählter Bevölkerungsgruppen mit Thiamin, Riboflavin, Pyridoxin, Pantothensäure, Folsäure. **Examination of selected population groups as to the status of supply with thiamine, riboflavin, pyridoxine, and pantothenic acid.**

19502 Wirths, W.   DE 111570/73/0002 N
Nährstoffversorgung von Schülern in der Ganztagsschule. **Nutrient supply of pupils in schools with lectures till 4 p.m. – so–called full–time schools – .**

19503 Wirths, W.   DE 111570/73/0003
Nährstoffzufuhr und Ernährungszustand von Hochleistungssportlern. **Nutrient intake and nutritional status of high–performance sportsmen.**

19504 Wirths, W.   DE 111570/77/0001
Zufuhr an Quellstoffen von verschiedenen Bevölkerungsgruppen in der Bundesrepublik Deutschland. **Intake in thickeners in various groups of the population in the Federal Republic of Germany.**

19505 Wirths, W.   DE 111570/78/0004 N
Berufsschwere und Ernährungsstatus der Bevölkerung in der Bundesrepublik Deutschland. **Occupational activities and nutritional status of the population in the Federal Republic of Germany.**

19506 Wirths, W.   DE 111570/78/0005 N
Unterschiede im Energieumsatz bei ausgewählten Tätigkeiten unter Kontrolle und ad libitum. **Differences in energy expenditure in selected activities under control and ad libitum.**

19507 Kluthe, R.; Schaeffer, G.   DE 126840/75/0001 N
Eiweissbedarf des Menschen. **Human requirement of protein.**

19508 Kluthe, R.; Quirin, H.   DE 126850/73/0001 N
Einfache biochemische Parameter zur Festlegung des Eiweissernährungszustandes des Menschen. **Simple biochemical parameters for the determination of the status of protein supply in man.**

19509 Bodenstedt, A.A.; Rahier, M.–L.   DE 129340/78/0001 N
Ernährungsgewohnheiten deutscher Aussiedler aus Polen. **Food behaviour of German migrants from Poland.**

19510 Bitsch, I.; Kunze, K.   DE 129900/72/0006
Die Erzeugung und Charakterisierung ernährungsbedingter Polyneuropathien an der Ratte. **Generation and characterization of nutritionally induced polyneuropathies in rat.**

19511 Cremer, H.–D.; Panten, I.; Wagner, M.   DE 129900/72/0007
Einfluss der Ernährung in früher Kindheit auf die geistige Entwicklung. **Influence of nutrition in early childhood on mental development.**

19512 Menden, E.   DE 129900/72/0009
Einfluss von Aminosäureimbalanzen auf die Entstehung einer Fettleber. **Influence of amino acid imbalances on the genesis of fatty liver.**

19513 Oltersdorf, U.; Cremer, H.–D.; Bitsch, I.   DE 129900/72/0010
Wechselwirkungen zwischen Arzneimitteln und defizitärer Vitamin–Versorgung. **Interrelations between medicaments and deficient vitamin supply.**

19514 Rehner, G.; Koopmann, M.   DE 129900/72/0011
Einfluss der Nahrungszusammensetzung auf den Trinkwasserbedarf – physiologische und biochemische Wirkungen limi– tierter Trinkwasserzufuhr. **Influence of food composition on the demand for drinking water – physiological and biochemical effects of limited drinking–water supply.**

19515 Aign, W.; Cremer, H.–D.; Menden, E.   DE 129900/72/0012
Prüfung und Entwicklung von Reduktionskostformen. **Testing and development of reduction diets.**

19516 Oltersdorf, U.   DE 129900/74/0004
Untersuchungen über das Erythrogramm als Indikator für Fehlernährungszustände. **Analysis of erythrogram as indicator of false nutrition.**

19517 Piendl, A.; Geiger, E.; Heyse, K.–U.; Wagner, D.

Bier und Gesundheit. **Beer and health.**

DE 161770/77/0005

19518 Jork, H.; Weiss, M.　DE 167102/77/0003
Bestimmung biogener Amine im Harn in Abhängigkeit von
der Ernährung. **Determination of biogenic amines in urine as
affected by nutrition.**

19519 Bomar, M.T.; Popken, A.–M.　DE 211010/75/0003
Bakteriologische Aspekte der Gemeinschaftsverpflegung.
Bacteriological aspects of catering.

19520 Ulrich, H.–J.　DE 211100/78/0004 N
Untersuchung des Ernährungsverhaltens berufstätiger Frauen.
Investigation of the nutritional behaviour of employed women.

19521 Kappus, W.　DE 914002/78/0001 N
Änderung der Ernährungssituation der land– und
forstwirtschaftlichen Bevölkerung. **Change in nutritional
situation of population in agriculture and forestry.**

19522 Kappus, W.　DE 914002/78/0002 N
Verbesserung der Lebensqualität durch Änderung des
Ernährungsverhaltens – Entwicklung und Erprobung von
Beratungsmethoden unter Berücksichtigung der zeitlich,
personell und finanziell begrenzten Möglichkeiten der
Beratungsträger sowie bisher schwer ansprechbarer Gruppen
–. **Improvement of life quality by change of nutrional behaviour
– development and testing of advisory methods with respect to
adviser's opportunities limited in time, staff and finances and to
groups difficult to contac sofar.**

19523 Ebbesen, F.; Hertel, J.; Edelsten, D.
DK 030193/77/0001 N
Indflydelse af fototerapi på tarmpassage og
lactosemalabsorption hos spædbørn. **The effect of phototherapy
on gut transit time and lactose malabsorption in babies.**

19524 Grignon, C.　FR 011706/75/3336
Sociologie des pratiques alimentaires. **Sociology of food habits.**

19525 Bassecoulard–Zitt, E.　FR 012400/78/8557
Systemes de preparation de repas et restauration collective.
Catering systems.

19526 Scott, J.; Molloy, A.; O'Broin, J.D.; Temperley, I.J.
IE 140203/00/9062 N
**Folate and vitamin B12 nutritional status of the Irish
community.**

19527 Kevany, J.P.; McNamara, C.; O'Rathaille, M.
IE 140401/77/9114 N
**A computer based system for determining low–cost diets for
human populations, based on current food prices.** Publications.

19528 Staveren, M. W. van　NL 020062/68/4995
De ontwikkeling van methoden en technieken en het gebruik
ervan ter bepaling van de voedselconsumptie en de
samenstelling van het voedselpakket. **Development and use of
methods and techniques for determination of the food
consumption and composition of foods.** Publications.

19529 Hautvast, J.G.A.J.　NL 020062/72/4993
Onderzoek naar het niveau van risico–indicatoren voor het
ontstaan van atherosclerotische complicaties op latere leeftijd
en de factoren die dit bepalen; een studie bij kinderen van 5–12

jaar in diverse regio's in Nederland. **The level of risk–indicators
for atherosclerotical complications on older age; a study with
5–12 years old children in the Netherlands.** Publications.

19530 Hautvast, J.G.A.J.　NL 020062/78/8656 N
Bepaling (bio) chemische parameters voedingstoestand van de
bevolking. **Assessment of the nutritional status of selected
groups by (bio) chemical methods.** Publications.

19531 Kouwenhoven, T.　NL 020062/78/8863 N
Methodenontwikkeling ter beschrijving van de relatie tussen
perceptuele indrukken en cognitieve beslissingsprocessen bij
de keuze van voedingsmiddelen. **Development of methods for
describing the relation between perceptual impressions and
cognitive decision processes in the choice of foods.**

19532 Edema, J.M.P.　NL 020062/78/8864 N
Sociale en culturele achtergronden van
voedingsmiddelenkeuze en van voedselbereiding. **Social and
cultural roots of food choices and of food preparations.**

19533 Wijn, J.F. de　NL 050301/64/6759
7e Oriënteringsonderzoek voedingstoestand 8–jarige
schoolkinderen. **Investigation about nutritional status of
schoolage–children (8 y) in the Netherlands. 7 th Orientation
1976/77.** Publications.

19534 Luyken, R.; Wijn, J.F. de　NL 050301/65/6448
Uitwerken van somatometrische, fysiologische en
biochemische kriteria voor het vaststellen van de
voedingstoestand. **Testing of somatometric, physiological and
biochemical parameters to evaluate the nutritional status of
men.**

19535 Kamer, J.H. van de　NL 050301/72/6493
Onderzoek betreffende glutamine– en/of
pyrrolidoncarbonzuurbevattende peptiden bij tarwegevoelige
patiëntjes. **Investigation in coeliac patients into the small
intestinal permeability for peptides from gliadin and casein,
with special emphasis on pyrrolidonelcarboxylicacid containing
peptides.** Publications.

19536 Luyken, R.　NL 050301/73/5320
Peiling ("surveillance") voedingstoestand adolescenten
(scholieren en werkende jeugd) in Nederland. **Surveillance of
nutritional status of adolescents at school and of wage earning
young men.** Publications.

19537 Wijn, J.F. de　NL 050301/73/6466
Verband tussen obesitas op jeugdige leeftijd en hart – en
vaatziekte op latere leeftijd. **Relations between overweigh at an
early age on the occurrence of heart – and coronary diseases at
an older age.**

19538 Zaal, J.　NL 050301/75/6463
Ontwikkeling van methodieken voor meting van lichamelijke
activiteiten en het dagelijks activiteitenpatroon. **Evaluation of
physical methods for (daily) energy expenditure measurements.**

19539 Luyken, R.　NL 050301/76/6760
Onderzoek naar de voedingstoestand van 15–16 jarige
schoolkinderen. **Nutritional status of 15–16 year old youths
visiting schools.**

19540 Berg, H. van den　NL 050301/76/6761
Onderzoek foliumzuurmetabolieten in serum en volbloed.

Studies on the folate compounds in human blood.

19541 Butter, H. den; Luyken, R.　　NL 050301/76/6762
Voedingstoestand van Bosland–creolen in Suriname.
Nutritional status of Bushnegroes in Surinam.

19542 Ruiter, D. de　　NL 050302/76/6599
De betekenis van de onverteerbare bestanddelen van brood
voor de gezondheid van de mens. **The importance of the
indigestible constituents of bread for human health.**

D 7300 – Public health and medicine

See also 1831, 1867, 5082, 7738, 10327, 13518, 13784, 13785,
14389, 15764, 15861, 16009, 16724, 16725, 18322, 19074, 20072

19543 Istas, J.; Termonia, M.; Alaerts, G.; Monseur, X.;
Walravens, J.　　BE 100000/78/0036 R
Kwalitatieve en kwantitatieve bepaling van organische
gasvormige luchtpolluenten. **Qualitative and quantitative
determination of gaseous organic air polluants.**

19544 Salmon Legagneur, E.; Gayral, J.P.; Roustan, J.L.
　　FR 010206/68/2931
Etude de la pollution due aux effluents de porcherie. **Pollution
from piggery effluents.** Publications.

19545 Hobson–Frohock　　GB 010205/18/0046 N
Determination of ethoxyquin in poultry meat, eggs and milk.

19546 Dixon; Heitzman　　GB 010404/18/0059 N
**The measurement of residues of zeranol in edible tissues of
cattle and sheep.**

19547 Smart　　GB 010603/00/0070 R
**Study of sources of contamination of meat and animals and
products by bacteria of public health significance.**

19548 Norris　　GB 010603/75/0090 R
Developing rapid methods for identifying microorganisms.

19549 Roberts　　GB 010605/00/0030 R
**Defining factors affecting inhibition of bacteria by salt, water,
pH. and temperature in foods.**

19550 Stayner; Talamo　　GB 011602/00/0003 R
Tractor and machinery noise.

19551 Lord　　GB 012005/00/0045 R
**Influence of distribution on effectiveness of chemicals for
controlling moulding of hay.**

19552 Hamilton　　GB 030903/00/0207 R
**Occurrence of organochlorine pesticides in the environment of
South–West Scotland.**

19553 Brodie　　GB 030903/00/0404 R
Distribution of resistance to anticoagulant rodenticides.

19554 Ruthren; Hamilton　　GB 030903/65/0201 R
**Quinquennial monitoring of organochlorine and mercury
residues in soils.**

19555 Findlay　　GB 030903/75/0205 R
**Occurrence of organochlorine residues in milk from treatment
of pastures to control leatherjackets.**

19556 Kolb　　GB 030903/77/0403 R
Ecology and behaviour of foxes in an urban area.

19557 Patterson　　GB 040102/79/0009 N
Inhibition of salmonella by competing organisms.

19558 Lloyd; Bell　　GB 050201/61/0021 N
**Development of techniques for studies on protection of
operators from pesticides.**

19559 Smart; Hill　　GB 050201/62/0017 N
**Extraction cleanup and estimation procedures in determination
of pesticides in agriculture samples.**

19560 Cann; Hodgkiss　　GB 051003/76/0020 R
**Investigations of the incidence of clostridium botulinum and
vibrio parahaemolyticus in fishery products.**

19561 McWeeny　　GB 051101/79/0001 N
**Studies of C–N and S nitrosation in relationship to
nitrosamines.**

19562 Carr　　GB 051101/79/0003 N
Radioactive elements in the food chain.

19563 Carr　　GB 051101/79/0004 N
Radioactive elements in food associated with Windscale.

19564 Lindsay　　GB 051101/79/0005 N
Mercury intakes and effects on human populations.

19565 Lindsay　　GB 051101/79/0008 N
Mycotoxins: surveys on edible nuts.

19566 Lindsay　　GB 051101/79/0010 N
Lead; critical group studies.

19567 Buss　　GB 051101/79/0014 N
Household waste survey.

19568 Singer　　GB 051101/79/0015 N
Garbage waste assessment.

19569 Cermak　　GB 060224/79/0022 N
Safety of man in livestock buildings.

19570 Spillane, T.A.; O'Shea, J.; Flynn, A.V.; Sugrue, J.J.;
Wheeler, B.M.　　IE 060100/69/0352 R
**Protection of the environment. (A) silage effluent disposal
studies. (B)nutrient build up in natural waters.** Publications.

19571 Dempster, J.F.　　IE 060100/70/0526 R
**An evaluation of a low cost cleaning procedure for bacon
factories.** Publications.

19572 Palmer, J.　　IE 060400/72/0476 R
**Testing for cleaning effictivness of detergent–sterilizer and
cleanability of dairy equipment surfaces.** Publications.

19573 Palmer, J.　　IE 060400/75/0474 N
Cold cleaning of pipe line milking machines. Publications.

19574 Mantovani, A.; Baldelli, R.; Pampiglione, S.; Zanetti,
R.; Battelli, G.　　IT 040229/75/0001
Malattie professionali in agricoltura. **Professional diseases in**

agriculture. Publications.

D 7310 – Public health engineering

See also 158, 340, 429, 1349, 1373, 1687, 1873, 1986, 2099, 2372, 5201, 5687, 5850, 7784, 8505, 8591, 8644, 8645, 8646, 8647, 8699, 8714, 8715, 8755, 8786, 8946, 9393, 9705, 9803, 9848, 10044, 10199, 10251, 10253, 10273, 13511, 13682, 13877, 15117, 15286, 15301, 15675, 15708, 15710, 15991, 16264, 16270, 16626, 17054, 18819, 18825, 18869, 18870, 18874, 18884, 18934, 18954, 19085, 19143, 19181, 19192, 19221, 19322, 19682

19575 Briquet, M.; Goffeau, A.; Hutchemakers, J.; Convent, B.   BE 020105/70/0003 N
Etude comparative des effets biochimiques et génétiques des pesticides organiques de la série des urées substitués sur le métabolisme respiratoire des cellules des organismes faisant partie de la chaîne alimentaire et de l'environnement de l'homme. **Comparative study of the biochemical and genetical effects of organic pesticides such as substituted urea on the respiratory metabolism of organism included in the alimentary chain or important to the environment of man.**

19576 Schamp, N.; Van Wassenhove, F.; Velghe, K.
          BE 030005/75/0004
Onderzoek over de geur in en rond mesthokken van varkens en kippen. **Investigation of odors in and around pig and chicken houses.** Publications.

19577 Schamp, N.; Van Langenhove, X.
          BE 030005/77/0006 N
Geurhinder rond destructiebedrijven. **Odor nuisance by rendering.**

19578 Cottenie, A.; D'Haese, A.   BE 030008/70/0003
Kwalitatief onderzoek van oppervlaktewaters. **Qualitative study of surface waters.** Publications.

19579 Cottenie, A.; D'Haese, A.   BE 030008/72/0004 R
Studie van het loodgehalte in planten en gronden langs de verkeerswegen en geïndustrialiseerde zones. **Study of the lead content in plants and soils near highways, and industrialised zones.**

19580 Cottenie, A.; D'Haese, A.   BE 030008/76/0006 R
Opmaken van de balans van atmosferische polluenten, fall-out van zware metalen. **Balance sheet of atmospheric pollution, fall-out of heavy metals.**

19581 Cottenie, A.; Kiekens, L.; Verloo, M.; Velghe, G.; Camerlynck, R.; Van de Maele, F.   BE 030008/77/0007 R
Chemische Ecologie. **Chemical Ecology.** Publications.

19582 Verachtert, H.; Ramasamy, J.   BE 040503/70/0005 R
De rol van de cellulolyse bij afvalwaterzuivering en de studie van cellulosen van bacteriële oorsprong. **Study of cellulolytic organisms and bacterial celluloses in waste water purification processus.** Publications.

19583 Verachtert, H.; Houtmeyers, J.   BE 040503/72/0004 R
Studie van de microbiële flora van biologische afval waterzuiveringsinstallaties, speciaal de draadvormende bacteriën. **Study of the microbial populations of biological sewage treatment plants especially the filamentous bacteria.** Publications.

19584 Van Hoof, J.; De Zutter, L.   BE 051200/77/0005 R
Fysico–chemische en microbiele aspecten van slachthuis –en pluimveeslachterij–afvalwater. **Physical, chemical and microbiological aspects of waste water from slaughterhouses and poultry abattoirs.**

19585 Maton, A.; Priem, R.   BE 070300/73/0001 R
Studie van de hinderlijke reukgassen uit stallen, hun absorptie, de arbeidsbehoefte en kostprijs van de bestrijdingstechnieken. **Research on bad smells from stalls, their absorption, their labour time requirement and cost–price.**

19586 Maton, A.; Priem, R.   BE 070300/73/0002 R
Onderzoek van reukbestrijdingsprodukten in mengmestkelders. **Research on deodorizers in liquid manure cellars.**

19587 Maton, A.; Priem, R.   BE 070300/73/0003 R
Dispersie van reukgassen afkomstig van veestallen. **The dispersion of bad smells from livestock buildings.**

19588 Maton, A.; Priem, R.   BE 070300/73/0004 R
Invloed van het gebruik van ozon als reukbestrijdingsmiddel op de produktiviteit van een varkensbedrijf. **Influence of using ozone as desodorization on the productivity of fatting–pigs.** Publications.

19589 Maton, A.; Priem, R.   BE 070300/73/0005 R
Studie van de arbeidsbehoefte, reukhinder en kostprijs bij het gebruik van verregeningsinstallatie voor het toedienen van mengmest. **Study of the labour time requirement, the evil smiling gass and costprice by application of liquid manure by raingun.**

19590 Maton, A.; Priem, R.   BE 070300/73/0007 R
Studie van de aërobe afbraak van mengmest door beluchting. **Research on the aerobic treatment of liquid manure by means of aeration.** Publications.

19591 Maton, A.; Priem, R.   BE 070300/76/0045 R
Studie van de biologische afbraak van mengmest door middel van "bio schijven". **The use of "Bio–discs" in the aerobic treatment of liquid manure.** Publications.

19592 Hovart, P.; Vyncke, W.; Baeteman, M.; Maertens, D.
          BE 070800/69/0010 R
Studie van de verontreiniging van de zee. **Study on the pollution of the sea.** Publications.

19593 Waes, G.; Vandamme, K.   BE 070900/77/0039
De bakteriologie van aktief slib. **The bacteriology of activated sludge.**

19594 Bossuyt, R.   BE 070900/78/0032 R
Studie van de waarde van produkten voor de reiniging en desinfektie van de melkwinningsapparatuur op de hoeve. **Study of the value of products for cleaning and disinfecting the milking equipment on the farm.**

19595 Vandamme, K.; Waes, G.   BE 070900/79/0043 N
Invloed van verschillende faktoren op de vokvorming in aktief slibinstallaties. **The influence of different factors on the floc formation in activated sludge installations.**

19596 Istas, J.; Hofman, M.; Monseur, X.; Neirinckx, G.; Buttiens, A.   BE 100000/76/0028 R

Studie over anaërobe gisting van de organische afvalstoffen. **Organic wastes, anaerobic fermentation studies.** Publications.

19597 Monseur, X.; Termonia, M.; Dourte, P.; Walravens, J.
BE 100000/78/0026 R
Etude des odeurs du lisier. **Study of manure odours.**

19598 Reuter, G.; Marquardt, E.; Stolle, A.
DE 104302/77/0002
Gegenwärtige Struktur der Schlachtbetriebe in der Bundesrepublik Deutschland. **The present status of slaughterhouses in the Federal Republic of Germany.**

19599 Bussler, W.; Traulsen, B.   DE 105202/78/0008 N
Reaktion von höheren Pflanzen auf die Einwirkung von Luftverunreinigungen und ihre Verwendung zur Frühindikation. **Reaction of higher plants on air pollution and their use for early diagnosis.**

19600 Wasmund, R.; Sprung, V.; Bultmann, H.
DE 105750/72/0001
Untersuchung der Gefahr von Staubbränden und Staubexplosionen in der Lebensmittelindustrie. **Investigation on the danger of dust fires and dust explosions in food industry.** Publications.

19601 Stan, H.-J.; Abraham, B.; Kassner, H.
DE 105900/78/0005 N
Reaktionen von höheren Pflanzen auf die Einwirkung von Luftverunreinigungen und ihre Verwendung zur Frühindikation. **Reactions of higher plants under influence of air pollutants and their application for an early detection.**

19602 Hötzel, D.; Pietrzik, K.   DE 111550/75/0004
1. Ermittlung des Versorgungszustandes an Folsäure und Pantothensäure 2. Ermittlung des Pantothensäurebedarfs. **1. Evaluation of the nutritional status of folic acid and pantothenic acid 2. Evaluation of pantothenic acid requirement.** Publications.

19603 Matthies, H.J.; Paolim, K.   DE 114201/75/0001
Schwebegeschwindigkeit von Gutwolken. **Floating speed of dust–clouds.**

19604 Collins, H.-J.; Spillmann, P.   DE 114302/78/0002 N
Verlängerung der Nutzungsdauer von Abfalldeponien und Minderung des Verdichtungsaufwandes durch Mischung der Abfälle vor deren Einbau. **Prolongation of landfills' lifetime as well as reducing the compacting requirement by means of mixing the refuse before placing.**

19605 Zöttl, H.W.; Hädrich, F.; Keilen, K.; Stahr, K.
DE 126050/75/0008
Untersuchungen zur Spurenelementdynamik – Be, Cd, Co, Cu, Mn, Ni, Pb, V, Zn – einer Kleinlandschaft des Südschwarzwaldes. **Turnover of trace elements – Be, Cd, Co, Cu, Mn, Ni, Pb, V, Zn – in a small landscape of the southern Black Forest.** Publications.

19606 Rheinbaben, W.von; Niese, G.   DE 129080/72/0001
Untersuchung von anaeroben Prozessen und deren Wirkung auf die Kompostierung von Siedlungsabfällen. **Studies on the influence of anaerobic processes on the composting of town refuses.** Publications.

19607 Küster, E.; Löw, E.von   DE 129080/75/0002
Vorkommen von cancerogenen, aromatischen Polycyclen in Siedlungsabfällen und deren Um– und Abbau durch Mikroorganismen. **Occurrence of carcinogenic aromatic polycyclic compounds in town refuses and their transformation and decomposition by microorganisms.**

19608 Kowald, R.; Hohn; Niese, G.   DE 129080/78/0004 N
Untersuchung von Klärschlämmen im Bereich des Wasserwirtschaftsamtes Dillenburg. **Analysis of sewage sludges in the district of the Water Management Office Dillenburg.**

19609 Niese, G.; Fertig, J.   DE 129080/78/0005 N
Bestimmung des optimalen Belüftungsgrades bei der Heissrotte fester und schlammiger Siedlungs– und Produktionsabfälle. **Determination of the optimal rate of aeration during the decomposition of garbage and sewage at high temperatures.**

19610 Stein, W.   DE 129200/74/0001
Die Fliegen von Mülldeponien und ihre hygienische Bedeutung. **The flies in refuse depots and their hygienic importance.**

19611 Stein, W.; Lüchtrath, L.   DE 129200/77/0001
Unterschiede zwischen Laboratoriums– und Freilandstämmen bei synanthropen Fliegen. **Differences between laboratory and field strains of synanthropic flies.**

19612 Stein, W.; Shahen, A.   DE 129200/77/0002
Intra– und interspezifische Konkurrenz bei Larven synanthroper Fliegen. **Intra– and interspecific competition in larvae of synanthropic flies.**

19613 Stein, W.; Weber, G.; Simmonds, M.
DE 129200/77/0003
Untersuchungen zur hygienischen Bedeutung der Insekten, insbesondere der Fliegen, auf Autobahnrast– und Parkplätzen. **Investigations on the hygienic importance of insects, especially of flies, at parking places and rest areas by motor highways.**

19614 Lang, K.   DE 129700/78/0001 N
Lebensmittelkontamination insbesondere durch den Menschen und Verbraucherschutz. **Human–borne food contamination and consumer protection.** Publications.

19615 Bombosch, S.; Peters, L.   DE 132660/75/0001
Untersuchungen über Vorkommen und Verbleib von Quecksilber in Nahrungsketten. – Modelluntersuchungen in Niedersachsen –. **Studies on distribution and pathways of mercury in food chains. – Model investigations in Lower Saxony –.** Publications.

19616 Düvel, D.   DE 135053/70/0001
Cancerogene Kohlenwasserstoffe in der Umgebung des Menschen. Untersuchungen zur endogenen Bildung von polycyclischen Kohlenwasserstoffen in höheren Pflanzen 1966. **Cancerogenic hydrocarbons in the environment of man. Studies on the endogenous formation of polycyclic hydrocarbons in higher plants.**

19617 Hilliger, H.G.; Hartung, J.   DE 139260/75/0002
Methodenentwicklung zur Feststellung und Bewertung von Stallgerüchen. **Development of methods for statement and evaluation of stable odours.**

19618 Hilliger, H.G.; Ackemann, H.H.   DE 139260/77/0002

Prüfung von Oberflächenkeimen in Nutztierställen. **Research of surface germs in livestock houses.**

19619 Bürger, H.–J.; Rieso, A.; Stoye, M.
DE 139500/78/0013 N
Resistenz parasitärer Entwicklungsstadien in Klärschlamm gegenüber Elektronenbestrahlung. **Resistance of parasitic eggs, oocysts and larvae in sewage sludge to electron rays.**

19620 Barth, H.
DE 142102/78/0001 N
Hygienische Untersuchungen im Rahmen der Entwicklung und Erprobung neuer Technologien zur wirtschaftlichen Aufbereitung und Kompostierung von Siedlungsabfällen durch die Verfahrenskombination Cascadenmühle–Tunnelmiete. **Hygienic investigations within development and testing of new technologies for economic treatment and composting of domestic waste by the combined system of cascade mill and tunnel clamp silo.**

19621 Müller, W.; Hartmann, F.
DE 144610/77/0004
Ausbreitung von mikrobiellen Aerosolen in der Freiluft. **Dispersion of pathogenic agents from stable exhausts.** Publications.

19622 Strauch, D.; Dietz, P.
DE 144610/78/0001 N
Dekontamination von Anthrax–Sporen. **Decontamination of anthrax–spores.**

19623 Strauch, D.; Dietz, P.
DE 144610/78/0002 N
Desinfektion mittels Aerosolen. **Disinfection by aerosols.**

19624 Strauch, D.; Becker, K.H.
DE 144610/78/0003 N
Untersuchungen zur Verbesserung der Nachweisverfahren für Pseudomonas mallei. **Trials on improvement of methods for detection of Pseudomonas mallei.**

19625 Rüprich, W.; Vetter, R.
DE 144710/77/0002
Untersuchungen zur Aufbereitung von tierischen Exkrementen durch Belüftung mit dem Ziel der Geruchsverminderung, Entseuchung und Gehaltsverminderung. **Investigations regarding the treatment of animal excrement by aeration with the aim of reducing smell, disinfecting and reducing its volume.**

19626 Höschele, K.
DE 145050/71/0001
Mobile Messungen der SO2, CO, NOX–Konzentration der bodennahen Luft zur Untersuchung der Herkunft, des Transports und der atmosphärischen Verweilzeit von Luftverunreinigungen. **Mobile measurements of SO2, CO, NOX–concentrations of the air near the ground. Study of origin, transport and atmospheric life time of air pollution.**

19627 Isensee, E.; Schuldt, E.
DE 148150/74/0001
Entwicklung von Verfahrenselementen zum biologischen Abbau von Flüssigdung. **Development of methods for the biological decomposition of liquid manure.**

19628 Isensee, E.; Wagner, M.
DE 148150/78/0001 N
Ermittlung der Geruchsquellen in Tierhaltungsanlagen, insbesondere Schweinemastställen. **Investigation of the sources of odour in livestock farms especially in swine finishing houses.**

19629 Mahnel, H.
DE 160764/73/0002
Untersuchungen über die viruzide Wirkung von Desinfektionsmitteln und die Eignung der Prüfverfahren. **Studies on the virucidal effect of disinfectants and on the suitability of test methods.**

19630 Mahnel, H.
DE 160764/73/0003
Trinkwasserdesinfektion unter spezieller Berücksichtigung der Viren. **Drinking water disinfection with special regard to viruses.**

19631 Forstner, M.J.
DE 160820/70/0013
Untersuchungen über die Lebensfähigkeit von pathogenen Vermehrungsstadien tierischer Parasiten in Abwasser und Stallabgängen. **Investigations on the viability of pathogenic stages of animal parasites in sewage and manure.**

19632 Kessler, H.G.; Bürgmayr, J.
DE 161350/78/0004 N
Untersuchungen über Reinfektionsbekämpfung in Rohrleitungssystemen in Molkereien. **Investigations on control of recontamination in pipeline systems in dairies.**

19633 Künast, C.
DE 161361/78/0006 N
Lockstoffe bei Stubenfliegen. **Attractants in common house–flies.**

19634 Künast, C.; Messner, M.
DE 161361/78/0007 N
Resistenz bei Stubenfliegen. **Resistance in common house–flies.**

19635 Künast, C.
DE 161361/78/0008 N
Larvizide Wirkung von Permethrin auf Stubenfliegen. **Larvicidal effect of permethrin on common house–flies.**

19636 Mändl, B.; Heyse, K.–U.
DE 161770/78/0001 N
Schwermetalle in der Brauereianalytik. **Heavy metals in brewing analysis.**

19637 Bischofsberger, W.; Hruschka, H.
DE 161860/77/0003
Anwendung von Fällungsverfahren mittels Kalk und Eisensalzen zur Verbesserung der Leistungsfähigkeit biologischer Kläranlagen. **Application of chemical precipitation with lime and iron as means of increase in capacity of biological waste water treatment plants.**

19638 Thoss, R.; Wiik, K.
DE 164350/72/0001 R
Ein lineares Entscheidungsmodell zur Planung der regionalen Abwasserwirtschaft 1971. **A linear decision model for planning of regional sewage disposal.**

19639 Thoss, R.; Döllekes, H.P.
DE 164350/72/0002 R
Die Optimierung der Abgasbelastung in der Bundesrepublik Deutschland 1971. **Optimization of exhaust–gas impact in the Federal Republic of Germany.**

19640 Thoss, R.; Brasse, P.
DE 164350/72/0003 R
Ein regionalisiertes Optimierungsmodell einer integrierten Abfallwirtschaft 1971. **A regional optimization model of integrated waste disposal.**

19641 Schweisfurth, R.; Kaiser, R.
DE 167150/78/0002 N
Untersuchungen zum Vorkommen von Hefen und Fadenpilzen in Trinkwasser. **Experiments of yeasts and moulds in drinking water.**

19642 Schweisfurth, R.; Lührs, A.
DE 167150/78/0003 N
Untersuchungen zur Ermittlung der Wiederverkeimungstendenz von Trinkwasser. **Experiments on determining the new growth of bacteria in drinking water.**

D 7310 – Public health engineering

19643 Domsch, K.H.; Munnecke, D.; Fischer, H.–F.
DE 201020/78/0005 N
Entwicklung mikrobieller Entgiftungssysteme für Pestizide.
Development of microbial pesticide detoxification systems.

19644 Graef, M.
DE 201060/71/4013 R
Massnahmen zur Bekämpfung der Schwingungsbelastung an Arbeitsplätzen in der Landwirtschaftlichen Produktion.
Methods for the control of vibration stress at workingplaces of agricultural production.

19645 Mejer, G.–J.
DE 201060/71/5008
Erfassung und Bewertung von geruchsintensiven Stoffen.
Determination and evaluation of malodorous gases.

19646 Hinz, T.
DE 201060/75/0001
Staubbekämpfung und Untersuchungen an Entstaubungsanlagen. **Dust control and studies on dust removing systems.**

19647 Witte, E.
DE 201060/75/0002 R
Verminderung der Lärmbelastung durch aktive und passive Bekämpfungsmassnahmen. **Reduction of noise stress by active and passive methods of control.**

19648 Batel, W.
DE 201060/77/0002
Messen der Dauerbelastung durch Staub, Lärm, Geruch und Schwingungen in der landwirtschaftlichen Produktion.
Measuring of permanent stress by dust, noise, odour and vibrations in agricultural production.

19649 Batel, W.
DE 201060/77/0003 R
Staubschutzeinrichtungen für die Beschäftigten in der landwirtschaftlichen Produktion. **Facilities for dust control for people employed in agricultural production.**

19650 Witte, E.
DE 201060/78/0001 N
Messen der Dauerbelastung durch Lärm. **Measurement of continuous stress by noise in agricultural production.**

19651 Graef, M.
DE 201060/78/0002 N
Messen der Dauerbelastung durch Schwingungen an Arbeitsplätzen der landwirtschaftlichen Produktion.
Measurement of continuous stress by shock and vibration at working places in agricultural production.

19652 Krause, K.–H.
DE 201060/78/0004 N
Bestimmung der physikalischen, chemischen und biologischen Eigenschaften von Staub aus der landwirtschaftlichen Produktion. **Determination of physical, chemical and biological properties of dust inhaled by men in agricultural production.**

19653 Krause, K.–H.
DE 201060/78/0005 N
Ausbreitung von luftgetragenen Schadstoffen von der Produktionsstätte. **Emission and transmission of air pollution at agricultural working places.**

19654 Löliger, H.–C.; Matthes, S.; Platz, S.
DE 201300/75/0003
Keim– und Staubemissionen aus Geflügel–Intensivhaltungen.
Germs and dust emissions from confined poultry housing.

19655 Matthes, S.
DE 201300/78/0002 N
Kinetik der Ei– und Fleischinfektionen bei Legehennen und Broilern. **Kinetics of egg and meat infections in laying hens and broilers.**

19656 Löliger, H.–C.; Platz, S.; Matthes, S.
DE 201300/78/0011 N
Tenazität von aus Geflügelställen emittierten Keimen in der Luft, an Pflanzen und im Boden. **Tenacity of microorganisms emitted from laying hen houses in the air, on plants and in the soil.**

19657 Kaminsky, G.; Lembke, E.
DE 202030/75/0005
Folgen langfristiger Lärmeinwirkung auf die Hörfähigkeit der Waldarbeiter. **Influences of long–term noise exposure of forest workers on their hearing capacities.** Publications.

19658 Wobbe, G.
DE 202030/75/0008
Die Koordination des Material– und Informationsflusses am Beispiel der Holzindustrie. **The coordination of material and information flow e.g. in timber industry.** Publications.

19659 Eisenhauer, G.; Bloch, G.; Kaminsky, G.
DE 202030/78/0001 N
Untersuchungen und Massnahmen zur Humanisierung der Motorsägenarbeit. **Investigations on and methods for humanization of power saw operation.**

19660 Tolle, A.; Hahn, G.; Otte, I.
DE 207020/74/0004
Schnellidentifizierung pathogener Mikroorganismen in Milchprodukten. **Rapid identification of pathogens in milk products.**

19661 Tolle, A.; Hahn, G.; Heeschen, W.
DE 207020/78/0004 N
Analyse von Virulenz–Faktoren und Nachweis von PathogenitätsMechanismen bei Streptokokken. **Analysis of virulence factors and detection of pathogenicity mechanisms on streptococci.**

19662 Heine, K.; Wiechen, A.
DE 207050/78/0001 N
Radioökologische Untersuchungen zum Verhalten von Radionukliden in Nahrungsketten auf dem Lande zur Beurteilung potentieller Kontaminationen in der Umgebung kerntechnischer Anlagen. **Radio–ecological investigations on the action of some radio–nuclides in food chains in the country as basis of valuation of potential environment contamination near nuclear power stations.**

19663 Feldt, W.; Lauer, R.
DE 208050/74/5003
Untersuchung der Pu–239–Abgaben von Kernkraftwerken.
Investigation of the Pu–239 output of nuclear power stations.

19664 Ocker, H.–D.; Fretzdorff, B.; Nierle, W.
DE 209010/78/0004 N
Toxische Schwermetalle in Getreide und Getreideprodukten.
Toxic heavy metals in cereals and cereal products.

19665 Weipert, D.; El–Baya, A.W.
DE 209020/78/0001 N
Untersuchungen über die Toxizität von 5–Alkyl–Resorcinol in Vermahlungsprodukten. **Investigation of the toxicity of 5–alkyl–resorcinol in milling products.**

19666 Schmidt, U.
DE 210030/77/0005
Prüfverfahren und Verfahrenstechnik für Reinigungsmittel, die in fleischverarbeitenden Betrieben zum Einsatz kommen. **Evaluation and application of detergents in use in meat processing plants.**

19667 Hamm, R.; Hecht, H.
DE 210040/78/0006 N

Untersuchung der Kontamination von Fleisch und Organen von frei weidenden Schafen und von Wild aus originär metallhaltigen und metallfreien Gebieten an toxischen Elementen. Untersuchung des Carry–over–Effektes. **Studies on the contamination of meat and organs of sheep and game from areas which are more or less contaminated with toxic elements. – Investigation of the carry–over effect.**

19668 Mirna, A.   DE 210060/78/0002 N
Untersuchungen über Rückstände in Schlachtfetten. **Investigation on residues in fat of animal origin.**

19669 Fischer, E.; Frindik, O.; Schelenz, R.
       DE 211030/78/0002 N
Untersuchungen zur Überwachung von Lebensmitteln auf eine radioaktive Kontamination durch natürliche und künstlich erzeugte Radionuklide. **Investigations on the control of foods for radioactive contamination by natural and artifical radionuclides.**

19670 Neudecker, C.   DE 211050/78/0003 N
Tierversuche zur gesundheitlichen Prüfung von phytoalexinhaltigen Lebensmitteln. **Studies on animals for safety evaluation of foods containing phytoalexins.**

19671 Renner, H.   DE 211050/78/0005 N
Mutagenitätsprüfung von mit Zusatzstoffen versehenen Lebensmitteln. **Mutagenicity testing of foods containing additives.**

19672 Reichmuth, C.; Noack, S.   DE 215030/78/0006 N
Wirkung von hochtoxischen gasförmigen Insektenbekämpfungsmitteln auf die Umgebung von Vorratslägern in Grossstädten. **Effect of very toxic stored food fumigants on the surroundings of warehouses in cities.**

19673 Schoenhard, G.   DE 215060/78/0002 N
Die Auswirkungen des Benzin–Blei–Gesetzes auf die Kontamination von Nahrungs– und Futterpflanzen mit Blei. **Effects of the law on reduction of lead in petrol on the contamination of food plants and forage crops with lead.**

19674 Gärtel, W.   DE 215220/78/0003 N
Untersuchungen über den Gehalt an Mineralstoffen, insbesondere an Schwermetallen von Weinausscheidungen – Weinstein, Schleimsäure –. **Investigations on the content of mineral substances, especially heavy metals, in wine sediments – cream of tartar, mucic acid –.**

19675 Hansen, K.   DE 305010/75/0004
Pathomorphologie von Organohalogenverbindungen. **Pathomorphology of organic halides.**

19676 Roll, R.   DE 305010/78/0001 N
Mutagenitätsuntersuchungen von polycyclischen aromatischen Kohlenwasserstoffen mit Hilfe des Dominant–Letal–Tests an der Maus. **Mutagenic studies on polycyclic aromatic hydrocarbons using the Dominant Lethal Test on mice.**

19677 Beck, T.; Bucher, E.   DE 502055/72/0007
Untersuchungen zur Strahlensensibilität von Mikroorganismen in Klärschlämmen. **Studies of radiological resistance of micro–organisms in sewage sludge.** Publications.

19678 Rosopulo, A.   DE 502055/73/0020
Die Quecksilberbestimmung in Boden und Pflanzen sowie Siedlungsabfällen mittels flammenloser Atomabsorption. **Determination of mercury content in soil, plants and wastes by means of flameless atomic absorption methods.**

19679 Maier, J.; Liebl, J.   DE 502059/74/0001
Untersuchungen zu Pflanzenschutzmittelrückständen bei Hopfen. **Analysis of pesticide residues in hops.**

19680 Blendl, H.M.   DE 502300/77/0003
Minderung von Emissionen aus Betrieben mit konzentrierter Tierhaltung. **Reduction of emissions in farms with intensive animal production.**

19681 Researcher not indicated   DE 502650/78/0012 N
Analytik organisch–chemischer Schadstoffe aus Oberflächenwasser. **Analytics of organo–chemical pollutants from surface water.**

19682 Ruf, M.; Scherb, K.; Hübel, K.; Kucklentz, V.
       DE 502657/74/0001
Strahlenbehandlung von Klärschlamm und Abwasser. **Radiation treatment of sewage sludge and waste water.**

19683 Merkel, D.   DE 507051/75/0002
Fluorgehalte von Pflanzen und Rinderknochen in der Umgebung einer Aluminiumhütte. **Fluorine contents of plants and bones of dairy cows in the environment of an aluminium smelting work.**

19684 Vetter, H.; Kowalewsky, H.H.   DE 507400/78/0001 N
Untersuchungen über die Ausbreitung von Geruchsemissionen aus Schweine– und Hühnerhaltungsbetrieben. **Investigations on the extension of odour emission from pig and poultry farms.**

19685 Vetter, H.; Grummer, H.–J.; Klasink, A.; Mählhop, R.
       DE 507400/78/0002 N
Ermittlung von Schadensschwellenwerten für Quecksilber in Pflanzen und tierischen Organen. **Concentration of mercury in plants and animal organs in relation to different amounts in soil and feedstuff respectively.**

19686 Sunkel, R.   DE 508302/74/0002
Die Ermittlung des Nitrataustrages mit dem Sickerwasser in der Schutzzone II eines Wasserwerkes. **The determination of nitrate leaching along with seepage water within the protected zone II of a water work.**

19687 Jung, M.   DE 910001/72/0001
Über das Vorkommen von Aflatoxin M in Trockenmilcherzeugnissen. **The occurrence of aflatoxin M in dried–milk products.**

19688 Riemann, F.; Pieper, I.   DE 914005/78/0002 N
Untersuchungen über die gesundheitlichen Verhältnisse und die medizinische Versorgung der in den Ortskrankenkassen versicherten deutschen landwirtschaftlichen Arbeitnehmer. **Studies on hygienic conditions and medical services of German employees in agriculture insurea in local health insurance.**

19689 Riemann, F.; Harbeck, H.   DE 914006/78/0003 N
Ergänzende Formen der sozialen Sicherung landwirtschaftlicher Familien und die Belastung der Betriebe mit Sozialabgaben. **Supplementary forms of social security for farmers' families and charge of enterprises with social duties.** Publications.

19690 Hutterer, R.   DE 936001/75/0001 R
Der Rückgang der Bestände der Feldspitzmaus – Crocidura leucodon – im Rheinland als Beispiel für die Beeinflussung von Ökosystemen durch Umweltchemikalien. **The decrease in population of the bicoloured white–toothed shrew – Crocidura leucodon – in the Rhineland as an example of the influence of chemical environmental pollutants on ecosystems.**

19691 Christensen, S.G.; Hald, E.   DK 030137/79/0001 N
Forekomst af Yersinia enterocolitica i fødemiddelkæden. **The occurrence of Yersinia enterocolitica in foods.**

19692 Nansen, P.; Aalbæk, B.; Schlundt, J.
                    DK 030137/79/0005 N
Smitstoffers overlevelsesevne ved biogasudvikling af gylle. **Survival of infectious agents during anerobic digestion and methanogenesis of slurry.**

19693 Lund, E.; Lydholm, B.; Nielsen, A.L.
                    DK 030138/77/0015 N
Påvisning af virus i spildevand, slam og recipienter. **The detection of virus in waste waters, sludges and recipient waters.**

19694 Lund, E.; Jahn, S. al A.   DK 030138/79/0002 N
Undersøgelser af forskellige sudanske jordarters virusbindende evne i forbindelse med vandrensning. **Studies on the virus binding capacity of soil samples from Sudan.**

19695 Salmon–legagneur, E.; Roustan, J.L.
                    FR 010206/74/2942
Etude des composés odorants des déjections animales. **Study of smelling compounds of animal manure.**

19696 Catroux, G.; Germon, J.C..   FR 011002/71/0588
Epuration du lisier de porcherie : évolution au stockage et épandage. **Purification of pig–semi–liquid manure : evolution during storage, problems arising at spreading.** Publications.

19697 Bidan, P.; Dubois, P.   FR 011009/71/2210
Epuration biologique des vinasses de distilleries de betteraves. **Biological treatment of wastes from sugar beet distilleries.** Publications.

19698 Morfaux, J.N.; Goyet, C.   FR 011009/71/2211
Epuration des eaux résiduaires des usines de panneaux de fibre de bois. **Purification from wood fiber board factories. Wastes.** Publications.

19699 Echaubard   FR 011800/72/5289
Action des radiations ionisantes sur la physiologie de la mouche domestique. **The effect of ionizing radiations on housefly physiology.**

19700 McGrath, D.   IE 060200/73/0823 R
Reduction of odour of pig slurry. Publications.

19701 Sherwood, M.; Kiely, P.V.; Burke, W.
                    IE 060200/76/1177 R
Land spreading of animal manures – effects on water quality. Publications.

19702 McMahon, E.; Malone, D.; Hopkins, L.
                    IE 070300/77/9121 N
Industrial and solid wastes and their disposal in Ireland.

19703 O'Gara, F.; Gumbleton, B.   IE 110102/79/9229 N

Mechanism of the proliferation of plasmid mediated multiple drug resistance in agricultural environments. Publications.

19704 Collins, J.D.; O'Mahony, H.; Dunne, C.
                    IE 120206/78/9237 N
Hygiene and salmonella surveillance in an integrated poultry processing unit. Publications.

19705 Hannan, J.; Dunne, C.; Collins, J.D.; Hall, J.; O'Mahony, H.   IE 120206/78/9238 N
The prevalence of r–factor–positive escherichia coli and salmonellae in effluents from sewage plants.

19706 Dodd, V.A.; Tunney, H.; Murphy, M.J.
                    IE 120301/77/9054 N
Disposal of sewage sludge by land spreading.

19707 Bracken, J.J.   IE 120403/00/9094 N
Heavy metal studies in three Irish rivers. Publications.

19708 Colzani, G.; Nuccitelli, G.   IT 020600/77/0002 N
Sicurezza degli operatori nella distribuzione meccanizzata dei fitofarmaci.. **About the operator's security in the mechanical gear of the phitomedicines..**

19709 Meijboom, F.W.   NL 010102/75/6737
Aërobe biologische zuivering van kalverdrijfmest op semitechnische schaal (ca 4m^3). **Aerobic biological purification of liquid manure of milk fed calves in a 4m^3 Pilot plant.** Publications.

19710 Lande Cremer, L.C.N. de la   NL 010103/68/2598
Oplossing van het vraagstuk van de verwerking van mestoverschotten. **Disposal of excess manure.** Publications.

19711 Lande Cremer, L.C.N.de la   NL 010103/71/3557
Bestrijding van de stank van mest door regulering van de microbiologische omzettingen. **Control of the offensive odours from manure through regulation of the microbiological transformations.** Publications.

19712 Geelen, M.A. van   NL 010106/72/4724 R
Stankbestrijding bij ventilatielucht uit stallen en hokken door middel van luchtwassers. **Odour abatement of exhaust ventilation air from livestock houses by air washing.** Publications.

19713 Kroodsma, W.   NL 010106/72/4729
Het drogen van kippemest met behulp van ventilatielucht om stankoverlast te beperken. **Drying of poultry manure by means of ventilating air for odour abatement.** Publications.

19714 Benders, G.A.   NL 010106/75/6421
Onderzoek m.b.t. het doelmatig gebruik van water bij het reinigen van melkstal, van melkapparatuur en in aanliggende ruimten. **Research related to the efficient use of waters for cleaning of the milking parlour, milking equipment and adjacent rooms.**

19715 Jongebreur, A.A.   NL 010106/76/6713 R
Ontwikkelen van meetmethoden voor het bepalen van de stank veroorzaakt door varkensstallen, pluimveehokken en mestopslagputten. **Development of measuring methods for determining the odours emanating from piggeries, poultry houses and dung storages.** Publications.

19716 Haartsen, P.I. NL 010106/76/7383 R
De verspreiding van stank–bevattende ventilatielucht uit stallen. **The dispersion of odourous ventilation air from animal houses in the atmosphere.**

19717 Klarenbeek, J.V. NL 010106/78/8367
Eenvoudige sensorische meetmethoden voor het bepalen van de stank in de landbouw. **Simple sensory methods for the determination of malodourous emissions in agriculture.**

19718 Klarenbeek, J.V. NL 010109/78/8367
Eenvoudige sensorische meetmethoden voor het bepalen van de stank in de landbouw. **Simple sensory methods for the determination of malodourous emissions in agriculture.**

19719 Dorp, F. van NL 010110/76/7283
Scheme for decontamination of agricultural areas after severe nuclear accidents.

19720 Schipper, C.J.; Brouwer, J. NL 010213/61/3383
Onderzoek naar de bruikbaarheid van diverse methoden van reiniging en desinfectie van melkwinningsapparatuur. (o.a. afvoer van afvalwater). **Methods for cleaning and disinfection of milking equipment (a.o. discharge of waste water). Publications.**

19721 Hoeks, J. NL 010501/73/5209
Biochemische processen in afvalwater onder aerobe respectievelijk anaerobe omstandigheden. **Biochemical processes in waste water under aerobic resp. anaerobic conditions. Publications.**

19722 Mayhew, S.C. NL 020006/75/4818
Onderzoek van de redox reacties van anaerobe bacteriën, in het bijzonder met betrekking tot de afbraak van aromatische verbindingen. **Studies on the anaerobic degrations by microorganisms with special reference to aromatic compounds.**

19723 Koopal, L.K. NL 020016/75/6295
Fundamenteel onderzoek naar de fysische–chemische technieken ter verwijdering van vast kolloidaal materiaal uit water, speciaal vlokking m.b.v. polymeren en onderzoek naar de verwijdering van laagmolekulaire organische stoffen uit waterige oplossing d.m.v. adsorptie aan kool en het effect van concurrerende adsorbaten hierop. **Flocculation of carbon suspensions with polymers and the competitive adsorption on carbon.**

19724 Biersteker, K. NL 020019/78/8634 N
Arbeidsgezondheidkunde en Bedrijfshygiëne. **Occupational Health and Industrial Hygiene.**

19725 Tamminga, S.K.; Kampelmacher, E.H.
NL 020031/71/5118
Bedrijfshygiënische onderzoekingen; bakteriologische gesteldheid van oppervlakken. **Plant hygienic investigations; Bacteriological condition of surfaces. Publications.**

19726 Beverloo, W.A.; Akse, H. NL 020031/74/6377
Sorptiekinetik van organische componenten (insecticiden e.d. vanuit water aan actieve kool). **Sorption of organic compounds from aqueous solution on active carbon. Publications.**

19727 Deinema, M.H. NL 020033/69/4715
Ecologisch onderzoek naar de voorwaarden voor groei van draadvormige bacteriën in actief slib met behulp van batch en continue cultures. **Investigations on physiology and ecology of filamentous and non–filamentous bacteria in activated sludge studied in batch and continue cultures. Publications.**

19728 Adamse, A.D. NL 020033/76/4385
Microbiologisch onderzoek van de anaërobe slibgisting. **Microbiological research of anaerobic sludge fermentation.**

19729 Deinema, M.H. NL 020033/78/8801 N
Biologische fosfaatverwijdering uit afvalwater m.b.t. actief slib. **Biological removal of phosphate from waste waters by activated sludge.**

19730 Rensink, J.H. NL 020064/68/4647
Ontstaan, voorkomen en bestrijden van licht slib. **Development, prevention and combating of bulking sludge.** Publications.

19731 Leentvaar, J. NL 020064/71/4987
Toepassing a–kool bij de zuivering van afvalwater en bereiding van drinkwater. **Application of activated carbon for waste water treatment and drinking water production.** Publications.

19732 Lettinga, G. NL 020064/71/8458
Anaërobe zuiveringsmethoden voor de behandeling van afvalwater. **Anaerobic treatment methods for waste water purification.** Publications.

19733 Buuren, J.C.L. van NL 020064/73/4990
Effect van chelaterende natuurlijke en kunstmatige organische stoffen op het gedrag van zware metalen in het waterig milieu. **The effect of natural and artificial chelating agents in the behaviour of various heavy metals in the aquatic environment.**

19734 Klapwijk, A. NL 020064/74/6334
Nitrificatie en denitrificatie processen bij de zuivering van afvalwater met het oog op N.eliminatie. **Nitrification and denitrification processes in connection with N–elimination during purification of waste waters.** Publications.

19735 Cuppen, J.G.M. NL 020064/76/6843
Structuur en funktie van het oecosysteem van het Callitricho–Batrachion. **Structure and function of the ecosystem Callitricho–Batrachion.**

19736 Velsem, A.F.M. van NL 020064/76/8465
Anaerobe vergisting van varkensdrijfmest. **Anaerobic digestion of wet piggery waste.**

19737 Zeeuw, W.J. de NL 020064/77/8457
Adaptatie van anaëroob slib. **Adaptation of anaerobic sludge.**

19738 Rensink, J.H. NL 020064/78/8831 N
Biologische defosfatering van afvalwater d.m.v. aktief slib. **Biological removal of phosphate in wastewater by activated sludge.**

19739 Boleij, J.S.M. NL 020070/76/7379
Onderzoek naar de grootteverdeling van het stedelijk aerosol. **Size–distribution of urban aerosols.**

19740 Harssema, H. NL 020070/76/7383
De verspreiding van stank–bevattende ventilatielucht uit stallen. **The dispersion of odourous ventilation air from animal houses in the atmosphere.**

D 7310 – Public health engineering

19741 Hofschreuder, P.   NL 020070/78/8395
Monstername – efficiency voor grote deeltjes onder
buitenlucht omstandigheden. **Sampling efficiency for large
wind–borne particles.**

19742 Snijders, J.M.A.; Gerats, G.E.; Corstiaensen, G.P.;
Logtestijn, J.G. van   NL 030008/76/6926
Hygiëne van slachtprocessen. **Hygiene of slaughter processes.**
Publications.

19743 Logtestijn, J.G. van   NL 030008/76/7771 R
Hygiënische aspekten van het (her)gebruik van water in de
vleeslijn. **Hygienic aspects of the (re)use of water in the meat
industry.** Publications.

19744 Logtestijn, J.G. van   NL 030008/77/7774 R
Arbeidsmilieu en hygiëne. **Environment and hygiene.**

19745 Jong, J. de   NL 040007/76/8431
Reiniging van effluenten en verontreinigd water met behulp
van riet- of biezenvelden. **Purification of effluents and polluted
water with the help of reed and rush fields.**

19746 Hoek, K.W. van de   NL 040010/72/4728
Stankbestrijding bij mest en gier door middel van beluchting;
mestafvoersystemen uit stallen. **Odour abatement by aerating
manure and liquid manure; dung removal systems in stables.**
Publications.

19747 Schothorst, M. van   NL 040011/64/7437
Het tegengaan van Salmonella besmetting van kalveren in
slachthuizen. **Prevention and decreasing of
Salmonella–contamination of calves in slaughterhouses.**
Publications.

19748 Schaefer, J.   NL 050301/72/5308
Analyse en bestudering van de aard, hoeveelheid en oorsprong
van stoffen en mengsels van stoffen die stankoverlast
veroorzaken met behulp van instrumenteel–analytische en
sensorische methoden. **Study and analysis of odorous pollutants
in the environment.**

19749 Waart, J. de   NL 050301/72/6480
Verwijderen van chemische afvalstoffen uit afvalwater door
middel van microorganismen. **Disposal of chemical waste
products from effluent by means of micro–organisms.**

19750 Reuzel, E.   NL 050301/74/6758
Toxiciteitsonderzoek van luchtverontreinigende stoffen, in het
bijzonder fotochemische luchtverontreiniging. **Research on the
toxicity of air pollutants, especially photochemical pollutants.**
Publications.

19751 Schaefer, J.   NL 050301/75/6750
Ontwikkeling van objectieve instrumentele methodes voor de
bepaling van de intensiteit van onwelriekende lucht in de
landbouw. **Development of objective instrumental methods for
measurement of the intensity of malodorous air in agriculture.**

19752 Berende, P.L.M.   NL 050305/75/8031
Persistentie van veevoederadditieven en contaminanten in
excreta, mestopslag, biologische afbraakinstallaties, slib en
effluent. **Persistency of feed additives and contaminants in
excreta, stored manure, bio degradation units, its silt and
effluent.**

19753 Brasser, L.J.; Giezen, J.J. van; Guicherit, R.
     NL 050401/51/6235
Verontreiniging van water en bodem, voor zover afkomstig
van luchtverontreiniging. **Pollution of water and soil as far as
originating from atmospheric pollution.** Publications.

19754 Jeltes, R.; Tonkelaar, W.A.M. den
     NL 050401/70/6690
Melieuchemisch onderzoek bij lozingen, lekkages, ongevallen
e.d. (o.a. van olie). **Application of environmental chemistry in
case of spills, leakages, accidents a.s.o. (a.o. of oil).**
Publications.

19755 Heide, B.A.   NL 050401/73/6688
Aerobe zuivering in laag belaste actief–slib systemen (i.v.m.
kwaliteitsbeheer oppervlaktewater). **Aerobic purification in
very low loaded activated sludge systems.** Publications.

19756 Heide, B.A.   NL 050401/74/6689
Surplusslibverwerking. **Treatment and disposal of sewage
sludges.** Publications.

19757 Kooij, E.G.   NL 060002/68/4019
Ontwikkeling van een voor meer doeleinden toe te passen
reinigings–middel voor machines en hulpmiddelen in de
zuivelindustrie. **Development of a cleaning agent for dairy
machinery which can be used for more purposes.** Publications.

19758 Jansen, L.A.   NL 060002/74/6088
Lawaaibestrijding in de zuivelindustrie. **Fighting of noise in
dairy industry.** Publications.

19759 Nieuwenhof, F.F.J.   NL 060002/76/6612
Gedeeltelijke voorzuivering van afvalwater. **Partial
pre–purification of waste water.**

19760 Langeveld, L.P.M.   NL 060002/77/7311
Effect van Cleaning in Place van vulmachines op het
besmettingsniveau van het produkt. **Effect of the
cleaning–in–place of filling machines on the microbiological
contamination level of the product.**

19761 Goren, E.   NL 060010/65/7292 R
Verbetering van hygiënische maatregelen, o.a. desinfectie, op
pluimveehouderij bedrijven. **Improvement of hygienic
measures, a.o. desinfection, on poultry farms.**

D 7320 – Medicine

19762 Bitsch, I.   DE 129900/73/0002
Biochemie der chronischen Alkoholintoxikation und des
Alkoholentzuges. **Biochemistry of chronic intoxication with
alcoholics and of withdrawal.**

19763 Borneff, J.; Edenharder, R.   DE 154070/72/0001
Der bakterielle Steroidabbau als vermutliche Ursache des
Dickdarmkrebses. **Bacterial steroid degradation as the
probable etiologic factor of large bowel cancer.**

19764 Jensen, A.T.; Jensen, E.   DK 030106/78/0002 N
Undersøgelse af reaktivitet og neutraliserende virkning af
antacida til humant brug. **Investigation of reactivity profile and
neutralizing effect of antacida in human medicine.**

19765 Aalund, O.   DK 030129/76/0011 N
Patofysiologiske studier på porcin hud eksponeret for termisk
og elektrisk energi. **Patho–physiological studies on porcine skin
exposed to thermal and electrical energy.**

19766 Tomassone, R.; Jolivet, E.   FR 010214/77/8269
Transmission de la balharziose: étude en guadeloupe (3).
Transmission of bilharzia: case study in guadeloupe.

19767 Hasan, S.; Duthoit, J.L.; Louis, C.; Croizier, G.; Plus,
N.; Fosset, J.   FR 010612/69/5192
Recherche d'infections naturelles chez les moustiques.
Research on the natural infection of mosquitos.

19768 Plus, N.; Jousset, F.X.; Croizier, G.; Veyrunes, J.C.;
Duthoit, J.L.   FR 010612/69/5193
Virus endémiques des populations de Diptères apparemment
normales. **Endemic viruses of apparently normal Drosophila
and Mosquito populations.**

19769 Giban, J.; Kermarrec, A.; Delattre, P.
                         FR 011605/77/5275
Rôle du rat dans la dynamique des foyers de Bilharziose à
Schistosoma Mansoni en Mangrove, écologie de la Bilharziose.
Rats, shistosomiasis, mangroves, bionomics and epidemiology.

19770 Scardovi, V.   IT 040210/77/0295 R
Ecologia, evoluzione e tecnologia dei bifidobatteri. **Ecology,
evolution and technology of L. bifidus.**

19771 Pauluzzi, S.   IT 041029/78/1155 N
Studio del ruolo degli Herpesvirus, Papovavirus, Adenovirus,
Oncornavirus e Poxvirus nei processi neoplastici umani ed
animali. **A study on the influence of Herpesvirus, Papovavirus,
Adenovirus, Oncornavirus and Poxvirus on human and animal
neoplastic growths.**

19772 Zonneveld, R.J. van   NL 020019/77/8635 N
Sociale gerontologie. **Social gerontology.**

19773 Biersteker, K.   NL 020019/77/8638 N
Milieu–gezondheidsrelaties; Capita–Selecta uit studies in
Nederland of daarbuiten naar stoffen en verschijnselen in het
fysisch–chemisch milieu en hun invloed op de menselijke
gezondheid. **Relations between environment and health; Capita
Selecta from studies in and outside the Netherlands on
chemicals and phenomena in the physical/chemical environment
and their effects on human health.**

19774 Bausch – Goldbohm, R.A.   · NL 020019/77/8798 N
Onderzoek naar de vraag hoe zinvol screening op
risicofactoren voor hart en vaatziekten in de Nederlandse
situatie is. (Kaunas–Rotterdam, Invention study). **An estimate
of the usefulness of screening on risk for coronavy and
heartdisease in the Netherlands (Kaunas–Rotterdam, Invention
study).**

19775 Pelt, F.L.   NL 020019/78/8799 N
Zorg voor moeder en kind. **Mother and child care.**

19776 Visser, G.R.   NL 020023/75/4512
Besturing regionale gezondheidszorg. **Regional health
management.** Publications.

19777 Defares, P.B.   NL 020048/77/7566
De invloed van stress en persoonlijkheidsfactoren op cognitief
funktioneren. **The influence of stress and personality variables
on cognition.**

19778 Ploeg, J.D. van der   NL 020048/78/8806 N
Stress bij groepsleiding. **Organizational stress in a residential
setting.**

19779 Schuller, P.L.   NL 040011/76/7475
Het ontwikkelen van een methode van onderzoek voor het
aantonen van aflatoxine in menselijke/dierlijke organen;
onderzoek naar het vóórkomen van aflatoxin in menselijke
levers in Nederland. **The development of a detection method for
aflatoxin in human and animal organs; investigation of the
prevalence of aflatoxin in human livers in the Netherlands.**

19780 Greve, P.A.   NL 040011/76/7516
Onderzoek naar het voorkomen van chloorhoudende
bestrijdingsmiddelen, PCB's en andere accumulerende stoffen
in het lichaamsvet van de Nederlandse bevolking. **Examination
on the prevalence of chlorinated pesticides, PCB's and other
accumulating agents in the body fat of the dutch population.**
Publications.

D 8100 – Documentation, publication and information

See also 1786, 4853, 10133, 13663, 15029, 15547, 15550, 17352, 17895, 20334

19781 Dagnelie, P.; Rousseaux, G.; Carletti, G.; Laustriaux, J.; Debouche, C.; Oger, R. BE 010010/70/0002 R
Organisation d'une bibliothèque de programmes statistiques pour ordinateur. **Organization of a computer statistical program library.** Publications.

19782 Dagnelie, P.; Rousseaux, G.; Kindermans, M.
BE 010010/75/0007 R
Constitution d'une banque de données pédologiques. **Composition of a data bank of pedological information.**

19783 Goffinet. R.; Hellemans, R.; Van Haeperen, J.
BE 120000/77/0024
Classification et caractérisation des exploitations agricoles. **Classification and characterization of the holdings.** Publications.

19784 Goffinet, R.; Stuyck, D.; Vanorlé, L.; Van Lierde, D.; Devisch, N. BE 120000/77/0026 R
Recherches sur le fonctionnement économique des exploitations agricoles et horticoles, ainsi que sur celui des élevages spécialisés. **Study of the economic functionning of agricultural, horticultural and specialised breeding farms.**

19785 Everaet, H. BE 120000/77/0028 N
De verspreiding van innovaties in de landbouw. **The diffusion of innovations in agriculture.** Publications.

19786 Rogister, J. BE 130000/56/0007 R
Cartographie écologique et forestière des diverses forêts domaniales belges. **Ecological and sylvicultural mapping of the Belgian State Forests.** Publications.

19787 Weiling, F.; Unger, C. DE 111151/75/0001
Erstellung von Rechenprogrammen zur multivariaten – und univariaten – Analyse. **Establishment of computing programs for multivariate – and univariate – analysis.**

19788 Pacher, J.; Zimmermann, G. DE 126505/75/0005 N
Die Geschichte des Waldes auf der heutigen Gemarkung Stuttgart. **History of the forest in the today landmark of Stuttgart.**

19789 Keuffel, W.; Schumann, G. DE 132840/75/0008
Untersuchung über das Berichtswesen staatlicher Forstämter. **Study on the reporting practices of State Forestry Departments.**

19790 Schulze, W.; Heller, P. DE 139750/78/0019 N
Maschinengerechte Dokumentationsverfahren in der Tierärztlichen Praxis. **Machine–compatible documentation procedures in a veterinary practice.**

19791 Haendler, H.; Neese, U. DE 144030/75/0001
Integration der Hohenheimer Datenbank für Futtermittelbefunde in das "International Network of Feed Information Centres" – INFIC –. **Integration of the Hohenheim data bank for feed analyses data into the "International Network of Feed Information Centres" – INFIC –.**

19792 Haendler, H.; Jager, F.; Neese, U.; Mayr, H.
DE 144030/78/0001 N
Erarbeitung eines mehrsprachigen Thesaurus zur Deskription von Futtermitteln für die besonderen Belange der Datendokumentation. **Development of a multilingual thesaurus for describing feeds for the special purposes of data documentation.** Publications.

19793 Albrecht, H.; Hildt, U. DE 144960/78/0006 N
Die Behandlung der Umweltschutzproblematik in Schulbüchern der Sekundarstufe I. **The presentation of environmental problems in school–books of secondary schools – 11–16 years –.**

19794 Researcher not indicated DE 161000/78/0001 N
Aufbau eines EDV–Informationssystems für Entscheidungsträger der Gemeinschaftsverpflegung. **Setup of EDP information system for decision makers of catering.**

19795 Seidewitz, L. DE 201040/75/0002
Erarbeitung von Grundlagen für den internationalen Informationsaustausch. **Elaboration of a basis for international exchange of information.**

19796 Hondelmann, W. DE 201040/75/0004
Sammelaktionen durch Materialaustausch. **Collections carried out by exchange of material.**

19797 Rhody, B.; Panzer, K.F. DE 202010/75/0003
Eignung mechanischer und optischer Messgeräte zur Erstellung maschinenlesbarer Datenträger für die terrestrische Datenerfassung bei Waldinventuren. **Capability of mechanical and optical measurement instruments for computer–compatible recording for terrestrial data collection in forest inventories.**

19798 Laux, W. DE 215300/77/0001
Analyse von Anfrageart, Anfragethematik und Anfrageanlass zur Verbesserung der Recherchequalität im Fach Phytomedizin. **Analysis of kind, reasons and subjects of inquiry for improvement of retrieval quality in phytomedicine.**

19799 Sicker, W. DE 215300/77/0003
Vergleich von Suchstrategien und Rechercheergebnissen bei Recherchemassnahmen im Fach Phytomedizin mit Handkarteien und elektronischer Datenverarbeitung. **Comparison of search strategies and results in phytomedicine with hand card files and electronic data processing.**

19800 Laux, W. DE 215300/77/0004
Auslegung der Deskriptorenstruktur im Fach Phytomedizin auf Verwendbarkeit im EDV–System. **Interpretation of structure of descriptors in phytomedicine for use in EDP system.**

19801 Blumenbach, D. DE 215300/77/0005
Registerverbesserung für Spezialbibliographien. **Improvement of indices for special bibliographies.**

19802 Laux, W. DE 215300/77/0007
Analyse der Aussagefähigkeit von Sachtiteln im Fach Phytomedizin im Hinblick auf die Aussagefähigkeit von Titelbibliographien. **Analysis of the informative value of titles in phytomedicine with regard to informative value of title bibliographies.**

D 8100 – Documentation, publication and information

19803 Blumenbach, D.   DE 215300/77/0008
Entwicklung von Dokumentationssprachen bzw.
Deskriptorsystemen für phytomedizinische Spezialgebiete –
z.B. Virologie, Pflanzenschutzmittel usw. –. **Development of
documentation languages resp. descriptor systems for special
fields in phytomedicine – e.g. virology, plant protectives, etc. –.**

19804 Laux, W.   DE 215300/77/0009
Verbesserung der Zugriffsmöglichkeit zu verschiedenen
systematischen Einheiten bei biologischen Objekten
einschliesslich der Lösung des Synonymproblems in der
Dokumentation. **Improvement of access to different systematic
units of biological objects including the solution of the problem
of synonyms in documentation.**

19805 Sicker, W.   DE 215300/77/0011
Kostenanalyse für die Recherchebearbeitung in der
Pflanzenschutzdokumentation. **Cost analysis of operation of
search in documentation on plant protection.**

19806 Blumenbach, D.   DE 215300/77/0012
Untersuchungen und EDV–Tests zu einer Neuordnung der
Bibliographie der Pflanzenschutzliteratur. **Studies on EDP tests
for rearrangement of bibliography on documents of plant
protection.**

19807 Liebscher, H.–J.; Fischer, P.   DE 218000/75/0001
Bearbeitung und Herausgabe des IHD–Jahrbuchs der
Bundesrepublik Deutschland. **Compilation and edition of the
IHD–Yearbooks of the Federal Republic of Germany.**

19808 Hansen, I.B.; Sørensen, F.T.   DK 030195/78/0001 N
Anvendelse af AGRIS–databasen til on–line litteratursøgning.
Use of the AGRIS database for on–line information retrieval.

19809 Millier, C.; Pierrat, J.C.   FR 010312/75/8293
Evaluation des langages de simulation discrète (4). **Evaluation
of some discrete events simulation languages.**

19810 Masson, J.P.; de Nancy   FR 010312/76/8292
Bibliothèque d'analyse de variance (4). **Analysis of variance
program library.**

19811 Boussard, J.M.; Mamoun, M.; David, C.
                    FR 012212/75/8668
Programme MADS (Multipurpose Agricultural Data System).
Multipurpose Agricultural Data System.

19812 Marin–Lafleche, A.; Remy, J.C.   FR 012503/69/6147
Contribution à la compréhension d'un problème par voie
d'enquête. **Contribution to the intelligence of an agronomic
problem by means of enquiries.**

19813 Pernet, F.; Bel, F.   FR 012600/78/8569
Etat des informations disponibles sur les "zones
marginalisées". **An outlook on available knowledge about
marginalised areas.**

19814 Millen   GB 010810/00/0001 R
Production of weed abstracts.

19815 Braude   GB 011711/00/0009 R
**Information retrieval and publication of index of current
research on pigs.**

19816 Smith   GB 030303/77/0010 R
**The collation and analysis of statistical information on hill and
upland farming and land use.**

19817 Mcburney   GB 040601/79/0009 N
Northern Ireland contribution to national cereals survey 1979.

19818 Lilwall   GB 060108/00/0007 R
Information services.

19819 Antonietti, A.   IT 040206/73/0340
Ricerca per l'armonizzazione dei catasti terreni. **Research for
the standardization of land registers.** Publications.

19820 Morandi Cecchi, M.   IT 063500/77/0641
Elaborazione automatica dei dati di natura territoriale.
Automatic elaboration of territorial data.

19821 Burg, J. van der   NL 010117/71/4366
Ontwikkeling van een gemechaniseerd systeem voor de
landbouwkundige documentatie en informatie. **Development of
a mechanized system for agricultural documentation and
information.** Publications.

19822 Dorgelo, F.   NL 010117/78/8301
Onderzoek naar nieuwe mogelijkheden voor het publiceren
van wetenschappelijke literatuur. **Research of new possibilities
in scientific publishing.**

19823 Stol, Ph.Th.   NL 010501/79/9059 N
Conversationele tekstverwerking. **Conversational compilation
of information data.**

19824 Stol, Ph.Th.   NL 010501/79/9060 N
Programmeertaal GENSTAT. **Programming language
GENSTAT.**

19825 Heisterkamp, S.H.   NL 010601/62/1890
Onderzoek naar de toepassingsmogelijkheden van
programmeermethoden en het gebruik van elektronische
apparatuur bij mechanische administratie, archivering en
verwerking in het bosbouwkundig onderzoek. **Research into
the possibilities of using electronic computers and similar
equipment in forest research.** Publications.

19826 Kettenis, D.L.   NL 020066/72/4899
Ontwikkeling van een algemene programmeertaal voor
continue en discrete simulatie. **A simulation language for
combined continuous system and discrete system simulation.**
Publications.

D 8200 – General research methodology

See also 1828, 8992, 16729, 18056

19827 Nielsen, H.E.   DK 010202/76/0009
EDB–system og –metoder til bearbejdning af data fra
undersøgelser i svinebesætninger. **An electronic data system
and methods for processing data from investigations with pig
herds.**

19828 Grebet, Ph.   FR 010101/75/5039
Comparaison et analyse critique des différentes méthodes
d'estimation de l'ETP en fonction du type de temps du
moment. **Comparison and critical analysis of different
estimating methods of potential evapotranspiration according to**

climatic conditions.

19829 Joannes, H.; Aries, F.　　　FR 010312/76/8278
Prédiction et régression (1). **Prediction and regression.**

19830 Masson, J.P.　　　FR 010312/76/8280
Optimisation de plans d'expériences (1). **Optimization of experimental designs.**

19831 Monestiez, P.　　　FR 010312/76/8290
Classification avec contraintes (2). **Classification with constraints.**

19832 Masson, J.P.　　　FR 010312/78/8281
Plans d'expériences optimaux discrets et surfaces de réponse (1). **Discrete optimal designs and response curves.**

19833 Felix, L.; Gosselin, M.; Rauzy, G.　　　FR 011104/75/0245
Inventaire des facteurs induisant des variations dans les données recueillies sur essais de plantes de grande culture. **Inventory of the factors inducing variations of the data of tests on large scale plants.**

19834 Badia, J.; Charpenteau, J.L.　　　FR 011409/77/8270
Modèles et dispositifs expérimentaux: cas de non indépendance des termes d'erreurs (1). **Models and experimental designs: non independence of error terms.**

19835 Nefussi, J.; Mergui, G.　　　FR 012205/76/8562
Mésoanalyse des IAA. **Mesoanalysis for food industry.**

19836 Truter　　　GB 012011/00/0007 R
Determination of crystal structures of macromolecules (peptides, polysaccharides and proteins).

19837 Mcmurray; Mccaughey　　　GB 041608/79/0004 N
Stormont investigative recording operation (SIRO).

19838 Gelman　　　GB 060219/00/0012 R
Recovery experiments for analytical methods.

19839 Manmana Novaro, P.; Mariani, B.M.; Stefanini, R.　　　IT 020800/68/0004
Cereali – Pianificazione di prove sperimentali ed analisi statistica dei risultati mediante un calcolatore elettronico. **Cereals – Planning of experimental trials and statistical computer analysis of results.** Publications.

19840 Stoutjesdijk, J.F.　　　NL 010110/64/7954
Ontwikkeling, verbetering en bevordering van nucleaire en verwante fysische en chemische methoden in biologie en landbouw. **Development, improvement and promotion of appliaction of nuclear and related physical and chemical methods in biology and agriculture.**

19841 Hag, B.A. ten; Haan, G.H. de　　　NL 010207/77/7648
Eenvoudige opbrengstbepalingsmethoden bij snijmais. **Simple methods for yield determination in silage maize.**

19842 Eenkhoorn, W.　　　NL 040007/60/4285
Verbetering van de in gebruik zijnde (of komende) analyse–methoden en –technieken voor grond–, water–, en gewasonderzoek. **Improvement of new and existing methods and techniques for soil, water and crop analysis.**

D 8210 – Mathematics

See also 6147, 10399, 13043, 13263, 13679, 18101, 20174

19843 Liard, O.　　　BE 010002/71/0007
Recherche de méthodes de détermination anticipée de récoltes de fruits à pépins. **Research of the methods of anticipated determination of the harvest of pit fruit.**

19844 Dagnelie, P.; Palm, R.　　　BE 010010/68/0003 R
Etude biométrique de différentes essences forestières et comparaison de différentes méthodes d'échantillonnage et de cubage. **Biometrical study of different forest tree species and comparison of different methods of sampling and cubage.** Publications.

19845 Dagnelie, P.; Debouche, C.　　　BE 010010/74/0005
Etude de modèles mathématiques non–linéaires dans leur application aux courbes de croissance. **Study of non–linear mathematical models and their application on growth curves.** Publications.

19846 Dagnelie, P.; Carletti, G.　　　BE 010010/74/0006
Recherche de méthodes de détection automatique de valeurs anormales. **Research of automatical detection methods of the abnormal values.** Publications.

19847 Dagnelie, P.; Debouche, C.　　　BE 010010/76/0008 R
Exécution par ordinateur de comptabilités agricoles et d'analyses de groupes. **Execution by computer of the agricultural book–keeping and groups analysis.**

19848 Vansteenkiste, C.; De Schutter, F.　　　BE 030003/72/0001 R
Optimalisering van de rekentechnieken voor simulatie van verdeelde parameter –systemen uit de milieuwetenschappen. **Optimilization of computation techniques for simulation of distributed parameter systems in environmental sciences.** Publications.

19849 Vansteenkiste, G.; Rotti, A.; Ottoy, J.; Calus, A.; Callewier, J.　　　BE 030003/72/0002 R
Onderzoek naar de geldigheid van statistische modellen. **Research concerning the validity of statistical models.** Publications.

19850 Van Steenkiste, G.; Spriet, J.　　　BE 030003/76/0003 R
Fundamentele studie, modelbouw en identificatie van deelsystemen met biologische aktiviteit met het doel interaktieve optimale sturing uit te voeren. **Fundamental study, modelbuilding and identification of subsystems in biological activity in order to carry out interactive optimal control.** Publications.

19851 Welvaert, W.; Poppe, J.　　　BE 030011/76/0007
Identifikatie van ectomycorrhiza door myceliumkarakterisatie en door artificiële fruktifikatie in rein kultuur. **Identification of ectomycorrhiza by characterization of the mycelium and by artificial fructification in pure culture.**

19852 Wijnhoven, J.　　　BE 040602/73/0002
Oplossen van statische methodologische problemen bij het experimenteren in de landbouwwetenschappen. **Research on statisticalproblems by experimenting in agricultural sciences.**

19853 Motoulle, A.　　　BE 120000/77/0027 N
Amélioration de la statistique des prix agricoles. **Amelioration**

D 8210 – Mathematics

of statistics concerning prices of agricultural products. Publications.

19854 Franz, F.; Flurl, H.　　　　DE 160210/77/0003
Entwicklung eines vereinfachten Verfahrens der Holzvermessung und Holzaufnahme im Schwachholz. **Development of a rapid method of timber scaling of slender wood.**

19855 Dempfle, L.　　　　DE 161300/78/0004 N
Relative Effizienz von statistischen Methoden zur Schätzung von genetischen Parametern, insbesondere genetische Varianzen und Kovarianzen. **Relative efficiency of various statistical methods for estimating genetic parameters, especially genetic variances and covariances.**

19856 Stuhler, E.　　　　DE 161420/75/0001
Ein Modellversuch im Hochschulbereich zur Harvard–CaseMethod. **An experiment concerning the Harvard–Case–Method.**

19857 Dietz, P.　　　　DE 501505/77/0004
Laufende Überprüfung und Verbesserung der Vermessungstechnik. **Continuous control and improvement of measuring technology.**

19858 Sandvad, K.; Kristensen, K.　　　　DK 010118/73/4702
Udvikling og afprøvning af forsøgsteoretiske metoder og EDB–programmer med henblik på planteavlsforsøg. **Development and testing of theoretical methods and EDP programmes with reference to crop husbandry experiments.**

19859 Rudemo, M.; Mason, V.C.　　　　DK 030107/76/0002
Sammenligning af metoder til bestemmelse af aminosyrer. **A comparison of the methods used in the determination of amino acids.**

19860 Flensted–Jensen, M.　　　　DK 030107/79/0001 N
Matematikkens anvendelse inden for jordbrugs– og veterinærvidenskaberne. **Application of mathematics in the agricultural and veterinary sciences.**

19861 Denis, J.B.　　　　FR 010111/77/8273
Tables de fréquences multidimensionnelles (2). **Multidimensional contingency tables.**

19862 Denis, J.B.　　　　FR 010111/77/8274
Analyse statistique des notations (1). **Statistical analysis of notations.**

19863 Kobilinsky, A.　　　　FR 010111/77/8275
Analyse multicanonique (caroll) (2). **Multicanonical analysis (caroll).**

19864 Brugere, D.; Deffontaines, J.P.; Arnoux, J.; Briand, P.
　　　　FR 010112/72/9114
Mise au point d'un dispositif de cartographie thématique automatique (carat). **Development of a computer program ("CARAT") for automatic thematic mapping.**

19865 Brugere, D.; Michel, G.; Hurpin, B.; Rebischung, J.; Leroux, M.; Rives, M.　　　　FR 010112/75/9113
Réalisation d'une expérience pilote de traitement informatique d'opérations de recherche en cours dans le domaine de la production végétale en utilisant le système "ariane" du cated. **Pilot testing of the ARIANE (CATED) conversational**

retrieval computerized system as applied to a number of I.N.R.A. plant research projects.

19866 Brugere, D.; Valery, P.; Boissard, P.; Briand, P.
　　　　FR 010112/78/9116
Mise au point d'un dispositif semi–automatique de reconnaissance de ressemblances multidimensionnelles par visualisation et manipulation de matrices polychromes réalisées par ordinateur sur écran cathodique "péricolor". **Development of a semi–automatic multidimensional resemblance identifying system through the visualization and manipulation of polychrome matrices, computer produced on "PERICOLOR" screen.**

19867 Desnoyers, F.; Vodovar, N.　　　　FR 010205/78/9564
Mise au point d'une méthode morphométrique en microscopie électronique pour la détermination de la cellularité des tissus adipeux. **An electron microscopic morphometric method for evaluation of adipose tissues cellularity.**

19868 Ley, J.P.　　　　FR 010214/74/8253
Modélisations de la croissance: courbes de croissance (3). **Modelisation of growth: growth curves.**

19869 Vila, J.P.　　　　FR 010214/74/8255
Minimisation de fonction (4). **Function minimization.**

19870 Minato, P.　　　　FR 010214/74/8257
Chronique multivariable (3). **Multivariate time series.**

19871 Vila, J.P.　　　　FR 010214/74/8262
Structure de covariances: analyse factorielle (1). **Covariance structures: factor analysis.**

19872 Jolivet, E.　　　　FR 010214/75/8258
Mesures de condensation, d'agglomération liées à des processus ponctuels (3). **Condensation and agglomeration measures linked with stochastic point process.**

19873 Ley, J.P.　　　　FR 010214/76/8261
Structure de covariances: croissance, composantes de la variance (1). **Covariance structures: growth and variance components.**

19874 Jacob, C.　　　　FR 010214/76/8264
Elimination d'un facteur de croissance (1). **Elimination of growth factor.**

19875 Tomassone, R.　　　　FR 010214/77/8251
Statistique non paramétrique (2). **Non parametric statistics.**

19876 Ley, J.P.; Vila, J.P.　　　　FR 010214/77/8252
Méthodes graphiques en biométrie (4). **Graphical methods in biometry.**

19877 Dervin, C.; Tomassone, R.　　　　FR 010214/77/8265
Classification non hiérarchique de grands corpus de données (2). **Partition of large sets of data.**

19878 Vila, J.P.　　　　FR 010214/78/8254
Analyse factorielle sur données binaires (1). **Factor analysis of dichotomized variables.**

19879 Vila, J.P.　　　　FR 010214/78/8256
Approximation et optimisation stochastique. **Approximation and stochastic optimization.**

19880 Ley, J.P.; Vila, J.P. FR 010214/78/8263
Structure de covariances: piste, autorégressif, simplex et circumsimplex (1). **Covariance structures: path, autoregressives, simplex and circumsimplex.**

19881 Masson, J.P.; Millier, C. FR 010312/76/8277
Analyse de variance multivariable: dépouillement de données (1). **Multivariate analysis of variance: case studies.**

19882 Masson, J.P. FR 010312/76/8279
Les modèles linéaires adaptés aux plans d'expérience utilisés en agronomie (1). **Linear models fitted to field experiments used in agronomy.**

19883 Haeflinger, R. FR 010312/77/8291
Modèles arima uni et multivariables (3). **Arima models: uni and multivariate.**

19884 Masson, J.P.; Danzart, M. FR 010312/78/8282
Discrimination entre modèles (1). **Model discrimination.**

19885 Routchenko, W.; Soyer, J.P. FR 010704/65/0554
Recherche d'indices permettant de donner une expression mathématique à l'intensité de croissance des plantes cultivées. **Determination of indexes allowing a mathematical expression of growth intensity of crops.** Publications.

19886 Boussard, J.M.; Bourliaud, J.; Jaffrelot, J.J.
FR 011706/74/3331
La vérification des modèles économétriques de grande dimension : utilisation des méthodes de classification automatique. **Validation of large econometric models : using automatic clustering techniques.** Publications.

19887 Foulhouze, I.; Boussard, J.M. FR 012212/77/8664
Repondération d'un mauvais échantillon statistique. **Reweighting a bad sample.**

19888 Taylor; St GB 010104/00/0004
Multibreed theory.

19889 Taylor; St GB 010104/00/0005
Growth theory.

19890 Sales GB 010105/77/0006
Statistical analysis of animal breeding experiments and bioassays.

19891 Rowlands; Pocock GB 010408/00/0033
Development of general statistical programs for large scale models.

19892 Clark; Filshie GB 010702/00/0003 R
Development of real time data processing systems.

19893 Mccorquodale GB 010709/00/0005 R
Environmental and other errors in poultry experiments.

19894 Morley–Jones GB 010709/00/0006
Devise or adapt statistical and computational techniques for general use.

19895 Holland; Barlow GB 011009/00/0001
Methodology : experimental design.

19896 Rutherfrd; Tamsett GB 011009/75/0007
Methodology of data analysis.

19897 Holland; Moore GB 011009/75/0008
Biometry of plants, pests and diseases.

19898 Rutherford; Cumming GB 011009/75/0009
Recording methods and data handling.

19899 Thornley GB 011107/00/0001
The use of mathematical models to study plant growth and development.

19900 Luckwill; Williams, R.R. GB 011510/00/0022
Productivity of british apple and pear orchards.

19901 Dumont GB 011611/00/0007
Hay production systems.

19902 Dumont; Boyce GB 011611/00/0009
Protein production from forage crops.

19903 Boyce GB 011611/74/0010
Systems studies of machinery for reduced cultivations.

19904 Dumont GB 011611/76/0013
To determine the effects of different types of farm transport.

19905 Boyce; Price GB 011611/77/0014
Sugar beet production mathematical models to analyse unit operations and determine their economic importance.

19906 Audsley; Boyce GB 011611/78/0015
System studies on irrigation.

19907 Boyce GB 011611/78/0016
Operational research studies to identify energy effective food production systems and separate operations.

19908 Clough; Broster GB 011704/00/0022
Computer programmed feeding systems for lactation period.

19909 Mulvany GB 011704/00/0024
Development of farm management information systems.

19910 Draycott GB 011809/00/0005
Development and support of general computer programs.

19911 Freeman; Barnes GB 011809/00/0009
Development of dynamic models for biological systems.

19912 Barnes; Phelps GB 011809/77/0010
Statistical methods applied to problems in vegetable research.

19913 Freeman; Morris GB 011809/77/0011
Theoretical statistical investigations arising out of problems in vegetable research.

19914 Kempton GB 011909/00/0002
Statistical and mathematical investigation on data.

19915 Kempton GB 011909/76/0003
Statistical programming.

19916 Wright GB 011910/00/0003
Theoretical and empirical evaluation and comparison of

breeding methods and selection techniques.

19917 Radley   GB 012002/00/0011 R
Devise or adapt statistical and computational techniques for general use.

19918 Nelder   GB 012014/00/0001
Statistical programming.

19919 Gower   GB 012014/00/0003
Statistical and mathematical investigations.

19920 Rowell; Walters   GB 013401/00/0012
Statistical research.

19921 Rowell   GB 013401/76/0888
Programming of general application.

19922 Maxwell; Sibbald   GB 030303/00/0009
Simulation models of hill and upland sheep production systems.

19923 Inkson   GB 030407/00/0001
Theory of experimental design and statistical analysis.

19924 Inkson   GB 030407/00/0002
Crop yield and composition in relation to soil properties, and the numerical classification of soils.

19925 Inkson   GB 030407/00/0003
Development of computer techniques and programs.

19926 Topham   GB 030701/00/0042
Statistical studies in plant variation.

19927 Topham; Cowan   GB 030701/00/0043
Computer applications to genetics and plant breeding.

19928 Green   GB 030901/00/0403
Evaluation of characteristics and techniques for identifying and classifying root and vegetable varieties.

19929 Green   GB 030901/00/0405
Study of analysis systems in varietal taxonomy of cross–pollinated species.

19930 Stewart   GB 040201/75/0003 R
Mathematical modelling applied to ecosystems of Lough Neagh.

19931 McCallion   GB 040201/78/0004
Investigation of sampling techniques in relation to the farm census.

19932 Miller   GB 050510/00/0009
Epidemic planning and information computer assisted.

19933 Miller; Richards   GB 050510/00/0010
Disease models.

19934 Richards; Dragon   GB 050510/00/0013
The development of on line access to disease data banks.

19935 Richards; Dragon   GB 050510/00/0014
Computerisation of zoonoses order data.

19936 Davies; Bell   GB 050510/00/0020
Abortion statistics.

19937 Parkinson   GB 060313/00/0001
Extended use of milk recording in scotland.

19938 Heemst, H.D.J. van   NL 010104/75/6225
Praktische toepassing van simulatieprogramma's op het gebied van gewasverdamping en produktie. **Application of simulation models on transpiration and production of crops.** Publications.

19939 Hamming, G.   NL 010116/70/6556
Het gebruik van wiskundige methoden in economische analyses (kreukel analyse). **The use of mathematical methods in economic analysis (Crumple analysis).**

19940 Boer, P.B. de   NL 010116/73/5920
Normative bedrijfsmodellen voor de rundveehouderij en weidebouw. **Normative farmmodels for cattle–and grasslandhusbandry.**

19941 Wieling, H.; Meijer, A.B.   NL 010208/73/5920
Normatieve bedrijfsmodellen voor de rundveehouderij en weidebouw. **Normative farm models for cattle–and grassland–husbandry.**

19942 Straten, H. van der   NL 010208/78/7960 R
Het ontwikkelen, aanpassen en actueel houden van modellen voor weidebedrijven m.b.v. lineaire programmering. **Development and keeping up to date of models for grassland farms by means of linear programming.**

19943 Stol, Ph.Th.   NL 010501/73/5274 R
Multicriteria–analyse. **Multi–criteria–analysis.**

19944 Stol, Ph.Th.   NL 010501/77/7216
Ontwikkeling verwerkingssystemen voor lange reeksen van gegevens. **Development of computer systems to process extensive data series.** Publications.

19945 Stol, Ph.Th.   NL 010501/79/9057 N
Bepaling van de kans van samengestelde gebeurtenissen op basis van de kansen van elk der samenstellende gebeurtenissen afzonderlijk. **Determination of the probability of compound events from empirical distributions of each event separately.**

19946 Heisterkamp, S.H.   NL 010601/60/1889
Wiskundig–statistisch methodenonderzoek ten behoeve van het bosbouwkundig onderzoek. **Application of mathematical and statistical methods to forest research.** Publications.

19947 Berg, A. van den   NL 010601/76/6680
Onderzoek naar methoden van electronische verwerking van vegetatiekundige gegevens ten behoeve van het landschapsecologisch onderzoek. **Research on the development of computer routines for ecological data handling.**

19948 Berg, A. van den   NL 010601/76/6681
Het operationeel en bruikbaar maken van het computer plotprogramma SYMVU ten behoeve van onderzoek in de landschapsbouw. **The development of SYMVU plots as a tool in landscape planning.**

19949 Vries. P.G.de   NL 020009/72/4825
Onderzoek naar en bestudering van wiskundig–statistische methoden t.b.v. bosinventarisatie. **Statistical methods in forest inventory.** Publications.

19950 Corsten, L.C.A. NL 020066/72/4903
Optimale proefschema's en hun constructie onder ruime voorwaarden. **Optimal experimental design.**

19951 Corsten, L.C.A. NL 020066/72/4904
Analyse van multi variabelen bij groeikrommen. **Growth curves and multivariate analysis.**

19952 Keuls, M. NL 020066/73/6315
Gevolgtrekkingen na uitvoering van de F–toets in de variantieanalyse. **Statements following an F–test on means.**

19953 Laan, P. van der NL 020066/75/6320
Verdelingsvrije methoden bij twee–steekproeventoetsen, variantieanalyse, tellingen en ordenings– en selectieproblemen. **Distribution–free methods for two–sample problems, analysis of variance, categorical data and order– and selection problems.** Publications.

19954 Hendriks, T.H.B. NL 020066/76/6824
Netwerk optimalisering. **Networkoptimization.**

19955 Beek, P. van NL 020066/76/6825
Decompositie technieken. **Decomposition techniques.**

19956 Beek, P. van NL 020066/76/6826
Toepassingen van dynamische programmering. **Application of dynamic programming techniques.** Publications.

19957 Hendriks, M. NL 020066/77/8556
Fuzzy set theory; toepassingsmogelijkheden van wiskundige modellen, die hun oorsprong hebben in fysische systemen, in systemen waarin het menselijk gedrag een grote rol speelt. **Fuzzy set theory; application of mathematical models, which come from physical systems, in systems in which the human behaviour plays a main part.**

19958 Otten, A. NL 020066/78/8555
Kwantiel–analyse met niet–symmetrische tolerantieverdeling. **Quantal response analysis with a non–symmetrical distribution of the tolerances.**

19959 Verdooren, L.R. NL 020066/78/8557
Populatieomvang schatten m.b.v. terugvangmethode. **Capture recapture methods.**

D 8220 – Chemical techniques

See also 1017, 2091, 5286, 5287, 8979, 19042, 19543, 20092, 20094, 20142

19960 Deltour, J.; Dreze, P.; Paquot–Gasia, M.C.
BE 010018/73/0001 R
Application des méthodes isotopiques dans la recherche agronomique. **Application studies of isotopic methods in agricultural research.** Publications.

19961 Nangniot, P.; Impens, R. BE 010021/72/0003
Etude sur la présence de composés métalliques dans les plantes, les sols, les eaux et l'atmosphère. **Study on the present of metallic componds in plants, soils, water and atmosphere.** Publications.

19962 Naveau, H. BE 020101/76/0002 N
Evaluation chimique des substances fermentescibles et des déchets obtenus après fermentation anaérobic de déchets organiques. **Chemical evaluation of primary and of residue obtained in anaerobic fermentation of organic wastes.** Publications.

19963 André, P.; Lheureux, C.; Winand, M.; Giot–Wirgot, P.
BE 020301/75/0006 R
Etude de la translocation des éléments minéraux et de phytocides dans l'arbre à l'aide de radioisotopes. **Study of the translocation of mineral elements and phytocides in trees with radioisotopes.**

19964 Vanbelle, M.; Arnould, R.; Fockedey, J.
BE 020601/77/0015
Estimation de la teneur en azote des carcasses de rats et de poussin à partir de leur teneur en eau. **Estimation of nitrogen content of rat and chicken carcasses by estimation of their water.** Publications.

19965 Casier, J.; Storme, H.; Van der Bruel; Goffings, G.; Meskens, J.; Claeys, L. BE 040501/67/0004 N
Structuuranalyse van de wateronoplosbare endospermcelwandpentosanen van tarwe en rogge. **Structural analysis of the water insoluble pentosanfraction from the endosperm cell walls of wheat and rye.** Publications.

19966 Casier, J.; Ahmadi, A. BE 040501/71/0003
Studie van de chemische structuur en de vorming van de kleurstoffen in de suikerbiet melasse. **Research on the chemical structure and the color formation in sugar beet melasse.**

19967 De Vos, R.; Lauwers, H.; Nicaise, X.; Simoens, X.
BE 050400/78/0002 N
Morfologisch opsporen van hormonengebruik in de vetmesting van rund en varken. **Morphological methods for the detection of hormonal treatment in ox and pigs.** Publications.

19968 Van Onsem, J.G.; Heursel, J. BE 070600/62/0033
Onderzoek naar de kwalitatieve bepaling van aromaatcomponenten in de bloemen van Azalea indica. **Research into the qualitative and quantitative determination of aromatic components in the flowers of Azalea indica.**

19969 Van Onsem, J.; Gabriels, R. BE 070600/69/0025 R
Uitwerken van kwantitatieve analytische methodes voor bodem– en gewas– gietwateronderzoek. **Development of quantitative analytical methods for soil, plant and water research.** Publications.

19970 Henriet, J.; Van Damme, J. BE 080700/46/0002
Mise au point des méthodes d'analyse chimique des pesticides dans les formulations commerciales nouvelles. **Study on analytical methods for the determination of pesticides in new commercial formulations.** Publications.

19971 Henriet, J.; Van Damme, J. BE 080700/65/0003
Etude des spécifications ou normes de qualité des produits pesticides. **Study on specifications for pesticides formulations.** Publications.

19972 Fekete, M. de; Vieweg, G. DE 117030/74/0003 N
Stoffwechsel der Stärke. **Amyl metabolism.**

19973 Heilenz, S. DE 129045/71/0001
Spektrochemische Verfahren zur quantitativen Simultanbestimmung von etwa 40 Elementen in biologischen Materialien. **Spectrochemical methods for determination of**

approx. 40 elements simultaneously in biological materials.

19974 Menden, E.   DE 129900/72/0015
Entwicklung von Methoden zur Bestimmung der
Proteinqualität im Laboratorium. **Development of methods for
determination of protein quality in laboratory.**

19975 Wessolek, G.   DE 132063/77/0001
Vergleich zwischen Keramik– und Nickelintermetallkerzen zur
Bestimmung von Nährstoffen – N, P, K – im Grundwasser
unter Brache und landwirtschaftlich genutzten Flächen.
**Comparison of ceramic– and Ni–intered vacuum chambers to
determine the nutrients – N, P, K – in groundwater under
fallow and agricultural fields.**

19976 Bassler, R.; Putzka, H.–A.   DE 135056/74/0001
Es wird die Anwendbarkeit verschiedener
Bestimmungsverfahren für die Analytik der Vitamine C und E
sowie einiger Antioxydantien in Abhängigkeit von der Matrix
untersucht; entsprechendes gilt für die Analytik von
Mykotoxinen unter Berücksichtigung störender
Begleitsubstanzen in pflanzlichen Produkten. **Various
determination methods for the analysis of vitamins C und E and
some antioxydants in dependence on the matrix as well as for
the analysis of myco– toxins with reference to disturbing
accompanying substances in plant products.**

19977 Buchloh, G.; Neubeller, J.   DE 144445/77/0020
Bestimmung von Zuckern in Obstfrüchten mittels
Gaschromatographie. **Determination of sugars in fruits by
means of gas chromatography.** Publications.

19978 Kirchhoff, J.   DE 144540/70/0004 R
Überprüfung und Verfeinerung vorhandener sowie
Entwicklung neuer Verfahren für den Nachweis von Pestiziden
und ihren Umwandlungsprodukten in Pflanzen und Böden
1970. **Testing and improvement of existing as well as
development of novel methids for the indentification of
pesticides and their residues in plants and soils.**

19979 Kirchgessner, M.; Steinhart, H.   DE 161280/77/0004
Eine Methode zur Bestimmung von Tryptophan in
biologischen Substanzen. **The determination of tryptophan in
biological material.**

19980 Jork, H.; Kerling, W.   DE 167102/78/0001 N
Phytotechnische Untersuchungen terpenoider Inhaltsstoffe bei
Euphorbia lathyris. **Phytochemical investigations on terpenoid
constituents of Euphorbia lathyris.**

19981 Jork, H.; Nachtrab, M.   DE 167102/78/0002 N
Phytochemische Untersuchungen an Artemisia maritima L.
unter besonderer Berücksichtigung der
Sesquiterpen–Derivate. **Phytochemical investigations on
Artemisia maritima L. with special regard to sesquiterpene
derivatives.** Publications.

19982 Jork, H.; Mang, P.   DE 167102/78/0003 N
Vergleichende analytische Untersuchungen zur selektiven
Nikotin–Bestimmung in Kautabak. **Comparative analyses for
selective determination of nicotin in chewing tobacco.**

19983 Brieskorn, C.H.; Schwack, W.   DE 176150/78/0002 N
Reaktion zwischen Thujon und biogenen Aminen. **Reaction
between thujone and biogenic amines.**

19984 Neumann, H.–G.   DE 176300/74/0001 N
Analyse und Stoffwechsel von Aflatoxinen. **Analysis and
metabolism of aflatoxins.**

19985 Ellwardt, P.–C.   DE 201010/71/4004 N
Chemische Reaktionen zur Bildung von Huminstoffsystemen:
zur Chemie der Aminosäurechinone. **Chemical reactions for
formation of humic substances: Chemistry of amino acid
quinones.**

19986 Adam, S.   DE 211040/77/0004
Verbesserung gaschromatographischer Methoden.
Improvement of gas chromatographic methods.

19987 Seher, A.; Scholter, U.   DE 213010/78/0001 N
Wirkung von alpha–Linolensäure und anderen ungesättigten
Fettsäuren auf den Stoffwechsel der Linolsäure. **Influence of
linolenic acid and other unsaturated fatty acids on the
transformation of linoleic acid to arachidonic acid.**

19988 Seher, A.; Cetin, M.   DE 213010/78/0002 N
Gelenkte Umesterung von Baumwollsaatöl. **Directed
transesterification of cottonseed oil.**

19989 Seher, A.; Fujikawa, T.   DE 213010/78/0003 N
Umesterung pflanzlicher und tierischer Fette.
Interesterification of fractions of animal fats and vegetable oils.

19990 Rosopulo, A.; Hahn, M.; Stärk, H.; Fiedler, I.
     DE 502055/77/0006
Einfluss der Veraschungsmethode auf die Ergebnisse der
chemischen Analyse von Kulturpflanzen. **Influence of different
burning methods on the results of chemical analysis of
cultivated plants.** Publications.

19991 Mason, V.C.   DK 010206/75/0004
Udvikling af hydrolysemetode til aminosyrebestemmelse med
mindre arbejdsforbrug og større kapacitet. **Development of a
hydrolysis method for amino acid determination requiring less
labour and having an increased capacity.**

19992 Middelboe, V.; Johansen, H.S.   DK 030105/77/0005
Udvikling af et grundlag for en ^{13}C–analog til den
kommercielle ^{15}N–analysator. **Development of a basis for a
^{13}C–analog to the commercial ^{15}N–analyser.**

19993 Madsen, H.E.L.; Christensson, F.
     DK 030106/65/0025 N
Krystallisations– og opløsningskinetik af biologisk vigtige
tungtopløselige salte. **Kinetics of crystallization and dissolution
of biologically important sparingly soluble salts.**

19994 Christensen, F.; Kaas, K.; Springborg, J.
     DK 030106/70/0030
Dimere m–hydroxo og m–aniono forbindelser med Chrom
(III) og Cobalt (III). **Dimer m–hydroxo and m–aniono
connections with Chrom (III) and Cobalt (III).**

19995 Sørensen, H.   DK 030106/73/0010
Undersøgelser og indhold af aminer og aminosyrer i forskellige
planter, specielt fra familierne Resedaceae, Cruciferae og
Filicates. **Investigations of the amine and amino acid content of
various plants, particularly from the Resedaceae, Cruciferae
and Filicate families.**

D 8220 – Chemical techniques

19996 Skibsted, L.H. DK 030106/74/0028
Guldkomplexer. **Gold complexes.**

19997 Madsen, H.E.L. DK 030106/75/0026
Bestemmelse af stabilitetskonstanter for komplexer mellem
metalioner og N–(phosphonomethyl) glycin. **A determination
of the stability constants of complexes formed between metal
ions and N–(phosphonomethyl) glycine.**

19998 Springborg, J. DK 030106/75/0031
Reaktivitet af ligander koordineret til Cobalt(III). **Reactivity of
ligands coordinated to Cobalt (III).**

19999 Clausen, S. DK 030106/77/0006 N
Omsætningen mellem carboxylsyrechlorider og svovlsyre.
Reactions of carboxylic acid chlorides with sulfuric acid.

20000 Larsen, L.M.; Olsen, O.; Sørensen, H.
DK 030106/77/0007 N
Studier over aminosyreoxidaser og glycosidaser. **Amino acid
oxidases, cyanide, and glycosidaser.**

20001 Springborg, J.; Laier, T.; Schäffer C.E.
DK 030106/78/0005 N
Monomere cobalt (III) komplexer med pyridin som ligand.
Monomeric cobalt (III) complexes with pyridine as a ligand.

20002 Jakobsen, P.E.; Rotenberg, S. DK 030141/73/0001 N
Forskellige kulhydratfraktioners (bl.a. pektiners) indflydelse
på lipogenesens omfang. **The effect of carbohydrates (pectin)
on the rate of lipogenesis.**

20003 Boudon, M.; Flanzy, J. FR 010205/76/9555 N
Analyse des esters méthyliques d'acides gras par
chromatographie gaz–liquide sur colonne capillaire en verre.
**Gaz–liquid chromatography of methyl esters of fatty acids on
glass capillary column.**

20004 Boudon, M.; Flanzy, J. FR 010205/78/9556
Analyse des triglycérides par chromatographie gaz–liquide sur
colonne capillaire en verre. **Gaz–liquid chromatography
analysis of triglycerides on glasscapillary column.**

20005 Routchenko, W.; Soyer, J.P. FR 010704/70/0555
Analyse de sève. Interprétation automatique des résultats. **Sap
analysis. Automatical data processing.**

20006 Prugnaud, J.; Pion, R.; Champredon, C.
FR 010815/76/9578 N
Mise au point de la méthodologie de détermination des acides
aminés marqués au 14–C et 35–S. **Measurement of the specific
activity of 14–C and 35–S labelled amino acids.**

20007 Carr GB 010106/00/0004 R
Purify and assay hormones and other proteins.

20008 Byast GB 010802/00/0002 R
**Development of analytical methods for herbicides and their
decomposition products.**

20009 Smith GB 010802/00/0011 R
**Effect of high applications upon the rate of decomposition of
Simazine and Linuron.**

20010 Horne GB 011403/00/0002 R
Analytical methods techniques, computer processing etc.

20011 Trim; Johnson GB 011404/00/0003 R
Nucleic acid analysis techniques.

20012 Bradfield GB 011507/00/0011 R
Development of chemical methods for plant and soil analysis.

20013 Florence GB 011703/00/0021 R
**Develop analytical methods for milk, milk products, feedstuffs
and biological materials.**

20014 Hunt; Scaife GB 011802/00/0017 R
**Development of new methods of chemical analysis of soils and
plants.**

20015 Elliott; Janes GB 012005/00/0025 R
**Development of pyrethroids discovered at Rothamsted
Experimental Station.**

20016 Parsons GB 012011/00/0001 R
Synthesis of potential complexing agents.

20017 Wingfield GB 012011/00/0002 R
Coordination chemistry of alkali and alkaline earth metals.

20018 Parsons; Wingfield GB 012011/00/0004 R
Ion uptake and transport through membranes.

20019 Owen GB 012011/00/0005 R
**Determination of crystal structures of metal complexes and
ligands.**

20020 Owen GB 012011/00/0006 R
Crystal structures of insecticides.

20021 Truter GB 012011/79/0011 N
Complexes between macrobicyclic compounds or peptides.

20022 Pringle GB 012901/00/0001 R
**Contractile mechanism of insect fibrillar muscle using
physico–chemical methods.**

20023 Sweetsur GB 030201/00/0013 R
Development and use of modern methods of chemical analysis.

20024 Noble; Shand GB 030202/77/0022 R
Research techniques in radiobiochemistry.

20025 Nicholson GB 030402/00/0006 R
**Flame emission and atomic absorption methods:
instrumentation and techniques for trace and major elements.**

20026 Ellinger GB 030601/00/0012 R
Estimate availability of methionine using GLC.

20027 Ellinger; Duncan GB 030601/78/0011 N
**Development of new method of estimation of methionine by
GLC.**

20028 Hamilton GB 030903/00/0206 R
**Development of analytical methods especially for pesticides and
heavy metals.**

20029 Jason; Smith GB 051005/00/0025 R
**Pattern matching of chromatograms as an aid to rapid
identification.**

D 8220 – Chemical techniques

20030 O'Keeffe, M.; Eades, J.F.K.   IE 060500/77/1332 R
Development and/or modification of analytical techniques for residue studies. Publications.

20031 Molinari, G.P.; Del Re, A.; Battini, G.
IT 040406/78/0001
Analisi di contaminanti ambientali: policlorobifenili e policlorodibenzofurani derivati. **Analysis of environment contaminants: polychlorinated biphenyls and derivative polychlorinate dibenzofurans.** Publications.

20032 Zamorani, A.; Dal Belin Peruffo, A.; Spettoli, P.; Pallavicini, C.   IT 040802/78/0001 N
Sintesi di plasteine con proteasi immobilizzate. **Synthesis of plastein by immobilized enzymes.** Publications.

20033 Vertregt, N.; Braber, J.M.; Broekhoven, L.W. van
NL 010102/70/6738
Chemisch–analytische begeleiding van onderzoek. **Analytical participation in research.** Publications.

20034 Sinnaeve, J.   NL 010110/76/7288
Behaviour of radionuclides in biological and nonbiological processes at very low concentration. Publications.

20035 Lieshout, C.G. van   NL 010401/66/1639
Ontwikkeling van residu–analysemethoden in verband met het aantonen van vergiftigingen door bestrijdingsmiddelen en andere stoffen. **Development of methods for residue analysis for demonstration of poisoning of animals by pesticides and other products.** Publications.

20036 Burg, J. van den   NL 010601/70/3112
Internationale vergelijking van methoden van grond– en gewasanalyse t.b.v. het bosbouwkundig onderzoek. **International comparison of methods of soil and plant analysis in forestry research.** Publications.

20037 Schouwenburg, J.Ch. van   NL 020007/72/4971
Ontwikkeling en verfijning van methoden voor grond– en gewasanalyse. **Development and improvement of methods of soil– and plant analysis.** Publications.

20038 Novazamski, I.   NL 020007/76/6787
Ontwikkeling en aanpassing van analysemethoden en apparatuur voor het onderzoek aan grond en gewas. **Development and adaptation of analytical methods and apparatus for soil and cropanalysis.**

20039 Schuller, P.L.   NL 040011/76/7481
Het ontwikkelen van een methode van onderzoek voor het bepalen van citrinine in cultuurfiltraten en veevoeders. **Development of a detection method for determination of citrinin in culture filtrates and animal feeds.**

20040 Schelhaas, R.M.   NL 040012/78/8944 N
Het ontwikkelen van analysemethodieken voor het onderzoek naar organische mestmonsters. **Development of analytical methods for the analysis of organic material to be used as soil amendments.**

20041 Hofstee, J.; Janzen, G.J.   NL 050208/50/5096
Analyse en methoden van onderzoek inzake zetmeel en zijn afgeleiden. **Development of methods of analysis on starch and derivatives.** Publications.

20042 Slump, P.   NL 050301/70/6469
Verbetering van analysemethoden van aminozuren peptiden en nucleinezuren. **Improvement of the methods for the determinations of aminoacids, peptides and nucleicacids in foods.** Publications.

20043 Maarse, H.   NL 050301/70/6502
Beproeven en zo nodig verbeteren van bestaande en ontwikkelen van nieuwe apparatuur en methoden voor de cumulatie, afscheiding, concentratie en scheiding van geur– en smaakstoffen uit produkten en lucht– en dampmonsters. **Development and improvement of equipment and methods of accumulation, separation and concentration of flavours from products, air– and vapour samples.**

20044 Quirijns, J.K.   NL 050301/73/6472
Ontwikkeling van automatische analysemethoden voor residuen van chloorhoudende bestrijdingsmiddelen in plantaardig en dierlijk materiaal. **Development of automated analytical techniques for organochlorine pesticide residues in plant material and animal tissues.** Publications.

20045 Koops, J.   NL 060002/70/3987
Ontwikkeling en aanpassing van chemische analyse–methoden voor het zuivelonderzoek. **Development and adaptation of analytical chemical methods for dairy research.** Publications.

D 8230 – Physical techniques

See also 7753, 9407, 10510, 10722, 19866, 20003, 20004, 20006, 20022, 20043, 20089, 20174

20046 Baltes, W.; Hörtig, W.   DE 105900/75/0012
Pyrolytische Spaltungen von N–p–Chlorphenyl–D–isoglucosamin und seinen braunen Folgeprodukten. **Pyrolytic fragmentations of N–p–chlorophenyl–Disoglucosamine and of brown consecutive products.**

20047 Hildebrandt, G.; Schaden, J.   DE 126451/78/0001 N
Ein mehrstufiges Stichprobenmodell für grossräumige Waldinventuren mit Hilfe von Fernerkundungsaufzeichnungen. **A multistage sampling design for large area forest inventories using remotely sensed data.**

20048 Eder, H.; Reisinger, W.; Fritsche, H.
DE 129640/74/0001
Entwicklung fluoreszenzmikroskopischer Färbemethoden für die differentielle Darstellung von Blutzellen. **Development of specific staining methods for fluorescence microscopy of blood cells.**

20049 Kramer, H.; Akca, A.   DE 132720/78/0001 N
Verfahrensverbesserungen bei der Waldkartierung und Waldinventur durch EDV–unterstützte photogrammetrische Luftbildauswertung und Fernerkundungsdaten. **Methodical improvements of forest–stand–mapping and forest inventory by means of computer–aided photogrammetric methods and remote sensing data.**

20050 Bors, J.; Fendrik, I.; Kiselnic, L.   DE 138181/73/0001
Wirkung kleiner Strahlendosen auf Pflanzen. **Effect of low radiation doses on plants.** Publications.

20051 Ernst, D.E.W.; Zelles, L.; Seibold, H.W.; Christoffers,

D.; Georgi, B.   DE 138181/77/0001
Quantitative Mikroskopie an Mikroorganismen. **Quantitative microscopy of microorganisms.** Publications.

20052 Kühn, W.K.G.; Schätzler, H.P.   DE 138181/77/0002
Messung der Biomasse an Beständen durch Gamma–Scanning. **Biomass measurement by gamma–scanning.** Publications.

20053 Stephan, E.   DE 139260/73/0001
Untersuchungen zur Prüfung der Verwendungsmöglichkeiten von mit dem Katathermometer gemessenen Abkühlungsgrössen –Katawertenzur weitergehenden Kennzeichnung des lokalen Mikroklimas in Tier– ställen. **Testing studies on possibilities of utilizing catathermometric cooling–down values –cata–values– as continuative indicators of local microclimate in stables.**

20054 Plonait, H.; Reinhard, H.J.   DE 139750/78/0003 N
Erfassung und Auswertung biologischer Messwerte bei Verwendung implantierbarer Miniatursender und elektronischer Datenverarbeitung. **Collection and evaluation of biological data using implantable miniature transmitters and electronic data processing.** Publications.

20055 Hentschel, G.   DE 144400/78/0004 N
Optimierung der Probenaufbereitung zur emissionsspektrometrischen Bestimmung des stabilen Stickstoff–Isotops 15N. **Optimization of test–sample preparation for emission spectrophotometric determination of the stable nitrogen–isotope 15N.**

20056 Zöhrer, F.   DE 160210/77/0007 N
Synoptische Darstellung der Forstinventur–Methodik. **Synoptical presentation of forestry inventory.**

20057 Schwertmann, U.; Murad, E.   DE 161020/78/0005 N
Mössbauerspektren natürlicher und synthetischer Eisenoxide. **Moessbauer spectroscopy of natural and synthetic Fe–oxides.**

20058 Ahlgrimm, H.–J.   DE 201070/73/5001
Schnellbestimmung des Feuchtegehalts organischer Stoffe, insbesondere von Halmgut unter Ausschaltung verfahrensspezifischer und stoffspezifischer Störgrössen. **Rapid measuring of the moisture content in organic matter esp. of roughage excluding method–specific and matter– specific interfering factors.**

20059 Wiechen, A.; Heine, K.   DE 207050/74/5001
Entwicklung und Anwendung von Tracerverfahren mit Radioisotopen zur Lösung von Problemen der Milch/ Ernährungsforschung. **Development and use of tracer methods with radioactive isotopes for the solution of problems in dairy research.**

20060 Bisgård, K.M.; Nielsen, B.S.   DK 030105/74/0001
Udvikling og anvendelse af energidispersiv røntgenfluorescensspektrometri. **The development and application of energy dispersing X–ray fluorescent spectrometry.**

20061 Bisgård, K.M.; Svendsen, K.H.; Wismer–Pedersen, J.
                    DK 030105/79/0001 N
Røntgendiffraktionsmålinger på collagen. **X–ray diffraction studies of collagen.**

20062 Borggaard, O.K.; Lindgreen, H.B.; Mørup, S.

DK 030106/79/0001 N
Termisk oxidation af chlorit. **Structural investigation of chlorite after heating.**

20063 Guennelon B.; Cabibel, B.   FR 010601/74/6261
Mise en oeuvre de méthodes de mesures physiques utilisant les techniques nucléaires. **Implementing methods of physical measure making use of nuclear radiation techniques.**

20064 Mosse, J.; Baudet, J.; Renard, H.A.
                    FR 011103/76/0428
Mesure du taux des protéines: dosage quantitatif non destructif de l'azote des graines par radioactivation neutronique. **Measuring proteins rate: a non destructive quantitative method for determining nitrogen of seeds by neutronic radioactivation.**

20065 Filshie   GB 010702/00/0002 R
Design, testing and production of radiotelemetry systems.

20066 Fitter   GB 011112/79/0001 N
Application of microelectronics in the measurement and control of plant environments.

20067 Buchan   GB 012701/00/0014 R
Design and development of electrophysiological instrumentation and experimental techniques – insects.

20068 Roberts; Hutcheson   GB 030704/00/0021 R
Techniques of electron microscopy.

20069 Stewart; White   GB 040303/00/0013 R
Investigation of the possible discrimination of cereal cultivars by use of electron microscope techniques.

20070 Researcher not indicated   GB 050454/00/0001 R
Vida, diagnostic data recording system.

20071 Harkness   GB 050508/75/0003 R
Electron microscopy research projects in collaboration with other departments and other organisations.

20072 Houston; Hodgkiss   GB 051003/69/0025 R
The electron microscopy of bacteria of interest in food microbiology and taxonomy.

20073 McCarthy, D.D.   IE 060400/77/1297 R
Calibration studies on the cromic oxide techniques. Publications.

20074 Aldrich, J.C.   IE 140202/76/9050 N
Portable recording respirometers for in situ measurements of oxygen consumption in marine environments.

20075 Resmini, P.; Volonterio, G.; Albonico, F.; Piergiovanni, L.; Cerutti, G.   IT 040609/77/0001
Studio dei composti fenolici mediante cromatografia su strato sottile e cromatografia liquida ad alta pressione. **Studies on phenolic substances by TLC and HPLC.**

20076 Salerno, A.   IT 040722/74/0623
Valutazione della massa muscolare nei suini mediante la ricerca del K–40. **Evaluation of muscular mass in pigs by tracing of K–40.**

20077 Kasteren, H.W.J. van   NL 010104/73/3969

Onderzoek naar de reflectie van ingestraalde energie, van diverse golflengten, door begroeiingen (toepassingsmogelijkheden moderne waarnemingstechnieken op afstand). **Spectral reflectance studies of vegetative canopies (applicability of modern remote sensing techniques).** Publications.

20078 Post, C.J. van der   NL 010106/77/7592
Ontwerpen van een centrale klimaatregeling voor de IMAG proefkassen. **Development of a central climate control for the IMAG experimental greenhouses.**

20079 Puite, K.J.   NL 010110/64/7282
Development and improvement in accuracy and reproducibility of dosimetric systems for x–ray intercomparison, neutron and high level gamma radiation. Publications.

20080 As, H. van   NL 020034/75/6326 R
De studie van watertransport in planten m.b.v. kernresonantie. **Watertransport in plants as studied by NMR.**

20081 Bot, G.P.A.; Dixhoorn, J.J. van; Udink ten Cate, A.
NL 020036/74/6337
Fysische modelbouw, digitale simulatie en regeling van kasklimaat. **Modelling, digital simulation and control of glass–house climates.** Publications.

20082 Udink ten Cate, A.J.   NL 020036/77/8561
Automatisering kassen vakgroep Tuinbouwplantenteelt. **Automation of the glasshouses of the departement of horticulture.**

20083 Bottemanne, F.A.   NL 020036/78/8558
Eddy–correlatie metingen. **Eddy–correlation measurements.**

20084 Udink ten Cate, A.J.   NL 020036/78/8559
Adaptief regelen gebaseerd op stabiliteitsmethoden. **Adaptive control based on stability methods.**

20085 Driessen, W.F.M.   NL 020036/78/8560
Microprocessors in meteorologische instrumenten. **Microprocessors in meteorological instruments.** Publications.

20086 Knegt, E.   NL 020041/72/4509
De ontwikkeling van fysio–chemische bepalingsmethoden voor gytohormonen. **Development of chemico–physical methods for the determination of plant growth substances.** Publications.

D 8240 – Biological techniques

See also 2093, 2701, 2801, 5287, 8289, 9069, 14352, 19142, 19867, 20061, 20067

20087 Van den Bruel, W.; Quoilin, J.   BE 010017/72/0004 R
Faunistique et mise au point de techniques d'extraction de la microfaune du sol. **Faunistique and researchs on the technics of microfauna's extraction.**

20088 Lints, F.; Hoste, G.; Gosseye, F.   BE 020304/71/0001 R
Etude du déterminisme de l'héritabilité en vue d'améliorer les schémas de sélection. **Study in heritability determinism viewing selection schema improvement.** Publications.

20089 Meire, R.; De Baerdemacker, J.   BE 040402/76/0002
Numerische en experimentele studie van mechanische processen in biologische produkten. **A numerical and experimental study of mechanical processes in biological products.**

20090 Hörchner, F.; Gerber, H.C.; Zander, B.
DE 104200/72/0003 N
Zusätze von humoralen und sekretorischen Antikörpern zu in vitro–Kulturen von Nippostrongylus brasiliensis. Zusätze zellulärer Elemente – Mastzellen, Lymphozyten – zu in vitro–Kulturen. **Supplementary humoral and secretory antibodies to in vitro–cultures of Nippostrongylus brasiliensis. Addition of cellular elements – fattening cells, lymphocytes – to in vitro–cultures.**

20091 Juhr, N.–C.   DE 104351/74/0001
Gnotobiotische Modelle zur symbiontischen Assoziation der Laboratoriumsnager. **Gnotobiotic experiments for symbiotic association of laboratory rodents.**

20092 Limberg, P.   DE 105201/71/0001
Internationale ökologische Stickstoff–Dauerversuche – ISDV –. **International ecological permanent experiments with nitrogen.**

20093 Zenk, M.H.; Stöckigt, J.; Gross, G.G.
DE 108100/71/0001 N
Biosynthese des Lignins. **Biosynthesis of lignin.**

20094 Grosse–Brauckmann, E.   DE 111100/72/0003
Zur Technik des Gefässversuches. **Advanced techniques in pot experiments.**

20095 Weiling, F.; Unger, C.   DE 111151/70/0005
Die multi– und die univariaten Analysen als biometrische Methoden. **Multi– and univariate analyses as biometric methods.** Publications.

20096 Ullrich, W.   DE 117030/74/0002 N
Wege der Regulation des photosynthetischen Nitratstoffwechsels bei Algen durch ökologische Faktoren. **Regulation of photosynthetic nitrate metabolism in algae influenced by ecological factors.**

20097 Zimmermann, F.   DE 117400/75/0001 N
Genetik der Regulation des Kohlenhydratstoffwechsels bei der Hefe Saccharomyces cerevisiae – Katabolitrepression. **Genetic regulation of carbohydrate metabolism in Saccharomyces cerevisiae: repression of catabolites.**

20098 Marquardt, H.; Bayer, U.   DE 126100/74/0002 N
Mutationsuntersuchungen mit aromatischen Kohlenwasserstoffen an somatischen Zellen. **Mutation experiments on somatic cells with aromatic hydrocarbons.**

20099 Barner, J.; Al–Tayyar, A.J.   DE 126400/77/0001
Ökologische Untersuchungen über Lepidium sativum und Marchantia polymorpha und ihren Bioindikatorwert gegenüber Luftverunreinigungen. **Ecological investigations on Lepidium sativum and Marchantia polymorpha and on their value as indicator of air pollution.** Publications.

20100 Steubing, L.; Cornelius, R.; Simmermacher, W.; Kirschbaum, U.   DE 129064/77/0001
Messung spezieller Luftverunreinigungskomponenten mit Hilfe biologischer Indikatoren. **Measuring of special air pollution components by biological indicators.** Publications.

20101 Eder, H.; Brix, W. DE 129640/74/0002
Vergleichende automatische Thrombozytenzählung bei Pferd, Rind, Schwein, Schaf, Hund, Ratte. **Comparative automatic platelet counts in the blood of horse, cow, pig, sheep, dog and rat.**

20102 Blobel, H.; Gupta, K.G. DE 129740/75/0005
Produktion, Nachweis– und Reinigungsverfahren von Staphylokokken–Koagulase. **Production and procedures of identification and purification of staphylococcal coagulase.**

20103 Schön, W.J.; Winkler, U. DE 132180/75/0002
Methoden der N– und Proteinbestimmung. Eine vergleichende Untersuchung. **Methods for the determination of nitrogen and protein. A comparative analysis.**

20104 Francke, W.; Hindorf, G. DE 135151/75/0001
Flüchtige Inhaltsstoffe in Wespen. **Volatile substances in wasps.**

20105 Ernst, D.E.W.; Georgi, B. DE 138180/78/0001 N
Messung der planktischen Primärproduktion durch Chlorophyllfluoreszenz. **Mesurement of planctic primary production by stabilized chlorophyll fluorescence.**

20106 Schulze, W.; Hazem, A.S.; Cramon, A.von
  DE 139750/74/0028
Das Schwein als Versuchstier. **Swine as experimental animals.**

20107 Müller, W.; Kunkel, D.; La–Hong, B.
  DE 144610/77/0003 R
Lebensfähigkeit von Bakterien in Luft. Experimentelle Untersuchungen in einer Aerosolkammer und im Mikrofadentest. **Survival of airborne bacteria – experiments in an aerosol chamber and in micro–thread test.**

20108 Dennig, H.K.; Högner, W. DE 160822/78/0002 N
Untersuchungen zur Haltung von Trypanosoma evansi in verschiedenen Kulturmedien. **Cultivation of Trypanosoma evansi in different cultural media.**

20109 Röschenthaler, R. DE 164100/74/0001
Untersuchungen zur Definition der Bedingungen, die in vivo zu einer Hemmung des Bakterienwachstums durch Ochratoxin A führen In vitro–Untersuchungen über den Mechanismus der Hemmung der bakteriellen Zellfunktionen durch Ochratoxin mit Hilfe zellfreier Extrakte. **Definition of conditions resulting in an in vivo inhibition of bacterial growth by Ochratoxin A In vivo studies on the mechanism of inhibition in bacterial cell functions by Ochratoxin and by means of cell–free extracts.**

20110 Schweisfurth, R.; Rinck, M. DE 167150/78/0001 N
Weitere Untersuchungen an Hyphomicrobium manganoxidans. **Further studies on Hyphomicrobium manganoxidans.**

20111 Oberwinkler, F.; Blanz, P. DE 173051/78/0001 N
Vergleichende Merkmalsanalysen an Exobasidium–Arten und verwandten Basidiomyceten. **Comparative analyses of characteristics of Exobasidium strains and related Basidiomycetes.** Publications.

20112 Oberwinkler, F.; Deml, G. DE 173051/78/0002 N
Vergleichende feinstrukturelle und chemische Merkmalsanalysen an Ustilaginales–Arten. **Comparative analyses of fine structural and chemical characteristics of** Ustilaginales strains. Publications.

20113 Wöhrmann, K. DE 173400/75/0001 N
Populationsgenetische Untersuchungen an Saccharomyces cerevisiae. **Population genetic studies on Saccharomyces cerevisiae.**

20114 Martens, R. DE 201020/75/0011
Nachweis, Aufnahme, Transport und Abbau von polyclischen aromatischen Verbindungen – PCA's – in bzw. aus Müllkomposten. **Evidence, intake, transport, and degradation of polycyclic aromatic compounds – PCA's – in resp. from composted municipal waste.**

20115 Reber, H.; Karanth, N. DE 201020/78/0001 N
Regelung des Abbaus von Substanzpaaren in kontinuierlichen Kulturen von Pseudomonaden. **Regulation of the utilization of binary substrate mixtures in continuous cultures of pseudomonads.**

20116 Czeratzki, W. DE 201040/75/0008
Untersuchungen über den Einfluss der Bodenwasserspannung in unterschiedlichen Wurzelzonen auf Wachstum und Wasserverbrauch der Pflanzen mit Hilfe von Unterdrucklysimetern. **Studies on the influence of soil moisture tension in different root zones on growth and water consumption of plants carried out by means of low–pressure lysimeters.**

20117 Sator, C. DE 201040/75/0029
Entwicklung von Serien–Methoden für pflanzliche Inhaltsstoffe. **Development of serial methods for vegetable constituents.**

20118 Speckmann, H. DE 201060/74/0007 R
Herabsetzen des Rohstoff– und Energiebedarfs bei Verfahren der technischen Mikrobiologie. **Reduction of demand for raw materials and energy in using methods of technical microbiology.**

20119 Kossmann, A. DE 215010/73/0002
Entwicklung automatisch arbeitender komplexer Identifizierungsund Bestimmungssysteme für die Analytik multipler Pflanzenschutz– mittelrückstände. **Development of automatized working identification and determination systems for analysis of multiple residual plant protectives.**

20120 Hassan, S.A.; Franz, J.M. DE 215170/70/4001
Weiterentwicklung von Methoden zur Prüfung der Nebenwirkungen von Pflanzenschutzmitteln auf Nutzarthropoden. **Further development of methods to test the side–effects of pesticides on entomophagous arthropods.**

20121 Ahl, R. DE 216030/77/0009 N
Die Interferonbildung in Zellkulturen und Infektionsschutz von Zellkulturen durch Interferon. **Interferone formation in cell cultures and protection of cell cultures against infection by interferone.**

20122 Häckel, H. DE 301100/78/0001 N
Entwicklungen über ein elektronisches Verfahren zur Messung der Benetzungsdauer unmittelbar an Pflanzen. **Developments of an electronic method for measuring the wetting duration immediately on plants.** Publications.

20123 Häckel, H. DE 301100/78/0002 N

Photosynthetisch aktive Strahlung: Messtechnik, klimatologische Auswertung und Zusammenhang mit anderen Strahlungsgrössen. **Photosynthetically active radiation: measuring technique, climatological evaluation and correlation to other parameters of radiation.**

20124 Pietzsch, O.   DE 305030/75/0029
Standardisierung der Salmonella–Nachweisverfahren. **Standardization of methods of salmonella identification.** Publications.

20125 Walther, M.   DE 305030/75/0035
Standardisierung serologischer Verfahren zur Feststellung von Cysticercose und Echinokokkose sowie Errichtung einer internationalen Antigenbank. **Standardization of serological methods for the detection of cysticercosis and echinococcosis and establishment of an international antigen bank.**

20126 Levetzow, R.   DE 305030/75/0043
Verbesserung der Kultivierung aerober und anaerober Keime. **Improvement of cultivation of aerobic and anaerobic organisms.**

20127 Andersen, P.E.; Thomsen, K.V.
                    DK 010201/75/0004 R
Nye analysemetoder i fodermiddelvurderingen. **New analytical methods for feed–evaluation.**

20128 Vestergaard Thomsen, K.   DK 010201/76/0003
Laboratoriemetoder til vurdering af fodermidlers og foderblandingers næringsværdi til drøvtyggere. **Laboratory methods for the nutritive value assessment of food stuffs and food mixes for ruminants.**

20129 Sørensen, M.   DK 010201/76/0006
Forsøg til vurdering af in vitro analysens værdi til bestemmelse af den energetiske næringsværdi i fodermidler og foderblandinger til fedekalve. **Experiments to assess the value of in vitro analysis of energetic nutritive value in food stuffs and feed mixtures for fattening calves.**

20130 Larsen, P.O.; Dalgaard, L.; Al–Abassi, F.; Wieczorkowska, E.   DK 030106/72/0001 N
Undersøgelse over forekomst, biosyntese og nedbrydning af aromatiske aminosyrer og carboxylsyrer i planter. **Studies on occurrence, biosynthesis and metabolic degradation of aromatic amino acids and aromatic carboxylic acids in plants.**

20131 Bresciani, J.; Andersen, C.   DK 030109/79/0002 N
Elektronmikroskopiske undersøgelser af stor regnorms konkretionslegemer. **Investigation of brown bodies in earthworms (Lumbricidae) by electron microscopy.**

20132 Agergaard, N.   DK 030126/79/0003 N
Blodtypebestemmelsers reaktionskinetik. **The reaction kinetics of blood group determination.**

20133 Christensen, K.   DK 030127/75/0020 N
Cytogenetiske studier af husdyr. C–bånd polymorfier hos svin. **Cytogenetic studies in farm animals. C–band polymorphism in swine.**

20134 Lehn–Jensen, H.; Greve, T.; Kullander; Liedholm
                    DK 030128/78/0003 N
Dybfrysning af humane oocyter og embryoner. **Low temperature preservation of early stages of human embryos.**

20135 Andersen, J.M.; Jensen, C.J.   DK 030146/79/0003 N
Planteregeneration og vækst i in vitro kulturer. **Plant regeneration and growth in in–vitro cultures.**

20136 Kristensen, H.Ø.   DK 030601/79/5011 N
Dynamiske modeller for genetisk bestemte vært–patogen systemer. **Dynamic models for genetic host–pathogen systems.**

20137 Lefebvre, J.; Bocquet, G.; Louis, J.; Guillaumin, M.; Laurent, P.   FR 010202/62/2507
Application des analyses multidimensionnelles en biologie aux problèmes de morphométrie et de taxonomie. **Utilization of multivariate analysis in biological studies of morphometry and taxonomy.** Publications.

20138 Vila, J.P.; Bouvier, A.; Astier, R.   FR 010214/78/8268
Enquête éco–pathologique continue (2). **Continuous eco–pathological survey.**

20139 Rerat, A.; Roger; Vaugelade, P.; Villiers, P.A.
                    FR 010217/77/9590 N
Mise au point d'une méthode de mesure du débit de sang dans la veine porte. Analyse des facteurs de variation du débit sanguin porte. **Development of quantitative–method for measuring portal blood flow application to the study of the variation factors of portal blood flow.**

20140 Becker, M.; Picard, J.F.; Timbal, J.   FR 010303/66/4162
Méthodologie des études phyto–écologiques. **Methodology of phyto–écological studies.**

20141 Becker, M.; Perrin, J.R.   FR 010303/69/4163
Méthodologie de l'écologie expérimentale. **Methods of experimental ecology.**

20142 Fournier, J.C.   FR 011002/72/6300
Constitution d'un laboratoire d'étude de la biodégradabilité. **Constitution of a laboratory for study of biodegradability.**

20143 Pearson; Hutchings   GB 010308/19/0016 N
Metabolism and function of differentiated cells in culture.

20144 Lynch   GB 010502/79/0019 N
Measurement of soil biomass.

20145 Arnold   GB 012005/00/0037 R
Design of apparatus and techniques for studying insect activity and the effects of insecticides.

20146 Borrill; Tyler   GB 012106/00/0009 R
Systems for rapid identification and classification of herbage plants using botanical characteristics and place of origin.

20147 Burnett; Hirsh   GB 023801/79/0004 N
Use of the high voltage electron microscope (hvem) with biological materials.

20148 Kilpatrick   GB 040201/75/0001 R
Forest sampling techniques.

20149 Camlin   GB 040303/00/0008 R
Biochemical and physiological techniques to aid varietal identification and classification.

20150 Pearson; Greer   GB 041607/79/0006 N
Standardisation and interpretation of electronic cell count of

somatic cells in bulk milk.

20151 Roberts; Sellwood GB 050322/76/0041 R
Development of determinative methods for Pseudomonas group 1.

20152 Knight; Oberts, R. GB 050322/76/0051 R
Diagnosis of bacterial diseases by immunofluorescent methods.

20153 Mackinnon GB 050504/00/0005 R
Standardisation of brucellosis techniques.

20154 Gower GB 050504/00/0007 R
Rapid automation of rose bengal plate test (with Searle Ltd).

20155 Robinson GB 060220/00/0007 R
Respirometric techniques with microorganisms.

20156 Collins, J.K.; Vaughan, A.; McCarthy, A.M.;
Loughman, D.F.G.; Cotter, J. IE 110102/78/9140 N
Mechanism of viral oncogenesis using simian virus 40 and host cell mutants. Publications.

20157 Tobin, J.J. IE 130102/78/9158 N
Studies on cytochromes p450 and 65 in fat globule membrane and in membrane preparations from bovine mammary tissue.

20158 Gosling, J.P.; McNamara, E.M.; Ryan, M.A.
IE 130102/78/9218 N
Characterisation of the biological effects of pmsg (potency as a regulator of receptors; kinetics of binding to receptors). Publications.

20159 Rotili, P. IT 020900/73/2553
Struttura e funzionamento di sistemi biologici sperimentali. Studio della competizione intra e intergenotipica in piante foraggere. I anno. Nel quadro dell'accordo di collaborazione Italia–Francia. **Structure and functioning of experimental biological systems. Study of intra and inter–genotypical competition in forage plants. 1 year. Within the framework of Italo–French collaboration.** Publications.

20160 Scossiroli, R.E. IT 040213/77/0807
Analisi biometrica per la interpretazione delle variabili dei processi biologici. **Biometric analysis allowing the interpretation of variables occurring in biological processes.**

20161 Porceddu, E. IT 060500/74/0178
Colture in vitro di gemme. **Buds in vitro culture.**

20162 Noordwijk, M. van NL 010103/78/7972
Werkzaamheden ter verbetering en vernieuwing van methoden in gebruik bij het wortelonderzoek. **Improvement and research on new methods for root investigation.**

20163 Es, A. van NL 010105/73/8328
Ontwikkeling van een methode voor de voorspelling van de blauwgevoeligheid bij aardappelen. **Development of a method to predict the susceptibility of potatoes to blackspot.** Publications.

20164 Mulder, R.W.A.W.; Dorresteijn, L.W.J.
NL 010109/73/3906
Onderzoek naar betere microbiologische bepalingsmethoden voor pluimvee– en eiprodukten. **The improvement of microbiological methods used for poultry and egg products.**

Publications.

20165 Scheele, C.W. NL 010109/73/5410
Ontwikkeling van apparatuur voor meting van de energiebalans bij pluimvee. **Development of methods for energy balance experiments in poultry.** Publications.

20166 Janssen, W.M.M.A.; Terpstra, K.; Weijland, B.
NL 010109/75/6067
De verteerbaarheid van gras bij ganzen. **The digestibility of grasses by geese.**

20167 Bergström, P.L. NL 010112/67/1201
Eenvoudige methoden voor de bepaling van de karkassamenstelling bij landbouwhuisdieren. **Simplified methods to determine carcass composition in farm animals.** Publications.

20168 Gersons, L. NL 010118/73/4185
Selectie en toepassing van sensorische analyse voor verse en verwerkte groente– en vruchtenprodukten. **Selection and application of sensoric analysis for fresh and processed vegetables and fruit products.**

20169 Wal, A.F. van der NL 010120/77/8890 N
Ontwikkeling van de sapstroommeter en onderzoek naar de toepassingsmogelijkheden. **The development of 'sapstreammeter' and investigations on application.** Publications.

20170 Lamers, J.G. NL 010207/78/6625 N
Onderzoek naar de mogelijkheden van remote sensing technieken ten behoeve van het landbouwkundig onderzoek. **Research for the possibilities of remote sensing techniques in agricultural research.**

20171 Kersting, K.; Dijk, C. van NL 010602/77/7204
Onderzoek naar het ecosysteem metabolisme als waterkwaliteitparameter. **Investigation of the ecosystem metabolism as a water quality parameter.**

20172 Egberts, E. NL 020071/78/8392
Prolifererende hybride cellen met gedifferentieerde kenmerken: modelsystemen voor zuiver wetenschappelijk en toegepast onderzoek. **Proliferating somatic cell hybrids with differentiated characteristics: Model systems for fundamental and applied research.**

20173 Cornelisse, J.L. NL 030002/72/5666 R
Salmonella–isolatie (salmonella, isolatie, sublethale beschadiging, resuscitatie). **Salmonella–isolation (salmonella, isolation, sublethally injured, resuscitation).** Publications.

20174 Bercken, J. van den NL 030003/78/8954 N
Elektrofysiologische technieken en automatische gegevensverwerking. (intracellulaire mikroëlektroden, 'voltage clamp' techniek, minicomputer, automatische gegevens–verwerking). **Electrophysiological techniques and automatic data analysis (intracellular microelectrodes, voltage clamp technique, minicomputer, automatic data analysis).**

20175 Peterse, D.J. NL 030009/71/5699
Vaststellen en interpreteren van parameters ter beoordeling van de klauw van het rund. **The determination and interpretation of parameters for evaluation of bovine claw quality.**

D 8240 – Biological techniques

20176 Harrewijn, G.A. NL 050301/60/6497
Ontwikkelen en verbeteren van methoden voor de
microbiologische beoordeling van voedingsmiddelen.
**Development and improvement of methods for
microbiological evaluation of foods.** Publications.

20177 Hellemond, K.K. van NL 050305/76/8040
Ontwikkeling van technieken voor langduring infuseren van
oplossingen en bemonsteren van het bloed bij schapen,
varkens en vleeskalveren. **Development of techniques for long
term infusion of solutions and sampling of the blood of sheep,
pigs and veal calves.**

D 8290 – Other methods or techniques

20178 Dagnelie, P.; Laustriaux, J. BE 010010/70/0001
Simulation sur ordinateur d'expériences en champs. **Simulation
of field experiments on computer.** Publications.

20179 Wels, A. DE 129640/73/0001
Stoffaufnahme und Stoffabgabe lebender Zellen.
Mikrophotometrische Messung der Diachromaufnahme und
–abgabe lebender Lymphozyten in einer
Durchströmungskammer –Teil II. **Absorption and excretion of
living cells – microphotometric experiments on diachrome
absorption and excretion of living lymphocytes in a perfusion,
pt. 2.**

20180 Eder, H. DE 129640/73/0004
Stoffaufnahme und Stoffabgabe lebender Zellen.
Mikrofluorometrische Untersuchungen über die
Fluorochromaufnahme und –abgabe von Lymphozyten.
**Absorption and excretion of living cells – microfluorometric
experiments on the fluorochrome absorption and excretion of
lymphocytes 1971 (Forts..**

20181 Köhne, M. DE 132361/73/0001
Theorie und Praxis der Bewertung in der Landwirtschaft.
Theoretical and practical estimation in agriculture.

20182 Haen, H.de; Behrens, R. DE 132367/77/0001
Ökonometrisches Mehrprodukt–Produktionsmodell des
Agrarsektors. Eine theoretische und empirische Analyse.
**Econometric multi–product production model of the
agricultural sector. Theoretical and empirical analysis.**

20183 Hanf, C.H. DE 148405/78/0005 N
Berücksichtigung von Unsicherheiten in dynamischen Nutzen
– Kosten - Analysen. **Dynamic cost–benefit analysis under
consideration of uncertainties.**

20184 Wiebecke, C. DE 202010/77/0007
Methodische Fragen der Quantifizierung der Sozialleistungen
des Waldes. **Methodical problems of quantification of social
services of forests.**

20185 Hoyningen–Huene, J.von DE 301030/77/0006
Funktionsmodelle für die Wechselbeziehung zwischen
meteorologischen und pflanzenphysiologischen Parametern.
**Functional models of interactions between meteorological and
plant physiological parameters.** Publications.

20186 Jensen, E. DK 030107/75/0003
Semantisk informationsteori. **Semantical information theory.**

20187 Chavagnat, A. FR 011103/75/0431
Essais biochimiques de viabilité et radiographie des semences.
Biochemical tests for viability and radiography in seeds.

20188 Agronomie :) Hutter, W.; Biométrie : Badia; Marty,
J.R.; Charpenteau; Rellier, J.P.; Sabarthez
FR 011401/69/6210 R
Méthodologie d'Etude des Systèmes de culture (Dispositif
expérimental d'AUZEVILLE). **Methodology of study of
Cultural Systems..**

20189 Langlet, A. FR 011401/71/0644
Utilisation de divers exemples en vue de la construction d'une
méthodologie d'étude des problèmes de diagnostic et
d'aménagement régional. **Studies on the methodology of
regional diagnosis and planning based on some examples.**
Publications.

20190 Luisoni, E. IT 060100/74/0100
Indagini sul miglioramento della sierodiagnosi. **Studies on the
improvement of serum diagnosis.**

20191 Bottemanne, F.A. NL 020036/71/5389
Ontwikkeling van en onderzoek aan een automatisch
meteorologisch waarnemingsstation. **Development of and
investigations on an automatic meteorological observation
station.**

D 8900 – Routine research and services

See also 24, 127, 287, 340, 1582, 1585, 1805, 1815, 2177, 2178,
2182, 2383, 2428, 3302, 4766, 5320, 5330, 5333, 5334, 5354,
5368, 5824, 5915, 5920, 6083, 8386, 9067, 9068, 9223, 9229,
9234, 9349, 9447, 9516, 11759, 13184, 13292, 13293, 13665,
14102, 14686, 15925, 16019, 16060, 17488, 18324, 18411, 18911,
19046, 19398, 19797, 19808, 20191, 20809

20192 Wilssens, A.; De Mey, L. BE 030012/78/0005 N
Taxonomische studie van enkele groepen sporenvormers.
Taxonomic study of some sporeforming rods. Publications.

20193 Mülling, M.; Rohloff, D. DE 104400/72/0004 R
Histometrische Untersuchungen an Hoden von Wildtieren.
Histometrical investigations of tests in wild animals.

20194 Blanckenburg, P.von; Metz, M. DE 105351/75/0004
Neuorientierung der Nahrungshilfe zur Deckung mittelfristig
zu erwartender grosser Nahrungsdefizite in
Entwicklungsländern. **Reorientation of food assistance to meet
medium–term high food deficiencies in developing countries – to
be expected at medium–term –.**

20195 Wasmund, R.; Apelt, J. DE 105750/75/0001
Untersuchung der Notwendigkeit und Zweckmässigkeit des
Arbeitens mit Modellgemischen beim Bestimmen von
Stoffwerten flüssiger Lebensmittel. **Investigation on necessity
and suitability of working with model mixtures when
determining material values of fluid foodstuffs.** Publications.

20196 Bielig, H.J.; Rouwen, F.M. DE 105813/75/0002
Physikalische Stoffeigenschaften pflanzlicher Lebensmittel.
Physical properties of vegetable foodstuffs. Publications.

20197 Meuser, F.; Suckow, P. DE 105820/75/0001
Optimierung von Clean–up–Verfahren für die
gaschromatographische Bestimmung von

Schädlingsbekämpfungsmittelrückständen in Getreide und Getreideprodukten. **Optimization of clean–up procedures for the gas chromatographic determination of pesticide residues in cereals and cereal products.**

20198 Baltes, W.; Block, H.   DE 105900/75/0004
Untersuchungen an den braunen Teerstoffen von Raucharomaessenzen. **Investigation of brown tars of liquid smoke essences.**

20199 Baltes, W.; Braun, M.   DE 105900/75/0005
Untersuchung der braunen Kaffeeröststoffe. **Investigations of brown roast–compounds of coffee.**

20200 Stan, H.–J.; Pfannkuchen, M.   DE 105900/75/0016
Isolierung und Charakterisierung von LipoxygenaseIsoenzymen aus Sojabohnen. **Isolation and characterization of lipoxygenase isoenzymes from soybeans.**

20201 Stan, H.–J.   DE 105900/75/0017
Nachweis von Pestizid–Rückständen in Lebensmitteln durch GC–MS–Kopplung. **Determination of pesticide residues in food with gaschromatography–mass spectrometry.** Publications.

20202 Stölzle, H.   DE 105953/73/0001
Thesaurus Zucker. **Thesaurus of sugar terms.**

20203 Kick, H.; Götz, W.   DE 111100/75/0005
Stickstoffrückstände von Kunstdüngern. **Nitrogen residues of artifical manure.**

20204 Breuer, L.   DE 111990/72/0001 N
Beziehung zwischen Radar–Echointensität und Niederschlag zur quantitativen Analyse der in Westdeutschland vorkommenden Niederschlagsstrukturen. **Correlations between radar–echo intensity and precipitation for quantitative analysis of precipitation structures occurring in West Germany.**

20205 Maier, H.G.; Wewetzer, H.   DE 114100/75/0001
Bestimmung des Extraktionsgrades von Kaffee–ExtraktPulver. **Estimation of the degree of extraction of coffee extract powder.**

20206 Gressel, P.; Boehme, C.   DE 114450/77/0001 N
Untersuchungen über den Einfluss verschiedener verfahrenstechnischer Parameter auf die Formbeständigkeit von Buchenfunierplatten. **Studies on the influence of different process technological parameters on the dimensional stability of beech veneer boards.**

20207 Gressel, P.; Mohl, H.R.   DE 114450/77/0002 N
Untersuchungen über die Feuchtbeständigkeit verschiedener formaldehydarmer Harnstoff–Formaldehyd–Harze. **Studies on moisture stability of different low–formaldehyde urea–formaldehyde–resins.**

20208 Schmidt–Vogt, H.   DE 126300/78/0001 N
Fichtenmonographie Band 2. **Monograph of spruce, vol. 2.**

20209 Pacher, J.; Kretschmar, S.   DE 126505/75/0003
Die Wechselbeziehungen zwischen Forstorganisation und forstlicher Ausbildung im zeitlichen Rückblick und in ihrer gegenwärtigen Problematik. **The interdependency of forest organization and forest education in the past and in its problems of today.**

20210 Kuhlmann, F.; Hedtrich, G.   DE 129301/77/0002 N
Ablaufsteuerung bei der Milchproduktion. **Controlling in milk production.**

20211 Zilahi–Szabo, M.G.; Teuteberg, G.
   DE 129304/71/0002 N
Grundlagen und Organisation einer landwirtschaftlichen Datenbank, bezogen auf die Regionen Hessens. **Principles and organization of agricultural data bank referring to regions in Hesse.**

20212 Seuster, H.; Müller, H.   DE 129310/75/0001
Ausbau eines Unternehmungsplanspiels als Ausbildungsmethode in der Landwirtschaft. **Further development of a management game as instructional method in agriculture.**

20213 Hadlok, R.; Karo, M.; Binzel, R.–M.; Mabrouk, H.
   DE 129700/75/0001
Schimmelpilze und Fleischerzeugnisse. **Moulds and meat products.** Publications.

20214 Kielwein, G.; Bezler, A.; Melling, H.
   DE 129701/75/0003
Der Pyruvatgehalt der Milch als Kriterium der hygienischen und technologischen Wertigkeit der Milch. **Pyruvate content in milk with respect to hygienic and technological value of milk.**

20215 Kielwein, G.; Luh, H.–K.   DE 129701/78/0001 N
Dokumentation zu Kulturgeschichte, Herstellung, Zusammensetzung und Verbreitung international bedeutender Käse. **Documentation into history, production, composition and distribution of cheeses of international importance.**

20216 Müller, K.   DE 132062/75/0003
Ermittlung analytisch fassbarer Indikatoren zur genaueren Fixierung physiologisch bedeutender Stoffwechselsituationen in Pflanzen und pflanzlichen Produkten – Ausreife, Keimung u.a. –. **Determination of analytical indicators for the fixation of physiologically important metabolic states in plants and plant products – maturity, sprouting, etc. –.**

20217 Röbbelen, G.; Thies, W.   DE 132184/75/0003
Bestimmung und Selektion auf Ölgehalt bei Raps durch NMR–Spektroskopie. **Determination and selection of oil content in rape seed by NMR–spectroscopy.**

20218 Zimmer, K.; Nolting, G.   DE 138270/70/0001
Sortimentprüfung bei Sommerblumen, internationale Registrierung der Sortimente von Callistephus chinensis, Petunia x hybrida Vilm., Tagetes erecta und T. patula, Begonia semperflorens 1952. **Testing of assortments of summer flowers, international registration of assortments of Callistephus chinensis, Petunia x Hybride Vilm., Tagetes erecta and T. patula, Begonia semperflorens.**

20219 Landzettel, W.   DE 138630/71/0001
Dokumentation bäuerlicher Wohnformen. **Documentation of agricultural dwelling.**

20220 Schulze, W.; Cramon–Taubadel, A.von
   DE 139750/78/0015 N
Weltkatalog der veterinärmedizinischen Lehranstalten nach dem Stand von 1976/77. **World catalogue of veterinary schools according to the situation of 1976/77.**

20221 Schulze, W.; Droege, P.   DE 139750/78/0016 N
Eine Kasuistik der seit Inkrafttreten des neuen deutschen
Tierschutzgesetzes vom 24. Juli 1972 bis Juni 1977 an
Gerichten der Bundesrepublik Deutschland und Westberlins
aktenkundig gewordenen Verstösse gegen dieses Gesetz. **Cases
of offence against the new German animal protection laws filed
from July 24 1972 to June 1977 at lawcourts in the Federal
Republic of Germany and West Berlin.**

20222 Schulze, W.; Elhardt, W.–R.   DE 139750/78/0017 N
Jahresbericht 1975/76 der Schweinepatienten einer
Tierärztlichen Landpraxis im Kreis Wesel 'Niederrhein'.
**Annual report of 1975/76 of pig patients in a rural veterinary
practice in the Wesel district 'Lower Rhine'.**

20223 Schulze, W.; Hanke, H.   DE 139750/78/0018 N
Statistische Übersicht einer Grosstierpraxis im Mittleren
Niedersachsen der Jahre 1958 bis 1975. **Statistical survey of a
large–animal practice in central Lower Saxony from 1958 to
1975.**

20224 Koch, W.; Sanwald, E.; Walter, H.
                                    DE 144540/74/0002 N
Möglichkeiten der Erfassung von Remissionsspektren von
Pflanzen und Untersuchungen zu Wechselwirkungen zwischen
Strahlungseinflüssen und Pflanzen. **Possibilities of determining
remission spectra in plants and studies on interactions between
radiation effects and plants.**

20225 Reisch, E.; Wenzel, K.   DE 144745/73/0002
Erarbeitung, Fortschreibung und Aufbereitung von
betriebswirtschaftlichen und arbeitswirtschaftlichen
Kalkulationsdaten für einen bundeseinheitlichen
Datenkatalog. **Collecting, updating and preparing of economic
and labour calculation data for a Federal standard data bank.**

20226 Mosonyi, E.; Kiefer, W.; Hauck, E.
                                    DE 145302/75/0005
Effizienz der Hochwasservorhersage im Hinblick auf die
Steuerung von Speichern. **Efficiency of flood forecasting with
regard to reservoir control.**

20227 Teichgräber, R.   DE 160331/75/0001
Versuche zum Zwecke der Vereinheitlichung internationaler
Brandprüfverfahren; Vergleich zwischen ISO und DIN 4102.
**Tests with the aim of coordinating international fire testing
methods; comparison between ISO and DIN 4102.**

20228 Schulz, H.; Henrici, D.; Heimeshoff, B.
                                    DE 160336/75/0001
Beitrag zur Spannungsermittlung in ausgeklinkten
Brettschichtträgern. **Computation of stresses in endnotched
glued laminated beams.** Publications.

20229 Terplan, G.; Schegger, G.; Zaadhof, K.–J.
                                    DE 160731/75/0001
Nachweis von Staphylokokkenenterotoxin in Lebensmitteln
nach Ultrafiltration anhand der Immunelektrophorese nach
Laurell und der Gegenstromelektrophorese. **Detection of
staphylococcal enterotoxins in food after ultrafiltration by
means of immuno–electrophoresis – Laurell – and
counter–current immuno–electrophoresis.**

20230 Terplan, G.; Baath, C.; Ebner, R.; Gedek, W.
                                    DE 160731/75/0002

Nachweis und Identifizierung von Antibiotika in Milch mittels
Dünnschichtchromatographie. **Detection and identification of
antibiotics in milk by means of thin–layer chromatography.**

20231 Gedek, W.   DE 160731/75/0011
Einsatz von Penicillinase zur Identifizierung von
biosynthetischen und penicillinasestabilen Penicillinen.
**Application of penicillinase for the identification of
biosynthetic and penicillinase–stable penicillins.**

20232 Terplan, G.; Arold, W.; Grove, H.–H.
                                    DE 160731/75/0013
Einfluss von psychrotrophen Mikroorganismen auf den Gehalt
der Milch an Pyruvat, L–Lactat und D–Lactat. **Psychrotrophic
microorganisms and the pyruvate, L–lactate and D–lactate
content in milk.**

20233 Pirchner, F.; Förster, M.; Zwiauer, D.
                                    DE 161300/78/0006 N
Genkartierung Rind. **Gene mapping of cattle.** Publications.

20234 Gränzer, W.   DE 161360/78/0001 N
Entwicklung optimierter Miniatursender zur
pH–Wertmessung. **The development of optimized miniature
transmitter for the measurement of the pH–value.** Publications.

20235 Heimeshoff, B.; Bauler, H.; Krzykacz, B.; Spengler, R.
                                    DE 161582/75/0001
Beanspruchungsverhalten finiter Brettelemente unter
zweiachsiger Beanspruchung. **Load behaviour of finite boards
elements under biaxial load.**

20236 Heimeshoff, B.; Krzykacz, B.; Glos, P.
                                    DE 161582/75/0003
Beanspruchungsverhalten finiter Brettelemente unter
einachsiger Beanspruchung nach einer
Langzeit–Vorbelastung. **Load behaviour of finite boards
elements under single–axle load after long duration preload.**

20237 Narziss, L.; Schuster, I.   DE 161790/75/0001
Fettsäuren und Lipide in Malz, Würzen und Bier. **Fatty acids
and lipids in malt, wort and beer.**

20238 Rehm, H.J.   DE 164100/75/0001
1.Abbau von Aflatoxinen durch Mikroorganismen
2.Bedingungen zur Aflatoxinbildung. **1.Breakdown of
aflatoxins by micro–organisms 2.Conditions of aflatoxin
formation.**

20239 Bösenberg, H.; Norpoth, K.   DE 164200/75/0001
Verbesserungen der Spurenanalytik von Mykotoxinen und
Mykotoxin–Metaboliten. **Improvement of analytical tracing of
mycotoxins and mycotoxin metabolites.**

20240 Bergner, K.–G.; Ha, Y.–D.   DE 170050/75/0003
Versuche zur schnellen Identifizierung von
Fungicid–Rückständen. **Experiments on rapid identification of
fungicide residues.**

20241 Brieskorn, C.H.; Mahlmeister, K.   DE 176150/75/0003
Polarographische Bestimmung von Vitamin E und
Antioxydantien in Körperflüssigkeiten. **Polarographic analysis
of vitamin E and antioxidants in body fluids.**

20242 Niebergall, H.; Hartmann, M.   DE 176150/75/0005
Entwicklung und Anwendung einer neuen Messanordnung

zum Bestimmen der Stoffmigration aus Folien in Lebensmittel und Simulantien unter Einsatz der Hochdruckflüssigkeitschromatographie. **Development and application of a new method for measuring the migration of additives and other contents from plastics into foodstuffs and simulants using the high pressure liquid chromatography.**

20243 Rietz, E. DE 201010/77/0003
Automatisierung der Messwerterfassung und –verarbeitung mittels elektronischer Datenverarbeitungsanlagen für den variablen Einsatz der instrumentellen Analytik bei den verschiedenen Forschungsvorhaben der Institute. **Automation of collection and processing of data by means of electronic data processing systems for variable use of instrumental analytics in different research projects of the institutes.**

20244 Rohrmoser, K. DE 201030/77/0002
Zentrale Erfassung und Auswertung von Daten der pflanzlichen Produktion aus Projekten der Deutschen Technischen Zusammenarbeit. **Central collection and evaluation of data on plant production from projects of the German Technical Co–operation.**

20245 Seidewitz, L. DE 201040/75/0003
Internationale Standardisierung von Deskriptoren und Deskriptorwerten. **International standardization of descriptors and descriptor values.**

20246 Alleweldt, G.; Berndt, H.; Wolfrom, I.
DE 204000/71/4036
Dokumentation der Weinbauforschung. **Documentation of viticultural research.**

20247 Hamann, J.; Blüthgen, A.; Heeschen, W.; Tolle, A.
DE 207020/74/0009
Erarbeitung eines Systems zur Isolierung und Identifizierung von Antibiotika aus Milch. **Elaboration of a system of isolation and identification of antibiotics in milk.**

20248 Hahn, G.; Tolle, A. DE 207020/77/0002
Klassifizierung von Streptokokkenstämmen Human– und Veterinärmedizinischer Institute und Aufbau einer Datenbank im Rahmen der Streptokokkenzentrale. **Classification of strains of streptococci in institutes for human and veterinary medicine and establishment of a data bank in streptococci center.**

20249 Reuter, H.; Meier, R. DE 207060/78/0001 N
Verbesserung der automatischen Probenahme von Rohmilch in Milchsammelwagen. **Improvement of automatic sampling of raw milk in milk collecting tanks.**

20250 Rehbein, H.; Kress, G. DE 208040/75/0004
Analytik von frischem und gefrorenem Fisch; Entwicklung von enzymologischen Methoden zum Gefriernachweis. **Analytics of fresh and frozen fish; development of enzymological methods for recognizing frozen fish.**

20251 Feldt, W.; Siebert, W. DE 208050/75/0002
Radioökologische Analyse im Bereich des Kernkraftwerks Unterweser. **Radioecological investigations carried out in the surroundings of the nuclear power station Unterweser.**

20252 Weipert, D. DE 209020/75/0004
Messungen der Viskosität und des rheologischen Verhaltens von Roggen– und Weizenmehlteigen. **Measurement of viscosity and rheological properties of rye and wheat flour doughs.**

20253 Klettner, P.G. DE 210020/75/0004
Festigkeitsuntersuchungen an frischem und zubereitetem Fleisch und Fleischerzeugnissen mit rheologischen Messgeräten. **Testing of solidity in fresh and prepared meat and meat products by rheological measurements.**

20254 Rödel, W. DE 210030/75/0006
Vorschlag transportabler Messgeräte für die Qualitätskontrolle in fleischverarbeitenden Betrieben und für die amtliche Lebensmittelüberwachung. **Recommendation of transportable measuring units for quality control in meat processing enterprises and for the official food control.**

20255 Linke, H. DE 210030/75/0013
Ermittlung der Streuung von Qualitätskriterien im Rahmen der Aufstellung sachgerechter Prüfpläne für Fleischerzeugnisse. **Determination of dispersion of quality criteria in connection with establishment of appropriate meat products control programmes.**

20256 Leistner, L. DE 210030/75/0015
Entwicklung von Starterkulturen für IM–Meats. **Development of starter cultures for IM meats.**

20257 Linke, H. DE 210030/78/0011 N
Erstellung eines Wurstatlanten. **Catalogue of German meat products.**

20258 Arneth, W. DE 210040/75/0008
Entwicklung von Schnellmethoden zur Routineanalyse von Fleisch und Fleischerzeugnissen. **Development of rapid methods for routine analysis of meat and meat products.**

20259 Arneth, W. DE 210040/75/0009
Entwicklung automatischer Verfahren zur raschen Routinebestimmung bestimmter Bestandteile von Fleisch und Fleischerzeugnissen. **Development of automatic methods for rapid routine analysis of certain constituents in meat and meat products.**

20260 Arneth, W.; Hofmann, K. DE 210040/75/0014
Entwicklung von Methoden zur Bestimmung von Muskeleiweiss in Fleischerzeugnissen. **Development of methods for determination of myosin in meat products.**

20261 Hamm, R.; Honikel, K. DE 210040/75/0016
Beziehungen zwischen biochemischen Faktoren und Kriterien der Fleischqualität bei Rindfleisch unter besonderer Berücksichtigung der Geschwindigkeit von Reaktionen post mortem. **Correlations between biochemical factors and quality criteria in beef with special regard to velocity of post mortem reactions.**

20262 Hamm, R.; Gottesmann, P. DE 210040/78/0003 N
Untersuchungen zur Entwicklung einer einfachen Methode zur Unterscheidung zwischen Frischfleisch und aufgetautem Gefrierfleisch. **Investigations on the development of a simple method for differentiation between fresh meat and frozen/thawed meat.**

20263 Schön, I. DE 210050/75/0001
Erarbeitung international bedeutsamer Fleischstandards. **Elaboration of meat–standards of international significance.**

20264 Folkers, D.   DE 211100/78/0005 N
Wirkungsanalyse von Massnahmen zur
Verbraucheraufklärung. **Analysis of the effectiveness of selected consumer information methods.**

20265 Mangold, H.K.; Reichwald, I.; Hudalla, B.; Kaiser, H.
            DE 213020/75/0001
Ernährungsphysiologische und toxikologische Bewertung
neuer Nahrungsfette. **Nutritional and toxicological evaluation of new edible fats.**

20266 Mukherjee, K.D.; Ilsemann, K.   DE 213020/75/0009
Entstehung ungewöhnlicher Lipide bei konventioneller
Verarbeitung von natürlichen Fetten. **Formation of unusual lipids in conventional processing of natural fats.**

20267 Mukherjee, K.D.; Richter, I.   DE 213020/75/0011
Neue Technologien zur Fettgewinnung. **New technologies for the extraction of fats.**

20268 Mangold, H.K.; Moety, E.A.   DE 213020/75/0013
Neue Produkte aus pflanzlichen Ölen. **New products from vegetable oils.**

20269 Mangold, H.K.   DE 213020/75/0016
Fette und andere Lipide aus Schlachttieren. **Fats and other lipids from slaughter animals.**

20270 Schuphan, I.; Kossmann, U.; Kossmann, A.;
Pflugmacher, J.   DE 215010/75/0003
Untersuchungen zum Schicksal der
PerhalogenalkylmercaptanFungizide. **Investigations of the residue and degradation behaviour of perhalogeno alkylthiol fungicides.**

20271 Lyre, H.; Ehle, H.; Heidler, G.; Martin, J.
            DE 215090/77/0001
Untersuchungen zur Wirksamkeit und Phytotoxizität von
Fungiziden und Herbiziden im Rahmen des
Zulassungsverfahrens. **Investigations on efficiency and phytotoxicity of fungicides and herbicides in admittance process.**

20272 Lyre, H.   DE 215090/77/0004
Biometrische Grundlagen und Aufstellung von Codes –
Schlüssel – für die Einführung der EDV für das
Zulassungsverfahren. **Biometric principles and establishment of codes for introduction of EDP into the admittance process.**

20273 Laermann, T.T.   DE 215090/77/0006
Prüfung von Wirksamkeit und Phytotoxizität bei
Wachstumsreglern im Rahmen des Zulassungsverfahrens.
Testing of efficiency and phytotoxicity of growth regulators in admittance process.

20274 Becker, H.; Riepert, F.   DE 215100/77/0001
Untersuchungen zur Wirksamkeit und Phytotoxizität von
Insektiziden, Akariziden, Nematiziden, Molluskiziden,
Rodentiziden und Wildschadenverhütungsmitteln im Rahmen
des Zulassungsverfahrens. **Investigations on efficiency and phytotoxicity of insecticides, acaricides, nematicides, molluscicides, rodenticides and agents against damages by game in admittance process.**

20275 Becker, H.; Grasblum, M.; Riepert, F.; Rothert, H.
            DE 215100/77/0003

Entwicklung von Richtlinien für die Prüfung von Mitteln gegen
tierische Schädlinge. **Development of guidelines for testing pesticides.**

20276 Herfs, W.; Brasse, D.   DE 215100/77/0004
Untersuchungen zur Wirkung von
Pflanzenbehandlungsmitteln auf die Honigbiene im Rahmen
des Zulassungsverfahrens. **Investigations on effects of plant protectives on honeybee in admittance process.**

20277 Herfs, W.; Brasse, D.   DE 215100/77/0005
Untersuchungen zur Wirkung von
Pflanzenbehandlungsmitteln auf Nutzarthropoden im Rahmen
des Zulassungsverfahrens. **Investigations on effects of plant protectives on useful arthropods in admittance process.**

20278 Kohsiek, H.   DE 215110/77/0002
Richtlinien für die Prüfung von fahrbaren Sprühgeräten für
Zeilenanlagen im Obst– und Weinbau. **Guidelines for testing of mobile sprayers for row planting in fruit culture and viticulture.**

20279 Kohsiek, H.   DE 215110/77/0004
Erarbeitung von Methoden für die Beurteilung von
Pflanzenschutzgeräten. **Development of methods for valuation of plant protection equipment.**

20280 Stegemann, H.; Loeschcke, V.   DE 215140/75/0003
Index europäischer Kartoffelsorten. **Index of European potato varieties.**

20281 Casper, R.   DE 215150/78/0011 N
Routinenachweis von Kartoffelviren mit dem
ELISA–Verfahren. **Routine testing for potato viruses by ELISA.**

20282 Weidemann, H.–L.; Koenig, R.; Casper, R.; Paul,
H.L.   DE 215150/78/0014 N
Vergleichende Untersuchungen für die Entwicklung von
serologischen Schnellverfahren zur Routinetestung von
Pflanzkartoffeln. **Comparative studies on the development of serological rapid methods for routine testing of seed potatoes.**

20283 Blumenbach, D.   DE 215300/77/0002
Erstellung eines Führers für die Benutzung der
Pflanzenschutzdokumentation. **Establishment of a guide for use of documentation on plant protection.**

20284 Blumenbach, D.   DE 215300/77/0006
Fortschreibung des Thesaurus Phytomedizin unter
Berücksichtigung der aktuellen fachlichen und methodischen
Erfordernisse des Pflanzenschutzes. **Updating of thesaurus on phytomedicine with regard to actual technical and methodical requirements for plant protection.**

20285 Laux, W.   DE 215300/77/0010
Erstellung und Veröffentlichung einer Konkordanzliste für
russische Namen von schädlichen und nützlichen Arthropoden
und den entsprechenden wissenschaftlichen Namen. **Collection and publication of a concordance list for Russian names of injurious and useful arthropods and corresponding scientific names.**

20286 Blumenbach, D.   DE 215300/77/0013
Erarbeitung eines Führers für die in der Bundesrepublik
Deutschland Pestiziddokumentation betreibenden

Dokumentationsstellen im Hinblick auf Austausch und Zusammenarbeit. **Development of a guide on documentation centres in the Federal Republic of Germany with documentation on pesticides with regard to exchange and cooperation.**

20287 Laux, W.   DE 215300/77/0014
Erstellung eines Gesamtzeitschriftenkataloges der Bibliotheken der Biologischen Bundesanstalt für Land– und Forstwirtschaft. **Establishment of overall catalogue of periodicals in libraries of the Biologische Bundesanstalt für Land– und Forstwirtschaft.**

20288 Wagner, C.   DE 301100/77/0002
Hopfenperonospora Warndienst. **Warning service on Peronospora in hops.**

20289 Uehleke   DE 305010/75/0002
Toxikologie von Bioziden. **Toxicology of biocides – pesticides –.**

20290 Toth, L.; Kellert, M.   DE 305010/75/0006
Isolierbarkeit von Aflatoxinen. **Possibilities of isolating aflatoxins.**

20291 Toth, L.; Tiebach, R.   DE 305010/75/0007
Bestimmung von Dickungsmitteln. **Determination of thickening agents.**

20292 Toth, L.   DE 305010/75/0008
Entwicklung und Einsatz der Kapillargaschromatographie in der Lebensmittelanalytik. **Development and application of capillary gas chromatography in food analysis.**

20293 Toth, L.   DE 305010/75/0010
Überprüfung und Standardisierung analytischer Verfahren in der Lebensmittelchemie. **Verification and standardization of analytical methods in food chemistry.**

20294 Bressau, G.   DE 305010/75/0017
Bewertung von Pestizidrückständen in und auf Lebensmitteln. **Evaluation of pesticide residues in and on foods.**

20295 Junge, C.; Olschimke, D.   DE 305010/75/0023
Erarbeitung von analytischen Eigenschaften für Fruchtsäfte und gleichartige Erzeugnisse sowie den dazu erforderlichen Untersuchungsmethoden. **Development of analytical characteristics for fruit juices and products of identical type and of methods of analysis required for this purpose.**

20296 Junge, C.   DE 305011/77/0003
Weinstatistik. **Wine statistics.**

20297 Levetzow, R.   DE 305030/75/0002
Kontrolle der Desinfektionswirkung durch standardisierte bakteriologische Methoden. **Control of disinfecting effects by standardized bacteriological methods.**

20298 Levetzow, R.   DE 305030/75/0003
Vermeidung unspezifischer Reaktionen durch Testmodifikationen. **Avoidance of non–specific reactions by modifications of tests.**

20299 Levetzow, R.   DE 305030/75/0005
Spezies–Diagnose beim Clostridium–Nachweis. **Identification of Clostridia; species diagnosis.**

20300 Levetzow, R.   DE 305030/75/0007
Entwicklung einer Temperaturmesstechnik für die ambulante Kontrolle von Tiefkühlkost. **Development of a temperature measuring technique for ambulant inspection of deep–frozen meals.**

20301 Schwarz, O.   DE 501500/75/0001
Forstlicher Schneemessdienst im Süd– und Nordschwarzwald. **Forest service for snow measuring in the southern and northern Black Forest.**

20302 Volk, H.   DE 501504/75/0005
Benutzungshäufigkeit von Walderholungseinrichtungen. **Frequency of utilization of forest recreation facilities.**

20303 Fuchs, H.   DE 502058/78/0001 N
Verbesserung der Aussagekraft von Labor–Keimprüfungsverfahren bei Saatgut. **Improvement of the quality of seed–germination testing in laboratory. Publications.**

20304 Haisch, K.–H.; Brünn, K.   DE 502552/75/0001
Qualität der Milch und ihre wirtschaftliche Bewertung. **Milk quality and its economical evaluation.**

20305 Strehler, A.; Schulz, H.; Perwanger, A.; Hofstetter, N.   DE 502600/75/0001
Energiegewinnung aus Stroh und Holz – Verfügbare Reststoffe in der Landwirtschaft zur Strohgewinnung – Hochverdichtung von Stroh – Solarenergie in der Landwirtschaft –. **Winning of energy from straw und wood.**

20306 Wenner, H.L.; Boxberger, J.   DE 502602/75/0003
Untersuchungen zur Optimierung der elektrischen Energiebedarfsdeckung in der Landwirtschaft. **Studies on optimizing the meeting of electric energy demand in agriculture.**

20307 Zakosek, H.; Becker, H.; Horney, G.   DE 506050/70/0001
Weinbau–Standortkarte der hessischen Weinbaugebiete 1:5.000. **Map of habitats of viticulture in Hesse 1:5.000.**

20308 Bargon, E.; Ziehlke, C.P.   DE 506051/75/0001
Bodenkarte von Hessen 1:25 000, Bl. 4622 Kassel–West. **Soil map of Hesse scale 1:25 000, sheet no. 4622 Kassel–West.**

20309 Bargon, E.; Schrader, L.   DE 506051/75/0002
Bodenkarte von Hessen 1:25 000, Bl. 5518 Butzbach. **Soil map of Hesse scale 1:25 000, sheet no. 5518 Butzbach.**

20310 Bargon, E.   DE 506051/75/0004
Bodenkarte von Hessen 1:25 000, Bl. 5819 Hanau a.M.. **Soil map of Hesse scale 1:25 000, sheet no. 5819 Hanau a.M..**

20311 Bargon, E.; Fickel, W.   DE 506051/75/0005
Bodenkarte von Hessen 1:25 000, Bl. 6118 Darmstadt–Ost. **Soil map of Hesse scale 1:25 000, sheet no. 6118 Darmstadt–Ost.**

20312 Schrader, L.   DE 506051/78/0001 N
Bodenkarte von Hessen 1:25 000, Blatt 5519 Hungen. **Soil map of Hesse scale 1:25 000, sheet no. 5519 Hungen.**

20313 Schrader, L.   DE 506051/78/0002 N
Bodenkarte von Hessen 1:25 000, Blatt 5418 Giessen. **Soil map**

of Hesse scale 1:25 000, sheet no. 5418 Giessen.

20314 Fickel, W.   DE 506051/78/0003 N
Bodenkarte von Hessen 1:25 000, Blatt 6117 Darmstadt–West.
**Soil map of Hesse scale 1:25 000, sheet no. 6117
Darmstadt–West.**

20315 Fickel, W.   DE 506051/78/0004 N
Bodenkarte von Hessen 1:25 000, Blatt 5717 Bad Homburg
v.d.H.. **Soil map of Hesse scale 1:25 000, sheet no. 5717 Bad
Homburg v.d.H..**

20316 Fickel, W.   DE 506051/78/0005 N
Bodenkarte von Hessen 1:25 000, Blatt 5716 Oberreifenberg.
**Soil map of Hesse scale 1:25 000, sheet no. 5716
Oberreifenberg.**

20317 Puffe, D.; Morgner, F.; Zerr, W. DE 506156/78/0001 N
Untersuchungen über spezielle Inhaltsstoffe bei
Futterpflanzen. **Investigations on special constituents of forage
plants.**

20318 Weimann   DE 506401/70/0001
Überprüfung des Hessischen Verfahrens der
Zustandsaufnahme im Rahmen der Forsteinrichtung durch
eine Inventur für die Fichtenbestandsklasse im hessischen
Staatswald. **Control of the usual store inventories of the forest
management in Hesse by sampling in the spruce stands.**

20319 Struff, R.   DE 915500/75/0001
Sachliche und räumliche Schwerpunktbildung für integrierte
Programmplanung der Gemeinschaftsaufgabe "Verbesserung
der Agrarstruktur und des Küstenschutzes". **Formulation of
the main concern as to subject and space in integrated planning
of the joint programme "Improvement of agrarian structure
and of coastal protection".**

20320 Wagn, O.   DK 010116/19/0002
Undersøgelse over forekomst af forskellige plantesygdomme
og skadedyr samt anvisning af den mest hensigtsmæssige
bekæmpelse af disse. **Investigation of the occurrence of various
plant diseases and pests, and recommendations for their
control.**

20321 Jensen, A.   DK 010116/77/0011
Specielle opgaver, diagnosticering og registrering af sygdomme
i havebrugsplanter. **Special projects, diagnosis and registration
of diseases in horticultural plants.**

20322 Jørgensen, G.; Poulsen, J.S.D.; Jepsen, Ø.R.
                                        DK 010204/78/0003 N
Standardisering af blodprøveudtagning og fastlæggelse af
normalværdier for blodparametre hos mink. **Standardization of
bloodsampling technique and determination of normal blood
values in mink.**

20323 Madsen, E.   DK 020500/79/9181 N
Udvikling af metode til bestemmelse af frøkvalitet baseret på
indholdet af ATP (adenosintrifosfat) i den initiale spiringsfase.
**The content of ATP in the initial stage of germination as a
method for determination of seed quality.**

20324 Schultz, C.; Roulund, H.; Ditlevsen, B.; Hagman, M.;
Skröppa, T.; Ifver, J.   DK 030102/78/0001 N
Koordinering af EDB–registrering af genressourcemateriale
vedr. skovtræer i norden. **Coordination af EDP–registration af**

forest genetic material in the nordic countries.

20325 Jensen, A.T.; Jensen, E.; Pedersen, M.B.
                                        DK 030106/73/0023 N
Sammenligning af samtlige jordbrugskalksorters reaktivitet. **A
comparative study of the reactivity of all agricultural limes
marketed in Denmark.**

20326 Rudemo, M.   DK 030107/78/0001 N
Statistisk metodeudvikling og konsulentvirksomhed inden for
det jordbrugs– og veterinærvidenskabelige område. **Statistical
methods development and consulting within the agricultural
and veterinary sciences.**

20327 Bloch, B.   DK 030138/70/0002
Elektronmikroskopiske undersøgelser af en række organer og
cellekulturer fortrinsvis med virologisk sigte.
**Electron–microscopic investigations of a series of organs and
cell cultures viewed from a virological standpoint.**

20328 Lund, E.; Nissen, B.   DK 030138/78/0002 N
Undersøgelse af forskellige kemiske desinfektionsmidler.
**Studies on the efficiency of various chemical disinfectants
against virus.**

20329 Pedersen, T.T.; Have, H.   DK 030144/78/0001 N
Regional analyse af mængder og fordeling af halm og
affaldstrææ. **Regional analysis of amount and utilization of waste
products especially straw in Denmark.**

20330 Lundsgaard, T.   DK 030147/79/0002 N
Udbygning og vedligeholdelse af en antiserumbank samt
udvikling af serologiske metoder til rutinetestning af frø for
virusinfektion. **Extension of a bank holding antisera against
seed–borne viruses, and elaboration of routine seed health
testing methods.**

20331 Jensen, P.F.   DK 030149/79/0008 N
Landbo– og miljørettens udvikling. **The development of
environmental and agricultural law.**

20332 Jacobi, P.   DK 030161/78/0002 N
Anvendelse af grafisk databehandling i landskabsanalyse.
**Implementation of computer aided design in landscape
analysis.**

20333 Jakobsen, S.J.   DK 030181/79/0003 N
Udarbejdelse af tilvækstoversigt for bøg i Danmark. **Yield
table for beech, based on permanent sample plots.**

20334 Hansen, I.B.; Sørensen, F.T.; Pedersen, K.B.
                                        DK 030195/74/0001 R
Udarbejdelse af input til FAO's AGRIS–1
dokumentationsprojekt. **Preparation of the input for FAO's
AGRIS–1 documentation project.**

20335 Robert, M.   FR 010103/73/6347
Essai d'estimation quantitative et développement des profils.
Tests for quantitative evaluation of profile development.

20336 Lefèvre, E.; Calvet, R.   FR 010103/74/6337
Tests biologiques rapides de l'activité des herbicides. **Quick
biological tests on herbicide activity.**

20337 Raichon, C.; Damour, L.; Guibert, P.; Billot, C.;
Guimbard, C.; Brun, R.   FR 010112/70/3032

Collecte de données économiques dans des domaines expérimentaux. **Collecting economic datas on experimental farms.** Publications.

20338 Grandclaude, L.; Delarbre, F.　　　FR 010112/73/3030
Etablissement de modèles d'entreprises de polyculture – élevage bovin. **Elaboration of farm models in mixed farming (plant production and cattle).**

20339 Bouchon, J.; Bachacou; Le Goff, N; Ottorini, J.M.
　　　　　　　　　　　　　　　　　FR 010301/73/4060
Méthodes d'échantillonnage en forêt : utilisation de la méthode des variables régionalisées. **Sampling methods in forestry : use of regionalized variables method.**

20340 Clement, A.　　　　　　　FR 010303/69/4159
Amélioration du diagnostic foliaire. **Improvement of the foliar diagnostic.**

20341 Bachacou, J.　　　　　　　FR 010312/75/8297
Cartographie automatique (3). **Automatic cartography.**

20342 Millier, C.　　　　　　　FR 010312/77/8276
Dictionnaire de modeles. **Model dictionary.**

20343 Haeflinger, R.; Conesa, A.　　　FR 010312/77/8283
Dépouillement enquête betterave alsace. **Data analysis of a sugar–beet survey in alsace.**

20344 Barral–Mazoyer, R. Mme; Agius, I.
　　　　　　　　　　　　　　　　　FR 010502/74/6013
Dosage, en agronomie, du bore par ionométrie. **Ionometric analysis of boron in agricultural samples.**

20345 Lecomte, A.　　　　　　　FR 010601/75/8299
Traitement automatique des données d'analyseur de gaz (4). **Automatic data analysis from a gas analyzer.**

20346 Lecomte, A.　　　　　　　FR 010601/75/8300
Pesage automatique et traitement des informations recueillies sur le terrain (4). **Automatic weighing and data analysis of field informations.**

20347 Lecomte, A.　　　　　　　FR 010601/77/8298
Pesage automatique du bétail et de son alimentation; mise en mémoire des données (4). **Automatic weighing of cattle and cattle feeding; data storage.**

20348 Arnoux, M.; Defrance, H.; Verbruge
　　　　　　　　　　　　　　　　　FR 010615/74/9036
Peintures réfléchissantes et antiseptiques pour troncs d'arbres fruitiers. **Testing reflecting and antiseptic points for the protection of fruit tree trunks.**

20349 Gachon, L.; Triboi, E.　　　　FR 010802/76/6110
Mise au point d'une technique simplifiée de mesure du phosphore isotopiquement diluable. **A simplified technique for appreciate of isotopically exchangeable phosphate.**

20350 Naert, B.; Servat, E.　　　　FR 011211/72/0611
Cartographie pédologique au 1/100 000. Feuille de Millau. **Soilmap (1/100 000) of Millau country.** Publications.

20351 Soignet, G.　　　　　　　FR 012216/68/0511
Structure et organisation du laboratoire "Unité de service". **Management of soil analysis as a "Unit laboratory".**

20352 Bracquart; Lefebvre, R.　　　FR 012222/25/6040
Utilisation des données climatiques annuelles Comparaisons pluriannuelles. **Climatology of Picardy.**

20353 Hiroux, G.; Desmet Mme; Cousin　FR 012222/75/6046
Titrage ampérométrique pour le dosage iodométrique de l'amylose dans les pois de conserve (T.N.B.E. Miller. Technique générale de...). **Amperometric titration of amylose in peas.**

20354 Maucorps, J.; Rouil; Guerin, B.; Salin, R.
　　　　　　　　　　　　　　　　　FR 012503/59/6145
Cartographie des sols du Département de l'Aisne. **Soil survey of the department of Aisne.**

20355 Researcher not indicated　　　GB 060117/00/0002 R
Minor investigations.

20356 Reseacher not yet known　　　GB 060117/78/0003 N
Minor Investigation.

20357 Researcher not indicated　　　GB 060325/00/0001 R
Minor investigations.

20358 Connaughton, M.J.; Keane, T.　IE 030100/65/7301 R
Agroclimatological study of Ireland. Publications.

20359 O'Brien, D.; Fitzsimons, B.; Keogh, R.
　　　　　　　　　　　　　　　　　IE 050100/69/7520 N
Growth, yield and production models for trees. Publications.

20360 McEntee, M.　　　　　　　IE 060300/71/0162 R
Climatic regionalisation in Ireland. Publications.

20361 Staunton, W.P.　　　　　　IE 060300/73/0871 R
Algae, fungi and moss on the surface of growing media. Publications.

20362 Connolly, J.F.　　　　　　IE 060400/69/0284 N
Biochemical parameters and animal performance. Publications.

20363 McGann, T.C.A.　　　　　IE 060400/76/2010 R
Large scale monitoring of milk constituents. Process and product control in the dairy food industry by infrared absorbance/reflectance techniques. Publications.

20364 Rea, M.; O'Connor, F.　　　IE 060400/77/2075 R
Improved methods of the isolation of staphylococcus aureus and screening of foods for staphylococcal enteroxins.

20365 Fitzgerald, P.; O'Connor, L.　IE 060500/58/0219 R
Sugar beet seed germination testing. Publications.

20366 Morandini, R.; Tocci, A.; Pelizzo, A.
　　　　　　　　　　　　　　　　　IT 021700/48/0001 R
Libro nazionale boschi da seme. **Registry of forest tree seed stands.** Publications.

20367 Preto, G.　　　　　　　　IT 021700/75/0001
Utilizzazione della fotografia aerea per inventari e cartografia forestale. **Aerial survey for forest inventoring and mapping.**

20368 Castellani, C.; Scrinzi, G.　　IT 021800/78/0003 R
Rilevamento dei soprassuoli boschivi mediante campionamento al fine di ridurre le spese d'inventario. **Forest survey by sampling methods in order to reduce inventory costs.**

20369 Vlahov, G.; Cucurachi, A.; Brighigna, A.
IT 022100/75/0001
L'evoluzione degli acidi volatili nelle salamoie di fermentazione delle olive da tavola. **Volatile acids evolution in table olive brines.**

20370 Casalicchio, G.; Rosciglione, L.; Vianello, G.; Del Monte, M. IT 040202/78/0001
Carta pedologica dell'emilia – romagna. **Soil survey of the emilia – romagna region.**

20371 Pirola, A. IT 040226/77/0804
Atlanti regionali della vegetazione. **Regional atlases of plant life.**

20372 Gariboldi, P.L. IT 040604/78/1137 N
Sintesi di campioni per test biologici, derivati saturi e insaturi dell'omoleucina, sintesi eterociclici vari contenenti catene laterali terpenoidiche. **Synthesis of samples for biological tests; saturated and non saturated derivates of homo–leucine; synthesis of various heterocyclic substances containing terpenic lateral chains.**

20373 Segre, L. · IT 040618/77/0298 R
Ricerca di reperti agricoli per la creazione in Italia del museo storico dell'agricoltura. **The collection of agricultural items in view of the creation in Italy of a Museum of the History of Agriculture.**

20374 Calandra, R. IT 041014/75/0002
Carta dei suoli e delle limitazioni nell'uso dei suoli della provincia di Ascoli Piceno. **Soil maps concerning also the limitations in the use of land in the province of Ascoli Piceno (Italy). Publications.**

20375 Geri, G. IT 041111/76/0001
L' aereofotogrammetria nello studio dei terreni agrari. **The aerial photographs in the agricultural soil study.**

20376 Nassimbeni, P.; Nazzi, P. IT 090701/79/0003 N
Carta pedologica della Regione Friuli Venezia Giulia alla scala 1 : 25.000. **Soil map of Friuli Venezia Giulia region in the scale of 1 : 25.000.**

20377 Santen, A. van NL 010101/57/1983
Bedrijfsbeheer en uitvoering van werkzaamheden voor proeven op proefboerderijen ten dienste van onderzoek instellingen. **Farmmanagement and execution of work on experimental farms for the use of research institutions.**

20378 Caem, H.E. van NL 010101/57/1984 R
Uitvoering van proefveldwerkzaamheden en verbetering van de proefveldtechniek van landelijk verspreide proefvelden ten dienste van onderzoekinstellingen. **Execution of work on experimental fields and improvement of experiment techniques for field experiments scattered all over the country for the use of research institutions.**

20379 Elbertsen, R.W.J. NL 010101/57/1986
Uitvoering en verbetering van diverse administratieve en ondersteunende werkzaamheden zoals boekhouding, projectenadministratie, foto–, film– en lichtdrukwerk, ten dienste van onderzoekinstellingen. **Execution and improvement of various adminstrative and service tasks such as bookkeeping, projectadminstration, photography, filmaking,** photo–typing, for the use of research institutes.

20380 Steiner, A.A. NL 010102/76/7305
Internationale samenwerking plantenteelt zonder aarde. **International co–operation soilless culture. Publications.**

20381 Bergh, J.P. van den NL 010102/79/8932 N
Adviezen voor onderzoek naar in mengsels groeiende plantesoorten. **Advices for research on plant species growing in mixtures.**

20382 Reuderink, R. NL 010103/55/0504
Aangelegenheden in verband met het meststoffenbesluit. **Matters concerning the fertilizers regulations. Publications.**

20383 Dijk, H.van NL 010103/60/0521
Karakterisering van organische meststoffen en potgronden in het laboratorium. **Laboratory characterization of organic soil amendments, and of potting soils. Publications.**

20384 Ris, J. NL 010103/73/4353
Onderricht in methoden van onderzoek en van bewerking der verkregen resultaten toegepast bij het bodemvruchtbaarheidsonderzoek. **Instruction in methods of investigation and of analysis of results applied in soil fertility research. Publications.**

20385 Smilde, K.W. NL 010103/78/8617 N
Nederlands–Voltaanse samenwerking binnen de "Service National des Sols" van Boven–Volta. **Cooperation between The Netherlands and Upper Volta to reinforce the "Service National des Sols", Upper Volta.**

20386 Helwig, A.J.G. NL 010106/49/2232
Algemene handelsvoorwaarden voor de bedrijfsuitrusting in land en tuinbouw. **General trading regulations for the equipment in agriculture and horticulture.**

20387 Fluit, J. NL 010106/69/2684
Merkenonderzoek grondbewerkingswerktuigen. **Comparative research of soil tillage implements. Publications.**

20388 Velde, J.J. van de NL 010106/69/2686
Merkenonderzoek van werktuigen voor het zaaien, poten, planten en kunstmest strooien. **Comparative research of implements for sowing, planting and spreading of fertilizers. Publications.**

20389 Velde, J.J. van de NL 010106/69/2688
Merkenonderzoek voor oogstwerktuigen voor hakvruchten. **Comparative research of harvesting machines for raw crops.**

20390 Velde, J.J. van de NL 010106/69/2690
Merkenonderzoek trekkers en trekker toebehoren. **Comparative research of tractors and tractor accessories. Publications.**

20391 Fluit, J. NL 010106/69/2691
Merkenonderzoek mechanisatie weidebouw. **Comparative research of the mechanization for pastural farms. Publications.**

20392 Verkaik, A.P. NL 010106/69/2692
Merkenonderzoek van werktuigen t.b.v. melken en voeren in de rundveehouderij. **Comparative research of implements in behalf of milking and feeding for live stock farming. Publications.**

20393 Kraai, A.R.   NL 010106/69/6424
Merkenonderzoek intern en extern transport t.b.v. de rundveehouderij. **Comparative research of internal and external transportation equipment for livestock farming.** Publications.

20394 Kraai, A.R.   NL 010106/69/7580
Merkenonderzoek oogstwerktuigen maai– en plukbare gewassen. **Comparative research of harvesting machines.**

20395 Porskamp, H.A.J.   NL 010106/70/2687
Merkenonderzoek van verzorgingswerktuigen i.c. spuitapparatuur. **Comparative research of crop husbandry implements, i.c. sprayers.** Publications.

20396 Porskamp, H.A.J.   NL 010106/70/6408
Merkenonderzoek ventilatoren in de agrarische sector. **Comparative research of fans in the agricultural sector.** Publications.

20397 Bijl, R.S.   NL 010106/72/3652
Merkenonderzoek van machines en werktuigen voor de bloembollenteelt. **Comparative research of machines and implements for bulb growing.** Publications.

20398 Siepman, A.H.J.   NL 010106/72/3714
Mechanisatie – en rationalisatie – onderzoek t.b.v. ontwikkelingslanden. **Research in relation to mechanisation and rationalisation in developing countries.** Publications.

20399 Letter, R.   NL 010106/72/5341
Merkenonderzoek van werktuigen voor de groenvoorziening en de recreatie. **Comparative research of implements for public gardens and recreation grounds.**

20400 Werken, G. van de   NL 010106/72/8347
Uitbreiding en onderhoud van een rekenservice en databank ter ondersteuning van de bedrijfsvoering (IMAG–DATASERVICE). **Extension and updating of a calculation service and databank as a help in farm management (IMAG–DATASERVICE).** Publications.

20401 Verkaik, A.P.   NL 010106/73/3844
Merkenonderzoek mechanisatie van stallen. **Comparative research of mechanization in stables.** Publications.

20402 Vries, R.L. de   NL 010106/73/5187
Verkrijging en verwerking van gegevens van de landbouwwerktuigeninventaris. **Obtaining and processing of data of the inventory of agricultural machinery.** Publications.

20403 Post, C.J. van de   NL 010106/73/5366 R
Tuinbouwtechnisch onderzoek ten behoeve van of in samenwerking met ontwikkelingslanden. **Horticultural engineering research in relation to or in cooperation with developing countries.** Publications.

20404 Foeken, D.   NL 010106/74/5189
Het opstellen van statistieken betreffende technische ontwikkelingen en prijsgedrag van technische hulpmiddelen in land– en tuinbouw. **Arranging statistics related to technical developments and price level of technical aids in agriculture and horticulture.** Publications.

20405 Lieftink, D.A.   NL 010106/75/6416 R
Merkenonderzoek van apparatuur en werktuigen voor kassen. **Comparative research of apparatus implements and machines for use in greenhouses.**

20406 Lieftinck, D.A.   NL 010106/75/6417
Merken onderzoek werktuigen voor buitenteelten in de tuinbouw. **Comparative research of implements for outdoor crops in horticulture.**

20407 Lieftink, D.A.   NL 010106/76/7575 R
Merkenonderzoek watergeefsystemen in de plantaardige sector. **Comparative machinery research of watering systems in plant production.** Publications.

20408 Vries, R.L. de   NL 010106/77/7672
Landbouwmechanische aspecten van nationale en internationale overheidsactiviteiten. **Agricultural engineering aspects of national and international governmental activities.** Publications.

20409 Tijen, W.F. van   NL 010109/73/8382
Onderzoek naar de eikwaliteit bij proeven van de Pluimveeteeltproefbedrijven. **Research into the egg quality of the eggs collected at the poultry experimental farms.**

20410 Holsheimer, J.P.   NL 010109/76/7228
Het coördineren van onderzoek ter ondersteuning van pluimveevoorlichting,– managementtraining en –troubleshooting t.b.v. c.q. in ontwikkelingslanden. **Research–coordination to support poultry–extension, –management training and –troubleshooting for or in developing countries.**

20411 Meijaard, D.   NL 010116/74/6546 R
Samenstelling en representativiteit van het tuinbouwboekhoudnet. **Composition and the representativity of the Dutch horticultural accountancy data net–work.**

20412 Koppert, G.   NL 010116/77/7736 R
Het samenstellen van een overzicht inzake bedrijfseconomische en statistische gegevens m.b.t. boomkwekerij. **Composition of a review about farm–economical and statistical data in ornamental plant growing.**

20413 Goedewaagen, T.   NL 010117/57/1593
Het verlenen van hulp aan instellingen van landbouwkundig onderzoek bij de redactionele verzorging of vormgeving, het uitgeven en verspreiden van hun publikaties. **Assisting agricultural research bodies in the editing and publishing of their publications.** Publications.

20414 Burg, J. van der   NL 010117/57/1594 R
Het verzorgen van een literatuur informatie dienst op het gebied van de landbouw. **Provision of a litterature information service in the field of agriculture.** Publications.

20415 Heuvel, J. van den   NL 010117/57/9046 N
Het verzorgen van landbouwkundige documentatiesystemen ten behoeve van de landbouw. **Provision of an agricultural documentation system for agriculture in the Netherlands.**

20416 Burg, J. van der   NL 010117/72/9045 N
Attenderingsdienst landbouwliteratuur met behulp van computersystemen. **Current awareness service on agricultural literature, using computer retrieval systems.**

20417 Greidanus, P. NL 010118/73/4217
Produktie- en opslagstatistiek van hard fruit. **Statistics of storage and production of top fruit.** Publications.

20418 Greidanus, P. NL 010118/73/4219
Produktgegevens groente en fruit. **Facts and pointers of vegetable and fruit products.** Publications.

20419 Rudolphij, J.W. NL 010118/76/6652 R
Servicecomputerprogramma voor de berekening van te installeren koelvermogen. **Service computer programme for the calculation of the refrigeration capacity for cold stores.** Publications.

20420 Staden, O.L. NL 010118/77/7261
Overzichtelijke rangschikking van gegevens over de behandeling van snijbloemen na de oogst. **Composing a review of data concerning post–harvest treatment of cut–flowers.**

20421 Nieuwenhuizen, G.H. van NL 010118/77/7265
Het testen van luchtkoelers. **The testing of evaporators.**

20422 Beek, G. van NL 010118/78/7847
Verzamelen van technische gegevens die van belang zijn voor de bewaring van tuinbouwprodukten. **Collection of technical data for the storage of horticultural products.**

20423 Westerveld, G.J.W. NL 010119/62/2074 R
De systematische kaartbladen–kartering van Nederland (1 : 50.000). **Systematic soil mapping of the Netherlands (1 : 50.000).** Publications.

20424 Steur, G.G.L. NL 010119/70/1447 R
Samenstellen van een handleiding voor bodemkartering in Nederland. **Compilation of a Netherlands soil survey manual.**

20425 Haans, J.C.F.M. NL 010119/77/7786 R
Coördinatie van de interpretatie van bodemkaarten volgens het systeem van de Werkgroep Interpretatie Bodemkaarten. **Correlations of the interpretation of soil maps.**

20426 Schelling, J. NL 010119/78/9070 N
Ontwikkeling en beproeving van de automatische verwerking van puntopnamen. **Automatic processing of borelogs for soil survey.**

20427 Kuilenburg, J. van NL 010119/78/9075 N
Ontwikkeling, opbouw en gebruik database–systeem Rijks Geologische Dienst. **Database development and operation for geological borelogs.**

20428 Bakker, H. de NL 010119/79/9074 N
Herziening en aanvulling leerstof cursus Veldbodemkunde. **Review and completion matter of teaching of the course Soil survey.**

20429 Wal, A.F. van der NL 010120/78/8886 N
Literatuurstudie van enige belangrijke graanziekten. **Literature review of some major cereal diseases.**

20430 Henstra, S. NL 010121/64/0984
Toegepast elektronenmicroscopisch onderzoek. **Electronmicroscopical studies of biological and non–biological objects.** Publications.

20431 Bosch, H. NL 010121/64/0986
Ontwikkeling van werktuigbouwkundige instrumenten, machines en hulpmiddelen. **Mechanical design of scientific apparatus.** Publications.

20432 Borel, G.; Schurer, K. NL 010121/64/0987
Elektronische en fysische instrumentatie. **Development of fysical technics; optical radiation measurements. Development of electronic measuring and control apparatus. Development of electronic circuits.** Publications.

20433 Koppe, R. NL 010121/64/0988
Advies en onderhoud van de vaste technische en technisch–wetenschappelijke installaties van de Instellingen. **Consulting engineering for the design of scientific installations for agricultural research and for the maintenance of utilities.**

20434 Beuzenberg, M.P. NL 010201/75/0982
Onderzoek naar de werking van nieuwe bestrijdingsmiddelen tegen dierlijke en plantaardige parasieten in de bloementeelt. **Effects of new chemicals for the control of diseases and pests in floriculture.** Publications.

20435 Muller, P.J. NL 010205/65/1490 R
Diagnostisch onderzoek bij bol– en knolgewassen. **Diagnostic investigations in flower bulbs.** Publications.

20436 Buschman, J.C.M. NL 010205/67/1504 R
Voorlichting buitenlandse afnemers van bloembollen. **Instruction of bulb customers in foreign countries.** Publications.

20437 Bijl, R.S. NL 010205/72/3652
Gebruikswaarde–onderzoek van machines en werktuigen voor de bloembollenteelt. **Comparative research of machines and implements for bulb growing.** Publications.

20438 Ende, J. van den NL 010206/62/0931
Chemisch grondonderzoek voor glasteelten. **Soil testing for glasshouse crops.** Publications.

20439 Noordam, W.P.; Ham, M. van der NL 010207/71/3259
Onderzoek ten behoeve van de verstrekking van kwantitatieve informatic voor de bedrijfseconomische advisering in de akkerbouw en de vollegrondsgroenteteelt. **Preparation of a data book for farm management advice concerning arable crops and outdoor vegetables.** Publications.

20440 Wieling, H. NL 010208/70/8729 N
Normen voor de voedervoorziening (Technische data op het terrein van de voedervoorziening). **Standards for feed supply.** Publications.

20441 Wieling, H. NL 010208/72/8730 N
Invloed van technische ingrepen op de voedervoorzieningsdata. **Influence of technical measures on feed supply data.** Publications.

20442 Kekem, A.J.T. van NL 010208/78/8727 N
De computerisering van het bedrijfseconomisch advies (Blauwe boek). **The automating of the farm economical advice.**

20443 Buizer, F.G. NL 010209/54/1165
Microbiologisch routine–onderzoek van monsters veevoeder. **Microbiological routine examination of samples of feedingstuffs.**

20444 Buizer, F.G.   NL 010209/54/1166
Researchwerk t.b.v. microbiologische
onderzoekingsmethoden voor monsters veevoeder. **Research
work on behalf of the microbiological methods of analyses for
samples of feedingstuffs.** Publications.

20445 Buizer, F.G.   NL 010209/54/1167
Het routine–onderzoek van monsters op Salmonellae en
Enterobacteriaceae. **The routine examination of samples of
Salmonellae and Enterobacteriaceae.**

20446 Buizer, F.G.   NL 010209/54/1168
Het researchwerk voor de onderzoekingsmethoden voor
monsters op Salmonellae en Enterobacteriaceae. **The research
work for the methods of analysis for the determination of
Salmonellae en Enterobacteriaceae in samples.**

20447 Langerak, C.J.   NL 010210/52/0041
Onderzoek naar methoden ter meting van de weerstand van
zaden tegen ongunstige uitzaai–omstandigheden. **The study of
methods for measuring seed vigour.** Publications.

20448 Bekendam, J.   NL 010210/63/0037
Het versneld opheffen van kiemrust bij zaden. **Accelerating the
breaking of dormancy of seeds.** Publications.

20449 Heuver, M.   NL 010210/69/0441
Werkzaamheden voortvloeiende uit het lidmaatschap van het
Rijksproefstation voor de Zaadcontrole van de International
Seed Testing Association. **Activities of the station as a member
of the International Seed Testing Association.**

20450 Burg, W.J. van der   NL 010210/69/2366
Onderzoek naar kenmerkende eigenschappen voor het
sorteren van zaden. **Evaluation of characteristics of seeds for
mechanical cleaning and fractionating.**

20451 Vuurde, J.W.L. van   NL 010210/69/2371 R
Onderzoek over pathogene bacteriën en virussen in zaaizaden.
Investigations on pathogenic bacteria and viruses.

20452 Langerak, C.J.   NL 010210/69/2664
Ontwikkeling en waardering van bepalingsmethoden voor
schimmelinfecties bij zaaizaden. **Development and evaluation
of methods for determination of infections by fungi in sowing
seeds.** Publications.

20453 Langerak, C.J.   NL 010210/69/2731
Beoordeling van de gebruikswaarde van
zaaizaadontsmettingsmiddelen. **Quality testing of pesticides for
seed dressing.** Publications.

20454 Burg, W.J. van der   NL 010210/71/3624 R
Rassenonderscheiding met behulp van zaadkenmerken.
Identifying of cultivars by means of seeds characteristics.

20455 Burg, W.J. van der   NL 010210/72/3453 R
Ontwikkeling van methoden voor de ploidiebepaling van
zaden van diverse gewassen. **Development of methods for
ploidie determination of seeds of different crops.**

20456 Burg, W.J. van der   NL 010210/72/3623 R
Speciale methodieken in de zuiverheidsanalyse van zaaizaad.
Special methods of analysis of purity of seeds.

20457 Bekendam, J.   NL 010210/72/3626
Verbetering van de methoden voor de bepaling van de
kiemkracht van zaaizaden. **Improving germination test
methods for seeds.** Publications.

20458 Bekendam, J.   NL 010210/72/3627 R
Onderzoek op grond van praktijkproblemen, samenhangend
met kiemkracht, opkomst en bewaring van zaden.
**Investigation of practical problems in relation with germination
emergence and storage of seeds.** Publications.

20459 Burg, W.J. van der   NL 010210/75/7754
Vereenvoudiging van de zuiverheidsanalyse bij het onderzoek
inzake dubbele zaden in graszaadsoorten. **Simplification of the
purity analysis in the examination of multiple florets in grass
seed species.** Publications.

20460 Burg, W.J. van der   NL 010210/78/7755
Identificatie van zaden langs chemische weg. **Identification of
seed by chemical means.**

20461 Oppenoorth, W.F.F.; Eisses, J.   NL 010211/03/0016
Ontwikkeling van methoden voor routine–onderzoek van
melk, melkprodukten en zuivelprodukten. **Development of
methods of analysis for routine examination of milk and milk
products.** Publications.

20462 Oppenoorth, W.F.F.; Krol, B.M.   NL 010211/04/0012
Onderzoek van monsters melkprodukten en zuivelprodukten
en het houden van toezicht op de laboratoria der
zuivelcontrole–instellingen ten dienste van het rijkstoezicht.
**Examination of milk products within the framework of the
State Supervision over the laboratories of the dairy control
institutions.** Publications.

20463 Tuinstra, L.G.M.T.; Ruig, W.G. de
   NL 010211/10/0017
Ontwikkeling van methoden voor routine–onderzoek van
oliehoudende zaden, oliën, vetten, vethoudende produkten,
vlees, vleesprodukten, vis en visprodukten en verwante
voedings– en voedermiddelen. **Development of methods of
analysis for routine examination of oil–seeds, oils, fats, fat
products and related foods and fodders.** Publications.

20464 Oppenoorth, W.F.F.; Eisses, J.   NL 010211/32/0013
Onderzoek monsters melk, melkprodukten en
zuivelprodukten anders dan ten dienste van het Rijkstoezicht.
**Examination of milk and milk products otherwise than within
the framework of the State Supervision over the laboratories of
the dairy control institutions.** Publications.

20465 Tuinstra, L.G.M.T.; Ruig, W.G. de
   NL 010211/32/0014
Onderzoek van monsters oliehoudende zaden, oliën, vetten,
vethoudende produkten, vlees, vleesprodukten, vis en
visprodukten en verwantevoedings– en voedermiddelen.
**Examination of oil–seeds, oils fats, fat products, meat, meat
products, fish and fish products and related foods and fodders.**
Publications.

20466 Tuinstra, L.G.M.T.; Ruig, W.G. de
   NL 010211/56/0018
Ontwikkeling van methoden van onderzoek voor
toevoegingen, pesticiden en contactmaterialen m.b.t. melk,
melkprodukten, zuivelprodukten, oliën, vetten, vethoudende
produkten, eiprodukten, vlees, vleesprodukten, vis,

visprodukten en verwante voedings- en voedermiddelen. **Development of methods of analysis for food additives and pesticides in relation to and for materials in contact with milk, milk products, oils, fats, fat products, egg products, meat, meat products, fish, fish products and related foods and fodders.** Publications.

20467 Oppenoorth, W.F.F.; Tuinstra, L.G.M.T.
NL 010211/61/0015
Onderzoek van monsters eiprodukten. **Examination of egg products.**

20468 Dijkman, A.J.; Vries, T. de   NL 010213/60/3378
Onderzoek van reinigings- en desinfectiemiddelen op hun praktische bruikbaarheid in de melkevij. **Research about detergents and sanitizers for practical use on dairy farms.** Publications.

20469 Vries, T. de   NL 010213/62/3382
Beproeving van melkkoeltanks. **Testing of farm bulk tanks.** Publications.

20470 Dijkman, A.J.   NL 010213/71/3386
Onderzoek naar laboratoriumapparatuur, welke gebruikt kan worden bij de beproeving van reinigings- en desinfectiemiddelen voor melkwinningsapparatuur. **Research about laboratory equipment which can be used in testing detergents and sanitizers.**

20471 Rossem, G. van   NL 010300/44/9082 N
Verzamelen van informatie t.a.v. vóórkomen, verspreiding en economische betekenis van insektenplagen in en buiten Nederland. **Information on occurrence, distribution, control and economic importance of insect pests in and outside the Netherlands.**

20472 Miller, H.J.   NL 010300/48/9090 N
Inventarisatie van in Nederland voorkomende planteparasitaire bacteriën. **Maintenance of an inventory of plant pathogenic bacteria which occur in the Netherlands.**

20473 Boerema, G.H.   NL 010300/48/9110 N
Inventarisatie van in Nederland voorkomende planteparasitaire schimmels. **Maintenance of an inventory of plant pathogenic fungi which occur in the Netherlands.**

20474 Rossem, G. van   NL 010300/51/9080 N
Diagnose van insekten die schade aan planten veroorzaken. **Entomological diagnosis of insect damage to plants.**

20475 Miller, H.J.   NL 010300/51/9085 N
Diagnose van door bacteriën aangetast plantenmateriaal; identificatie van de bacterie die de ziekte veroorzaakt. **Diagnosis of diseased plant material due to bacteria; identification of the plant pathogenic bacteria concerned.**

20476 Maas, P.W.Th.   NL 010300/51/9091 N
Aaltjesanalyse van grond- en gewasmonsters t.b.v. veldinspectie bij diverse gewassen. **Nematological soil and crop sample analysis for field inspection in several crops.**

20477 Maas, P.W.Th.   NL 010300/51/9094 N
Nematologische diagnose van afwijkingen (slechte groei, rot e.d.) bij diverse gewassen. **Nematological diagnosis of poor growth in various crops.**

20478 Boerema, G.H.   NL 010300/54/9106 N
Diagnose van schimmelziekten bij planten, resp. identificatie van plantepathogene schimmels. **Diagnosis of fungal plant diseases and identification of the plant pathogenic fungi.**

20479 Kort, J.   NL 010300/57/1391 N
Toetsing van aardbeiklonen op aanwezigheid van virusziekten. **Testing of strawberry clones on presence of virus diseases.**

20480 Kort, J.   NL 010300/62/8612 N
Instandhouding en vermeerdering van toetsklonen van aardappelsoorten met specifieke resistentie-eigenschappen ten behoeve van het biotypenonderzoek bij twee soorten van aardappelcysteaaltje, alsmede van zuivere populaties van deze biotypen ten behoeve van het resistentie-onderzoek bij nieuwe aardappelrassen. **Maintenance and propagation of potato clones for testing of resistance against wart disease and potato cyst nematodes.**

20481 Boerema, G.H.   NL 010300/70/9087 N
Verzamelen van informatie t.a.v. uitheemse schimmels en schimmelziekten die een potentiëel gevaar vormen voor de Nederlandse cultuurgewassen. **Information on foreign fungi and fungal diseases which could be dangerous for Dutch crops.**

20482 Boerema, G.H.   NL 010300/70/9107 N
Nomenclatuur van planteparasitaire schimmels. **Nomenclature of plant pathogenic fungi.**

20483 Bruin, Th. de   NL 010300/72/9101 N
Veldinspektie importpartijen pootaardappelen. **Field inspection of imported seed–potatoes on the occurrence of undesired diseases.**

20484 Miller, H.J.   NL 010300/76/9116 N
Verzamelen van informatie t.a.v. in- en uitheemse bacteriën en bacterieziekten die een potentieel gevaar vormen voor de Nederlandse cultuurgewassen. **Information on native and foreign bacteria and bacterial diseases which could be dangerous for Dutch crops.**

20485 Kooistra, T.   NL 010300/78/9097 N
Determinatie van pathogenen in grond en gewas ten behoeve van bestrijdingsmiddelenproeven in sla. **Identification of fungi in soil and crop for fungicide experiments in lettuce.**

20486 Kooistra, T.   NL 010300/78/9098 N
Het bepalen van resistentie van pathogenen bij sla tegen fungiciden en bactericiden. **Determination of resistance of pathogens in lettuce against fungicides and bactericides.**

20487 Lensing, H.H.   NL 010401/70/6529
Ontwikkelings- en standaardisatie-onderzoek ten behoeve van de kwaliteitscontrole van zowel middelen ter onderkenning, voorkoming en genezing van dierziekten als van proefdieren. **Investigation of development and standardization for the quality control of means for diagnosis, prevention and curing of animal diseases, as well as the quality control of laboratory animals.** Publications.

20488 Bekkum, J.G. van   NL 010402/67/1218 R
Productie van mond- en klauwzeervaccin. **Foot- and–mouth disease vaccine production.** Publications.

20489 Lensing, H.H.   NL 010402/73/9063 N
Onderzoek van ontsmettingsmiddelen voor veterinair gebruik.

Investigation on disinfectants for veterinary use.

20490 Kleef, H.A. van   NL 010501/73/5259 R
Cultuurtechnische inventarisatie Nederland; opdrachten. **Land division survey Netherlands; surveys on commission.**

20491 Ernst, L.F.   NL 010501/79/9062 N
Samenstellen van een lijst met definities en symbolen voor hydrologische termen. **Hydrological terminology.**

20492 Leek, N.A.   NL 010601/72/3719
Beoordeling van de gebruikswaarde van machines en werktuigen met betrekking tot beheer en exploitatie van bos en landschap. **Testing machines and tools for forestry and landscaping.**

20493 Leek, N.A.   NL 010601/72/6764
Testen van machines en werktuigen op hun gebruikswaarde voor de bosbouw. **Testing machines and tools for use in forestry.** Publications.

20494 Dam, H. van   NL 010602/77/8605 N
Inventarisatie van artikelen en rapporten waarin hydrobiologische waarderingscriteria zijn gebruikt. **Inventory of articles and reports in which criteria for the hydrobiologicalal assesment of water are used.**

20495 Staveren, J.M. van   NL 020000/74/5470
Ontwikkeling van interdisciplinaire planmethodieken voor overwegend agrarische gebieden in de ontwikkelingslanden. **Development of interdisciplinary planning methods for rural regions in developing countries.** Publications.

20496 Schouwenburg, J.C. van   NL 020007/72/6518
Het toetsen en verbeteren van het analytisch peil van laboratoria. **Testing and improvement of the analytical level of laboratories.**

20497 Bijsterbosch, B.H.   NL 020016/73/4939
De invloed van geadsorbeerde polymeren op de transportsnelheid van elektrolyten door een vloeistof–vloeistof grensvlak. **The influence of adsorbed polymers on the rate of transport of ions through a liquid–liquid interface.** Publications.

20498 Hoven, T.J.J. van den   NL 020016/78/8512
Elektrokinetiek van polystyreenproppen; invloed van gemengde milieus. **Electrokinetics of polystyrene plugs; influence of mixed media.**

20499 Lyklema, J.   NL 020016/78/8513
Polymeer gestabiliseerde vrije vloeistoffilms. **Polymer–stabilized free liquid films.** Publications.

20500 Roeterdink, F.   NL 020038/77/8442
Reactiviteit van N–aminopyrimidinen in basisch milieu en de fotochemie van pyrimidine N–yliden. **Reactivity of N–aminopyrimidines toward bases and the photochemistry of pyrimidine–N–ylids.**

20501 Munters, Ø.J.   NL 020051/78/8808 N
Het begrip sociale integratie in de sociologische en daarmee verwante literatuur. **The concept social integration in the sociological and the allied literature.**

20502 Oomkes, F.R.   NL 020063/78/8873 N
Het schrijven van een leerboek 'Inleiding in de communicatieleer'. **An introduction to communicology.**

20503 Arnoldussen–v.d.Lugt, A.   NL 020066/72/6831
Geschiedenis van begrippen continue en discontinue lijnen en functies en infinitesimalen in begin 19e eeuw. **Geometrical and analytical concepts in Bolzano.**

20504 Ente, P.J.   NL 040007/60/4082
Kartering van de bodemgesteldheid van de Markerwaard. **Soil–survey and mapping of the Markerwaard.**

20505 Ente, P.J.   NL 040007/62/2074
De systematische kaartbladenkartering van Nederland (1:50.000). **Systematic soil mapping of the Netherlands (1:50.000).** Publications.

20506 Brinkhorst, W.   NL 040007/67/4103
Vervaardiging grondwaterstandskaarten van Oostelijk Flevoland. **Mapping of the ground water level of Oostelijk Flevoland.** Publications.

20507 Jong, J. de   NL 040007/67/8479
Routinematig waterkwaliteitsonderzoek in het IJsselmeergebied. **Routine research on water quality in the IJsselmeer area.**

20508 Ente, P.J.   NL 040007/68/4077
Kartering van de bodemgesteldheid van Zuidelijk Flevoland. **Soil survey and mapping of Zuidelijk Flevoland.**

20509 Eenkhoorn, W.   NL 040007/68/4124
Het in stand houden van een beperkte bacterie– en schimmelcollectie. **Maintenance of a small collection of bacteria and fungi.**

20510 Ente, P.J.   NL 040007/71/4084
Kartering van de bodemgesteldheid van het Grevelingen–bekkengebied. **Soil survey and mapping of the Grevelingen bekken area.**

20511 Ente, P.J.   NL 040007/74/5540
Kartering van de bodemgesteldheid van het gebied Ooster–Schelde. **Soil–survey in the Oosterschelde area.**

20512 Brook, R.H.   NL 040012/78/8943 N
Ontwikkeling van een algemeen bodemvruchtbaarheidsschema op basis van bodemanalyse data. **Soil Test Data Interpretation Guide, with special reference to RTI methods (Royal Tropical Institute methods).**

20513 Slump, P.   NL 050301/67/6475
Aminozuren in Nederlandse veevoedercomponenten. **Aminoacids in Dutch feed ingredients.** Publications.

20514 Belderok, B.   NL 050302/70/6602
Onderzoek, bewaking en verbetering van de kwaliteit van voedingsmiddelen uit granen en grondstoffen daarvoor. **Quality testing of cereal foods and their raw materials.**

20515 Jorritsma, J.   NL 060003/30/7727 R
Analyse suikerbietenmonsters voor derden. **Analysis of sugar beet samples for outside organizations.**

20516 Heijbroek, W.   NL 060003/32/7723
Waarnemingen t.b.v. de vergelingsziekte

waarschuwingsdienst. **Observations on behalf of the virus yellows warning service.** Publications.

20517 Jorritsma, J.   NL 060003/62/7713
Vaststelling van de verzaaibaarheid van suikerbietenzaad.
Testing of suitability for sowing of sugar beet seed.
Publications.

20518 Jorritsma, J.   NL 060003/62/7714
Onderzoek suikerbietenzaad op andere eigenschappen dan
verzaaibaarheid. **Research on properties of sugar beet seed
other than suitability for sowing.** Publications.

D 9900 – Research which cannot be classified in the fields mentioned above

D 9900 – Research which cannot be classified in the fields mentioned above.

See also 3884, 8400, 20496, 20810

20519 Germain, R.; Stainier, F.   BE 020303/63/0004 R
Etude morphologique de grains de pollens en vue d'éclaircir certains problèmes de taxonomie. **Morphological studies on pollen grains in order to resolve taxonomic problems.** Publications.

20520 Verachtert, H.; Van Der Leyden, J.
    BE 040503/66/0001
Studie van de biochemie van osmofiele gist en in het bijzonder de CN – ongevoelige ademhaling in monibiela tomentosa. **Biochemical study of osmophilic yeasts, especially the CN insensitive respiration in Monibiela tomentosa.** Publications.

20521 Rixhon, L.; Delhaye, R.   BE 080800/76/0009
Phytoclimatologie et phénologie des plantes de grande culture. **Phytoclimatology and phenology of some field crops.**

20522 Schein, E.; Warnecke, M.; Parfeit   DE 104201/75/0001
Entwicklungszyklus von Babesien in den Überträgerzecken. **Life cycle of Babesia in vector ticks.**

20523 Trautvetter, E.; Pagel, B.   DE 104500/77/0001 R
Postnatale Entwicklung kardiovaskulärer Funktionen bei Hunde–und Katzenwelpen. **Postnatal evolution of cardiovascular functions in young dogs and cats.**

20524 Bornkamm, R.   DE 105100/70/0008
Soziologie und chemische Ökologie von Sukzessionsstadien auf verschiedenen Versuchsflächen. **Phytocenological and chemical ecology of successional stages in different experimental plots.** Publications.

20525 Bornkamm, R.; Overdieck, D.; Blume, H.–P.
    DE 105100/74/0003
Photosynthese und Stoffproduktion von Licht– und Schattenpflanzen im Rot– und Blaulicht. **Photosynthesis and dry matter production of light and shade plants in red and in blue light.**

20526 Göhlich, H.; Heidt, H.   DE 105601/75/0002
Automatisierung der Massenbestimmung von chemischen Pflanzenschutzmittelbelägen. **Automation of quantity analysis of chemical deposits from plant protection products.**

20527 Beck, G.; Marquardt, K.; Schalt, W.
    DE 105650/70/0001
Die Bedarfsermittlung für eine offengelegte wirtschaftliche Planung von öffentlichen innerstädtischen Erholungs-einrichtungen für überwiegend im Freien stattfindende Er-holungsformen 1971. **Determination of the needs for clear economic planning of public recreationeal facilities in the centre of towns for recreational activities executed chiefly in open air.**

20528 Dellweg, H.   DE 105981/72/0001 N
Reaktionskinetische Grundlage der Fermentation von Escherichiacoli–Mutanten. **Reaction kinetic conditions of fermentation of Escherichia coli mutants.**

20529 Rudolph, H.; Zscheile, D.   DE 105987/70/0003
Bestimmungsgründe für die Konzentration in der deutschen Brauindustrie seit der Währungsreform 1970. **Determinant factors of the concentration of brewing industry in Germany since the currency reform 1970.**

20530 Windisch, S.; Henninger, W.   DE 105990/72/0001
Ergänzung und wissenschaftliche Bearbeitung der Hefesammlung als anerkanntem Teil der Deutschen Sammlung von Mikroorganismen. **Complementing and scientific work at the yeast collection as a recognized part of the German Collection of Micro–organisms.**

20531 Esser, K.; Stahl, U.   DE 108051/77/0001
Züchtung von Alkan– und Methanolhefen im Hinblick auf hohe Proteinausbeute. **Breeding of alkane and methanol yeasts with regard to high yield in protein.** Publications.

20532 Zenk, M.H.; Gross, G.G.; Klischies, M.; Stöckigt, J.
    DE 108101/74/0001
In–vivo und in–vitro Untersuchungen zur Biosynthese des Lignins. **In–vivo and in–vitro experiments on the biosynthesis of lignin.**

20533 Zenk, M.H.; Stöckigt, J.; Klischies, M.
    DE 108101/75/0002
In–vivo Untersuchungen zur Biosynthese von Lignanen. **In–vivo experiments on the biosynthesis of lignans.**

20534 Klämbt, D.; Maass, H.   DE 111121/72/0002
Die Biosynthese der Cytokinine. **The biosynthesis of cytokinins.**

20535 Kausch, W.   DE 111150/70/0001
Physiologie des Wurzelwachstums unter dem Einfluss ökologischer Faktoren. **Physiology of root–growth influenced by ecological factors.**

20536 Kausch, W.; Spengler, H.; Wolf, D.
    DE 111150/70/0002
Ökologie der Formbildung, am Beispiel der Sonnen–Schattenblätter. **Ecological aspects of morphogenesis for example in sun–shade leaves.**

20537 Kausch, W.; Potthof, H.; Scharrenberg, U.
    DE 111150/70/0003
Ökologische Untersuchungen im Stadtbereich – Ein Beitrag zu den Problemen des Umweltschutzes –. **Ecological research in town – as a contribution to environmental protection –.**

20538 Weiling, F.   DE 111150/74/0002
Über Wechselbeziehungen zwischen der deutschen und russischen Botanik im vergangenen Jahrhundert. **On interrelations between German und Russian botany in the past century.**

20539 Weiling, F.   DE 111151/70/0003
Untersuchungen zur Entwicklung der Statistik im vergangenen Jahrhundert 1968. **Development of statistics in the past century.** Publications.

20540 Franke, W.; Werner, R.   DE 111152/77/0001 R
Über die Abhängigkeit des Ektoteichodennachweises in Blättern von inneren und äusseren Faktoren, Ektoteichodenvorkommen in Wurzeln. **On the demonstration of ectoteichodes depending upon inner and outer factors, existence of ectoteichodes in roots.**

D 9900 – Research which cannot be classified in the fields mentioned above

20541 Franke, W.; Mentges, A. DE 111152/77/0002
Elektronenmikroskopische Untersuchungen zur Frage des
Vorkommens interner Cuticulae und einer Cuticula an
Wurzelhaaren. **Electronmicroscopical investigations on the
existence of internal cuticles and of cuticles of roothairs.**

20542 Claussen, W. DE 111300/78/0003 N
Beziehung zwischen Assimilatanreicherung und
Photosyntheseleistung von Blättern. **Relationship between
accumulation of assimilates and photosynthetic efficiency of
leaves.**

20543 Krampitz, G.; Potz, A. DE 111401/75/0004
Beeinflussung der Ca–Bindung und der
Carboanhydrase–Aktivität durch Hormone 'speziell
Steroidhormone'. **Influence of hormones 'especially steroid
hormones' on Ca–bond and on carboanhydrase activity.**

20544 Krampitz, G.; Paeffgen, D. DE 111401/75/0006
Vergleichende Untersuchungen der
Aminosäurekompositionen in Vogeleischalen: Biochemische
und taxonomische Beziehungen zwischen Tauben, Papageien,
Spechten und Kuckucken. **Comparative studies of amino acid
compositions in avian egg shells: biochemical and taxonomic
relations between pigeons, parrots, woodpeckers and cuckoos.**

20545 Wirths, W. DE 111570/74/0002
Anthropometrische Untersuchungen in verschiedenen
Bevölkerungsgruppen. **Anthropometric studies on different
groups of population.**

20546 Skomroch, W.; Schulte–Geers, R. DE 111702/72/0002
Problematik der kommunalen Kreisreform für die
Vergleichbarkeit von Zeitreihen 1972. **Problems of the
municipal district reform with regard to the comparability of
time series.**

20547 Maier, H.G.; Rohrdanz, D. DE 114100/75/0002
Hydrolyse von Estern aus organischen Säuren und Zuckern.
Hydrolysis of esters from organic acids and sugars.

20548 Kratz, W. DE 114450/74/0015
Dampfsperre in hölzernen Aussenwandelementen. **Vapour
barrier in exterior timber constructions.**

20549 Kratz, W. DE 114450/74/0016
Vergleichende Untersuchung von genagelten und geleimten
hölzernen Verbundelementen unter natürlicher
Beanspruchung. **Comparative investigations on nailed or glued
exterior timber constructions under natural conditions.**

20550 Heumann, W. DE 120100/71/0001
Gentransfer bei der Konjugation von Rhizobium.
Conjugational gene transfer in rhizobium.

20551 Pühler, A. DE 120100/71/0002
Fertilitätsinhibierung durch R Faktoren bei Rhizobium.
Plasmide in Rhizobium. **Fertility inhibition by R factors in
rhizobium. Plasmids in Rhizobia.**

20552 Ciriacy, M.von DE 126100/75/0001
Genetik und Regulation von Enzymen der Gluconeogenese
bei Saccharomyces cerevisiae. **Genetics and regulation of
gluconeogenetic enzymes in Saccharomyces cerevisiae.**

20553 Hildebrandt, G.; Kadro; Abdulhanan

DE 126451/74/0001
Untersuchungen über spektrale Eigenschaften von Wald– und
anderen Vegetationsbeständen. **Investigations of the spectral
properties of forest stands and other vegetation communities.**

20554 Mantel, K.; Pacher, J. DE 126505/71/0001
Untersuchungen zur forstlichen Biographie, Band 2.
Researches on forest biography, volume 2.

20555 Pacher, J. DE 126505/71/0002
Untersuchungen zu den Auswirkungen der
Naturwissenschaften auf die Forstwissenschaft und die
forstliche Lehre in historischer Sicht. **Researches on the effects
of the natural sciences to the sience of forestry and to the
forestry education in historical view.**

20556 Pacher, J.; Pesch, H. DE 126505/75/0002
Die forstliche Entwicklung im Raum Schelklingen zwischen
1800 und 1900. **Forest development in the territory of
Schelklingen between 1800 and 1900 1975 (Diss.–Forts..**

20557 Pacher, J.; Scheifele, M. DE 126505/78/0001 N
Baden–Württembergische Forstliche Biographie. **Forest
biography of Baden–Wuerttemberg.**

20558 Mitscherlich, G. DE 126600/72/0002 R
Untersuchungen über die Lärmdämmung verschiedener
Waldbestände 1972–1978. **Investigations into noise inhibition in
various forest stands.**

20559 Mitscherlich, G.; Wetzler, H. DE 126600/75/0001
Der Einfluss des Waldes auf das Stadtklima von Freiburg i.Br..
**The influence of the forest on the urban climate of Freiburg
i.Br..**

20560 Grammel, R.; Behler, H. DE 126650/78/0001 N
Untersuchungen zur Charakterisierung und Bewertung von
Sägerestholz. **Investigations to characterize and classify
residual wood of sawmills.**

20561 Degkwitz, E. DE 129000/74/0001
Elimination des Vitamins C. Adaptation an den Vitamin
C–Gehalt der Nahrung. **Elimination of vitamin C – Adaptation
to vitamin–C content in foods.**

20562 Neumann, K.–H.; Dadkah, T. DE 129041/70/0003
Untersuchungen über Beziehungen zwischen der hormonal
gesteuerten Zellteilungsaktivität, dem Proteinstoffwechsel und
der Enzymaktivität bei Pflanzen in Gewebekulturen.
**Investigations of the correlations between hormonally
determined cell division activity, protein metabolism and
enzyme activity in plant tissue cultures.**

20563 Neumann, K.–H.; Schäfer, A.; Dührssen, E.
DE 129041/70/0004
Untersuchungen über Beziehungen zwischen hormonal
gesteuerter Zellteilungsaktivität, der Differenzierung und dem
Nukleinsäurewechsel von Karotten–Gewebekulturen 1961.
**Correlations between cell division activity controlled by
hormones, differentiation and change of nucleic acid in tissue
cultures of carrots.**

20564 Neumann, K.–H.; Pertzsch, C. DE 129041/70/0005
Der Einfluss verschiedener Zuckerarten und –konzentrationen
in der Nährlösung auf die Aufnahme und den Stoffwechsel von
$C-14-CO_2$ aus Bikarbonat bei pflanzlichen Gewebekulturen.

The influence of various sugars and sugar concentrations in the nutrient solution on the uptake and metabolism of C–14–CO2 of bicarbonate in plant tissue cultures.

20565 Neumann, K.–H.; Forche, E.   DE 129041/73/0001
Untersuchungen zur Erstellung haploider Zellkulturen von Datura und Papaver. **Investigations on production of haploid cell cultures of datura and papaver.**

20566 Pauler, B.   DE 129043/71/0008
Einbau von markiertem Schwefel in Blattproteine – Methodik der Trennverfahren –. **Input of radioactive sulphur in leaf proteins – methods of separation –.**

20567 Küster, E.   DE 129080/75/0001
Physiologie und Ökologie von halophilen Organismen. **Physiology and ecology of halophilic micro–organisms.**

20568 Küster, E.; Neumeier, W.   DE 129080/77/0006
Einfluss steigender NaCl–Konzentrationen auf die Antibiotika–Bildung bei Streptomyceten. **Influence of increasing NaCl–concentrations on the production of antibiotics by Streptomycetes.**

20569 Küster, E.; Attaby, H.   DE 129080/77/0007
Einfluss von biogenen Faktoren auf Luftmycel– und Sporenbildung bei Streptomyceten. **Influence of biogenic factors on the formation of aerial mycelium and conidia in Streptomycetes.**

20570 Stein, W.   DE 129200/75/0004
Untersuchungen zum Blütenbesuch synanthroper Fliegen. **Investigation of the visit of flowers by synanthropic flies.**

20571 Senft, B.; Erhardt, G.; Meyer, F.   DE 129251/75/0001
Beta–Laktoglobulin – Polymorphismus und Eiweissleistung beim Rind. **Beta–Lactoglobulin – polymorphism and protein production in cattle.**

20572 Renner, E.; Schmidt, R.   DE 129252/75/0002
Variabilität im Fettsäuremuster verschiedener Nahrungsfette. **Variability in the fatty acid pattern of different edible fats.**

20573 Renner, E.; Hanspach, I.   DE 129252/75/0003
Bildung von Aromasubstanzen während der Reifung von Milchprodukten. **Synthesis of aromatic compounds during the ripening of milk products.**

20574 Habermehl, K.–H.; Rach, A.   DE 129600/77/0001
Die Blutgefässe der Zunge und ihre Geschmackspapillen bei kleinen Wiederkäuern und Fleischfressern. **Blood–vessels of the tongue and gustatory papillae in small ruminants and carnivores.**

20575 Rufeger, H.   DE 129640/75/0001
Regulation und Adaptation des Stickstoff–Stoffwechsels der Monogastriden. **Regulation and adaptation of the nitrogen metabolism of monogastrides.** Publications.

20576 Hadlok, R.; Samson, R.A.; Schipper, M.A.A.   DE 129700/75/0002
Wildfleischhygiene: Der Schimmelpilzgehalt von Wild–Faeces. **Game hygiene: the mould content in game excrements.**

20577 Kitzrow, D.   DE 129740/78/0001 N
Oberflächenstrukturen und Koagulasen von Staphylococcus aureus. **Surface cell structures and coagulases of Staphylococcus aureus.** Publications.

20578 Blobel, H.; Berete, Y.; Schaeg, W.   DE 129740/78/0002 N
Phospholipasen von Staphylococcus aureus. **Phospholipases of Staphylococcus aureus.** Publications.

20579 Blobel, H.; Schaeg, W.; Brückler, J.   DE 129740/78/0003 N
Bestimmung von Protein A. **Estimation of protein A.**

20580 Kloos, W.; Kopp, U.; Blobel, H.   DE 129740/78/0004 N
Plasmide von Staphylokokken. **Plasmids of staphylococci.**

20581 Schoner, W.; Pauls, H.; Patzelt, R.   DE 129760/74/0004
Struktur und Funktion der Na–Pumpe der Zellmembranen der Tiere. **Structure and function of the sodium pump of mammalian cell membranes.**

20582 Schoner, W.; Eigenbrodt, E.   DE 129760/74/0005
Hormonelle Regulation der Pyruvatkinaseaktivität in der Leber und die damit gekoppelte Steuerung der Gluconeogenese. **Hormonal regulation of pyruvate kinase activity in liver and of gluconeogenesis.**

20583 Balke, E.   DE 129820/75/0002
Die Klassifizierung von Brucellenstämmen. **Classification of strains of Brucella.**

20584 Eikmeier, H.; Kraft, W.   DE 129881/75/0002
Normalwerte in der klinischen Labordiagnostik. **Standard values in clinical laboratory diagnostics.** Publications.

20585 Feldheim, W.   DE 129900/72/0017
Mikroalgenprojekte. **Projects on micro–algae.**

20586 Przemeck, E.; Lüdtke, M.   DE 132061/75/0003
Über die chemische Bindung der Stärkeproteine an ihre Kohlenhydrate. **On the chemical binding between starch proteins and carbohydrates.**

20587 Knackmuss, H.–J.   DE 132121/72/0003
Abbau chlorierter und sulfonierter aromatischer Kohlenwasserstoffe durch Bakterien. **Degradation of chlorinated and sulphonated aromatic hydrocarbons by bacteria.**

20588 Schlegel, H.G.; Weiss, A.R.   DE 132121/75/0002
Induktion des Nukleinsäureabbaus durch Hitzeschock; Isolierung der Ribonuklease und kinetische Untersuchungen; Analyse der ausgeschiedenen Produkte. **Induction of nucleic acid degradation by heat treatment; Isolation of ribonuclease and kinetic studies; Analysis of excreted products.**

20589 Schlegel, H.G.; Bowien, B.; Mayer, F.; Amachi, T.   DE 132121/75/0003
Reinigung der Ribulosediphosphat–Carboxylase aus verschiedenen Wasserstoffbakterien und anderen autotrophen Bakterien; Mikromorphologische Untersuchungen zur Struktur des Enzyms; Glycolsäure–Ausscheidung. **Purification of ribulosediphosphate carboxylase from several hydrogen bacteria and other autotrophic bacteria; Micromorphological studies on the enzyme structure; Excretion of glycolic acid.**

20590 Schlegel, H.G.; Conrad, R.   DE 132121/75/0004

Abbauwege von Fruktose und Glukose in Rhodopseudomonas capsulata; Analyse der Zwischenprodukte und Enzyme; Embden–Meyerhof–Weg und Entner–Douderoff–Weg. **Degradation pathways of fructose and glucose in Rhodopseudomonas capsulata; Analysis of intermediary products and enzymes; Embden–Meyerhof pathway and Entner–Douderoff pathway.**

20591 Schlegel, H.G.; Jüttner, R.; Ibrahim, M.
DE 132121/75/0005
Massenkultur von Wasserstoffbakterien unter autotrophen Bedingungen in statischer und kontinuierlicher Kultur; Einfluss der Partialdrucke der Gase, Sauerstoff und Wasserstoff; Gas–chromatographische Analyse. **Mass culture of hydrogen bacteria under autotrophic conditions in batch and continuous culture. Influence of the partial pressure of gases, oxygen and hydrogen; Gas–chromatographic analysis.**

20592 Schlegel, H.G.; Vollbrecht, D.; El–Nawawy, M.
DE 132121/75/0006
Optimisierung der Bedingungen für die Ausscheidung von 2–Keto–3–deoxy–6–phospho–gluconsäure durch eine Mutante von Alcaligenes eutrophus H 16; Ausscheidung von beta–Hydroxy–buttersäure. **Optimisation of the conditions for the excretion of 2–keto–3–deoxy–6–phospho–gluconic acid by a mutant of Alcaligenes eutrophus H 16; Excretion of beta–hydroxybutyric acid.**

20593 Schlegel, H.G.; Ibrahim, M.　　DE 132121/77/0001
Belüftung von Bakterien und Hefen mit Wasserstoffperoxid in Gegenwart von Katalase. **Aeration of bacterial and yeast suspensions by addition of hydrogen peroxide at the presence of catalase.** Publications.

20594 Schlegel, H.G.; Berndt, H.　　DE 132121/78/0001 N
Stickstoffixierung durch Wasserstoffbakterien unter autotrophen und heterotrophen Bedingungen, insbesondere Charakterisierung der Nitrogenase, Ferrexodine und Hydrogenase von Xanthobacter autotrophicus. **Nitrogen fixation by hydrogen bacteria under autotrophic and heterotrophic conditions, especially the characterization of the enzyme nitrogenase, ferrexodin and hydrogenase from Xanthobacter autotrophicus.** Publications.

20595 Schlegel, H.G.; Vollbrecht, D.　DE 132121/78/0002 N
Ausscheidung von organischen Säuren durch aerobe Bakterien unter Begrenzung des Stoffwechsels durch Sauerstoffmangel. **Excretion of organic acids by aerobic bacteria by limiting the metabolism by oxygen deficiency.**

20596 Schlegel, H.G.; Bowien, B.; Friedrich, C.; Friedrich, B.　　DE 132121/78/0003 N
Regulation der an der autotrophen CO2-Fixierung und an der Aktivierung von Wasserstoff beteiligten Enzyme, untersucht an Mutanten von Alcaligenes eutrophus H16. **Regulation of enzymes of autotrophic CO2–fixation and of the activation of molecular hydrogen, using mutants of Alcaligenes eutrophus H16.**

20597 Schlegel, H.G.; Reh, M.; Clayton, R.
DE 132121/78/0004 N
Übertragung von Autotrophiemerkmalen von Nocardia und neu isolierten Stämmen auf heterotrophe Bakterien; gelelektrophoretischer und elektronenmikroskopischer Nachweis der Autotrophieplasmide. **Transfer of autotrophic markers from Nocardia opaca and newly isolated strains to**

heterotrophic members of the same taxonomical group. Gel electrophoretical and electron microscopical proof for autotrophic plasmids.

20598 Schlegel, H.G.; Probst, I.; Schneider, K.
DE 132122/73/0004
Die Komponenten des Elektronentransports, Eigenschaften der Wasserstoff–Dehydrogenase und partikulären Hydrogenase von Hydrogenomonas eutropha. **Components of electron transport, properties of hydrogen dehydrogenase and of the particular hydrogenase of Hydrogenomonas eutropha.**

20599 Thiele, O.W.; Imre, S.; Plotkin, J.; Petri, M.S.
DE 132150/72/0001 N
Über Eigenschaften und chemische Zusammensetzung der Erythrozytenmembran beim erwachsenen Rind und beim Kalb. **On properties and chemical composition of the red–cell membrane of adult cattle and of calf.**

20600 Schön, W.J.　　DE 132180/75/0001
Biosynthese und Stoffwechsel der Zimtsäure–Glucoside in der Wildform und Mutanten von Melilotus albus. **Biosynthesis and metabolism of cinnamic acid glucosides in Melilotus albus and induced mutants.**

20601 Glodek, P.; Hörstgen, G.; Rapp, K.
DE 132274/75/0001
Genetische Differenzierung durch Selektion auf verschiedene quantitative Leistungseigenschaften bei der Maus. **Genetic differentiation by selection for different quantitative production traits in the mouse.**

20602 Abel, H.　　DE 132300/78/0003 N
Fütterungseinflüsse auf Enzymaktivitätsmuster der tierischen Zelle. **Nutritional effects on enzyme activity patterns in living animal cells.**

20603 Delorme, A.　　DE 132780/73/0002
Aufbau einer Eichenjahrringchronologie des Postglazials aus subfossilen Baumfunden. **The setup of an oak dendrochronology from post–glacial subfossil tree finds.**

20604 Zundel, R.; Rozsnyay, Z.　　DE 132870/70/0004 R
Motive und Wünsche von Waldbesuchern nach Repräsentativbefragungen in Ziel– und Quellgebieten 1970. **Motives and wishes of forest frequenters by representative survey in regions of destination and of origin.**

20605 Zundel, R.; Rozsnyay, Z.　　DE 132870/70/0006 R
Heinrich Christian Burckhardt und seine Bedeutung für die Forstwirtschaft und Forstwissenschaft 1968. **Heinrich Christian Burckhardt and his importance to forestry and science of forestry.**

20606 Hasel, K.; Klein, H.–J.　　DE 132870/72/0001
Die Geschichte der Forsten des Hann. Allgemeinen Klosterfonds 1972. **The history of the forests owned by the Common Hanoverian Conventual Fund.**

20607 Häberle, S.; Meyer, H.　　DE 132900/74/0001
Untersuchungen zur Vermessung von FichtenLangholz. **Investigations on spruce long–wood measuring.**

20608 Brunner, H.　　DE 135050/74/0001
Stoffwechselphysiologische Veränderungen der Regeneration eines Wurzelsystems. **Variations in metabolism physiology**

during the regeneration of a root system.

20609 Sol, R.   DE 135052/77/0003
Die Zucht von Otiorrhynchus sulcatus und anderen
Rüsselkäfern für die Prüfung von Insektiziden. **Breeding of
Otiorrhynchus sulcatus and other weevils for testing of
insecticides.**

20610 Deutschmann, F.; El–Sherif   DE 135055/74/0001
Anatomie der Blätter ölsaatliefernder Pflanzen. **Anatomy of
the leaves of plants yielding oilseeds.**

20611 Francke, W.   DE 135151/72/0003
Stoffwechselprodukte von Ascoidea hylecoeti, des
symbiontischen Pilzes von Hylecoetus dermestoides.
**Metabolites from Ascoidea hylecoeti, the symbiontic fungus of
Hylocoetus dermestoides.**

20612 Francke, W.; Haase, R.   DE 135151/75/0002
Chemische Kommunikation bei Vorratsschädlingen. **Chemical
communication in Coleoptera of stored products.**

20613 Friedrich, W.; Moskophidis, M.; Klotz, C.M.
                        DE 135202/75/0001
Natürliche und partialsynthetische Analoga des Vitamins B12.
Natural and partially synthetic analogues of vitamin B12.
Publications.

20614 Wilmers, F.   DE 138150/74/0001
Messung der Verdunstung einer freien Wasserfläche im
Zusammenhang und Vergleich mit meteorologischen
Messungen und daraus resultierenden Berechnungen des
Wärme– und Wasserhaushaltes der bodennahen Luftschicht
der Atmosphäre. **Evaporation measurement of a free area of
water surface in correlation and comparison with
meteorological measurements and with resulting calculations of
heat and water relationships in the near ground air stratum of
the atmosphere.**

20615 Ernst, D.E.W.; Reinhardt, D.   DE 138180/77/0002
Untersuchung der Primärproduktion niedersächsischer
Flachseen. **Investigation of the primary production of shallow
lakes in Lower Saxony.**

20616 Gopal–Ayengar; Pahlow, R.; Umi–Salamah, H.;
Fendrik, I.   DE 138180/77/0004
Cytologische Untersuchungen der Wirkung von Strahlen und
anderen Umweltfaktoren an Pflanzen. **Cytological effects of
radiation and environmental factors on plants.**

20617 Kühn, W.K.G.; Alps, W.   DE 138181/77/0005
Untersuchungen über Ausbreitungsvorgänge in der
bodennahen Atmosphäre unter Berücksichtigung der
Bodenrauhigkeit. **Investigations on the spread of aerosols in the
atmosphere near the soil surface under the influence of the soil
roughness.** Publications.

20618 Schmidt–Stohn, G.; Wricke, G.   DE 138300/74/0003
Isoenzym–Analysen beim Roggen. **Analyses of the isoenzymes
in rye.**

20619 Storck, H.; Hinken, J.   DE 138360/77/0003
Forschungssystem und –prozess in den
Gartenbauwissenschaften – Ein empirischer Beitrag zur
Wissenschaftsforschung –. **System and process of horticultural
sciences – An empirical contribution to the sociology of sciences**

20620 Zabeltitz, C.von; Kohlmeier, D.   DE 138390/72/0003
Untersuchungen über die zeitliche Abhängigkeit der
Lichtdurchlässigkeit bei verschiedenen Kunststoffen.
**Investigations into the temporal dependence of light–
transmission by several plastic covers.**

20621 Herrmann, K.; Kunzemann, J.; Schulz, J.; Vösgen, B.;
Schäfers, F.–I.   DE 138750/75/0001
Phenolische Inhaltsstoffe und Wirkstoffe der Gewürze.
Phenolic constituents and active substances in spices.

20622 Messow, C.   DE 139102/73/0008
Histometrische Untersuchungen an der Schilddrüse.
Histometrical studies on thyroid gland.

20623 Hapke, H.–J.; Abel, J.; Ghosh, M.; Tachampa, S.;
Youssef, S.   DE 139151/75/0001
Versuche zur Feststellung akuter Enzymwirkungen durch
Chloramphenicol. **Trials for estimation of acute action of
chloramphenicol on enzyme systems.**

20624 Hapke, H.–J.; Abel, J.   DE 139151/75/0002
Versuche zur Mobilisation von im Organismus deponiertem
Blei. **Trials to mobilize lead deposited in organisms.**

20625 Böhm, K.H.; Nicklas, R.   DE 139451/75/0002
Untersuchungen über pyrogene Inhaltsstoffe von Hefen.
Investigations into pyrogens of yeasts.

20626 Hörnicke, H.; Ehrlein, H.–J.   DE 144140/72/0001
Mechanismus und biologische Bedeutung der Coecotrophie
bei Lagomorpha. **Mechanism and biological significance of
coecotrophy in Lagomorpha.**

20627 Siebert, G.; Stärk, D.   DE 144190/75/0002
Stoffwechsel von NAD und Adenosindiphosphat–ribose.
Metabolism of NAD and adenosine diphosphate ribose.

20628 Siebert, G.; Schnell, E.   DE 144190/75/0004
Stoffwechsel von Sorbit. **Metabolism of sorbitol.**

20629 Ottow, J.C.G.; Fabig, W.   DE 144320/74/0002
Isolierung und Eigenschaften denitrifizierender Bakterien aus
Festbettreaktionen. **Isolation and properties of denitrifying
bacteria from laboratory plants.**

20630 Beringer, H.; Nothdurft, F.   DE 144400/70/0001
Beziehungen zwischen Tocopherolgehalt und Fettsäuremuster
von Samen. **Relationship between tocopherol content and fatty
acid pattern of seeds.**

20631 Martin, P.; Weckenmann, D.   DE 144400/75/0002
Aktivität proteolytischer Enzyme und Stickstoff–Mobilisation
während der Seneszenz von Blättern. **Activity of proteolytic
enzymes and nitrogen mobilization during senescence of leaves.**

20632 Schnell, F.W.; Utz, H.F.   DE 144420/74/0002
Effizienz der Selektion in spaltenden Generationen von
autogamen und allogamen Pflanzenarten. **Efficiency of
selection in segregating generations of autogamous and
allogamous plants.**

20633 Liegel, W.   DE 144445/77/0011
Zur Akkumulationsfähigkeit von Schwermetallionen bei

D 9900 – Research which cannot be classified in the fields mentioned above

grünen Mikroalgen. **On the ability of accumulation of heavy metal ions in green microalgae.**

20634 Gebbing, H.   DE 144450/72/0002
Elektrophoretische Untersuchungen über spezielle Eiweissstoffe der Rebe. **Electrophoretical investigations of special grape proteins.**

20635 Strauch, D.; Hundeloh, H.   DE 144610/75/0003
Aerosol–Dekontamination von bakteriellen Infektionserregern. **Aerosol–decontamination of pathogenic bacteria.**

20636 Franz, G.   DE 144885/75/0001
Geschichte des Gartenbaus – Deutsche Agrargeschichte 6 –. **History of Horticulture – German Agricultural History 6 –.**

20637 Heimann, W.; Gumbert, W.   DE 145100/74/0003
Reaktionsmechanismen der enzymatischchemischen Umlagerung von Lipid–Hydroperoxiden. **Reaction mechanism in enzymatic–chemical rearrangement of lipid hydroperoxides.**

20638 Loncin, M.; Hahn, G.; Weiser, H.   DE 145150/74/0001
Untersuchungen über die Kristallisation von Fetten. **Studies on the crystallization of fats.**

20639 Jaenicke, L.   DE 151050/72/0001
Biosynthese von Folsäurecofaktoren und ihren Konjugaten. **Biosynthesis of folic acid cofactors and their conjugates.** Publications.

20640 Jaenicke, L.; Boland, W.   DE 151050/74/0002
Sexuallockstoffe der Braunalgen –Phaeophytae. **Sex attractants in brown algae –Phaeophytae–.** Publications.

20641 Jaenicke, L.   DE 151050/78/0001 N
Regulation der Folatenzyme des Methylgruppenstoffwechsels in Abhängigkeit von Stoffwechsellage und Alter. **Regulation of folate enzymes of methyl group metabolism in relation to metabolic state and age.**

20642 Zahn, R.K.; Müller, W.E.G.   DE 154200/78/0001 N
Der Einfluss der Pollution auf die Programmierte Synthese. **The impact of pollution on programmed synthesis.** Publications.

20643 Lang, K.J.   DE 160060/75/0001
Wechselwirkung zwischen Mikroorganismen. **Interrelations between microorganisms.**

20644 Blaschke, H.   DE 160061/75/0004
Wachstumsregulationen in Laub- und Nadelstreu. **Growth regulators in tree leaf and conifer needle litter.**

20645 Schwenke, W.; Doppelreiter, H.   DE 160090/75/0003
Untersuchungen zur Entwicklung, Biologie und Ökologie einiger im Nadelwald lebender Collembolen–Arten. **Studies on development, bionomy and ecology of some species of Collembola living in the soil of coniferous stands.**

20646 Bäumler, W.   DE 160092/72/0006 R
Möglichkeiten der Verbesserung des Giftköder–Verfahrens zur Mäusebekämpfung 1972. **Possibilities of improving the poison ous–bait method for mice control.**

20647 Baumgartner, A.; Enders, G.   DE 160121/73/0001 N
Standortsklima Alpenpark Königssee. **Topoclimatology in the alpine park of Koenigssee.** Publications.

20648 Schulz, H.; Patzak, W.   DE 160330/75/0001
Energiegewinnung aus Holz – Holz– und HolzabfallVerwertung für die Eigen–Energieversorgung von Unternehmen der Holzwirtschaft und unter dem Aspekt des Umweltschutzes. **Energy from wood – utilization of wood and wood residues for the energy self–sufficiency of the wood–working industry and with reference to environmental aspects.**

20649 Grosser, D.   DE 160330/78/0001 N
Mikroanatomische Beschreibungen der Hölzer Israels. **Description of the microanatomy of the woods in Israel.**

20650 Fengel, D.   DE 160332/75/0002
Fraktionierungsversuche am Alkali–Extrakt aus Holocellulose. **Fractionation experiments on the alkali extract from holocellulose.** Publications.

20651 Fengel, D.; Stoll, M.   DE 160332/78/0001 N
Untersuchungen an ägyptischem Leinen. **Studies on Egyptian linen.**

20652 Aufsess, H.von   DE 160333/74/0005
Gegenseitige Beeinflussung verschiedener Mikroorganismen im Holz. **Interactions between various microorganisms in wood.**

20653 Schneider, A.   DE 160334/78/0003 N
Untersuchungen über die Porengrössenverteilung in Hölzern und Holzwerkstoffen mit dem Quecksilber–Porosimeter. **Investigations on the pore size distribution in woods and wood–based materials with the mercury porosimeter.**

20654 Schulz, H.; Grosser, D.   DE 160335/77/0001
Holzfehler. **Wood defects.**

20655 Grosser, D.   DE 160335/78/0001 N
Holzartenbestimmungen an ägyptischen Särgen. **Wood species identification of ancient Egyptian coffins.**

20656 Grosser, D.   DE 160335/78/0002 N
Mikroanatomische Beschreibungen der Hölzer Persiens. **Description of the microanatomy of Iranian woods.**

20657 Tempel, K.   DE 160550/72/0005
Untersuchungen zum Wirkungsmechanismus von Polyanionen in vivo. **Investigations into mechanisms of action of polyanions in vivo.**

20658 Tempel, K.; Hollatz, R.; Raake, W.   DE 160551/75/0002
Wirkung von Nucleinsäuren und Nucleinsäure–Basen auf Säugetiere nach Einwirkung von ionisierenden Strahlen und biologischen Alkylantien. **On the effect of nucleic acids and nucleic acid bases on mammals under the influence of ionizing radiations and/or alkylating agents.** Publications.

20659 Petry, H.   DE 160600/75/0006
Motilitätsuntersuchungen durch Magnetinduktion. **Motility measurements by magnetic induction.**

20660 Sambraus, H.H.   DE 160705/75/0004
Futterprägung von Meerschweinchen. **Food imprinting in**

Guinea pigs.

20661 Mayr, A.; Bibrack, B.; Wizigmann, G.; Thein, P.; Bachmann, P.A.   DE 160763/74/0001
Aktive Interferonisierung neugeborener Tiere. **Active interferonization of newborn animals.**

20662 Drawert, F.; Beier, J.   DE 161100/75/0006
Biosynthese Hopfenbitterstoffe Biosynthese Aromastoffe 'Terpene'. **Biosynthesis of bitter substances of hops Biosynthesis of aromatic substances 'terpenes'.** Publications.

20663 Drawert, F.; Görg, A.; Staudt, G.; Müller, W.
          DE 161100/75/0017
Über die elektrophoretische Differenzierung und Klassifizierung von Proteinen. **On electrophoretic differentiation and classification of proteins.** Publications.

20664 Feucht, W.; Nachit, M.   DE 161265/75/0002
Die phenolischen Komponenten in Prunus–Arten und deren Verteilung innerhalb des Baumes. **Phenolic compounds and their distribution among the different organs of Prunus trees.** Publications.

20665 Feucht, W.; Schmid, P.; Gebhardt, K.
          DE 161265/78/0003 N
Histochemische Untersuchungen des Phloemgewebes von Kirscharten und –sorten auf Polyphenole und Oxidationsenzyme. **Histochemical investigations on phloem tissue of species and varieties of cherries for polyphenols and oxidation enzymes.**

20666 Kirchgessner, M.; Gerum, J.   DE 161280/74/0001
Ansatz und Verwertung von Energie und Eiweiss bei Broilern. **Retention and utilization of energy and protein in broilers.**

20667 Kirchgessner, M.; Krziwanek, S.von
          DE 161280/74/0011
Einfluss der Proteinversorgung auf Stoffwechselenzyme. **Influence of protein supply on enzymes in metabolism.**

20668 Kirchgessner, M.; Steinhart, H.; Wieninger, R.
          DE 161280/74/0012
Interaktionen zwischen Spurenelementen und Verdauungsenzymen. **Interactions between trace elements and gastrointestinal enzymes.**

20669 Rottmann, O.   DE 161300/75/0008
Automatisierung von zytogenetischen Vorsorgeuntersuchungen. **Automatization of cytogenetic prophylactic investigations.**

20670 Pirchner, F.; Butler, I.von; Willeke, H.
          DE 161300/78/0002 N
Vergleich der Effizienz verschiedener Methoden bei Selektion auf antagonistische Eigenschaften bei der Hausmaus – Mus musculus domesticus –. **Comparison of the efficiency of different selection methods on antagonistic traits in mice – Mus musculus domesticus –.**

20671 Narziss, L.; Neidhardt, W.   DE 161790/75/0002
Über den Komplex der Beta–Glucane beim Mälzen und Brauen. **The beta glucans complex during malting and brewing.**

20672 Rehm, H.J.; Röschenthaler, R.   DE 164100/71/0001

Bildung und Wirkung verschiedener Mykotoxine. **Formation and effect of some mycotoxins.**

20673 Schweisfurth, R.; Wenzel, A.   DE 167150/77/0001
Untersuchungen an eisenpräzipitierenden Bakterien. **Experiments on iron precipitating bacterial.** Publications.

20674 Müller, P.; Klomann, U.; Reis, H.; Nagel, P.; Bartholome, S.; Thome, M.   DE 167200/73/0001
Diversität von Biozönosen auf unterschiedlich belasteten Standorten und ihre Indikatorbedeutung. **Diversity of biocenoses at varying impaired sites and the significance of indicators.**

20675 Müller, P.; Schreiber, H.; Klomann, U.
          DE 167200/74/0001
Erfassung der Europäischen Invertebraten. **Survey of European invertebrates.**

20676 Oberwinkler, F.; Blanz, P.; Deml, G.
          DE 173051/74/0001
Parasitische Basidiomyceten – Exobasidiales, Uredinales, Ustilaginales –. **Parasitic Basidiomycetes – Exobasidiales, Uredinales, Ustilaginales –.**

20677 Brieskorn, C.H.; Seifert, M.   DE 176150/75/0002
Über die Triterpensäuren aus einigen Gewürzkräutern. **The triterpenic acids of some aromatic plants.**

20678 Brieskorn, C.H.; Noble, P.   DE 176150/78/0001 N
Die Sesquiterpenoide des Myrrhenharzes. **The sesquiterpenoides of the resin of myrrh.**

20679 Jagnow, G.   DE 201020/75/0010
Abbau von Antibiotika in Abgängen aus der Geflügelhaltung. **Degradation of antibiotics in faeces of poultry.**

20680 Eckstein, D.; Bauch, J.   DE 202040/70/5001
Dendrochronologische Untersuchungen an ausgewählten Holzarten. **Dendrochronological studies of selected wood species.**

20681 Parameswaran, N.; Kruse, J.; Liese, W.; Bauch, J.
          DE 202040/77/0001
Feinstrukturelle Untersuchungen an Zellen und Zellwandkomponenten. **Microstructural examinations of cells and cell wall components.**

20682 Noack, D.; Brettel, G.   DE 202060/75/0001
Untersuchung zum Stoff– und Wärmetransport in Holz und Holzwerkstoffen. **Investigation of flow of water and heat transport in wood and wood materials.**

20683 Rapp, A.; Bachmann, O.; Steffan, H.
          DE 204000/73/4004
Untersuchungen über die Phenolcarbonsäuren und Flavonoide bei der Rebe. **Investigations on phenolic carboxylic acids and flavonoids in vines.**

20684 Blaich, R.   DE 204000/78/0017 N
Die Rolle extrazellulärer toxischer Substanzen bei Botrytis cinerea. **The function of extracellular toxic substances in Botrytis cinerea.**

20685 Erz, W.; Blab, J.; Bless, R.; Haarmann, K.; Nowak, E.
          DE 205020/78/0004 N

D 9900 – Research which cannot be classified in the fields mentioned above

Wissenschaftliche Entscheidungshilfen bei Entwicklung, Durchführung und Verbesserung internationaler Übereinkommen. **Scientific aids for resolutions in the development, realization and improvement of national and international laws or conventions.**

20686 Suhren, G.; Heeschen, W.; Tolle, A.
DE 207020/77/0003
Pyruvatbildungsvermögen von Bakterienzellen. **Formation of pyruvate by bacterial cells.**

20687 Bühringer, H.
DE 208050/74/0005
Aufnahmestudien mit Radionukliden an Süss–, Brack– und Seewasserorganismen. **Studies of the accumulation of radionuclides in fresh–, brackish and seawater organisms.**

20688 Leistner, L.
DE 210030/75/0001
Sammlung von Mikroorganismen für die Fleischforschung. **Collection of microorganisms for research on meat.**

20689 Mangold, H.K.; Gomaa, C.S.; Kaiser, H.; Hudalla, B.
DE 213020/78/0001 N
Oberflächenlipide der Samen von verschiedenen Rapssorten. **Surface lipids of the seeds of different varieties of rape.**

20690 Richter, I.; Krain, H.; Kiewitt, I.; Mukherjee, K.D.
DE 213020/78/0002 N
Biochemie ungewöhnlicher Lipide in Pflanzen und Tieren. **Biochemistry of unusual lipids in plants and animals.**

20691 Kossmann, A.
DE 215010/77/0003
Ausarbeitung von Rechenprogrammen und Programmpflege für die Auswertung wissenschaftlicher Versuchsanstellungen. **Development of calculating programmes and programme maintenance for evaluation of scientific experiments.**

20692 Stegemann, H.
DE 215140/77/0008
Verbesserung von Trenn– und Identifizierungs–Methoden bei Makromolekülen. **Improvement of methods for separation and identification of macromolecules.**

20693 Becker, G.
DE 217030/75/0001
Beiträge zur Ökologie und Physiologie von Termiten. **Contributions to the knowledge of the ecology and physiology of termites.**

20694 Böhme, C.; Grunow, W.
DE 305010/75/0005
Stoffwechsel von Fremdstoffen und biochemische Analytik im Rahmen von Tierversuchen. **Metabolism of foreign substances and biochemical analysis: animal experiments.**

20695 Hilbig, V.
DE 305030/73/0005
Stoffwechseluntersuchungen von Pflanzenschutzmitteln in der isoliert perfundierten Ratten– und Hühnerleber. **Metabolic studies of pesticides in the isolated perfused liver of rats and chickens.**

20696 Bulling, E.
DE 305030/75/0051
Typisierung von Resistenzfaktoren. **Typifying of R–factors.**

20697 Bulling, E.; Stephan, R.
DE 305030/75/0054
Antibiotika–Resistenz von Salmonella–Bakterien. **Antibiotics resistance of salmonella bacteria. Publications.**

20698 Dietz, P.
DE 501505/77/0011
Sortierung von Industrieholz Orientierende Untersuchungen zur Erarbeitung einer praktikablen Industrieholzsortierung. **Classification of industrial wood. Orientation studies for development of practicable classification of industrial wood.**

20699 Schöpfer, W.; Sieder
DE 501507/77/0004
Vermessung und Sortierung von Rohstangen. **Measuring and classification of raw poles.**

20700 Pommer, G.
DE 502058/78/0007 N
Assimilatumverteilung in Vicia faba. **Assimilate distribution in Vicia faba.**

20701 Mergenthaler, E.
DE 502501/70/0002
Untersuchungen an Polysacchariden. **Investigations into polysaccharides.**

20702 Belitz, H.–D.; Seilmeier, W.; Wieser, H.
DE 502502/75/0001
Partialsequenzen der Prolaminfraktion aus Mais – Zein – und Weizen – Gliadin –. **Partial sequences of the prolamin fraction from maize – zein – and wheat – gliadin –.**

20703 Kiermeier, F.; Buchberger, J.
DE 502553/72/0001
Probleme der Milcherfassung mit Tanksammelwagen. **Tanker collection of bulk milk and its problems.**

20704 Researcher not indicated
DE 502650/78/0001 N
Blähschlammbildende Bakterien – Ringtest –. **Bloating sludge forming bacteria – ring test –.**

20705 Dittrich, H.H.; Sponholz, W.R.
DE 506105/77/0001
Die Bildung neuer SO2–bindender Stoffwechselprodukte durch Hefe, Botrytis und Essigbakterien. **Formation of new SO2–binding metabolites by yeats, Botrytis and Acetobacter.**

20706 Schmid, P.; Behre, K.–E.; Zimmermann, W.–H.
DE 507150/71/0001 R
Die Entwicklungsgeschichte einer Siedlungskammer im ElbeWeser–Winkel seit dem Neolithikum – mit besonderer Berück– sichtigung der Wirtschaftsformen – 1971. **Historical development of settlement in Elbe–Weser angle since neolithic period with special regard to forms of cultivation.**

20707 Schmid, P.; Brandt, K.; Behre, K.–E.
DE 507150/75/0001
Siedlungsarchäologische Untersuchungen zur mittelalterlichen Wirtschafts– und Herrschaftsstruktur Ostfrieslands. **Archaeological settlement studies on the medieval history of economy and social structure in Eastern Frisia – W. Germany –.**

20708 Behre, K.–E.
DE 507151/73/0001
Die Pflanzenreste der wikingerzeitlichen Siedlung Haithabu bei Schleswig. **Plant remains in the viking–age settlement Haithabu near Sleswig.**

20709 Beran, N.
DE 509154/75/0002
Untersuchungen über den Einfluss der Luftfeuchte auf die Photosynthese. **Studies on the influence of air humidity on photosynthesis.**

20710 Beran, N.
DE 509154/75/0004
Der Verlauf der Transpiration unter verschiedenen ökologischen Bedingungen. **The course of transpiration under different ecological conditions.**

D 9900 – Research which cannot be classified in the fields mentioned above

20711 Berge, H.; Orgis, K. DE 904000/78/0001 N
Schwefeldioxid als notwendiger Bestandteil der Biosphäre.
Sulfur dioxide a necessary component of biosphere.
Publications.

20712 Gressel, P. DE 913000/74/0001
Das Verhalten von Holzwerkstoffen – Sperrholz und
Spanplatten – bei natürlicher Bewitterung, verglichen mit
Ergebnissen spezieller Kurzprüfverfahren zur Beurteilung der
Verleimungsgüte, vornehmlich neuartiger Bindemittel. **The
behaviour of timbers – plywood and chip board – subjected to
natural weathering in comparison with results of special short
test procedures for estimating the glueing quality especially of
new agglutinants.**

20713 Mortensen, B.K.; Jansen, K. DK 010300/78/0012 N
Fedtspaltning i smør. **Lipolysis in butter.**

20714 Møller–Madsen, A.; Jensen, H. DK 010300/78/0061 N
Smørsyrebakterier i ensilage, gødning og mælk. **Chlostridia in
silage, manure and milk.**

20715 Keiding, J. DK 020600/79/5121 N
Populationsdynamiske undersøgelser over voksne stuefluer,
Musca domestica, med henblik på udvikling af strategisk
bekæmpelse. **Population dynamic investigations of adult
houseflies, Musca domestica, with special reference to the
development of a stragetic method for the control.**

20716 Lund, M. DK 020600/79/5177 N
Undersøgelse af lækattes indflydelse på en ø–bestand af
mosegrise med sigte på en praktisk biologisk bekæmpelse.
**Investigation of stoats as a practical biological method for the
control of an island population of water voles.**

20717 Henningsen, K.W.; Bishop, N.I.; Kaufmann, U.;
Stummann, B.M. DK 030101/78/0001 N
Genetisk kontrol af fotosyntetisk effektivitet og
hydrogenproduktion hos alger. **Genetic control of
photosynthetic efficiency and hydrogen production in algae.**

20718 Rajagopal, R.; Allerup, S.; Møller, I.
DK 030104/78/0001 N
Den hormonale kontrol af plantevækst: cykliske nukleotiders
rolle i betacyanin syntese og xylogenesen. **The hormonal
control of plant growth: The role of cyclic nucleotides in
betacyanin synthesis and xylogenesis.**

20719 Lyshede, O.B. DK 030104/78/0002 N
Elektronmikroskopiske undersøgelser af kartoffelknoldens
celler. **Electronmicroscopic examination of potato tuber cells.**

20720 Lyshede, O.B.; Løschenkohl, B. DK 030104/78/0003 N
Flerkernede celler i kartoffelknolden. **Multinucleate cells in
potato tubers.**

20721 Rajagopal, R.; Møller, I.; Olsen, C.E.
DK 030104/79/0003 N
Syntese og biologisk aktivitet af N–hydroxytryptophan.
Synthesis and biological activity of N–hydroxytryptophan.

20722 Lyshede, O.B.; Barthlott, W.; Allerup, S.
DK 030104/79/0004 N
Mikrokanaler i epidermiscellernes ydervæg hos Welwitschia
mirabilis. **Microchannels in the outer cell wall of epidermal cells
of Welwitschia mirabilis.**

20723 Høgh–Schmidt, K. DK 030105/77/0002
Undersøgelse af dråbefordeling i nedbør. **An investigation of
drop distribution during a downpour of rain.**

20724 Middelboe, V. DK 030105/78/0001 N
Frembringelse af Cerenkov–lys i transparentia. **Production of
Cerenkov radiation in transparent media.**

20725 Skibsted, L.H. DK 030106/78/0004 N
Fotokemiske og fotofysiske egenskaber af rhodium (III)
komplexer. **Photochemical and photophysical properties of
rhodium (III) complexes.**

20726 Larsen, P.O.; Olsen, C.E.; Sørensen, F.T.;
Wieczorkowska, E. DK 030106/79/0006 N
Forekomsten af aromatiske aminosyrer og carboxylsyrer i Iris
familien i sammenhæng med den systematiske inddeling af
denne familie. **The distribution of aromatic amino acids and
aromatic carboxylic acids in Iridaceae in relation to its
chemotaxonomical classification.**

20727 Bresciani, J. DK 030109/72/0005
Undersøgelse af krebsdyrenes seksualitet. **An investigation of
crustacean sexuality.**

20728 Arnbjerg, J. DK 030129/78/0001 N
Betydning af øget ilttryk for øjets udvikling hos mus. **The
influence of elevated oxygen tension on the ocular development
in mice.**

20729 Lyshede, O.B.; Løschenkohl, B.
DK 030147/78/0001 N
Flerkernede celler i kartoffelknolden. **Multinucleate cells in
potato tubers.**

20730 Jart, A. DK 030192/78/0003 N
Forestring af glycerol med fedtsyrer. **Esterification of glycerol
with fatty acids.**

20731 Jart, A.; Badir, S. DK 030192/78/0004 N
Trans–omlejringen under forskellige fedtstofteknologiske
processer. **The formation of trans–isomers during various
processes in fat technology.**

20732 Refstrup, E.; Vogensen, F.K. DK 030193/79/0003 N
Genetiske forhold i gruppe N streptokokker. **Genetics of the
group N streptococci.**

20733 Cruiziat, P.; Bodet, C.; Bethenod, O.
FR 010101/75/5036
Modélisation du déterminisme climatique de la résistance
stomatique. **Modelisation of the climate factors affecting the
stomatal resistance.**

20734 Delmas, A. FR 010103/70/6333
Recherches expérimentales sur les mécanismes de la mise en
solution des composés peu solubles. **Experimental research on
the mechanisms leading to the taking in solution of little soluble
compounds.**

20735 Dumortier, B. FR 010106/72/1775
Physiologie des rythmes biologiques. **Physiology of biological
rythms.** Publications.

20736 Dumortier, B.; Rospars, J.P.; Lavialle, M.; Brachet,
R.; Brunnarius, J. mme FR 010106/72/5248

D 9900 – Research which cannot be classified in the fields mentioned above

Information sensorielle et rythmes circadiens. **Sensory information and circadian rhythms.**

20737 Chambon, J.P.; Genestier, G.; Martinez
FR 010106/74/5251
Faunistique écologique – Etude globale des biocénoses céréalières. **Study on biocenosis of cereales crop.**

20738 Lavialle, M.; Rospars, J.P.; Dumortier, B.; Brachet, R.; Brunnarius, J. Mme; Charles, M.   FR 010106/74/5254
Information photopériodique et rythme circadien chez Carausius Morosus. **Photoperiodic information and circadien rhythm in Carausius morosus.**

20739 Rospars, J.P.   FR 010106/74/5255
Action des substances actives sur le système nerveux central au niveau synaptique. **Action of drugs on the central nervous system at the synaptic level.**

20740 Dumortier, B.; Lavialle, M.; Brunnarius, J. Mme; Brachet, R.; Rospars, J.P.; Charles, M.   FR 010106/74/5256
La mesure photopériodique du temps : un modèle pour l'étude de l'information sensorielle chez l'insecte. **Photoperiodic time–measurement: a model for the study sensory information in Insects.**

20741 Dumortier, B.; Lavialle, M.; Brunnarius, J. Mme; Brachet, R.; Rospars, J.P.   FR 010106/75/5257
Diapause et modification périodique d'un paramètre physique. **Amplitude modulation of a physical parameter as an inducing factor of diapause.**

20742 Lavialle, M.; Rospars, J. P.; Dumortier, B.; Brachet, R.; Brunnarius, J. Mme   FR 010106/76/5264
Action photodynamique. **Photodynamic action.**

20743 Dumortier, B.; Rospars, J. P.; Brunnarius, J. Mme; Brachet, R.; Lavialle, M.   FR 010106/76/5265
Information photopériodique chez les Lépidoptères tropicaux. **Photoperiodic information in tropical species of Lepidopters.**

20744 Lavialle, M.; Brachet, R.; Rospars, J.P.; Dumortier, B.; Brunnarius, J. Mme   FR 010106/77/5266
Information sensorielle et photoréception extraoculaire. **Sensory information and extraoptic photoreception.**

20745 Rospars, J.P.; Brunnarius, J. Mme; Lavialle, M.; Charles, M.; Dumortier, B.   FR 010106/77/5267
Physiologie des neurones sensoriels antennaires. **Physiology of antennal sensory neurones.**

20746 Rospars, J.P.; Brunnarius, J. Mme; Lavialle, M.; Dumortier, B.   FR 010106/77/5268
Anatomie du deutocérébron d'un insecte (Première partie). **Anatomy of an Insect deutocerebrum.**

20747 Desnoyers, F.; Vodovar, N.   FR 010205/69/2717
Etude morphologique des tissus adipeux. **Morphological study of adipose tissues.** Publications.

20748 Desnoyers, F.; Vodovar, N.   FR 010205/74/2718
Influence de la nutrition sur le développement morphologique des tissus adipeux. **Influence of nutrition on the morphological development of adipose tissues.** Publications.

20749 Pascal, G. et Peret, J.   FR 010205/74/2719

Rythme des activités mitochondriases et lipogénique du foie au cours du nycthémère. **Nycthemeral Rythm of mitochondriase activity and lipogenesis of liver.**

20750 Dziedzic, A.; Andrieu, A.J.   FR 010208/75/3207
Propagation des bruits et leur absorbtion dans la nature en fonction des variations atmosphériques et des sols. **Noise propagation and absorbtion in nature, in correlation with soil and atmospheric variations.**

20751 Jacob, C.   FR 010214/78/8267
Périodicité et rythmes biologiques (3). **Periodicity and biological rythms.**

20752 Ducluzeau, R.; Hudault, S.; Galpin, J.V.
FR 010216/73/9612 N
Ecologie microbienne: facteurs contrôlant le développement des bacteries psychrophiles dans l'eau minérale plate. **Microbial ecology: factors controlling the phychrophilic bacteria development in flat mineral water.**

20753 Raibaud, P.; Roustan, J.   FR 010216/76/9611 N
Ecologie microbienne: isolement de souches méthanogenes dans les digesteurs alimentés avec du fumier de porc. **Microbial ecology: isolation of methanogenic bacterial strains from digestors fed with pig manure.**

20754 Delatour, C.; Guinot, G.   FR 010305/69/4130
Microflore interne des troncs d'épicéa sur pied. **Internal microflora of living spruce timber.**

20755 Buttoud, G.   FR 010308/78/8600
La politique forestière sous la monarchie de juillet. **French foresty politics between 1830 and 1848.**

20756 Bachacou, J.; Monestiez, M.   FR 010312/75/8296
Processus spatiaux et expérimentation (3). **Spatial processes and field experiments.**

20757 Millier, C.   FR 010312/76/8287
Propriétés de stabilité d'écosystèmes (3). **Stability properties of ecosystems.**

20758 Duron, M.   FR 010401/74/0224
Culture in vitro de quelques espéces ligneuses. **In vitro culture of some woody plants.**

20759 Robichet, O.; Salette, J.   FR 010403/76/6022
Techniques d'étude histologique de différents organes végétaux, application aux feuilles de graminées et aux boutures herbacées de plantes ornementales. **Histological study of different plant parts. Application to grass leaves and ornemental cuttings.**

20760 Andre, J.P.; Blanc, D. Mme; Gras, R.; Bellenand–Mayeur, P.   FR 010502/66/6008
Culture sur substrats non terreux. **Soilless culture.**

20761 Morisot, A.   FR 010502/74/6254
Déplacement avec mélange des solutions (nitrates). **Miscible displacement of solutions (nitrates).**

20762 Lyon, J.P.; Leclant, F.; Panis, A.; Bonfils, J.; Marro, J.P.   FR 010503/73/5046
Entomocénoses des maquis (et éventuellement des garrigues). **The entomocenoses of Scrub (and possibly of garrigue).**

20763 Cayrol, J.C.; Couderc, C.   FR 010504/71/5159
Etude des possibilités d'utilisation des nématodes libres
comme vecteurs de bactéries utiles dans certains milieux
cultivés. **Study of the ability of free–living nematodes to carry**
useful bacteria in some cultivated media.

20764 Scotto la Massese, C. ; baujard, P. ; kermarrec, A. ;
bordeaux, U.E.R. ; doucet, M.   FR 010504/73/5160
Nématofaune des écosystèmes naturels. **Nematofauna of the**
wild ecosystems.

20765 Cayrol, J.C.; Scotto la massese, S. Mme; Combettes, S.
Mme   FR 010504/73/5165
Recherches sur la biologie et le rôle des nématodes
mycophages associés aux mycorrhizes. **Investigations on the**
biology and the role of the mycophagous Nematodes associated
with Mycorrhiza.

20766 Cardin, M. C. Mme; Laumond, C.; Scotto la Massese,
C.   FR 010504/75/5171
Utilisation de la microscopie électronique en taxonomie des
nématodes. **Taxonomy of Nematodes using electron**
microscopy.

20767 Vey, A.; Fargues, J.; Quiot, J.B.; Ferron, F.; Ratault,
C.   FR 010612/53/5177
Réactions hémocytaires chez les invertébrés. **Hemocytic**
reactions in invertebrates.

20768 Quiot, J.B.   FR 010612/55/5178
Etude de la pathogénèse des virus et des rickettsies des
invertébrés en culture cellulaire. **Studies on the pathogenesis of**
invertebrate viruses and rickettsia in cell culture.

20769 Quiot, J.M.; Cousserans, F.   FR 010612/55/5179
Etablissement de primo–cultures et de lignées cellulaires
d'invertébrés. **Establishment of invertebrate cell cultures and**
cell lines.

20770 Boemare, N.; Vago, C.; Vey, A.; Fargues, J.; Pascal,
M.; Bavo, L.   FR 010612/56/5186
Enchaînement des maladies chez les invertébrés avec
participation de bactéries potentiellement pathogènes. **Effect**
of Potentially pathogenic Bacteria on Invertebrates.

20771 Vago, C.   FR 010612/58/1761
Action pathologique de la pollution chimique physique et
microbienne sur les invertébrés. **Pathological action of**
chemical, physical and microbiological pollution on
invertebrates. Publications.

20772 Louis, C.; Lepage, J.; Vago, C.; Vey, A.; Ayglon, D.;
Bonami, J.R.   FR 010612/58/5180
Action pathogène de la pollution chimique, physique et
microbienne sur les invertébrés. **Pathogenic effect on**
invertebrates of chemical, physical and microbial pollution.

20773 Fosset, J.; Meynadier, G.   FR 010612/60/5181
Elevage aseptique d'invertébrés. **Axenic rearing of**
invertebrates.

20774 Bergoin, M.; Meynadier, G.; Amargier, A. Mme;
Veyrunes, J.C.; Duthoit, J.L.; Hurpin, B.
          FR 010612/63/5188
Etude des Entomopoxvirus. **Study of Entomopoxviruses.**

20775 Bergoin, M.; Quiot, J. M. Mme; Boemare, N.;
Duthoit, J.L.; Croizier, G.; Diallo, B.   FR 010612/64/5185
Etude comparée des viroses de type densonucléose.
Comparative virology of insect densonucleosis.

20776 Vago, C.; Amargier, A. Mme; Meynadier, G.; Duthoit,
J.L.; Lyon, J.P.   FR 010612/65/5183
Etude des formations tumorales et du rôle oncogène de
certains virus chez les invertébrés. **Studies on tumors and**
oncogenic effect of viruses in invertebrates.

20777 Giannotti, J.; Leclant, F.; Louis, C.; Benhamou, N.
          FR 010612/66/5184
Etude des relations entre vecteurs et germes transmis
biologiquement. **Study of relationships between vectors and**
transmitted microorganisms.

20778 Vago, C.; Croizier, G.; Giannotti, J.; Hurpin, B.;
Meynadier, G.; Robert, P.   FR 010612/66/5187
Etude d'un type nouveau de procaryotes : l'agent de la
léthargie. **Study of a new type of procaryotes : the lethargy**
agent.

20779 Croizier, G.; Vago, C.; Odier, F.; Quiot, J.B.
          FR 010612/70/5194
Etude de l'immunité antivirale chez les insectes. **Antiviral**
immunity in insects.

20780 Meynadier, G.; Louis, C.; Vago, C.; Duthoit, J.L.;
Croizier, G.; Lopez, A.   FR 010612/70/5195
Etude ultrastructurale des Rickettsiales d'invertébrés et de leur
cycle. **Ultrastructure and developmental cycle of invertebrate**
Rickettsiales.

20781 Vey, A.; Amargier, A. Mme; Ratault, C.; Duthoit,
J.L.; Quiot, J. B.; Fargues, J.   FR 010612/70/5196
Pathogénèse des mycoses d'insectes. **Pathogenesis of fungal**
infections in insects.

20782 Croizier, G.; Odier, F.; Vey, A.; Duthoit, J.L.;
Veyrunes, J.C.; Amargier, A. Mme   FR 010612/71/5197
Etude des processus de résistance de type humoral chez les
insectes. **Studies on humoral resistance mechanisms in insects.**

20783 Plus, N.; Jousset, F.X.; Croizier, G.; Veyrunes, J.C.;
Duthoit, J.L.   FR 010612/71/5198
Etude comparée des Picornavirus d'invertébrés et de
vertébrés. **Comparative study of invertebrate and vertebrate**
Picornaviruses.

20784 Vey, A.; Quiot, J. B.; Moussa, J.B.; Yousfi, A.
          FR 010612/72/5199
Mycoses à champignons levuriformes chez les invertébrés.
Infections by yeast like fungi in invertebrates.

20785 Quiot, J.B.; Croizier, G.; Vey, A.; Ratault, C.;
Veyrunes, J.C.   FR 010612/72/5200
Etude de l'action des toxines fongiques et bactériennes à l'aide
de cultures cellulaires d'invertébrés. **Action of fungal and**
bacteriol toxins in invertebrate cell cultures.

20786 Quiot, J.B.; Bergoin, M.; Croizier, G.; Odier, F.
          FR 010612/73/5201
Mise au point du titrage de virus d'invertébrés à l'aide de
cultures cellulaires. **Improvement of invertebrate virus titration**
by means of cell cultures.

20787 Plus, N.; Duthoit, J.L.; Quiot, J.B.   FR 010612/74/5205
Association de virus et de lignées cellulaires. Etude sur cellules de Drosophiles. **Association of viruses with cell lines Studies on Drosophila cells.**

20788 Boemare, N.; Laumond, C.   FR 010612/74/5206
Relations entre nématodes entomophages et bactéries associées. **Relationships between entomophagous nematods and associated bacteria.**

20789 Bergoin, M.; Jousset, F.X.   FR 010612/75/5208
Caractérisation du Picornavirus C. **Characterization of Drosophila C Picornavirus.**

20790 Quiot, J.B.; Croizier, G.; Bergoin, M.; Grignon, C.; Vago, C.   FR 010612/75/5209
Etude de l'association permanente des Parvovirus et des lignées cellulaires. **Studies of persistent' association of a Parvovirus.**

20791 Louis, C.; Duthoit, J.L.; Giannotti, J.; Quiot, J.B.; Meynadier, G.; Massonie, G.   FR 010612/75/5210
Modifications induites des enveloppes de procaryotes. **Experimental changes in the envelopes of the procaryotes.**

20792 Louis, C.; Meynadier, G.; Giannotti, J.
    FR 010612/75/5211
Etude par cryodécapage de procaryotes intracellulaires symbiotiques ou pathogènes aux invertébrés et aux vertébrés. **Comparative freeze etching study of procaryotes infecting invertebrate and vertebrate cells.**

20793 Bouquet, A.; Doazan, J.P.; Leglise
    FR 010702/73/0110
Cultures d'anthères, culture de tissus et régénération. **Anther cultures – vine tissue culture and regeneration.**

20794 Couvy, J. Mme; Eyme, J.   FR 010703/72/0381
La constitution cellulaire d'Agaricus Silvicola et Agaricus Bisporus au cours du développement. **Cytological study of Agaricus Silvicola and Agaricus Bisporus during differenciation.**

20795 Laborde, J.; Pradet, M.   FR 010703/73/0382
Evaluation de la biomasse mycélienne de champignons saprophytes croissant sur milieux solides. **Determination of the mycelium biomass of saprophytic fungi growing on solid media.**

20796 Poitou, N.; Delmas, J.; Mousain, D.
    FR 010703/75/0397
Influence des champignons mycorhiziens sur la croissance des espèces forestières. **Effect of mycorrhizal fungi on the growth of forest tree species.**

20797 Triboi, A.M. Mme   FR 010802/71/6111
Activité de la nitrate réductase et génétique. **Nitrate reductase activity and genetics.**

20798 Robelin, M.; Mingeau, M.; Blanchet, R.
    FR 010802/76/6116
Echanges gazeux chez deux variétés de soja à feuilles larges ou étroites. **Gas exchange in two soja varieties with either wide or narrow leaves.**

20799 Labadie, J.; Gouet, Ph.   FR 010809/73/9523
Recherches de collagénases bactériennes. **Research of collageneses of bacterial origin.**

20800 Obaton, M.   FR 011002/67/0596
Ecologie des Rhizobium. **Rhizobium ecology.** Publications.

20801 Catroux, G.   FR 011002/69/0587
Eaux résiduaires des sucreries et distilleries de betteraves. **Effluents of sugar–refinery and beet distillery.** Publications.

20802 Soulas, G.; Fournier, J.C.   FR 011002/72/0591
Constitution d'un laboratoire d'étude de la biodégradabilité. **Setting up a laboratory for studying biodegradation.**

20803 Cornu, A.; Dulieu, H.; Maizonnier, D.
    FR 011003/75/0440
Transfert d'information génétique sans fusion gamétique. **Gene transfer without gametic fusion.**

20804 Pussard, M.; Pons, R.   FR 011007/75/5015
Ultrastructure générale de quelques Amibes libres – Mitose. **General ultrastructure of some free living Amoebas – Mitosis.**

20805 Perringer, P.; Nicoli, J.   FR 011010/72/2226
Modélisation de la croissance de la levure. **Yeast growth model.**

20806 Renard, H.A.   FR 011103/72/0295
Action d'ondes électromagnétiques sur les potentialités des semences. **Effect on electromagnetic pwaves on the seeds potentialities.**

20807 Casas, J.   FR 011205/76/8658
Les systèmes de recherche–développement agronomique dans les pays sous–développés et moyennement développés. **Agricultural Research Systems in less and middle developed countries.**

20808 Galzy, P.; Radier, M.   FR 011208/69/2238
Etude de la sexualité des levures. **Study on sexuality in yeast.** Publications.

20809 Galzy, P.; Vezinhet, F.   FR 011208/70/2236
Régulation enzymatique au cours de la sporulation de la levure. **Enzymatic regulation during yeast sporulation.** Publications.

20810 Missonnier J.; Robert, Y.   FR 011306/72/1735
Influence du bocage sur la faune des animaux d' intérêt agronomique. **Effect of the "bocage" field pattern on agricultural fauna.** Publications.

20811 Robert, Y.; Brunel, E.; Dedryver, Ch.
    FR 011306/72/5124
Facteurs de fluctuation des populations d'insectes dans les zones bocagères. **Factors causing fluctuations in insect populations of bocage areas.**

20812 Decau, J.   FR 011401/74/6195
L'équilibre photo–protéosynthèse chez le Maïs. Influence de facteurs exogènes (alimentation hydrique et azotée) ou endogènes (aptitude à la fructification, transferts). **Photo–protéosynthesis balance in Maize. Effects of nitrogen and water feedings (exogenous factors) and of fructification and translocation potentials (endogenous factors).**

20813 Hutter, W.   FR 011401/75/6203

D 9900 – Research which cannot be classified in the fields mentioned above

Jours disponibles pour les travaux des champs. **Available days for agricultural labour.**

20814 Caboche, M.   FR 011406/71/2527
Etude de la résistance à la 5–bromodeoxyuridine dans des souches cellulaires de hamster (bhk 21/13). **Studies of 5–bromodeoxyuridine resistance in syrian hamster fibroblasts (bhk 21/13).** Publications.

20815 Caboche, M.   FR 011406/73/2528
Etude génétique du métabolisme homocystéine / méthionine sur souches cellulaires de hamster (bhk 21/13). **Homocystein and methionine metabolism in bhk 21/13 hamster cells.**

20816 Gillois, M.   FR 011406/73/2529
Etude biochimique des protéines chromosomiques de lignées cellulaires porcines (pk 15) normales et portant des mutations chromosomiques. **Biochemical studies of chromosome proteins in normal and mutant pk 15 cells.**

20817 Gillois, M.   FR 011406/73/2530
Obtention de lignées cellulaires porcines (pk) photorésistantes, photosensibles, thermodépendantes de 2.000 à 3.000 å. **Induction and characterization of photoresistant, photosensible, thermodependant cells in 2.000 to 3.000 å ultraviolet light.**

20818 Dubois, M.; Martinat, N.   FR 011501/77/7532
La relaxine: Préparation, dosage radioimmunologique, immunocytologie. **Preparation, immunocytology – DOSAGE radioimmunoassay of Relaxin.**

20819 Heslot, H.; Maldonado, P.; Gaillardin, C.; Beckerich, J.M.   FR 011707/72/0162
Etude génétique de la biosynthese de la lysine chez la levure candida lipolytica. **Genetic study of lysin biosynthesis in candida lipolytica (yeast).** Publications.

20820 Heslot, H.; Treton, B.   FR 011707/72/0302
Etude du cycle de Krebs chez saccharomycopsis. **Krebs cycle on saccharomycopsis.**

20821 Strebler, G.; Touber, M.   FR 011800/75/5294
Production de protéines par les Acridiens. **Production of proteins by Acrididae.**

20822 Berchu, L.; Errecart, M.; Hy, M.; Mainsant, P.; Dussaigne, A.; De Fontguyon, C.   FR 012205/78/8560
Histoire des industries alimentaires. **Food industry history.**

20823 Duval, L.   FR 012208/60/6181
Etude de la réaction céruléomolybdique des phosphates, des arseniates, des silicates et des germanates. **The ceruleomolybdic reaction of phosphate, arsenate, silicate and germanate.**

20824 Reboul, C.; Al Hamchari, M.C.; Desbrosses, B.; Badis, M.F.: Mamoun, M.   FR 012212/75/8515
Jours disponibles pour les travaux agricoles et statistiques météorologiques. **Available days for agricultural landworks and meteorological statistical records.**

20825 Ricou, G. Mme; D'Aguilar, J.   FR 012220/60/5282
Etude des échanges de faune entre la prairie permanente et les autres systèmes d'une microrégion. **Study of the faunal movings between the permanent grassland and the other systems of a micro area.**

20826 Lefevre, G.   FR 012222/00/0503
Inventaire et repérage des caractéristiques du milieu cultural. Classification et évaluation de l'importance des divers facteurs intervenant dans l'ensemble des conditions culturales. **Surveying and marking cultural environment. Classification and evaluation of various factors involved in the whole cultural conditions.**

20827 Descoins, C.; Lettere, M.; Gallois, M.
                                        FR 012225/73/5172
Méthodes de synthèses stéréo–sélectives de systèmes diéniques conjugués. Application à la synthèse de phéromones sexuelles. **Stereoselective synthesis of dienic conjugated systems. Applications to synthesis of sex pheromones.**

20828 Kalaora, B.   FR 012303/78/8584
Ecologie, mouvement écologique et relation à la nature. **Ecology, ecological movement and relation to nature.**

20829 Meunier, A.   FR 012502/78/8547
Environnement économique des isoglucoses. **Economic context of H.F.C.S.**

20830 Hebert, J.; Remy, J.C.   FR 012503/72/6162
Valeur azotée des vinasses de distillerie de betteraves. **Nitrogen value of washy–wine of sugar–beet distillery.**

20831 Hall   GB 010103/00/0007
Blood groups in farm animals.

20832 Spooner   GB 010103/00/0009
Iron binding proteins (transferrin and lactoferrin), their structure and relationship to disease.

20833 Baldwin   GB 010301/78/0087
Ingestive and thermoregulatory behaviour in sheep and goats.

20834 Kemp; Coleman   GB 010302/00/0021
Fatty acid metabolism of rumen ciliate protozoa.

20835 Kemp; Dawson   GB 010302/00/0022
Biohydrogenation of dietary unsaturated fatty acids in the rumen and attempts to control this reaction.

20836 Wright   GB 010303/00/0035
IgM and IgG antibody production by spleen cells.

20837 Beale   GB 010303/00/0037
Binding properties of ligandin.

20838 Daniel; Davies   GB 010303/00/0050
Factors involved in tolerance of liver transplants in the pig.

20839 Evans; Smith   GB 010304/74/0036
Actions of synthetic insecticides on mammalian nervous system.

20840 Peaker   GB 010305/00/0050
Mechanism of milk secretion, particularly components of the aqueous phase of milk.

20841 Wooding; Morgan   GB 010308/76/0009
Structure and function of the milk fat globule membrane (Mfgm) and other cellular inclusions in milk.

20842 Greaves; Wingfield   GB 010803/75/0005
The effect of herbicides and breakdown products on the microflora of the root region of plants.

20843 Chancellor   GB 010804/00/0002
Vegetative regeneration of weeds.

20844 Oswald; Kirkham   GB 010812/00/0004
The agroecology and control of important grass weeds in leys and seed crops.

20845 Flegg; McNamara   GB 011001/00/0014
Ecology of nematode vectors of virus diseases.

20846 Cockshull   GB 011102/00/0015
Experimental and anatomical studies of the control of flower initiation and development.

20847 Rose   GB 011102/75/0062
Physics in relation to crop processes.

20848 Acock   GB 011102/76/0064
Analysis of crop canopy photosynthesis.

20849 Moorby   GB 011105/75/0014
Interrelationships between nutrient supply and photosynthesis.

20850 Morgan   GB 011402/00/0002
Fungal virus genetics.

20851 Horne; Johnson   GB 011403/78/0011
Image processing.

20852 Hewitt; James   GB 011509/00/0002
Metallo–proteins and other enzymes from chloroplasts.

20853 Smith; Best   GB 011509/00/0003
Amine metabolism in plants (barley etc. as models).

20854 Dunn; Kempton   GB 011806/00/0011
Study resistance to root and foliage aphids.

20855 Entwistle; Munasin   GB 011807/00/0009
Biology, epidemiology and control of white rot disease of onion.

20856 Miflin; Lea   GB 012001/76/0023
The pathway of nitrogen assimilation and transport in nitrogen fixing legumes.

20857 Whittngham; Keys   GB 012002/00/0014
Potential increase in cereal yield by the control of photorespiration.

20858 Wood; Antoniw   GB 012002/77/0016
Physiological studies in relation to agronomy of the potato crop.

20859 Wingfield; Truter   GB 012011/00/0003
Coordination chemistry of trace elements.

20860 Hughes   GB 012011/00/0008
Crystal structures of compounds from blighted potatoes.

20861 Walters; Evans   GB 012105/76/0028
Evaluate feed quality characteristics of potential varieties of red and white clovers.

20862 Clerihew; Mitchell   GB 030112/77/0014
Restriction of placentation.

20863 Moore   GB 030202/00/0005
The metabolism of lipids by rumen microflora.

20864 Peaker   GB 030204/78/0028
Mechanism and control of milk uptake.

20865 Webley   GB 030405/00/0003
Microorganisms involved in the decomposition of peat and its components.

20866 Jones   GB 030405/00/0007
Ultrastructure and chemical composition of soil fungi, including plant pathogens.

20867 Clarke; Woodham   GB 030601/00/0015
The biological and laboratory evaluation of novel and conventional protein feeding stuffs including cereals.

20868 Cutler; Symonds   GB 030903/74/0104
Survey of pesticide usage on arable crops.

20869 Hewson; Kolb   GB 030903/74/0401
Population dynamics of the fox in scotland.

20870 Wright; McBratney   GB 040301/00/0002
Yield and its distribution in four grasses suitable for grass drying.

20871 McNulty; Todd   GB 041601/00/0018
Purification and biochemical characterisation of viruses.

20872 Saunders; Wilson   GB 050511/78/0013
The regulation of the oestrus cycle in cattle.

20873 Wignall; Potter   GB 051009/00/0009
Reduction of air, water and noise pollution from fish handling and processing plants.

20874 Wignall; Tatterson   GB 051009/00/0011
Methods of analysis of fish by–products in relation to feedstuffs standards.

20875 Rogers, P.A.M.; Poole, D.B.R.   IE 060100/71/0346 R
A survey of blood copper levels of Irish cattle based on the indirect ceruloplasmin test. Publications.

20876 Cunningham, E.P.; More O'Ferrall, G.J.; Poole, D.B.R.   IE 060100/77/1278 R
Comparison of metabolic profiles of beef breed bulls on performance testtest. Publications.

20877 Tunney, H.   IE 060200/73/0828 R
Chemical composition of cattle, pig and poultry slurry. Publications.

20878 Brereton, A.J.; Coulter, B.S.   IE 060200/73/0835 R
Mathematical model of plant growth. Publications.

20879 Connolly, J.F.; Phelan, J.A.   IE 060400/77/2073 R
Butter hardness: an examination of the factors in milkfat which determine inter alia the spreadability of butter.

20880 Neenan, M.; Lyons, G.; Hammond, R.F.; Hickey, B.;

Comerford, P.J.; Kelly, J.   IE 060500/76/1268 R
Biomass for energy production phase 2. Publications.

20881 Prendeville, G.N.; Helleris, A.   IE 110202/78/9180 N
Interactions between herbicides and cytokinins and gibberellins in terms of membrane integrity in phaseolus.

20882 Baker, K.P.; Townley, P.   IE 120208/77/9198 N
The genus culicoides in ireland, and its distribution: aspec ts of their biology relative to their life cycle and the rep ellent activity of selected chemicals.

20883 Valenziano, S.; Sabato, S.   IT 011801/75/0001
Flora e vegetazione di una zona dell'Appennino centro–settentrionale (Rincine). **Flora and vegetation of an area in the north–central Apennines (Rincine).** Publications.

20884 Valenziano, S.   IT 011801/75/0002
Tentativo di revisione sistematica del Populus tremula. **Reclassification attempt for Populus tremula.** Publications.

20885 Eccher, A.   IT 011801/75/0011
Studio comparato di provenienze dei pini mediterranei della Sezione Halepensis. (Progetto FAO/SCM/CRFM/4bis). **Comparative investigation of Halepensis Section pine provenances. (FAO/SCM/CRFM/4bis project).**

20886 Cale, M.T.; Figliolia, A.; Izza, C.   IT 020200/50/0001
Metabolismo delle piante in diversi ambienti climatici. **Plant metabolism in different environments.** Publications.

20887 Luzzati, A.; Siragusa Campanello, N.
                                          IT 020200/79/0002 N
Purificazione e caratterizzazione di enzimi ossido–riduttasi. **Purification and characterization of oxido–reductase enzymes.**

20888 Marinari Palmisano, A.; Ambrogioni, L.
                                          IT 020400/72/0005
Specie del gen.Heterodera in Italia. **Heterodera spp. in Italy.**

20889 Marinari Palmisano, A.   IT 020400/75/0001
Ultrastruttura degli spermi in alcuni nematodi Criconematoidea. **Sperm ultrastructure in some nematodes Criconematoidea.**

20890 Bagnoli, B.   IT 020400/78/0002
Sistematica dei Lepidotteri Nottuidi. **Systematics of Lepidoptera Noctuidae.**

20891 Bagnoli, B.   IT 020400/78/0003
Specie di Lepidotteri Nottuidi associati al mais in Toscana. **Species of Lepidoptera Noctuidae living on Zea mais in Tuscany.**

20892 Bagnoli, B.   IT 020400/78/0004
Specie di Lepidotteri Nottuidi associati all' erba medica in Toscana. **Species of Lepidoptera Noctuidae living on Medicago sativa in Tuscany.**

20893 Lanza, F.; Lopez, G.; Rizzo, V.; Spallacci, P.; Onofrii, M.; Venezian Scarascia, M.E.   IT 020500/75/0009
Relazioni tra evaporazione potenziale variamente calcolata ed evaporazione effettiva. **Relationship between calculated and measured evaporation.**

20894 Fortini, S.; Galterio, G.; Alessandroni, A.; Nardi, S.;

D'Egidio, M.G.; Sgrulletta, D.   IT 020800/74/0002 R
Frumento duro – Ricerche biochimiche sulle relazioni tra attività enzimatiche di tessuti fogliari e produzione di granella e di proteine. **Durum wheat – Biochemical relationships between leaf enzyme activities and grain and protein yield.** Publications.

20895 Palmieri, S.   IT 021000/78/0001
Studi sulle cinetiche di reazione ossido riduttive catalizzate da metallo enzimi. **Studies of metal enzimes catalyzed oxydo reductive reactions in biological systems.**

20896 Rusconi Camerini, G.; Biancardi, E.; De Biaggi, M.
                                          IT 021100/75/0009 R
Studio delle caratteristiche chimico–qualitative della barbabietola da zucchero. **Study of the sugar beet chemical and quantitative traits.** Publications.

20897 Iannotta, N.; Pantusa, M.; Garofalo, M.G.; Rizzuti, B.; Perri, L.   IT 021400/74/0001
Studio sulla incidenza e localizzazione dell'aborto dell'ovario di alcune cultivar di olivo. **Researches on incidence and localization of ovary abortion of some olive cultivars.**

20898 Ciancio, O.; Mercurio, R.; Nocentini, S.
                                          IT 021700/22/0001 R
Sperimentazione di specie esotiche. **Experiment on exotic forest trees.** Publications.

20899 Tocci, A.; Fusaro, E.; Pelizzo, A.; Avolio, S.; Guidi, G.   IT 021700/29/0001 R
Ricerche sulle provenienze di specie forestali indigene ed esotiche. **Provenance trials of indigenous and exotic forest trees.** Publications.

20900 Ciancio, O.   IT 021700/63/0001
Ricerche sugli eucalitteti. **Researches on eucalyptus stands.** Publications.

20901 Guidi, G.; Avolio, S.; Fusaro, E.; Ciancio, O.; Ranalli, A.; Menguzzato   IT 021700/68/0002 R
Studi ecologici sull'abete in Molise e in Calabria. **Ecologic studies on Abies alba in Molise and Calabria.** Publications.

20902 Mirabella, A.   IT 021700/69/0004 R
(Analisi chimiche su piante forestali) e pedologia. **(Chemical analysis on forest tree species) and pedology.** Publications.

20903 Spagnesi, M.   IT 022800/76/0002 N
Osservazioni stagionali delle variazioni per concentrazioni di melatonina ed altri parametri nella Lepus timidus. **Seasonal variations of the concentration of melatonine and other parametrs in Lepus timidus..**

20904 Giordano, E.; Santostasi, M.   IT 040116/72/0001
Ricerche sulle provenienze di Pinus Halepensis. **Researches on provenances of Aleppo Pine.**

20905 Giavarini, I.; Negrini, F.; Minoccheri, F.; Dalla Pozza, G.; Giordani, G.   IT 040212/78/0001
La fosfatasi nelle ovaiole a livello di circolo e di tessuti. **Phosphatase in the blood and tissues of laying hens.**

20906 Cultrera, R.   IT 040217/72/0440
Ossidazione enzimatica di antociani. **Enzymatic oxidation of anthocyanin.** Publications.

D 9900 – Research which cannot be classified in the fields mentioned above

20907 Guerzoni, M.E.　　　　　IT 040240/74/0568
Produzione di composti antifungini da parte di Saccharomyces Cereviae. **Production of fungicidal compounds from Saccharomyces Cereviae.**

20908 Grasso, S.　　　　　IT 040302/77/0839
Individuazione di sostanze antivirali isolate da piante. **Identification of antivirus substances isolated from plants.**

20909 Damigella, P.; Tribulato, E.; Continella, G.
　　　　　IT 040307/74/0001
Progetto speciale C.I.P.E. n.11 – Ricerche collegiali sugli agrumi. Ricerche sulle varietà e portinnesti. **C.I.P.E. Speciel Plan n.11. Collegial researches on citrus trees. Researches on varieties and rootstocks.** Publications.

20910 Silva, S.; Carini, F.; Rastelli, A.　　IT 040406/79/0001 N
Decadimento biologico di alcuni radionuclidi in vegetali. **Biological decay of some radionuclides in plants.**

20911 Dellaglio, F.　　　　　IT 040408/73/0191
DNA–DNA omologia tra organismi del genere lactobacillus. **DNA–DNA homology between organisms of the lactobacillus genus.** Publications.

20912 Dellaglio, F.　　　　　IT 040408/77/0166 R
I fermenti lattici quali componenti della microflora intestinale degli animali domestici. **Lactobacilli as part of the bowel microflora of domestic animals.**

20913 Bottazzi, V.　　　　　IT 040409/77/0121 R
Caratterizzazione del sistema proteasico presente in lattobacilli termofili. **Characterization of the proteasic system present in Lactobacillus thermophilus.**

20914 Ciampi, C.　　　　　IT 040505/73/0176
Indagine sui rapporti ultrastrutturali nei casi di interazione fra organismi vegetali. **Survey of ultrastructural relations in cases of interaction between plant organisms.** Publications.

20915 Ciampi, C.　　　　　IT 040505/77/0147 R
Indagine sui rapporti ultrastrutturali nei casi di interazione fra organismi vegetali. **Research on ultra–structural relations in cases of interaction between vegetable organisms.**

20916 Ruffini Castrovilli, C.M.　　　　IT 040602/74/0621
Indagini sperimentali sull'influenza del retinolo dei carotinoidi del mais e della surgelazione sulle performances e sul valore commerciale del fegato grasso pregiato di palmipedi. **Experimental research on the influence of retinol, of maize carotinoids and of freezing on the performances and commercial value of highly rated fat liver of palmipeds.**

20917 Volonterio, G.　　　　　IT 040609/77/0316 R
La distribuzione del 14c nei vegetali. **14C distribution in plants.**

20918 Corberi, E.　　　　　IT 040611/73/1189
Ricerche sull'ecologia di bdellovibrio bacteriovorus. **Research on the ecology of Bdellovibrio Bacteriovorus.**

20919 Fossati Galli, E.　　　　IT 040611/77/0185 R
Degradazione microbica dei composti organici di sintesi anticrittogamici ed erbicidi, e degli acidi biliari. **Bacterial degradation of synthetic organic components used as fungicides and herbicides, and of biliary acids.**

20920 Basadonna Baggi, G.　　　　IT 040611/77/0789
Accertamento della biodegradabilità di composti organici di sintesi. **Assessment of the biological degradation of organic synthetic compounds.**

20921 Baglioni, T.; Locatelli, A.; Genchi, C. – Agnes, F.; Arrigoni, C. – Traldi, G.; Sartorelli, P.; Simonic, T. – De Luca, A.　　　　　IT 040641/76/0001
Polimorfismi Enzimatici nei bovini. **Cattle Enzymatic Polymorphism.** Publications.

20922 Cocucci, S.　　　　　IT 040645/77/0151
Meccanismi della dormienza nei semi e negli organi quiescenti. **Mechanisms of latency in seeds and quiescent organs.**

20923 Tranfaglia, A.　　　　　IT 040703/71/0001
Ricerche di sistematica e biologia sugli Homoptera coccoidea. **Taxonomic and biological researches on Homoptera coccoidea.** Publications.

20924 Trembla, E.　　　　　IT 040703/73/0321
Immunodiagnosi di insetti di interesse agrario "G. Pseudococcus. **Immunodiagnosis of insects of interest to agriculture – G. Pseudococcus.** Publications.

20925 Pizzolongo, P.　　　　　IT 040704/72/0119
Ricerche ultrastrutturali su piante parassite e saprofite. Ricerche sulla origine e sulla evoluzione degli organuali cellulari. Rapporti tra microorganismi ed insetti. **Ultra–structural research on parasitic and saprophyte plants. Research on the origin and on the evolution of the cellular organs. Relation between microorganisms and insects.** Publications.

20926 Rossi–Doria, M.　　　　IT 040706/74/0619
Analisi economica delle informazioni di una rete contabile. **Economic analysis of information from an accounting network.**

20927 Coppola, S.　　　　　IT 040713/73/0919
Citochinine nei microrganismi e nelle interazioni piante–microrganismi. **Cytoquinines in microrganisms and in plant–microorganisms interactions.** Publications.

20928 Buonocore, V.　　　　IT 040746/78/1040 N
Studi sulle interazioni tra inibitori amilasici di natura proteica presenti nella cariosside di frumento e amilasi animali. **A study on the interaction of non proteinic amilase inhibitors present in wheat caryoxide and animal amilase.**

20929 Ferrari, G.　　　　　IT 040802/77/0180 R
Miglioramento dell'efficenza dei sistemi di assorbimento e traslocazione dei vegetali. **Improvement in the efficiency of the absorption an translocation systems of plants.**

20930 Alghisi, P.　　　　　IT 040808/74/0502
Studio dell'origine citoplasmatica o nucleare dell'attività perossidasica in frazioni subcellulari di piante di mais maschiofertili e maschiosterili sane ed inoculate con Helminthosporium Maydis razza T. **Study of cytoplasmatic or nuclear origin of peroxydasic activity in subcellular fractions of sterile and fertile male maize plants, healthy and inoculated with Helminthosporium Maydis T. strain.**

20931 Bianchi, A.A.　　　　　IT 041001/72/0395

Ricerche sulle foraggere e i pascoli. **Research on forage plants and pastures.** Publications.

20932 Mennella, V.; Mastroforti, G.; Sediari, T.; De Angelis, M.E.   IT 041016/77/0002
Recupero statico e funzionale del patrimonio architettonico rurale umbro. **The structural and functional recovery of architectonic property of Umbrian country.**

20933 Rossi, J.; Costamagna, L.   IT 041023/74/0001 N
Enzimologia. **Enzymology..**

20934 Lotti, G.   IT 041103/74/0578
Studi sul ruolo dello zinco nel biochimismo vegetale. **Studies on the role of zinc in plant biochemistry.**

20935 Pelosi, P.   IT 041108/74/0599
Composti metallo–organici nella pianta. **Metal–organic compounds in plants.**

20936 Pelosi, P.   IT 041108/77/0257 R
Identificazione del codice olfattivo. **Identification of the olfactory code.**

20937 Olmi, M.   IT 041206/77/0250 R
Studi sulla entomofauna di risaia. **Study on the insect population of rice–fields.**

20938 Bosticco, A.; Tartari, E.   IT 041216/77/0002 N
Indagini preliminari sulla disponibilità ed utilizzazione di alcuni sottoprodotti dell'azienda agraria. **Preliminary studies on the availability and utilization of some agricultural by–products..**

20939 Gessa, C.   IT 041305/78/1061 N
L'acidità delle acque di coordinazione del ferro ed alluminio nei complessi organo–minerali e meccanismi di interazione con composti umici e fulvici. **Water coordination of iron and aluminum in organic–mineral complexes; interactions with humic and fulvic substances.**

20940 Sarfatti, G.; Pacini, E.; Cresti, M.; Ciampolini, F.
                                                IT 041402/72/0001
Ricerche ultrastrutturali sul meccanismo della autoincompatibilità e della incompatibilità unilaterale interspecifica nelle Angiosperme. **Ultrastructural researches on the mechanism of self and of unilateral interspecific incompatibility in Angiosperms.** Publications.

20941 Carilli, A.   IT 042201/77/0131
Produzione e saggio di materiali biologici ottenuti da colture di funghi entomopatogeni. **Production and testing of biological materials obtained from entomopathogenic fungi cultures.**

20942 Sarti, A.   IT 060200/74/0090
Studio della influenza della fotorespirazione sul bilancio fotosintetico durante lo sviluppo di piante a ciclo C_4 e C_3. **Photorespiration intensity and growth development of C_3 and C_4 plants.**

20943 Veri, G.   IT 060200/77/0984 R
Micrometeorologia delle piante. **Micro–meteorology of plants.**

20944 Porceddu, E.   IT 060500/77/1004
Studio della variabilità genetica presente in popolazioni di piante coltivate e selvatiche. **A study of genetic variability in groups of cultivated and wild plants.**

20945 Tedeschi, P.   IT 060700/74/0121
Ricerche lisimetriche. **Lysimetric studies.**

20946 Crescimanno, F.G.   IT 060900/73/0167
Osservazioni su piante nucellari in via di selezione in pieno campo e proseguimento delle ricerche sull'embrionia nucellare. **Observations on nucellary plants and the continuing of researches on the nucellary embrion.** Publications.

20947 Caggiati, P.   IT 061000/74/0023
Analisi storica dei costi di alcune colture. **Historical analysis of the costs of some croppings.**

20948 Florenzano, G.   IT 061300/63/0154
Ricerche di base sui microrganismi autotrofi e studio delle applicazioni dei processi autotrofici in agricoltura, nella produzione di alimenti e nella difesa dell'ambiente. **Basic researches on autotrophic microorganisms and development of applications of autotrophic processes in agriculture, in food and feed production and in the control of environment's pollution.** Publications.

20949 Ceruti, A.   IT 061400/70/0157
Strutture submicroscopiche. **Submicroscopic structures.** Publications.

20950 Ceruti, A.   IT 061400/77/0913
Ecologia dei funghi. **Fungi ecology.**

20951 Ceruti, A.   IT 061400/77/0914
Processi di antibiosi e di micotossicosi. **Antibiosis and mycotoxicosis mechanisms.**

20952 Lepidi, A.   IT 061900/73/0010
Variabilità di caratteri morfo–fisiologici di Humicola sp. ed altri funghi terricoli, infettati con particelle micoplasma–simili. **Variability of morpho–physiological characters of Humicola sp. and other soil fungi infected with mycoplasma –like particles.** Publications.

20953 Jona, R.   IT 062100/72/0150
Caratterizzazione cariologica ed istologica del patrimonio ereditario delle diverse cultivar. **Histochemical determination of cell wall components in fruit pulp.**

20954 Liberatori, J.   IT 062500/68/0205
Sulla struttura e sulla funzione di alcune proteine del latte di particolare interesse biologico. **Structure and function of some milk proteins of particular biological interest.** Publications.

20955 Liberatori, J.   IT 062500/71/0203
Studi chimici, chimico fisici ed immunochimici sulle IgA, IgG e IgM del latte di diverse specie animali. **Chemical, physical–chemical and immunochemical studies on IgA, IgG and IgM from colostrum and milk of different animal species.** Publications.

20956 Liberatori, J.   IT 062500/72/0206
Sulla degradazione enzimatica delle caseine. **Enzymatic degradation of caseins.** Publications.

20957 Liberatori, J.   IT 062500/74/0204
Azione di enzimi proteilitici sulle IgA e sulle IgG isolate da latti animali. **Activity of proteolytic enzyms on IgA and IgG**

D 9900 – Research which cannot be classified in the fields mentioned above

isolated from animal milks.

20958 Nuti Ronchi, V.   IT 064300/78/1190 N
Fusione genetica tra protoplasti vegetali. **The genetic fusion of plant protoplasts.**

20959 Veen, H.   NL 010102/69/7980
Onderzoek inzake groeiregulatoren ten behoeve van toepassingen in de praktijk. **Research on plant growth regulators for practical purposes.** Publications.

20960 Wit, C.T. de   NL 010102/78/7996
Samenwerking tussen de onderzoekprojecten ten behoeve van voeder- en voedselgewassen en van natuurlijke weilanden in ontwikkelingslanden en het onderzoek ten behoeve van de Stichting Onderzoek Wereldvoedselvoorziening. **Co–ordination between research projects on productivity of food and fodder crops and natural pastures in developing countries and the research projects of the "Centre for World Food Studies".** Publications.

20961 Chadwick, K.H.   NL 010110/71/7281
A study of dose effects responses and the interrelationship between cell survival, mutation and chromosomal aberrations in plant cells. Publications.

20962 Metz, S.H.M.   NL 010115/74/5400
Studie van biochemische en fysiologische grondslagen en parameters van groei en karkassamenstelling. **Study of biochemical and physiological bases and parameters for growth and carcass composition.** Publications.

20963 Rijneveld, R.   NL 010116/77/8910 N
Onderzoek naar projecten t.b.v. de ontwikkelingssamenwerking in de visserij. **Research into projects for development co–operation in fishing industry.**

20964 Boer, W.C.   NL 010118/77/7260
Kwaliteitsomschrijving van snijbloemen. **Quality description of cut–flowers.**

20965 Duvekot, W.S.   NL 010118/77/7268
Vastlegging knopstadia van snijbloemen. **Recording bud development stages of cut flowers.** Publications.

20966 Locht, L.J.   NL 010501/73/5267 R
Problematiek van de verdeling van waterschapslasten. **Cost allocation for regional water management.**

20967 Wijngaard, J.K.R. van den   NL 010601/74/6673
Ontwikkeling van methoden ter bepaling en afweging van ruimtelijke aanspraken in een landschappelijk en natuurwetenschappelijk waardevol gebied. (Midden–Brabant) – bosbouw en landinrichting. **Development of methods for determination and evaluation of multiple land–use in areas with high landscape and nature values – forestry and land allocation.** Publications.

20968 Biezen, J.B.   NL 010602/68/4564
Gebruik van wiskunde enstatistiek bij oecologisch onderzoek. **Mathematical and stetistical aspects of ecological research.**

20969 Mueller, F.   NL 020006/61/4815
De samenhang tussen structuur en functie van redox–enzymen, in het bijzander flavoproteïnen. **Structure and function of redox enzymes with special reference to flavoproteins.**

Publications.

20970 Mueller, F.   NL 020006/67/4817
Het mechanisme van redox–enzymen m.l.v chemische modellen. **Model studies in relation to the catalytic action of redox enzymes.** Publications.

20971 Kok, A. de   NL 020006/72/6283
Structuur en functie van a–ketozuur dehydrogenase complexen uit prokaryoten en eukaryoten. **Structure and function of a–keto acid dehydrogenase complexes from prokaryotes and eukaryotes.** Publications.

20972 Hartog, N.A. den   NL 020010/74/6581
Kengetallen matrialen; inzicht in de schaarste van hout als grondstof. **Indexnumbers of materials; Understanding of scantiness of wood as raw material.**

20973 Dorsman, W.   NL 020013/73/6303
Onderscheiden van geslachten en soorten van voornamelijk Paramphistomum (Trematoda) door electrophorese. **Differentiation among genera and species of mainly Paramphistomum (Trematoda) by electrophoresis.**

20974 Stam, P.   NL 020015/69/4420
De veranderingen in de genetische structuur van populaties die op weg zijn naar een koppelingsevenwicht. Experimenteerobjecten: muizen, meelkevers, drosophilia. **Changes in genotypic composition of populations approaching linkage–equilibrium. Experimental animals: mice,flour beetles, drosophilia.** Publications.

20975 Boer, P. de   NL 020015/71/4984
Het effect van chromosomale aberraties op fertiliteit en embryonaalletaliteit bij zoogdieren. **Chromosomal aberrations, fertility and embryonic lethality in mammals.** Publications.

20976 Broek, H.W.J. van den   NL 020015/72/4423
De rol van nucleaire eiwitten bij de transcript–regulatie van het genetisch materiaal. **Regulation of transcription in Eucaryotes.** Publications.

20977 Visser, J.; Bos, C.J.   NL 020015/74/6346
Onderzoek van het centraal metabolisme m.b.v. mutanten. (Aspergillus). **Characterization of mutant dehydrogenases in Aspergillus nidulans.** Publications.

20978 Bos, C.J.; Visser, J.   NL 020015/75/6347
Biochemische en genetische analyse van pectolytische enzymen bij schimmels en bacteriën. **Biochemical and genetical analysis of pectolytic enzymes in fungi and bacteria.** Publications.

20979 Koornneef, M.   NL 020015/77/8793 N
Genetica van het planthormoon metabolisme bij Arabidopsis thaliana. **Genetics of planthormone metabolism in Arabidopsis thaliana.**

20980 Koopal, L.K.; Hibma, J.T.   NL 020016/68/4929
Eigenschappen van de dubbellaag van zilveriodide bij aanwezigheid van geadsorbeerd polyvinylalcohol en de karakterisering van het geadsorbeerde polymeer. **The electrical double layer of silver iodide in the presence of adsorbed polyvinyl alcohol and the characterization of the adsobed polymer.** Publications.

20981 Springer, M.M. NL 020016/71/4933
Diëlektrisch onderzoek van de fasegrensstructuur van polystyreen latices met en zonder adsorptie van laag- of hoog-moleculaire verbindingen. **Dielectric investigation of the phase boundary structure of polystyrene latics with and without adsorption of low or high molecular compounds.**

20982 Keuskamp, J.W.; Wegh, R.A. NL 020016/71/4937
Evenwichtsdikten en stratificatie van vrije vloeistoffilms. **Equilibrium thickness and stratification of free liquid films.** Publications.

20983 Fleer, G.J. NL 020016/72/4932
Stabiliteit van kolloidale systemen in aanwezigheid van polymeren. **Stability of colloids in the presence of polymers.** Publications.

20984 Keizer, A. de; Lande Gremer, L.C.N. de la
NL 020016/72/4935
De elektrische dubbellaag en solstabiliteit van zilveriodide in de aanwezigheid van kationogene en niet–iogene oppervlakteactieve stoffen. **The electrical double layer and sol stability of silveriodide in the presence of cationic and non–ionic surface–active materials.** Publications.

20985 Leeuwen, H.P. van NL 020016/74/4940
Relaxatieverschijnselen in niet–diffuse dubbellagen. **Relaxation phenomena in non–diffuse double layers.** Publications.

20986 Cohen–Stuart, M.A. NL 020016/75/4256
Conformatie van geadsorbeerde polymeren. **Conformation of adsorbed macromolecules.**

20987 Norde, W. NL 020016/77/7312
Eigenschappen van geadsorbeerde biopolymeren. **Properties of adsorbed biopolymers.** Publications.

20988 Scheutjens, J.M.H.M. NL 020016/77/7313
De adsorptie van oligomeren en polymeren: een theorie gericht de kwantitatieve verklaring van de uitvlokking door polymeren. **The adsorption of oligomers and polymers: a theory aimed at the quantitative explanation of the flocculation by polymers.**

20989 Schee, H.A. van der NL 020016/77/7314
Adsorptie van oligomeren aan geladen grensvlakken. **Adsorption of oligomers at charged interfaces.**

20990 Mattheij, J.A.M. NL 020017/72/4682
Centrale regulatie van de prolactine secretie bij de rat en de fysiologische functies ván dit hormoon. **The central regulation of the prolactin secretion in the rat and the physiological functions of this hormone.** Publications.

20991 Hijwegen, T. NL 020018/77/8439
Taxonomische betekenis van de compatabiliteit van in de natuur voorkomende plant – parasiet combinaties. **Taxonomic significance of host – parasite compatibility existing in nature.**

20992 Biersteker, K. NL 020019/76/7318 R
Effecten van milieuverontreinigingen op bodem, water, lucht en de daaruit voortvloeiende effecten op menselijke gezondheid, welzijnsbelevenis en schade aan planten, dieren en ecosystemen (Provincie onderzoek Milieuhygiëne). **Effects of environmental pollution on soil, water and air and the consequent effects on human health, well–being and damage to plants, animals and ecosystems (Provincial Environmental Health Research Project).**

20993 Krabbe, J.J. NL 020025/78/8807 N
Het historisme in het economisch denken. **Historism in economic thought.**

20994 Antheunisse, J. NL 020033/62/4697
De levensvatbaarheid van micro–organismen na langdurige bewaarperioden met toepassing van verschillende technieken. **The viability of micro–organisms after long storage periods with application of different techniques.** Publications.

20995 Zevenhuizen, L.P.T.M. NL 020033/66/4699
Chemische structuur en functie van exopolysacchariden van Gram–negatieve bacteriën. **Chemical structure and function of exopolysaccharides of Gram–negative bacteria.** Publications.

20996 Middelhoven, W.J. NL 020033/70/4700
Genetische en fysiologische karakterisering van katabolietrepressie door stikstofverbindingen in saccharomyces cerevisiae. **Genetical and physiological characterization of catabolite repression exerted by nitrogenous compounds upon enzyme systems in Saccharomyces cerevisiae.** Publications.

20997 Kortstee, G.J.J. NL 020033/71/5007
De aerobe afbraak van choline door micro–organismen. **The aerobic decomposition of choline by micro–organisms.** Publications.

20998 Middelhoven, W.J. NL 020033/75/4390
Ammonium-, glutamaat- en glutamine– huishouding van Saccharomyces cerevisiae. **Metabolism of ammonium, glutamate and glutamine in Saccharomyces cerevisiae.** Publications.

20999 Zevenhuizen, L.P.Th.M. NL 020033/76/7355
Effect van zware metalen, in het bijzonder koper, op bacteriën. **Influence of copper on the growth of bacteria.**

21000 Kooyman, R. NL 020034/75/6325
Structuur en aggregatie–eigenschappen van aggregatiemodellen van chlorophyl i.v.m. energie–overdracht. **Structure of aggregates of chlorophyll and related compounds.** Publications.

21001 Hemminga, M.A. NL 020034/75/6808
Landbouwkundige toepassingen van de moleculaire biofysica. **Applied molecular biophysics in agriculture.**

21002 Schaafsma, T.J. NL 020034/77/7562
De moleculaire fysica van de fotosynthese in algen. **Molecular physics of algal photosynthesis.**

21003 Schaafsma, T.J. NL 020034/77/7563
Magneto optische verschijnselen en ladingsscheiding in chlorophyll. **Magneto–optics and charge separation in chlorophyll.**

21004 Haneghem, I.A. van NL 020036/71/4690
Warmte geleiding in bevochtigde korrelstapelingen (grond) bij temperaturen beneden 0C. **Thermal conductivity in moist granular materials (soil) of temperatures below 0C.**

21005 Birmie, J.　　　　　　　　NL 020036/71/4691
Data acquisitie en rerwerking t.b.v. microklimatologisch
onderzoek. **Data acquisition for micro meteorological research.**
Publications.

21006 Derksen, W.J.　　　　　　NL 020036/73/5074
Invloed van microklimaatsfactoren op Infrared Line Scanning
(IRLS) beelden. **Influence of micrometeorological parameters
on IRLS pictures.** Publications.

21007 Groot, A.E. de　　　　　　NL 020038/73/4894
Synthese en structuur–werkingsrelaties van plantenhormonen
en andere fysiologische actieve natuurprodukten. **Synthesis
and structure–activity relationships of planthormones and other
physiological active natural products.**

21008 Peterse, A.J.G.M.　　　　NL 020038/74/6339
Synthese en structuur–werkingsrelaties van podolacton en
endosmaan derivaten. **Synthesis and structure–activity
relationships of podolactone and endosmane derivatives.**
Publications.

21009 Tramper, J.　　　　　　　NL 020038/75/6297
Toepassing van geïmmobiliseerde enzymen in organisch
chemische synthesen. **Application of immobilised enzymes in
organic chemical syntheses.** Publications.

21010 Stoel, R.F. van der　　　　NL 020038/75/6298
Reactiviteit van pyrimidinen ten opzichte van alkyl (aryl)
lithium. **Reactivity of pyrimidines towards alkyl (aryl) lithium.**
Publications.

21011 Streef, J.W.　　　　　　　NL 020038/75/6299
Reactiviteit van azepinen ten opzichte van nucleofielen.
Reactivity of azepines towards nucleophiles.

21012 Sanders, G.M.　　　　　　NL 020038/75/6300
Reactiviteit van quaternaire bicyclische aza–aromaten.
Reactivity of quaternary bicyclic aza–aromatic compounds.
Publications.

21013 Breuker, J.　　　　　　　NL 020038/76/4394
Nieuwe ontwikkelingen in Chichibabin reacties van
azahetarenen. **New development in the Chichibabin reactions of
azaaromatics.**

21014 Kos, N.J.　　　　　　　　NL 020038/76/4478
Chemie van purines. **The chemistry of purines.**

21015 Counotte–Potman, A.　　NL 020038/76/7366
Nieuwe ontwikkelingen in reacties van azahetarenen met
hydrazine. **New evolutions in reactions of aza–hetarenes with
hydrazine.** Publications.

21016 Haak, H.J.W. van der　　NL 020038/76/7367
De chemie van de naftyridines. **The chemistry of
naphthyridines.**

21017 Bie, D.A. de　　　　　　　NL 020038/78/8443
Alkyleringsreacties van azahetarenen onder invloed van
oxiderende agentia. **Alkalisation of azahetarenes by oxidative
agents.** Publications.

21018 Luteijn, J.　　　　　　　NL 020038/78/8444
Synthese van Clerodanen. **Synthesis of Clerodanes.**

21019 Sicherer–Roetman, A.　　NL 020038/78/8445
Synthese van Momilactones. **Synthesis of Momilactones.**

21020 Smit, P.　　　　　　　　NL 020038/78/8446
Synthese van analoga van nucleosiden. **Synthesis of Nucleoside
Analogues.**

21021 Loon, L.C. van　　　　　　NL 020041/75/4496
Regulatie van eiwitopbouw en –afbraak tijdens de
ontwikkeling van de plant. **Regulation of protein turnover
during plant growth and senescence.** Publications.

21022 Rombach, J.　　　　　　　NL 020042/56/5022
De analyse van het effect van licht op groei, differentiatie en
stofwisseling van planten. **The effect of light on growth,
differentiation and metabolism of plants.** Publications.

21023 Kronenberg, G.H.M.　　NL 020042/60/4717
Onderzoek van fysiologische, fysische en chemische aspecten
van chlorofylsystemen, in het bijzonder die van
purperbacteriën. **Study of physiological, physical and chemical
aspects of chlorophyll systems, especially in purple bacteria.**
Publications.

21024 Kuiper, F.　　　　　　　NL 020042/64/5014
Onderzoek naar wortelpermeabiliteit in afhankelijkheid van
diverse factoren (druk, temperatuur, energievoorziening,
opkweek osmotica, enz.) en de betekenis hiervan voor de
waterhuishouding. **Root permeability in relation to several
factors (pressure, temperature, energy supply, cultivation
conditions, osmotica etc.) and its significance for the water
relationships of plants.** Publications.

21025 Spruit, C.J.P.　　　　　　NL 020042/68/5019
Photomorphogenetische regulering van de ontwikkeling van
het photosynthese–apparaat. **Photomorphogenetic regulation
of the development of the photosynthetic apparatus.**
Publications.

21026 Spruit, C.J.P.　　　　　　NL 020042/69/5024
Spectrofotometrie van fytochroom en andere tetrapyrrolen in
vivo. **Spectrophotometry of phytochrome and other
tetrapyrroles.** Publications.

21027 Spruit, C.J.P.　　　　　　NL 020042/70/5020
Biosynthese van chlorophyllen in geïsoleerde etioplasten.
Chlorophyll biosynthesis in isolated etioplasts.

21028 Spruit, C.J.P.　　　　　　NL 020042/70/5023
Localisatie van phytochroom in verband met physiologische
reacties. **Phytochrome localisation as related to physiological
effects.** Publications.

21029 Spruit, C.J.P.　　　　　　NL 020042/70/5025
Lichtreacties en electronentransport in de photosynthese.
Photo reactions and electron transport in photosynthesis.

21030 Wesselius, J.C.　　　　　NL 020042/71/4719
Rendement van de lichtenergie bij de groei van algen–culturen
in vergelijk met gewassen. **Light energy conversion during the
growth of algae cultures compared with crops.** Publications.

21031 Lindeman, W.　　　　　　NL 020042/71/5018
Fotosynthese en lichtfosforylering bij groene planten in
afhankelijkheid van lichtintensiteit, golflengtegebied en

andere in- en uitwendige factoren. **Photosynthesis and photophosphorylation in green plants in dependency on light intensity, wavelength area and other internal and external factors.** Publications.

21032 Bensink, J.   NL 020042/72/5013
Onderzoek naar regelmechanismen die een rol spelen bij de aanleg, uitgroei en vormgeving van het bladapparaat. **Studies on the morphogenesis of leaves.**

21033 Wit, H.C.D. de   NL 020044/55/5459
Taxonomie van Cryptocoryne. **Taxonomy of Cryptocoryne.**

21034 Leeuwenberg, A.J.M.   NL 020044/59/5466
Taxonomische revisie van Afrikaanse Loganiaceae. **Taxonomical revision of African Loganiaceae.** Publications.

21035 Wit, H.C.D. de   NL 020044/60/5460
Taxonomie van lagenandra. **Taxonomy of lagenandra.**

21036 Breteler, F.J.   NL 020044/66/5463
Taxonomie van Afrikaanse Dichapetalaceae. **Taxonomy of African Dichapetalaceae.** Publications.

21037 Bos, J.J.   NL 020044/68/5462
Phytotaxonomische revisie van het genus Dracaena met speciale betrekking op Afrika. **Phytotaxonomic revision of the genus Dracaena (lilliaceae) with special reference to the African species.**

21038 Leeuwenberg, A.J.M.   NL 020044/70/5467
Phytotaxonomische revisie van de familie Apocynaceae van Afrika. **Phytotaxonomical revision of the African Apocynaceae.**

21039 Wijnands, D.O.   NL 020044/70/8870 N
Clavis Commeliniana; de taxonomische en nomenclatorische status van de afbeeldingen van planten in de werken van G. and C. Commelijn. **Clavis Commeliniana; the taxonomic and nomenclatural status of the plant illustrations in the works of G. en C. Commelijn.**

21040 De Wilde, J.J.F.E.   NL 020044/73/5464
Taxonomie van de wilde Afrikaanse Begoniaceae. **Taxonomy of African Begoniaceae.**

21041 Arends, J.C.   NL 020044/73/5468
Cytotaxonomie van enige Afrikaanse genera. **Cytotaxonomy of various taxa of African Plants genera.** Publications.

21042 Wit, H.C.D. de   NL 020044/75/5465
Taxonomie ficus van Ethiopië. **Taxonomy ficus of Ethiopia.**

21043 Willemse, M.T.M.   NL 020046/75/8450
Sporogenese en gametogenese van planten (Lillium, Gasteria, Azolla). **Sporogenesis and gametogenesis of plants (Lillium, Gasteria, Azolla).** Publications.

21044 Outer, R.W. den   NL 020046/75/8451
Floëem en houtanatomie van Angiospermen. **Anatomy of phloem and xylem of Angiosperms.**

21045 Schel, J.H.N.   NL 020046/77/8453
Structuur en functie van endosperm: De opzet van een in vitro cultuur van endosperm cellen van Zea mays en de ultrastructuur en ontwikkeling van het embryo. **Structure and function of endosperm: The establishment of an in vitro culture**
of endosperm of Zea mays and the ultra–structure and development of the embryo. Publications.

21046 Willemse, M.T.M.   NL 020046/77/8454
Morfogenese van transportweefsels in stengel, blad en bloem. **Morphogenesis of conducting tissue in stem, leafe and flower.**

21047 Wit, C.T. de   NL 020054/74/6291
Toegevoegde energie en arbeid bij landbouwkundige produktie. **Added energy and labour of agricultural production.** Publications.

21048 Goudriaan, J.   NL 020054/77/7344
Vorm en functie bij planten. **Form and function in plants.** Publications.

21049 Wit, C.T. de   NL 020054/78/7996
Samenwerking tussen de onderzoekprojecten ten behoeve van voeder en voedselgewassen en van natuurlijke weilanden in ontwikkelingslanden en het onderzoek ten behoeve van de Stichting Onderzoek Wereldvoedselvoorziening. **Co–ordination between research projects on productivity of food and fodder crops and natural pastures in developing countries and the research projects of the "Centre for World Food Studies".** Publications.

21050 Ven, W.S.M. van de; Schrijver, H.   NL 020055/73/5103
De invloed van vergiften op enkele geisoleerde organen. **The influence of toxic substances on isolated organs.**

21051 Strik, J.J.T.W.A.   NL 020055/76/7502
Porfyrie en hepatotoxiciteit bij warmbloedigen. **Porphyria and hepatotoxicity of warm–bloodeds.**

21052 Alink, G.M.   NL 020055/77/7503
Ontwikkeling en toepassing van celmodellen ten behoeve van het in vitro toxiciteitsonderzoek. **Development and application of cell models for in vitro toxicity studies.** Publications.

21053 Debets, F.M.H.   NL 020055/78/8545
Interakties van lichaamsvreemde stoffen met cytochroom P–450 en verwante cytochromen als indicatie voor leverschade. **Interaction of xenobiotic chemicals with cytochrome P–450 and related cytochromes as indication of liver damage.**

21054 Rootselaar, B. van   NL 020066/67/6827
Structuur en representatie van zekere niet–communatieve algebra's. **Structure and representation of certain non–communative algebra's (semi–nearrings).**

21055 Rootselaar, B. van   NL 020066/68/6829
Monografie over algebraische systemen met partiele structuur. **Monography about algebraic structures.**

21056 Rootselaar, B. van   NL 020066/68/6830
Miscellana mathematica; uitgaven manuscripten van Bolzano. **Miscellaneous mathematics; publishing manuscripts of Bolzano.**

21057 Nieuwenhuis, C.J.H.   NL 020066/73/6833
Modelonderzoek en systeemanalyse betreffende de dynamica van instellingen van wetenschappelijk onderwijs in Nederland. **A model for Dutch university planning dynamics.**

21058 Rootselaar, B. van   NL 020066/73/6834
De structuur van hiërarchische systemen. **The structure of**

D 9900 – Research which cannot be classified in the fields mentioned above

hierarchial systems. Publications.

21059 Damste, B.R.   NL 020066/76/6823
Theorieën van R. Thom betreffende toepassingen van
differentiaaltopologie, o.a. in de biologische wetenschappen.
**R. Thom's theories concerning applications of
differentialtopologies a.o. in biological sciences.**

21060 Hoorn, W.G. van   NL 020066/77/8550
Algebraïsche structuren. **Algebraic structures.**

21061 Putten, B. van   NL 020066/77/8551
Vectoriële normen op lineaire ruimten. **Vectorial norms on
linear spaces.**

21062 Verdooren, L.R.   NL 020066/78/8552
Analyse van log lineaire modellen. **Analysis of log linear
models.**

21063 Koningsveld, H.   NL 020069/73/4928
Theorievorming in de wetenschap – een rationele
onderneming? Een methodologisch onderzoek. **Theory
formation in science – a rational enterprise? A methodological
investigation.** Publications.

21064 Boers, C.C.   NL 020069/75/6310
Verantwoorde wetenschap en wetenschappelijke ethiek. Een
wetenschaps–theoretisch en ethisch onderzoek. **Responsible
science and scientific ethics. A methodological and ethical
investigation.** Publications.

21065 Visser, M.B.H.   NL 020069/77/8388
Demokratisering van de wetenschap. **Democratization of
science.**

21066 Meyer, A.M.T.   NL 020069/78/8865 N
Achtergrond en ontwikkeling van de antropologische en
politieke ideeën van John Locke (1632–1704). **The background
and development of John Locke's beliefs concerning society and
man.**

21067 Akster, H.A.; Barends, P.   NL 020071/74/6304
Structuur, histochemie en innervatie van kopspieren van vissen
(percidae) met verschillende contractie patronen. **Structure,
histochemistry and innervation of fisch headmuscles with
different contraction patterns.** Publications.

21068 Barends, P.M.G.   NL 020071/75/4253
Biochemische en quantitatief histochemische kenmerken van
kopspieren van vissen (Percidae) met verschillende
activiteitspatronen. **Biochemical and quantitative histochemical
characters of fish head muscles (Percidea) differing in patterns
of activity.**

21069 Muiswinkel, W.B. van   NL 020071/75/6306
De ontwikkeling van het immunologisch apparaat bij de vis.
The ontogeny of the fishimmune system. Publications.

21070 Rombout, J.H.W.M.   NL 020071/75/6307
Onderzoek naar de morfologie, de ontogenie en de funcie van
endocriene cellen in de darm van vissen (Cyprinidae). **A study
of the morphology, origin and function of endocrine cells in the
intestinal tract of fishes. (Cyprinidae).** Publications.

21071 Voogd van der Straaten, W.A. de

NL 030001/73/5859 R

Regeneratie kinetiek in epitheel van de kippetracheam in
vitro. **Regeneration kinetics of tracheal epithelium in vitro.**

21072 Wensing, C.J.G.   NL 030001/74/5853 R
De ontwikkeling van het steroid producerend apparaat in de
testes van foetale en prepuberale varkens. **Investigation of the
development of the steroid–producing apparatus in the testes of
fetal and prepuberal piglets.** Publications.

21073 Wensing, C.J.G.   NL 030001/75/6048 R
De ontwikkeling van de processus vaginalis bij de mannelijke
en vrouwelijke hond. **Investigations in the development of the
vaginal process in the male and female dog.**

21074 Bosma, A.A.   NL 030001/75/6140 R
Cytotaxonomie van de varkensachtigen (suidae).
Cytotaxonomy of the Suidae. Publications.

21075 Wensing, C.J.G.   NL 030001/75/7758 R
Experimenteel onderzoek naar de oorzaken van de
idiopathische hypotrofie van het spermatogenetisch epitheel.
**Experimental investigations into the causal factors of the
idiopathic hypotrophy of the spermatogenic epithelium.**
Publications.

21076 Badoux, D.M.   NL 030001/75/8892 N
Biomechanisch onderzoek van het spanzaagmechanisme in het
achterbeen van het paard. **Biomechanical aspects of the
reciprocal apparatus in the hind limb of the horse.**

21077 Wensing, C.J.G.   NL 030001/77/7743 R
Onderzoek naar de ontwikkeling en bouw van het
bloedvaatstelsel van de testis. **Investigation of the development
and structure of the vasculature of the testis.**

21078 Voogd van der Straten, W.A. de

NL 030001/77/7745 R

Onderzoek naar de regulatie van chondrogene aktiviteit in
vitro. **The regulation of chondrogenic activity in vitro.**

21079 Schlimme, J.F.C.   NL 030014/73/5662
Onderzoek naar de mogelijkheden van klinische toepassing
van de vectorcardiografie bij honden. **Vectorcardiography in
dogs.**

21080 Geelen, M.J.H.   NL 030015/73/6052 R
Hormonale regulatie van lipogenese in rattelever. **Hormonal
regulation of lipogenesis in rat liver.** Publications.

21081 Golde, L.M.G. van   NL 030015/74/5762 R
Metabole regulering van de biosynthese van fosfolipiden en
triglyceriden in de lever. (regulatie, metabolisme,
trygliceriden, fosfolipiden, lever). **Metabolic regulation of the
biosynthesis of phospholipids and triacylglycerols in the liver.
(regulation, metabolism, triacylglycerols, phospholipids, liver).**
Publications.

21082 Golde, L.M.G. van   NL 030015/74/6055 R
Metabolisme van fosfolipiden in de volwassen en foetale long.
**Metabolism of phospholipids in the adult lung and during
maturation of the developing lung.** Publications.

21083 Vaartjes, W.J.   NL 030015/75/8947 N
De regulering in rattelever van vetzuursynthese uit C2– of
C3–eenheden. **Regulation of fatty acid synthesis from C2– or
C3–precursors in the rat liver.** Publications.

21084 Batenburg, J.J.   NL 030015/77/8949 N
Lipide metabolisme in pulmonaire type II epitheelcellen. **Lipid
metabolism in pulmonary type II epithelial cells.** Publications.

21085 Mulder, I.   NL 030015/78/8946 N
Veranderingen in levermitochondriën gedurende ketosis
(acetonaemie, acetoacetylcoenzym A,
Hydroxmethyglutarylcoenzym–A–synthase, calciumionen,
ATP). **Change in liver mitochondria during ketosis
(acetonaemia, acetoacetyl coenzyme A, hydroxymethylglutaryl
coenzyme A synthase, calcium ions, ATP).** Publications.

21086 Geelen, M.J.H.   NL 030015/78/8948 N
Hormonale regulatie van de synthese van komplexe lipiden in
rattelever (regulatie, hormonen, synthese glycerolipiden).
**Hormonal regulation of glycerolipid synthesis in rat liver
(regulation hormones, glycerolipid synthesis).** Publications.

21087 Helle, W.   NL 040001/73/4681
Populatie–biologisch onderzoek aan Tsetsevliegen. **Population
biological research on Tsetse flies.** Publications.

21088 Vonk, J.W.; Barug, D.; Meinema, H.A.
                NL 050104/76/7571
Omzetting van (organo–) metaalverbindingen in het milieu.
**Conversion of (organo–) metal compounds in the
environment.**

21089 Treurniet, D.M.L.   NL 050301/75/6501
Waterhuishouding van slachterijen en vleeswarenbedrijven.
**Water management in slaughterhouses and meat processing
units.**